Volume A

TEACHER'S GUIDE

IMPACT MATHEMATICS

Algebra and More for the Middle Grades

Course 2

Developed by
Education Development Center, Inc.

Nina Arshavsky, Ricky Carter, Sydney Foster,
E. Paul Goldenberg, Susan Janssen, Charles Lovitt, Joan Lukas,
Michelle Manes, Cynthia J. Orrell, Faye Nisonoff Ruopp, Daniel Lynn Watt

Chicago, Illinois

Photo Acknowledgments

Cover image: *Paddy Grass,* Toyohiro Yamada/FPG International LLC

Photo credits are given on pages A416–A417 and constitute a continuation of the copyright page.

Education Development Center Staff

Principal Investigators: E. Paul Goldenberg, Faye Nisonoff Ruopp

Senior Project Director: Cynthia J. Orrell

Senior Curriculum Developers: Nina Arshavsky, Ricky Carter, Sydney Foster, Susan Janssen, Charles Lovitt, Joan Lukas, Michelle Manes, Daniel Lynn Watt

Curriculum Developers: Phil Lewis, Debbie Winkler

Administrative Assistant: Christine Brown

Everyday Learning Development Staff

Editorial: Anna Belluomini, Mary Cooney, Susan Halko, Eric Karnowski, Kathleen Ludwig

Design: Fran Brown, Jess Schaal

Production: Annette Davis

Additional Credits

Nancy Anderson, Kathleen Burke, Carlisle Communications, Lindaanne Donohoe, Herman Adler Design Group, Huffman and Associates, Inc., Stacey Miceli, Precision Graphics

ISBN 1-57039-856-9

The algebra content for *Impact Mathematics* was adapted from the series, *Access to Algebra*, by Neville Grace, Jayne Johnston, Barry Kissane, Ian Lowe, and Sue Willis. Permission to adapt this material was obtained from the publisher, Curriculum Corporation of Level 5, 2 Lonsdale Street, Melbourne, Australia.

Everyday Learning Corporation
P.O. Box 812960
Chicago, IL 60681
www.everydaylearning.com

1 2 3 4 5 6 7 8 9 10 BP/VHG 04 03 02 01 00 99

Impact Mathematics Project Reviewers

Everyday Learning Corporation and Education Development Center appreciate all the feedback from the curriculum specialists and teachers who participated in review and testing.

Special thanks to:

Peter Braunfeld
Professor of Mathematics Emeritus
University of Illinois

Sherry L. Meier
Assistant Professor of Mathematics
Illinois State University

Judith Roitman
Professor of Mathematics
University of Kansas

Marcie Abramson
Thurston Middle School
Boston, Massachusetts

Denise Airola
Fayetteville Public Schools
Fayetteville, Arizona

Chadley Anderson
Syracuse Junior High School
Syracuse, Utah

Jeanne A. Arnold
Mead Junior High
Elk Grove Village, Illinois

Joanne J. Astin
Lincoln Middle School
Forrest City, Arkansas

Jack Beard
Urbana Junior High
Urbana, Ohio

Chad Cluver
Maroa-Forsyth Junior High
Maroa, Illinois

Robert C. Bieringer
Patchogue-Medford School Dist.
Center Moriches, New York

Susan Coppleman
Nathaniel H. Wixon Middle School
South Dennis, Massachusetts

Sandi Curtiss
Gateway Middle School
Everett, Washington

Alan Dallman
Amherst Middle School
Amherst, Massachusetts

Sharon DeCarlo
Sudbury Public Schools
Sudbury, Massachusetts

David P. DeLeon
Preston Area School
Lakewood, Pennsylvania

Jacob J. Dick
Cedar Grove School
Cedar Grove, Wisconsin

Sharon Ann Dudek
Holabird Middle School
Baltimore, Maryland

Cheryl Elisara
Centennial Middle School
Spokane, Washington

Patricia Elsroth
Wayne Highlands Middle School
Honesdale, Pennsylvania

Dianne Fink
Bell Junior High
San Diego, California

Terry Fleenore
E.B. Stanley Middle School
Abingdon, Virginia

Kathleen Forgac
Waring School
Massachusetts

Steven J. Fox
Bendle Middle School
Burton, Michigan

Kenneth L. Goodwin Jr.
Middletown Middle School
Middletown, Delaware

Fred E. Gross
Sudbury Public Schools
Sudbury, Massachusetts

Penny Hauben
Murray Avenue School
Huntingdon, Pennsylvania

Jean Hawkins
James River Day School
Lynchburg, Virginia

Robert Kalac
Butler Junior High
Frombell, Pennsylvania

Robin S. Kalder
Somers High School
Somers, New York

Darrin Kamps
Lucille Umbarge Elementary
Burlington, Washington

Sandra Keller
Middletown Middle School
Middletown, Delaware

Pat King
Holmes Junior High
Davis, California

Kim Lazarus
San Diego Jewish Academy
La Jolla, California

Ophria Levant
Webber Academy
Calgary, Alberta
Canada

Mary Lundquist
Farmington High School
Farmington, Connecticut

Ellen McDonald-Knight
San Diego Unified School District
San Diego, California

Ann Miller
Castle Rock Middle School
Castle Rock, Colorado

Julie Mootz
Ecker Hill Middle School
Park City, Utah

Jeanne Nelson
New Lisbon Junior High
New Lisbon, Wisconsin

DeAnne Oakley-Wimbush
Pulaski Middle School
Chester, Pennsylvania

Tom Patterson
Ponderosa Jr. High School
Klamath Falls, Oregon

Maria Peterson
Chenery Middle School
Belmont, Massachusetts

Lonnie Pilar
Tri-County Middle School
Howard City, Michigan

Karen Pizarek
Northern Hills Middle School
Grand Rapids, Michigan

Debbie Ryan
Overbrook Cluster
Philadelphia, Pennsylvania

Sue Saunders
Abell Jr. High School
Midland, Texas

Ivy Schram
Massachusetts Department of Youth Services
Massachusetts

Robert Segall
Windham Public Schools
Willimantic, Connecticut

Kassandra Segars
Hubert Middle School
Savannah, Georgia

Laurie Shappee
Larson Middle School
Troy, Michigan

Sandra Silver
Windham Public Schools
Willimantic, Connecticut

Karen Smith
East Middle School
Braintree, Massachusetts

Kim Spillane
Oxford Central School
Oxford, New Jersey

Carol Struchtemeyer
Lexington R-5 Schools
Lexington, Missouri

Kathy L. Terwelp
Summit Public Schools
Summit, New Jersey

Laura Sosnoski Tracey
Somerville, Massachusetts

Marcia Uhls
Truesdale Middle School
Wichita, Kansas

Vendula Vogel
Westridge School for Girls
Pasadena, California

Judith A. Webber
Grand Blanc Middle School
Grand Blanc, Michigan

Sandy Weishaar
Woodland Junior High
Fayetteville, Arkansas

Tamara L. Weiss
Forest Hills Middle School
Forest Hills, Michigan

Kerrin Wertz
Haverford Middle School
Havertown, Pennsylvania

Anthony Williams
Jackie Robinson Middle School
Brooklyn, New York

Deborah Winkler
The Baker School
Brookline, Massachusetts

Lucy Zizka
Best Middle School
Ferndale, Michigan

CONTENTS

Program Philosophy

In developing *Impact Mathematics: Algebra and More for the Middle Grades,* we, the authors at Education Development Center, Inc., have relied on our collective experiences as teachers, parents, and former students. Our main goal is to offer a curriculum that respects the background and knowledge of middle school teachers, recognizes the competence and energy of middle school students, and addresses the need for intellectually challenging and inclusive mathematics materials. With *Impact Mathematics,* we have combined the best of what is known as "reform" curricula with the best of "traditional" curricula, incorporating more active involvement on the part of students in making sense of important mathematical ideas.

With middle grades teachers and students in mind, we have created a comprehensive curriculum for Grades 6 through 8 that completes a full year of algebra by the end of Grade 8. While the number and operations, geometry, and data and probability strands were created especially for this program, the algebra strand is based on the highly successful Australian program, *Access to Algebra,* developed by Curriculum Corporation.

The rewarding and interesting introduction to algebra offered by this program can help develop and maintain students' ongoing interest in all areas of mathematics. The materials created for *Impact Mathematics* follow the *Access to Algebra* material in style: use of narrative and realistic contexts, personalization in the form of cartoons in which middle grades students explain how they approach problems, and opportunities for students to choose or create their own problems.

Conceptual Understanding and Basic Skills

Discussions regarding mathematics learning in both professional circles and the popular media might lead you to believe that teaching for conceptual understanding and teaching basic skills are mutually exclusive. But, in fact, the opposite is true. Conceptual understanding and basic skills are not opposing interests; they go hand in hand and support each other.

Impact Mathematics makes the big ideas as well as the important skills of mathematics accessible to middle school students. It presents mathematical ideas intact, not broken down into bite-sized bits that lack the big idea. *Impact Mathematics* helps students both build new mathematical ideas and see how these new ideas relate to ideas they have already developed. In this way, *Impact Mathematics* takes a conceptual approach.

At the same time, *Impact Mathematics* recognizes that for students to be able to use the new ideas and procedures effectively, they need practice. Practice need not be the enemy of learning; the enemy of learning is mindless drill. Instead, practice can encourage students to stay interested in the mathematical concepts. *Impact Mathematics* provides plenty of opportunity for practice, but with variety and contrast to keep students' attention focused.

Algebraic Focus in a Comprehensive Program

Impact Mathematics is a comprehensive program including number and operations, proportional reasoning, geometry, probability, and data, with a focus on the development of algebraic thinking. The program takes a developmental approach to algebra. Student understanding of the algebra strand—interwoven with and related to the other mathematical strands—evolves over a three-year period, allowing the ideas and skills to develop and become familiar over time.

Most students develop strong algebraic ideas in the early years of elementary school, but they don't acquire ways of expressing and manipulating them in algebraic terms until later, when algebra is formally taught. For example, young children know how to share \$36 among three people by first distributing the ten dollar bills and then distributing the ones. Later, if children learn a standard method for dividing $3\overline{)36}$ they may see again that the process is like dividing $3\overline{)30}$, then dividing $3\overline{)6}$, and finally adding the results. If this process is written out as $\frac{36}{3} = \frac{30}{3} + \frac{6}{3}$, that concise statement contains an important idea about adding fractions and an even more general algebraic idea. Students who understand *why* $\frac{36}{3} = \frac{30}{3} + \frac{6}{3}$ know that the sum of $\frac{30}{3}$ and $\frac{6}{3}$ must be $\frac{36}{3}$, and not $\frac{36}{6}$. The idea, expressed more generally, is $\frac{a}{3} + \frac{b}{3} = \frac{a+b}{3}$, and even more generally, is $\frac{a}{c} + \frac{b}{c} = \frac{a+b}{c}$, and so leads to the distributive law of division over addition.

Our approach in *Impact Mathematics* is to start with algebra as a notation for "generic" arithmetic, a description of processes that students understand. Later, algebra also becomes a handy language for "unlocking secrets" (equation solving) and building mathematical models. By the end of the third book, students will have learned both to express functions using variables and to graph these functions. They will have also learned how to use variables to set up and solve equations, as well as how to factor some familiar polynomials, and to understand the origin and use of the quadratic formula.

Use of Manipulatives and Calculators

Manipulatives and calculators can be powerful tools for teaching and learning mathematics. There is, however, much discussion and controversy about the appropriateness of their use. As the authors of *Impact Mathematics,* we believe that when manipulatives and calculators are used, they must be used to support the content learning. More specifically, we consider the important mathematical ideas first and then determine whether manipulatives or calculators can be used in learning those ideas more completely.

We believe it's critical that students develop good number sense and calculation skills before they work extensively with calculators. For example, we incorporate graphing calculators in Course 3 to explore families of functions, but only *after* students have a firm idea of how to graph "parent" functions by hand. Graphing technology can then be used to allow students to graph more complex functions, analyze their behavior, and compare representations. Similar to our philosophy of integrating skills with understanding, we believe that students need experiences with pencil and paper along with graphing technology.

Organization by Content

Impact Mathematics often uses applications to help develop a particular mathematical concept or place it in context. However, *Impact Mathematics* remains organized by mathematical content, not by contexts. This organization helps both teacher and student keep the mathematical ideas at the fore, easily recognizable and never buried or lost in the settings. While the mathematical focus shifts with each chapter, the *Impact Mathematics* approach offers opportunities to connect topics to one another so that earlier learning is not abandoned as new ideas are introduced.

Developing Concepts in Varied Contexts

The contexts used for developing concepts and practicing skills include real-world applications, as well as mathematical settings such as number puzzles, and the world of the imagination such as a factory that uniformly resizes rods using stretching machines. Sometimes, *Impact Mathematics* provides exercises that are *not* set in contexts or integrated into word problems precisely so that students can focus on the mathematical ideas, undistracted by surrounding material.

Stretching machines such as this are used in Chapter 3 to study the law of exponents.

A Final Note

The unique power of mathematics stems from the world of the imagination in which one envisions triangles with perfectly straight sides, or two-dimensional objects embedded in perfectly smooth planes. In the real world, all objects are three dimensional (even a line drawn on paper has thickness, or it wouldn't be visible!), all lines are irregular, and all surfaces are pitted. Likewise, all measurements are only approximations, and no physical object can have an irrational length. Our minds reason well precisely because we can ignore irregularities and focus instead on the essential features. We can reason about quantities that no physical ruler can measure but that we can "measure" with our mental rulers. In sum, we reason well because we can abstract reality.

We, the authors of *Impact Mathematics,* recognize that all people, from early childhood on, do reason abstractly, and that what grows over time is both their ability to recognize the abstractions, and the formality with which they are able to express abstractions. We also recognize that mathematics, while not simply common sense, is rooted in common sense. Mathematics is a human product that has developed as an extension and a codification of ways of thinking that are natural to us all. Students must not think of mathematics as a departure from natural, logical thinking. To that aim *Impact Mathematics* is written to help students use and sharpen their own logical thinking, learn to be comfortable with the abstractions that give mathematics its power, develop their ideas and mathematical imagination, and acquire the skills that support all that good thinking and the ability to express it clearly to others.

We hope you will enjoy teaching and learning with these materials.

Scope and Sequence

Number and Operations

Topics	Course 1										Course 2										Course 3									
	1	2	3	4	5	6	7	8	9	10	1	2	3	4	5	6	7	8	9	10	1	2	3	4	5	6	7	8	9	10
Numbers and Number Sense	Develop										Develop										Apply									
Whole Numbers	C	F	C				C	C			C	C	C	C			C	C					C				C	C		
Signed Numbers	C	F							C					F	C						C		C							
Exponents and Roots							F					F	F	F	C				F			F	F				F			
Rationals and Irrationals	Develop										Apply										Apply									
Fractions and Decimal Concepts		F	F	C			C											C								C				
Percents				F									C		C		C	F					C			C				
Ratios and Rates	Expose										Develop										Apply									
Meaning and Representations		C		C						C		C			F	F	C	F			F				C					
Proportions				C					C	C		C			F	F	C	F							C					
Algorithms and Operations	Apply										Apply										Apply									
Fractions	C	F	F	F				C			C							C								C				
Decimals		F	F	F				C			C																			
Signed Numbers														F																

Algebra

Topics	Course 1										Course 2										Course 3									
	1	2	3	4	5	6	7	8	9	10	1	2	3	4	5	6	7	8	9	10	1	2	3	4	5	6	7	8	9	10
Algebraic Representations	Develop										Develop										Develop									
Coordinate Graphs		C			F	F		C	F		C		C	F	F	F	C	C	F	C	F	F	F	F	F			F		F
Tables and Graphs	C	C			F	F		F	F	C	C		C	F	F	F			F	F	F	F	F	F		C	C	F		F
Algebraic Reasoning	Develop										Develop										Develop									
Patterns and Numeric Forms	F	F		C	C	C		F	F		F	F	F	F	F	F	C	C	F	F	F	F	F	C		F	F	F		F
Properties and Rules	F	C	C				F	F	C		F		F	F	C	F					C	C	F	C		F	F	C		
Functions and Relations	Expose										Develop										Develop									
Linear Expressions/Equations					C	C			F		F			C	F	F	C	F	F		F			F				F		F
Quadratic Expressions/Equations									C		C	C	C		C				F			F	F	F			F	F		C
Exponential Expressions/Equations					C	C		C	C				F	C					F				F	F		F		F		C
Rational Expressions/Equations																		C	C					F		F		C		C

F = This topic is a Focus of Instruction in this chapter.

C = This topic is Connected to the content of the chapter and is either reviewed in this chapter or informally introduced.

Expose: Ideas are introduced at an informal concrete level and will be fully developed later in the program.

Develop: Ideas are formalized and fully developed.

Apply: Ideas are reviewed and used to extend understanding of related ideas.

Geometry

Topics	Course 1										Course 2										Course 3									
	1	2	3	4	5	6	7	8	9	10	1	2	3	4	5	6	7	8	9	10	1	2	3	4	5	6	7	8	9	10
Two-Dimensional Shapes	Develop										Apply										Apply									
Polygons	F	C	C				F					C					C	C							C					
Quadrilaterals	F						F					C					C	C							C					
Triangles	F						F					C		C			F	F							C					
Angles	C						F										C	C							C					
Geometric Relationships	Expose										Develop										Apply									
Congruence																	F	C							C					
Similarity							C			C		C		C	C		F	F			C				C					
Three-Dimensional Figures	Expose										Develop										Apply									
Spatial Visualization												F					C													
3-D Solids												F					C													
Measurement	Develop										Develop										Apply									
Perimeter and Area		C	C					F				F		C			F	C							C					
Surface Area and Volume								C				F					F	C							C					
Coordinate Geometry	Develop										Develop										Develop									
Coordinate Representations					F	F		C	C		C		F	F	F	F	C	C	F	C	F	F	F	F	C			F		F
Transformations												C		C			F								F			C		

Data and Probability

Topics	Course 1										Course 2										Course 3									
	1	2	3	4	5	6	7	8	9	10	1	2	3	4	5	6	7	8	9	10	1	2	3	4	5	6	7	8	9	10
Data Analysis	Develop										Develop										Apply									
Graphs and Displays	C	C		C	F	F				F									C	F	C									
Modeling and Analysis	C	C			F	F				F		C			C					F	C									F
Statistical Measures						F				C										F									C	
Surveys and Sampling										F								C		F									C	
Probability	Develop										Develop										Develop									
Basic Concepts and Rules										F										F									F	
Counting Methods																				F									F	
Experiments and Simulations										F										F									F	

Assessment in *Impact Mathematics*

The assessment tools in *Impact Mathematics* are broader than those in traditional mathematics programs. They encompass the processes of problem solving, reasoning, communication, connections, concepts, applications, representational strategies, and procedures.

The flexibility and variety of assessment in *Impact Mathematics* addresses the various ability levels and learning styles of students, as well as the instructional needs of teachers.

In the Student Edition

- **Share & Summarize** questions provide a forum for students to summarize and share their learning with the class.
- **On Your Own Exercises,** an integral part of daily instruction, are independent assignments intended for individual work outside of class.
- **Review & Self-Assessment** provides students with an opportunity to reflect on the important topics within the chapter and to prepare for formal assessment.

In the Teacher's Guide

- **Problem Set Wrap-Ups** ensure students are making appropriate progress through an Investigation.
- **Troubleshooting** notes provide remedial work students might need in order to move on to the next Investigation successfully.
- **Additional Examples** can be used as on-the-run assessment tools.
- **Quick Checks** provide checklists of what students should be able to do at the end of each lesson.
- **Quick Quizzes** provide brief end-of-lesson assessment opportunities.

In the Assessment Resources Book

- A **Pretest** determines whether students have the prerequisite skills for the course.
- **Refresher Worksheets** help students review prerequisite skills.
- **Chapter Tests** provide a comprehensive evaluation of chapter content.
- **Performance Assessments** provide open-ended opportunities to measure student achievement. They can be used to supplement or replace items on chapter and semester tests, as take-home assignments, as group assessments, or as challenge or extra-credit problems.
- **Semester Tests** provide cumulative mid-year and end-of-year evaluations.

The Instructional Cycle

Impact Mathematics is designed to actively engage students in their own learning. To facilitate the learning and teaching process, *Impact Mathematics* is designed around a three-step instructional cycle.

Introduce

Each multiday lesson begins with a class discussion, activity, or problem designed to introduce the mathematics and help set a context for learning. To help guide the introduction, **Explore** activities and **Think and Discuss** questions are provided in the student materials.

Develop

Each lesson in *Impact Mathematics* is composed of in-class **Investigations** that provide a mix of worked-out examples, direct modeling through cartoons, and interactive problem sets. During Investigations, the mathematics, not an artificial format, determines the approach and the day's activity. Each Investigation is designed to last about 45 minutes or one class period. Positioned at logical breaking points, Investigations help teachers determine pacing and help make multiday lessons manageable.

The **Share & Summarize** questions signal the end of each Investigation. These questions offer students an opportunity to share what they did and what was learned. They also provide a summary of major points. For teachers they offer an important assessment opportunity. When used as part of class discussion, Share & Summarize questions serve as a checkpoint to make sure that appropriate learning has taken place and that students can move forward in the lesson successfully.

Assign & Assess

Independent assignments and opportunities to assess what students have learned are a regular part of the curriculum. The **On Your Own Exercises** at the end of each lesson are an integral part of program instruction and are intended for individual work done primarily outside of class. You will find three types of problems in each set of On Your Own Exercises.

- *Practice & Apply* problems provide opportunities for students to reinforce and directly apply the skills and concepts they have learned in each of the Investigations.
- *Connect & Extend* problems relate student learning in the lesson to other mathematical topics and strands, and sometimes require students to stretch their thinking. Connections may reach back to ideas previously developed in the program or might offer a preview of how current topics are related to what's to come.
- *Mixed Review* problems are important part of the instructional and assignment structure. Frequent review of previously learned skills helps students maintain mastery and replaces the need to reteach topics.

Assignment guides for each Investigation are provided in the Teacher's Guide.

Overview of Student Materials

Lesson Stucture

3.3 Growing Exponentially

Have you ever heard someone say, "It's growing exponentially"? People use this expression to describe things that grow very rapidly.

In this lesson, you will develop a more precise meaning of *exponential growth.* You'll also investigate what it means to decrease, or decay, exponentially.

Explore

Suppose you make up a funny joke one evening. The next day, you tell it to two classmates. The day after that, your two classmates each tell it to two people. Everyone who hears the joke tells two new people the next day.

How many new people will hear the joke on the fourth day after you made it up? 16

On which day will more than 1,000 new people hear the joke? the 10th

If the joke was told only to people in your school, how many days would it take for everyone in your school to hear it? Answers will vary, depending on school size.

The number of students who hear the joke for the first time doubles each day. *Repeated doubling* is one type of exponential growth. In the next two investigations, you will look at other situations in which things grow exponentially.

Investigation 1 Telling the Difference

The expressions 2^x, $2x$, and x^2 look similar—they all include the number 2 and the variable x—but they have very different meanings. The same is true of 3^x, $3x$, and x^3. Looking at tables and graphs for these expressions will help you discover just how different they are.

176 CHAPTER 3 Exploring Exponents

Just the facts

The fruit fly is one of the world's most studied animals. Because it reproduces so rapidly, it is ideal for many scientific experiments.

Problem Set A

Ms. Nisonoff brought two fruit flies to her biology class. She told her students that the flies would reproduce, and that the population of flies would double every week. Luis and Zoe wanted to figure out how many flies there would be each week.

Luis made this table:

Week	1	2	3	4	5
Flies	2	4	6	8	10

Zoe made this table:

Week	1	2	3	4	5
Flies	2	4	8	16	32

1. Whose table is correct? That is [illegible]

7. Possible answer: All the graphs have the point (2, 4). The graph for the (x, 2x) points lie on a line; both of the other two graphs lie on a curve. The curve for the (x, 2^x) points becomes very steep as x increases.

Problem Set B

Remember

The formula for the volume of a cube with edge length x is $V = x^3$.

Kate and Darnell made tables to show the relationship between the edge length and the volume of a cube.

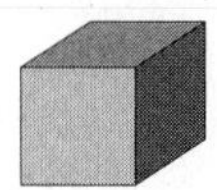

Kate made this table:

Edge Length	1	2	3	4	5
Volume	3	9	27	81	243

Darnell made this table:

Edge Length	1	2	3	4	5
Volume	1	8	27	64	125

1. Whose table shows the correct volumes? Darnell's
2. Complete this table to compare the expressions $3x$, 3^x, and x^3.

x	0	1	2	3	4	5
$3x$	0	3	6	9	12	15
3^x	1	3	9	27	81	243
x^3	0	1	8	27	64	125

3. As x increases from 0 to 5, which expression's values increase most quickly? 3^x
4. Which expression describes Kate's table? Which describes Darnell's table? 3^x, x^3
5. Look at the values in the table for 3^x. Describe in words how to get from one value to the next. multiply by 3
6. Look at the values in the table for $3x$. Describe in words how to get from one value to the next. add 3

Share & Summarize

1. Compare the way the values of $2x$ change as x increases to the way the values of 2^x change as x increases.
2. Consider the expressions $4x$, 4^x, and x^4. Without making a table, predict which expression's values grow the fastest as x increases. 4^x

On Your Own Exercises

Practice & Apply

1. Possible answers: ×1 or ×3^0
2. ×5
3. 5-ft output
4. 3-cm input
5. Possible answer: ×25×4
6. Possible answer: ×3×33
7. not possible
8. Possible answer: ×11×101

Supply the missing information for each diagram.

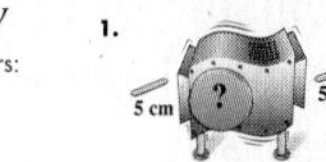

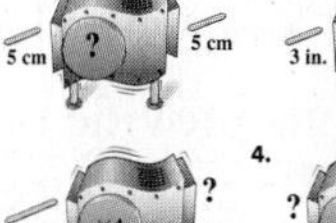

If possible, find a hookup that will do the same wo[illegible] ing machine. Do not use ×1 machines.

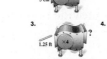

9. Find two repeater machines that will do t[illegible] machine. ×9^2, ×3^4
10. Find a repeater machine that will do the [illegible] machine. ×$(\frac{1}{2})^3$

Lab Investigation Using a Spreadsheet to Guess-Check-and-Improve

MATERIALS computer with spreadsheet software (1 per group)

Guess-check-and-improve is a great method for solving simple equations, but it can be tedious when the equations are more complicated. The process is a lot faster and more fun when you have a computer do the calculations while you do the thinking.

Sonia decided to use a spreadsheet to help her solve this equation using guess-check-and-improve:

$$\frac{3n + 5}{2} = \frac{5n + 3}{3}$$

Setting Up the Spreadsheet

First, Sonia entered headings and formulas in the top two rows of the first four columns of her spreadsheet.

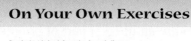

	A	B	C	D
1	Test Variable n	Left Side $(3n + 5)/2$	Right Side $(5n + 3)/3$	Differ[illegible]
2		[illegible]	[illegible]	[illegible]

Top clockwise:

The introduction to each multiday lesson includes an ***Explore*** activity or ***Think & Discuss*** questions.

Students work through the problems sets in an **Investigation** individually or in groups.

Share & Summarize questions at the end of each investigation help students pull together key ideas.

Optional ***Lab Investigations*** provide extended explorations and the use of software.

On Your Own Exercises can be assigned as homework.

Student Book Features

Just the Facts engages students with interesting facts related to problem contexts.

Worked out ***Examples*** provide direct instruction when appropriate.

Vocabulary is highlighted and defined in context.

Cartoons provide direct modeling of mathematical reasoning and problem solving strategies in an accessible and inviting format.

Remember markers remind students about information they learned in previous lessons.

In Your Own Words features encourage students to write about mathematical ideas.

Overview of Teacher Materials

The *Chapter Organizer* at the front of each chapter provides all chapter planning information in a convenient and easy-to-use format.

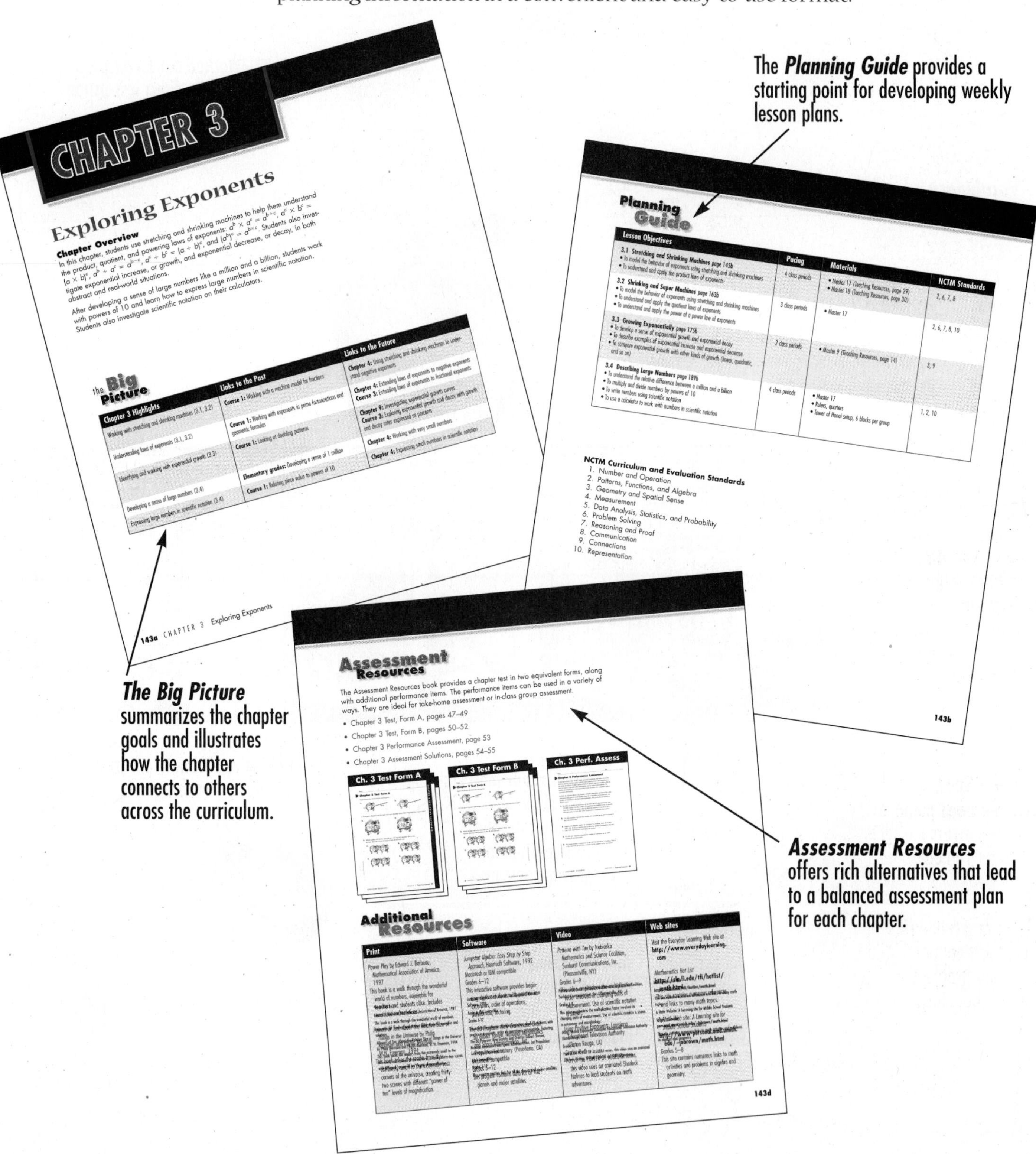

The ***Planning Guide*** provides a starting point for developing weekly lesson plans.
The Big Picture summarizes the chapter goals and illustrates how the chapter connects to others across the curriculum.
Assessment Resources offers rich alternatives that lead to a balanced assessment plan for each chapter.

In-depth teaching notes are provided for each Investigation page. *Impact Mathematics'* unique arrow cues help teachers make a quick visualconnection between in-depth teaching notes and the corresponding location on the student page.

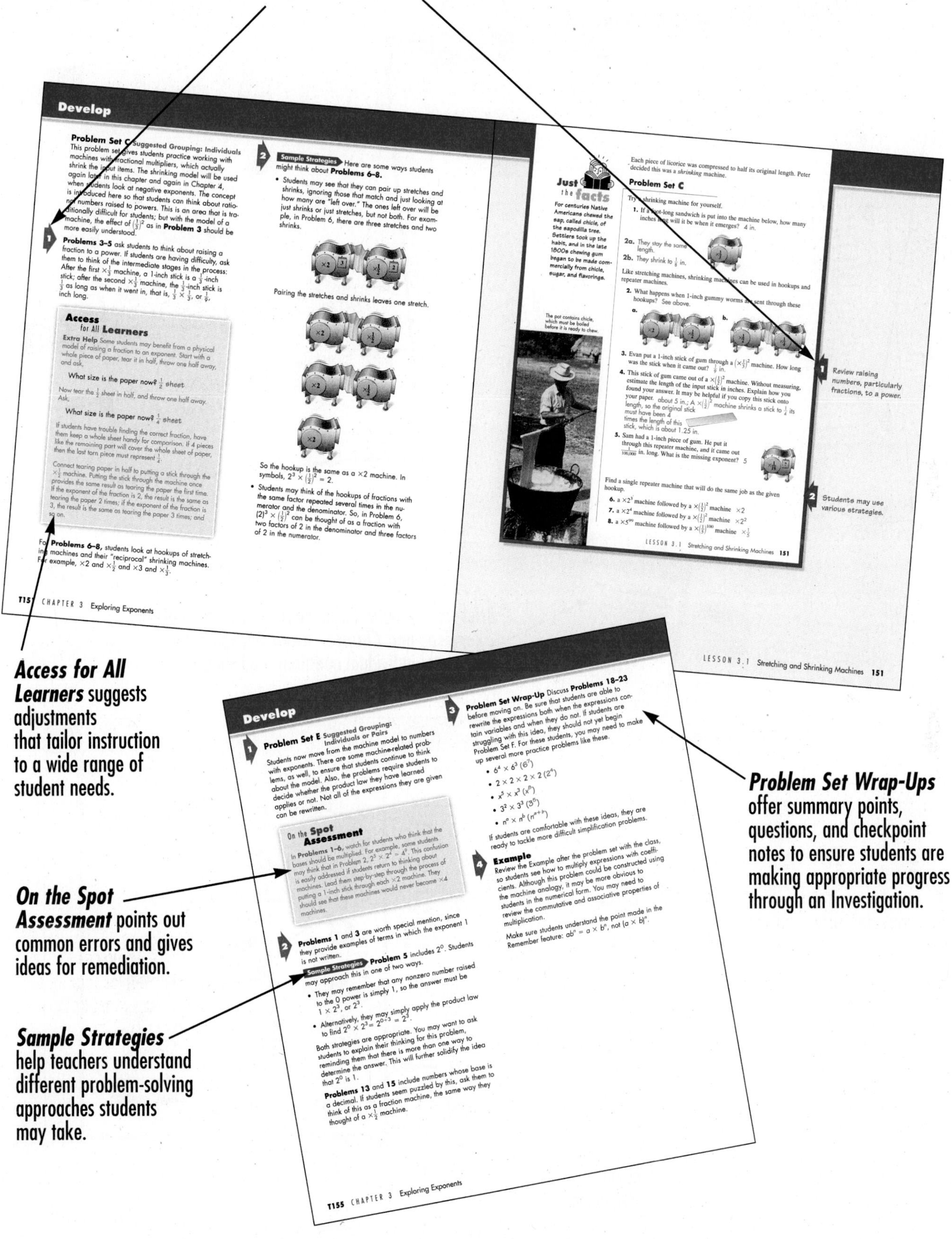

Access for All Learners suggests adjustments that tailor instruction to a wide range of student needs.

On the Spot Assessment points out common errors and gives ideas for remediation.

Sample Strategies help teachers understand different problem-solving approaches students may take.

Problem Set Wrap-Ups offer summary points, questions, and checkpoint notes to ensure students are making appropriate progress through an Investigation.

If students struggle with ***Share & Summarize*** questions, ***Troubleshooting*** notes provide the remediation they need in order to move on to the next Investigation.

Additional Examples offer instructional support. Use them to assist struggling students or as an impromptu assessment tool.

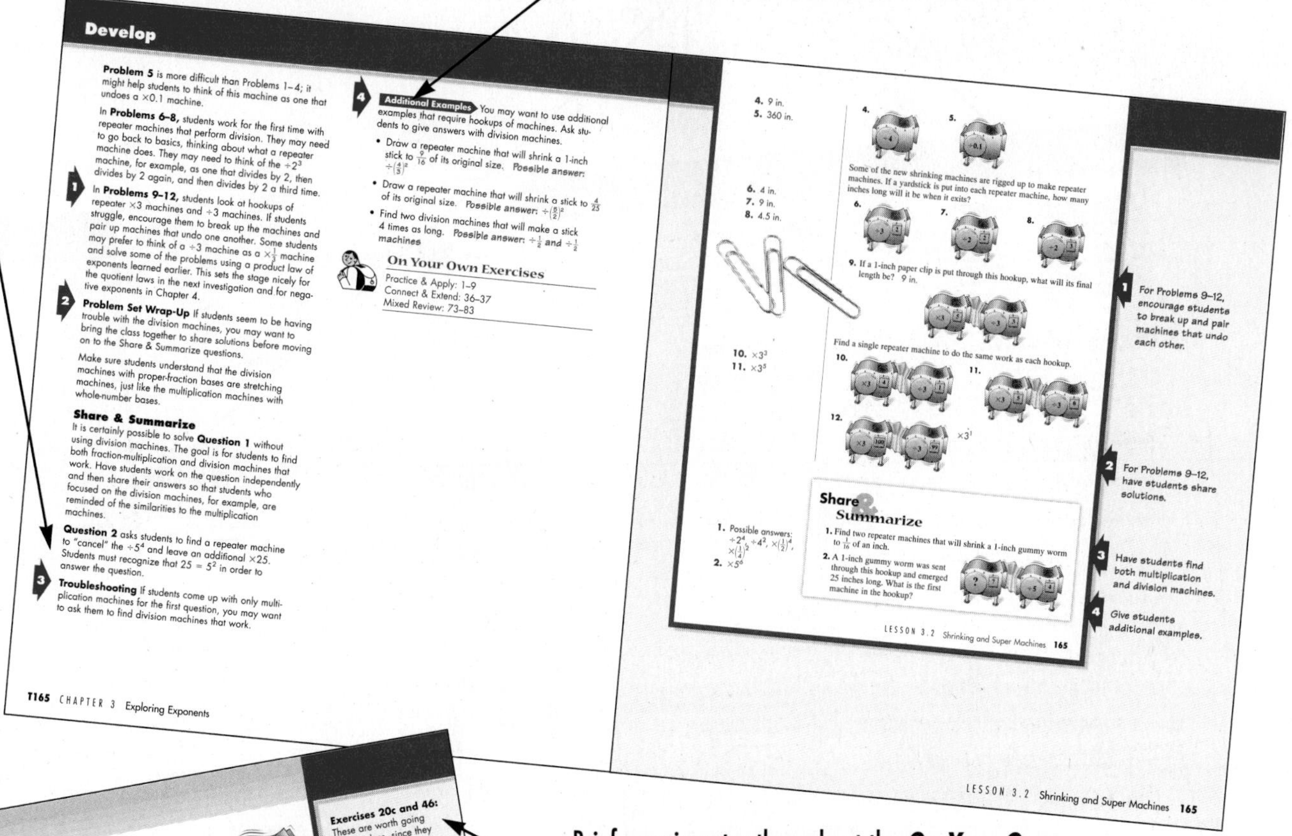

Develop

Problem 5 is more difficult than Problems 1–4; it might help students to think of this machine as one that undoes a ×0.1 machine.

In **Problems 6–8,** students work for the first time with repeater machines that perform division. They may need to go back to basics, thinking about what a repeater machine does. They may need to think of the $\div 2^3$ machine, for example, as one that divides by 2, then divides by 2 again, and then divides by 2 a third time.

1 In **Problems 9–12,** students look at hookups of repeater ×3 machines and ÷3 machines. If students struggle, encourage them to break up the machines and pair up machines that undo one another. Some students may prefer to think of a ÷3 machine as a $\times\frac{1}{3}$ machine and solve some of the problems using a product law of exponents learned earlier. This sets the stage nicely for the quotient laws in the next investigation and for negative exponents in Chapter 4.

2 **Problem Set Wrap-Up** If students seem to be having trouble with the division machines, you may want to bring the class together to share solutions before moving on to the Share & Summarize questions.

Make sure students understand that the division machines with proper-fraction bases are stretching machines, just like the multiplication machines with whole-number bases.

Share & Summarize

It is certainly possible to solve **Question 1** without using division machines. The goal is for students to find both fraction-multiplication and division machines that work. Have students work on the question independently and then share their answers so that students who focused on the division machines, for example, are reminded of the similarities to the multiplication machines.

Question 2 asks students to find a repeater machine to "cancel" the $\div 5^4$ and leave an additional ×25. Students must recognize that $25 = 5^2$ in order to answer the question.

3 **Troubleshooting** If students come up with only multiplication machines for the first question, you may want to ask them to find division machines that work.

4 **Additional Examples** You may want to use additional examples that require hookups of machines. Ask students to give answers with division machines.

- Draw a repeater machine that will shrink a 1-inch stick to $\frac{9}{16}$ of its original size. *Possible answer:* $\div\left(\frac{4}{3}\right)^2$
- Draw a repeater machine that will shrink a stick to $\frac{4}{25}$ of its original size. *Possible answer:* $\div\left(\frac{5}{2}\right)^2$
- Find two division machines that will make a stick 4 times as long. *Possible answer:* $\div\frac{1}{4}$ and $\div\frac{1}{2}$

On Your Own Exercises

Practice & Apply: 1–9
Connect & Extend: 36–37
Mixed Review: 73–83

T165 CHAPTER 3 Exploring Exponents

1 For Problems 9–12, encourage students to break up and pair machines that undo each other.

2 For Problems 9–12, have students share solutions.

3 Have students find both multiplication and division machines.

4 Give students additional examples.

LESSON 3.2 Shrinking and Super Machines 165

Brief margin notes throughout the ***On Your Own Exercises*** and ***Chapter Review*** explain the purpose of individual questions, and suggest problem extensions.

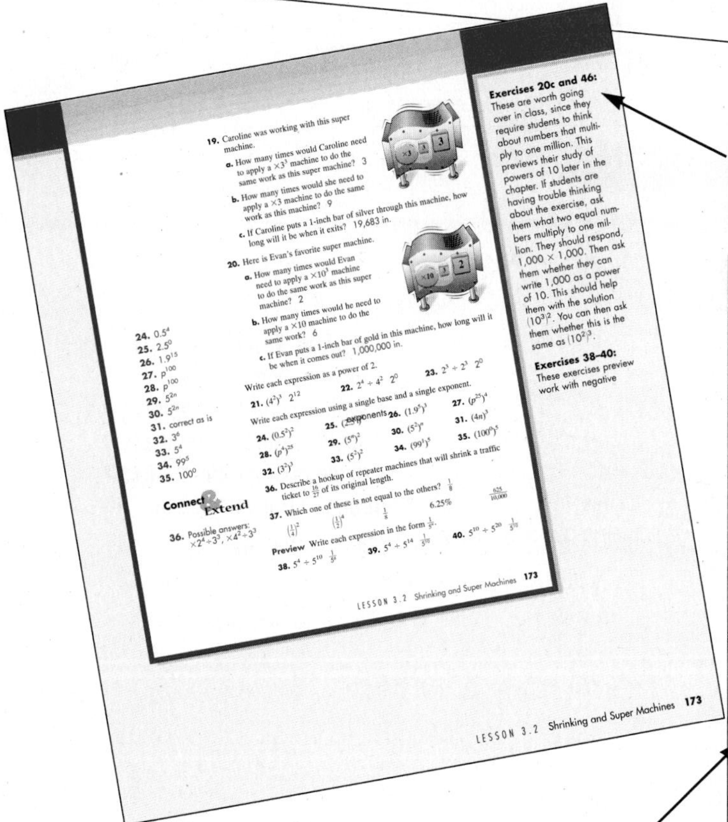

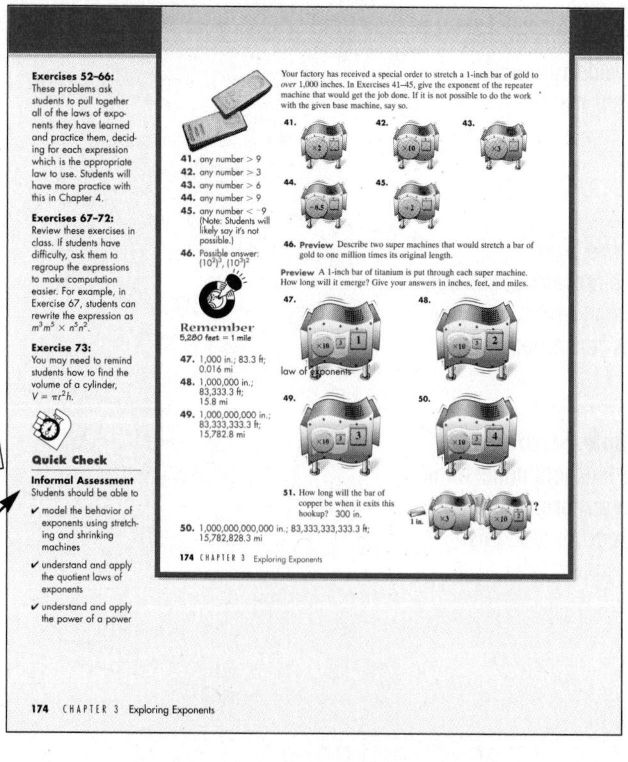

Exercises 20c and 46: These are worth going over in class, since they require students to think about numbers that multiply to one million. This previews their study of powers of 10 later in the chapter. If students are having trouble thinking about the exercise, ask them what two equal numbers multiply to one million. They should respond, 1,000 × 1,000. Then ask them whether they can write 1,000 as a power of 10. This should help them with the solution $(10^3)^2$. You can then ask them whether this is the same as $(10^2)^3$.

Exercises 38–40: These exercises preview work with negative

LESSON 3.2 Shrinking and Super Machines 173

Exercises 52–66: These problems ask students to pull together all of the laws of exponents they have learned and practice them, deciding for each expression which is the appropriate law to use. Students will have more practice with this in Chapter 4.

Exercises 67–72: Review these exercises in class. If students have difficulty, ask them to regroup the expressions to make computation easier. For example, in Exercise 67, students can rewrite the expression as $m^3m^5 \times n^5n^2$.

Exercise 73: You may need to remind students how to find the volume of a cylinder, $V = \pi r^2 h$.

Quick Check

Informal Assessment

Students should be able to:

- ✓ model the behavior of exponents using stretching and shrinking machines
- ✓ understand and apply the quotient laws of exponents
- ✓ understand and apply the power of a power

174 CHAPTER 3 Exploring Exponents

Quick Check provides informal end-of-lesson opportunities for assessing students' understanding.

Course 2

CONTENTS

Volume A

Chapter One

Understanding Expressions 1a

Chapter Two

Geometry in Three Dimensions .. 75a

Chapter Three

Exploring Exponents 143a

Chapter Four

Working with Signed Numbers . 215a

Chapter Five

Looking at Linear Relationships ..297a

Volume B

Chapter Six

Solving Equations 381a

Chapter Seven

Similarity 447a

Chapter Eight

Ratio and Proportion 517a

Chapter Nine

Interpreting Graphs 599a

Chapter Ten

Data and Probability 663a

CHAPTER 1

Understanding Expressions

Chapter Overview

In this chapter, students will manipulate expressions beginning at the concrete level by using bags and blocks to model the expressions. After becoming familiar with modeling expressions, students will investigate writing algebraic expressions and formulas that relate to specific situations.

Then students are introduced to the distributive property at the concrete level using bags and blocks. As they become familiar with the models, they are introduced to symbolic representations using flowcharts and tables.

Chapter 1 Highlights	Links to the Past	Links to the Future
Matching expressions and situations (1.1, 1.2)	**Course 1:** Writing expressions to describe patterns; translating written descriptions into symbols	**Chapter 2:** Writing expressions for block patterns **Chapter 3:** Working with exponential expressions **Chapter 9:** Working with inverse and quadratic expressions
Using formulas and evaluating expressions (1.1, 1.2)	**Course 1:** Developing and applying area and perimeter formulas; playing *What's My Rule?;* evaluating expressions	**Chapter 2:** Developing and applying volume and surface area formulas
Solving equations by backtracking (1.2)	**Course 1:** Solving equations by backtracking and guess-check-and-improve	**Chapter 6:** Solving equations by doing the same thing to both sides **Chapter 9:** Using graphs to estimate solutions **Course 3:** Solving systems of equations
Using the distributive property (1.3)	**Course 1:** Finding equivalent expressions to represent a situation	**Course 3:** Factoring quadratic expressions

Planning Guide

Lesson Objectives	Pacing	Materials	NCTM Standards
1.1 Variables and Expressions page 3b • To use variables to write expressions • To understand the order of operations • To practice using expressions to represent specific situations • To use flowcharts to build expressions • To solve equations using backtracking	4 class periods	• Master 1 • Master 2 • Master 3	1, 2, 6
1.2 Expressions and Formulas page 31b • To practice using variables to write expressions • To use expressions to solve problems • To develop and use formulas to find specific quantities • To identify restrictions on variables • To use a spreadsheet to make a chart	3 class periods	• Master 3 • Master 4	2, 5, 6
1.3 The Distributive Property page 51b • To understand and apply the distributive property • To remove parentheses by multiplying • To insert parentheses by factoring expressions • To perform numerical calculations using the distributive property	4 class periods	• Master 3 • Master 5	1, 2, 5, 6, 9, 10

NCTM Curriculum and Evaluation Standards

1. Number and Operation
2. Patterns, Functions, and Algebra
3. Geometry and Spatial Sense
4. Measurement
5. Data Analysis, Statistics, and Probability
6. Problem Solving
7. Reasoning and Proof
8. Communication
9. Connections
10. Representation

Assessment Opportunities

Standard Assessment

Impact Mathematics offers three types of formal assessment. The Chapter 1 Review & Self-Assessment in the Student Edition serves as a self-assessment tool for students. In the Teacher's Guide, a Quick Quiz at the end of each lesson allows you to check students' understanding before moving to the next lesson. The Assessment Resources include blackline masters for chapter and semester tests.

- **Student Edition** Chapter 1 Review & Self-Assessment, pages 74–75
- **Teacher's Guide** Quick Quizzes, pages 31, 51, 73
- **Assessment Resources** Chapter 1 Test, Form A, pages 27–29; Chapter 1 Test, Form B, pages 30–32

Ongoing Assessment

Impact Mathematics provides numerous opportunities for informal assessment of your students as they work through the investigations. Share & Summarize questions help you determine whether students understand the important ideas of an investigation. If students are struggling, Troubleshooting tips provide suggestions for helping them. On the Spot Assessment notes appear throughout the teaching notes. They give you suggestions for preventing or remedying common student errors. Assessment Forms in the Assessment Resources provide convenient ways to record student progress.

- **Student Edition** Share & Summarize, pages 9, 13, 18, 21, 36, 42, 55, 58, 63, 67
- **Teacher's Guide** On the Spot Assessment, pages T6, T11, T15, T16, T20, T34, T36, T39, T41, T54, T60, T62, T65
  Troubleshooting, pages T9, T13, T18, T21, T36, T42, T55, T58, T63, T67
- **Assessment Resources** Chapter 1 Assessment Forms, pages 27–32

Alternative Assessment, Portfolios, and Journal Ideas

The alternative assessment items in *Impact Mathematics* are perfect for inclusion in student portfolios and journals. The In Your Own Words feature in the Student Edition gives students a chance to write about mathematical ideas. The Performance Assessment items in the Assessment Resources provide rich, open-ended problems, ideal for take-home or group assessment.

- **Student Edition** In Your Own Words, pages 27, 48, 71
- **Assessment Resources** Chapter 1 Performance Assessment, pages 33–34; Chapter 1 Assessment Forms, pages 27–32

Assessment Resources

The Assessment Resources provide a chapter test in two equivalent forms, along with additional performance items. The performance items can be used in a variety of ways. They are ideal for take-home assessment or in-class group assessment.

- Chapter 1 Test, Form A, pages 27–29
- Chapter 1 Test, Form B, pages 30–32
- Chapter 1 Performance Assessment, pages 33–34
- Chapter 1 Assessment Solutions, pages 35–36

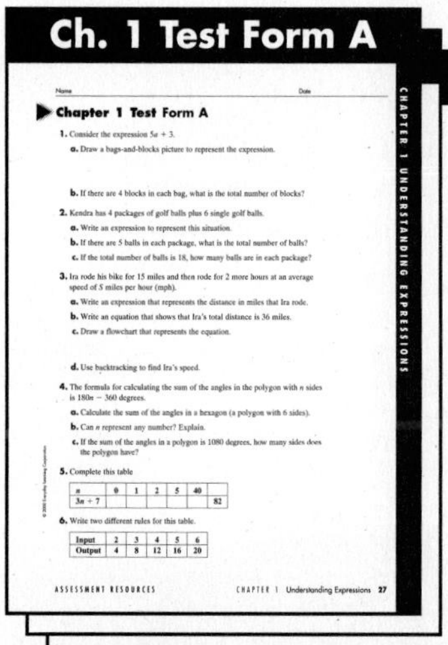

Ch. 1 Test Form A

Name Date

Chapter 1 Test Form A

1. Consider the expression $5a + 3$.
   a. Draw a bags-and-blocks picture to represent the expression.
   b. If there are 4 blocks in each bag, what is the total number of blocks?
2. Kendra has 4 packages of golf balls plus 6 single golf balls.
   a. Write an expression to represent this situation.
   b. If there are 5 balls in each package, what is the total number of balls?
   c. If the total number of balls is 18, how many balls are in each package?
3. Ira rode his bike for 15 miles and then rode for 2 more hours at an average speed of S miles per hour (mph).
   a. Write an expression that represents the distance in miles that Ira rode.
   b. Write an equation that shows that Ira's total distance is 36 miles.
   c. Draw a flowchart that represents the equation.
   d. Use backtracking to find Ira's speed.
4. The formula for calculating the sum of the angles in the polygon with n sides is $180n - 360$ degrees.
   a. Calculate the sum of the angles in a hexagon (a polygon with 6 sides).
   b. Can n represent any number? Explain.
   c. If the sum of the angles in a polygon is 1080 degrees, how many sides does the polygon have?
5. Complete this table

n	0	1	2	5	40	
$3n + 7$						82

6. Write two different rules for this table.

Input	2	3	4	5	6
Output	4	8	12	16	20

ASSESSMENT RESOURCES CHAPTER 1 Understanding Expressions 27

CHAPTER 1 UNDERSTANDING EXPRESSIONS

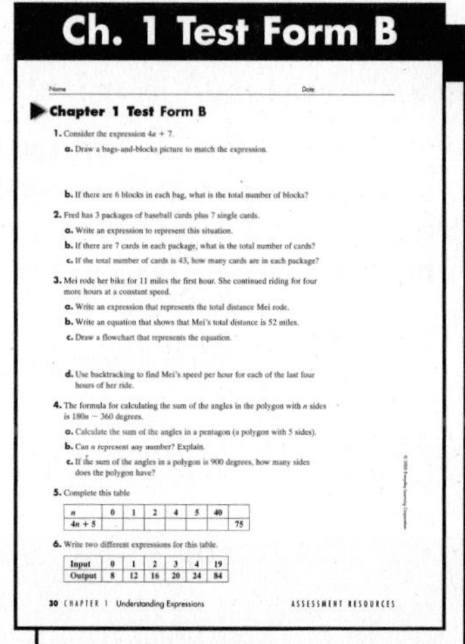

Ch. 1 Test Form B

Name Date

Chapter 1 Test Form B

1. Consider the expression $4a + 7$.
   a. Draw a bags-and-blocks picture to match the expression.
   b. If there are 6 blocks in each bag, what is the total number of blocks?
2. Fred has 3 packages of baseball cards plus 7 single cards.
   a. Write an expression to represent this situation.
   b. If there are 7 cards in each package, what is the total number of cards?
   c. If the total number of cards is 43, how many cards are in each package?
3. Mei rode her bike for 11 miles the first hour. She continued riding for four more hours at a constant speed.
   a. Write an expression that represents the total distance Mei rode.
   b. Write an equation that shows that Mei's total distance is 52 miles.
   c. Draw a flowchart that represents the equation.
   d. Use backtracking to find Mei's speed per hour for each of the last four hours of her ride.
4. The formula for calculating the sum of the angles in the polygon with n sides is $180n - 360$ degrees.
   a. Calculate the sum of the angles in a pentagon (a polygon with 5 sides).
   b. Can n represent any number? Explain.
   c. If the sum of the angles in a polygon is 900 degrees, how many sides does the polygon have?
5. Complete this table

n	0	1	2	4	5	40	
$4n + 5$							75

6. Write two different expressions for this table.

Input	0	1	2	3	4	19
Output	8	12	16	20	24	84

30 CHAPTER 1 Understanding Expressions ASSESSMENT RESOURCES

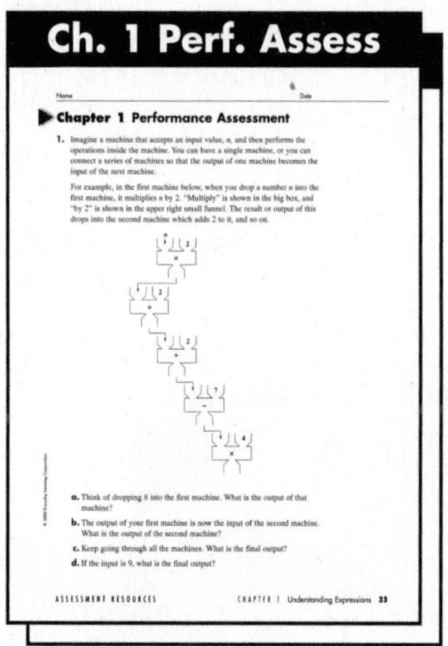

Ch. 1 Perf. Assess

Name Date

Chapter 1 Performance Assessment

1. Imagine a machine that accepts an input value, n, and then performs the operations inside the machine. You can have a single machine, or you can connect a series of machines so that the output of one machine becomes the input of the next machine.

   For example, in the first machine below, when you drop a number n into the first machine, it multiplies n by 2. "Multiply" is shown in the big box, and "by 2" is shown in the upper right small funnel. The result or output of this drops into the second machine which adds 2 to it, and so on.

   a. Think of dropping 8 into the first machine. What is the output of that machine?
   b. The output of your first machine is now the input of the second machine. What is the output of the second machine?
   c. Keep going through all the machines. What is the final output?
   d. If the input is 9, what is the final output?

ASSESSMENT RESOURCES CHAPTER 1 Understanding Expressions 33

Additional Resources

Print

Expressions and Formulas, Wisconsin Center for Educational Research, Encyclopedia Britannica Educational Corporation, 1998
This 15-day unit introduces students to informal forms of mathematical expressions and the use of the order of operations.

Key to Algebra, Book 2: Variables, Terms and Expressions by Julie King, Key Curriculum Press, 1990
The second book of a 10-book set examines basic algebraic concepts of variables, terms, and expressions using only integers.

Software

The Cruncher, Davidson & Associates
Students learn how to use spreadsheets in contextual situations and gain skill in understanding and applying numerical data.

Expressions & Formulas, Edunetics Corporation
Students write the steps of solving a problem in words and then translate the words to algebraic expressions.

Video

Beginning Algebra: Exponents, Video Resources, 1992
The video covers exponents, order of operations, as well as introducing variables and variable instructions.

Algebraic Expressions, Sunburst Communications, Inc., 1997
This video is one of four videos in the MATH VANTAGE series for Grades 5 to 8. It develops fundamental concepts of constants, operations, and variables as related to algebraic expressions.

Web sites

Visit the Everyday Learning Web site at **http://www.everydaylearning.com**

Youth Net
http://youth.net/
This World Wide Web site describes and provides links to interactive projects and resources, other online projects, and school-home pages.

Math Online; KQED Center for Education & Lifelong Learning
http://www.kqed.org/cell/school/math/mathonline/index.html
Users can choose from three main menu items: Lessons, News and Events, and Resources.

Introduction

The pictures on the opening spread show three specific situations that involve the use of algebra. As you discuss the path of a football kick with students, ask a volunteer to draw the path on the chalkboard. Explain that a path of this type is a parabola. Ask students to think of other specific contexts in which algebraic equations might be used.

Understanding Expressions

In this chapter, you will explore *algebraic expressions*—the combinations of number, letters, and mathematical symbols that form the language of algebra. This language allows you to express many kinds of relationships that exist all around you.

Algebra in the Strangest Places

You might think that algebra is a topic found only in textbooks, but you can find algebra all around you—in some of the strangest places.

Did you know there is a relationship between the speed ants crawl and the air temperature? If you were to find some ants outside and time them as they crawled, you could actually estimate the temperature. Here is the algebraic equation that describes the relationship.

$$t = 15s + 3$$

Celsius temperature (t); ant speed in $\frac{\text{cm}}{\text{s}}$ (s)

There are many ordinary and extraordinary places where you will encounter algebra.

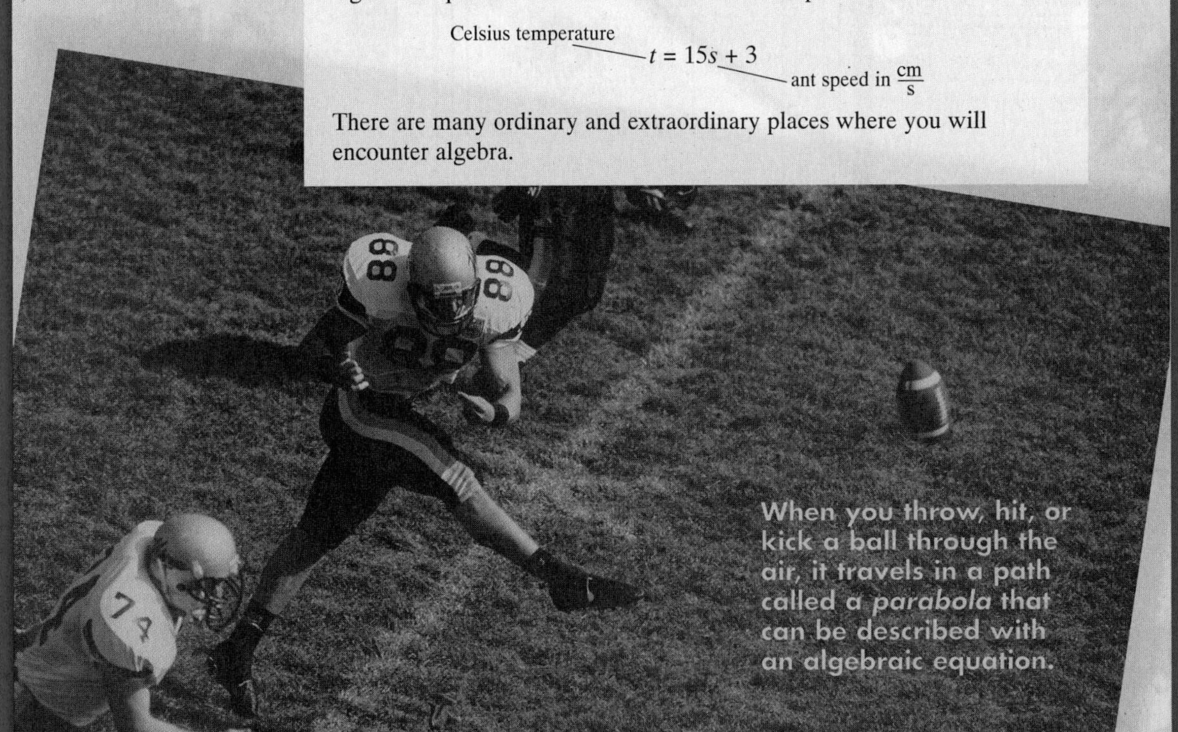

When you throw, hit, or kick a ball through the air, it travels in a path called a *parabola* that can be described with an algebraic equation.

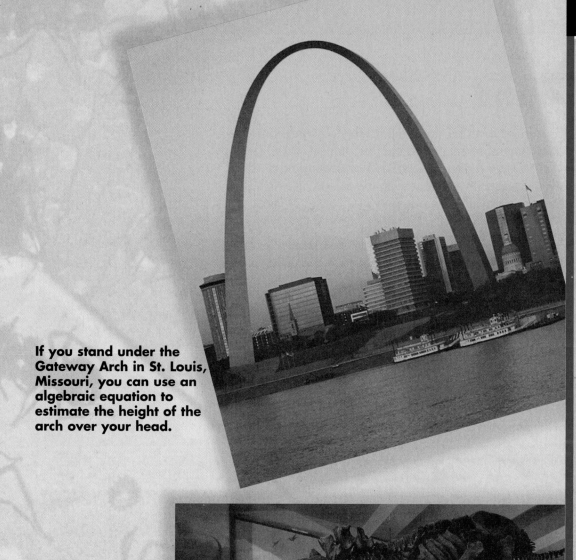

If you stand under the Gateway Arch in St. Louis, Missouri, you can use an algebraic equation to estimate the height of the arch over your head.

By measuring radioactive carbon and solving algebraic equations, scientists can estimate the age of bones and other fossils.

3

Ch. 1 Family Letter

family*letter*

CHAPTER 1 UNDERSTANDING EXPRESSIONS

Dear Family,

Our class is about to begin an exciting year of *Impact Mathematics*. Some of the topics we will study include negative numbers, exponents, three-dimensional geometry, ratios, probability, and data analysis. Throughout the year, your son or daughter will also develop and refine skills in algebra.

Your child will have many opportunities to develop an understanding about how mathematical concepts work the way they do. Since problem solving is the heart of all our work in mathematics, many activities and problems will be open-ended so that your child can explore a variety of problem-solving strategies.

In our first chapter, your child will be introduced to algebraic expressions—the combinations of numbers, letters, and mathematical symbols that form the language of algebra. We will begin by learning about variables—letters or symbols that can change or that represent unknown quantities. For example, in the expression $b + 2$, the variable is b. Ask your child to give other examples after finishing Investigation 1 in the chapter.

Once your child is familiar with variables and expressions, we will create flowcharts to match expressions and then use the flowcharts to solve equations. Your child will also explore formulas used in everyday life, such as the formula used to convert degrees Celsius to degrees Fahrenheit: $F = \frac{9}{5}C + 32$.

Encourage your child to explain the kinds of problems he or she is solving in class. In addition, help him or her think about common occurrences of algebraic expressions in daily life. Your interest in your child's work helps underscore the importance of mathematics and its usefulness in daily life.

TEACHING RESOURCES — CHAPTER 1 Understanding Expressions 1

Mathematical Background

An important part of algebra is developing facility in manipulating expressions, regardless of the real quantities they represent. In this chapter, students take first steps in that direction. The Theory of Multiple Intelligences states that students have varied learning styles and various ways of cognitively processing ideas. The investigations in this chapter deliberately activate kinesthetic, concrete, and visual styles of learning, particularly in the bags-and-blocks model.

In addition, students will learn some ways in which expressions can be manipulated, especially those related to the distributive property of multiplication over addition and over subtraction. This important property of the real number system underpins the simplification and factoring of expressions, which in turn provide powerful means of gaining algebraic insight into the nature of a particular expression. Chapter 1 also introduces some of the major algebraic conventions used in forming expressions, especially those with multiplication, division, and exponents. Two meanings of *variable* are introduced (a quantity that can vary and an unknown). For a further discussion of the many meanings of *variable,* see Chapter 2, *NCTM 1988 Yearbook,* "The Ideas of Algebra, K–12."

Students use flowcharts to build expressions and reinforce the concepts of order of operations. Backtracking formalizes the intuitive process that many students use to solve equations; it is also a powerful strategy for solving a particular class of equations.

1.1 Variables and Expressions

Objectives

- To use variables to write expressions
- To understand the order of operations
- To practice using expressions to represent specific situations
- To use flowcharts to build expressions
- To solve equations using backtracking

Overview (pacing: about 4 class periods)

Change is all around us. Sometimes we can use mathematics to help us make sense of the changing world. In this lesson, students learn how algebraic expressions can be used to describe these kinds of situations. Students are introduced to a bags-and-blocks model to show quantities that can change. Then they use variables to show unknown quantities and practice using expressions to represent situations. In the last investigation, students use flowcharts to build expressions and to solve equations by backtracking.

Advance Preparation

You will need 3 paper bags and 30 blocks for Investigation 1 to use in a whole-class demonstration. Later in this investigation, you may wish to use Master 1, Input/Output Tables, for students to record their answers. Master 2, Row of Houses, helps students organize their thinking and record their answers in a logical manner. Master 3, Flowcharts, also provides a method of recording answers when working on problems involving flowcharts.

	Summary	Materials	On Your Own Exercises	Assessment Opportunities
Investigation 1 page T4	Students translate between expressions and bags-and-blocks situations.	• Master 1 (Teaching Resources, page 3) • 3 paper bags • 30 blocks	Practice & Apply: 1–6 Connect & Extend: 37–39 Mixed Review: 49–67	Share & Summarize, pages T9, 9 On the Spot Assessment, page T6 Troubleshooting, page T9
Investigation 2 page T10	Students write algebraic expressions to represent situations in context.	• Master 2 (Teaching Resources, page 4)	Practice & Apply: 7–17 Connect & Extend: 40–42 Mixed Review: 49–67	Share & Summarize, pages T13, 13 On the Spot Assessment, page T11 Troubleshooting, page T13
Investigation 3 page T13	Students learn conventions for representing operations and exponents in expressions and practice evaluating expressions.	• Master 3 (Teaching Resources, page 5)	Practice & Apply: 18–27 Connect & Extend: 43–45 Mixed Review: 49–67	Share & Summarize, pages T18, 18 On the Spot Assessment, pages T15, T16 Troubleshooting, page T18
Investigation 4 page T18	Students use flowcharts to build expressions and to solve equations by backtracking.	• Master 2 • Master 3	Practice & Apply: 28–36 Connect & Extend: 46–48 Mixed Review: 49–67	Share & Summarize, pages T21, 21 On the Spot Assessment, page T20 Troubleshooting, page T21 Informal Assessment, page 30 Quick Quiz, page 31

Introduce

Tell students that they will be learning how to use expressions to describe situations. Read the opening paragraphs with students. You may wish to review the definition of an *expression,* a mathematical phrase that uses numbers and/or variables and operations.

Students may find that some material introduced in the first lesson is a review. If your students are familiar with writing expressions and using flowcharts, you may want to move quickly through these investigations.

Think & Discuss

One way to introduce the bags-and-blocks scenario is to have students participate in setting up the problem. This should help them remember the model. Have four students come to the front of the room and form a line facing the class. Have 3 bags and 30 blocks placed on a desk.

Hand 2 blocks to the student on the right. Give each of the other three students an empty bag to hold. Students now mirror the arrangement in the illustration in the text. Show the class that the bags are empty. Then ask the class:

> How many blocks do these four students have altogether? 2

Now place 5 blocks in each of the bags. Ask students:

> What is the total number of blocks now? 17

Encourage students to predict the total number of blocks by asking:

> What would be the total number of blocks if there were 8 blocks in each bag? 26

Tell students that it isn't always practical to use a model. You may want to illustrate this point by asking:

> Suppose there were 100 blocks in each bag. What is the total number of blocks now? 302

To encourage students to generalize their experiences, ask:

> When you know how many blocks are in each bag, how do you find the total number of blocks? Multiply the number of blocks in each bag by 3, and then add 2.

1.1 Expressions

Every day people are confronted with problems they have to solve. Many of these problems involve such quantities as the amount of spice to add to a recipe, the cost of electricity, and interest rates. In some problem situations, it helps to have a way to record information without using a lot of words. For example, both boxes present the same idea.

To convert a Celsius temperature to a Fahrenheit temperature, find nine-fifths of the Celsius temperature and then add 32.	$F = \frac{9}{5}C + 32$

While the statement on the left may be easier to read and understand at first, the statement on the right has several advantages. It is shorter and easier to write, it shows clearly how the quantities—Celsius temperature and Fahrenheit temperature—are related, and it allows you to try different Celsius temperatures and compute their Fahrenheit equivalents.

In this lesson, you'll see that by using a few simple rules, you can write powerful algebraic expressions and equations for a variety of situations.

1 Review the introductory text with students.

Think & Discuss

2 Have students "act out" the Think & Discuss situation.

Shaunda, Kate, and Simon are holding bags of blocks. Erin has just two blocks.

If you know how many blocks are in each bag, how can you figure out how many blocks there are altogether? See ①.

① Add the number in the first bag, the number in the second bag, the number in the third bag, and 2. Or, since the number in each of the bags is the same, multiply this number by 3 and add 2.

Students should understand that since the number of blocks in each bag can change, or vary, the quantity can be represented by a *variable*. They should be aware that it is customary to use letters to represent a number, such as the varying quantity of blocks in each bag.

On the board, draw a picture of 3 bags and 2 blocks, writing the letter n on each of the bags. Ask students questions such as:

> How can we add to find the total number of blocks? Add n three times, then add 2: $n + n + n + 2$.
>
> What is another way to find the total number of blocks? Multiply 3 by n, then add 2.
>
> How can you write the expression using multiplication? $3n + 2$

Continue the demonstration by having students find how many blocks are in each bag when there are 29 blocks altogether. Leave 29 blocks on the desk. Tell students that one student will have 2 blocks and the remaining blocks will be divided evenly among the bags. Encourage students to provide ways to find the number of blocks that will be in each bag. Some students may suggest that you give 2 blocks to the student on the right and divide the remaining 27 blocks equally among the three students.

Investigation 1

In this investigation, students use a bags-and-blocks model to write and evaluate algebraic expressions. They work forward to find the value of an expression when given the value of a variable. They work backward to find the value of a variable when given the value of an expression. Be sure students understand that no matter how many times a variable is used in an expression, it always represents the same quantity.

You may continue to use the 3-bags-and-2-blocks model from the introduction. Ask students:

> What rule could you use to find the total number of blocks if you know how many blocks are in each bag? $3n + 2$

Write the rule on the board. Tell students that this rule is an example of an *algebraic expression,* since it contains variables and operations.

If you know the number of blocks in each bag, it's not hard to express the total number of blocks. For example, if there are 20 blocks in each bag, you can just add:

$$20 + 20 + 20 + 2 = 62$$

Or you can multiply and add:

$$3 \times 20 + 2 = 62$$

VOCABULARY
variable

What if you don't know the number in each bag? First, notice that, in this situation, the number of bags and the number of loose blocks don't change, but the number of blocks in each bag can change. Quantities that can change, or vary, are called **variables.**

In algebra, letters are often used to represent variables. For example, you can let the letter n stand for the number of blocks in each bag.

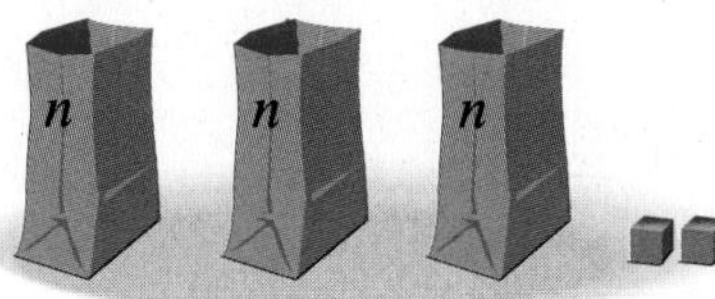

Remember
Multiplication can be shown in several ways:
$3 \times n$ $3(n)$
$3 \cdot n$ $3 * n$

Now you can find the total number of blocks as you did before—by adding:

$$n + n + n + 2$$

or by multiplying and adding:

$$3 \times n + 2$$

In algebra, the multiplication symbol between a number and a variable is usually left out. So $3 \times n + 2$ can be written $3n + 2$.

Investigation 1 Bags and Blocks

In the bags-and-blocks situation above, you can think of $3n + 2$ as a *rule* for finding the total number of blocks when you know the number of blocks in each bag. Just substitute the number in each bag for n. For example, for 100 blocks in each bag, the total number of blocks is

$$3n + 2 = 3 \times 100 + 2 = 302$$

1 Review the concept of a variable.

2
- Discuss the rule for finding the number of blocks if there are n in each bag.
- Have students find the number of blocks in each bag if there are 29 blocks altogether.

3
- Review the rule for 3 bags and 2 blocks.
- Introduce the term *algebraic expression.*

Develop

Problem Set A **Suggested Grouping: Pairs**
Problem Set A provides students with practice evaluating the expression $3n + 2$ for different values of n. Students also informally practice backtracking, or working backward, to find the value of n when given the total number of blocks.

Circulate around the room to make sure students know how to complete the table in **Problem 1.** You may want to complete the table as a whole-class activity, having volunteers complete individual table entries on the board. You may wish to use Master 1, Input/Output Tables, as a means of having students record their answers in an orderly fashion.

Sample Strategies The reasoning processes students use to solve **Problem 5** are essential for solving equations. Here students work from the total number of blocks to the number of blocks in each bag. Many students may have previous experiences in solving this kind of problem. In the later investigations, students will learn the technique of backtracking more formally. At this stage, students may employ these strategies:

- Some may want to work with the blocks and bags. Students may model the problem by counting out 20 blocks, and then putting 2 blocks aside. The remaining 18 blocks must be divided equally among the 3 bags. Students can find the number of blocks in each bag by either physically counting and putting the blocks in each bag or by simplifying $\frac{18}{3}$.
- Other students may use guess and check.

Encourage students to explain their solving strategies.

On the Spot Assessment

Watch for students who add 3 and the number representing n when evaluating the expression $3n + 2$. Review with them the meaning of the notation in which a number followed by a variable indicates multiplication. You might wish to have students use bags and blocks to find the value of the expression $3n + 4$ when n has these values:

$n = 5$ $\quad 3 \times 5 + 4 = 19$

$n = 2$ $\quad 3 \times 2 + 4 = 10$

$n = 6$ $\quad 3 \times 6 + 4 = 22$

Teaching Resources

Master 1 Activity Master
Input/Output Tables

VOCABULARY
algebraic expression

Rules written with numbers and symbols, such as $n + n + n + 2$ and $3n + 2$, are called **algebraic expressions.**

As you study algebra, you will work with algebraic expressions often. Using bags and blocks is a good way to start thinking about expressions. Imagining the variable as a bag that you can put any number of blocks into can help you see how the value of an expression changes as the value of the variable changes.

Problem Set A

1 Have students work in pairs.

In these problems, you will continue to explore the situation in which there are 3 bags, each containing the same number of blocks, plus 2 extra blocks.

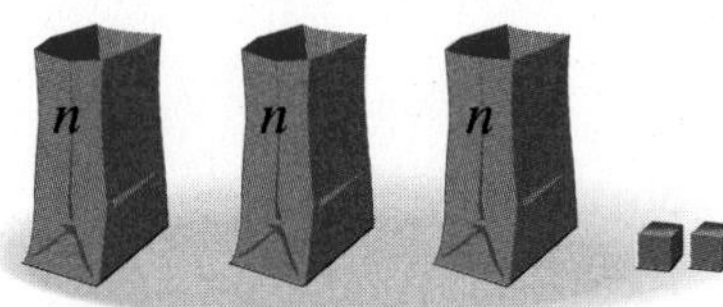

1. Copy and complete the table.

Number of Blocks in Each Bag, n	0	1	2	3	4	5
Total Number of Blocks, $3n + 2$	2	5	8	11	14	17

2 Make sure students know how to complete the table.

2. If $n = 7$, what is the value of $3n + 2$? 23
3. If $n = 25$, what is the value of $3n + 2$? 77
4. If there are 50 blocks in each bag, how many blocks are there altogether? 152
5. If there are 20 blocks altogether, how many blocks are in each bag? 6
6. Copy and complete the table.

3 Look for a variety of strategies for Problem 5.

n	10	5	40	25	100	7	30	22	42	1,047
$3n + 2$	32	17	122	77	302	23	92	68	128	3,143

7. Compare the tables in Problems 1 and 6. Which table do you think was more difficult to complete? Why?

   Possible answer: The tables use the same rule, but the table in Problem 1 has inputs that are in order, and was only missing outputs. The table in Problem 6 was more difficult because the numbers aren't in order and we had to find some inputs as well as outputs.

Develop

Sample Strategies Students may use one of the following strategies to solve **Problem 8.**

- Some students may need to use bags and blocks to model the problem. They may need to put blocks in the bags to discover that the situation is impossible with whole units. As students reconstruct the problem in these concrete or visual terms, they find that the difficulties often disappear because they better understand the question.
- Some students may use number sense. They may subtract the 2 blocks first and then realize that 16 is not divisible by 3.
- Other students may use logical reasoning. They may recognize that since $3 \times 6 = 18$, there must be fewer than 6 blocks in each bag. If there were 5 blocks in each bag, there would only be 17 blocks in all. If each bag held fewer than 5 blocks, the total number of blocks would be less than 17. Therefore it is not possible to have exactly 18 blocks in all.

Problem Set Wrap-Up Students should understand how the expression $3n + 2$ relates to the bags-and-blocks model before doing Problem Set B. Check their work on **Problems 8–10** before proceeding. If needed, work through an additional example like the one that follows.

Additional Example Make up an expression such as $2n + 1$ that can be modeled using bags and blocks.

- Have one student use bags and blocks to model the expression. Then ask that person to determine the total number of blocks if there are 8 blocks in each bag. After the student solves the problem, you might want to write on the board: $2(8) + 1 = 17$.
- Have a second student find the number of blocks per bag if the total number of blocks is 21. *10*

Problem Set B **Suggested Grouping: Pairs**
This problem set focuses on relating expressions with bags-and-blocks situations. Students are asked to explain what the numbers and variables in expressions represent for a given situation. They are introduced to the use of letters other than *n* as variables, and they write simple expressions for models. They also explore the meaning of subtracting a constant.

8. no; Possible explanation: If 5 blocks are in each bag, there are a total of 17 blocks. If 6 blocks are in each bag, there are a total of 20 blocks. The number that gives a total of 18 must be between 5 and 6. Since the number of blocks must be a whole number, it is not possible to have a total of 18 blocks.

9. If the bags contained different numbers of blocks, the number of blocks in a bag could not be represented by a single variable, *n*.

10a. five bags, each containing the same number of blocks, plus 6 extra blocks

10b. The $5n$ represents the 5 bags with *n* blocks each, and the 6 represents the 6 extra blocks.

8. Could the total number of blocks in this situation be 18? Explain.

9. To represent the number of blocks in 3 bags plus 2 extra blocks with the expression $3n + 2$, you need to assume that all the bags contain the same number of blocks. Why?

10. The expression $3n + 2$ describes the total number of blocks in 3 bags, each with the same number of blocks, plus 2 extra blocks.

a. Describe a bags-and-blocks situation that can be represented by the expression $5n + 6$.

b. Explain how the expression fits your situation.

You have spent a lot of time exploring the number of blocks in three bags plus two extra blocks. Now you'll investigate some other bags-and-blocks situations.

Problem Set B

1. Here are 5 bags and 4 extra blocks.

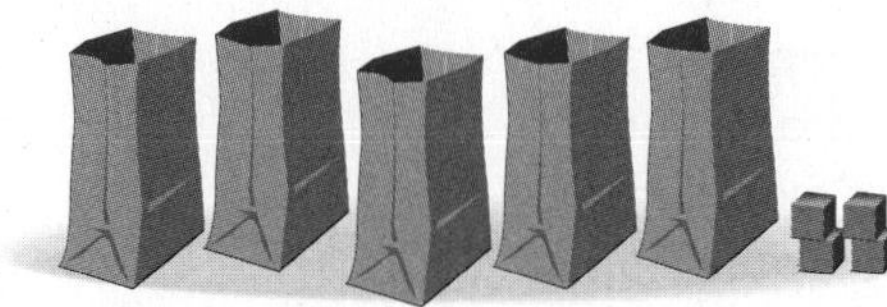

a. What is the total number of blocks if each bag contains 3 blocks? If each bag contains 10 blocks? 19, 54

b. Using *n* to represent the number of blocks in each bag, write an algebraic expression for the total number of blocks. $5n + 4$

c. Find the value of your expression for $n = 3$ and $n = 10$. Do you get the same answers you found in Part a? 19, 54, yes

2. Now suppose you have 4 bags, each with the same number of blocks, plus 2 extra blocks.

a. Draw a picture of this situation.

b. Write an expression for the total number of blocks. $4n + 2$

3. Write an expression to represent 7 bags, each with the same number of blocks, plus 5 extra blocks. $7n + 5$

4. Write an expression to represent 10 bags, each with the same number of blocks, plus 1 extra block. $10n + 1$

1 Look for a variety of strategies for Problem 8.

2
- Check students' work on Problems 8–10.
- Present additional examples if needed.

3 Have students work in pairs.

LESSON 1.1 Variables and Expressions 7

Develop

In **Problem 5,** students have their first exposure in this course to using a letter other than *n* as a variable when they match expressions to drawings. You may wish to discuss various ways to approach the problem. Some students may look at a picture and then find the expression that describes it. Others may choose an expression and look for a drawing that matches that expression. Some students may count the bags in a picture and find expressions that have the correct corresponding coefficient. Then they can count the number of blocks to narrow their choices and choose the correct expression. Others may approach it from the constant perspective, counting the blocks first, narrowing their search, and then looking at the bags to find the correct expression.

In **Problem 6,** students define different components of a given expression. They also think forward and backward to complete a table. Students will get more formal practice with working backward in the subsequent investigations.

5. Any letter can be used to stand for the number of blocks in a bag. Match each expression below with a drawing.

$2c + 4$ $4m + 2$ $4y + 5$ $2f + 5$

a. $4m + 2$

b. $2f + 5$

c. $2c + 4$

d. $4y + 5$

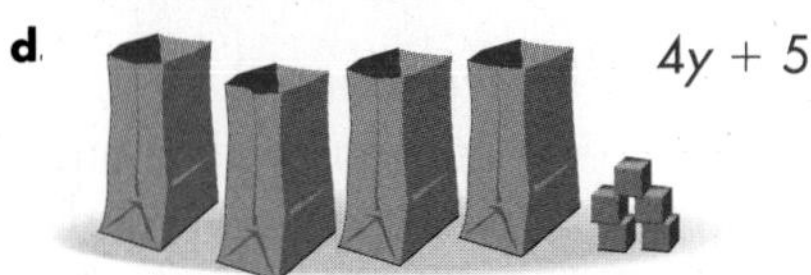

1 Discuss using a letter for a variable other than *n*.

6. Rebecca wrote the expression $3b + 1$ to describe the total number of blocks represented in this picture.

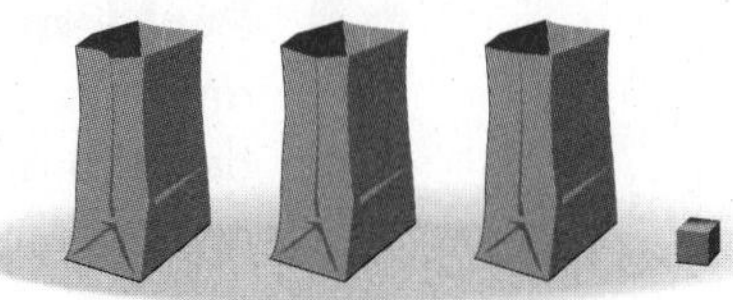

a. What does the variable *b* stand for in Rebecca's expression?

6a. the number of blocks in each bag

b. What does the 3 stand for? the number of bags

c. What does the 1 stand for? the number of loose blocks

d. Complete the table for Rebecca's expression.

b	1	2	3	10	23	25	100
$3b + 1$	4	7	10	31	70	76	301

2 Be sure students understand what each number and each variable in the equation represents.

Develop

In **Problem 7,** students are exposed to the limitations of models. Students may question how the situation in **7b** can occur if there is only 1 block in each bag. Since there would only be 5 blocks in all, they may wonder how it would be possible to have 7 fewer blocks. In this case, the model doesn't make sense. Point out that the bags-and-blocks model is merely one way to help us think about a situation. Remind them that this model, like most models, sometimes has limitations.

In **Problem 7c,** students are given the total number of blocks and take away bags of blocks.

In **Problems 8a and 8b,** students are given the number of blocks for Sascha. They can then use that information to find how many blocks Chris and Dean have. Then they add the number of blocks each boy has to find the total number of blocks. Some students may focus on finding the number of blocks held by Chris and Dean and forget to add Patrick's blocks when finding the total quantity.

Sample Strategies Students may use one of these strategies to solve **Problem 8c.**

- Some students may use logic and the information given in the directions to write an expression. They know that Sascha has one more block than Chris and one fewer block than Dean. Therefore if b represents the number of Sascha's blocks, then the total number of blocks for the three boys can be represented by $b + (b - 1) + (b + 1) = 3b$. To find the total number of blocks, they can add the 2 blocks for Patrick to $3b$.
- Other students may need to look at the answers to 8a and 8b to see whether the data forms a pattern. They may need to experiment with giving Sascha different quantities of blocks in order to establish and test their theories.
- Still other students may need to use concrete materials. Have them give Sascha 2 blocks and then find the number of blocks for Chris and Dean. Chris: 1; Dean: 3

If students need more assistance in understanding why you can multiply the number of blocks Sascha has by 3 and then add 2, you may wish to ask questions such as these:

> How many blocks would Chris have if Dean gave him one block? 2
>
> How many blocks would Dean have left after he gave Chris one block? 2
>
> How can you multiply to find the total number of blocks that Sascha, Chris, and Dean have in all? Multiply 2 by 3.
>
> How will you account for Patrick's blocks? Add 2 to the product.
>
> How could you find the total if there were n blocks? Multiply n by 3, then add 2.

Problem 8d is more challenging. Students may reason that if there are 26 blocks altogether, they can take away 2 blocks for Patrick. That leaves 24 blocks to be divided among the other three boys. Using their logic from 8c, students can find $\frac{24}{3} = 8$, so Sascha has 8 blocks, Chris has one fewer block than Sascha, or 7, and Dean has one more block than Sascha, or 9.

In **Problem 8 e–g,** students must realize that the expressions with c and s name the same total quantity. However, since c and s stand for the number of blocks for different people, the written expressions are not the same. Students may choose to verify their answers using different values for Sascha's blocks.

Problem Set Wrap-Up Ask students to share their answers to **Problem 8.** Since this problem allows students to apply what they have learned, it is a good opportunity to ensure that students understand the material. Encourage them to share their strategies.

Share & Summarize

These three questions ask students to make their own bag-and-block drawing and write an expression describing it. Ask students to share their pictures with partners, and have the partners write expressions that represent the pictures.

Troubleshooting If students are still having difficulty understanding expressions, they may need more experience modeling bags-and-blocks situations. As students experiment with different quantities, have them record their answers in a table.

Start by giving each group of students 2 bags and 3 extra blocks. Have them find the total number of blocks if each bag has 7 blocks. Continue with different numbers of blocks per bag. They can use their tables to help them find a rule and write an expression.

On Your Own Exercises

Practice & Apply: 1–6
Connect & Extend: 37–39
Mixed Review: 49–67

7a. Possible answer: 1 block less than 4 bags' worth

7b. Possible answer: 7 blocks less than 5 bags' worth

7c. Possible answer: the number of blocks left after 3 bags' worth are removed from a group of 14 blocks

8a. Chris: 5; Sascha: 6; Dean: 7; Patrick: 2; total: 20

8b. Chris: 14; Sascha: 15; Dean: 16; Patrick: 2; total: 47

8c. The total is 3 times the number Sascha has, plus 2.

8d. The total, 26, is 3 times the number Sascha has, plus 2. So 3 times the number Sascha has must be 24. Sascha must have 8 blocks. So, Chris has 7, Dean has 9, and Patrick has 2.

7. Zoe thought of a new situation:

"Imagine that the total number of blocks is 2 blocks less than 3 bags' worth. This is hard to draw, but I just described it easily in words—and I can write it algebraically as $3n - 2$."

a. Describe a situation that $4n - 1$ could represent.

b. Describe a situation that $5x - 7$ could represent.

c. Describe a situation that $14 - 3p$ could represent.

8. Sascha has 1 more block than Chris, and Dean has 1 more block than Sascha. Patrick has just 2 blocks.

a. If Sascha has 6 blocks, how many blocks does each boy have? How many do they have altogether?

b. If Sascha has 15 blocks, how many blocks does each boy have? How many do they have altogether?

c. If you know how many blocks Sascha has, how can you determine the total number of blocks without figuring out how many blocks each of the other boys has?

d. If the boys have 26 blocks altogether, how many does each boy have? Explain how you arrived at your answer.

e. Let s stand for the number of blocks Sascha has. Write an expression for the number each boy has. Then write an expression for the total number of blocks. See below.

f. Let c stand for the number of blocks Chris has. Write an expression for the number each boy has. Then write an expression for the total number of blocks. See below.

g. Your expressions for Parts e and f both tell how many blocks the group has, and yet the expressions are different. Explain why. $3s + 2$ tells the total number of blocks in terms of the number Sascha has. $3c + 5$ tells the total number of blocks in terms of the number Chris has. They are different because the variables s and c stand for different values.

Share  Summarize

Answers will vary.

1. Make a bags-and-blocks drawing.

2. Write an expression that describes your drawing.

3. Explain how you know your expression matches your drawing.

8e. Chris: $s - 1$; Sascha: s; Dean: $s + 1$; Patrick: 2; total: $s + s + s + 2$, or $3s + 2$

8f. Chris: c; Sascha: $c + 1$; Dean: $(c + 1) + 1$; Patrick: 2; total: $c + c + c + 5$, or $3c + 5$

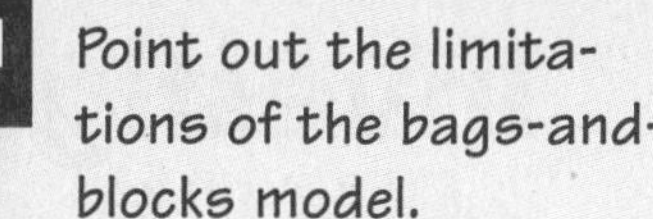

1 Point out the limitations of the bags-and-blocks model.

2 Assist struggling students with Problem 8.

3 Encourage students to share their answers and strategies for Problem 8.

4 Have students exchange drawings with their partners.

LESSON 1.1 Variables and Expressions 9

Investigation 2

In this investigation, students move from using bags and blocks to modeling algebraic expressions. They begin to explore situations with unknown quantities as well as those with quantities that can change. Students are immersed in situations where they must write expressions and then find values for the expressions that fit the parameters of the problem. Students are asked to think of situations that can be described by a given algebraic expression.

Problem Set C Suggested Grouping: Small Groups

The puzzle in this problem set provides an example of how expressions can be used to solve complex problems. It involves logical thinking as well as the skills of writing and using expressions. It highlights the power of breaking a big problem into manageable parts.

In **Problem 1,** students will not need to use their algebra skills to determine which person lives in each house. They can use logical reasoning to solve the problem. Most will start by placing Bart in house number 2 and Freda in house number 6 because that information is given in the clues. Students may then place Lyndal, Jay, Davina, and Tara respectively. You may wish to use Master 2, Row of Houses, to help students record their answers in a logical manner.

Tips from Teachers

I often read aloud important information and hints so that students have a chance to use both auditory and visual skills in understanding the problem. For example, I read aloud and emphasize the hint in **Problem 1** that suggests students ignore any information not needed to solve the problem, such as how many CDs are owned by each person.

2 **Sample Strategies** For **Problems 1 and 2,** you may want to suggest that students plan how they will organize their data before they start to solve the problem.

- Some students may use a table, like the one below to organize their data.

House	1	2	3	4	5	6
Person	Tara	Bart	Lyndal	Jay	Davina	Freda
Expression	$4p - 13$	$p + 4$	$p - 2$	p	$3(p - 2)$	$17 - p$

- Other students may record the data in a less formal way. These students may prefer to sketch the houses or use Master 2 and write the data below each house.

In **Problem 2,** students use the clues to find the number of CDs owned by each person. Students must translate key words into symbols in order to write expressions. For example, the phrase *2 fewer* is shown by the expression $p - 2$.

Problem 3 asks students to find what value of p will result in Davina having the most CDs. Students evaluate expressions for different values of p to find the answer. Students may find it helpful to organize their data in a table like the one below.

Tara	Bart	Lyndal	Jay	Davina	Freda
$4p - 13$	$p + 4$	$p - 2$	p	$3(p - 2)$	$17 - p$
3	8	2	4	6	13
7	9	3	5	9	12
11	**10**	**4**	**6**	**12**	**11**
15	11	5	7	15	10
19	12	6	8	18	9

House 5 has the most CDs when Jay has 6 CDs.

By substituting several values for p, students see that when p is less than 6, Freda has the most CDs. When p is greater than 6, Tara has the same number of or more CDs as Davina. Only when p equals 6, does Davina have more CDs than anyone else.

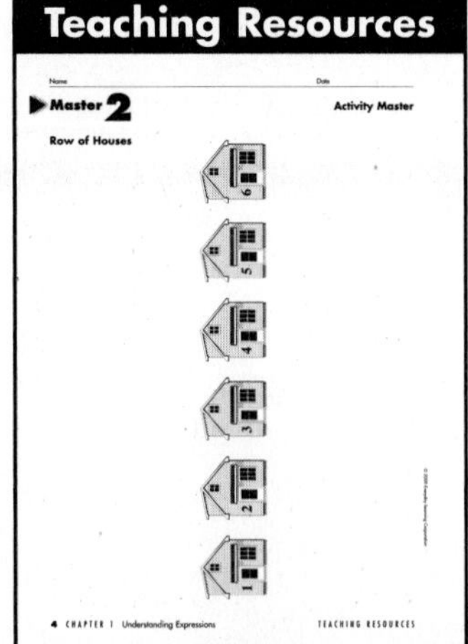

Investigation  Writing Expressions

You have seen that algebraic expressions can be used to represent situations in which a quantity changes, or *varies*. So far, you've worked a lot with bags and blocks. In this investigation, you will write algebraic expressions to describe many other situations.

Problem Set C

- Have students work in small groups.
- Distribute copies of Master 2.

Jay, Lyndal, Davina, Bart, Tara, and Freda live in a row of houses that are numbered 1 to 6. Use the clues below to help you solve Problems 1–3.

- Jay owns some CDs.
- Lyndal lives next to Jay and three houses from Freda. Lyndal has 2 fewer CDs than Jay.
- Davina lives on the other side of Jay and has three times as many CDs as Lyndal.
- Bart lives in House 2 and has 4 more CDs than Jay.
- If Tara had 13 more CDs, she would have four times as many as Jay.
- Jay acquired all his CDs from Freda, who lives in House 6. Freda had 17 CDs before she gave p of them to Jay.
- The person in House 5 owns the most CDs.

Suggest that students think about how to organize their data before they begin.

1. Figure out who lives in each house. (Hint: Focus on where the people live. Ignore the other information.)
2. Let p stand for the number of CDs Jay has. Write an expression containing the variable p for the number of CDs each person has.
3. Use your expressions to help determine how many CDs Jay has. (Hint: Experiment with different values of p. Only one value of p gives the person in House 5 the most CDs.) 6

1. 1: Tara; 2: Bart; 3: Lyndal; 4: Jay; 5: Davina; 6: Freda

2. Jay: p; Lyndal: $p - 2$; Davina: $3(p - 2)$; Bart: $p + 4$; Tara: $4p - 13$; Freda: $17 - p$

Problem Set D **Suggested Grouping: Pairs**
This problem set contains a number of contexts for writing expressions. The wording of each problem emphasizes that a variable represents a number. For example, **Problem 2** refers to the number of pounds, rather than merely to the weight, emphasizing that it is the *number* that is represented by a variable.

On the Spot Assessment

Watch for students who use the number of pounds of a bag of potatoes as the basis for writing the expression in **Problem 2c and 2d.** For example, some students may not read the problem carefully and decide that a bag of broccoli is 5 lb lighter than a bag of potatoes, when it is actually lighter than a bag of corn. These students would write the expression as $t - 5$ instead of $(t - 2) - 5$, or $t - 7$. Encourage students to make a list of the vegetables and the expression showing how many pounds each bag weighs for a quick reference.

1b. $N - 11$
2c. $(t - 2) - 5$, or $t - 7$
2d. $(t - 2) - 2$, or $t - 4$
2e. broccoli, beans, corn, potatoes, carrots

In Problem Set C, the variable p could have only one value. The variable was used to represent an unknown quantity: the number of CDs Jay has. As you saw, it is helpful to be able to use a variable to represent an unknown quantity. Now you have two ways to think about variables: as a quantity that can change and as an unknown quantity.

Problem Set D

Have students work in pairs.

For these situations, the variables represent unknown quantities rather than quantities that change.

1. Jonathan bought N apples.

a. Granny Smith bought four times as many apples as Jonathan. Write an expression to show how many apples she bought. $4N$

b. Jonathan used 11 apples in a pie. How many does he have left?

2. Suppose a bag of potatoes weighs t pounds. Write an expression for the number of pounds in each bag of vegetables below. Each expression should include the variable t.

a. a bag of carrots weighing 3 lb more than a bag of potatoes $t + 3$

b. a bag of corn weighing 2 lb less than a bag of potatoes $t - 2$

c. a bag of broccoli weighing 5 lb less than a bag of corn

d. a bag of beans weighing 3 lb more than a bag of broccoli

e. Order the five bags from lightest to heaviest.

3. Baby Leanne is L inches tall. Write expressions, in terms of the variable L, to represent the heights in inches of these members of Leanne's family:

a. her 4-year-old brother Tim, who is twice as tall as Leanne $2L$

b. her 6-year-old sister Kerry, who is 5 in. taller than Tim $2L + 5$

c. her mother, who is 15 in. shorter than four times Leanne's height

d. her father, who is 15 in. shorter than twice Kerry's height

e. Baby Leanne is about 20 in. long. Check the expressions you wrote in Parts a–d by substituting this value and determining whether the heights are reasonable.
Tim is 40 in., or 3 ft 4 in.; Kerry is 45 in., or 3 ft 9 in.; her mother is 65 in., or 5 ft 5 in.; her father is 75 in., or 6 ft 3 in.; The heights seem reasonable.

Just the facts

The average newborn is about 20 inches long. It takes people about 4 years to double their length at birth, and 8 more years to grow to three times their birth length. A person "only about 3.5 times the height of a newborn" is quite tall!

3c. $4L - 15$
3d. $2(2L + 5) - 15$, or $4L - 5$

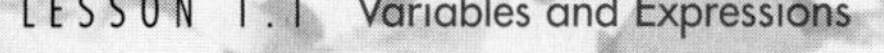

LESSON 1.1 Variables and Expressions **11**

In **Problems 4 and 5,** students are asked to consider possible restrictions on given variables. This may be a student's first exposure to the concept of domain. Encourage students to talk about these limitations. After discussing these problems, you may want to have students identify any limitations on other expressions they have written for bags-and-blocks situations in prior investigations.

In **Problem 4,** students need to realize that Maya must have at least 70¢, or 14 nickels, in order to purchase the pencil. It follows that when k is less than 14, the problem doesn't make sense.

In **Problem 5,** students are exposed to an upper limitation. If the fare is greater than 50¢, then the $5 that Neeraj has will not be enough money to ride the bus 10 times in one week.

Problem Set Wrap-Up Students may like to share their scenarios for **Problem 6** with the class. This would provide a forum to check for the reasonableness of the situations. The variety of situations may help students realize how they can use expressions in their lives.

Before moving on, be sure students understand that expressions for specific situations may not make sense for certain values. Have students decide which situations in **Problems 1-5** would not make sense if the value of the variable were 0. Then have students provide examples of instances when it only makes sense for a variable to be replaced by a whole number. Students may suggest people waiting in line, the number of computers in a classroom, and so on.

The first U.S. nickel, the "Shield nickel," was minted in 1866. If you found one of these in your attic today, it could be worth hundreds to thousands of dollars!

4d. $5k - 70$; No; since 70¢ is 14 nickels, k must be 14 or greater.

4. Maya has k nickels in her pocket.

a. Write an expression for the value of Maya's nickels in cents. Find the value of the expression for $k = 4$. $5k$, 20¢

b. Maya also has 60¢ in other coins. Write an expression for the total value, in cents, of all her change. $5k + 60$

c. Find the total value for $k = 5$ and $k = 12$. 85¢, $1.20

d. Yesterday Maya had k nickels in her pocket and no other money. She spent 70¢ on a pencil. What was the total value of her coins after she bought the pencil? Could k be *any* whole number? Why?

5. Neeraj rides the city bus to school and back each weekday. The bus fare is F cents each way. He starts each week with $5 for bus fare. Write an expression for each of the following:

a. the amount, in cents, Neeraj spends on bus fare in one day $2F$

b. the amount he has left when he gets home on Monday $500 - 2F$

c. the total bus fare he has spent by lunch time on Thursday $7F$

d. the amount of bus fare he spends each week $10F$

e. the amount he has left at the end of the week $500 - 10F$

f. What would happen if F were 60? See Additional Answers.

6. You can sometimes make sense of an expression by inventing a meaning for its symbols. For example, for the expression $k - 4$, you can let k represent the number of kittens in a pet shop. Then $k - 4$ could stand for the number of kittens in the shop after 4 have been sold.

Interpret each expression below by making up a meaning for the symbols. See Additional Answers.

a. $d + 10$ **b.** $3a$ **c.** $f - 4$

1 Encourage students to talk about restrictions in Problems 4 and 5.

2 Have students share their scenarios for Problem 6.

3 Review the idea of restrictions on variables.

Additional Answers
Problem Set D

5f. Possible answer: $5 would not be enough for a week's bus fare.

6. Possible answers:

a. If I have d dollars, $d + 10$ is the number of dollars I have after my brother gives me 10 more dollars.

b. If a is the number of apples picked by each student, $3a$ is the number picked by 3 students.

c. If a leaky radiator starts with f quarts of fluid, $f - 4$ is the amount of fluid left after 4 quarts have escaped.

Share & Summarize

Have students discuss their answers to Share & Summarize in pairs. You may want to have students decide whether there are any values of h that do not make sense. Some students may note that while h must be greater than or equal to 0, its value does not have to be a whole number since someone may study for part of an hour.

Troubleshooting If students are having difficulty writing expressions, suggest that they first assign a value for the variable and then write a numerical expression. They can use the numerical expressions to help find any patterns or rules. For example, in **Problem 5a** of Problem Set D, students could start by saying the fare is 40¢ for each ride. The cost for two rides is 2×40, or 80¢. Substituting F for 40, the cost for two rides is $2F$.

On Your Own Exercises

Practice & Apply: 7–17
Connect & Extend: 40–42
Mixed Review: 49–67

Investigation 3

This investigation introduces the conventions used to write and evaluate expressions. In previous investigations, students learned to write repeated addition as either $a + a + a + a$ or as $4a$. They will now study ways to write repeated multiplication as $a \times a \times a \times a$ or as a^4. Students then use the order of operations to evaluate expressions.

Discuss the use of an *exponent.* Be sure students understand that an exponent tells how many times a number or a variable is multiplied by itself. You may wish to write these two expressions on the board and discuss with students the standard notation for writing expressions:

- $d \times d \times d$ is written d^3. Students should know that this can be read as *d cubed* or as *d to the third power.*
- $a \times 4 \times a$ is written $4a^2$, **not** as $a^2 4$ or $4aa$ or $a4a$. Students should be aware of the two conventions illustrated in this expression: using exponents and writing the number factor before the variable factor.

Share & Summarize

1 Have students discuss their answers to Questions 1–3 in pairs.

Let h represent the number of hours Shaunda spent on homework last week.

1. Zach spent half as much time on his homework as Shaunda had on hers. Write an expression for the number of hours he spent. $\frac{1}{2}h$
2. Describe a situation that the expression $2h + 1$ might represent.
3. Write another algebraic expression containing the variable h, and describe a situation your expression might represent.

2. Possible answer: Leslie spent twice as much time as Shaunda did on her homework, plus 1 hour.

3. Possible answer: $\frac{1}{7}h$ is the average number of hours Shaunda spent doing homework each day last week.

Investigation  Evaluating Expressions

When you study mathematics, it is important to know the shortcuts that are used for writing expressions. You already know that when you want to show a number times a variable, you can leave out the multiplication sign: instead of $6 \times t$ or $6 \cdot t$, you can write $6t$. Note that the number is normally placed before the variable.

VOCABULARY
exponent

2 Discuss the use of an exponent.

What if you want to show that the variable t is multiplied by itself? You could write $t \times t$ or $t \cdot t$ or tt. However, an **exponent** is usually used to tell how many times a quantity is multiplied by itself. So $t \times t$ is written t^2, and $t \times t \times t$ is written t^3.

Here are some other examples.

- The expression $m \times 5 \times m$ is written $5m^2$.
- The expression $2 \cdot s \cdot s \cdot s$ is written $2s^3$.
- The expression $x \times x \times y \times 7$ is written $7x^2y$ or $7yx^2$.
- The expression $2p \cdot p \cdot p$ is written $2p^3$.

It is also important to understand the rules for *evaluating,* or finding the value of, expressions. You learned some of these rules when you studied arithmetic.

LESSON 1.1 Variables and Expressions 13

Think & Discuss

As part of a whole-class discussion, have students evaluate the first two expressions in this section. Record volunteers' answers on the board. Then have students use their calculators to evaluate the expression and compare their answers to those on the board. Discuss the *order of operations* with students, explaining that it is a convention that was devised so that everyone calculates expressions in the same way.

Students need to know whether or not their calculators compute using the order of operations. For calculators that don't follow this convention, students will have to learn to insert parentheses when entering expressions in the calculators in order to get the correct answer. For example, on a calculator that does not automatically multiply first, $2 + 8 \times 9$ would have to be entered as $2 + (8 \times 9)$ or as $8 \times 9 + 2$.

Write $2 + 3 \cdot 5$ on the board. Ask students questions such as these:

> In the expression $2 + 3 \cdot 5$, which operation do you perform first? Second? Why? **Multiply 3 and 5 first. Add 2 and 15 second. This follows the order of operations.**

Challenge students to find a way to rewrite the expression $2 + 3 \cdot 5$ so that everyone would add 2 and 3 before they multiply. Lead the discussion so that students suggest putting parentheses around $2 + 3$, so, $(2 + 3) \times 5 = 25$.

Then ask students:

> Which expression means add 4 and 6 and then multiply by *n*: $4 + 6n$ or $(4 + 6)n$? **$(4 + 6)n$**

Have students read the cartoon about $4m^2$ in their texts.

① 47, 4 (Note: Some students may not use the correct order of operations.)

② Answers will vary. (Note: Most calculators will use the correct order of operations, but some will not.)

③ $(4 + 6)n$, $4 + 6n$

Think & Discuss

Evaluate each expression without using a calculator. See ①.

$$7 + 8 \times 5 \qquad 7 - 6 \div 2$$

Now use your calculator to evaluate each expression. Did you get the same answers with the calculator as you did without? See ②.

Most calculators will multiply and divide before they add or subtract. This *order of operations* is a convention that everyone uses to avoid confusion. If you want to indicate that the operations should be done in a different order, you need to use parentheses. Look at how the use of parentheses affects the value of the expressions below.

$$2 + 3 \cdot 5 = 2 + 15 = 17 \qquad 7 - 6 \div 2 = 7 - 3 = 4$$

$$(2 + 3) \cdot 5 = 5 \cdot 5 = 25 \qquad (7 - 6) \div 2 = 1 \div 2 = \frac{1}{2}$$

Which expression below means "add 4 and 6, and then multiply by n"? Which means "multiply 6 by n, and then add 4"? See ③.

$$4 + 6n \qquad (4 + 6)n$$

There are also rules for evaluating expressions involving exponents.

Zach, 4m² means "find m² and multiply it by 4"!
You're reading it backward, Neeraj! 4m² means "find 4m and square it"!
4m²

1 Use the Think & Discuss as a part of a whole-class discussion.

2 Have students read the cartoon.

Think & Discuss

Have students think about whether Zach or Neeraj has made the right calculation.

If students think the expressions are the same, have them substitute a number for *m*, such as 2, and evaluate the expression Zach's way, $4 \times (2)^2 = 16$, and then Neeraj's way, $(4 \times 2)^2 = 64$. Obviously the results are different. Explain that in order to keep expressions like $4m^2$ unambiguous, we agree to the convention that exponents are evaluated before multiplication. In this expression, we square *m* before we multiply by 4.

Students should recognize that once parentheses are inserted around $4m$ in $4m^2$, the expression $(4m)^2$ means *take 4m and square it.*

Some students have difficulty distinguishing expressions such as $4m^2$ and $(4m)^2$ since both expressions may be read as *four em squared.* Distinguishing between these two expressions is vital. Students may distinguish the two expressions by reading them differently. Many people use the term *quantity* to designate the amount in parentheses, so $(4m)^2$ may be read as *four em the quantity squared.*

Problem Set E **Suggested Grouping: Individuals**

This problem set gives students practice using the conventions for writing and evaluating expressions with addition, multiplication, and exponents. Students then use their knowledge to identify errors in calculations.

In **Problems 1-8,** students simplify addition and multiplication expressions. They need to use the order of operations to correctly place parentheses.

On the Spot Assessment

Watch for students who confuse addition and multiplication of variables. Suggest that they substitute numbers for variables in **Problems 1 and 2** to see whether the expressions are equal.

In **Problems 9-12,** students evaluate expressions containing exponents.

Problem Set Wrap-Up In **Problem 13** various misinterpretations of the expression $3t^2$ are dealt with explicitly. Have students report their thinking to the whole class. It is especially important that students analyze the errors in the other four calculations so that they see where mistakes are often made in evaluating expressions.

Think & Discuss

Who is correct, Neeraj or Zach? Neeraj

Does "find m^2 and multiply it by 4" give the same result as "find $4m$ and square it"? Try it for $m = 2$ to see. See ①.

① No; for $m = 2$, the first statement gives $2^2 \times 4 = 16$, and the second gives $(4 \times 2)^2 = 64$.

Think again about who is correct, Neeraj or Zach. Then add parentheses to the expression $4m^2$ so it will give the other boy's calculation. $(4m)^2$

1 Discuss Neeraj's and Zach's statements.

Problem Set E

2 Have students work individually.

Rewrite each expression without using multiplication or addition signs.

1. $r + r$ $2r$ **2.** $r \times r$ r^2 **3.** $t + t + t$ $3t$

4. $5 \cdot g \cdot g \cdot g$ $5g^3$ **5.** $5s + s$ $6s$ **6.** $2.5m \times m$ $2.5m^2$

7. Copy the expression $6 + 3 \times 4$.

a. Insert parentheses, if necessary, so the resulting expression equals 18. Parentheses are not necessary.

b. Insert parentheses, if necessary, so the resulting expression equals 36. $(6 + 3) \times 4$

8. Write an expression that means "take a number, multiply it by 6, and cube the result." $(6m)^3$

Evaluate each expression for $r = 3$.

9. $5r^2$ 45 **10.** $(5r)^2$ 225

11. $2r^4$ 162 **12.** $(2r)^4$ 1,296

13. When Kate, Jin Lee, Darnell, Zach, and Maya tried to find the value of $3t^2$ for $t = 7$, they got five different answers! Only one of their answers is correct.

3 Have students present their thinking for Problem 13.

Kate: $t^2 = 49$, so $3t^2 = 349$

Jin Lee: $3t^2 = 3 \times 7^2 = 42$

Darnell: $3t^2 = 3 \times 7^2 = 3 \times 49 = 147$

Zach: $3t^2 = 37^2 = 1{,}369$

Maya: $3t^2 = 3 \times 7^2 = 21^2 = 441$

a. Which student evaluated the expression correctly? Darnell

b. What mistake did each of the other students make in thinking about the problem?

13b. Kate found that t^2 was 49, but then she put 3 in front of 49 instead of multiplying 49 by 3. Jin Lee interpreted 7^2 as 7×2, rather than as 7×7. When Zach substituted 7 for t, he wrote 37^2 instead of $3(7^2)$. Maya evaluated $3t$ and then squared the result, rather than finding t^2 and multiplying the result by 3.

LESSON 1.1 Variables and Expressions 15

Example

Have students read the example in the student text showing different ways to express division. The cartoon presents conventions for representing division in expressions. Students need to understand that although the expressions all look different, the expressions are equivalent in terms of their meaning.

Some students may have difficulty with the idea that $\frac{P}{3}$, $P \div 3$ and $\frac{1}{3}P$ represent the same quantity because they have difficulty with the arithmetic equivalents, like $\frac{5}{3}$, $5 \div 3$ and $\frac{1}{3} \times 5$. Some may need to substitute numbers for P to be convinced.

After they read the example, have students continue with Problem Set F.

Problem Set F **Suggested Grouping: Individuals**

Problem Set F gives students practice in evaluating different expressions using division. They will use these skills to solve simple equations.

You may wish to discuss **Problem 4** as a class. Some students may have difficulty evaluating the expression. These students may square and divide before they subtract, thinking $(5 \cdot 5) \div 12 - 1 = \frac{25}{12} - 1 = \frac{13}{12}$. Remind them that the numerator and the denominator of a fraction each represent one value and should be evaluated separately. Only after evaluating the numerator and denominator can the fraction be evaluated.

On the **Spot Assessment**

In **Problems 5 and 6,** watch for students who do not realize that $\frac{7k}{5}$ is the same as $\frac{7}{5}k$. In the first case, 7 is multiplied by k and then the result is divided by 5. In the second case, 7 is divided by 5, and the result is multiplied by k. If students don't see this, ask them to substitute a value for k in each expression. This will bring up some conversation about the fact that the order in which multiplication and division are performed in these expressions doesn't make a difference.

You have explored ways of expressing multiplication and repeated multiplication, like $3t$ and t^2. Now you will look at some ways to express division.

EXAMPLE

Three friends won a prize of P dollars in the community talent show. They want to share the prize money equally. There are several ways to express the number of dollars each student should receive.

All three expressions in the example above are correct, but the forms $\frac{1}{3}P$ and $\frac{P}{3}$ are used more commonly in algebra than $P \div 3$.

Problem Set F

1. In the prize-money example, P stands for the dollar amount of the prize, and $\frac{P}{3}$ shows each friend's share.
   a. If the prize is \$30, how much will each friend get? \$10
   b. Suppose $\frac{P}{3}$ = \$25. How much prize money is there? \$75

Find the value of each expression for $k = 5$.

2. $k^3 - 2$ 123
3. $12 - k$ 7
4. $\frac{k^2 - 1}{12}$ 2
5. $\frac{7k}{5}$ 7
6. $\frac{7}{5}k$ 7

1 Have the class read and discuss the Example.

2 Have students work individually.

Develop

1 **Problem Set G** **Suggested Grouping: Pairs**
Problem Set G asks students to write expressions to represent a variety of situations. Since the problems in this set are a bit more difficult than previous ones, you may want students to work together in pairs.

2 In **Problem 2a,** some students might be uncomfortable that the answer is an algebraic expression, rather than a single number. Reassure these students that although each person's earnings will be a specific amount, that amount will vary based on the number of cards sold. Since we don't know the number of cards sold, the earnings are best expressed using a variable.

In **Problems 3–5,** students begin to work with multi-variable expressions, where the number of friends, cards, and price per card may vary. It is important for students to realize that there are several quantities in these problems that can vary.

3 The *What if?* format is useful in illustrating this variance as students build on a given situation. For example, after writing the expression for **Problem 3a,** students might ask themselves, what if the number of friends in the business changes? How would the expression change? This may help them solve **Problem 3b.** Likewise, to solve **Problem 3c,** they may ask, what if the number of cards sold changes? How would the expression change? Asking these questions can help them see exactly what is changing in each problem situation.

You might mention to students that they should be asking *What if?* questions in other situations as well in order to develop this questioning technique as a habit of mind.

4 **Problem Set Wrap-Up** Have students share their answers and strategies to **Problems 3–5.** If students are having difficulty following the progression of the problems, you may want to use whole numbers to illustrate the changes and then have students substitute the variables into the expressions. If you use this approach, you may want to ask students to write an expression for how much each of F friends would make after selling P cards in each situation below:

the price decreases by \$2, from B to $(B - 2)$

$$\frac{P(B-2)}{F}$$

the price decreases by K dollars, from B to $(B - K)$

$$\frac{P(B-K)}{F}$$

Problem Set G

Kate, Zach, Maya, and Darnell earn money by selling greeting cards they create on a computer.

1. In their first week in business, they sold 19 cards for B dollars each. They shared the money they collected equally.
   a. Write an expression that describes each friend's share. $\frac{19B}{4}$
   b. What is the value of your expression if B is \$2.00? If B is \$2.60? If B is \$3.00? \$9.50, \$12.35, \$14.25
   c. The friends wrote the equation $\frac{19B}{4} = 7.60$ to describe what happened their first week in business. What does the equation indicate about the money each friend made?
   d. Starting with the equation in Part c, find how much the friends charged for each card. \$1.60
2. This week the friends received orders for 16 greeting cards.
   a. If they sell the cards for B dollars each, how much will each friend earn? $\frac{16B}{4}$
   b. The friends would like to earn \$12 apiece for selling the 16 cards. How much will they have to charge for each card? \$3
3. In Problems 1 and 2, the price of a greeting card was the only variable. Kate wants to be able to vary three amounts—the number of friends working on the cards, the number of cards, and the charge per card—and still be able to calculate how much each person would make.

   Write an expression for how much each friend would earn in each situation.
   a. 3 friends sell 19 greeting cards for B dollars each $\frac{19B}{3}$
   b. F friends sell 19 cards for B dollars each $\frac{19B}{F}$
   c. 4 friends sell P cards for B dollars each $\frac{PB}{4}$
   d. F friends sell P cards for B dollars each $\frac{PB}{F}$
4. Suppose the price per card increases by \$2, from B to $(B + 2)$. Write an expression for how much F friends would each make after selling P cards at this new price. $\frac{P(B + 2)}{F}$
5. Suppose the price per card increases by K dollars, from B to $(B + K)$. Write an expression for how much F friends would each make after selling P cards at this new price. $\frac{P(B + K)}{F}$

1c. Each friend earned \$7.60.

1 Have students work in pairs.

2 Reassure students who are uncomfortable with an answer that is an algebraic expression.

3 Suggest that students ask *What if?* questions for Problems 3–5.

4 Have students share their answers for Problems 3–5.

LESSON 1.1 Variables and Expressions **17**

Develop

Share & Summarize

Ask students to complete all four steps in Question 1 and share their results before writing the equation. They should all get 2. Students may have seen these number tricks before. Although writing the expression is the focus of the lesson, some students may be interested in pursuing why the trick works. This can be motivating for students who want an additional challenge. Other students may be satisfied with verifying that the pattern holds for several different values of n.

> **Access for all Learners**
>
> **Extra for Experts** Have students explain why the trick in **Question 1** works. Students may note that some operations are undone. For example, the multiplication, or squaring, done in Step 1 is undone in Step 3. The division in Step 3 undoes the multiplication of n and 2. At this point, the expression is some number plus two, or $n + 2$. When the number, n, is subtracted in Step 4, the result is 2.

Troubleshooting If students are having difficulty using the conventions to write and evaluate expressions, you may need to discuss that changing the sequence of the steps may change the value of the expression. Students may find it helpful to record the order of operations as a list. After reviewing the list with students, have them evaluate the following expressions for $s = 3$:

s^2 9	$2s$ 6
$2s^3$ 54	2^3s 24
$(2s)^3$ 216	$\frac{3s}{2}$ $\frac{9}{2}$ or $4\frac{1}{2}$
$\frac{3}{2}s$ $\frac{9}{2}$ or $4\frac{1}{2}$	$3(s + 1)$ 12
$3s + 1$ 10	$2 \times 5 + s$ 13
$2 \times (5 + s)$ 16	

Have students explain how to evaluate each expression.

On Your Own Exercises

Practice & Apply: 18–27
Connect & Extend: 43–45
Mixed Review: 49–67

Investigation 4

In this investigation, students will be working with flowcharts to build expressions. Then they use the flowcharts to work backward and to solve some equations. The method of *backtracking,* or working backward from the output of an equation, allows students to formalize the thinking they did in Investigation 1 where they had to find the number of blocks in each bag given the total number of blocks. Flowcharts allow students to record their thinking in building and then "undoing" their equations. Some students may remember this method from a previous course. If so, have them review the method quickly or work immediately on the problem sets in the investigation. You may wish to use Master 3, Flowcharts, to provide a method for students to record answers.

Have students read the two paragraphs on page 18 in the text. Ask them to tell the expression that gives the total number of bagels, when n is the number of bagels in each bag. They should come up with $5n + 4$.

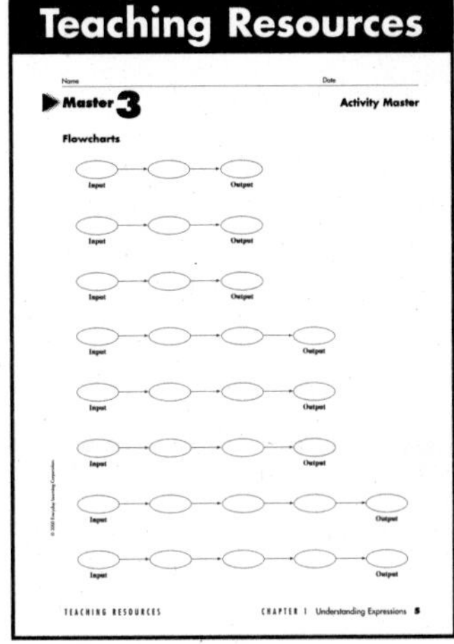

Just the facts

If you follow the steps in Question 1 carefully, your answer will be 2. Try it with your expression!

Share & Summarize

1. Write an algebraic expression that describes this set of calculations.

Step 1. Take some number and square it. $\frac{n^2 + 2n}{n} - n$

Step 2. Add 2 times the number you started with.

Step 3. Divide that result by your starting number.

Step 4. Subtract your starting number.

2. Write an expression that describes this set of calculations.

Step 1. Take some number and triple it. $10 - \frac{n - 3n}{n^2}$

Step 2. Subtract your result from your starting number.

Step 3. Divide that result by the square of your starting number.

Step 4. Subtract the result from 10.

3. Find the value of $\frac{5 + 15x^2}{13}$ when $x = 2$. 5

1 Have students share their answers for Question 1.

Investigation 4 Using Flowcharts

In this investigation, you will discover a tool that can help you evaluate expressions and solve equations.

In preparing for a party, Maya bought 5 bags of bagels and an extra 4 bagels.

2 Have students read these two paragraphs, and ask them what expression can be used to represent the bagel situation.

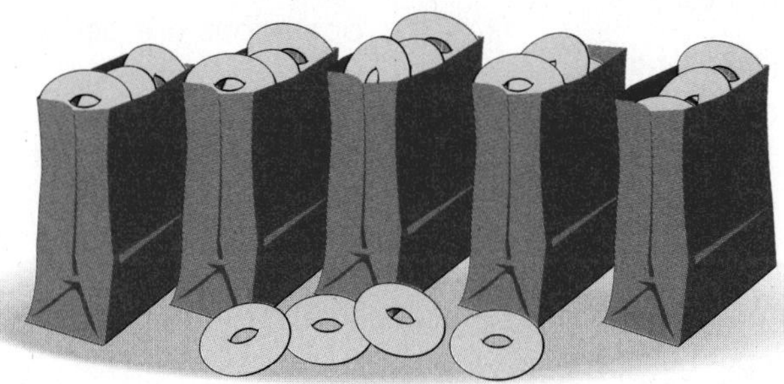

Develop

Tell students that they could use a diagram, or *flowchart,* to find the total number of bagels. Draw the flowchart below on the board.

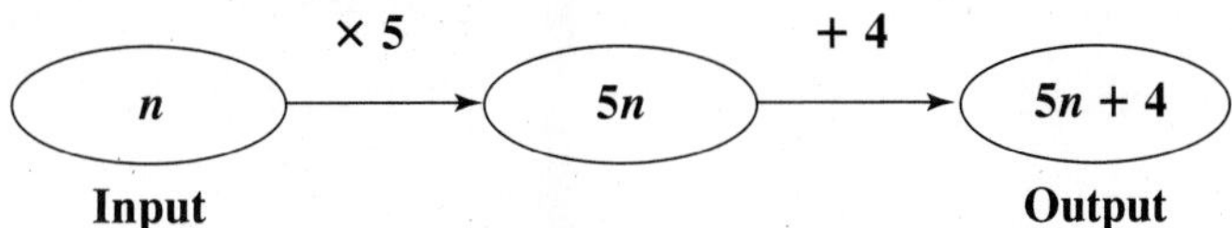

Explain that each arrow represents a *mathematical action* and each oval represents the result of an action. The *input* and the *output* are always ovals. Be sure students know that there are n bagels in each bag. Walk students through the flowchart by asking questions such as:

What is shown by the input? the number of bagels in each bag

What mathematical action is shown by the first arrow? Multiply by 5.

What result is shown by the middle oval? the number of bagels in 5 bags

What mathematical action is shown by the second arrow? Add 4.

What output is shown by the last oval? the number of bagels in 5 bags plus 4 more bagels

Be sure students understand that the sequence of the mathematical actions should follow the order of operations.

Additional Example If you have time, ask the class to build a flowchart providing three or four mathematical actions such as the ones below. Place the actions on the arrows; then ask a student to think of an input number. Complete the flowchart and compute the output, if $n = 5$.

a. $\frac{2n + 4}{2}$ 7

b. $n^2 - 2 \times 5$ 15

c. $n + 3 \times 4 - 2$ 15

Problem Set H **Suggested Grouping: Pairs**

In this problem set, students work with flowcharts in two ways. They complete flowcharts by filling in the ovals. Then they draw flowcharts to represent given expressions. Students need to understand that they must use the order of operations to help them correctly create the flowchart. Once the flowchart is finished, students compute the value of an expression by following the flowchart from left to right. You may wish to have students use Master 3, Flowcharts, when solving problems for this set.

In **Problems 4 and 5,** students will need to consider carefully what mathematical action or operation comes first. Flowcharts make it necessary for students to consider which operations are performed first, and they give students good practice with order of operations as well as understanding the use of parentheses.

In **Problem 5,** students may have difficulty figuring out what mathematical action, or operation, to put on the first arrow. If they find it difficult, ask them to think about telling a story about n that describes what happened to n first and continues for each step. They can ask themselves, what happened to n first? Then what happened? What happened after that? Often telling the story of the number helps students understand the order in which the operations are performed.

VOCABULARY
flowchart

If n represents the number of bagels in each bag, the total number of bagels Maya purchased is $5n + 4$. To find the total number of bagels, you multiply the number in each bag by 5 and then add 4. You can make a diagram, called a **flowchart,** to show these steps.

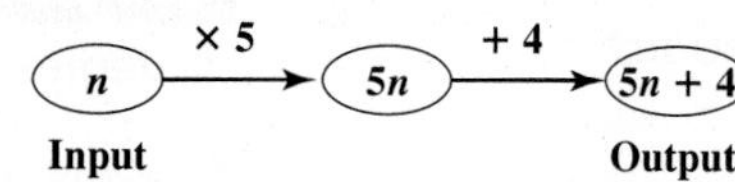

The oval at the left side of the flowchart represents the *input*—in this case, the number of bagels in each bag. Each arrow represents a *mathematical action.* The oval to the right of an arrow shows the result of a mathematical action. The oval at the far right represents the *output*—in this case, the total number of bagels.

To evaluate $5n + 4$ for a particular value of n, just substitute that value for the input and follow the steps until you reach the output. Here is the same flowchart, with an input—the value of n—of 3.

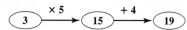

$3 \xrightarrow{\times 5} 15 \xrightarrow{+4} 19$

In Problem Set H you will use flowcharts to find outputs for given inputs, and you will create flowcharts to match algebraic expressions.

1 Walk students through the flowchart.

Problem Set H

2 Have students work in pairs.

Copy and complete each flowchart by filling the empty ovals.

1. $8 \xrightarrow{\times 4} 32 \xrightarrow{-5} 27$

2. $n \xrightarrow{\times 6} 6n \xrightarrow{-1} (6n - 1)$

3. $5 \xrightarrow{\times 3} 15 \xrightarrow{-1} 14 \xrightarrow{\div 3} \frac{14}{3}$

4, 5. See Additional Answers.

4. Consider the expressions $6y + 1$ and $6(y + 1)$.

a. Make a flowchart for the expression $6y + 1$.

b. Make a flowchart for the expression $6(y + 1)$. How is this flowchart different from the flowchart in Part a?

5. Consider the expressions $\frac{n+2}{3}$ and $n + \frac{2}{3}$.

a. Make a flowchart for each expression.

b. Use your flowcharts to find outputs for three or four n values. Do both flowcharts give the same outputs? Explain why or why not.

3 If students have difficulty, ask them to tell a story about what happens to n.

Additional Answers
Problem Set H

In this flowchart, addition comes before multiplication. In Part a, multiplication comes before addition.

5a. $n \xrightarrow{+2} (n + 2) \xrightarrow{\div 3} \frac{n+2}{3}$; $n \xrightarrow{+\frac{2}{3}} n + \frac{2}{3}$

5b. They give different outputs; in the first, $n + 2$ is divided by 3, and in the second, $\frac{2}{3}$ is added to n.

Develop

To introduce how flowcharts can be used to backtrack, draw the flowchart for Maya's bagels on the board.

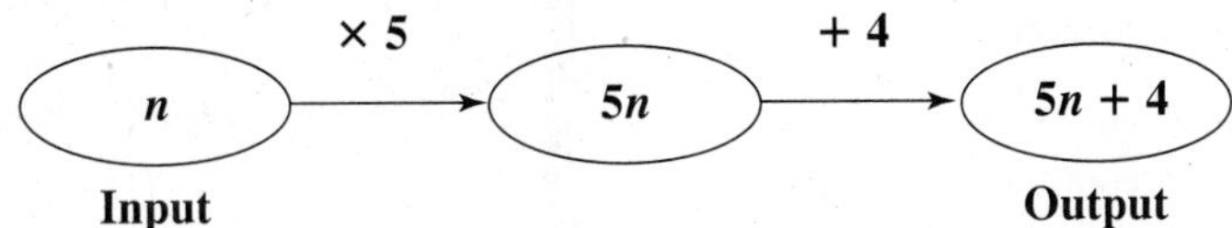

Walk through Luis's thinking on how to complete the flowchart. When discussing how to use the flowchart, some students may refer to "undoing" steps, for example, subtraction undoes addition, so the middle oval can be computed by finding $79 - 4 = 75$. Then since division undoes multiplication, the first oval can be computed by finding $75 \div 5 = 15$.

Additional Example Have students explain how to complete the flowchart for other output values. Students can check their answers by using their answer as the input value, completing the flowchart, and verifying that the output value is the original number.

Problem Set I Suggested Grouping: Individuals
In this problem set, students are given flowcharts with specific outputs and are asked to use backtracking to find the inputs. It is very important for students to write the equation that the flowchart represents so they can connect the idea of undoing with solving equations. Students can use Master 3, Flowcharts, when solving **Problems 1–4.**

> On the **Spot Assessment**
>
> Watch for students who forget that they should think about what must have happened to the number and who simply apply the operation on the arrows. For example, a common error in **Problem 2** would be to take 26 and simply subtract 7 to get the second oval. Encourage students to articulate what they are doing. At some point they will begin to automate the process by doing the inverse operation of each action.

Sample Strategies Students may use one of these strategies to solve the equations in **Problems 1–4:**

- Some students may notice when backtracking that whenever the operation is addition, they subtract; likewise, when the operation is multiplication, they divide to undo the mathematical action. They may use this observation to write clues beneath the original flowchart. For example, in **Problem 4,** they may write underneath the arrows, from right to left, $\div 2$, $+ 1$, and $\div 3$. Then given the output number, they can use the clues to work from right to left to find the input number.

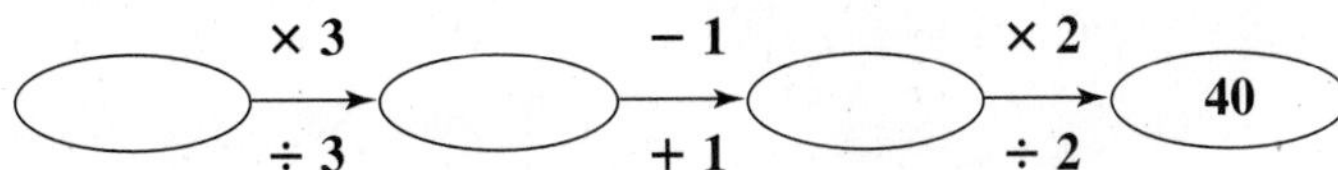

- Other students may solve by finding missing numbers. For example, in **Problem 4,** they will think what number times 2 equals 40. *20*
  Next they will think what number minus 1 is 20. *21*
  Finally they will think what number times 3 equals 21. *7*

At the beginning of this investigation, you saw that Maya had $5n + 4$ bagels, where n is the number of bagels in each bag. Suppose you knew she had a total of 79 bagels. How could you find the number of bagels in each bag? That is, how could you find the value of n for which $5n + 4 = 79$?

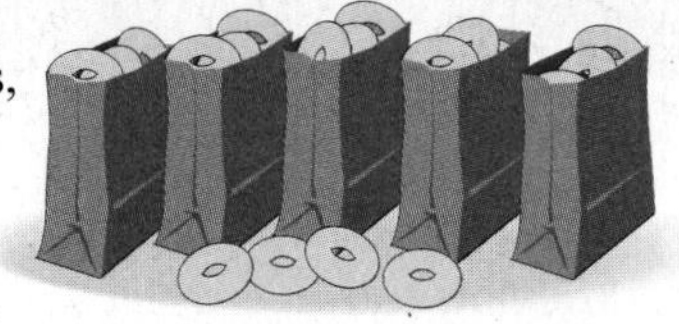

VOCABULARY **backtracking**

Luis used a flowchart to find this number by **backtracking,** or working backward. This is how he did it.

1 • Walk through Luis's thinking.
• You might refer to "undoing" the steps.

Since 79 is the output, I'll put it in the last oval.

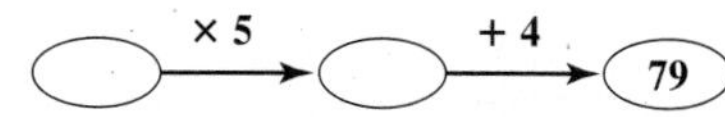

I add 4 to get 79, so the number in the second oval must be 75.

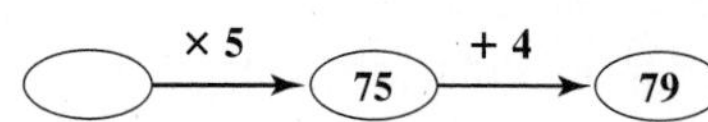

Since 5 times a number is 75, the number of bagels in each bag must be 15.

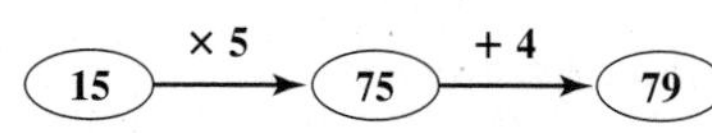

The input Luis found, 15, is the solution of the equation $5n + 4 = 79$. Now you will practice solving equations using the backtracking method.

Problem Set I

2 • Have students work individually.
• You might have students use Master 3 to record their answers.

1. Zoe put an input into this flowchart and got the output 53. Use backtracking to find Zoe's input. 12

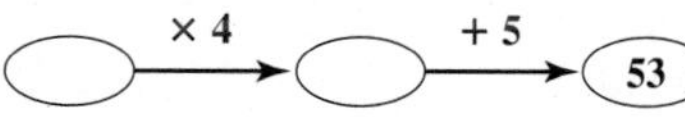

Luis solved some equations by backtracking. Problems 2–4 show the flowcharts he started with. Do Parts a and b for each flowchart.

a. Write the equation Luis was trying to solve.

b. Backtrack to find the solution.

2. (○) —× 3→ (○) —− 7→ (26)

a. $3n - 7 = 26$
b. 11

3. (○) —÷ 6→ (○) —+ 11→ (15)

a. $\frac{n}{6} + 11 = 15$
b. 24

4. (○) —× 3→ (○) —− 1→ (○) —× 2→ (40)

4a. $2(3n - 1) = 40$
4b. 7

Develop

Problem Set J **Suggested Grouping: Pairs**
In this problem set, students use backtracking to solve a *Think of a Number* game. In both problems, students are asked to describe the process using two different representations: a flowchart and an equation. Students can use Master 3, Flowcharts, to help them record their thinking.

Students may be surprised that they are able to solve an equation that looks as complicated as the one in **Problem 2.** Remind students having difficulty drawing the flowchart to think about the mathematical actions in the equation. Have them think about which operation happens first to the variable *n*. Encourage them to continue this process for each step. Students should realize that 1 was added to the number and then that sum was multiplied by 2. The product was divided by 3, and finally 1 was subtracted from the quotient.

Access for all Learners

For Early Finishers If you have time, let students make up some of their own *Think of a Number* games and play them with a partner.

Share & Summarize
Ask students to work on their descriptions in small groups. If you have each group read their descriptions aloud to the class, students may develop vocabulary for describing the "undoing" of the mathematical actions. If students are interested and have sufficient understanding of backtracking, you may wish to introduce the term *inverse operations.* Explain that addition and subtraction are inverse operations, as are multiplication and division.

Troubleshooting If students are having difficulty with backtracking, encourage them to write a simple equation, choose an input number and draw their own flowcharts. Then have them think about what would happen if they started with the output and needed to figure out the input. This skill will be revisited in future lessons, so students will have opportunities for additional practice.

On Your Own Exercises

Practice & Apply: 28–36
Connect & Extend: 46–48
Mixed Review: 49–67

Now that you have some experience using backtracking to solve equations, you can use backtracking to solve more challenging problems.

Problem Set J

1. Kristi and Zander were playing a game called *Think of a Number.*

Kristi must use Zander's output to figure out his starting number.

a. Draw a flowchart to represent this game. See below.

b. What equation does your flowchart represent? $10(2n + 3) = 210$

c. Use backtracking to solve your equation from Part b. Check your solution by following Kristi's steps. 9

2. Consider this expression.

$$\frac{2(n+1)}{3} - 1$$

a. Draw a flowchart for the expression. See below.

b. Use backtracking to find the solution of $\frac{2(n+1)}{3} - 1 = 5$. 8

Share & Summarize

Create an equation that can be solved by backtracking. Write a paragraph explaining to someone who is not in your class how to use backtracking to solve your equation.

Share & Summarize Answer

Possible answer: To solve the equation $3(2n + 1) = 15$, think, "Something times 3 is 15, so $(2n + 1)$ must be 5. And since $2n$ plus 1 is 5, $2n$ must be 4, which means n is 2."

Problem Set J Answers

1a. 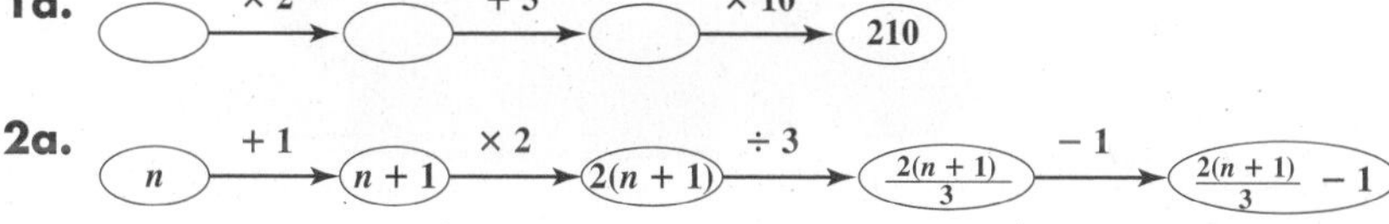

2a. n → (+ 1) → $n + 1$ → (× 2) → $2(n + 1)$ → (÷ 3) → $\frac{2(n+1)}{3}$ → (− 1) → $\frac{2(n+1)}{3} - 1$

1
- Have students work in pairs.
- You might have students record their work on Master 3.

2
- Have students work in small groups.
- After groups write their explanations, have them read their answers aloud.

On Your Own Exercises

On Your Own Exercises

Investigation 1
Practice & Apply: 1–6
Connect & Extend: 37–39

Investigation 2
Practice & Apply: 7–17
Connect & Extend: 40–42

Investigation 3
Practice & Apply: 18–27
Connect & Extend: 43–45

Investigation 4
Practice & Apply: 28–36
Connect & Extend: 46–48

Assign Anytime
Mixed Review: 49–67

Exercise 5:
Some students will substitute directly into the expression to find the total number of blocks. Others, however, may need to go back to the concrete image of 4 bags and 5 extra blocks to compute the total.

Practice & Apply

1. $3n + 4$
2. $2n + 3$
3. $n + 5$
4. $5n + 5$

5a. (4 bags and 5 blocks)

For each picture, write an expression for the total number of blocks. Assume each bag contains the same number of blocks.

1.

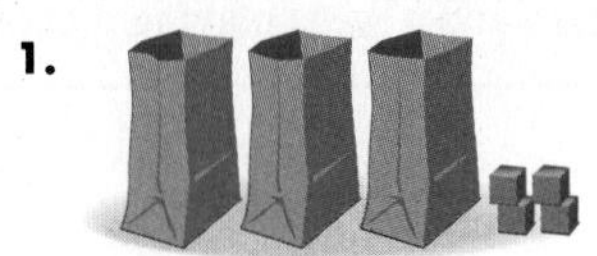

2.

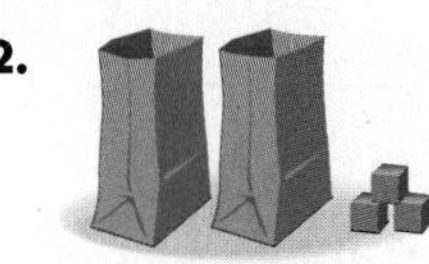

3.

4.

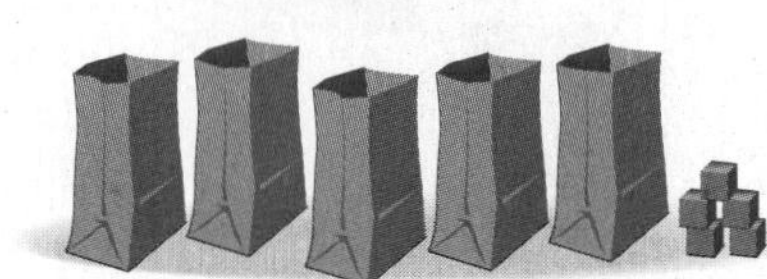

5. Consider the expression $4n + 5$.

a. Draw a bags-and-blocks picture for this expression.

b. Copy and complete the table.

n	0	1	2	3	26	66	79
$4n + 5$	5	9	13	17	109	269	321

c. If $n = 7$, what is the value of $4n + 5$? 33

d. If $n = 25$, what is the value of $4n + 5$? 105

6. A particular bags-and-blocks situation can be represented by the expression $5n + 3$. What is the value of $5n + 3$ if there are 38 blocks in each bag? 193

7. Here are clues for a logic puzzle.

- Five friends—Arnon, Bob, Carl, Dina, and Erin—live in a row of houses numbered 1 to 5.
- They all keep tropical fish for pets.
- Dina got her fish from Erin's next-door neighbor Arnon. Arnon had 21 fish before he gave f of them to Dina.
- Carl has twice as many fish as Dina, who lives in House 2. Carl does not live next to Dina.
- Erin lives in House 4 and has 3 fewer fish than Carl.
- Bob has 4 more fish than Dina.

a. Who lives in which house?

b. Write expressions to describe the number of fish each person has.

c. If the five neighbors have a total of 57 fish, how many fish does Dina have? 7

8. Keshon has s stamps in his collection.

a. Keshon's older sister Jamila has three times as many stamps as Keshon. Write an expression for the number of stamps she has.

b. Jamila decides to give Keshon 13 of her stamps. How many stamps will she have left? How many stamps will Keshon have?

9. Franklin, a golden retriever, weighs p pounds. In Parts a–c, write an expression for the weight of the dog in pounds. Each expression should include the variable p.

a. Tatu, a pug, weighs 49 pounds less than Franklin. $p - 49$

b. Mia, a Chihuahua, weighs $\frac{1}{17}$ as much as Franklin. $\frac{1}{17}p$

c. Lucy, a Great Dane, weighs twice as much as Franklin, minus 15 pounds. $2p - 15$

d. Franklin weighs 68 pounds. How much do Tatu, Mia, and Lucy weigh? Tatu: 19 lb; Mia: 4 lb; Lucy: 121 lb

7a. 1: Bob; 2: Dina; 3: Arnon; 4: Erin; 5: Carl

7b. Arnon: $21 - f$; Bob: $f + 4$; Carl: $2f$; Dina: f; Erin: $2f - 3$

8a. $3s$

8b. $3s - 13$, $s + 13$

Exercise 7:
Help students who are having trouble getting started to set up a table for organizing the information. Encourage them to record the known facts first and then to work through the rest of the clues. You may wish to distribute Master 2, Row of Houses, to help students record their thinking in a logical manner.

Exercise 9b:
Look for different ways students may write their answers: $\frac{1}{17}p$, $\frac{p}{17}$, and so on.

LESSON 1.1 Variables and Expressions 23

10. Mr. Karnowski has a stack of 125 sheets of graph paper. He is passing out g sheets to each of his students.

a. Write an expression for the number of sheets he will pass out to the first 5 students. $5g$

b. Write an expression for the number of sheets he will have left after he has given sheets to all 25 students in his class. $125 - 25g$

c. What would happen if g were 6?

10c. He would not have enough graph paper for the class.

11. The Marble Emporium sells individual marbles and bags of marbles. Each bag contains the same number of marbles.

a. Rita bought a bag of marbles, plus 1 extra marble. Is it possible that she bought an even number of marbles? Explain.

11a. Yes; if the bag contains an odd number of marbles, Rita must have bought an even number.

b. Helena bought 2 bags of marbles, plus 1 extra marble. Is it possible that Helena has an even number of marbles? Explain.

11b. No; if n is the number of marbles in each bag, the number in 2 bags is $2n$, which must be even. So the number in 2 bags plus 1 marble is $2n + 1$, which must be odd.

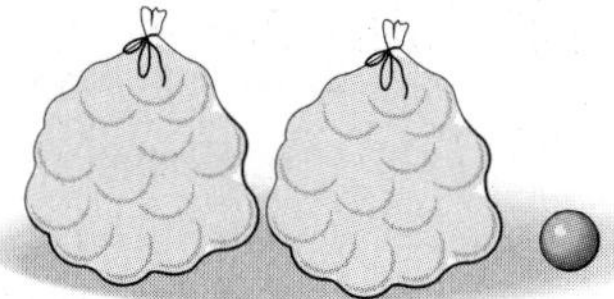

c. Challenge Let n stand for *any whole number.* Use what you have discovered in Parts a and b to write an algebraic expression containing n that means *any odd number.* Write another expression that means *any even number.*

11c. Possible answer: any odd number: $2n + 1$; any even number: $2n$

Interpret each expression by making up a meaning for the symbols.

12–17. See Additional Answers.

12. $7n$ **13.** $p - 6$ **14.** $25q - 50$

15. $2n + 1$ **16.** $3m - 6$ **17.** $5p - 3$

Rewrite each expression without using multiplication or addition signs.

18. $t + t + t + t$ $4t$

19. $4 \times xy \times xy$ $4(xy)^2$, or $4x^2y^2$

20. $6g + g + g$ $8g$

21. $8 \cdot c \cdot c \cdot d \cdot d$ $8(cd)^2$, or $8c^2d^2$

22. Find the value of $9 - 3D^2$ for $D = 1.1$. 5.37

23. Without using a calculator, find the value of $9 - 3D^2$ for $D = \frac{1}{2}$. $8\frac{1}{4}$

Evaluate each expression for $h = 4$.

24. $\frac{h^2 - 3}{13}$ 1 **25.** $\frac{3h}{4}$ 3 **26.** $9h \div 2$ 18

27. Shaunda, Neeraj, and Luis make and sell hand-painted T-shirts. They make a profit of D dollars for each shirt they sell.

a. If they sell 13 T-shirts, how much total profit will they make? $13D$

b. If the three friends equally divide the profit from selling the 13 shirts, how much will each receive? $\frac{13D}{3}$

c. Suppose each friend received $39 from selling the 13 shirts. How much profit did the students earn for each shirt? $9

d. Suppose F more friends join the business. If the group sells 20 T-shirts and divides the profit equally, how much will each friend receive? $\frac{20D}{F + 3}$

e. If the new, larger group of friends sells T shirts, how much profit will each friend receive? $\frac{TD}{F + 3}$

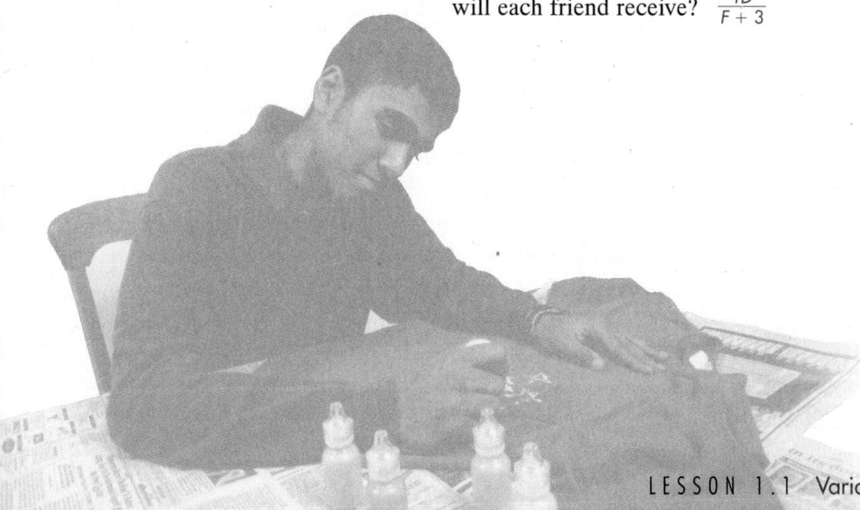

Exercises 22–23:
Students may be challenged by having to square a decimal or a fraction. Point out that both values for D are simple enough for them to square mentally. If students are confused about which operation to perform first, remind them that finding the value of a number raised to an exponent always occurs before other operations.

Exercise 25 Extension:
Students may notice that if $h = 4$, the expression simplifies to 3 because they are multiplying by 4 and then dividing by 4, which is the same as multiplying 3 by 1. Point out to them that they should be looking for these shortcuts in evaluating expressions.

Additional Answers

Possible answers:

12. If n is the number of newspapers I deliver each day, $7n$ is the number I deliver in a week.

13. If p is the number of math problems I was assigned for homework, $p - 6$ is the number I have left after I finish 6.

14. If q is the number of quarters in my pocket, $25q - 50$ is the amount of money in cents I have after I spend two of them.

15. If n is the number of ounces in a box of cereal, $2n + 1$ is the number of ounces in 2 boxes, plus 1 ounce.

16. If each FastPhoto developing lab has m machines, $3m - 6$ is the number of machines in 3 labs if 6 machines are out for repair.

17. If p is the number of pancakes Mr. Flanders is making for each of the five girls at his daughter's slumber party, $5p - 3$ is the number of pancakes left after he burns 3.

LESSON 1.1 Variables and Expressions 25

Assign and Assess

Exercises 28–36: You may wish to have students use Master 3, Flowcharts, as a way of recording their answers.

Exercise 32: Students are asked to create a flowchart from an equation. Remind them to interpret $3a$ as 3 times a in their flowcharts.

32b. 6

32c. 8; Multiply 6 by 4 and divide the result, 24, by 3.

Copy and complete each flowchart.

28.  (12) —× 2→ (24) —+ 12→ (36)

29. 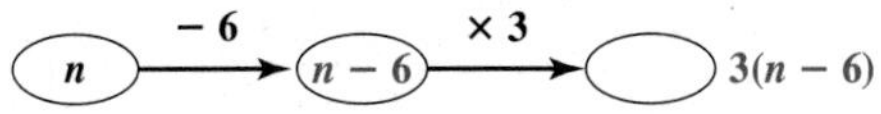 (n) —− 6→ ($n - 6$) —× 3→ ( ) $3(n - 6)$

30. 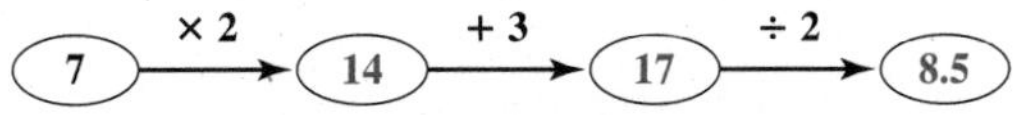 (7) —× 2→ (14) —+ 3→ (17) —÷ 2→ (8.5)

31.  (9) —× 5→ (45) —− 4→ (41)

32. Consider the expression $3a \div 4$.

a. Draw a flowchart to represent the expression. See below.

b. Use your flowchart to find the value of the expression for $a = 8$.

c. Use your flowchart to solve $3a \div 4 = 6$. Explain each step in your solution.

33. Lehie drew this flowchart.

(2) —× 16→ (32) —− 4→ (28)

a. What equation was Lehie trying to solve? $16n - 4 = 28$

b. Copy and complete the flowchart.

34. In a game of *Think of a Number,* Jin Lee told Darnell:

- *Think of a number.*
- *Subtract 1 from your number.*
- *Multiply the result by 2.*
- *Add 6.*

a. Draw a flowchart to represent this game. See below.

b. Darnell said he got 10. Write an equation you could solve to find Darnell's number. $2(n - 1) + 6 = 10$

c. Use backtracking to solve your equation. Check your solution by following Jin Lee's steps. 3

32a. 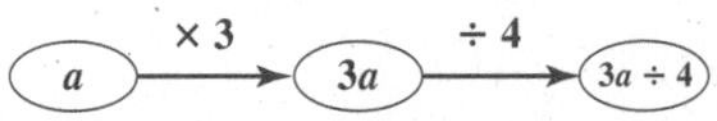 (a) —× 3→ ($3a$) —÷ 4→ ($3a \div 4$)

34a. 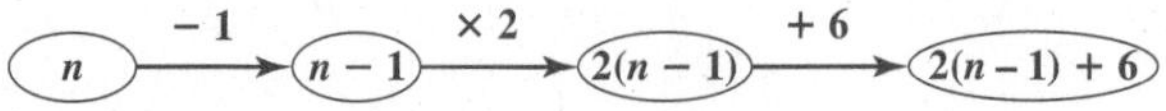 (n) —− 1→ ($n - 1$) —× 2→ ($2(n - 1)$) —+ 6→ ($2(n - 1) + 6$)

26 CHAPTER 1 Understanding Expressions

35. Luis wrote the expression $9(2x + 1) + 1$.

a. Draw a flowchart for Luis's expression. See Additional Answers.

b. Use your flowchart to solve the equation $9(2x + 1) + 1 = 46$. 2

36. Consider this equation.

$$\frac{3m \times 2}{6} = 1$$

a. Draw a flowchart to represent the equation. See below.

b. Use backtracking to find the solution. 1

Connect & Extend

37. Consider this expression.

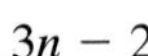

$$3n - 2$$

a. Why is it difficult to draw a picture of bags and blocks for this expression? It's hard to draw subtracted blocks.

b. Copy and complete the table.

n	15	24	30	38	45	60
$3n - 2$	43	70	88	112	133	178

38. James and Noah are packing the 27 prizes left in their booth after the school fair. They have 4 boxes, and each box holds 8 prizes.

a. How many boxes can they fill completely? 3

b. After they fill all the boxes they can, will they have any prizes left over to fill another box? If so, how many prizes will be in that box? yes, 3

c. How many empty boxes will there be, if any? none

39. Dave has 2 bags and a box. Each bag contains the same number of blocks. The box contains 10 more blocks than a bag contains.

a. Draw a sketch of this situation. Label each part of your sketch with an expression showing how many blocks that part contains.

b. Write an expression for the total number of blocks Dave has.

c. If Dave has a total of 49 blocks, how many blocks are in each bag? 13

In your own words

Describe a situation that can be represented by the expression $7n + 4$. Explain what the 7, the 4, and the n represent in your situation.

36a. $m \xrightarrow{\times 3} 3m \xrightarrow{\times 2} 3m \times 2 \xrightarrow{\div 6} \frac{3m \times 2}{6}$

39a.

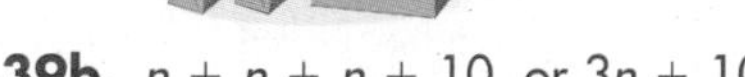

39b. $n + n + n + 10$, or $3n + 10$

Exercise 35b:
Encourage students to think carefully about which operations are performed first to yield 46. It may be useful to emphasize that the first step in undoing this equation, or in backtracking to find the solution, is to think about what number added to 1 gives 46 (or subtracting 1 from 46). This realization will help students later as they solve other kinds of equations.

Exercise 37:
You may wish to have students show their work on Master 1, Input/Output Tables.

Additional Answers

35a. $x \xrightarrow{\times 2} 2x \xrightarrow{+1} 2x + 1 \xrightarrow{\times 9} 9(2x + 1) \xrightarrow{+1} 9(2x + 1) + 1$

Exercise 42: Encourage students to think about Parts a and b without using a calculator. They should feel comfortable squaring 0.5 without a calculator. Students will probably guess in Part c that it would take 0.75 seconds to reach a height of 20 feet (halfway between 1 and 0.5, since 20 is halfway between 16 and 24). In Part d, you might ask whether they were surprised that when $t = 0.75$, their answer was 21, and not 20. This is a preview into their work with quadratic expressions later on. At this stage, you may want to leave them thinking about why the ball reached 21 feet, not 20 feet as predicted. Explain to them that they will be studying these kinds of relationships in Chapter 5.

40b. \$3.20, \$8

40d. \$3.20, \$8; The results are the same as for Part b; no

40. Tito's Taxi charges \$3.20 for the first mile plus \$2.40 for each additional mile.

a. Which expression gives the fare, in dollars, for a trip of d miles? (Assume that the trip is at least 1 mile.)

$d + 3.20 + 2.40$

$2.40(d - 1) + 3.20$ (circled)

$3.20(d + 2.40)$

$d(2.40 + 3.20)$

b. How much would it cost to travel 1 mile? To travel 3 miles?

c. Tito thought he might make more money if his drivers charged for every sixth of a mile, not every mile. The new rate is \$1.60 for the first $\frac{2}{6}$ of a mile, plus 40¢ for each additional $\frac{1}{6}$ mile.

If a person travels n sixths of a mile, which expression gives the correct fare? (Assume that the person travels at least $\frac{2}{6}$ of a mile.)

$1.60 + 40n$

$1.60 + 40(n - 2)$

$1.60 + 0.40n$

$1.60 + 0.40(n - 2)$ (circled)

d. Use the formula you chose in Part c to calculate fares for trips of 1 mile and 3 miles. Compare the results to those for Part b. Does Tito's Taxi make more money with this new rate plan?

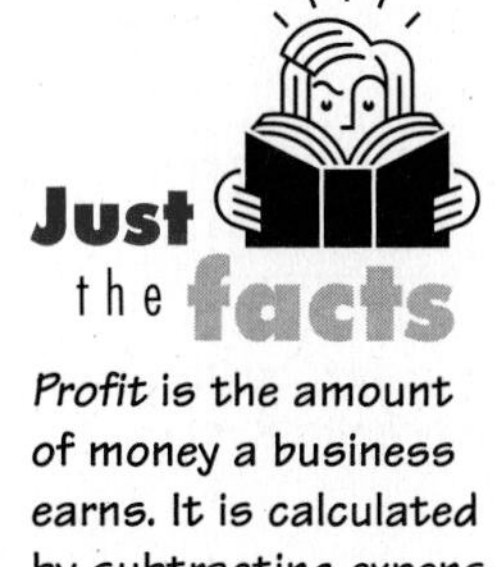

Just the facts

Profit is the amount of money a business earns. It is calculated by subtracting expenses (what was spent) from income (what was earned).

41. Challenge The members of the music club are raising money to pay for a trip to the state jazz festival. They are selling CDs and T-shirts.

a. Each CD costs the club \$2.40. The club is selling the CDs for \$12.00 apiece. Write an expression to represent how much profit the club will make for selling c CDs. $12c - 2.4c$, or $9.6c$

b. Each T-shirt costs the club \$3.50. The club is selling the T-shirts for \$14.50. Write an expression to represent how much profit the club will make for selling t T-shirts. $14.5t - 3.5t$, or $11t$

c. Now write an expression that gives the profit for selling c CDs and t T-shirts. $12c - 2.4c + 14.5t - 3.5t$, or $9.6c + 11t$

d. Ludwig sold 10 of each item. Johann sold 7 CDs and 12 T-shirts. Use your expression from Part c to calculate how much money each club member raised. \$206, \$199.20

42c. Answers will vary. A reasonable guess is 0.75 s; the actual time is about 0.691 s.

43b. Possible answer: The expressions seem to be the same.

44a. Answers will vary. Any number less than 0 or greater than 1 will work.

44b. Answers will vary. Any number between 0 and 1 will work.

44c. 0, 1

45a. $W = \frac{80}{L}$

42. Preview This equation describes how the height h of a particular baseball changed over time t after it was thrown from the ground. Height is in feet, and time is in seconds.

$$h = 40t - 16t^2$$

a. How high was the ball after 0.5 second? 16 ft

b. How high was the ball after 1 second? 24 ft

c. Based on what you learned in Parts a and b, guess how long it took the ball to reach a height of 20 feet.

d. Substitute your guess for t in the equation to find how high the ball was at that point in time. Were you close? Is your guess too high? Too low? Answers will vary.

43. Preview Consider the expressions $x(x - 1)$ and $x^2 - x$.

a. Choose five values for x. Evaluate both expressions for those values. Organize your results in a table. See Additional Answers.

b. What appears to be the relationship between the two expressions?

44. Challenge In this problem, you will compare x^2 and x for different values of x.

a. Find three values for x such that $x^2 > x$.

b. Find three values for x such that $x^2 < x$.

c. Find a value for x such that $x^2 = x$. Can you find more than one?

45. Geometry Franklin's garden is rectangular, with a length of L ft and an area of 80 square feet.

a. Write an equation you could solve to find the garden's width, W.

b. How wide is Franklin's garden if its length is 15 feet? $5\frac{1}{3}$ ft

c. If the width of Franklin's garden is 15 feet, how far does Franklin travel when he walks the perimeter of his garden? $40\frac{2}{3}$ ft

Exercise 43:
This exercise previews the distributive property which students will learn in Lesson 3 of this chapter. At this point, it is important only that they have an intuition that these expressions are equivalent. They will be able to prove this in Lesson 3.

Exercise 44:
Students have an opportunity to explore some of the properties of fractions and whole numbers in this exercise. If students have difficulty in answering Part b, they may not realize at first that they need to investigate numbers less than 1.

Exercise 45:
Students may resist writing the equation since they can easily find the width by dividing 80 by 15. Encourage them to write the equation, however, so that they have practice writing expressions involving division.

Additional Answers

43a. Possible table:

x	$x(x-1)$	$x^2 - x$
0	0	0
1	0	0
2	2	2
5	20	20
10	90	90

Assign and Assess

Exercise 46 Extension:
Challenge students to think of another *Think of a Number* game that would work for an input of 3 and an output of 2.

Exercise 48:
This exercise requires students to work with more than one variable. If students have difficulty using the variables, encourage them to work with numbers first in place of each of the variables.

Quick Check

Informal Assessment
Students should be able to

✔ translate between bags-and-blocks situations and expressions

✔ understand the order of operations

✔ use conventions for representing operations and exponents in expressions

✔ create flowcharts to represent input/output equations

✔ solve equations by backtracking

46. In a game of *Think of a Number,* the input was 3 and the output was 2. Tell whether each of the following could have been the game's rule.

a. Think of a number. Double it. Add 3 to the result. Then divide by 5. no

b. Think of a number. Subtract 2 from it. Multiply the result by 4. Then divide by 2. yes

c. Think of a number. Divide it by 3. Add 5 to the result. Then divide by 3 again. yes

47. Solve the equation $10 = 0.25x - 0.25$. You may want to draw a flowchart and use backtracking. $x = 41$

48. Challenge Mr. Frazier has a part-time job as a telemarketer. He earns $4.00 per hour, plus 50¢ for every customer he contacts.

a. Mr. Frazier works a 3-hour shift and contacts c customers. Write an equation for computing how many dollars he earns, e, during his shift. $e = 4(3) + 0.5c$

b. Use your equation to find Mr. Frazier's earnings if he contacts 39 customers during a 3-hour shift. $31.50

c. What total amount did Mr. Frazier make per hour, on average, for this shift? $10.50

Mixed Review

Find each product without using a calculator.

49. 98 × 54 5,292 **50.** 256 * 67 17,152 **51.** 2,692 · 53 142,676

Find each quotient.

52. 88 ÷ 11 8 **53.** 261 ÷ 9 29 **54.** 2,064 ÷ 86 24

55. Order these numbers from least to greatest: $^-7$, $^-2.5$, $^-3.8$, $^-3$, 0.

56. Order these numbers from least to greatest: $^-7$, 6, $^-2$, $^-\frac{1}{2}$, 0.

55. $^-7$, $^-3.8$, $^-3$, $^-2.5$, 0

56. $^-7$, $^-2$, $^-\frac{1}{2}$, 0, 6

Find each sum.

57. $\frac{1}{4} + \frac{3}{4}$ 1 **58.** $\frac{1}{3} + \frac{5}{3}$ 2 **59.** $\frac{1}{6} + \frac{1}{6}$ $\frac{1}{3}$

Fill in each blank to make a true statement.

60. $\frac{1}{7} + \underline{\ \frac{6}{7}\ } = 1$

61. $\frac{9}{3} - \underline{\ \frac{6}{3}, \text{ or } 2\ } = 1$

62. $\frac{1}{9} \times \underline{\ \frac{1}{9}\ } = \frac{1}{81}$

30 CHAPTER 1 Understanding Expressions

Find the value of a in each equation.

63. $3a = 12$ $a = 4$ **64.** $2a + 4 = 10$ $a = 3$ **65.** $5 - a = 0$ $a = 5$

66. Geometry Approximate the area of the spilled ink on the grid. Each square represents 1 square meter. about 43.5 m^2

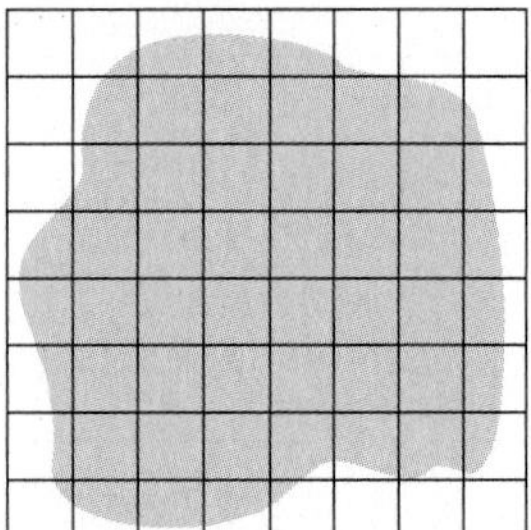

67a. mean: $159,980; median: $135,500; mode: $259,000

67b. Answers will vary. Good arguments can be made for the mean and the median.

67c. It will raise the mean and the median; the mode will stay the same.

67d. Answers will vary. The new mean is $262,481; the new median is $155,250. With this new piece of data, the median is a better indicator.

67. Statistics Kyle kept a list of the selling prices of the homes sold in his town during September.

$128,000	$85,500	$220,000	$105,000	$135,500
$259,000	$97,000	$98,500	$100,600	$263,000
$96,600	$175,000	$259,000	$187,000	$190,000

a. Find the mean, median, and mode of Kyle's data.

b. Which of these three measures do you think best represents the average selling price of a home in Kyle's town in September?

c. In November, Kyle read that one more home had sold in his town during September: a sprawling mansion, with a sale price of $1,800,000. Will this new piece of data change any of the measures you calculated in Part a? If so, how will it change them?

d. Does the new information in Part c change your answer to Part b?

Quick Quiz

1. Draw a bags-and-blocks picture for this expression: $5b + 15$. If the total number of blocks is 80, how many blocks are in each bag? 13

See Exercises 2–4 at bottom of this page.

2. Complete the flowchart.

Write the equation the flowchart represents. $4n + 5 = 21$

3. Make a flowchart to represent $3(n + 1) - 4 = 65$. Use backtracking to find n.

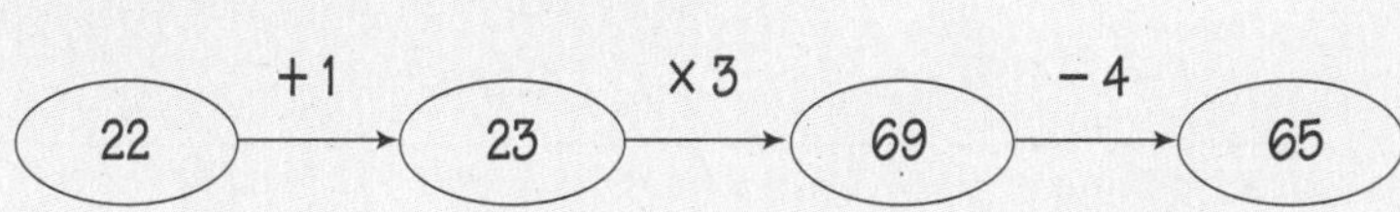

4. Evaluate each of the following if $g = 4$.

a. $\frac{2g}{5}$ $\frac{8}{5}$ or $1\frac{3}{5}$

b. $\frac{2}{5}g$ $\frac{8}{5}$ or $1\frac{3}{5}$

c. $3g^2$ 48

d. $\frac{g+2}{12}$ $\frac{6}{12}$ or $\frac{1}{2}$

LESSON 1.1 Variables and Expressions 31

Teacher Notes

1.2 Expressions and Formulas

Objectives

- To practice using variables to write expressions
- To use expressions to solve problems
- To develop and use formulas to find specific quantities
- To identify restrictions on variables
- To use a spreadsheet to make a chart

Overview (pacing: about 3 class periods)

Many students are not aware of how they can use algebraic expressions in their daily lives. Yes, they study it, but wonder when they will ever use this knowledge. In this lesson, students will discover how they might actually use algebra. They will write algebraic expressions to represent a variety of situations and describe situations that can be shown by a given expression. They use formulas and backtracking to find answers. In the last problem set, students use a table and graphs as representations for expressions to organize data and help them find who won a race. Finally, they use all these skills to make a spreadsheet for a business—one of the most common uses of algebra.

Advance Preparation

You may wish to use Master 4 Tortoise Table and Grid, as a way for students to record answers and a blank grid for making a graph.

	Summary	Materials	On Your Own Exercises	Assessment Opportunities
Investigation 1 page T34	Students use expressions to describe situations and solve problems. They also determine restrictions on variables.	• Master 3 (Teaching Resources, page 5)	Practice & Apply: 1–9 Connect & Extend: 14–15 Mixed Review: 19–32	Share & Summarize, pages T36, 36 On the Spot Assessment, pages T34, T36 Troubleshooting, page T36
Investigation 2 page T37	Students use and develop formulas for additional practice in finding the value of expressions.	• Master 3 • Master 4 (Teaching Resources, page 6) • Graph paper	Practice & Apply: 10–13 Connect & Extend: 16–18 Mixed Review: 19–32	Share & Summarize, pages T42, 42 On the Spot Assessment, pages T39, T41 Troubleshooting, page T42 Informal Assessment, page 50 Quick Quiz, page 51
Lab Investigation page T42	Students identify what is varying in given situations. They also invent situations from given expressions.	• Computer • Spreadsheet software		

Introduce

Introduce the lesson by telling students that they will learn how to use algebraic expressions to help them solve problems.

Emphasize to students that the situation represented by an algebraic expression represents both information you know and what information you want to find out. The variable represents what is *not* known about a situation in terms of what *is* known about the situation.

Think & Discuss

Have students read the first three paragraphs and the cartoon preceding the Think and Discuss section. Then have them answer the questions in the text. Be sure students understand the relationship between the number of calendars sold and the amount of money raised. Some students may write the expression as $12c + 2$. You may wish to remind them that this is also correct because of the commutative property of addition.

You may wish to take some time to review some of the properties of rational numbers. Knowing how to use and apply these properties can help students compute mentally and evaluate equations.

- Commutative property of addition: the order in which two or more numbers is added does not affect the sum: $a + b = b + a$
- Commutative property of multiplication: the order in which two or more numbers is multiplied does not affect the product: $a \times b = b \times a$
- Associative property of addition: how two or more addends are grouped does not affect the sum: $(a + b) + c = a + (b + c)$
- Associative property of multiplication: how two or more factors are grouped does not affect the product: $(a \times b) \times c = a \times (b \times c)$

If students need more practice with the properties of rational numbers, you may want to have them identify the property shown in each of the first four equations given below. Then have them use the properties to find the value of n in the last six equations.

$6.5 + 2.9 = 2.9 + 6.5$ commutative property of addition

$(3 \cdot 5) \cdot 8.2 = 3 \cdot (5 \cdot 8.2)$ associative property of multiplication

$6.4 + (2.7 + 2.3) = (6.4 + 2.7) + 2.3$ associative property of addition

$1.8 \cdot 4 = 4 \cdot 1.8$ commutative property of multiplication

$185 \cdot n = 216 \cdot 185$ $n = 216$

$(1.5 \cdot 8) \cdot 12 = n \ (8 \cdot 12)$ $n = 1.5$

$(450 + 147) + 53 = 450 + (n + 53)$ $n = 147$

$5.75 + (25 + n) = (5.75 + 25) + 106$ $n = 106$

$(5.2 \cdot 9.5) \cdot 10 = 5.2 \cdot (9.5 \cdot n)$ $n = 10$

$60 \cdot n = 35 \cdot 60$ $n = 35$

1.2 Expressions and Formulas

Before you write an expression to describe a situation, you need to figure out what is varying.

Zoe, Darnell, Maya, and Zach are members of a community group that raises money for various charities. Every year, the community group holds a calendar sale.

Last year's calendars pictured different animals, and all the profits from the sale were given to a wildlife preservation fund. The students agreed to each donate $2 of their own money to the fund in addition to the money they collected from the calendar sale. They sold the calendars for $12 each.

1 Emphasize that an algebraic expression represents information we know and information we want to find out.

Think & Discuss

How much money did each student collect for the fund? Consider both the money they earned for selling the calendars and the money they donated themselves.
Zoe: $26; Darnell: $86; Maya: $302; Zach: $1,202

What is varying in this situation? the number of calendars sold and the amount of money raised

Write an expression for the total amount of money given to the fund by each student. Tell what your variable stands for.
$12c + 2$, where c is the number of calendars sold

2 Have students read the cartoon and the paragraph before it, and then answer these questions.

Develop

1 This situation provides the students with an additional opportunity for guided practice before working independently. After determining what the variable will represent, students write an expression. Students will need to backtrack to answer the last question in the Think & Discuss section.

Students can read the first two paragraphs and the cartoon to gather the data needed to answer the discussion questions in the next section. If students notice that the number of hours that Zach worked is not given, tell them that they will find the information later in the problem.

2 **Think & Discuss**

Students should realize that the number of hours each person works preparing packets varies. As a result, the number of packets prepared by each person will also vary.

You may want to review how to complete a flowchart, as you or a volunteer draws one on the board.

Zoe: (4) —× 80→ (320) —+ 50→ (370)

3 Some students may prefer to use number sense to find the number of hours that Zach worked. They know that Darnell worked 7 hours to make 610 packets. Since Zach made 80 more packets than Darnell, he must have worked one hour longer, or 8 hours.

Other students may use guess-check-and-improve to find the answer. Encourage these students to find other ways to solve the problem.

For their summer project, the community group hosted a walkathon to raise money for cancer research. A successful radio campaign prompted a lot of people to request more information. The community group responded by sending informational packets.

Zoe, Darnell, Maya, and Zach each spent time one weekend preparing packets, including addressing them. It takes about an hour for one student to prepare 80 packets. On Monday, after school, they each completed another 50 packets.

Zoe, Darnell, and Maya discussed how much time they spent on the project.

Think & Discuss

About how many packets did each of the three students prepare? Consider both the packets prepared over the weekend and those completed on Monday. Zoe: 370; Darnell: 610; Maya: 1,010

When you calculated how many packets each student prepared, what was varying? See ①.

Write an expression for the total number of packets prepared over the weekend by a volunteer working for t hours. See ②.

Zach prepared 690 packets. How long did he spend preparing packets over the weekend? 8 h

① the amount of time spent on the weekend and the number of packets prepared

② $80t + 50$, where t is the number of hours spent

1 Have students read these paragraphs and the cartoon.

2 Discuss the questions as a class.

3 Discuss various solution strategies for finding how long Zach worked.

LESSON 1.2 Expressions and Formulas 33

Investigation 1

Students continue their work with algebraic expressions. Students are given situations and asked to write expressions that describe them. Then they must explain what the variable in their expressions represents. In the second problem set, students explore how a single expression can describe a multitude of situations.

Problem Set A **Suggested Grouping: Pairs**
This problem set gives students practice writing expressions for many situations. Students may find that there are different ways to approach these problems. Encourage students to explain their answers.

Problem 1 helps students understand how two expressions can contain a variable as well as the same numbers and operations, yet have different values and represent different situations. Have students test their expressions using different inputs to make sure that the expressions make sense.

In **Problem 2,** some students may think that every time Mr. Lopez adds the quantity of flour asked for in the recipe, he adds one additional cup. For example, they may think that if he doubles the recipe, he will add two additional cups of flour.

Students backtrack to find the value of the variable in **Problem 3.** Some students may have the variable represent the number of yards in one round trip. This will change their expression in 3a to $2d + 600$. To find the answer to 3b, students will need to solve the equation, then divide the value of d by 2.

In **Problem 4,** students are encouraged to use the formula to find the area of a square. Students who approach the problem in this way will use exponents when writing the expression. This previews the use of formulas studied in the next investigation.

On the **Spot Assessment**

Watch for students who let the variable in **Problem 4a** stand for data other than the side of the squares. Some students may let the variable represent either the area of each square section or the total area of the three square sections, and they may write expressions for the situation as $3a + 7$ and $a + 7$, respectively. While these are acceptable responses for the information given, encourage students to look at other alternatives. If necessary, review how to find the area of a square. Then ask students to write an expression based on that information.

Investigation 1 What's the Variable?

In this investigation, you will write algebraic expressions to match situations, and you'll figure out which of several situations match a given expression. You will also make up your own situations based on an expression and a given meaning for the variable.

Have students work in pairs.

Problem Set A

1a. $6 + 2B$, where B is the number of friends (or the number of boxes of popcorn)

1b. $6t + 2$, where t is the number of friends (or the number of tickets)

2. $\frac{w+1}{3}$, where w is the number of cups of flour in the recipe

3a. $2(2d) + 600$, or $4d + 600$, where d is the distance to the beach

3b. 246 yd

4a. $(3r^2 + 7)$ m^2, where r is the side length of a square section

1. A movie ticket costs \$6, and a box of popcorn costs \$2.

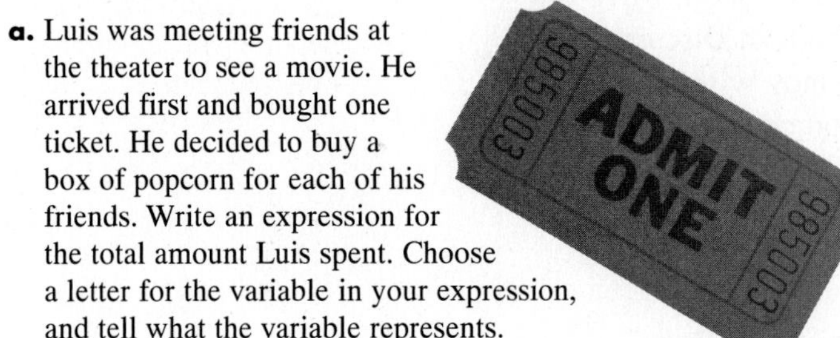

a. Luis was meeting friends at the theater to see a movie. He arrived first and bought one ticket. He decided to buy a box of popcorn for each of his friends. Write an expression for the total amount Luis spent. Choose a letter for the variable in your expression, and tell what the variable represents.

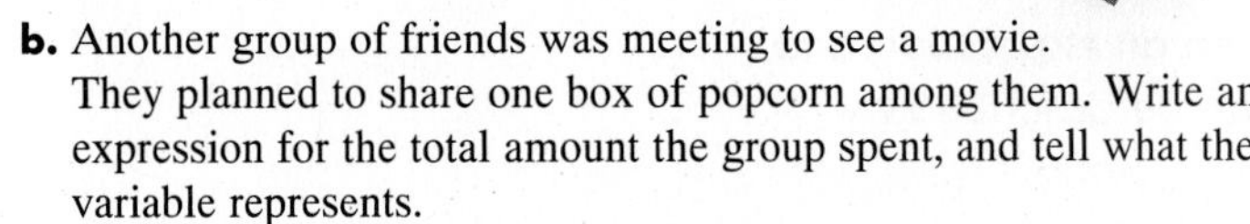

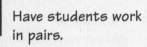

b. Another group of friends was meeting to see a movie. They planned to share one box of popcorn among them. Write an expression for the total amount the group spent, and tell what the variable represents.

2. A pancake recipe calls for flour. To make thicker pancakes, Mr. Lopez adds an extra cup of flour. He then divides the flour into three equal portions so that he can make blueberry pancakes, banana pancakes, and plain pancakes. Write an expression for how much flour is in each portion, and tell what your variable represents.

3. Luis made two round trips to the beach and then traveled another 600 yards to the concession stand.

a. Write an expression to represent the total distance Luis traveled. Be sure to say what your variable stands for.

b. If Luis walked a total of 1,584 yards, how far is it to the beach?

4. Ms. Franklin wants to break ground to add some new sections to her garden: three square sections with the same side length, and another section with an area of 7 square meters.

a. Write an expression to represent the total area of the sections Ms. Franklin needs to till.

b. Ms. Franklin's son Jahmall offers to help her. If they share the work equally, how many square meters will each have to dig up?

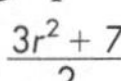

$\frac{3r^2 + 7}{2}$

Problem Set Wrap-Up Discuss the restrictions in **Problem 5b.** Most students will recognize that Simon will not have any money left after 15 weeks. They may be less likely to note that the variable must be a positive whole number.

Example

Write the expression $c + 10$ on the board and tell students that this expression describes a situation. Have a volunteer read the first situation in the text. Discuss how the situation fits the expression. You may wish to use numbers to illustrate why this situation can be shown by the expression. Repeat for the other two situations. Then have students tell about other situations that could be described by the expression.

Problem Set B **Suggested Grouping: Pairs**

In this problem set, students are given an expression and are asked to find a situation that can be described by that expression.

Be sure students understand that there can be two parts to each answer in **Problems 1–6.** They first decide whether the expression describes the situation. Then when the expression does describe the situation, students must explain what the variable stands for in the situation.

Access for all Learners

For Early Finishers Have students explain why the expression $2d + 5$ cannot be used to describe the situation in **Problems 1, 4, and 6.** Students can use their reasoning and language arts skills to write their explanations. Knowing why a situation is not described by a given expression can help students recognize when and why an expression does describe a situation.

5a. $60 - 4x$

5b. Since $4 \times 15 = 60$, Simon will spend all his money after 15 wk. So, x values greater than 15 don't make sense. Since x is the number of weeks, it must be a whole number greater than 0.

5. Simon received \$60 for his birthday. Each week, for x weeks, he spent \$4 of the money to go ice skating.

a. How much money, in dollars, did Simon have left after x weeks?

b. Does *any* number make sense for the value of x? If not, describe the values that don't make sense.

1 Discuss the restrictions in Problem 5b.

A single expression can represent lots of situations, depending on what the variable stands for.

2 Discuss the Example.

EXAMPLE

Consider the expression $c + 10$.

- If c is the number of cents in Jin Lee's piggy bank, $c + 10$ could represent the number of cents in the bank after she drops in another dime.
- If c is the number of gallons of gas left in Ms. Lopez's gas tank, $c + 10$ could represent the number of gallons after she adds 10 gallons.
- If there are c members in the science club, $c + 10$ could represent the number of members after 10 new students join.

Can you think of some other situations $c + 10$ could represent?

Problem Set B

3 Have students work in pairs.

In Problems 1–6, decide whether the expression $2d + 5$ can represent the answer to the question. If it can, explain what d stands for in that situation.

1. Lidia bought two tickets to a symphony concert and five tickets to a movie. How much did she pay? no (unless each movie ticket is \$1)

2. Sam bought several pens for \$2 each and a notebook for \$5. How much did he spend altogether? Yes; d stands for the number of pens.

On the **Spot Assessment**

Watch for students who confuse the variable *d* with an abbreviation for dogs in **Problem 4.** This is a common confusion when using a variable as an abbreviation for a word. For example, looking at the expression $2d + 5$, students often think of $2d$ as 2 dogs. They might then think that two dogs in the house can be abbreviated as $2d$. If they make this error, ask them what *d* stands for. They should respond the *number* of dogs. Therefore, $2d$ stands for 2 times the number of dogs, not 2 dogs. For example, if $d = 3$ dogs, then $2d = 2$ (3 dogs) $= 6$ dogs.

Problems 7–10 show students how the same expression can describe different situations depending on what the variable represents.

In **Problem 11,** students are asked to describe a situation shown by an expression that contains an exponent. Most students will remember using a number squared in Problem 4 of Problem Set A and use area as part of their descriptions.

Problem Set Wrap-Up Have students compare the expressions and variables in **Problems 7–10.** Students will see that the expressions are the same in all four problems. Then have students share their situations for each problem. Most students will supply the same situation, but students may find that the situation can vary even when parameters are given.

Share & Summarize

This kind of problem will be familiar to students by now. Students can exchange situations with a partner and check that their partner's situation is reasonable.

Troubleshooting If students have difficulty deriving situations in **Problems 7–10,** they will be provided the opportunity to refine their skills in future investigations.

On Your Own Exercises

Practice & Apply: 1–9
Connect & Extend: 14–15
Mixed Review: 19–32

3. A herd of zebras walked a certain distance to a watering hole. On the return trip, a detour added an extra 5 km. How many kilometers did they walk altogether?

4. There are two dogs in the house and five more in the yard. How many dogs are there altogether? no

5. Because their parents were sick, Maya and Santo spent twice as many hours as usual doing housework during the week plus an extra 5 hours on the weekend. How many hours of housework did they do?

6. Chau gets paid $5 for every hour he baby-sits, plus a $2 bonus on weekends. How much money does he earn if he baby-sits on Saturday? no

Describe a situation that can be represented by each expression.

7. $4m - 3$, if m stands for the number of pages in a book

8. $4m - 3$, if m stands for the distance in kilometers from home to school

9. $4m - 3$, if m stands for the number of eggs in a waffle recipe

10. $4m - 3$, if m stands for the number of grams of water in a beaker of water

11. Describe two situations that can be represented by the expression $10 - x^2$. Discuss with your partner how your situations match the expression.

① Possible situation: 7 more than the number of tea bags in 3 boxes of tea. t represents the number of tea bags in a box, so 3 boxes contain $3t$ tea bags; 7 more than the number of tea bags in 3 boxes is $3t + 7$.

1 After completing Problems 7–10, have students share their answers.

Share & Summarize

Describe two situations that can be represented by this expression:

$$3t + 7$$

Explain how your situations match the expression. Check by trying some values for the variable t and seeing whether the solutions make sense. See ①.

2 Have students exchange situations with a partner.

3. Yes; d stands for the distance to the water.
5. Yes; d stands for the usual number of hours they spend doing housework.
7. Possible answer: 3 fewer than the number of pages in 4 copies of a book
8. Possible answer: 3 fewer than the number of kilometers in 2 round trips to school
9. Possible answer: 3 fewer than the number of eggs in 4 waffle recipes
10. Possible answer: 3 fewer than the number of grams of water in 4 beakers of water
11. Possible answer: the unplanted portion of a 10 m^2 garden with an x-by-x square area planted; the front surface area of a picture frame that covers a 10 ft^2 area with an x-by-x square area reserved for the picture

Investigation 2

In this investigation, students are introduced to formulas. They learn that formulas are algebraic "recipes" used to represent relationships between variables that describe situations in contexts.

1 Begin the investigation by asking students what units are used to measure temperature. Most students will be familiar with both Fahrenheit and Celsius units of measurement from prior elementary and middle school mathematics courses.

2 Think & Discuss

Discuss the two questions as part of a whole-class discussion. You may want to have students tell how they came up with their answers. Some students will know the Celsius scale. Others may use benchmarks to compare the Celsius temperature to a Fahrenheit temperature before answering. Tell these students that they can use a *formula* to convert temperatures from degrees Celsius to degrees Fahrenheit.

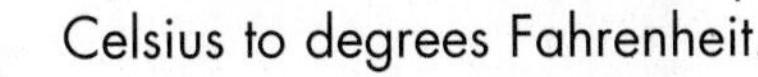

3 Explain to students that formulas are algebraic "recipes" used to represent relationships. Formulas are usually written as algebraic equations, with what you want to know by itself on the left-hand side, and the rule for calculating it on the right-hand side.

Direct students' attention to the formulas in the text. Point out what each variable represents and how the equation can be used. Ask questions such as:

> How can you find the temperature in degrees Fahrenheit if you know the temperature in degrees Celsius? Substitute the Celsius temperature for C in the equation and solve for F.
>
> Why can the formula be written in two ways? Possible answer: $\frac{9}{5}C$ and $\frac{9C}{5}$ are two ways to write the same amount.

Some students may need to substitute values into the two formulas to be reassured that they name the same amount.

Investigation  Using Formulas

Weather reports in most countries give temperatures in degrees Celsius. If you are like most Americans, however, a temperature of 20°C is something you've heard of, but you wouldn't know offhand whether it is very hot, pleasantly warm, or fairly chilly.

1 Ask students what units are used to measure temperature.

Think & Discuss

Test your sense of how warm these Celsius temperatures are.

- Which outdoor attire do you think is most appropriate when the temperature is 33°C: a winter coat, jeans and a sweatshirt, or shorts and a T-shirt? shorts and a T-shirt
- Which outdoor activity do you think is most appropriate in 10°C weather: swimming, soccer, or skiing? soccer

2 Ask students how they chose their answers.

VOCABULARY
formula

There is a **formula**—an algebraic "recipe"—for converting Celsius temperatures to the Fahrenheit system.

3
- Explain what a formula is.
- Ask questions about the formula used for converting Celsius temperatures to Fahrenheit temperatures.

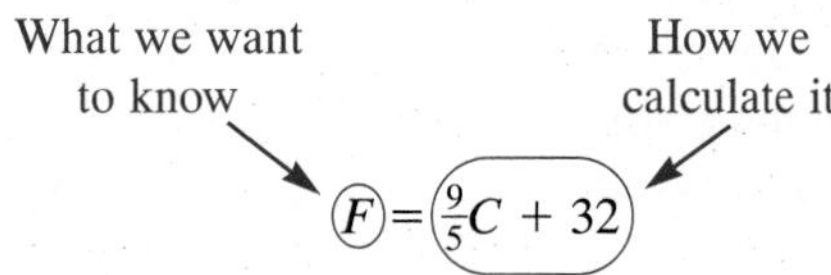

$$F = \frac{9}{5}C + 32$$

In the formula, the variable C represents the temperature in degrees Celsius, and the variable F represents the temperature in degrees Fahrenheit.

This formula can also be written like this:

$$F = \frac{9C}{5} + 32$$

LESSON 1.2 Expressions and Formulas 37

Develop

Example

Walk students through how to use the formula to convert temperatures from degrees Celsius to degrees Fahrenheit. Remind them to follow the order of operations. If you have students use the formula to check their answers to the Think and Discuss questions on the previous page, they should calculate 33°C = 91.4°F and 15°C = 59°F.

Problem Set C: Suggested Grouping: Pairs

This problem set gives students practice with using and evaluating formulas in a variety of contexts. Many of the problems engage students in formulating and solving equations in addition to evaluating expressions. Students have the opportunity to use the backtracking skills learned in the first lesson.

In **Problems 1–2,** students substitute values in a given formula to find quantities of flour. In **Problem 1b,** they need to backtrack to find the quantity of flour.

Problem 3 asks students to compare two formulas to determine which formula uses more shortening per quantity of flour. They verify their answers by substituting values in each formula, and testing that the expected results are obtained.

1 Walk students through the Example.

EXAMPLE

Use the formula to find the Fahrenheit equivalent of 20°C.

$F = \frac{9}{5}C + 32$	Start with the formula.
$F = \frac{9}{5} \times 20 + 32$	Substitute 20 for C.
$F = 68$	Simplify.

So 20°C is the same as 68°F.

Following the example above, find the Fahrenheit equivalents of 33°C and 15°C. Were your answers to the Think & Discuss questions on page 37 reasonable?

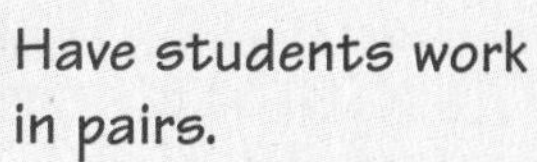

2 Have students work in pairs.

Problem Set C

1. Most pastry is made from flour, shortening, and water. There are different types of pastry. In *short pastry,* the relationship between the amount of flour F and the amount of shortening S is given by the formula

$$S = \frac{1}{2}F \qquad \text{or} \qquad S = \frac{F}{2}$$

a. Alice wants to make lemon tarts with short pastry using exactly 800 grams of flour. How much shortening should she use? 400 g

b. Daryl wants to make short pastry for cheese sticks, but he has only 250 g of shortening. What is the maximum amount of flour he can use? 500 g

2. The relationship between flour and shortening in *flaky pastry* is given by the formula

$$S = \frac{3}{4}F \qquad \text{or} \qquad S = \frac{3F}{4}$$

How much shortening would you need to add to 200 g of flour to make flaky pastry? 150 g

3. Which type of pastry—short or flaky—needs more shortening for a given amount of flour? Check your answer by testing the amount of shortening for two amounts of flour.

3. flaky pastry; for example, for 200 g of flour, 150 g of shortening for flaky pastry and 100 g of shortening for short pastry

In **Problem 4d,** students are asked to backtrack to convert from degrees Fahrenheit to degrees Celsius.

Problem 5 includes a brief discussion of the value of π, stating that it is not a variable. This problem reviews previous concepts and allows students to use π in area formulas.

On the Spot Assessment

In **Problems 5c and 5d,** watch for students who use the diameter instead of the radius to find the area of the pizza. This is a good opportunity to point out the helpful notes in the side margins of the student page. Remind students that in the area formula for a circle, it is the radius, not the diameter, that is squared.

Sample Strategies In **Problem 5d,** students may use one of these strategies to find the answer.

- Students may find the area of each pizza and then divide the price by the area to find the cost per square inch. Then they can compare the cost per square inch for each pizza to choose the more economical buy.
- Students may find the area of each pizza. They can compare the two areas to find that the area of the 24-inch pizza is four times as great as the area of the 12-inch pizza. If the costs were proportional, the cost of the larger pizza would be 4 times as great as the cost of the smaller pizza, or $4 \times \$7.50$, or \$30. Since the larger pizza costs less than \$30, it is the better buy.

Problem Set Wrap-Up Before moving to the next investigation, students should be able to substitute values and evaluate formulas. If students are having difficulty, you may wish to review **Problem 1a** and **Problem 2.**

4. You saw that the relationship between temperature in degrees Celsius and degrees Fahrenheit is given by the formula

$$F = \frac{9}{5}C + 32$$

a. Convert 38°C to degrees Fahrenheit. 100.4°F

b. Water freezes at 0°C. How many degrees Fahrenheit is this? 32°F

c. Water boils at 100°C. How many degrees Fahrenheit is this? 212°F

d. Convert 50°F to degrees Celsius. 10°C

Remember

The *diameter* is the longest measurement across a circle and equals twice the radius.

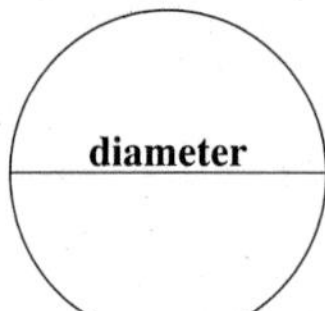

5. The formula for the area of a circle is $A = \pi r^2$, where r is the radius. The Greek letter π is not a variable. It is a number equal to the circumference of any circle divided by its diameter.

a. Your calculator probably has a button that automatically gives a good approximation for π. Do you recall some approximations you have used before? See below.

b. What is the value of πr^2 for $r = 5.6$? about 98.5

c. Tetromino's Pizza makes a pizza with a diameter of 12 in. Use the formula to find the area of a 12-in. pizza. about 113.1 in.^{2}

d. Tetromino's 12-in. pizza costs \$7.50. They also make a pizza with a diameter of 24 in., which sells for \$25. Which size is the better buy? Explain your answer. See below.

e. Tetromino's smallest round pizza has an area of 78.5 in.^{2}. Write the equation you would need to solve to find the radius of the pizza. Solve your equation. $78.5 = \pi r^2$; r is about 5.0 in.

5a. Answers will vary; some students may recall $\frac{22}{7}$ or 3.14.

5d. The 24-in. pizza; the 12-in. pizza costs about 6.6¢ per in.^{2} and the 24-in. pizza costs about 5.5¢ per in.^{2}.

1 Watch for multiple strategies for Problem 5d.

1

Problem Set D Suggested Grouping: Small Groups

Each problem in this problem set focuses on a tortoise race. These are complicated problems because students must consider three different formulas. Students must choose a formula, construct a table, make a graph, and then use these representations to answer questions.

Have students look at the illustration and read the information about the tortoises. You may want students to predict which tortoise will win the race. Accept any reasonable answer that students can support.

In **Problem 1,** students are asked to choose equations to describe the motion of each tortoise.

Now you will use formulas to help you analyze a race.

MATERIALS
graph paper

Problem Set D

Have students work in small groups.

Three tortoises entered a 10-meter race.

Tortoise 1 was especially slow. He moved at only 0.9 meter per minute, so he was given a 3.1-meter head start.

Tortoise 2 roared along at 1.3 meters per minute and received no head start.

Tortoise 3 also got no head start. Her speed was equal to the square of the time, in minutes, since the race began, multiplied by 0.165.

Just the facts

Tortoises live on land while their aquatic cousins, turtles, live in and around water. The limbs of tortoises and freshwater turtles have fingers and toes; marine turtles have flat flippers.

1. In investigating this problem, it would be useful to have a formula that tells each tortoise's distance from the starting line at any time after the race began. For each tortoise, choose the formula below that describes its distance D from the starting point m minutes after the race began.

$D = 3.1m + 0.9$ $\quad D = 1.3m$ $\quad D = 0.165 + m^2$

$D = 3.1 + 0.9m$ $\quad D = 0.165m^2$ $\quad D = 10 - 1.3m$

Tortoise 1: $D = 3.1 + 0.9m$; Tortoise 2: $D = 1.3m$; Tortoise 3: $D = 0.165m^2$

Develop

In **Problem 2** students are asked to make a table to show the positions of the tortoises at various times during the race. Remind students that when they choose a value of *m,* they must substitute it into each of the three equations, evaluate the equations, and record the answers in a table. You may wish to use Master 4 at this time.

In **Problem 3,** students graph points from the table they constructed in the prior problem. This method of representing data is especially effective for visual learners.

> ### On the **Spot Assessment**
>
> Watch for students who want to graph all the equations in **Problem 3** as linear equations. Remind them that not all graphs are straight lines. You may want to show them examples of nonlinear graphs.

Problem Set Wrap-Up Have students share their answers to **Problems 1–4.** Some students may find the correct times but choose the tortoise with the greatest time as the winner. Remind them that the winner of a race is the one with the shortest time. Encourage them to discuss their solving strategies. Students who have had experience in solving equations may prefer to solve the three equations for $D = 10$ and choose the fastest time.

Teaching Resources

Master 4 — Activity Master

Tortoise Table and Grid

You can use the formulas you found in Problem 1 to figure out the tortoises' positions at any time during the race. A table or a graph showing the positions of the tortoises at various times can help you understand how the race progressed.

2. Make a table like the one below that shows the tortoises' positions at various times during the race. To find a tortoise's distance at a given time, substitute the time value into the tortoise's formula. In your table, include whole-number minutes and any other time values that help you understand what happens during the race.

1 Have students use Master 4.

Possible table:

Time (min)	Distance from Start (m)			
	Tortoise 1	**Tortoise 2**	**Tortoise 3**	**Comments**
0	3.1	0	0	They're off!
1	4.0	1.3	0.17	Tortoise 1 is well in front.
2	4.9	2.6	0.66	Tortoise 3 looks hopeless!
3	5.8	3.9	1.49	
4	6.7	5.2	2.64	
5	7.6	6.5	4.13	
6	8.5	7.8	5.94	
7	9.4	9.1	8.09	
8	10.3	10.4	10.56	

3. On a single set of axes, make graphs that show the position of each tortoise at the times you have included in your table. Use a different color or symbol for each tortoise.

4. Use your table and graph to determine which tortoise won the race. You may need to add values to your table or extend your graph to find the winner.

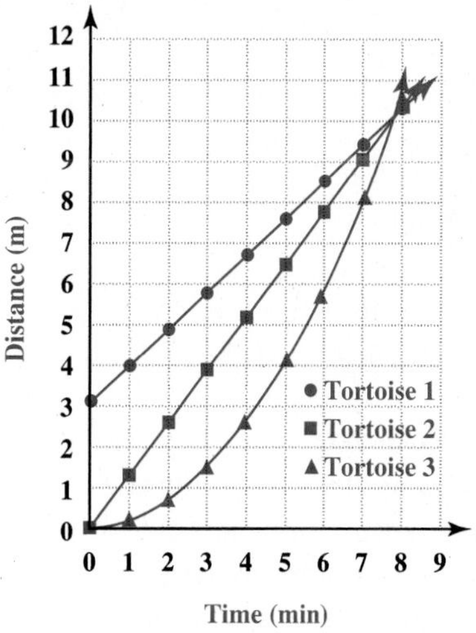

3. Note: Students may or may not connect the points on the graphs.

4. Tortoise 1 won. (Tortoise 1 reached the finish line in 7.67 min, Tortoise 2 in 7.69 min, and Tortoise 3 in 7.78 min.)

2 Have students share their answers and strategies.

LESSON 1.2 Expressions and Formulas **41**

Develop

Share & Summarize

Students are asked to write a formula for finding the surface area of a cube. Most students will find the area of each side, e^2, then multiply the area by the number of sides. So the formula to find the surface area is $A = 6e^2$. This problem also previews some of the work they will do in Chapter 2 on area.

Troubleshooting If students are having difficulty with writing and using formulas, they will have the opportunity for additional practice in subsequent investigations. If you have time, you may wish to revisit Problem Set C, Problem 4 and have students solve for different values of *C*.

On Your Own Exercises

Practice & Apply: 10–13
Connect & Extend: 16–18
Mixed Review: 19–32

Suggested Grouping: Small Groups

Materials and Preparation

Students will need access to a computer and to spreadsheet software to complete this investigation. It would be preferable to have all students perform the investigation at the same time in a computer lab. In this environment, you will be able to assess student understanding and address any problems that groups may encounter. If this is not an option, groups can take turns on the classroom computer, or you can use the computer to demonstrate how to use a spreadsheet. As a last resort, students can use pencil and paper to complete the spreadsheet. While not an ideal option, the last case will at least provide students with vicarious exposure to the mechanics of spreadsheet software.

Introduce the lesson and problem setting before allowing students to work with the spreadsheet software. Have students read the first three paragraphs. Be sure that students understand that Jo sells her cards in packs of 10 for $15 each. She charges a flat $7 fee to ship the cards, regardless of the size of the order.

Direct students' attention to the spreadsheet at the bottom of page 42. Discuss the labels in the spreadsheet. Students need to know spreadsheet terminology in order to follow the directions in this investigation. Review the terminology by asking questions such as:

How are the rows in a spreadsheet labeled? They are in numerical order.

How are the columns in a spreadsheet labeled? They are in alphabetical order.

What is a cell? The box at the intersection of a column and a row.

A cell is labeled by the column and the row. Which comes first? The column

What is in cell B1 on the spreadsheet? the label *Price*

What cell contains the label *Price with Shipping?* Cell C1

1. $S = 6e^2$; Each face has area e^2, and there are 6 faces, so the total area is $6e^2$.

Share & Summarize

A *cube* is a block with six identical square faces.

1. The *surface area* of a cube is the total area of all six faces. Write a formula for the surface area S of a cube with edge length e. Explain why your formula is correct.
2. Use your formula to find the surface area of a cube with edges of length 8 cm. 384 cm^2

1 Have students write a formula for the surface area of a cube.

Lab Investigation ▶ Formulas and Spreadsheets

MATERIALS
computer with spreadsheet software (1 per group)

Jo has started her own business selling hand-painted note cards. She designs and paints the front of the cards, and then she bundles the finished cards, with envelopes, in packs of 10.

2 Be sure students understand the context.

Using her own Web site, Jo has started to get orders from many specialty shops. She charges $15 for each pack of cards. By charging $7 for shipping regardless of the size of the order, she hopes to encourage large orders.

To help her calculate how much to charge for the various orders she gets, Jo set up a spreadsheet on her computer. She started by entering headings in the first three columns.

3 Review spreadsheet terminology.

	A	B	C
1	Number of Packs	Price	Price with Shipping
2			
3			
4			

Each box is called a *cell.* This is Cell A2.

Develop

Tell students that one of the benefits of a spreadsheet is that it does mathematical calculations. Formulas are used to tell the computer what calculations to perform. Direct students' attention to the spreadsheet at the top of page 43. Discuss how to write a formula, stressing that the equal sign in front of the formula allows the computer to recognize that it is to perform a calculation. Ask students questions such as:

> Look at Cell B2. What is this formula telling the spreadsheet to do? *Calculate the price of the number of packs entered in Cell A2.*
>
> Look at Cell C2. What is the formula doing? *It is calculating the price with shipping, using the value entered in Cell A2.*

Try It Out

Students set up spreadsheets to show Jo's business transactions. If any of your students are not familiar with computers or the very basic spreadsheet mechanics, you may need to supplement the directions in the text.

Students enter order data in the spreadsheet in **Question 2.** Most students should be able to follow the directions in the text.

In **Question 3,** students enter data for three more orders and calculate the total charge for each. Be sure that they understand that they are to replace the data in cell A2 for each order.

When she gets a new order, Jo enters the number of packs ordered into Column A, Row 2. This is Cell A2.

To have the spreadsheet do the calculations automatically, Jo entered formulas into Cells B2 and C2 to tell the spreadsheet what to do. When she entered the formulas, she used the name of Cell A2 as the variable. This tells the spreadsheet to use the value in Cell A2 for its calculations.

1 Discuss spreadsheet formulas and how to enter them.

	A	B	C
1	Number of Packs	Price	Price with Shipping
2		=A2*15	=A2*15+7
3			
4			

The = sign tells the spreadsheet that the entry is a formula to evaluate.

Look at the formula in Cell B2. It tells the spreadsheet to calculate the price of the number of packs entered in Cell A2: "Multiply the value in A2 by 15." The formula in Cell C2 calculates the price with shipping: "Multiply the value in A2 by 15, and then add 7."

1. Answers will vary. When no value is given in A2, most spreadsheets will evaluate the formula using an input of 0.
2. without shipping: $75; with shipping: $82

Try It Out

2 Have students set up their spreadsheets and answer the questions.

Set up a spreadsheet just like Jo's.

1. Without highlighting the cells, look at Cells B2 and C2. What do they display? Why do you think this may have happened?
2. Jo received an order from Carl's Cards and Gifts for 5 packs of cards. Use your spreadsheet to find how much Jo charges for 5 packs, both with and without shipping. To do this, select Cell A2. Then type "5" and press the return key or an arrow key.
3. Suppose Jo gets three more orders: 8 packs, 10 packs, and 30 packs. Find the charges with shipping for these orders.
8 packs: $127; 10 packs: $157; 30 packs: $457

Just the facts

When you start a spreadsheet program, Cell A1 is usually highlighted in some way. You can choose cells by using the arrows keys to move the highlight or by using a mouse to click on the cell you want.

LESSON 1.2 Expressions and Formulas 43

Develop

Try It Again

Students make a chart to show the charges for various orders. They use the Fill Down command to copy formulas from one cell to other cells. If possible, demonstrate how to use the Fill Down command. If a demonstration is not possible, be sure that students realize why the cells in the spreadsheet on page 44 are highlighted and that they understand how they can highlight the cells in their spreadsheet.

After groups complete the steps in **Question 4,** you may want the class to discuss how their spreadsheets look. Students should note that the formulas in the cells are similar. The operations remained the same in all cells within the same column, but the cell supplying the input data has changed. It names the cell in Column A to the left of the formula in each row.

Try It Again

After a while, Jo realized that most of her orders were in multiples of 5: 5 packs, 10 packs, 15 packs, 20 packs, and so on. Rather than changing her spreadsheet for every order, she wanted a more efficient way to compute the charges. A friend suggested she make a chart listing the charges for orders of various sizes. She could print the chart and then wouldn't have to turn to her computer so often.

To make her chart, Jo used the Fill Down command. To do this, she selected all the cells in Columns B and C, from Row 2 to Row 21.

	A	B	C
1	Number of Packs	Price	Price with Shipping
2		0	7
3			
4			
5			
6			
7			
8			
9			
10			
11			
12			
13			
14			
15			
16			
17			
18			
19			
20			
21			
22			

The Fill Down command took the formulas in the top cells, B2 and C2, and copied them into Cells B3–B21 and C3–C21. The formulas in Column B all looked like the formula in Cell B2, and the formulas in Column C all looked like the one in Cell C2.

4. Copy the formulas in your spreadsheet just like Jo did. Then look at the formulas in Cells B14 and C14. They don't look *exactly* like the formulas in Cells B2 and C2. For example, the formula in Cell B14 should be A14*15. What changed? Why do you think this happened?

4. The cell name, A2, changed to A14. Possible explanation: The spreadsheet changed the input cell so that the formula uses the value of the cell in Column A from that row.

1 If possible, demonstrate the Fill Down command.

Develop

If students are experienced with using spreadsheets, allow groups to complete the lab independently. In other cases, discuss what needs to be done to complete Jo's chart and how students should complete the spreadsheet.

Students predict answers in **Questions 5–7** to assess their understanding of how the spreadsheets work. They complete their spreadsheets in **Questions 8–10.**

In **Question 11,** the groups make a spreadsheet for the situation of their choosing. If students are having trouble thinking of a topic, remind them that there are many geometry formulas in Chapter 2 of this text that could be used in the spreadsheet. Some students may need help in labeling the columns as well as with writing and entering formulas. You may want to have groups either share their spreadsheets with the class or display their printouts.

3

What Did You Learn?

The two questions in this section help students look back on what they have learned from this lab activity. If time permits, have students answer the questions in class.

Students should be able to identify the variables in formulas entered in a spreadsheet, describe how a formula is changed when it is copied to another cell, and tell how a spreadsheet can be helpful.

To finish her chart, Jo needed to enter the order amounts into Column A—the numbers from 5 to 100 by fives—but she didn't want to take the time to type each number into its cell. She thought of an easier way to do it.

1 Discuss the steps Jo followed to finish her chart.

Jo entered the first number, 5, into Cell A2. Then she typed the formula A2+5 into Cell A3.

5. What number would the spreadsheet calculate for Cell A3? 10

Jo used the Fill Down command to fill the cells in Column A, from Row 4 to Row 21, with her formula for Cell A3.

6. Do you think the formula in Cell A4 is *exactly* the same as the formula in Cell A3? If not, what do you think the formula is? no, A3+5

7. What value would be calculated for Cell A4? 15

8. Try it with your spreadsheet. What happened? What does Column A look like now?

9. What numbers are given in Row 14 of your spreadsheet? What do these numbers mean?

10. Look at your spreadsheet to find what Jo should charge, with shipping, for an order of 45 packs of cards. $682

11. Design a spreadsheet of your own. Use a formula or equation from this chapter, or from a science book. Show a reasonable range of values, using an increment in the inputs to give about 20 to 30 rows of calculations. Label the columns clearly so someone could understand what your chart shows. Spreadsheets will vary.

8. The formula was copied into the cells, each using the cell in the previous row as its input. Column A now has the values 5, 10, 15, . . . , 100.

9. 65, 975, 982; For 65 packs of cards, the price without shipping is $975 and with shipping is $982.

2 If students have trouble thinking of a topic, suggest they use a geometry formula.

What Did You Learn?

3 If time permits, have students answer these questions in class.

12. A spreadsheet cell contains the formula D3*4–1.

a. What is the variable in this formula? D3

b. The formula in this cell is copied to the cell below it. What is the formula in the new cell? E3*4–1

13. Name at least one way in which spreadsheets can be helpful.
Possible answer: You can use them to make a lot of calculations quickly. You can make several calculations using different inputs without typing each calculation yourself.

LESSON 1.2 Expressions and Formulas 45

Assign and Assess

On Your Own Exercises

On Your Own Exercises

Investigation 1
Practice & Apply: 1–9
Connect & Extend: 14–15

Investigation 2
Practice & Apply: 10–13
Connect & Extend: 16–18

Assign Anytime
Mixed Review: 19–32

Exercise 1:
These exercises give students additional practice in writing expressions to describe situations.

Exercise 2b:
Most students will simply divide the answer to 2a by p. If no student comes up with the expression $40 + \frac{250}{p}$, challenge students to explain why it also is correct.

Practice & Apply

1. A ticket to the symphony costs $17 for adults and $8.50 for children.

a. Write an expression for the total ticket cost in dollars if A adults and three children attend the symphony. $17A + 25.5$

b. Write an expression for the total ticket cost if two adults and C children go to the symphony. $34 + 8.5C$

2. Josie and her friends are organizing a trip to the state skateboarding championships. The bus they will rent to take them there and back will cost $250, and Josie estimates that each person will spend $40 for meals and souvenirs.

a. If p people go on the trip, what will be the total cost for travel, meals, and souvenirs? $40p + 250$

b. What will be the cost per person if p people go on the trip?

c. What will be the total cost per person if 25 people go on the trip?

2b. $\frac{40p + 250}{p}$ or $40 + \frac{250}{p}$
2c. $50

3. A full storage tank contains 2,160 gallons of water. Every 24 hours, 4.5 gallons leak out.

a. How many gallons of water will be in the tank H hours after it is filled? $2{,}160 - \frac{4.5H}{24}$

b. How many gallons of water will be in the tank after D days?

c. How many gallons of water will be in the tank after W weeks?

3b. $2{,}160 - 4.5D$
3c. $2{,}160 - 31.5W$

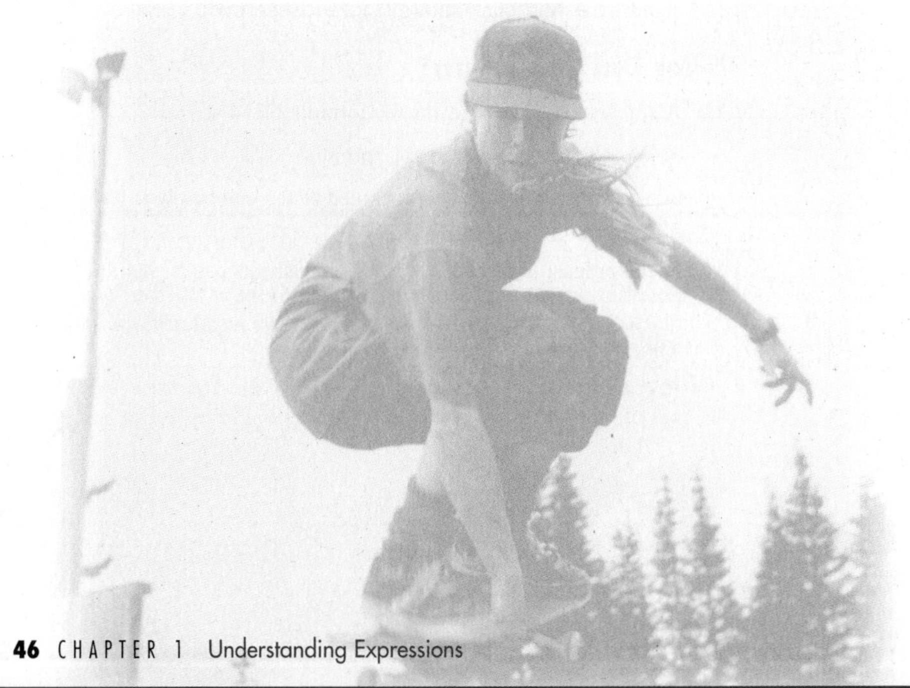

4. Yes; m is the price of a ticket.

6. Yes; m is the number of minutes it takes to play the CD once.

7. Possible answer: the total cost for having 3 pizzas delivered if the delivery fee is $2

8. Possible answer: the number of ounces left in 2 pitchers of lemonade after filling an 8-oz glass

9. Possible answer: the area of half the piece of paper

10. See Additional Answers.

In Exercises 4–6, determine whether the expression $9m - 4$ can be used to represent the answer to the question. If it can, explain what m stands for.

4. The ski club bought nine lift tickets and received a $4 discount on the total price. What was the total cost for the tickets?

5. Of the nine people on a baseball field, four are girls. How many are boys? no

6. Last Saturday, Tausha listened to her new CD nine times, but the ninth time she played it, she skipped a 4-minute song she didn't like. How much time did Tausha spend listening to her CD last Saturday?

In Exercises 7–9, describe a situation that the expression can represent.

7. $3p + 2$, if p is the price of a pepperoni pizza in dollars

8. $2x - 8$, if x is the number of ounces in a pitcher of lemonade

9. $\frac{L^2}{2}$, if L is the length of a square piece of paper

10. Three friends, Jody, Gemma, and Caitlin, have electronic robot toys that move at different speeds. They decide to have a 10-meter race.

- Jody's robot travels 1 meter per second.
- Gemma's robot moves 0.9 meter per second.
- Caitlin's robot's speed is 1.3 meters per second.

a. If they all start together, whose robot will win? How long will each robot take to reach the finish line?

b. To make the next race more interesting, the friends agree to give Gemma's and Jody's robots a head start.

- Gemma's robot has a 3-meter head start, so it has to travel only 7 meters.
- Jody's robot has a 2-meter head start, so it has to travel only 8 meters.

Whose robot wins this race? Whose comes in second? Whose comes in last?

c. The girls decide they would like the robots to finish as close to *exactly* together as possible. How much of a head start should Gemma's and Jody's robots have for this to happen?

Hint: Use your calculator. Caitlin's robot takes $10 \div 1.3 = 7.6923077$ seconds to travel 10 meters. How can you position the other two robots so that they take this same amount of time?

Exercises 7–9:
Students practice describing a situation represented by a given expression.

Exercise 10:
You may wish to read aloud the hint for Part c. Some students may use guess-check-and-improve to solve.

Additional Answers

10a. Caitlin's wins; Caitlin's: 7.7 s, Jody's: 10 s, Gemma's: 11.1 s

10b. Caitlin's (7.7 s) just wins, with Gemma's (7.8 s) second and Jody's (8 s) last.

10c. Jody's needs a 2.3076923-m head start, and Gemma's needs a 3.07692308-m head start.

In your **own words**

Knowing that there are 5 pennies in a nickel, Rob wrote the equation $5P = N$, where P is the number of pennies and N is the number of nickels. Explain why this equation does or does not represent this situation.

11. See Additional Answers.

12b. Answers will vary. If the counting takes 10 s, she will fall 490 m.

12d. Answers will vary. Using 3.6 and 3.8 for T, the cliff is between 63.5 m and 70.8 m high.

11. Measurement By measuring certain bones, forensic scientists can estimate a person's height. These formulas show the approximate relationship between the length of the tibia (shin bone) t and height h for males and females. The measurements are in centimeters.

males: $h = 81.688 + 2.392t$

females: $h = 72.572 + 2.533t$

tibia

a. How tall is a male if his tibia is 38 cm long? Give your answer in centimeters, and then use the facts that 2.54 cm is about 1 in. and 12 in. equals 1 ft to find the height in feet.

b. How tall is a female if her tibia is 38 cm long? Give your answer in centimeters and in feet.

c. If a woman is 160 cm tall (about 5.25 ft), how long is her tibia?

12. Physics The distance in meters an object falls in T seconds after it is dropped—not taking into account air resistance—is given by the formula $D = 4.9T^2$.

a. A stone is dropped from a high cliff. How far will it have fallen after 3 s? 44.1 m

b. After dropping from a plane, a parachutist counts slowly to 10 before pulling the ripcord to unfold her parachute. How far does she fall while she is counting?

c. Shelley dropped a pebble from a cliff and timed it as it fell. The pebble hit the water 3.7 s after she dropped it. How high is the cliff above the water? about 67 m

d. The watch Shelley used was accurate only to the nearest 0.1 s. This means that the actual time it took the pebble to fall may have been 0.1 s less or 0.1 s more than what Shelley timed. Find a range of heights for the cliff to allow for this error in timing the pebble's fall.

13. Geology Geologists estimate that Earth's temperature rises about 10°C for every kilometer below Earth's surface. $T = 50 + 10k$

a. If it is 50°C on the surface of Earth, what is the formula for the temperature T in degrees Celsius at a depth of k km?

b. If it is 50°C on the surface, what is the temperature at a depth of 15 km? 200°C

Additional Answers

11a. 172.584 cm, or about 5.66 ft

11b. 168.826 cm, or about 5.54 ft

11c. about 34.5 cm

Connect & Extend

14. A rental car costs \$35 per day plus \$.10 per mile.

a. What is the cost, in dollars, to rent the car for 5 days if you drive a total of M miles? $5(35) + 0.1M$ or $175 + 0.1M$

b. What is the cost to rent the car for 5 days if you drive M miles each day? $5(35 + 0.1M)$ or $175 + 0.5M$

c. What is the cost to rent the car for D days if you drive a total of 85 miles? $35D + 8.5$

d. What is the cost to rent the car for D days if you drive 85 miles each day? $D(35 + 0.1 \cdot 85)$ or $43.5D$

e. What would be the cost per person if three people share the cost of renting the car in Part d? $\frac{43.5D}{3}$ or $14.5D$

15. The diagram shows the square floor of a store. A square display case with sides of length 3 ft stands in a corner of the store. The manager wants the floor area painted. Assume the display case can't be moved.

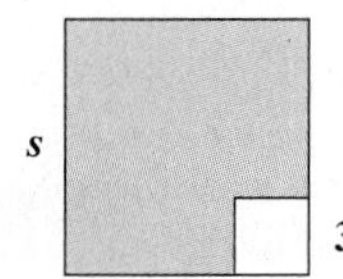

a. How many square feet need to be painted? $s^2 - 9$

b. The manager hires two people to paint the floor. How many square feet would each person have to paint if they share the job equally? $\frac{s^2 - 9}{2}$

c. Are there any restrictions on the value of s? If so, explain why and tell what the restrictions are. If not, explain why not.

15c. The value of s must be greater than 3 because the sides of the store's floor must be longer than the sides of the display case.

16. The formula below helps scuba divers figure out how long they can stay under water.

$$T = \frac{120V}{d}$$

T: approximate maximum time, in minutes, a diver can stay under water

V: volume of air in the diver's tank, in cubic meters, before compression

d: depth of the water, in meters

a. Machiko has 1 cubic meter of air compressed in her tank. She is 4 meters under water. How long can she stay down? 30 min

b. How long can Machiko stay 8 meters under water with 1 cubic meter of air in her tank? 15 min

c. If Machiko wanted to stay 4 meters under water for 1 hour, how much air would she need? 2 m^3

Exercise 15c:
Students are asked whether there are any restrictions placed on s. If students believe there are no restrictions, have them make a table of values for s using 1 to 5. Then ask whether there are any values that are too small.

Exercise 16:
Students use a formula with three variables to find the value of T, V, or d, depending upon the given information. Students can practice solving several different equations.

Assign and Assess

Exercise 17b:
Encourage students to work backward to solve the problem.

Exercise 18:
You may wish to have a student read Just the Facts aloud and then discuss the meaning of batting average and slugging percentage.

Quick Check

Informal Assessment
Students should be able to

- ✔ practice using variables to write expressions
- ✔ use expressions to solve problems
- ✔ develop and use formulas to find specific quantities
- ✔ identify restrictions on variables
- ✔ use a spreadsheet to make a chart

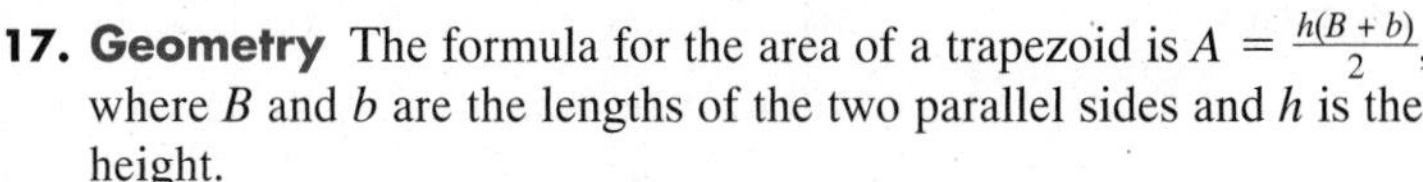

17. Geometry The formula for the area of a trapezoid is $A = \frac{h(B + b)}{2}$, where B and b are the lengths of the two parallel sides and h is the height.

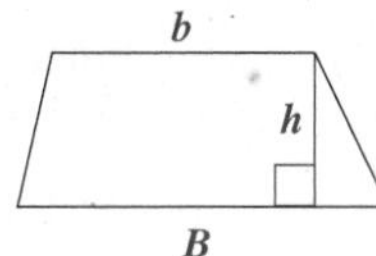

a. Find the area of a trapezoid with parallel sides of length 6 cm and 7 cm and height 5 cm. 32.5 cm^2

b. The area of a trapezoid is 6 cm^2. What might the values of h, B, and b be? Possible answer: $B = 4$ cm, $b = 2$ cm, $h = 2$ cm

18. Sports A baseball player's slugging percentage, P, can be computed with this formula:

$$P = \frac{S + 2D + 3T + 4H}{A}$$

where S is the number of singles, D is the number of doubles, T is the number of triples, H is the number of home runs, and A is the number of official at bats.

a. In 1998, Sammy Sosa of the Chicago Cubs hit 112 singles, 20 doubles, 0 triples, and 66 home runs in 643 at bats. What was his slugging percentage? 0.647

b. In 1998, Mark McGwire of the St. Louis Cardinals hit 61 singles, 21 doubles, 0 triples, and 70 home runs in 509 at bats. What was his slugging percentage? 0.752

Just the facts

A *single* hit enables the batter to reach first base; a *double,* to reach second base, a *triple,* to reach third base; and a *home run,* to make a complete circuit of the bases and score a run.

A batting average and a slugging percentage are different. A *batting average* is a measure of the number of hits a player makes for every time at bat. A *slugging percentage* figures in how many bases the batter ran for each hit.

Sammy Sosa

50 CHAPTER 1 Understanding Expressions

Mixed Review

19. $\frac{9}{8}$, or $1\frac{1}{8}$

Evaluate each expression.

19. $\frac{7}{8} + \frac{1}{4}$ **20.** $\frac{8}{11} - \frac{1}{2}$ $\frac{5}{22}$ **21.** $\frac{1}{10} \cdot \frac{1}{3}$ $\frac{1}{30}$ **22.** $\frac{2}{5} \div \frac{1}{2}$ $\frac{4}{5}$

Find each percentage.

23. 5% of 100 5 **24.** 100% of 5 5 **25.** 5% of 10 0.5

Find the value of b in each equation.

26. $\frac{3}{4}b = 6$ 8 **27.** $\frac{5}{2} - b = \frac{3}{2}$ 1 **28.** $2.2b - 4.2 = 2.4$

28. 3

29. Draw a factor tree to find all the prime factors of 100.

29. Possible tree:

100
25 4
5 5 2 2

30. Copy and complete the chart.

Fraction	Decimal	Percent
$\frac{1}{2}$	0.5	50%
$\frac{9}{20}$	0.45	45%
$\frac{1}{8}$	0.125	12.5%
$\frac{1}{20}$	0.05	5%

31. How many triangles are there in this figure? Be sure to look for different sizes! 27

32. Probability Kyle made up a game for the school carnival. He put 9 blocks in a container—3 red, 3 blue, and 3 yellow. To play his game, you choose one of the three colors and then—without looking into the container—select a block. If the block matches your color, you win 10 points.

a. What are the chances of selecting a blue block? A red block? A yellow block? $\frac{1}{3}$, $\frac{1}{3}$, $\frac{1}{3}$

b. Meela chose the color yellow and then reached into the container and pulled out a yellow block. Kyle says that if she picks one of the two remaining yellow blocks on her next draw, she will get 20 more points. What are the chances that Meela's second block will be yellow? $\frac{2}{8}$, or $\frac{1}{4}$

c. Meela does it again! Now Kyle says that if she chooses the last yellow block on her third draw, she will earn 30 more points. What are the chances that Meela's third block will be yellow? $\frac{1}{7}$

Exercise 31:

You may wish to give students this hint: There are more than 16 triangles and fewer than 30.

Quick Quiz

1. Write an expression that shows the number of inches in w feet, eight inches. $12w + 8$
2. Noah has y lacrosse balls.
   a. Write an expression for the number of balls Stella has if she has 3 less than twice the number of balls Noah has. $2y - 3$
   b. Are there any restrictions on y? Yes, Noah must have more than one ball.
3. Make up a story for the expression $12b + 7$. Possible answer: Jeremy has 7 more than 12 times the number of model airplanes that Elmore has.

LESSON 1.2 Expressions and Formulas 51

Teacher Notes

1.3 The Distributive Property

Objectives

- To understand and apply the distributive property
- To remove parentheses by multiplying
- To insert parentheses by factoring expressions
- To perform numerical calculations using the distributive property

Overview (pacing: about 4 class periods)

Sometimes a shortcut is a great aid in finishing a job correctly and on time, both in mathematics and in life. In this lesson, students learn about the distributive property of multiplication over addition and subtraction and how it can be used to make their lives easier. They learn about different ways to group blocks and then move on to rearranging symbolic expressions. It is important that students understand this property since it is a key element in elementary symbolic manipulation. It provides the backbone of the processes of collecting like terms and of factoring and expanding expressions.

Advance Preparation

You will need 3 bags and 6 blocks to demonstrate the Think & Discuss preceding Investigation 1. Copies of Master 3, Flowcharts, can be used to help students record their answers to problems involving flowcharts. You may also wish to use Master 5, Centimeter Dot Paper, in Investigation 3 and also with some exercises at the end of the chapter after Investigation 4.

Lesson Planner

	Summary	Materials	On Your Own Exercises	Assessment Opportunities
Investigation 1 page T54	Students learn that two forms of an expression can represent the same concrete situation.	• Master 3 (Teaching Resources, page 5) • 3 bags and 6 blocks	Practice & Apply: 1–3 Connect & Extend: 36–37 Mixed Practice: 56–74	Share & Summarize, pages T55, 55 On the Spot Assessment, page T54 Troubleshooting, page T55
Investigation 2 page T56	Students see that there are two different ways to write an expression.	• Master 3	Practice & Apply: 4–9 Connect & Extend: 38 Mixed Practice: 56–74	Share & Summarize, pages T58, 58 Troubleshooting, page T58
Investigation 3 page T59	Students practice using the distributive property in different contexts.	• Master 5	Practice & Apply: 10–23 Connect & Extend: 39–43 Mixed Practice: 56–74	Share & Summarize, pages T63, 63 On the Spot Assessment, pages T60, T62 Troubleshooting, page T63
Investigation 4 page T64	Students rewrite expressions inserting and removing parentheses	• Master 5	Practice & Apply: 24–35 Connect & Extend: 44–55 Mixed Practice: 56–74	Share & Summarize, pages T67, 67 On the Spot Assessment, page T65 Troubleshooting, page T67 Informal Assessment, page 72 Quick Quiz, page 73

Introduce

Ask students whether they have ever used shortcuts to do a multiplication problem, such as 4×24. Some may break apart the problem to find $4 \times 20 = 80$ and $4 \times 4 = 16$, then add those products to find $4 \times 24 = 96$. Explain that this strategy has a name. It is called the *distributive property of multiplication over addition.*

Tell students that they will begin to explore this property by using the bags-and-block model they learned when studying algebraic expressions in the first lesson.

Think & Discuss

Have 3 bags and 6 blocks in the front of the room, arranged in 3 groups of 1 bag and 2 blocks each. This mirrors the arrangement in the illustration in the text. Students should recognize this model.

1.3 The Distributive Property

If you have ever solved a multiplication problem like 4×24 by thinking, "It's 4×20 plus 4×4" or "It's 4 less than 4×25," you were using a mathematical property called the *distributive property.* Using this property, you can change the way you think about how numbers are grouped. For example, rather than think about 4 groups of 24, you can think about 4 groups of 20 added to 4 groups of 4. As you'll see, this property is helpful for more than just mental arithmetic.

1 Discuss the multiplication shortcuts presented in this paragraph.

You have used bags and blocks to help you think about algebraic expressions. Bags and blocks can help you look more closely at the distributive property, too.

Think & Discuss

2 Use bags and blocks to model the situation in the cartoon.

Shaunda, Kate, and Neeraj are each holding one bag and two extra blocks.

Find the total number of blocks if each bag contains

- 5 blocks 21
- 20 blocks 66
- 100 blocks 306
- b blocks $3b + 6$

How did you find your answers? Explanations will vary.

Develop

Have students look at page 53 to see how Jin Lee and Luis found the total number of blocks. Ask students to compare their strategies for finding the number of blocks with those given by Luis and Jin Lee. Students should see that Jin Lee first found the number of blocks in each group and then multiplied the number of blocks in each group by the number of groups. Luis found the number of blocks in all the bags and the total number of loose blocks and then added the answers together to find the total number of blocks. Each method of grouping shows that there are 66 blocks altogether.

Have students tell whose method they prefer and explain why.

Write the expressions showing Jin Lee's and Luis's methods on the board. Have students tell how you would rewrite the expressions if there were *b* blocks, then have students write their answers under the original expressions.

Jin Lee	Luis
$3(20 + 2)$	$(3 \cdot 20) + (3 \cdot 2)$
$3(b + 2)$	$(3 \cdot b) + (3 \cdot 2)$
	$3b + 6$

Students need to realize that these two expressions are different ways to think about, and to represent, the same situation. When the same value is substituted for the variable in each expression, the answer to both is the same.

Here's how Jin Lee and Luis found the total number of blocks when there were 20 in each bag.

1 Have students compare Jin Lee's and Luis's strategies.

Jin Lee's method:

"Each person has 22 blocks, so I multiplied 22 by 3 and got 66."

Luis's method:

"There are 3 bags—that's 60 blocks—and 3 sets of 2 leftover blocks—that's 6 more. So, there are 66 blocks."

Remember

These are four different ways to say the same thing:

3×22 $3(22)$

$3 \cdot 22$ $3 * 22$

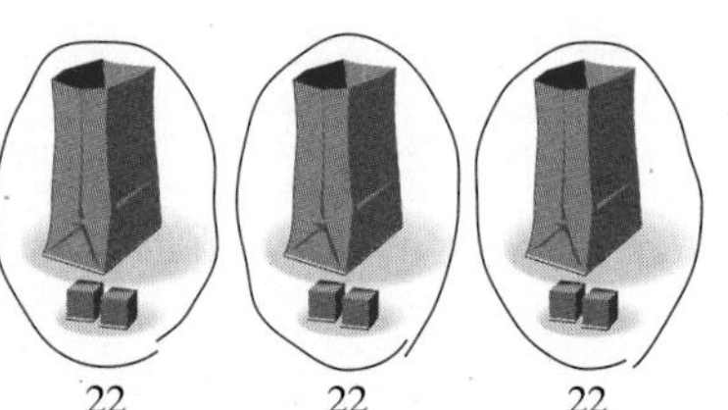
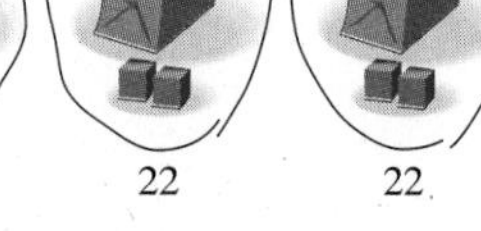

$3(20 + 2) = 3 \cdot 22 = 66$

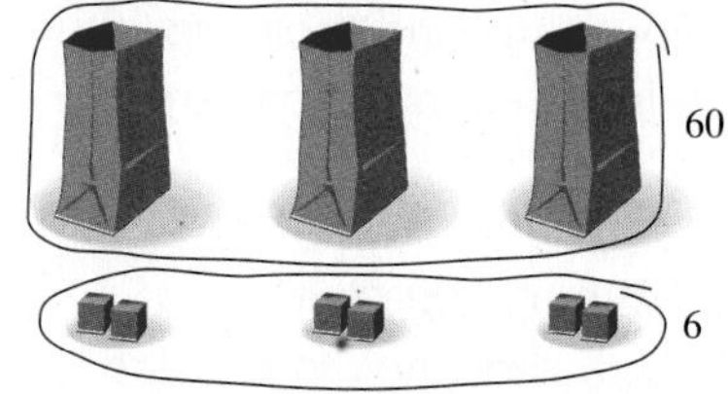

$3 \cdot 20 + 3 \cdot 2 = 60 + 6 = 66$

Jin Lee's and Luis's methods both work no matter how many blocks are in each bag. You can express their methods in symbols for b blocks in each bag.

Jin Lee's method	**Luis's method**
$3(b + 2)$	$3b + 3 \cdot 2 = 3b + 6$

Which way do *you* like to think about this situation? Or do you have another way?

Whichever method you prefer, the important thing to understand is that these two ways of looking at the problem give the same answer. That is,

$$3(b + 2) = 3b + 6$$

LESSON 1.3 The Distributive Property 53

Investigation 1

In this investigation, students are introduced to the distributive property using bags-and-blocks models. They use the distributive property to write an expression in two ways. Then they move to flowcharts and tables to show that the two ways of showing an expression have the same result.

Problem Set A **Suggested Grouping: Pairs**
Students use tables, flowcharts, and drawings to explore the distributive property and to show that the two alternative expressions have the same values. Students are introduced to a subtraction situation in the last problem.

In **Problems 1 and 2,** students use drawings of the bag-and-blocks models to show two ways to find the total number of blocks.

In **Problem 3,** students are asked to draw a flowchart showing the two ways used to find the total number of blocks in the previous problem. You may wish to have students record their work on Master 3, Flowcharts.

On the Spot Assessment

Watch for students who do not use the order of operations to complete their flowcharts in Problem 3. Have them use the values in Problems 2a and 2c as input values in their flowcharts. They can check to see whether their respective output values are the same as those calculated in Problem 2.

Investigation  Grouping Bags and Blocks

One way to see how different expressions can describe the same situation is to consider different groupings of a given number of bags and blocks. Each grouping will have the same total number of blocks, so the expressions you create must represent the same quantity.

1 Have students work in pairs.

Problem Set A

1, 2. See Additional Answers.

1. Brigitte placed 3 blocks in front of each of 4 bags. For each situation below, show two ways of finding the total number of blocks she has. If you need help, look back at Jin Lee's and Luis's methods.

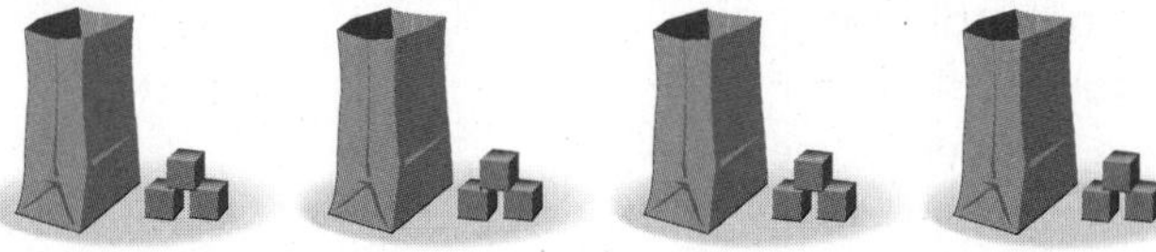

a. 6 blocks in each bag **b.** 15 blocks in each bag
c. 100 blocks in each bag **d.** b blocks in each bag

2. Keenan set 4 blocks in front of three sets of 2 bags. For each situation, show two ways of finding the total number of blocks he has.

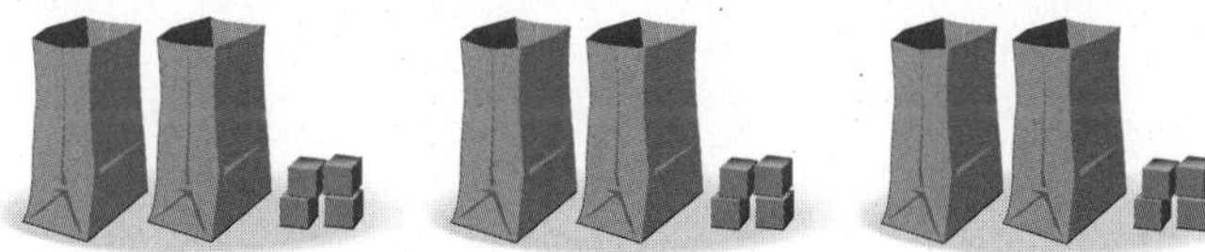

a. 7 blocks in each bag **b.** 11 blocks in each bag
c. 100 blocks in each bag **d.** b blocks in each bag

3. Flowcharts can also help you see different ways to express a quantity.
   a. Think about how you might create a flowchart to calculate the total number of blocks in the situation from Problem 2. Draw and label a flowchart that has four ovals. See below.
   b. Use an input of b for your flowchart. Find the output expression.
   c. Draw another flowchart to find the number of blocks in this situation, but this time use only three ovals. Use an input of b and find the output expression.

3b. Possible answer: $3(2b + 4)$

3a. Possible flowchart:

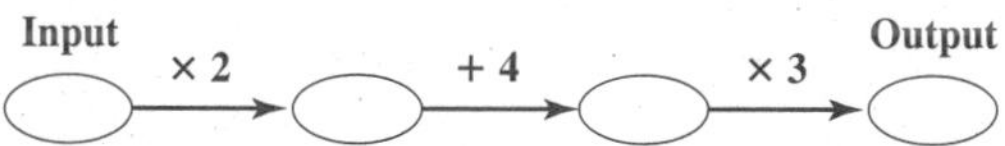

3c. Possible flowchart:

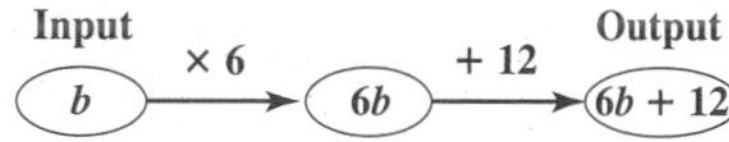

Additional Answers
Problem Set A

Possible answers:

1a. $4(6 + 3), (4 \cdot 6) + (4 \cdot 3)$
1b. $4(15 + 3), (4 \cdot 15) + (4 \cdot 3)$
1c. $4(100 + 3), (4 \cdot 100) + (4 \cdot 3)$
1d. $4(b + 3), 4b + (4 \cdot 3)$

Possible answers:

2a. $3(14 + 4), (3 \cdot 14) + (3 \cdot 4)$
2b. $3(22 + 4), (3 \cdot 22) + (3 \cdot 4)$
2c. $3(200 + 4), (3 \cdot 200) + (3 \cdot 4)$
2d. $3(2b + 4) = 6b + 12$,
$(3 \cdot 2b) + (3 \cdot 4) = 6b + (3 \cdot 4)$

In **Problem 5,** students encounter a subtraction situation for the first time in this lesson.

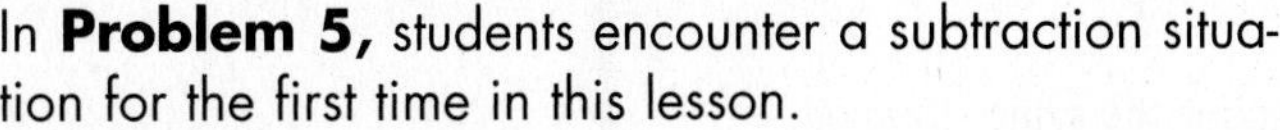

Problem Set Wrap-Up Discuss the subtraction situation in **Problem 5.** Have students present their answers for this problem and share their strategies. Emphasize that regardless of which calculation method is used, the total number of blocks is the same.

Share & Summarize

Students move from using words to describe a specific situation to using symbols to describe a general situation. They should realize that the two ways to find the total number of blocks result in the same answer. Some students may need to write an expression for Question 1 before making the generalization in Question 2.

Troubleshooting If students have difficulty understanding the different ways to find a total, you can still continue to the next investigation. Students will look at the distributive property again using a different context in future investigations.

On Your Own Exercises

Practice & Apply: 1–3
Connect & Extend: 36–37
Mixed Review: 56–74

4. Possible expressions: $4(b + 1)$, $4b + 4$

4. Lehie placed 1 block in front of each of 4 bags. Find two expressions for the total number of blocks she has.

5. Simon and Zoe's teacher held up 3 bags and told the class that each contained the same number of blocks. She removed 2 blocks from each bag. How can you express the number of blocks still in the bags?

To answer this question, Simon and Zoe decided to experiment by starting with 7 blocks in each bag.

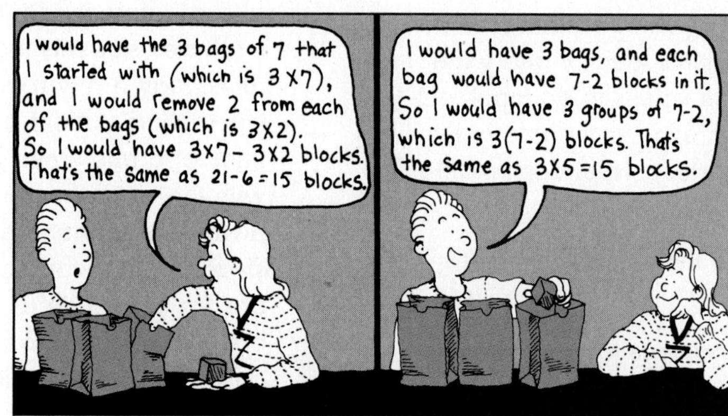

I would have the 3 bags of 7 that I started with (which is 3×7), and I would remove 2 from each of the bags (which is 3×2). So I would have 3×7 − 3×2 blocks. That's the same as 21−6=15 blocks.
I would have 3 bags, and each bag would have 7-2 blocks in it. So I would have 3 groups of 7-2, which is 3(7-2) blocks. That's the same as 3×5=15 blocks.

5a. $3(b - 2)$

a. If b blocks are in each bag, Zoe's reasoning can be expressed in symbols as $3b - 6$. Write an expression that fits Simon's reasoning.

b. Copy and complete the table to show the results of using Zoe's and Simon's methods for various numbers of blocks.

Number of Blocks	b	2	4	7	10	18	22
Zoe's Method	$3b - 6$	0	6	15	24	48	60
Simon's Method	$3(b - 2)$	0	6	15	24	48	60

1 Have students share their answers and strategies for Problem 5.

Share & Summarize

Dante put 5 blocks in front of each of 2 bags.

1. Describe, in words, two ways of finding the total number of blocks if you know the number of blocks in each bag.

1. Multiply the number of blocks in each bag by 2 and then add 10. Add 5 to the number of blocks in a bag and multiply the result by 2.

2. Write two rules, in symbols, for finding the total number of blocks if there are s blocks in each bag.
   Possible rules: $2s + 10$, $2(s + 5)$

2 Some students may need to write an expression for Question 1 before moving on to Question 2.

LESSON 1.3 The Distributive Property 55

Investigation 2

In this investigation, students are introduced to equivalent expressions by learning how to play *What's My Rule?* which provides a setting in which equivalent expressions arise naturally. Students identify and write equivalent expressions. They use values in an input/output table to find a rule and then express the rule in two ways. These activities reinforce students' understanding of the distributive property.

Students should understand that there is always more than one rule that will fit the data.

1 The best way to introduce the game is to play a round with the class. Here are the steps:

- Think of a rule and let students know that your rule can use one or more of the operations of addition, multiplication, and subtraction. Try, on the first round, to think of a rule that has a clear connection to the distributive property, such as $3x + 12$, or $3(x + 4)$.
- Tell students it is their job to figure out your rule by giving you inputs, one by one. Call on different students to supply inputs. You, in turn, will tell them the outputs for each input.
- Write their inputs in a table, with the corresponding outputs, and ask students to guess the rule at any point in the game.

As you play *What's My Rule?* with the class, you can help them observe patterns that can help them discover the rule, such as:

- Ask for inputs in an order that gives you information, such as, 0, 1, 2, ...
- The output for 0 tells you what is added.
- If all outputs are even, the number multiplying the input is an even number.

If students guess the rule $3x + 12$, and your rule was $3(x + 4)$, you can say that you had a different rule, but it gives the same result. Allow them to keep guessing until they find your rule. Likewise, $x + x + x + 12$ is also a different rule that gives the same result. The game motivates students to think of different ways to express rules. Play a few rounds with them, and if you have time, ask a student to come to the front of the room and think of a rule. Then have the student play the game with the class. Students should understand that there is always more than one rule that will fit the data. Some students may want to assert that $3(x + 4)$ and $3x + 12$ are the same rule. If you like, you can explain that they are equivalent rules, in that for each input, they will produce the same output, but the way they calculate the outputs is different. In the first rule, 4 is added to x first, and then the sum is multiplied by 3. In the second, x is multiplied by 3 first, and then 12 is added.

Discuss the cartoon and the algebraic expressions for Alana's and Maura's rules.

Investigation 2 The Same and Different

In the last investigation, you discovered more than one way to find the total number of blocks in a bags-and-blocks situation. You can also use tables and flowcharts to help figure out why two expressions can *look* different but produce the same outputs.

Alana, Maura, and Luis played the game *What's My Rule?* Luis made up a rule for finding the output for any input. Then, Alana and Maura gave Luis several inputs, and he told them the outputs his rule would produce. The girls organized the input/output values in a table.

Input	1	3	6	4	5
Output	8	12	18	14	16

Alana and Maura used their data to guess Luis's rule. When they gave their rules, Luis had a problem.

Alana and Maura described two rules that fit the table. If the input is represented by K, Alana's rule is written in symbols as $2K + 6$. Maura's rule is written as $2(K + 3)$.

It is reasonable to believe that the calculation $2K + 6$ will always give the same result as the calculation $2(K + 3)$. To help you see *why* this works—and why it *must* work no matter what K is—put back the missing multiplication signs.

1 Play a round of *What's My Rule?* with the class.

2 Discuss the cartoon and the expressions for the two rules.

Develop

1

Example
This example shows why two expressions are *equivalent*. This explanation gives students experiences in unpacking an expression. Make sure that students understand why these expressions give the same result.

Walk students through the example as you write the expressions on the board. If students are having difficulty following the logic, draw parentheses around each $K + 3$ in the second step to help them see the two groups of $K + 3$. Other students may need to replace K with a number to clarify their thinking.

Problem Set B **Suggested Grouping: Pairs**
Students draw flowcharts for equivalent expressions. You may wish to use Master 3, Flowcharts, at this time. Students show that two expressions are equivalent and then they are asked to find another expression that is equivalent to $2K + 6$.

In **Problem 1,** students draw flowcharts for two equivalent expressions. This gives students more practice in thinking about how the order of operations applies to expressions.

In **Problem 2,** students write expressions from statements. Then they show that their expressions are equivalent to $2K + 6$.

Access for all Learners

For Early Finishers Have these students write an expression for their rule in **Problem 3.** Encourage them to find another rule that is equivalent to $2K + 6$.

Problem Set Wrap-Up Ask students to share their rules from **Problem 3** with the class. Have them explain why each rule is equivalent to $2K + 6$.

EXAMPLE

Start with $2(K + 3)$, and put back the missing multiplication sign:

$$2 \times (K + 3)$$

This is two groups of $(K + 3)$, which can be written

$$K + 3 + K + 3$$

This is the same as $K + K + 3 + 3$, or

$$2K + 6$$

1 Walk students through the Example.

VOCABULARY
equivalent expressions

So, $2K + 6$ and $2(K + 3)$ are **equivalent expressions.** That means they must give the same result for every value of K.

Problem Set B

2 Have students work in pairs.

1. Let's look more closely at the expressions $2K + 6$ and $2(K + 3)$.
   a. Draw a flowchart for each expression. See below.
   b. For one of the expressions, you multiply first and then add. For the other, you add first and then multiply. Which expression is which?
2. You have seen that $2K + 6$ and $2(K + 3)$ are two ways of writing the same thing. And remember, Luis was thinking of a rule that was different from both of these but gave the same outputs.

   The rules below are also equivalent to $2K + 6$ and $2(K + 3)$. Using K for the input, write an expression for each rule, and show that your expression is equivalent to $2K + 6$.
   a. Add the input to 6 more than the input.
   b. Add 2 more than the input to 4 more than the input.
   c. Add 2 to the input, and double the sum. Add 2 to the result.
   d. Add 5 to the input, and double the sum. Subtract 4 from the result.
3. Write another rule, in words, that is equivalent to $2K + 6$.

1b. In $2K + 6$ you multiply first; in $2(K + 3)$ you add first.

2. See Additional Answers.

3. Possible rule: Add 2 less than the input to 8 more than the input.

3 Ask students to share their rules with the class.

You have seen that in the game *What's My Rule?* the rule can often be written in more than one way. You will now look at input/output tables from the game and express each rule in two ways.

1a.

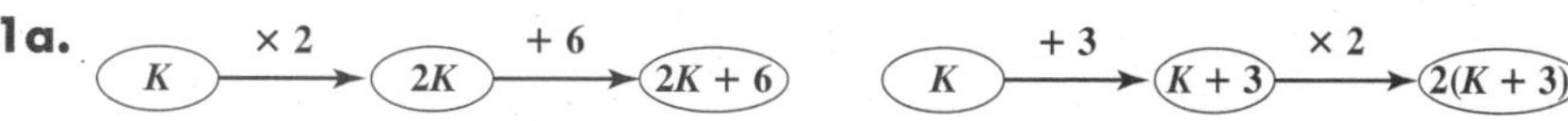

Additional Answers
Problem Set B Answers

2a. $K + (K + 6) = K + K + 6 = 2K + 6$

2b. $(K + 2) + (K + 4) = K + 2 + K + 4 = K + K + 2 + 4 = 2K + 6$

2c. $2(K + 2) + 2 = K + 2 + K + 2 + 2 = K + K + 2 + 2 + 2 = 2K + 6$

2d. $2(K + 5) - 4 = K + 5 + K + 5 - 4 = K + K + 5 + 5 - 4 = 2K + 6$

Develop

Problem Set C **Suggested Grouping: Pairs**
In this problem set, students are asked to find the rules for input/output tables. They are also asked to find equivalent expressions for each rule. In the first problems, students are given an order for the operations of the rule. In the last two problems, students are asked to find equivalent expressions for a given rule.

In **Problems 1–3,** students are asked to write two rules for each table. You may want to point out that the two rules use the same operations but in a different sequence.

Sample Strategies Students may use one of these strategies to find a rule for the table in **Problem 1** that involves adding first and then multiplying:

- Students may look at the output numbers to find a pattern. Since all the numbers are even, they are multiples of 2. So the output value is the sum of an input number and another number multiplied by 2. For example, when the sum of 0 and some number is multiplied by 2, the product is 6. So the number is 3. Students then try this rule to verify that it works for all values.
- Some may look at the patterns in output values. The difference between these output numbers is 2, indicating that the inputs are multiplied by 2. Students proceed from this step in the same way as in the first strategy.
- Others may concentrate on one pair and try to find a rule to get from the input number to the output number.

Problems 4 and 5 have tables but do not ask students to find rules. Students are asked to write another expression that gives the output value.

Share & Summarize

Problem 1 asks students to write equivalent expressions. Students should be able to explain why the expressions are equivalent.

Problem 2 asks students to write rules for a table of values. Be sure students' rules include two operations–multiplication and either addition or subtraction.

Troubleshooting Before moving on, be sure that students understand that for each input value, equivalent expressions must give the same result. If students are having trouble with this concept, you may want to use bags and blocks to illustrate the example on page 57.

On Your Own Exercises

Practice & Apply: 4–9
Connect & Extend: 38
Mixed Review: 56–74

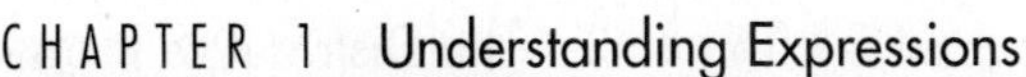

Problem Set C

1. Here's an input/output table for a game of *What's My Rule?*

Input	0	1	2	3	4
Output	6	8	10	12	14

1a. Possible rules: $2n + 6$, $2(n + 3)$

1b. Possible answer: Both rules are equal to $n + n + 6$. (Note: Students may use bags and blocks to explain their thinking.)

a. Use symbols to write two rules for this game. One rule should involve multiplying first and then adding, and the other should involve adding first and then multiplying. Substitute some other inputs to check that the two rules give the same output.

b. Why do the two rules give the same output for a given input?

Use symbols to write two rules for the data in each table. One rule should involve multiplying first and then adding or subtracting, and the other should involve adding or subtracting first and then multiplying.

2.

Input	2	3	4	5	6
Output	0	5	10	15	20

Possible rules: $5(n - 2)$, $5n - 10$

3.

Input	0	1	2	3	4
Output	4	4.5	5	5.5	6

Possible rules: $0.5(n + 8)$, $0.5n + 4$

Copy and complete each table. Then write another expression that gives the same outputs as the given expression. Check your expressions by substituting input values from your tables.

4.

j	0	1	3	8	17	20
$4(j + 2)$	8	12	20	40	76	88

4. Possible expression: $4j + 8$

5.

x	2	3	4	5	6	18	42	82
$5x + 5$	15	20	25	30	35	95	215	415

5. Possible expression: $5(x + 1)$

Share & Summarize

1. Write three expressions that are equivalent to $3P + 12$.

2. Use symbols to write two rules for the data in the table. One rule should involve multiplying first and then adding or subtracting; the other, adding or subtracting first and then multiplying.

Input, k	3	4	13	24	42	50
Output	0	4	40	84	156	188

1. Possible expressions: $2P + 6 + P + 6$, $P + P + P + 12$, $3(P + 4)$

2. Possible rules: $4(k - 3)$, $4k - 12$

1 Have students work in pairs.

2 Look for multiple strategies.

3 Make sure students can explain why their expressions are equivalent.

4 Be sure students' rules include multiplication and either addition or subtraction.

Investigation 3

In this investigation, students practice using the distributive property in various contexts. First, dot diagrams are used to show two ways to think about grouping numbers. Next, students receive a formal introduction to the distributive property. They use the distributive property to simplify some calculations. Then they test to see whether the distributive property works for various combinations of operations.

Call students' attention to the dot diagram on page 59. Discuss how the dot diagram shows different groupings. Some students will be familiar with this way to show the distributive property. Others will need a more comprehensive discussion.

Additional Example Relate the dot diagram to students' earlier work. Write 4×24 on the board. Remind students that they discussed shortcuts to find the product of these factors at the beginning of this lesson. Have students tell how they could make a dot diagram to show how to find the product. Students should describe two adjacent rectangles. The first rectangle has 4 rows with 20 dots in each row. The second rectangle has 4 rows of 4 dots each. You may wish to have students use Master 5, Centimeter Dot Paper, to model this example.

Teaching Resources

Master 5 — Activity Master

Centimeter Dot Paper

Investigation 3 Grouping with the Distributive Property

For the bags-and-blocks situation on page 53, Jin Lee and Luis found two ways to calculate the total number of blocks. In the *What's My Rule?* game on page 56, Alana and Maura found two rules for determining the output for a given input.

One way to find different rules is to look at different groupings of quantities, as you did with bags and blocks in Investigation 1. For example, you can think of the diagram below as a single rectangular array of dots or as two rectangular arrays put together.

1 Discuss the two ways to think about the groupings shown in the dot diagram.

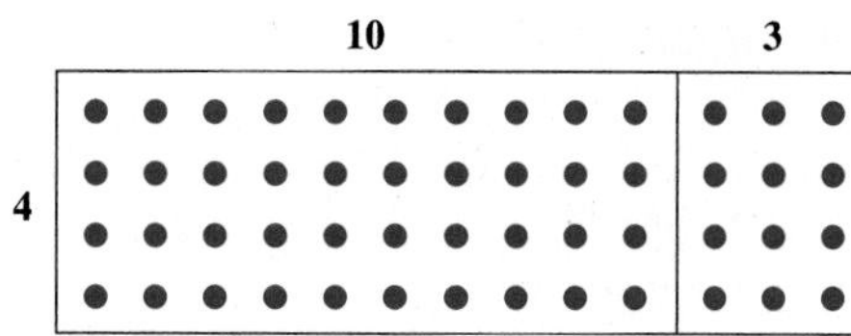

These two ways of thinking about the diagram lead to two ways of calculating the total number of dots in the diagram.

- The total number of dots can be found by noting that there are 4 rows with 10 + 3 dots each:

$$4(10 + 3)$$

- The total number of dots can be found by adding the number of dots in the left rectangle to the number of dots in the right rectangle:

$$4 \times 10 + 4 \times 3$$

Since both $4(10 + 3)$ and $4 \times 10 + 4 \times 3$ describe the total number of dots in the diagram,

$$4(10 + 3) = 4 \times 10 + 4 \times 3$$

LESSON 1.3 The Distributive Property 59

Problem Set D **Suggested Grouping: Pairs** Students interpret and make dot diagrams to show the distributive property visually. They could use Master 5, Centimeter Dot Paper, when answering Problems 2 and 5b. They are given a dot diagram and asked to solve for a variable. Students use dot diagrams to explain why an equation is false.

In **Problem 2,** students create a dot diagram. Although this is a new skill mentioned in the Additional Example, students should able to work independently to draw the diagram.

On the **Spot Assessment**

Watch for students whose diagram for **Problem 2** does not show that $3(4 + 5) = 3 \times 4 + 3 \times 5$. Some students may draw two diagrams to show that each side of the equation has the same number of dots. This would show that the two expressions are equivalent, but it is not the model used in this text. Review the example on page 59 with these students.

In **Problems 3 and 4,** students find the value of two variables in each picture. Students can discuss their strategies as a class in the Problem Set Wrap-Up.

Sample Strategies Students may use one of these strategies to find the variables in **Problem 3.**

- Some students may find the value of r first and then use that information to find the value of t. Students find $5 \cdot 10 = 50$, the number of dots in the first rectangle. They find $80 - 50 = 30$, the number of dots in the second rectangle. Then they use this information to find the value of the variables: $5 \cdot r = 30$, so $r = 6$, and $t = 10 + 6$, or 16.
- Other students may find the value of t first and then use that information to find the value of r. Students think $5t = 80$, so $t = 16$. Then they use this information to find the value of r: $t - 10 = r$, or $16 - 10 = 6$.

In **Problem 5,** students correct a common error, ignoring the parentheses in an expression. Students will study the use of parentheses in the next investigation.

In **Problem 6,** students are asked to interpret a dot diagram with three smaller rectangles.

Problem Set Wrap-Up Have students discuss the way they determined the value of the variables in **Problems 3 and 4.**

Problem Set D

1. Describe two ways to find the number of dots in this diagram. Write an expression for each method.

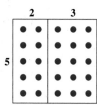

Possible answer: Multiply the number of rows by the number of dots in each row to get 5(2 + 3), or find the number of dots in each small rectangle and then add to get 5 × 2 + 5 × 3.

2. Create a dot diagram to show that 3(4 + 5) = 3 × 4 + 3 × 5.

2.

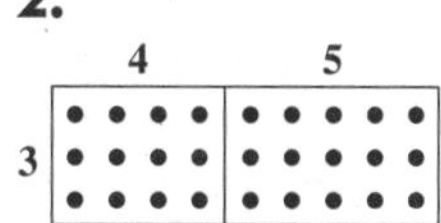

In the diagrams below, the dots are not shown, but the total number of dots is given and labels indicate the number of rows and columns. Use the clues to determine the value of each variable.

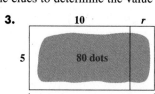

3. 10 r 5 80 dots t — $r = 6$, $t = 16$

4. $n = 12$, $q = 7$

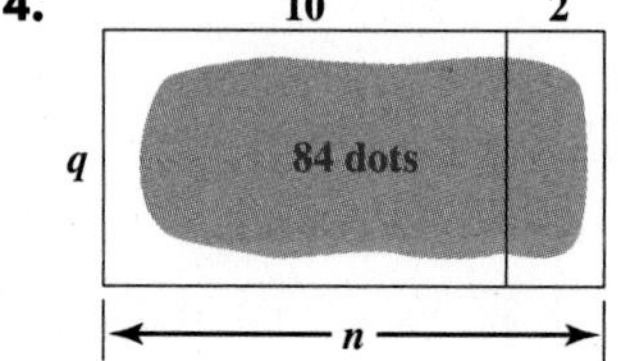

5. Jane wrote 5(10 + 6) = 5 × 10 + 6 in her notebook.

   a. Find the value of the expression on each side to show that Jane's statement is incorrect.

   b. Make a dot diagram you could use to explain to Jane why her statement doesn't make sense.

5a. 5(10 + 6) = 80, 5 × 10 + 6 = 56

5b. 10 6 5 50 dots 30 dots not 6 16

6. Describe two ways to find the number of dots in this diagram. Write an expression for each method.

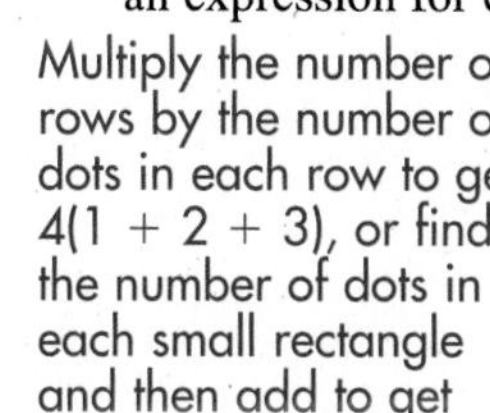

Multiply the number of rows by the number of dots in each row to get 4(1 + 2 + 3), or find the number of dots in each small rectangle and then add to get 4 × 1 + 4 × 2 + 4 × 3.

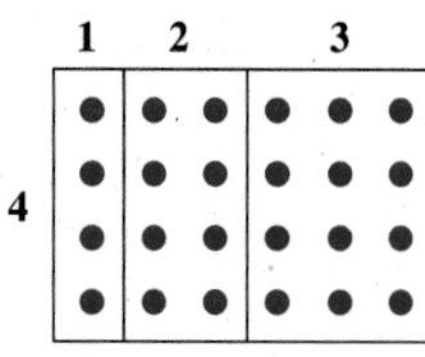

1 Have students work in pairs.

2 Discuss the sample strategies students may use to find the variable in Problems 3 and 4.

Develop

Think & Discuss

Discuss the meaning of *distribute*. Although the mathematical usage is more precise than the common usage, this association can help students remember the basic concept of the *distributive property*.

Direct students' attention to the equation in the Think & Discuss section. Have them tell what is being distributed in $3(10 + 9) = 3 \times 10 + 3 \times 9$. the 3

Discuss the shortcuts. You may wish to have students provide other examples of how to use these shortcuts to find products mentally.

Example

Write the expression $12 \times 77 + 12 \times 23$ on the board. Ask students:

> Which number is distributed in the expression? How do you know? 12; it is a factor in both multiplication steps.

Walk students through the shortcut in the example. Students should see that by writing the equation in this manner, they can use mental math to simplify the expression.

Dot diagrams help you see how different groupings can give equivalent expressions. In this lesson, you have seen many pairs of equivalent expressions, like $3(10 + 9)$ and $3 \times 10 + 3 \times 9$, or $2(n - 3)$ and $2n - 2 \times 3$. When you rewrite an expression like $3(10 + 9)$ or $3(20 - 1)$ as a sum or difference of products, you are using the *distributive property.*

Think & Discuss

What does it mean to *distribute* something? (A dictionary might help.) See ①.

① Possible answer: to pass something around or to give something out

What is being distributed in this equation: the 3

$$3(10 + 9) = 3 \times 10 + 3 \times 9$$

1 Discuss the meaning of *distribute.*

At the beginning of this lesson, you read about a shortcut that can be used to compute 4×24 mentally. Such shortcuts are examples of the distributive property.

2 Discuss the shortcuts.

Shortcut in Words	Shortcut in Symbols
"It's 4×20 plus 4×4."	$4 \times 24 = 4(20 + 4) = 4 \times 20 + 4 \times 4$
"It's 4 less than 4×25."	$4 \times 24 = 4(25 - 1) = 4 \times 25 - 4 \times 1$

Sometimes a calculation can be simplified by using the distributive property in reverse.

EXAMPLE

Find a shortcut for calculating $12 \times 77 + 12 \times 23$.

$$\begin{aligned} 12 \times 77 + 12 \times 23 &= 12(77 + 23) \\ &= 12(100) \\ &= 1{,}200 \end{aligned}$$

3 Walk students through the example.

LESSON 1.3 The Distributive Property 61

Problem Set E **Suggested Grouping: Individuals**
In this problem set, students practice using the distributive property to solve problems using mental math. They show how changing the grouping in expressions can make a hard problem easier. They review the order of operations to decide where to place parentheses to make an equation true.

Problems 1–6 reinforce students' mental calculation techniques.

In **Problems 7–10,** students must use the order of operations to make each equation true. Parentheses and order of operations were introduced in Lesson 1, Investigation 3. Parentheses can now play a role in understanding the distributive property.

On the **Spot Assessment**

Watch for students who insert parentheses around the factors in **Problems 8 and 9.** Remind them that this is not necessary since multiplication comes before addition in the order of operations.

In **Problems 11–14,** students use the distributive property to rewrite expressions and show shortcuts.

Problem Set Wrap-Up Have students explain their grouping methods to a partner. Students who are having difficulty placing the parentheses in **Problems 7–10** will have the opportunity to work on this skill in future investigations.

Have students recall which operations have been used together in the problems they have seen in this lesson. Most of the problems use multiplication and addition. Tell students that these problems are examples of the *distributive property of multiplication over addition.* Write the general form of this property on the board: $n(a + b) = na + nb$

Some students will recall problems that use multiplication and subtraction. Tell students that these problems are examples of the *distributive property of multiplication over subtraction.* Write the general form of this property on the board: $n(a - b) = na - nb$

Tell students that they will explore whether the distributive property is applicable to other pairs of operations.

Possible answers:
1. 85; 5(10 + 7) or 5(20 − 3)
2. 246; 6(40 + 1)
3. 76; 4(20 − 1)
4. 189; 7(20 + 7) or 7(30 − 3)
5. 270; 6(40 + 5) or 6(50 − 5)
6. 342; 9(40 − 2)

Problem Set E

1 Have students work individually and then explain their grouping methods to a partner.

Use the distributive property to help you do each calculation mentally. Write the grouping that shows the method you used.

1. $5 \cdot 17$ **2.** $6 \cdot 41$

3. $4 \cdot 19$ **4.** $7 \cdot 27$

5. $6 \cdot 45$ **6.** $9 \cdot 38$

Copy each equation, inserting parentheses if needed to make the equation true.

7. $4 \times (8 + 3) = 44$ **8.** $4 \times 8 + 3 = 35$

9. $3 \times 7 + 4 = 25$ **10.** $3 \times (7 + 4) = 33$

Find a shortcut for doing each calculation. Use parentheses to show your shortcut.

11. $9 \times 2 + 9 \times 8$ 9(2 + 8) **12.** $19 \times 2 + 19 \times 8$ 19(2 + 8)

13. $12 \times 4 + 12 \times 6$ 12(4 + 6) **14.** $7 \times \frac{3}{5} + 3 \times \frac{3}{5}$ $(7 + 3)\frac{3}{5}$

VOCABULARY
distributive property

2 Discuss the two versions of the distributive property.

You have been rewriting expressions as sums or differences of products using two versions of the **distributive property.** Each version has its own name.

When addition is involved, you use the *distributive property of multiplication over addition.* The general form of this property states that for any numbers *n, a,* and *b,*

$$n(a + b) = na + nb$$

The distributive property you have used to write an expression as a difference of products is the *distributive property of multiplication over subtraction.* The general form of this property states that for any numbers *n, a,* and *b,*

$$n(a - b) = na - nb$$

Each of these more specific names mentions two operations: multiplication, and either addition or subtraction. You distribute the number that multiplies the sum or difference to each part of the sum or difference.

In the next problem set, you will explore whether distribution works for several combinations of operations.

It's quite simple··· multiplication has a compound distributive effect by possessing the ultimate supremacy in its ability to dominate on a scale of mathematical precedence over weaker mathematical, or in this case algebraic, properties such as addition, which has a predisposition to be regressive.
OK?

Develop

Problem Set F **Suggested Grouping: Pairs**
This problem set addresses the misconception that any operation distributes over any other operation. This is an important consideration for students since it may affect their basic math computations when they solve more complex problems.

In **Problem 1,** students determine whether division can be distributed over addition.

In **Problem 2,** students find that division does not distribute over multiplication.

In **Problem 3,** students look at expressions involving exponents, which do not distribute over addition.

Access for all Learners

For Early Finishers Students may want to explore distributing with other pairs of operations, such as addition and subtraction or division and subtraction. Encourage students to write an expression using variables, try values for the variables, and decide whether the statement is true for all values of the variables.

Problem Set Wrap-Up Have students share their answers to all three problems in this problem set. You may want to point out which operation is distributing over another for each problem.

Share & Summarize

These problems focus on the basic concepts in this investigation.

Problem 1 asks students to make a dot diagram. They can use Master 5, Centimeter Dot Paper.

Problem 2 asks students to show how to use the distributive property to find answers mentally. You may want to provide students with additional practice by having students share the parts of their calculations that look difficult. Then have the class use the distributive property to simplify the calculation.

Troubleshooting If students are having difficulty showing the groupings of the distributive property, have them use concrete materials to model some of the problems in this investigation. Students may need to use bags and blocks in order for them to internalize the concepts. Once they have a basic grasp of the concepts, they can move on to symbolic representations.

On Your Own Exercises

Practice & Apply: 10–23
Connect & Extend: 39–43
Mixed Review: 56–74

Problem Set F

1. The statement is true for all values of the variables, provided $c \neq 0$.

1. The expressions in the following statement involve division rather than multiplication.

$$\frac{a+b}{c} = \frac{a}{c} + \frac{b}{c}$$

Choose some values for a, b, and c, and test the statement to see whether it is true. For example, you might try $a = 2$, $b = 5$, and $c = 7$. Try several values for each variable. Do you think the statement is true for all values of a, b, and c?

2. The statement is not true.

2. The expressions in the statement below are like those in Problem 1, but they involve multiplication rather than addition.

$$\frac{ab}{c} = \frac{a}{c} \times \frac{b}{c}$$

Choose some values for a, b, and c, and test the statement to see whether it is true. Try several values for each variable. Do you think the statement is true for all values of a, b, and c?

3. no (It works only when $a = 0$ or $b = 0$.)

3. Choose some values for a and b, and test this statement:

$$(a+b)^2 = a^2 + b^2$$

Do you think the statement is true for all values of a and b?

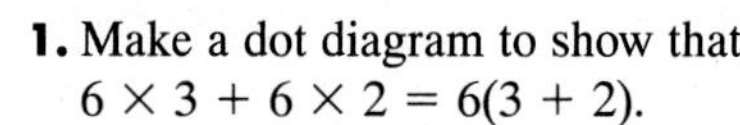

Share & Summarize

1. 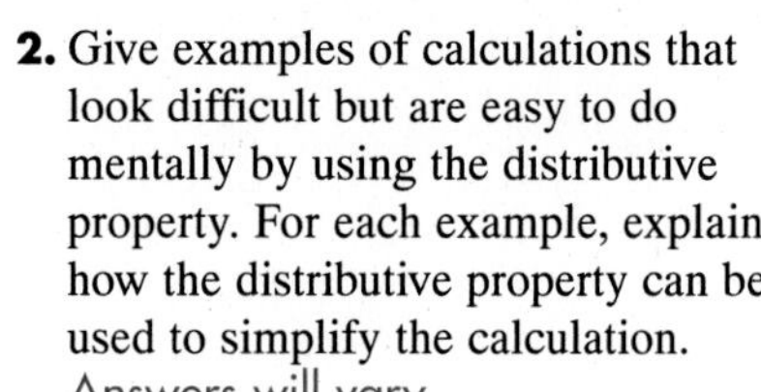

1. Make a dot diagram to show that $6 \times 3 + 6 \times 2 = 6(3 + 2)$.

2. Give examples of calculations that look difficult but are easy to do mentally by using the distributive property. For each example, explain how the distributive property can be used to simplify the calculation.
Answers will vary.

1 Have students work in pairs.

2 Have students share their answers to all three problems with the class.

3 You might have students use Master 5.

LESSON 1.3 The Distributive Property 63

Investigation 4

Begin the investigation by writing the equation $4(n + 2) = 4 \times n + 4 \times 2 = 4n + 8$ on the chalkboard. Remind students that they have already performed computations like this. Tell them that when you remove parentheses, it is called *expanding.* Ask students how the expanded form compares to the form using parentheses. Students should note that there is a change in the *form* of an expression without a change in the *value* that it gives.

Problem Set G **Suggested Grouping: Pairs**
Students use the distributive property to decide whether an equation is true. Then they practice expanding expressions with one or more variables.

The first seven problems give students practice comparing the factored and expanded forms of expressions.

In **Problem 1a,** students need to realize that checking whether the two expressions for $n = 2$ are true does not prove that the two expressions are equal for all values of n.

Sample Strategies Students may use one of these strategies to prove that the equation in **Problem 1b** is true:

- Some students may think of $4(n + 2)$ as 4 groups of $(n + 2)$ or $(n + 2) + (n + 2) + (n + 2) + (n + 2) = 4n + 8$.
- Other students may use a bags-and-blocks model to demonstrate their equivalency: 4 bags and 8 extra blocks has the same number of blocks as 4 groups, each containing 1 bag and 2 extra blocks.
- Others may rely on the distributive property to show that the equation is true.

Investigation 4 Removing and Inserting Parentheses

VOCABULARY
expand
factor

The distributive property explains how you can write expressions in different ways. Using the distributive property to remove parentheses is called **expanding.** Using the distributive property to insert parentheses is called **factoring.**

1 Discuss the idea of expanding.

removing parentheses (expanding)

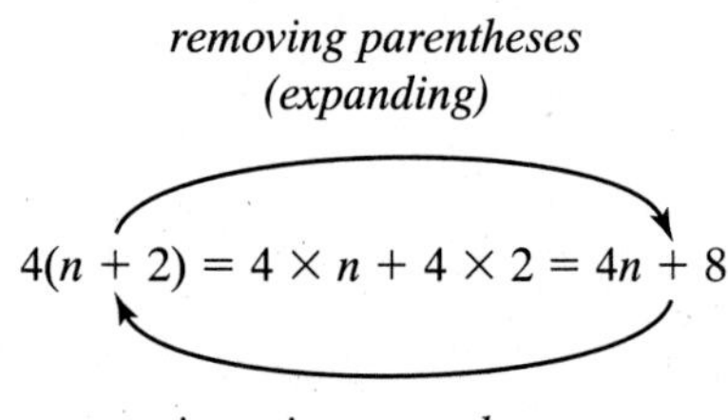

$4(n+2) = 4 \times n + 4 \times 2 = 4n + 8$

inserting parentheses (factoring)

Expanding and factoring allow you to change the *form* of an expression (what it looks like) without changing the output values it gives.

You have seen that rewriting an expression in a different form can be useful for simplifying calculations and comparing expressions. Later, you will see that rewriting expressions can help you solve equations.

In this investigation, you will practice using the distributive property to rewrite expressions. First, you'll focus on expanding expressions, or removing parentheses.

Problem Set G

2 Have students work in pairs.

1. Consider the equation $4(n + 2) = 4n + 8$.

a. Is the equation true for $n = 2$? yes

b. It is impossible to check that $4(n + 2) = 4n + 8$ for every value of n. How do you know that this equation is true for any value of n? The distributive property tells us that $4(n + 2) = 4n + 8$.

Decide whether each equation is true for all values of n. Explain how you decided.

2. $5(n + 6) = 5n + 30$

3. $7(n + 3) = 7n + 3$

4. $(n + 12) \cdot 9 = 9n + 108$

5. $1.5(n + 2.5) = 1.5n + 3.75$

6. $2(n + 4) = 2n + 4$

7. $(n + 9) \cdot 8 = n \cdot 8 + 72$

2. true, distributive property
3. not true, $7(n + 3) = 7n + 21$
4. true, distributive property
5. true, distributive property
6. not true, $2(n + 4) = 2n + 8$
7. true, distributive property

In **Problems 8–19,** students practice expanding expressions. Note that the manipulation is now quite decontextualized and that students are dealing with symbols irrespective of their contexts.

On the Spot Assessment

In **Problems 8–19,** watch for students who do not multiply each part when expanding an expression. These students only use expanding for the first part of the expression. For example, in **Problem 11,** students might show $3(n - 4) = 3n - 4$. Remind them to expand the entire expression. Encourage students to substitute values for n to make sure that the expressions name the same value.

In **Problems 20–25,** students work with expressions containing two variables. Students should be aware that the process of expanding is the same regardless of the number of variables.

Problem Set Wrap-Up Before moving on, make sure that students understand that expanding an expression changes the form but not the value. Students will have the opportunity for additional practice in later problem sets.

Example

Explain to students that in the previous examples, they used the distributive property to remove parentheses. Sometimes it is useful to take an expression and insert parentheses, or *factor* the expression.

Write $3d + 21$ on the board. Tell students that this is an expanded expression. Ask students how they think the expression looked before it was expanded. Walk students through the explanation in the Example on page 65.

Expand each expression. (That is, rewrite it to remove the parentheses.) Check the resulting expression by making sure it gives the same values as the original expression for at least three values of x.

8. $4(2x + 3)$ $8x + 12$

9. $4(3x + 7)$ $12x + 28$

10. $0.5(2x + 8)$ $x + 4$

Expand each expression.

11. $3(n - 4)$ $3n - 12$	**12.** $4(2n + 7)$	**13.** $8(3n - 3)$
14. $1(4n - 7)$ $4n - 7$	**15.** $2(2n - 3.5)$	**16.** $10(n + 10)$
17. $1(n + 1)$ $n + 1$	**18.** $0(n + 9{,}999)$ 0	**19.** $2(n + 0)$ $2n$

12. $8n + 28$
13. $24n - 24$
15. $4n - 7$
16. $10n + 100$

The expressions below look a bit different from those in Problems 11–19, but the distributive property still works. Expand each expression. If you are uncertain about a result, test it by substituting values for the variables.

20. $r(n + 1)$ $rn + r$	**21.** $n(2 + 7)$	**22.** $x(4 - 3n)$
23. $2(n + 9n)$	**24.** $n(2 + 18)$	**25.** $2(1.5n + 2.5n)$

21. $2n + 7n$, or $9n$
22. $4x - 3nx$
23. $2n + 18n$, or $20n$
24. $2n + 18n$, or $20n$
25. $3n + 5n$, or $8n$

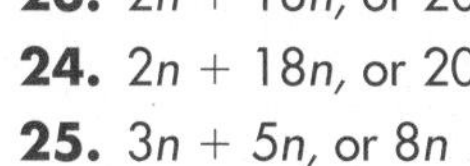

Now you will use the distributive property to insert parentheses.

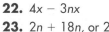

EXAMPLE

To rewrite $3d + 21$ by inserting parentheses, think about how the distributive property could have been used to produce the expression.

Both parts of the expression, $3d$ and 21, can be rewritten as 3 times something.

$$\begin{aligned} 3d + 21 &= 3 \times d + 3 \times 7 \\ &= 3(d + 7) \end{aligned}$$

You can check this result by using the distributive property to expand $3(d + 7)$.

$$\begin{aligned} 3(d + 7) &= 3 \times d + 3 \times 7 \\ &= 3d + 21 \end{aligned}$$

1 Walk students through the Example.

Just the facts

In your study of mathematics, you will sometimes use more than just standard parentheses. Here are a few styles of parentheses, brackets, and braces you might encounter.

{ [({ [( )] })] }

LESSON 1.3 The Distributive Property 65

Develop

Students may have given other ways to write the expression $3d + 21$. Some possibilities include $0.5(6d + 42)$, or $1.5\ (2d + 14)$. In most cases the last two expressions are not considered very useful. We are really interested in the simplest product: one with whole numbers and variables.

Tell students that when they factor a number, they should express it as the product of whole number factors (not including 1) unless there are fractions or decimals in the expression being factored. For example, the factored form of 35 is 5×7, not 0.5×70.

About the Mathematics

When mathematicians speak of factoring an integer like 35, they mean producing a set of integer factors whose product is 35. We cannot precisely describe what it means to factor an expression, but the general idea can be explained through examples. For example, the expression $\frac{1}{2}x + \frac{1}{2}$ is properly factored as $\frac{1}{2}(x + 1)$ even though the factor outside the parentheses is not an integer; and, similarly, $\frac{1}{2}\pi + \frac{1}{3}\pi x$ is properly factored as $\pi(\frac{1}{2} + \frac{1}{3}x)$ even though neither of the factors are integers. The notion of getting the simplest product is probably the least misleading, even though it doesn't say precisely what's meant by simplest. In this lesson, the term *whole number* is used in place of *integer.* Integers are taught in Chapter 4.

As you walk students through the examples of factoring on page 66, you may wish to ask students questions such as:

> Both parts of this expression can be rewritten as something times what number?
>
> What number should I write outside the parentheses when I factor this expression?
>
> What should I write inside the parentheses when I factor this expression?

If students don't give their answers in simplest form, you will need to preview the Example by asking whether the expression inside the parentheses can be factored.

Example

Tell students that they should factor an expression until it cannot be factored any further.

Walk students through the Example on page 66. Students should understand that if the expression inside the parentheses can be factored, then the expression can be factored further.

Be sure students understand that some expressions cannot be factored.

Rewriting an expression by inserting parentheses is called *factoring* because the resulting expression is the product of factors.

You could factor $3d + 21$ in other ways. For example, you could write $\frac{1}{2}(6d + 42)$ or $0.1(30d + 210)$. However, working with these expressions is a lot more complicated. Unless the expression you are factoring contains fractions or decimals, use only whole numbers in your factors.

The examples below show how some other expressions can be factored.

$$7 + 7x = 7 \times 1 + 7 \times x = 7(1 + x)$$

$$7t - 3t = 7 \times t - 3 \times t = (7 - 3)t = (4)t = 4t$$

$$6m + 3m^2 = 3m \times 2 + 3m \times m = 3m(2 + m)$$

$$s + ms + nms = s + m \times s + n \times m \times s = s(1 + m + nm)$$

After you factor, look carefully at the expression inside the parentheses. You may find that more factoring can be done.

EXAMPLE

Factor the expression $27p^2 + 18p$.

Since 9 divides both parts of the expression, it can be rewritten as follows:

$$27p^2 + 18p = 9(3p^2 + 2p)$$

Now look at the expression inside the parentheses. Since p divides both $3p^2$ and $2p$, the expression can be factored further.

$$9(3p^2 + 2p) = 9p(3p + 2)$$

So, $27p^2 + 18p = 9p(3p + 2)$.

Not all expressions can be easily factored. For example, no whole number or variable evenly divides both parts of $5x + 7$.

1 Discuss other possible ways to factor $3d + 21$.

2 Ask questions to guide students through the examples.

3
- Walk students through the Example.
- Help students understand that they should factor an expression until it can't be factored any further.

4 Explain that some expressions cannot be factored.

Problem Set H **Suggested Groupings: Pairs**
Students rewrite expressions using the distributive property. They practice expanding expressions with two and three terms.

In **Problems 1–6,** students determine whether an expression can be factored, and if so, factor it.

In **Problems 7–12,** students factor expressions with two parts.

Problems 13 and 14 ask students to factor an expression with three parts.

Students use data in a context in **Problem 15.** They write two expressions to describe the data. Depending on the first expression students write, they may use either factoring or expanding to write the second expression.

In **Problem 17,** students use factoring as a preview to adding terms in an expression. Students factor one side of an equation and show that it has the same value as the other side of the equation.

Problem Set Wrap-Up Discuss **Problems 16 and 17** as a class. Students' explanations for Problem 16 should have a reference to the fact that both terms in the first two expressions can be evenly divided by the same number. The terms in $4k + 9m$ do not have any common factors.

You may wish to discuss **Problem 17** further because it is a preview to adding like terms. If students understand the reasoning presented here, they will have a stronger basis when the skill is formally presented.

Share & Summarize
Encourage students to invent challenging expressions for their partners to factor and expand. The act of creating these problems gives students insight into the workings of the distributive property. Some students may come up with expressions that in fact cannot be factored. If they do, ask them to tell their partners why they can't be factored.

When explaining how expanding and factoring are related, students may use language such as, *one undoes the other.* In fact, this is a good way for them to think about these processes.

Troubleshooting If students are having difficulty with expanding and factoring, they probably need more practice. There are many additional problems in the On Your Own Exercises section, and you can use these to help them.

On Your Own Exercises

Practice & Apply: 24–35
Connect & Extend: 44–55
Mixed Review: 56–74

Problem Set H

Determine whether there is a whole number or variable that divides both parts of each expression. If there is, use the distributive property to rewrite the expression using parentheses. Check the resulting expression by expanding it.

1. $4a + 8$ $4(a + 2)$ **2.** $4b + 12$ $4(b + 3)$ **3.** $4c + 17$ no

4. $3g - 15$ $3(g - 5)$ **5.** $5f + 13$ no **6.** $8h - 24$ $8(h - 3)$

Factor each expression. You may need to look closely to see how to do it. Check the resulting expression by expanding it.

7. $22s + 33$ $11(2s + 3)$ **8.** $34t - 4$ $2(17t - 2)$

9. $45m + 25k$ $5(9m + 5k)$ **10.** $7j^2 + 3j$ $j(7j + 3)$

11. $4t + 9t$ $(4 + 9)t = 13t$ **12.** $8g^2 + 12g$ $4g(2g + 3)$

13. $10m + 15t + 25$ **14.** $8 - 16h^2 + 20h$

13. $5(2m + 3t + 5)$
14. $4(2 - 4h^2 + 5h)$
15. Possible answer: $7(800 + x)$; $5{,}600 + 7x$
16. $4t$ and $9t$ have t as a common factor, $6k$ and $9m$ have 3 as a common factor, but nothing evenly divides both $4k$ and $9m$.

15. Every morning Pamela and her dog Rex run to the local park, around the park, and back home. It is 400 meters to the park and x meters around the park. Write two expressions for the total distance, in meters, they run in a week. One of your expressions should involve parentheses.

16. Explain why $4t + 9t$ and $6k + 9m$ can be factored but $4k + 9m$ cannot.

17. Prove It! Show that $2k + 3k = 5k$ by first factoring $2k + 3k$. Then check that $2k + 3k = 5k$ for $k = 7$ and $k = 12$. $2k + 3k = (2 + 3)k = 5k$

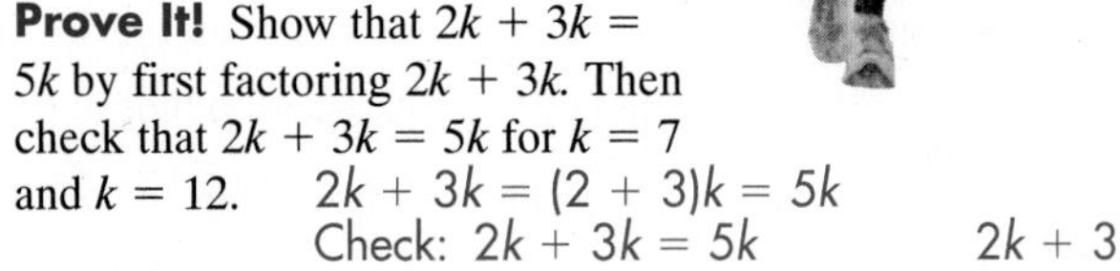

Check: $2k + 3k = 5k$ $2k + 3k = 5k$
$2(7) + 3(7) = 5(7)$ $2(12) + 3(12) = 5(12)$
$14 + 21 = 35$ ✓ $24 + 36 = 60$ ✓

Share & Summarize

1. Create an expression in factored form. Give it to your partner to expand. Expressions will vary.

2. Create an expression that can be factored. Give it to your partner to factor. Expressions will vary.

3. Explain how expanding and factoring are related. Both involve the distributive property and parentheses. When you expand you get rid of parentheses; when you factor you add parentheses.

1 Have students work in pairs.

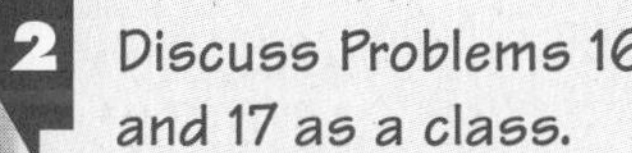

2 Discuss Problems 16 and 17 as a class.

3 Encourage students to invent challenging expressions for their partners.

LESSON 1.3 The Distributive Property 67

On Your Own Exercises

Investigation 1
Practice & Apply: 1–3
Connect & Extend: 36–37

Investigation 2
Practice & Apply: 4–9
Connect & Extend: 38

Investigation 3
Practice & Apply: 10–23
Connect & Extend: 39–43

Investigation 4
Practice & Apply: 24–35
Connect & Extend: 44–55

Assign Anytime
Mixed Review: 56–74

Exercise 1:
This problem is similar to the concrete models that students completed at the beginning of the chapter and should be relatively familiar to students.

On Your Own Exercises

Practice & Apply

1. Suppose there are 5 bags with N blocks in each bag, and 3 extra blocks beside each bag.

a. Write two expressions for the total number of blocks, as you did in Problem Set A. Possible answer: $5(n + 3)$, $5n + 15$

b. Check that your two expressions give the same total for $n = 8$, $n = 12$, and $n = 25$.

c. Explain—using a picture, if you like—why your two expressions must give the same total number of blocks for any value of n.

1b. Both expressions should give 55 for $n = 8$, 75 for $n = 12$, and 140 for $n = 25$.

1c. because 5 groups of 1 bag and 3 blocks is the same as 5 bags and $3 \cdot 5$, or 15, blocks

2. Suppose there are four sets of 3 bags, with 3 blocks in front of each set. For each situation, show two ways to find the total number of blocks.

a. 5 blocks in each bag Possible answer: $4(15 + 3)$, $4 \cdot 15 + 4 \cdot 3$

b. 100 blocks in each bag

c. b blocks in each bag Possible answer: $4(3b + 3)$, $4 \cdot 3b + 4 \cdot 3$

2b. Possible answer: $4(300 + 3)$, $4 \cdot 300 + 4 \cdot 3$

3. Shaunda has 5 bags, with the same number of blocks in each. She removes 2 blocks from each bag. For each situation below, show two ways of finding the total number of blocks in the bags.

a. The bags start with 7 blocks in each. $5(7 - 2)$, $5 \cdot 7 - 5 \cdot 2$

b. The bags start with 50 blocks in each. $5(50 - 2)$, $5 \cdot 50 - 5 \cdot 2$

c. The bags start with p blocks in each. $5(p - 2)$, $5 \cdot p - 5 \cdot 2$

4. Consider the expressions $3(T - 1)$ and $3T - 3$.

a. Copy the table, and complete the first four columns. In the last four columns, choose your own input values and calculate the output for both rules. Use fractions for at least two of your input values. The last four columns will vary.

T	4	11	100	30				
$3T - 3$	9	30	297	87				
$3(T - 1)$	9	30	297	87				

b. Show that $3(T - 1)$ and $3T - 3$ are equivalent expressions.

c. Find two more expressions that are equivalent to $3(T - 1)$ and $3T - 3$.

4b. Possible answer: $3(T - 1) = T - 1 + T - 1 + T - 1 = 3T - 3$

4c. Possible answer: $2(T - 1) + (T - 1)$, $T + T + T - 3$

Copy and complete each table. Then, for each table, write another expression that gives the same outputs. Check your new expression to make sure it generates the same values.

5.

h	0	1	2	7	42	47
$2(h + 3)$	6	8	10	20	90	100

Possible expression: $2h + 6$

6.

r	3	5	10	11	22	23
$5(r - 2)$	5	15	40	45	100	105

Possible expression: $5r - 10$

7.

n	4	5	6	8	44	100
$\frac{n-4}{4}$	0	0.25	0.5	1	10	24

Possible expression: $\frac{n}{4} - 1$

For each *What's My Rule?* table, find two ways to write the rule in symbols. Choose your own variable.

8.

Input	0	1	2	3	4
Output	8	10	12	14	16

Possible rules: $2(x + 4)$, $2x + 8$

9.

Input	0	1	2	3	4
Output	6	6.5	7	7.5	8

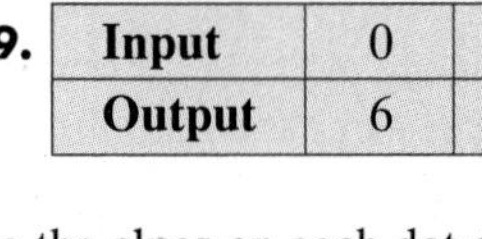

Possible rules: $\frac{1}{2}(x + 12)$, $\frac{1}{2}x + 6$

10. $a = 10$, $b = 126$
11. $g = 18$, $h = 4$
16. 170; Possible grouping: $17(2 + 8)$
17. 48; Possible grouping: $(16 - 4)4$
18. 100; Possible grouping: $(11 + 9)5$
19. $\frac{100}{87}$; Possible grouping: $\frac{1}{87}(20 + 80)$

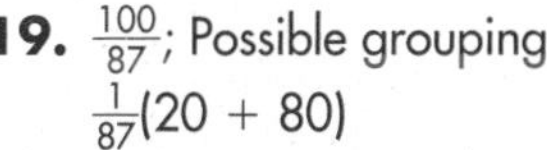

Use the clues on each dot diagram to find the unknown values.

10.

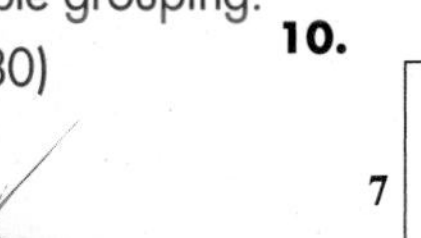

11.

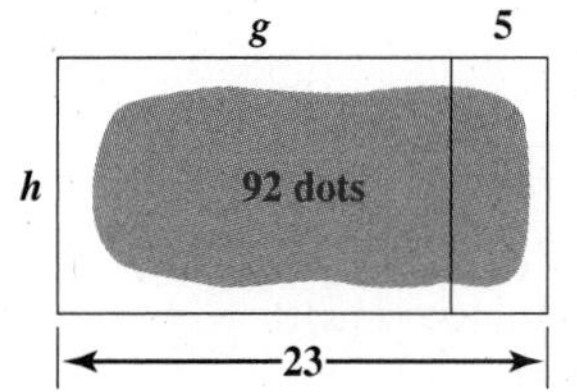

Copy each equation, inserting parentheses when needed to make the equation true.

12. $5 \times (2 + 3) = 25$

13. $(12 + 3) \times 7 = 105$

14. $11 + 8 \times 4 = 43$

15. $(0.2 + 0.2) \times 0.2 = 0.08$

Use the distributive property to help you do each calculation mentally. Write the grouping that shows the method you used. See margin.

16. $17 \cdot 2 + 17 \cdot 8$

17. $16 \cdot 4 - 4 \cdot 4$

18. $11 \cdot 5 + 5 \cdot 9$

19. $\frac{20}{87} + \frac{80}{87}$

Exercises 5–7: These problems give students more practice in using a table to generate different expressions that have the same value. Students can then check whether or not the new expression has the same value.

Exercises 10–11: Many students will find these problems to be an interesting challenge. However, if some students have difficulty, refer them to pages 59 and 60 for additional help.

LESSON 1.3 The Distributive Property 69

Assign and Assess

Exercises 24–29: These exercises involve expanding expressions and checking each new expression to make sure that it has the same value as the given expression.

Exercises 30–35: Students factor each expression. Remind them that not all the expressions can be factored.

20. not true, $6(W + 2) = 6W + 12$

21. true, distributive property

Remember

Expanding an expression means rewriting it to remove the parentheses.

Connect & Extend

22. true, distributive property

23. not true, $(a + 3) \times 7 = a \times 7 + 21$

25. $0.8k + 1.8$

26. $2n - 14$

31. not possible

32. $3(g - 5)$

34. $(11 + 3)v = 14v$

35. $(5z + 2)z$

36b. 4 bags with 3 blocks removed from each is the same as 4 bags with 12 blocks removed.

37b. Possible expressions: $15(5n - 100)$; or $75n - 1{,}500$

Decide whether each equation is true for all values of the variable. Justify your answers.

20. $6(W + 2) = 6W + 2$

21. $(Y + 176) \div 8 = \frac{Y}{8} + \frac{176}{8}$

22. $2.5(B + 12) = 2.5B + 30$

23. $(a + 3) \times 7 = a \times 7 + 3$

Expand each expression. Check the resulting expression by making sure it gives the same values as the original expression for several values of *x*.

24. $5(3j + 4)$ $15j + 20$

25. $0.2(4k + 9)$

26. $2(n - 7)$

27. $n(n - 6)$ $n^2 - 6n$

28. $3(3n + 3)$ $9n + 9$

29. $0(n + 875)$ 0

Factor each expression, if possible.

30. $4a + 8$ $4(a + 2)$

31. $18 + 5b$

32. $3g - 15$

33. $18 - 2A$ $2(9 - A)$

34. $11v + 3v$

35. $5z^2 + 2z$

36. Joshua has 4 bags of blocks. He removes 3 blocks from each bag.

a. Write two expressions for the total number of blocks in Joshua's bags now. Possible expressions: $4(n - 3)$, $4n - 12$

b. Explain—using a picture, if you like—why your two expressions must give the same total number of blocks for any value of the variable.

37. The rock band "The Accidents" brought five boxes of their new CD, *Waiting to Happen,* on their tour. Each box holds the same number of CDs. They hoped to sell all the CDs, but they sold only 20 CDs from each box.

a. Write an expression that describes the total number of unsold CDs. Possible expressions: $5(n - 20)$, or $5n - 100$

b. Write an expression that describes how much the band will earn, in dollars, by selling the remaining CDs for $15 each.

70 CHAPTER 1 Understanding Expressions

39. Possible answer:

a	b	c
3	20	8
5	16	10
11	10	16
15	8	20
27	5	32
35	4	40

40. Addition does not distribute over multiplication. For example, $2 + (3 \times 1) \neq (2 + 3) \times (2 + 1)$ because $5 \neq 15$.

41a. Multiply the number by 100, then subtract the number.

41b. $99n = (100 - 1)n = 100n - n$

In your own words

Assume you are talking to a student two years younger than you are. Explain why $3(b + 4) = 3b + 12$, not $3b + 4$. You might want to draw a picture to help explain the idea.

38. In this pattern of toothpicks, the width of the figure increases from one figure to the next. Using symbols, write two rules for finding the number of toothpicks in a figure. Use parentheses in one of your rules but not in the other. Use w to represent the width of a figure.

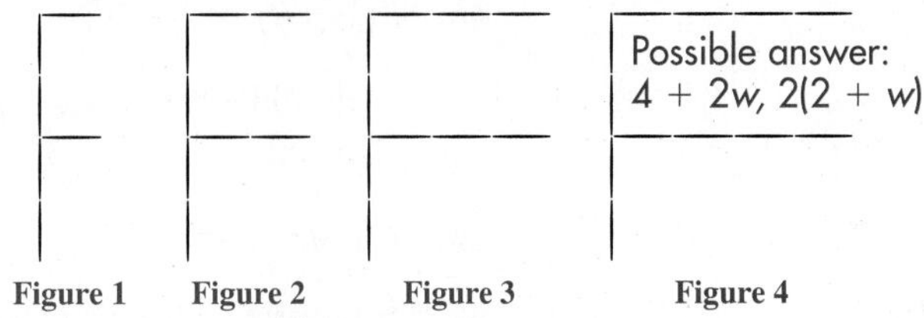

39. This dot diagram is missing so much information that many sets of numbers will work. Find at least three sets of values for a, b, and c.

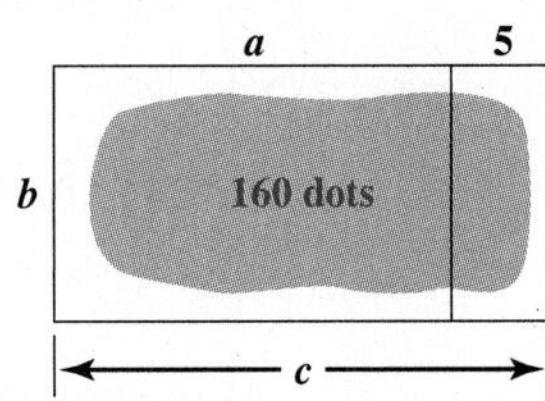

40. You have learned that multiplication distributes over addition. Do you think addition distributes over multiplication? That is, does $a + (b \times c) = (a + b) \times (a + c)$? Support your idea with numerical examples.

41. Marcus says he knows a shortcut for multiplying by 99 in his head. He claims he can mentally multiply any number by 99 within 5 seconds.

a. Find Marcus's shortcut for multiplying by 99.

b. Using symbols, explain why his shortcut works. (Hint: His shortcut uses the distributive property.)

Preview For each *What's My Rule?* table, fill in the missing numbers and find the rule. Hint: Consider exponents when you are looking for the rules.

Possible rule: n^2

42.

Input	0	1	2	3	5	8	10	25
Output	0	1	4	9	25	64	100	625

43.

Input	0	1	2	3	4	5	7	10
Output	3	4	7	12	19	28	52	103

Possible rule: $n^2 + 3$

Exercises 38–39:
Many students enjoy working on problems such as these in which they must use logical reasoning to find the answer. The basis for the logical reasoning in these two problems involves familiarity with the distributive property.

Exercises 42–43:
If students are having difficulty, point out the hint given at the end of the problem.

Assign and Assess

Exercises 56–64: Watch for students who misplace the decimal point when multiplying by a decimal.

Quick Check

Informal Assessment
At the end of the lesson, students should be able to

- ✔ use the distributive property to write two forms of the same expression
- ✔ rewrite expressions by inserting and removing parentheses
- ✔ perform numerical calculations using the distributive property

Expand each expression. Check your answer by substituting 1, 2, and 10 for the variable.

44. $7Q(Q + 8)$ $7Q^2 + 56Q$

45. $9L(L + 3L^2)$ $9L^2 + 27L^3$

46. $8R(\frac{1}{2} - R)$ $4R - 8R^2$

47. $3D(D^2 - \frac{D}{2})$ $3D^3 - \frac{3}{2}D^2$

Factor each expression.

48. $3m^3 + 6m$ $3m(m^2 + 2)$

49. $2t^3 + 4t^2$ $2t^2(t + 2)$

50. $4L + 3L^2$ $L(4 + 3L)$

51. $3P + mP$ $P(3 + m)$

52. $2(n + \frac{1}{2}) = 2n + 1$, and $2n$ must be even, so $2n + 1$ must be odd.

52. Challenge When you take any whole number, add $\frac{1}{2}$, and then multiply the sum by 2, the result is an odd number. Explain why.

53. Challenge This fraction contains variables.

$$\frac{8x + 4z + 2}{2}$$

To simplify this fraction, you might first think of it as

$$\tfrac{1}{2}(8x + 4z + 2)$$

Then you can apply the distributive property.

$$\tfrac{1}{2}(8x + 4z + 2) = \tfrac{1}{2}(8x) + \tfrac{1}{2}(4z) + \tfrac{1}{2}(2)$$
$$= 4x + 2z + 1$$

Use this method to simplify each fraction.

a. $\frac{12x + 6z + 3}{3}$ $4x + 2z + 1$ **b.** $\frac{10x^2 + 5x}{5}$ $2x^2 + x$

54. World Cultures In some countries, long multiplication is taught to students using a grid. Here's how to multiply 15 and 31 using a grid.

×	10	5
30	300	150
1	10	5

The product of 15 and 31 is 465, the total of the four numbers inside the grid. Use the grid method to find each product.

a. 14 × 56

b. 23 × 23

c. 45 × 21

54a. 784

×	10	4
50	500	200
6	60	24

54b. 529

×	20	3
20	400	60
3	60	9

54c. 945

×	40	5
20	800	100
1	40	5

Remember

A *prime number* has only two factors: itself and 1.

Mixed Review

55a. Possible answer: $x^2 + x = x(x + 1)$, which is the product of two whole numbers greater than 1 and therefore cannot be prime.

55b. Possible answer: $x^2 - x = x(x - 1)$, which is the product of two whole numbers greater than 1 and therefore cannot be prime.

59. 0.0064

66. $4.2r^3$

55. Challenge You can use factoring to prove some interesting facts about numbers.

a. If you start with a whole number greater than 1 and add it to its square, the result will never be a prime number. Explain why not. (Hint: Use x to stand for the whole number. Then x^2 is its square, and $x^2 + x$ is the whole number added to its square.)

b. If you start with a whole number greater than 2 and subtract it from its square, the result can never be a prime number. Explain.

Find each product.

56. 0.08×0.2 0.016 **57.** 0.15×0.4 0.06 **58.** 0.65×0.2 0.13

59. 0.08×0.08 **60.** 0.03×3 0.09 **61.** 0.06×0.02 0.0012

Find each percentage.

62. 70% of 1 0.7 **63.** 1% of 70 0.7 **64.** 16% of 50 8

Write each expression without using multiplication or addition signs.

65. $r + r + r$ $3r$ **66.** $4.2 \cdot r \cdot r \cdot r$ **67.** $5st + 2.7st$ $7.7st$

Find the value of each expression for $k = 1.1$.

68. $k^3 - 1^3$ 0.331 **69.** $\frac{7k}{5}$ 1.54 **70.** $\frac{7}{5}k$ 1.54

Geometry Find the area and perimeter of each figure.

71.

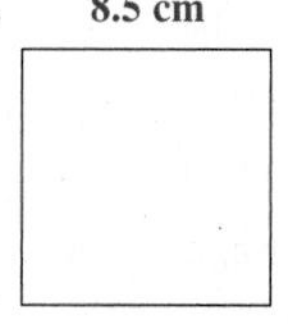

72.25 cm², 34 cm

72.

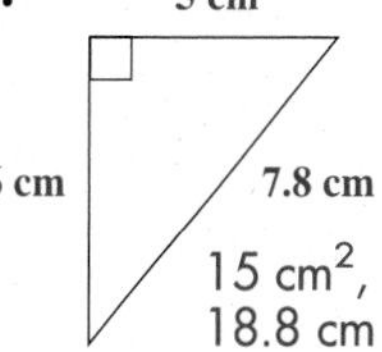

15 cm², 18.8 cm

73.

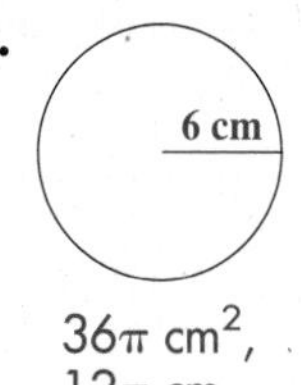

36π cm², 12π cm

74. The grid contains four types of squares: white, shaded, striped, and squares with stars.

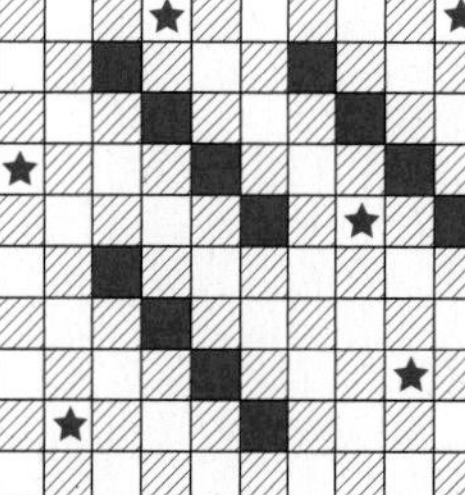

a. What percent of the squares in the grid are striped? 50%

b. What percent of the squares are shaded? 12%

c. What percent of the squares have stripes or stars? 56%

Exercise 66:

Watch for students who write $r \cdot r \cdot r$ as $3r$.

Quick Quiz

1. Explain how you can use the distributive property to do this calculation mentally: 5×99. Add 1 to 99, multiply by 5; then subtract 5. The expression $5(1 + 99) - 5$ shows these steps.
2. Rewrite this expression by removing the parentheses: $1.5(2C + 10)$. $3C + 15$
3. Use the distributive property to rewrite this expression: $24Y + 8Y^2$. $8Y(3 + Y)$
4. Insert parentheses to make this expression true: $8 \times 3 + 4 = 56$. $8 \times (3 + 4) = 56$
5. Find two different ways of writing a rule that produces the table below:

In	0	1	2	3	4
Out	2	6	10	14	18

$4n + 2$ or $2(2n + 1)$

LESSON 1.3 The Distributive Property **73**

Chapter Summary
This summary helps students recall the major topics of the chapter.

Vocabulary
Students should be able to explain each of the terms listed in the vocabulary section.

Strategies and Applications
The questions in this section help students review and apply the important mathematical ideas and problem-solving strategies developed in the chapter. The questions are organized by mathematical highlights. The highlights correspond to those in "The Big Picture" chart on page 1a.

Exercise 3:
Some students may need to be reminded to use 3.14 to represent π. You may also wish to ask students to round their answer to the nearest whole number.

Exercises 5 and 6:
You may wish to ask students to explain why the answers to these exercises are the same.

VOCABULARY
algebraic expression
backtracking
distributive property
equivalent expressions
expand
exponent
factor
flowchart
formula
variable

Chapter Summary

In this chapter, you learned that many situations can be described with algebraic expressions. In an *algebraic expression,* symbols—usually letters—are used as variables. *Variables* can be quantities that change or unknown quantities. By investigating different values for a variable, you can explore what happens in a situation as the variable changes.

You learned the standard ways of indicating multiplication, division, and repeated multiplication in algebraic expressions. You created flowcharts to match expressions, and you used flowcharts to backtrack to solve equations.

You found that the same situation can often be described with several *equivalent expressions,* and that sometimes one expression is more useful than another. You saw that you could change expressions into equivalent expressions by using the *distributive property* to *expand* and *factor* them.

Strategies and Applications

The questions in this section will help you review and apply the important ideas and strategies developed in this chapter.

Matching expressions and situations

1. Draw a bags-and-blocks picture to match the expression $2b + 6$. If there are 5 blocks in each bag, what is the total number of blocks?

1. 16 blocks in all.

2. Hector has h baseball caps.
   a. Rachel has 4 more than three times the number of caps Hector has. Write an expression for the number of caps Rachel has.
   b. Hector paid $10 for each of his caps. Write an expression for the amount he paid, in pennies, for all his caps. $1{,}000h$

2a. $3h + 4$

Using formulas and evaluating expressions

3. The formula for the circumference of a circle is $C = 2\pi r$, where r is the radius. If the radius of a circle is 4.3 cm, what is its circumference? about 27 cm

Evaluate each expression for $r = 2$.

4. $\frac{r}{2}$ 1

5. $\frac{3}{2}r$ 3

6. $\frac{3r}{2}$ 3

7. $3r^2$ 12

8. See below.

Solving equations by backtracking

8. Consider the expression $4(2n - 1) + 5$.
   a. Draw a flowchart to represent the expression.
   b. Use backtracking to solve the equation $4(2n - 1) + 5 = 21$.
9. Find the length of a rectangle with width 4.2 cm and area 98 cm^2. about 23.3 cm

Using the distributive property

10. $1.5r + 21$
11. $5x - 3$
12. $12r - \frac{1}{2}$
13. $7(2p + 3)$
14. $3g(1 + 3g)$
15. $7s(7 - 2)$, or $35s$
16. Possible rules: $4x + 4$, $4(x + 1)$

Use the distributive property to rewrite each expression.

10. $3(0.5r + 7)$ 11. $\frac{10x - 6}{2}$ 12. $\frac{1}{2}(24r - 1)$
13. $14p + 21$ 14. $3g + 9g^2$ 15. $49s - 14s$
16. Find two rules, using symbols, that could produce this table.

Input	0	1	2	3	4
Output	4	8	12	16	20

Demonstrating Skills

Rewrite each expression without using multiplication or addition signs.

17. $s + s + s + s$ 4s 18. $7 \cdot b \cdot b \cdot b$ $7b^3$ 19. $7g + 3g$ 10g
20. Find the value of $6y^2$ for $y = 4$. 96

Insert parentheses to make each equation true.

21. $3 \times (5 - 2) = 9$ 22. $(4 + 7) \times 3 = 33$

Use parentheses to show a shortcut for doing each calculation.

23. $17 \times (6 + 4)$
24. $8 \times (26 + 4)$

23. $17 \times 6 + 17 \times 4$ 24. $8 \times 26 + 8 \times 4$

Use the distributive property to expand each expression.

25. $5(x + 4)$ $5x + 20$ 26. $3(a + 2b + 3c)$ $3a + 6b + 9c$ 27. $3y(y - \frac{1}{3})$ $3y^2 - y$

Factor each expression. Check the resulting expression by expanding it.

28. $25r - 50$ $25(r - 2)$ 29. $16h - 4h^2$ $4h(4 - h)$ 30. $9x - 81y + 27z$ $9(x - 9y + 3z)$

8a. n —×2→ $2n$ —−1→ $2n - 1$ —×4→ $4(2n - 1)$ —+5→ $4(2n - 1) + 5$

8b. $n = 2.5$

Exercise 9:
Ask students to round their answers to the nearest tenth. Watch for students who label the length as cm^2.

Exercise 19:
Watch for students who write the answer as $g(7 + 3)$ or $g(10)$. While both represent the same amount, $10g$ is the most common way to represent this quantity.

Exercise 20:
Watch for students whose answer is 576. Remind them that exponents are evaluated before executing other operations.

Exercises 21–22:
Some students may need to review the order of operations before answering these exercises.

CHAPTER 2

Geometry in Three Dimensions

Chapter Overview

Almost every student has used blocks at one time or another to build structures. Now they will use blocks to build patterns and use algebraic expressions to describe their patterns. Students will describe the number of blocks in each stage of their patterns as well as the number of blocks added to go from one stage to the next.

Students learn to describe a three-dimensional structure by looking at different flat views. They explore the relationship between surface area and volume, and then they use this knowledge as they explore more deeply those relationships while learning about nets that fold into a solid.

the Big Picture

Chapter 2 Highlights	Links to the Past	Links to the Future
Working with block patterns (2.1)	**Course 1:** Describing and extending geometric and numeric patterns	**Chapter 5:** Writing linear equations for geometric patterns
Representing three-dimensional structures (2.2)	**Course 1:** Exploring the properties of polygons	**Course 3:** Identifying planes of symmetry and axes of rotation
Finding the volume of a solid (2.3)	**Course 1:** Finding areas and perimeters of two-dimensional figures	**Chapter 7:** Determining how a scale factor affects volume
Finding the surface area of a solid (2.3, 2.4)	**Course 1:** Finding areas and perimeters of two-dimensional figures	**Chapter 7:** Determining how a scale factor affects surface area

Lesson Objectives	Pacing	Materials	NCTM Standards
2.1 Block Patterns page 77b • To continue a block pattern given the first three stages • To describe block patterns visually and numerically • To describe block patterns with algebraic expressions	3 class periods	• Master 5 • Master 7 • Master 8 • Blocks	2, 3, 6, 7, 10
2.2 Visualizing and Measuring Block Structures page 90a • To draw front, top, and side views of block structures • To understand the difference between the three views (usually taught in middle school) which do not describe a unique structure and the three views used by engineers that do describe a unique structure • To understand volume as the number of blocks that make up a structure	4 class periods	• Masters 7, 8, 9, 10 • Blocks	2, 3, 6, 10
2.3 Surface Area and Volume page 108a • To find the volume of any prism as *area of base times height* • To understand that for a given volume of any prism, the cube is the rectangular prism with the minimum surface area • To articulate some applications of surface area and volume, in particular, the relationship of surface area per unit volume and what it tells you about heat loss	4 class periods	• Masters 7, 8 • Blocks • Decks of cards (optional) • Construction paper	2, 3, 4, 6, 10
2.4 Nets and Solids page 128a • To decide if a given net will fold into a closed three-dimensional solid • To create nets that will fold into given shapes • To use information about the nets of an object to find surface area and volume	3 class periods	• Masters 9, 11, 12, 13, 14, 15, 16 • 10 soft drink cans • Scissors • Tape • Rulers • Calculators	2, 3, 6, 7, 10

NCTM Curriculum and Evaluation Standards

1. Number and Operation
2. Patterns, Functions, and Algebra
3. Geometry and Spatial Sense
4. Measurement
5. Data Analysis, Statistics, and Probability
6. Problem Solving
7. Reasoning and Proof
8. Communication
9. Connections
10. Representation

Assessment Opportunities

Standard Assessment

Impact Mathematics offers three types of formal assessment. The Chapter 2 Review & Self-Assessment in the Student Edition serves as a self-assessment tool for students. In the Teacher's Guide, a Quick Quiz at the end of each lesson allows you to check students understanding before moving to the next lesson. The Assessment Resources include blackline masters for chapter and semester tests.

- **Student Edition** Chapter 2 Review & Self-Assessment, pages 141–143
- **Teacher's Guide** Quick Quizzes, pages 90, 108, 128, 140
- **Assessment Resources** Chapter 2 Test, Form A, pages 37–39; Chapter 2 Test, Form B, pages 40–42

Ongoing Assessment

Impact Mathematics provides numerous opportunities for informal assessment of your students as they work through the investigations. Share & Summarize questions help you determine whether students understand the important ideas of an investigation. If students are struggling, Troubleshooting tips provide suggestions for helping them. On the Spot Assessment notes appear throughout the teaching notes. They give you suggestions for preventing or remedying common student errors. Assessment Forms in the Assessment Resources provide convenient ways to record student progress.

- **Student Edition** Share & Summarize, pages 80, 82, 83, 93, 96, 97, 99, 112, 116, 119, 131, 134, 135
- **Teacher's Guide** On the Spot Assessment, pages T81, T83, T92, T99, T118, T121 Troubleshooting, pages T80, T82, T83, T93, T96, T97, T99, T112, T116, T119, T131, T134, T135, A383
- **Assessment Resources** Chapter 2 Assessment Checklists, pages 105–106

Alternative Assessment, Portfolios, and Journal Ideas

The alternative assessment items in *Impact Mathematics* are perfect for inclusion in student portfolios and journals. The In Your Own Words feature in the Student Edition gives students a chance to write about mathematical ideas. The Performance Assessment items in the Assessment Resources provide rich, open-ended problems, ideal for take-home or group assessment.

- **Student Edition** In Your Own Words, pages 89, 106, 125, 138
- **Assessment Resources** Chapter 2 Performance Assessment, page 43

Assessment Resources

The Assessment Resources provide a chapter test in two equivalent forms, along with additional performance items. The performance items can be used in a variety of ways. They are ideal for take-home assessment or in-class group assessment.

- Chapter 2 Test, Form A, pages 37–39
- Chapter 2 Test, Form B, pages 40–42
- Chapter 2 Performance Assessment, page 43
- Chapter 2 Assessment Solutions, pages 44–46

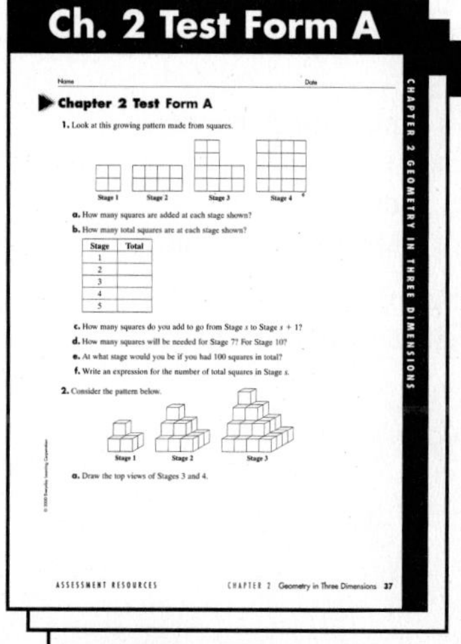

Ch. 2 Test Form A

Name Date

Chapter 2 Test Form A

1. Look at this growing pattern made from squares.

Stage 1 Stage 2 Stage 3 Stage 4

a. How many squares are added at each stage shown?

b. How many total squares are at each stage shown?

Stage	Total
1	
2	
3	
4	
5	

c. How many squares do you add to go from Stage s to Stage $s + 1$?

d. How many squares will be needed for Stage 7? For Stage 10?

e. At what stage would you be if you had 100 squares in total?

f. Write an expression for the number of total squares in Stage s.

2. Consider the pattern below.

Stage 1 Stage 2 Stage 3

a. Draw the top views of Stages 3 and 4.

CHAPTER 2 GEOMETRY IN THREE DIMENSIONS

ASSESSMENT RESOURCES CHAPTER 2 Geometry in Three Dimensions 37

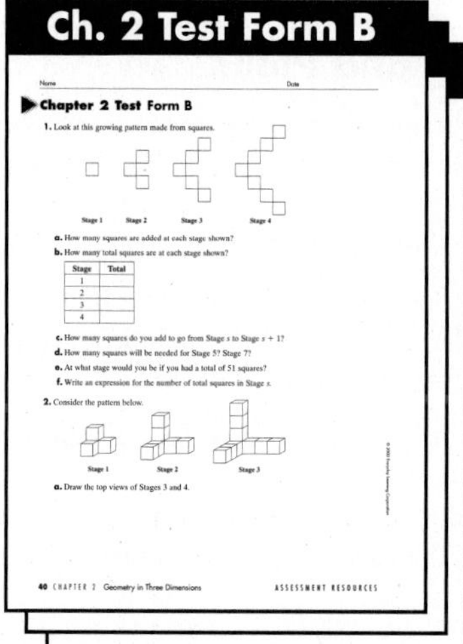

Ch. 2 Test Form B

Name Date

Chapter 2 Test Form B

1. Look at this growing pattern made from squares.

Stage 1 Stage 2 Stage 3 Stage 4

a. How many squares are added at each stage shown?

b. How many total squares are at each stage shown?

Stage	Total
1	
2	
3	
4	

c. How many squares do you add to go from Stage s to Stage $s + 1$?

d. How many squares will be needed for Stage 5? Stage 7?

e. At what stage would you be if you had a total of 51 squares?

f. Write an expression for the number of total squares in Stage s.

2. Consider the pattern below.

Stage 1 Stage 2 Stage 3

a. Draw the top views of Stages 3 and 4.

40 CHAPTER 2 Geometry in Three Dimensions ASSESSMENT RESOURCES

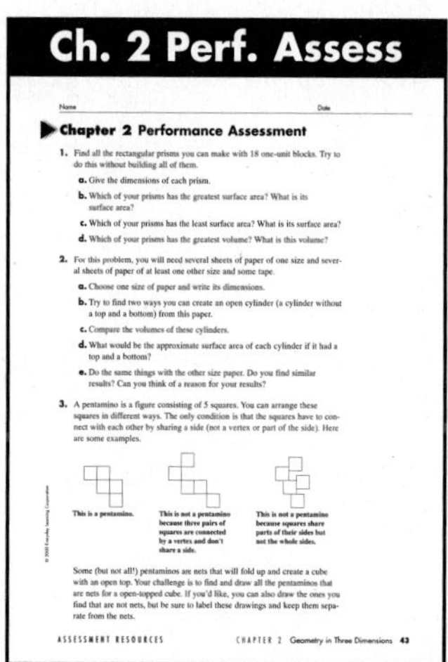

Ch. 2 Perf. Assess

Name Date

Chapter 2 Performance Assessment

1. Find all the rectangular prisms you can make with 18 one-unit blocks. Try to do this without building all of them.

a. Give the dimensions of each prism.

b. Which of your prisms has the greatest surface area? What is its surface area?

c. Which of your prisms has the least surface area? What is its surface area?

d. Which of your prisms has the greatest volume? What is this volume?

2. For this problem, you will need several sheets of paper of one size and several sheets of paper of at least one other size and some tape.

a. Choose one size of paper and write its dimensions.

b. Try to find two ways you can create an open cylinder (a cylinder without a top and a bottom) from this paper.

c. Compare the volumes of these cylinders.

d. What would be the approximate surface area of each cylinder if it had a top and a bottom?

e. Do the same things with the other size paper. Do you find similar results? Can you think of a reason for your results?

3. A pentamino is a figure consisting of 5 squares. You can arrange these squares in different ways. The only condition is that the squares have to connect with each other by sharing a side (not a vertex or part of the side). Here are some examples.

This is a pentamino.

This is not a pentamino because three pairs of squares are connected by a vertex and don't share a side.

This is not a pentamino because squares share parts of their sides but not the whole sides.

Some (but not all!) pentaminos are nets that will fold up and create a cube with an open top. Your challenge is to find and draw all the pentaminos that are nets for a open-topped cube. If you'd like, you can also draw the ones you find that are not nets, but be sure to label these drawings and keep them separate from the nets.

ASSESSMENT RESOURCES CHAPTER 2 Geometry in Three Dimensions 43

Additional Resources

Print	Software	Video	Web sites
Mathematics Through Paper Folding, Olson, Alton T. National Council of Teachers of Mathematics *Filling and Wrapping: Three-Dimensional Measurement* by Glenda Lappan, James T. Fey, William Fitzgerald, Susan N. Friel, Elizabeth Difanis Phillips Dale Seymour Publications *Mathematics Activities for Teaching* by Ed. R. Wheeler and Jane Thompson Barnard Kendall/Hunt Publishing Company In the Informal Geometry chapter, students use physical models to develop spatial understanding.	*Patterns and Relationships,* Edunetics Corporation Students identify, describe, and apply a pattern rule in graph and numeric sequence *Quadrilaterals, Polygons & Solid Geometry,* Queue, Inc. Students explore area and perimeter at a basic level and extend their thinking to finding area of combination figures. Volume is then explored as well as sum of angles and ratios of lines and areas. *Geometry Blaster,* Davidson & Associates Geometry is taught through an interactive adventure sequence.	*2D Visions in a 3D World,* Math Vantage: Spatial SenseUnit, Sunburst Communications This video focuses on comparing area and volume of various sized containers and illustrates techniques of making 2-dimensional surfaces appear 3-dimensional. *Containers: Surface Area and Volume,* Math Vantage: Spatial Sense Unit, Sunburst Communications This video, one of six in a series, presents an interview with a packaging designer and shows that surface area and volume are important considerations in economical packaging of frozen food.	Visit the Everyday Learning Web site at **http://www.everydaylearning.com** *Multiview Projections* **http://mane.mech.Virginia.EDU/~engr160/Graphics/Multiview.html** Students can find information about top, front, and side views of drawings. This site also includes drawing in perspective. *Find the Area of the Shape!* by Barbara Muenster, Math Forum Workshops, Summer, 1998 **http://forum.swarthmore.edu/workshops/sum98/participants/muenster/index2.html** Students can explore the meaning of area of geometric shapes.

Introduction

Direct students' attention to the drawing in the background of these pages and to the photo of the building at the top of page 77. Ask students whether they think the drawing and the photo represent the same building and whether they can identify certain features in both the photo and the drawing. What kinds of information are represented in the drawing? What is lost?

Then have a volunteer read aloud to the class the introductory paragraph and the first paragraph in the setion titled "Patterns and Plans" on page 76. Discuss the meaning of *two-dimensional* drawings and *three-dimensional* drawings. When students are comfortable with the meaning of these two terms, ask another volunteer to read aloud the last two paragraphs. Discuss the meaning of *elevations* and *blueprints.* Encourage students to think of places where they might use a blueprint.

Ch 2 Family Letter

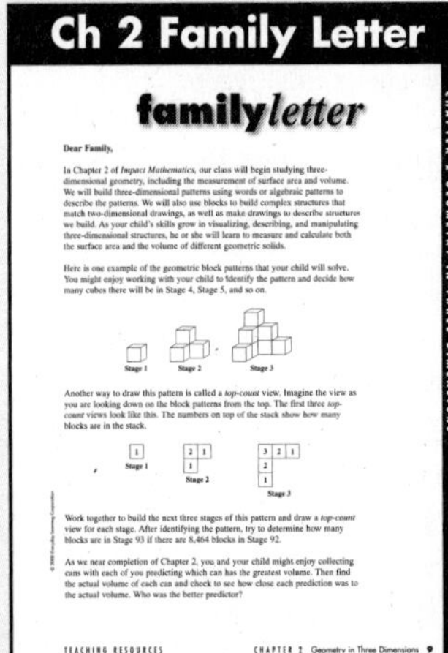

familyletter

Dear Family,

In Chapter 2 of *Impact Mathematics*, our class will begin studying three-dimensional geometry, including the measurement of surface area and volume. We will build three-dimensional patterns using words or algebraic patterns to describe the patterns. We will also use blocks to build complex structures that match two-dimensional drawings, as well as make drawings to describe structures we build. As your child's skills grow in visualizing, describing, and manipulating three-dimensional structures, he or she will learn to measure and calculate both the surface area and the volume of different geometric solids.

Here is one example of the geometric block patterns that your child will solve. You might enjoy working with your child to identify the pattern and decide how many cubes there will be in Stage 4, Stage 5, and so on.

Stage 1 Stage 2 Stage 3

Another way to draw this pattern is called a *top-count* view. Imagine the view as you are looking down on the block patterns from the top. The first three *top-count* views look like this. The numbers on top of the stack show how many blocks are in the stack.

Stage 1 Stage 2 Stage 3

Work together to build the next three stages of this pattern and draw a *top-count* view for each stage. After identifying the pattern, try to determine how many blocks are in Stage 93 if there are 8,464 blocks in Stage 92.

As we near completion of Chapter 2, you and your child might enjoy collecting cans with each of you predicting which can has the greatest volume. Then find the actual volume of each can and check to see how close each prediction was to the actual volume. Who was the better predictor?

TEACHING RESOURCES CHAPTER 2 Geometry in Three Dimensions 9

CHAPTER 2 GEOMETRY IN THREE DIMENSIONS

CHAPTER 2

Geometry in Three Dimensions

You live in a three-dimensional world. Everything around you has length, width, and thickness. Yet you often communicate in two dimensions: with pencil and paper. How can you represent three-dimensional shapes on paper? What kinds of measurements make sense when dealing with three-dimensional objects? This chapter will answer these questions.

Patterns and Plans

Some of the most powerful examples of using two-dimensional drawings to represent three-dimensional objects can be found in different types of designing. Architects must become very skilled at drawing three-dimensional objects so there is no confusion about what they represent.

Before a house is built, an architect makes drawings of what the house will look like. The drawings include *elevations* that show how the house will look from two sides.

The plans for a house also include blueprints, which show how the interior will be divided into rooms. Blueprints also show details such as where doors are, which way they open, and where to place items like sinks, the stove, and the bathtub.

The McCall Pattern Co.

A fashion designer will create a pattern that is used to cut cloth into the shapes that will be sewn together as the finished piece of clothing.

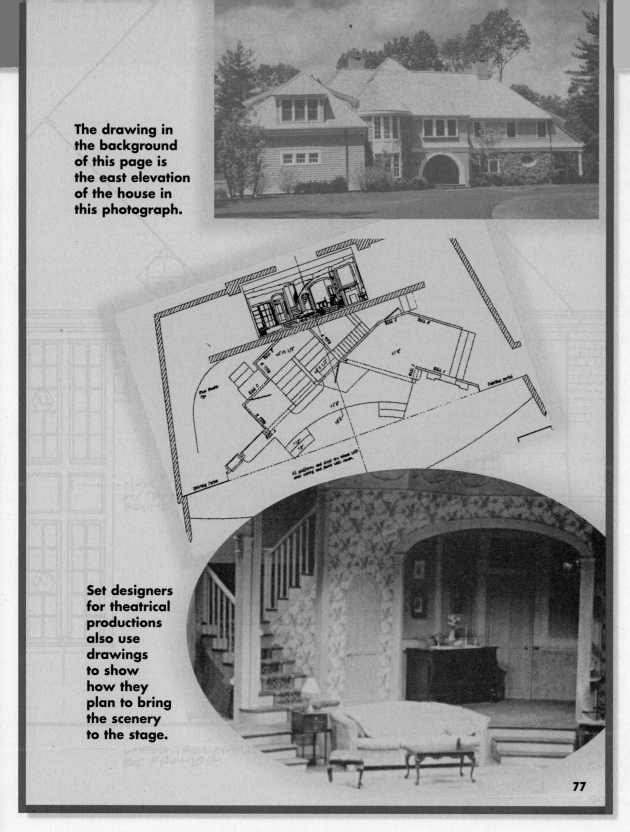

The drawing in the background of this page is the east elevation of the house in this photograph.

Set designers for theatrical productions also use drawings to show how they plan to bring the scenery to the stage.

77

Tell students that designers sometimes use geometric constructions to make their patterns and plans. Students can practice basic constructions using Master 6, Geometric Constructions.

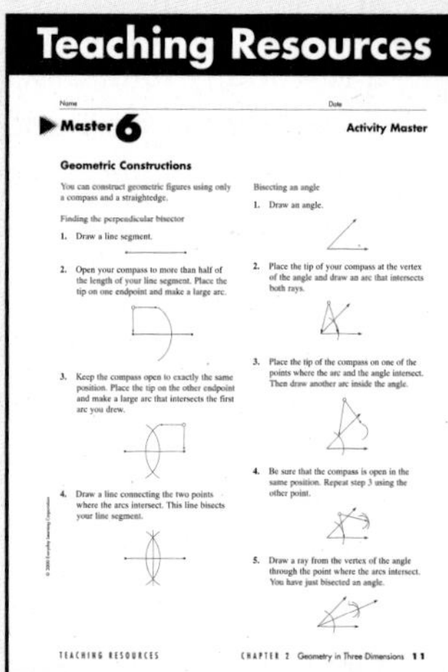

Teaching Resources

Name Date

Master 6 **Activity Master**

Geometric Constructions

You can construct geometric figures using only a compass and a straightedge.

Finding the perpendicular bisector

1. Draw a line segment.
2. Open your compass to more than half of the length of your line segment. Place the tip on one endpoint and make a large arc.
3. Keep the compass open to exactly the same position. Place the tip on the other endpoint and make a large arc that intersects the first arc you drew.
4. Draw a line connecting the two points where the arcs intersect. This line bisects your line segment.

Bisecting an angle

1. Draw an angle.
2. Place the tip of your compass at the vertex of the angle and draw an arc that intersects both rays.
3. Place the tip of the compass on one of the points where the arc and the angle intersect. Then draw another arc inside the angle.
4. Be sure that the compass is open in the same position. Repeat step 3 using the other point.
5. Draw a ray from the vertex of the angle through the point where the arcs intersect. You have just bisected an angle.

TEACHING RESOURCES CHAPTER 2 Geometry in Three Dimensions 11

Mathematical Background

An important part of our geometry strand is developing and improving students' visualization skills. Future mathematical study requires students to picture in their minds things they cannot see with their eyes. For example, in calculus, they must picture two-dimensional shapes rotating to create three-dimensional solids. In fields outside of mathematics, visualization is just as important. Architects must "see" a building from the plans, and surgeons must "see" their way through surgery without really seeing everything.

We work on developing these skills throughout the chapter, in part by introducing five different two-dimensional representations of three-dimensional figures:

- perspective (or isometric) drawings—Students are asked to look at a drawing of a block structure and create that structure with blocks.
- top-count views—These views show a top view of the object with numbers representing how many blocks are in each column. Students build from top-count views and draw top-count views for their own structures.
- front/top/side view triples—Students first discover why only three views are useful and then discover that while these views aid visualization, they do not always describe a unique structure.
- engineering views—Engineers use a different kind of front/top/side view triple than the ones generally taught in school. They hide some details, like the lines between blocks, but add some essential information, like where the blocks are at different levels. Though they are more difficult to interpret, the engineering views are also more useful in that they do describe a unique structure. In this chapter, students use a modified form of engineering views to describe their structures.
- nets—Students create their own nets for given solids and analyze whether given nets will, in fact, fold into a closed solid.

Students will also connect some of the algebra work, particularly writing expressions and using formulas in Chapter 1, to geometric contexts. First, students will analyze and create geometric patterns made from blocks, relating expressions to the numerical growth (the number of blocks used in each stage). Later, they develop and use formulas for the volume of a prism.

In the growth patterns, we encourage students to think about both closed-form rules (how many total blocks are in a given stage of the pattern) and recursive rules (how many blocks do I add to go from one stage of the pattern to the next). The first is common in mathematics curricula; the second is becoming more important both in mathematics and in other fields.

The closed-form rule used to be an important part of analyzing data, patterns, and so on; it was far more useful in computation. Imagine calculating the number of blocks in stage 1,000 of a given pattern if all you know is where you start and the number of blocks added at each stage! It would take you 999 computations to do it. With a closed-form rule, you could simply plug 1,000 into a formula, do one computation, and be done with it.

• ***Teaching notes continued on page A382.***

2.1 Block Patterns

Objectives

- To continue a block pattern given the first three stages
- To describe block patterns visually (where the blocks are placed) and numerically (how many blocks are added)
- To describe block patterns with algebraic expressions

Overview (pacing: about 3 class periods)

In this lesson, students build patterns from blocks. They write expressions to describe the number of blocks in each stage of a pattern and the number of blocks added to go from one stage to the next. This lesson is meant as a transition from Chapter 1 to the geometry and visualization of this chapter. The challenge to students comes in visualizing how blocks are added in a predictable way to create a pattern and in describing the growth numerically.

Advance Preparation

Make several copies of Master 7, 2-Centimeter Dot Paper, for each student. In some cases Master 5 can be used instead of Master 7. Students will find using them makes it much easier to record their work. Students will need to work with the blocks throughout the lesson, actually building and manipulating patterns. You may wish to have Master 8, Building Mat, available for students to use at this time. Have sets of 70 blocks per group of 4 ready each day of the lesson. You may use the 2-cm colored blocks from the manipulatives kit.

Lesson Planner

	Summary	Materials	On Your Own Exercises	Assessment Opportunities
Investigation 1 page T79	Students examine a staircase pattern made from blocks and write expressions to describe the number of blocks added and the total number of blocks for each stage	• Master 5 (Teaching Resources, page 7) • Master 7 (Teaching Resources, page 12) • 70 blocks (per group of 4)	Practice & Apply: 1–3 Connect & Extend: 9–12 Mixed Review: 19–38	Share & Summarize, pages T80, 80 Troubleshooting, page T80
Investigation 2 page T80	Students represent block structures with top-count views. They explore two more block patterns.	• Master 5 • Master 7 • Master 8 (Teaching Resources, page 13) • Blocks	Practice & Apply: 4–5 Connect & Extend: 13–16 Mixed Review: 19–38	Share & Summarize, pages T82, 82 On the Spot Assessment, page T81 Troubleshooting, page T81
Investigation 3 page A382	Students create block patterns that grow (numerically) in a prescribed way.	• Master 5 • Master 7 • Master 8 • Blocks	Practice & Apply: 6–8 Connect & Extend: 17–18 Mixed Review: 19–38	Share & Summarize, pages T83, 83 On the Spot Assessment, page T83 Troubleshooting, page T83 Informal Assessment, page 90 Quick Quiz, page, 90

Introduce

In this lesson, students will extend, generalize, and create block patterns. Some of the problems in this lesson preview the ideas of area and volume that follow in the chapter.

1 Begin the lesson by asking students how they would define a pattern. Are there specific criteria that need to be present to characterize something as a pattern? You might want to emphasize that one of the key characteristics of a pattern is *predictability.* If a large enough part of a pattern is shown, one should be able to figure out how the pattern should continue. This idea will be important when students create their own block patterns.

Ask students to provide specific examples of patterns, encouraging them to think of a variety of types of patterns, including visual patterns, numeric patterns, and growth patterns. Students might suggest

- patterns on wallpaper or fabric
- brick or tile patterns
- compound interest
- growth of bacteria
- number sequences, such as 3, 6, 9, 12, 15 . . .
- visual sequences, such as

Explain to students that, in this lesson, they will work with patterns made with blocks.

2 **Explore** **Grouping: Pairs**

Have students work in pairs on all but the last Explore question. Discuss the answers to these questions before going on to the last question which asks students to generalize the number of blocks at any stage, s.

It is important that students work with the blocks to do these problems since the act of building the next stage may contribute to their thinking about how to get from one stage to the next.

For example, some students may think of adding an outer "L" around Stage 2 to get to Stage 3, or adding $3 + 2$ blocks.

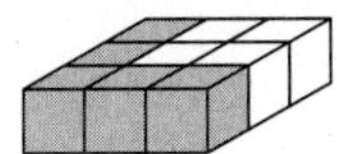

Similarly, to get from Stage 3 to Stage 4, they think of adding an "L" of $4 + 3$ blocks. Students can extend this thinking to the general case: To get from Stage s to Stage $s + 1$, you need to add $s + 1 + s$, or $2s + 1$ blocks.

Others may look at a numerical pattern of adding $3 + 5 + 7 + \ldots$ to get to Stages 2, 3, and 4 respectively. Encourage students to come up with different ways of looking at the problem. Note that the variable s will always represent the number of the stage.

After they finish these questions, ask students how they would describe how to get from one stage to the next. Discuss the last question with the whole class. To help students write an expression for the number of blocks in Stage s, help them look for a pattern in the answer to the previous question. What is true of each number in 1, 4, 9, 16, 25, and 36?

It is important that students understand the difference between the two expressions they wrote. The $2s + 1$ is the number of blocks added to build the next stage. The s^2 is the number of blocks in Stage s.

Notice that you can generate the pattern by using either expression or by building with blocks.

2.1 Block Patterns

Using algebra lets you communicate information in a concise way. In this lesson, you will see how you can write algebraic rules to describe geometric patterns made with blocks.

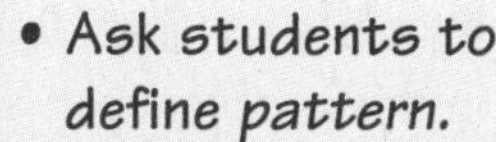

1
- Ask students to define *pattern.*
- Emphasize predictability of patterns.
- Have students provide specific examples of various types of patterns.

MATERIALS
cubes

Explore

The block pattern below grows from one stage to the next. The square in each stage is larger than the square in the previous stage.

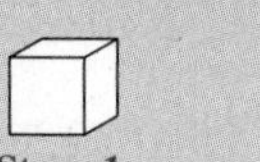
Stage 1

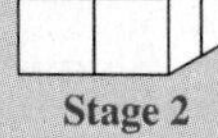
Stage 2

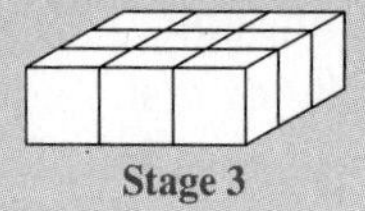
Stage 3

With your own blocks, build Stage 1. Add blocks to build Stage 2. Then add blocks again to build Stage 3.

Continue this pattern. Use your blocks to build Stages 4, 5, and 6.

- When you go from Stage 1 to Stage 2, how many blocks do you add? How do you arrange them? See ①.
- When you go from Stage 2 to Stage 3, how many blocks do you add? How do you arrange them? See ②.
- What would you do to go from Stage 3 to Stage 4? From Stage 4 to Stage 5? From Stage 5 to Stage 6? See ③.
- In general, how many blocks do you add to go from one stage to the next? In other words, how many blocks do you add to Stage s to make Stage $s + 1$? How do you arrange them? See ④.
- How many blocks in total are used in Stage 1? In Stage 2? In Stage 3? In Stage 4? In Stage 5? In Stage 6? 1, 4, 9, 16, 25, 36
- Write an expression for the number of blocks in Stage s. $s \times s$, or s^2

① Add 3 blocks, in an L-shape around the first block.

② Add 5 blocks, in an L-shape around the 2×2 square.

③ Add 7, 9, and then 11 blocks in an L-shape around the previous square.

④ Add $2s + 1$ blocks, in an L-shape around the $s \times s$ square.

2
- Have students work in pairs except for last question.
- Discuss answers to first five questions before proceeding.

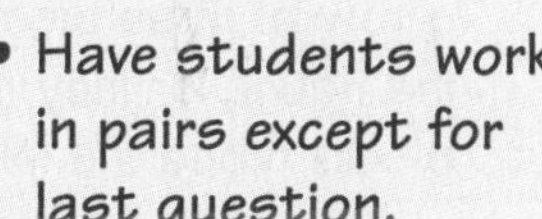

3
Discuss as a whole class.

Investigation 1

1 **Problem Set A** **Grouping: Pairs or Small Groups**
In this problem set, students look at a staircase pattern and consider both the number of blocks added to get from one stage to the next and the total number of blocks in any stage. The problems should be done in pairs (or small groups depending on the number of cubes available) so that students can see the variety of strategies that may be used to come up with the total number of blocks in each stage. If you have enough cubes, encourage students to work individually at first and later to work with a partner to share ideas and to generate more strategies.

As in the Explore activity, building the staircase may inform students of ways to generalize the pattern. For example, to build Stage 3, students may think of adding a row of three blocks along the right side or the top of the figure, or they may think of adding a diagonal of blocks along the left side of the figure.

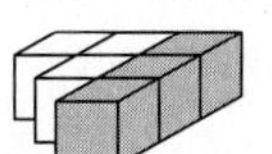

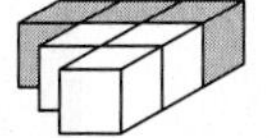
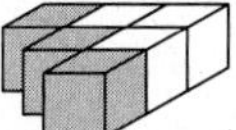

2 Encourage students to think about how to relate each stage to the stage that came before. This is the foundation of recursive thinking.

Problem 2 can help you assess whether students are able to think about how the number of blocks changes from one stage to the next without having to create all the stages up to that point. To get the number of blocks in Stage 275, they need to know that 274 blocks are added to get from Stage 273 to 274 and 275 blocks are added to get from Stage 274 to 275. So, if there are 37,401 blocks at Stage 273, there are 37,401 + 274 + 275 = 37,950 blocks at Stage 275.

If students have trouble answering **Problem 4,** ask them to extend the table through Stage 10.

In **Problem 6,** if students can state a general rule verbally, but have trouble writing a symbolic expression, encourage them to write the rule in words first. For example, if a student says, "It's the stage times one more and then half of that," you can help them write $\frac{(\text{stage}) \times (\text{stage} + 1)}{2}$. Then add the use of the variables.

If students have trouble coming up with a general rule for the number of blocks at each stage, you might suggest they put together two copies of each stage to form a rectangle or that they look at the pattern in their table (see "Sample Strategies").

Tips from Teachers

Finding the number of blocks at Stage *s* is difficult for students because they are looking for a two-column chart or for a rule rather than describing a pattern. Making a T-chart helps them see the input-output rule a little better and will help with functions, too.

Sample Strategies Here are some ways students might think about **Problems 4–7.**

Below are two ways to think about the pattern in order to write an expression for the number of blocks at any stage.

- A geometric solution is sometimes the easiest: To get the total number of blocks in Stage 4, for example, students can put two Stage 4 squares together to form a rectangle with dimensions 4 × 5.

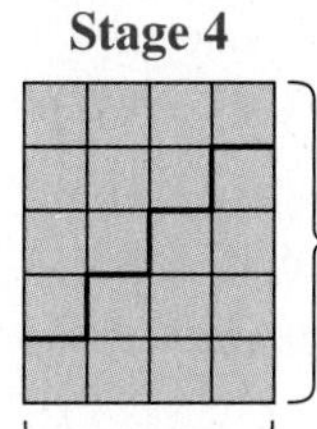

The number of blocks in one staircase is half the number in the rectangle, or $\frac{1}{2}(4 \times 5) = 10$. This can be generalized to Stage *s:* Two Stage *s* staircases can be put together to form an $s \times (s + 1)$ rectangle. The number of cubes in Stage *s* is half the number in the rectangle, or $(\frac{1}{2})s(s + 1)$.

- Some students may find a general expression by creating a table and looking for patterns.

Stage	Total Number of Blocks
1	1
2	3 (3 = half of 2 × 3 by looking at stage numbers in first column)
3	6 (6 = half of 3 × 4 by looking at stage numbers in first column)
4	10 (10 = half of 4 × 5 by looking at stage numbers in first column)

Students may realize that the total number of blocks at any stage is half the product of the stage number and the stage number plus 1.

Investigation 1 A Staircase Pattern

1. The number of blocks added is the same as the stage number. Possible arrangements: Add the blocks in a vertical row along the right side of the previous figure. Or, add the blocks in a horizontal row along the back side of the previous figure. Or, add the blocks along a diagonal to the left of the previous figure.

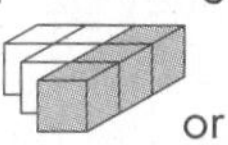

or

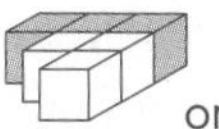

or

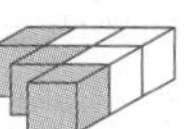

3. Add $s + 1$ blocks in, for example, a row along the right side of the previous figure.

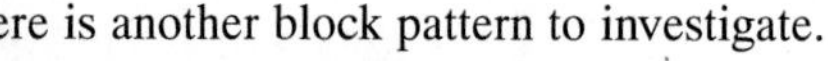

Here is another block pattern to investigate.

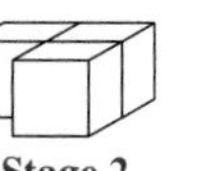
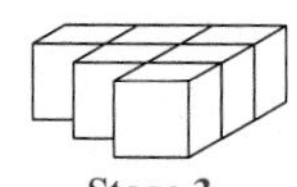

Stage 1 Stage 2 Stage 3

Problem Set A

Build the next three stages of this "staircase" pattern.

1. Describe how you add blocks to go from one stage to the next. That is, tell how many blocks you add, and how you arrange them. Draw pictures if they help to explain your thinking. You may want to use a table like the one below to organize your ideas.

To Create Stage	2	3	4	5	6
Add This Many Blocks	2				

2. Marty thinks there are 37,401 blocks in Stage 273. If he's right, how many blocks are in Stage 275? 37,950

3. How many blocks do you add to Stage s to make Stage $s + 1$? Write an expression to describe the number of blocks you add, and tell how you would arrange them.

Look at the number of blocks in each stage. If you made a table for Problem 1, you may want to add a row to your table to help you find a pattern to solve the next few problems.

To Create Stage	2	3	4	5	6
Add This Many Blocks	2				
Total Number of Blocks Needed	3				

4. How many blocks does it take to build Stage 10? 55

5. How many blocks does it take to build Stage 100? 5,050

6. Write an expression to describe the number of blocks you need to build Stage s. $\frac{1}{2}(s)(s + 1)$

1 Have students work in pairs or small groups.

2 Encourage students to think about how stages are related.

3 Some students may need to extend table.

Share & Summarize

Have groups come to the board to present their solutions for **Problems 3 and 6.** Encourage students to take turns in presenting the information, or adding to what has been said. Select students who came up with different strategies, rather than have presentations of the same strategy more than once. Make sure to ask students how they know their expression is right for any value of *s*.

Troubleshooting Students will be working with block patterns over the next two investigations. The important thing here is that they have started articulating rules and how they found them. If they are having difficulty with this investigation, you may want to present the additional examples below before moving on. The examples below are linear or constant growth, while the investigation focuses on more complicated patterns.

Additional Examples For a pattern that grows more slowly than any they've seen, simply show an "add one block each time" pattern like the one below. The new block is either added to the left or to the right. The number of blocks at Stage *s* is *s*.

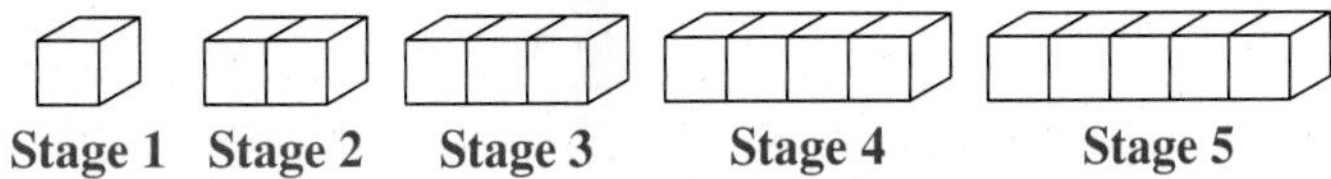

Stage 1 Stage 2 Stage 3 Stage 4 Stage 5

This pattern shows no change from one stage to the next. To get from one stage to the next, you don't add any blocks. The total number of blocks at Stage *s* is 3.

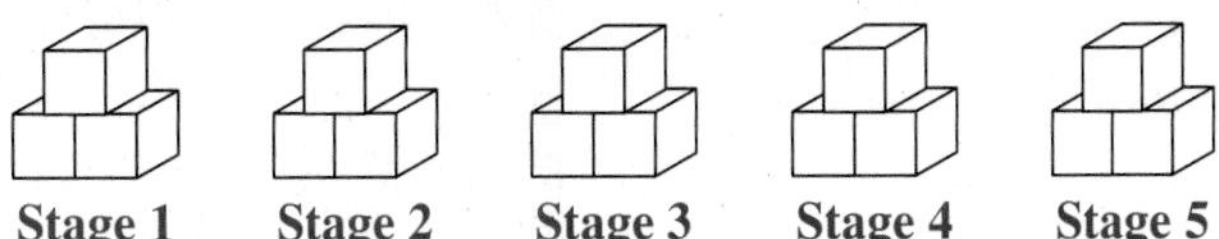

Stage 1 Stage 2 Stage 3 Stage 4 Stage 5

On Your Own Exercises

Practice & Apply: 1–3
Connect & Extend: 9–12
Mixed Review: 19–38

Investigation 2

This investigation introduces students to representing structures with *top-count views,* which show the number of blocks in each stack of a structure. This method will be used throughout this chapter, so it is important that students are comfortable using and interpreting these drawings.

Make sure that students understand how to create and interpret top-count views. Use either Master 5, Centimeter Dot Paper, or Master 7, 2-Centimeter Dot Paper, to practice drawing Stages 1, 2, and 3 with students for the figures given before they go on to Problem Set B. You may wish to have master 8, Building Mat, available for students if they need to build figures before answering the questions in Problem Set B. They may have to stand up to see the top views clearly. Some students will quickly learn how to represent these views and others may need more practice.

Teaching Resources

Teaching Resources

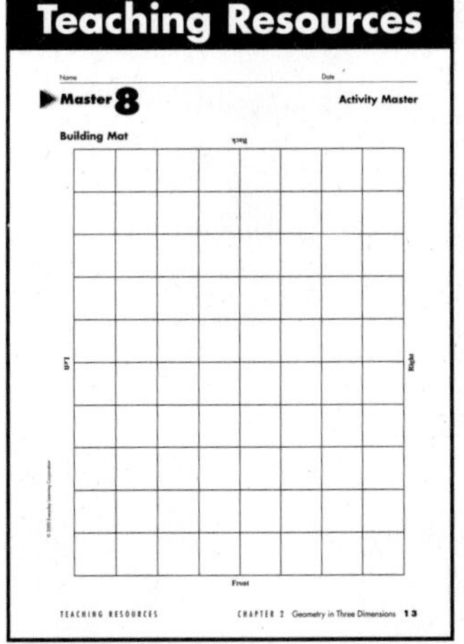

7. See Additional Answers.

7. Prove It! Find a way to explain why the expression you wrote for Problem 6 is correct, based on how you built each stage of the staircase pattern. To help you get started, you might try these ideas:

- Think about building two copies of one staircase and putting them together.
- Try breaking up a staircase into smaller pieces.
- Rewrite your expression in a different way, and try to fit both expressions to how the staircase grows.

Possible answer: built two staircases, looked for a pattern in the table

Describe how you found your answers to Problems 3 and 6.

1
- Have groups present solutions on the board showing various strategies.
- Ask how students know the expression is right for any value of s.
- Present additional examples if necessary.

Investigation 2 Other Block Patterns

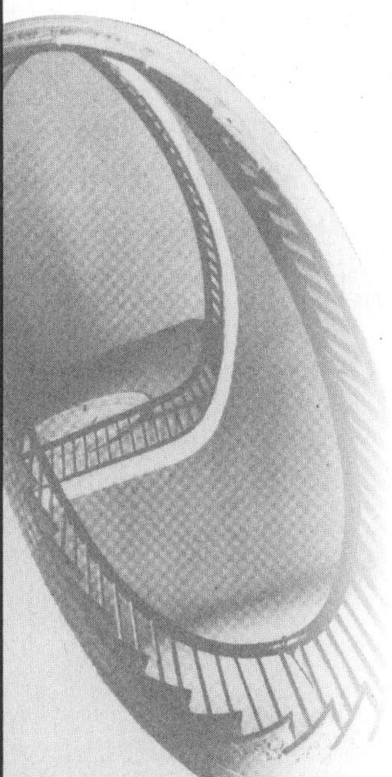

Here is another block pattern to build and investigate.

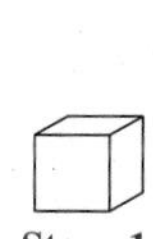
Stage 1

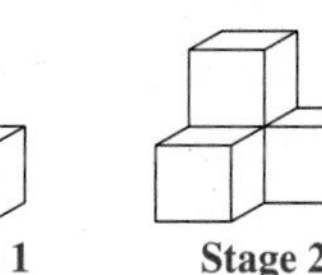
Stage 2

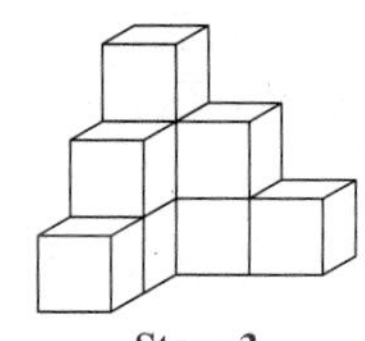
Stage 3

Another way to represent this "double staircase" pattern is to use a *top-count view.* Imagine you are looking down on the buildings from above. The numbers in the drawings below show how many blocks are in each stack.

1

Stage 1

2	1
1	

Stage 2

3	2	1
2		
1		

Stage 3

2 Be sure students understand *top-count views.*

Additional Answers
Problem Set A

7. Possible answers: Two Stage s figures put together form an $s \times (s + 1)$ rectangle, so one Stage s figure uses half as many blocks.

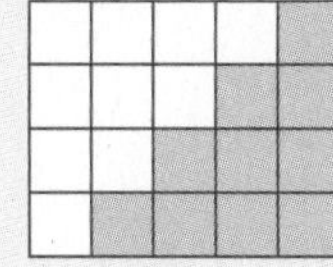

Or, looking at the expression as $\frac{s^2}{2} + \frac{s}{2}$, Stage s can be thought of as two pieces. In the two stages shown here, the blocks representing $\frac{s^2}{2}$ are shaded and the blocks representing $\frac{s}{2}$ are white.

Stage 2

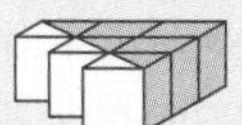
Stage 3

Problem Set B **Suggested Grouping: Pairs**
In this problem set, students may work from their top-view patterns or from numbers in a table they create to generalize about the stages.

Stage	1	2	3	4
Blocks to add to get to next stage	3	5	7	9
Total blocks	1	4	9	16

Some may quickly discover that the pattern in the number of blocks at each stage is the same as the pattern in the Explore activity they did at the beginning of the lesson. They will explore this connection more completely in Investigation 3.

In thinking about how many blocks are added at each stage, some students will see an L-shaped base on which the structure from the previous stage is built. If so, students may see the number added at each stage to be $(s + 1) + (s + 1) - 1$, or as 2 lines that are $s + 1$ long, sharing a vertex.

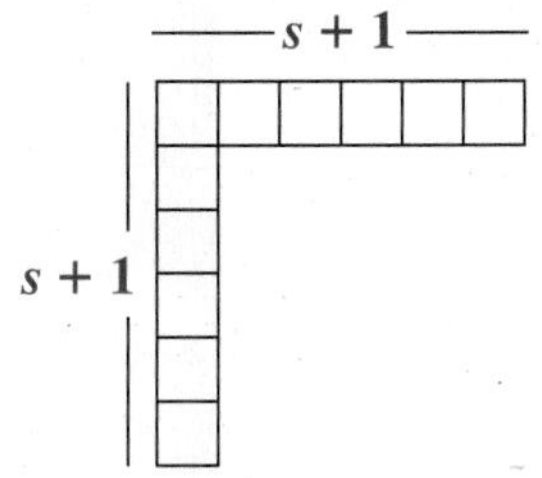

Answers to **Problem 4** should reflect an understanding that the pattern grows in a predictable way, both numerically and visually.

Problem 7 asks students to work backward: given the number of blocks, find the correct stage of the pattern. Some may do this by guess-check-and-improve. A student can guess what number multiplied by itself gives 100, check the guess by multiplying the number by itself, and then use the result to adjust the guess. You might take this opportunity to remind students about square roots and how to find them on their calculators. For Problem 7, students could simply find the square root of 100 to find the stage.

2

The case for **Problem 8** is more challenging. Students need to find a number whose square is close to but not over 79. They should find that squaring 8 gives 64 and squaring 9 gives 81, so the largest stage possible is 8. If they use calculators with square-root keys, students will find that the square root of 79 is between 8 and 9, so 8 is the largest stage possible.

On the Spot Assessment

For **Problem 8,** students who give the answer as "Stage 9" may be rounding up without thinking about the context of the problem. Ask these students, how many blocks are needed for Stage 9 and whether they have enough blocks. You might discuss other problems where the context influences whether you round up or down. For example, suppose 88 students are going on a field trip and each bus seats 28 students. How many school buses are needed? 88 ÷ 28 is just over 3, but rounding down does not make sense in this case. You need 4 school buses, even though there will be several empty seats on at least one of them.

Think & Discuss
Build the three Stage 2 pictures for the students in the front of the room, or draw them on an overhead transparency. Ask students to identify the Stage 2 cube from the three choices. Students may have already worked with cubes, but it is worth attending to the definition presented in the side margin and making sure that they understand what a *face* is. You may also want to discuss the meaning of *three-dimensional* and ask students to give you examples of figures that are not three-dimensional.

Problem Set B

1, 2. See Additional Answers.
3. 8,649
4. $2(s + 1) - 1$, or $2s + 1$; Possible arrangement: Add one block on top of each existing column and a single block at the end of each "arm."
6. 625; 1,000,000
9. s^2; Possible explanation: The number of blocks in each stage follows the pattern of the squares in the Explore: 1, 4, 9, 16, and so on. The blocks are just arranged differently.

1. Build the next three stages of this pattern. Draw a top-count view of each stage.

2. Think about how you go from one stage to the next.

a. How many blocks do you add to Stage 1 to make Stage 2? How do you arrange them?

b. How do you add blocks to Stage 2 to make Stage 3?

c. How do you add blocks to Stage 3 to make Stage 4?

3. If Stage 92 has 8,464 blocks, how many blocks are in Stage 93?

4. How many blocks do you add to Stage s to make Stage $s + 1$? Write an expression to describe the number of blocks you add, and tell how you would arrange them.

5. How many blocks does it take to build Stage 3? 9 Stage 4? 16 Stage 5? 25

6. How many blocks would it take to build Stage 25? Stage 1,000?

7. There are 100 blocks in a particular stage of this pattern. Which stage is it? Stage 10

8. If you have 79 blocks, which is the largest stage of the pattern you could build? Stage 8

9. Write an expression to describe how many blocks you need to build Stage s. Explain why your expression works.

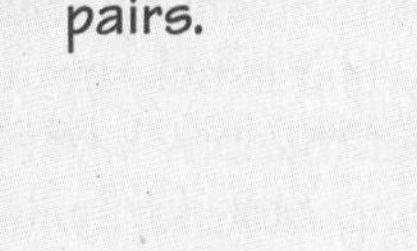

You may have students work in pairs.

2 Remind students about square roots.

Think & Discuss

Suppose you were making a pattern of larger and larger cubes. Stage 1 would look like this:

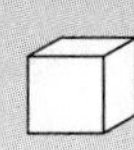

Stage 1

Which of these figures is Stage 2 in a growing pattern of *cubes*? C

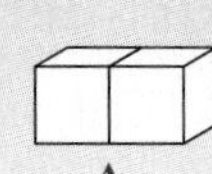

A

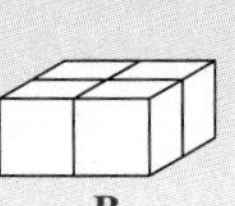

B

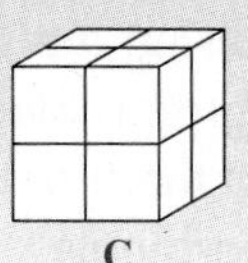

C

Remember

A cube is a three-dimensional figure with six square sides, or faces.

3 • Build models or display pictures for students.
• Discuss the meaning of three-dimensional.

Additional Answers
Problem Set B

1.

4	3	2	1
3			
2			
1			

Stage 4

5	4	3	2	1
4				
3				
2				
1				

Stage 5

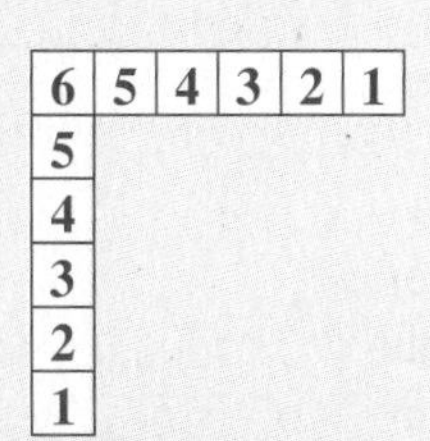

6	5	4	3	2	1
5					
4					
3					
2					
1					

Stage 6

2a. 3; Possible arrangements: Add 1 block to the existing stack and create two new 1-block stacks. Or build an L-shaped base from 3 blocks and set the single block on it at the corner.

2b. Possible arrangements: Add 1 block to each existing stack and create two new 1-block stacks. Or build an L-shaped base from 5 blocks and set Stage 2 on it.

2c. Possible arrangements: Add 1 block to each existing stack and create two new 1-block stacks. Or build an L-shaped base from 7 blocks and set Stage 3 on it.

Problem Set C Grouping: Individuals

In this problem set, students will need to think about how many unit cubes are used to build, or fit inside, larger cubes. You may want to provide students with Master 8, Building Mat, for building Stages 3 and 4 in Problem 1, and Master 7, 2-Centimeter Graph Paper, for recording top-count views.

Students should find that a Stage s cube requires s^3 blocks. This previews the idea of volume, since volume of a cube with edge length s is s^3. Volume is explored in depth later in this chapter.

> **Access for all Learners**
>
> **Language Diversity** To support students who don't read or use language easily, you might provide graphic (or visual) organizers in the form of table templates and large-block graph paper to aid students in creating their own three-dimensional patterns.

Problem Set Wrap-Up As a closing activity, ask students whether they needed to think about the number of blocks added at each stage in order to calculate the total number of blocks in a particular stage. Are they able to compute the number mentally without thinking about adding blocks?

As an extension, have students make a T-chart showing the stage number and the number of blocks in each stage. Then have them graph the values using the stage number as the x-coordinate. Discuss the graph. Students may note that the graph is not linear, that there are no negative values shown, and that the y-coordinate increases at a faster rate than the x-coordinate.

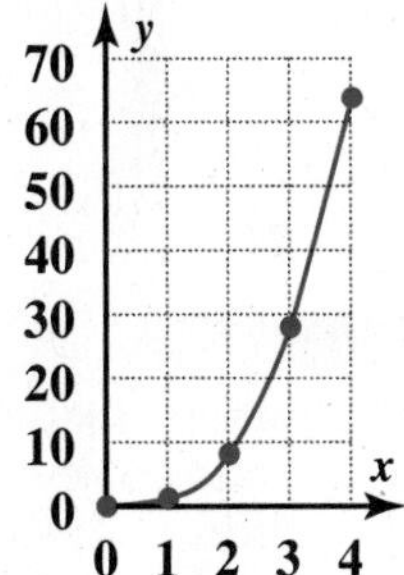

Share & Summarize

Students should notice that the square pattern and the double-staircase pattern have exactly the same number of blocks at each stage. They should also have an intuitive understanding that the cube number patterns seem to grow more quickly than the square-number patterns. You may want to relate this to the expressions for the total number of blocks in each stage. The expression s^3 grows faster than one that is s^2. Students will do more with this idea in Chapter 3 later in the year.

Troubleshooting If students are not clear about which patterns grow faster, you might go back and create, or extend, the tables for the slowest and fastest growing patterns. Then, if students still need help, present more examples.

Additional Examples For a pattern that grows more slowly than any students have seen, simply show an "add one block each time" pattern like the one below.

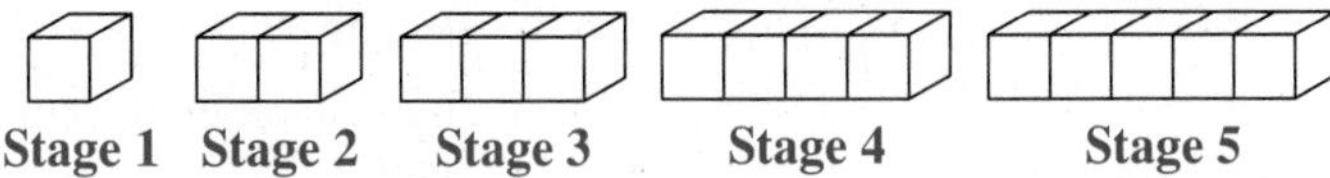

You could also show a "double the number of blocks each time" pattern, like this one.

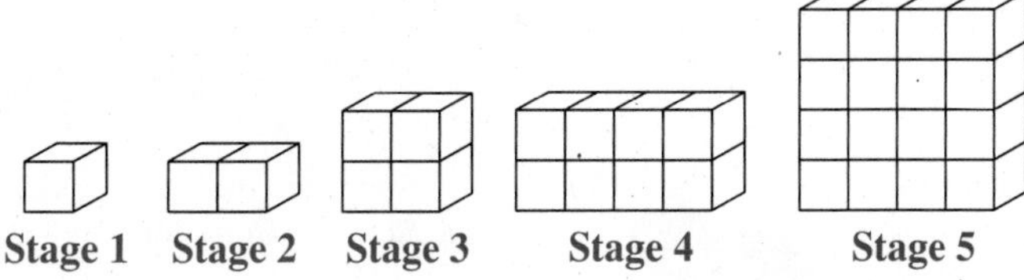

As a class, make a table of the total number of blocks in the first few stages of the different patterns. Then compare across columns of the table. Which grow fastest?

Stage	Square pattern	Cube pattern	"Add 1" pattern	Doubling pattern
1	1	1	1	1
2	4	8	2	2
3	9	27	3	4
4	16	64	4	8

At this point, students may mistakenly conclude that the squares and the cubes both grow faster than the doubling pattern. You can either ask them to continue the tables further by using their calculators to see that the doubling "overtakes" the others pretty quickly. Or you can leave it for now. Chapter 3 explores exponential growth and, in particular, comparisons like these in more detail.

• *Teaching notes continued on page A382.*

Problem Set C

1. Build Stages 3 and 4 of the growing pattern of cubes. Draw them using top-count views. See margin.
2. How many blocks did you use to build Stage 2? 8 Stage 3? 27 Stage 4? 64
3. Without building it, predict how many blocks you would need to build Stage 5. 125
4. Write an expression to describe how many blocks you need to build Stage s. Explain how you found your answer. See margin.

Share & Summarize

Possible answer: The staircase pattern grows most slowly. The square and the double-staircase patterns grow in the same way. The cube pattern grows most quickly.

Compare all the block patterns you have seen. Thinking only about the numbers of blocks needed to build each pattern, which of the patterns grow more quickly? Which grow more slowly? Do any grow in the same way, using the same numbers of blocks at each stage?

1.

3	3	3
3	3	3
3	3	3

Stage 3

4	4	4	4
4	4	4	4
4	4	4	4
4	4	4	4

Stage 4

Investigation 3 Building Block Patterns

4. $s \times s \times s$, or s^3; A Stage s cube has s layers of squares. There are s^2 blocks in a Stage s square, so there will be $s \times s^2$, or s^3, blocks in the cube.

Zoe noticed that the square pattern and the double-staircase pattern grow the same way numerically.

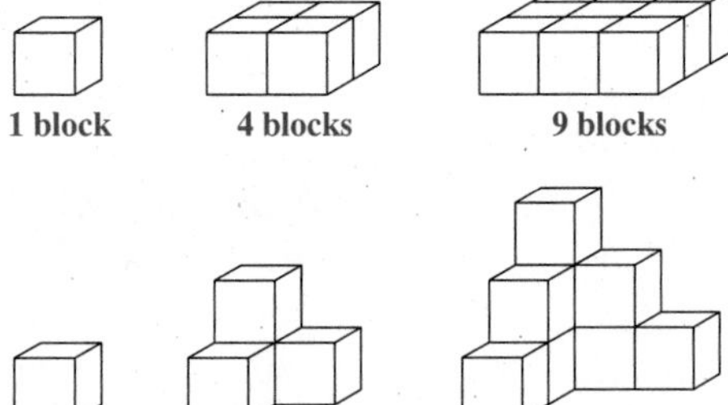

1 block 4 blocks 9 blocks

1 block 4 blocks 9 blocks

Think & Discuss Answer

Possible answer: Start with the front right corner of the square. Move that block up 1 unit, back 1 unit, and left 1 unit. Then move the Stage 2 double staircase (the 3 blocks in an L-shape with 1 block on top at the corner) up 1 unit, back 1 unit, and left 1 unit. Continue until you have the double staircase.

Think & Discuss

The cartoon on the next page shows how Zoe thought about creating the square pattern from the staircase pattern. Can you work the other way? That is, can you find a way to rearrange the blocks from the squares to form the double staircase? Describe your method.

1 You may give students Masters 7 and 8.

2
- Have students notice similarities and differences in patterns.
- If necessary, extend tables and present more examples.

3
- Have students analyze Zoe's strategy.
- Ask students to reverse the process.

Problem Set D Grouping: Small Groups or Pairs

The difficult part of this problem set is getting students to create patterns that satisfy the definition that the blocks must be added in a predictable way. When students are working in their groups, ask them to justify why their block patterns are, in fact, patterns. You may wish to use Master 7, 2-Centimeter Dot Paper, and Master 8, Building Mat, when building patterns and recording results.

In **Problem 2,** students may simply decide to rearrange the stairs and to center them on each row, rather than lining them up in stacks.

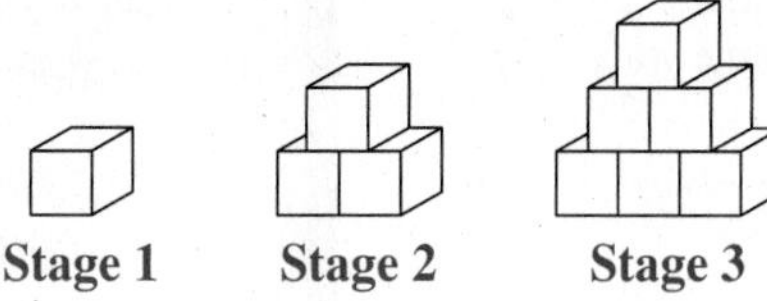

They could also do a simple row that grows in the prescribed way.

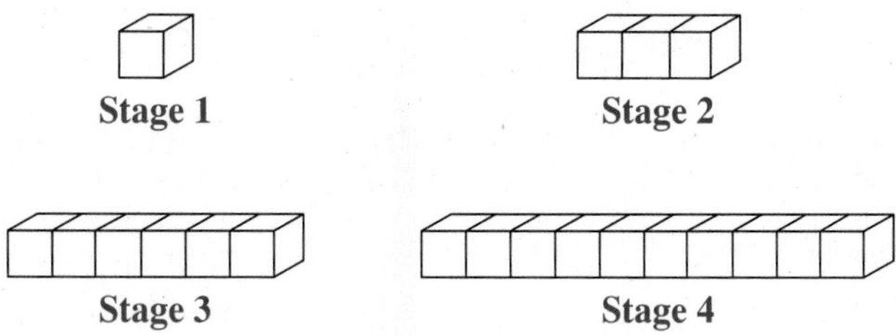

On the Spot Assessment

Students may create "patterns" where the number of blocks grows in a regular way but where the blocks are arranged somewhat randomly from one stage to the next. Here's one example, using the stairstep growth (1, 3, 6, 10, and so on) in **Problem 2**:

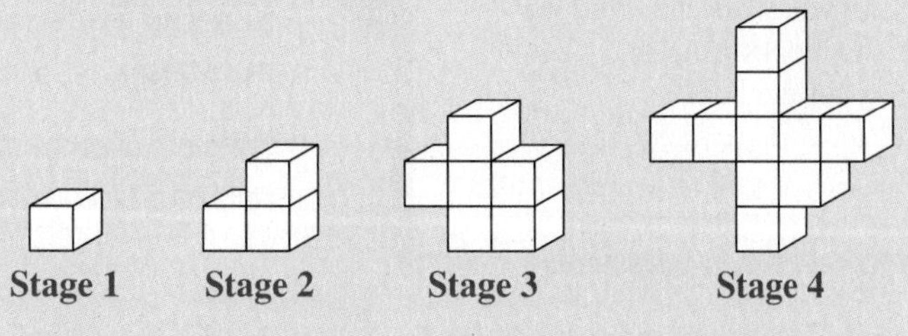

If students make this mistake, ask them to explain how they know where to add the blocks when they go from one stage to the next. You might ask them to sketch Stage 10. For a true pattern, the shape of the stages should make it clear how to add blocks to get from one stage to the next. In the case shown, it is impossible to know the "shape" of Stage 10.

In **Problem 3,** students may think about the problem in relation to the cube pattern they previously built. Since the rule for this pattern is $s^3 - 1$, rather than s^3, they must choose a systematic way to remove one block from each stage of the s^3 pattern. They might choose a specific corner and remove that block each time.

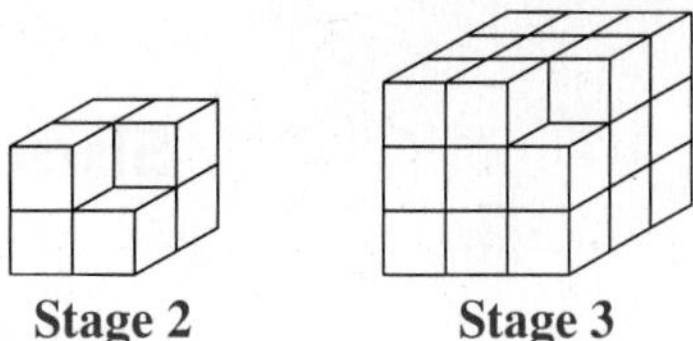

2 Note that, no matter how students arrange the blocks, Stage 1 always has 0 blocks. Since the idea of having a stage with no blocks is new to students, you might want to explore that with some other examples.

Additional Examples A simple example is a pattern in which the total number of blocks is $s - 1$, or one block less than the number of the stage. Stage 1 will have no blocks. In the other stages, the blocks could be arranged in a line.

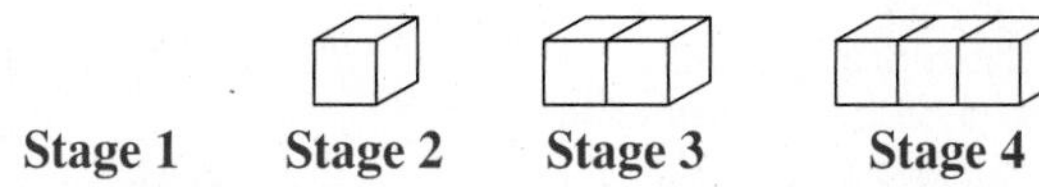

A pattern that shrinks, rather than grows, may eventually reach a stage with no blocks. For example, you might start with 20 blocks and remove 2 (in a regular way, of course!) each time. At Stage 11, you would run out of blocks. Here are the first few stages of such a pattern:

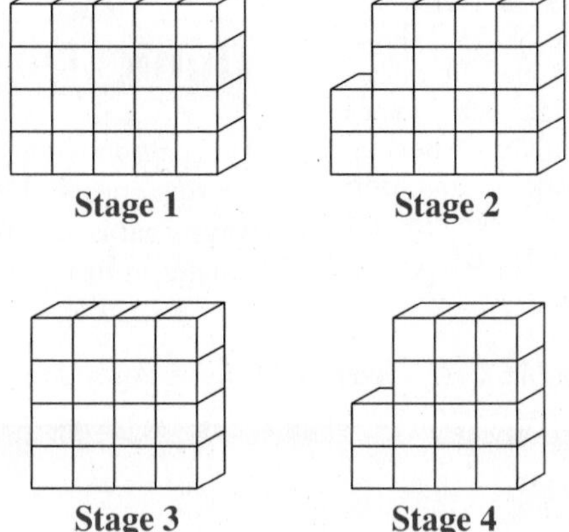

In this case, the rule for removal is "take away the top 2 blocks in the left-most stack." You might ask students to come up with other predictable ways to remove the blocks.

• ***Teaching notes continued on page A382.***

1. Possible pattern:

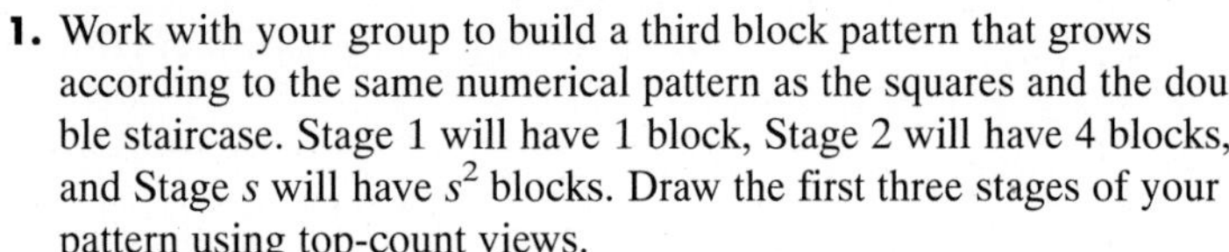

Problem Set D

Remember

To be a pattern, blocks must be added in a *predictable way*—both how many blocks you add and how you arrange them.

1. Work with your group to build a third block pattern that grows according to the same numerical pattern as the squares and the double staircase. Stage 1 will have 1 block, Stage 2 will have 4 blocks, and Stage s will have s^2 blocks. Draw the first three stages of your pattern using top-count views.
2. Now build another pattern that grows like the staircase pattern from Investigation 1: Stage 1 will have 1 block, Stage 2 will have $1 + 2$ blocks, Stage 3 will have $1 + 2 + 3$ blocks, and so on. Draw the first three stages of your pattern using any method you like.
3. Build a pattern with $s^3 - 1$ blocks in Stage s. Stage 1 will have no blocks, Stage 2 will have 7 blocks, Stage 3 will have 26 blocks, and so on. Possible pattern:

Stage 1

Stage 2

2	2
1	2

Stage 3

3	3	3
3	3	3
2	3	3

2. Possible pattern:

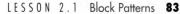

Stage 1

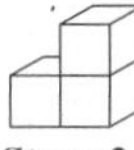

Stage 2

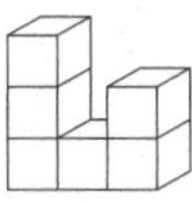

Stage 3

Share & Summarize

Answers will vary.

Create your own block pattern.

1. Draw at least the first three stages of your pattern.
2. Describe how your pattern grows from one stage to the next.
3. Write an expression for the number of blocks in each stage of your pattern.

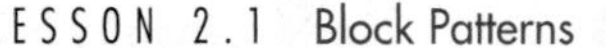

1 Have students work in small groups or pairs.

2
- Note that Stage 1 always has 0 blocks.
- Present more examples.

3
- Have 3 or 4 students give first 3 stages.
- Challenge class to find rules.

On Your Own Exercises

On Your Own Exercises

Investigation 1
Practice & Apply: 1–3
Connect & Extend: 9–12

Investigation 2
Practice & Apply: 4–5
Connect & Extend: 13–16

Investigation 3
Practice & Apply: 6–8
Connect & Extend: 17–18

Assign Anytime
Mixed Review: 19–38

Exercises 1–2: Students are asked to look at simple letter patterns and generalize the number of squares in Stage s. You may want to provide Master 5, Centimeter Dot Paper, for students to take home to make the drawing easier. For Part d in both exercises, you might need to discuss more than one way of looking for a pattern. For example, in **Exercise 2d,** consider this description for the number of blocks in each stage. $7, 7 + 5, 7 + 5 + 5, \ldots, 7 + (s - 1)5$ or $7 + 5s - 5$ which is $2 + 5s$. Another way is: $2 + 5, 2 + 5 + 5, 2 + 5 + 5 + 5, \ldots, 2 + s(5)$, or $2 + 5s$.

Practice & Apply

1. Squares can be used to make growing patterns. Here is a growing pattern of L-shapes.

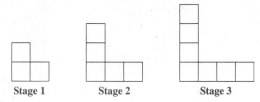

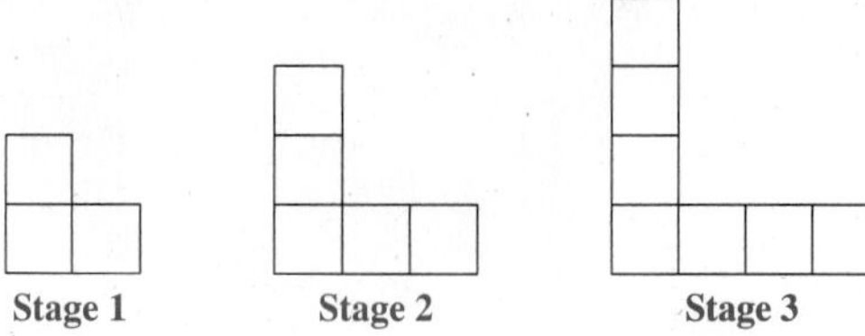

   a. How many squares are added to Stage 1 to make Stage 2? To Stage 2 to make Stage 3? 2, 2
   b. How many squares do you add to go from Stage s to Stage $s + 1$? 2
   c. How many squares are used in Stage 1? In Stage 2? In Stage 3? 3, 5, 7
   d. Write an expression for the number of squares in Stage s. $s + s + 1$, or $2s + 1$

2. Here is a growing pattern of H-shapes.

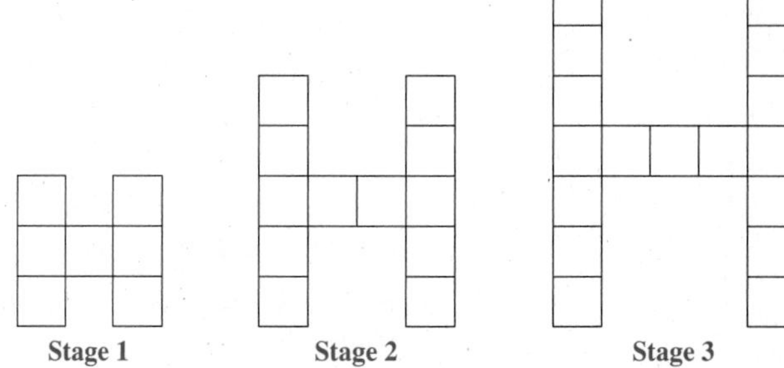

   a. How many squares are added to Stage 1 to make Stage 2? To Stage 2 to make Stage 3? 5, 5
   b. How many squares do you add to go from Stage s to Stage $s + 1$? 5
   c. How many squares are used in Stage 1? In Stage 2? In Stage 3? 7, 12, 17
   d. Write an expression for the number of squares in Stage s. $5s + 2$, or $4s + (s + 2)$

3. Choose a letter of the alphabet that you can draw with squares. Some good choices are A, C, E, F, I, O, T, U, and X.
   a. Draw Stage 1, Stage 2, and Stage 3 versions of your letter. Make sure the letter grows predictably from one stage to the next.
   b. How many squares are added from Stage 1 to Stage 2? From Stage 2 to Stage 3? for pattern in Part a: 3, 3
   c. How many squares do you add to go from Stage s to Stage $s + 1$? for pattern in Part a: 3

3a. Possible answer:

Stage 1 Stage 2

Stage 3

3d. for pattern in Part a: 5, 8, 11

d. How many squares are in Stage 1? In Stage 2? In Stage 3?

e. Write an expression for the number of squares in Stage s of your letter. for pattern in Part a: $3s + 2$, or $2(s + 1) + s$, or $2s + (s + 2)$

4a.

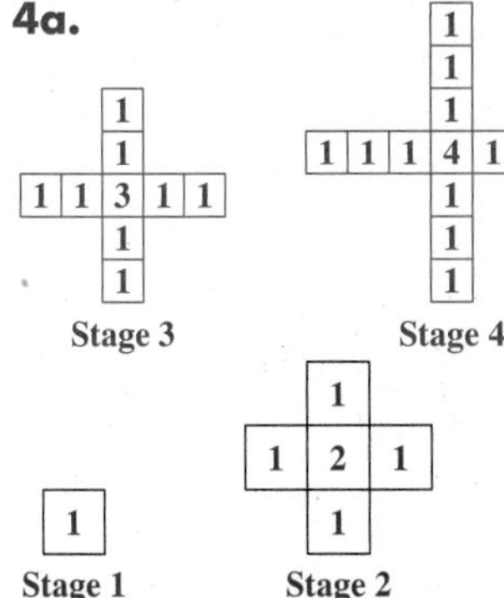

4. Here is a new block pattern.

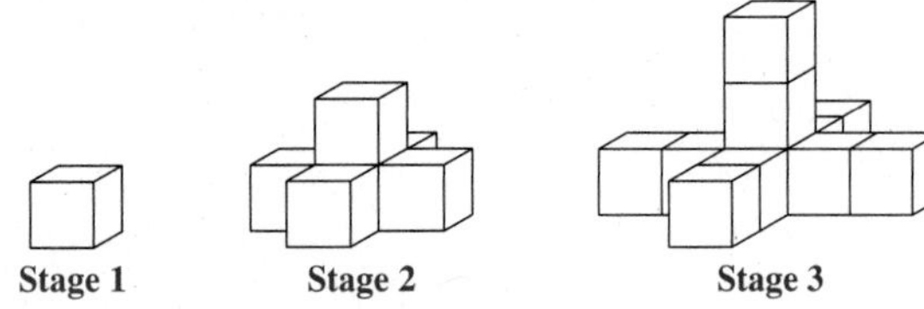

The top-count views of Stages 1 and 2 are shown at left.

a. Draw the top-count views of Stages 3 and 4.

b. How many blocks are added to Stage 1 to make Stage 2? To Stage 2 to make Stage 3? 5, 5

c. How many blocks do you add to go from Stage s to Stage $s + 1$? 5

d. How many blocks are used in Stage 1? In Stage 2? In Stage 3? 1, 6, 11

e. Write an expression for the number of blocks in Stage s. $5s - 4$, or $5(s - 1) + 1$, or $4(s - 1) + s$

5. Look at the block pattern in Exercise 4.

a. Describe how you could modify the pattern so that only 4 blocks are added from one stage to the next.

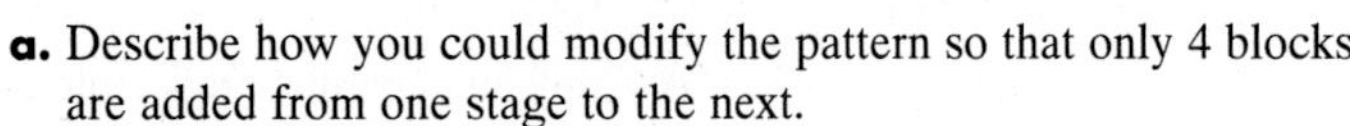

b. Use any method you like to draw the first three stages of your pattern.

Remember

To be a pattern, blocks must be added in a predictable way.

5a. Possible answer: Add blocks only around the sides, not on top.

5b. Possible answer:

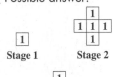

1
Stage 1

1
1 1 1
1
Stage 2

1
1
1 1 1 1 1
1
1
Stage 3

6. Here is another block pattern.

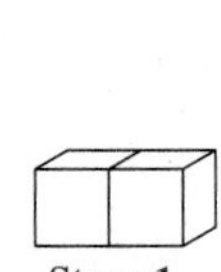

Stage 1

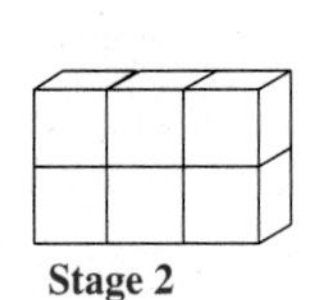

Stage 2

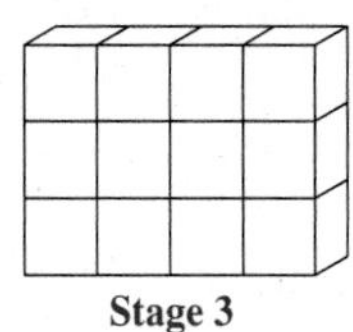

Stage 3

a. How many blocks are added to Stage 1 to make Stage 2? To Stage 2 to make Stage 3? 4, 6

b. How many blocks are added to get from Stage s to Stage $s + 1$? $2(s + 1)$

c. How many blocks are used to make Stage 1? 2 Stage 2? 6 Stage 3? 12

d. Write an expression for the number of blocks in Stage s. $s(s + 1)$

Exercise 3: Students will have to be careful about the letters they choose for generating a predictable pattern. You may want to ask them why they chose the particular letter they picked.

Exercise 8:
This problem is difficult because the solution is a quadratic: $2s^2 - s$. Although students may not come up with the general formula, they may discover some interesting number patterns:

Stage 1: 1

Stage 2: $1 + (1 + 4) = 2 \times 1 + 1 \times 4$

Stage 3: $1 + (1 + 4) + [(1 + 4) + 4] = 3 \times 1 + 3 \times 4$

Stage 4: $1 + (1 + 4) + [(1 + 4) + 4] + \{[(1 + 4) + 4] + 4\} = 4 \times 1 + 6 \times 4$

The number of 1s increases by 1, and the number of 4s increases by consecutive integers. That is, first there is 0, then there are 1 (1 more than last time), then 3 (2 more than last time), then 6 (3 more than last time), and so on.

7. Possible answer:

1	1

Stage 1

1	2	2	1

Stage 2

1	2	3	3	2	1

Stage 3

7. Draw the first three stages of another pattern that uses the same number of blocks in each stage as the pattern in Exercise 6. You may want to use top-count views.

8. Challenge To build Stage 2 of this block pattern, you could make its base (the bottom layer) and set Stage 1 on top of it. To build Stage 3, you could make its base and set Stage 2 on top of it.

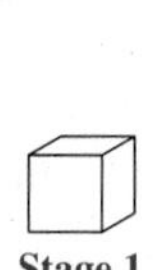
Stage 1

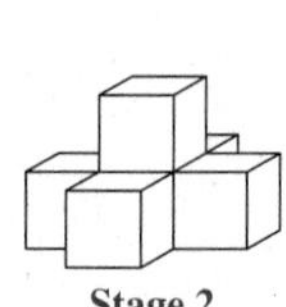
Stage 2

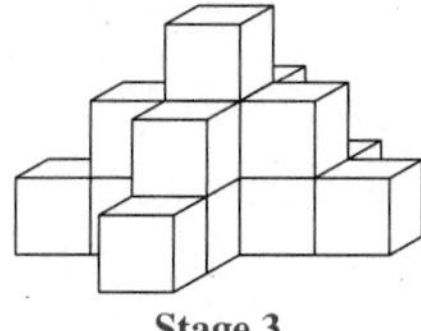
Stage 3

a. There are 5 blocks in the base of Stage 2. How many blocks are in the base of Stage 3? 9

b. How many blocks are in the base of Stage s? $4s - 3$

c. How many blocks are used in Stage 1? In Stage 2? In Stage 3?

8c. 1, 6, 15

d. Describe a rule for the number of blocks in Stage s. Write an expression for the rule, or describe it in words. Possible answer: $s(2s - 1)$

Connect & Extend

9. Jamie found that the number of blocks in Stage s of his block pattern was $2s$.

a. Copy and complete this table for Jamie's pattern.

Stage	1	2	3
Blocks	2	4	6

b. What might Jamie's block pattern look like? Draw the first three stages.

9b. Possible answer:

1	1

Stage 1

2	1	1

Stage 2

3	1	1	1

Stage 3

c. How many blocks are used in Stage 10 of Jamie's pattern? 20

d. How many blocks does Jamie add to Stage 1 to make Stage 2? To Stage 2 to make Stage 3? 2, 2

e. How many blocks does Jamie add to one stage to build the next stage in his pattern? 2

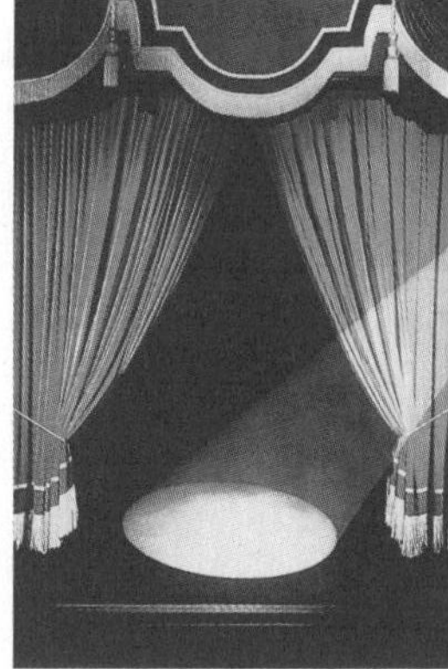

10b. Possible answer:

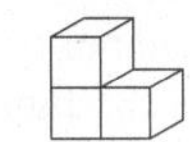

Stage 1 Stage 2

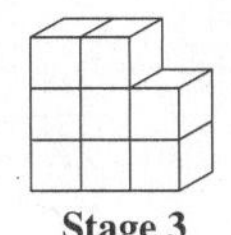

Stage 3

10e. Possible answer: From Stage s to Stage $s + 1$, Kate adds $2s + 1$ blocks.

Remember

To find the area of a figure on dot paper, you can count the squares inside the figure. Sometimes you have to count half squares.

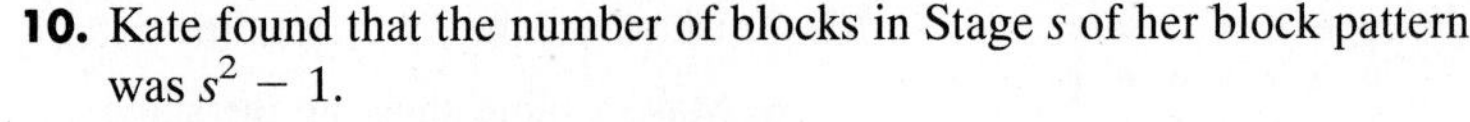

10. Kate found that the number of blocks in Stage s of her block pattern was $s^2 - 1$.

a. Copy and complete this table for Kate's pattern.

Stage	1	2	3
Blocks	0	3	8

b. What might Kate's block pattern look like? Draw the first three stages.

c. How many blocks are used in Stage 10 of Kate's pattern? 99

d. How many blocks does Kate add to Stage 1 to make Stage 2? 3 To Stage 2 to make Stage 3? 5

e. Describe how many blocks Kate adds to one stage to build the next.

11. Keisha drew a growing line pattern on dot paper.

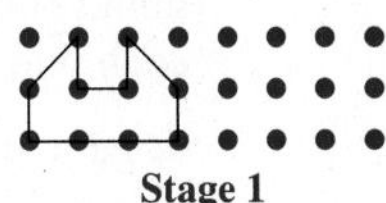

Stage 1

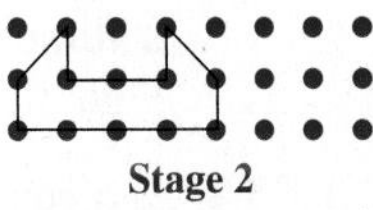

Stage 2

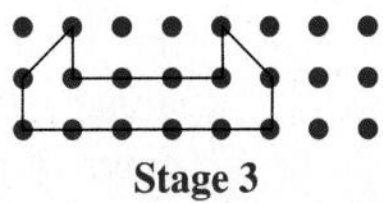

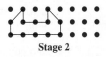

Stage 3

a. Make a table showing the stage, the number of dots on the perimeter of the figure, and the area of the figure.

Stage	1	2	3	4	5
Dots on Perimeter	10	12	14	16	18
Area (square units)	4	5	6	7	8

b. Write an expression for the number of dots on the perimeter in Stage s. $2(s + 4)$, or $2s + 8$

c. Write an expression for the area of Stage s. $s + 3$

Exercise 9:
The number of blocks, $2s$, was chosen deliberately as a way to get students picturing even numbers.

You may want to discuss this problem in class and follow one of many possible extensions. First, ask students to show their pictures, noting that the most useful picture of the even numbers is two lines of the same length. What do odd numbers look like visually? What do they look like algebraically? ($2s + 1$ or $2s - 1$; that simply says one more or one less than some even number.) Visually, how can you show that the sum of two even numbers is even? Can you show it algebraically? ($2s + 2p = 2(s + p)$ by the distributive property.) What about the sum of two odd numbers? And so on.

LESSON 2.1 Block Patterns **87**

Assign and Assess

Exercises 12:
This is the first pattern in which students see that the numbers decrease. Part d encourages them to think about the concept of a limit as the numbers get smaller. Students may be surprised by the "contradiction" that the perimeter never changes but the area decreases until the figure disappears. Remind students that shapes can have the same area while having very different perimeters. This will come up in surface area and volume relationships later in the chapter.

Exercises 13–16:
These problems are like the ones students solved in Chapter 1. The point is for them to realize that the process of finding a pattern, making an expression that fits the pattern, and using that expression to predict is the same, no matter where the pattern comes from.

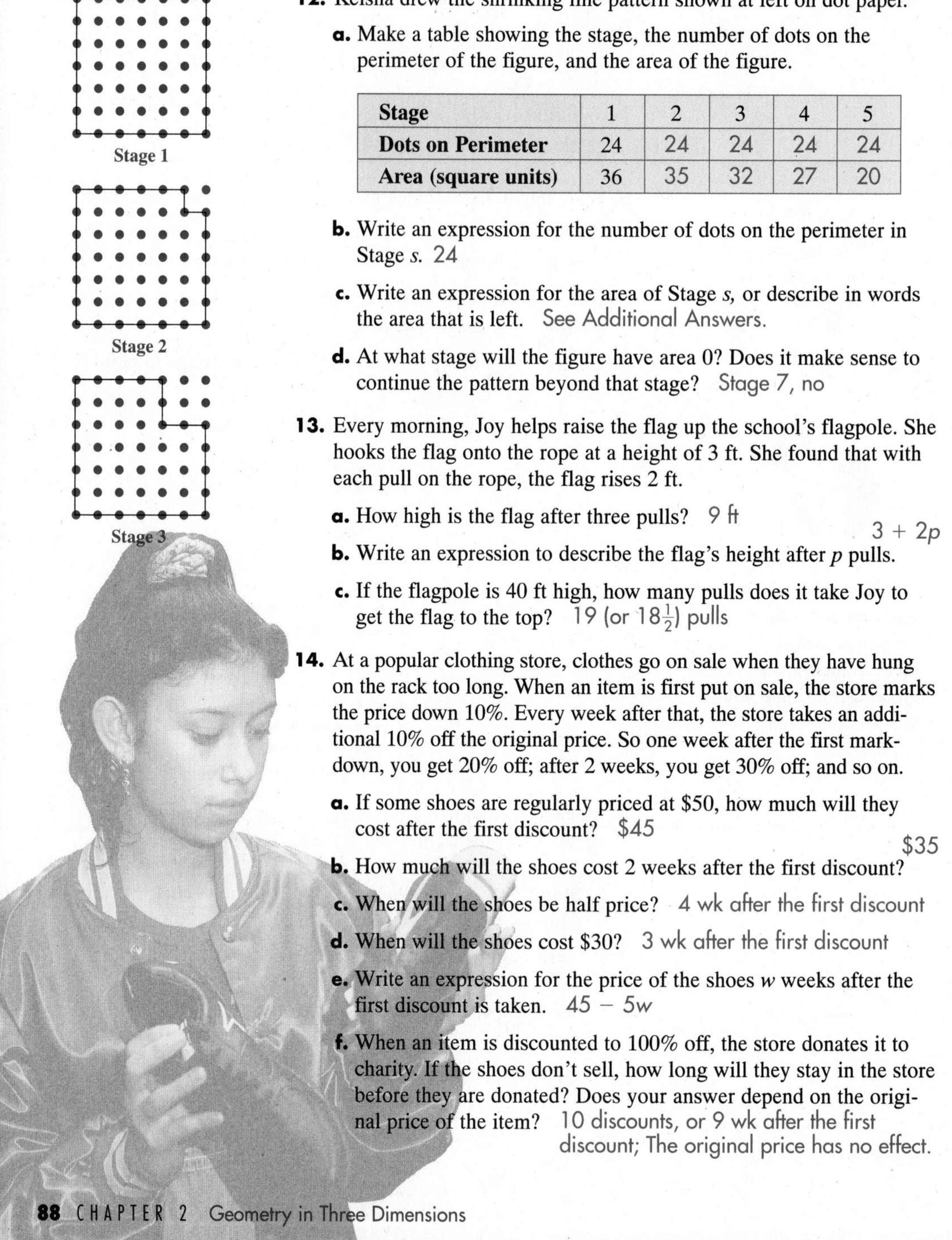

Stage 1

Stage 2

Stage 3

12. Keisha drew the shrinking line pattern shown at left on dot paper.

a. Make a table showing the stage, the number of dots on the perimeter of the figure, and the area of the figure.

Stage	1	2	3	4	5
Dots on Perimeter	24	24	24	24	24
Area (square units)	36	35	32	27	20

b. Write an expression for the number of dots on the perimeter in Stage *s*. 24

c. Write an expression for the area of Stage *s*, or describe in words the area that is left. See Additional Answers.

d. At what stage will the figure have area 0? Does it make sense to continue the pattern beyond that stage? Stage 7, no

13. Every morning, Joy helps raise the flag up the school's flagpole. She hooks the flag onto the rope at a height of 3 ft. She found that with each pull on the rope, the flag rises 2 ft.

a. How high is the flag after three pulls? 9 ft

b. Write an expression to describe the flag's height after *p* pulls. $3 + 2p$

c. If the flagpole is 40 ft high, how many pulls does it take Joy to get the flag to the top? 19 (or $18\frac{1}{2}$) pulls

14. At a popular clothing store, clothes go on sale when they have hung on the rack too long. When an item is first put on sale, the store marks the price down 10%. Every week after that, the store takes an additional 10% off the original price. So one week after the first markdown, you get 20% off; after 2 weeks, you get 30% off; and so on.

a. If some shoes are regularly priced at $50, how much will they cost after the first discount? $45

b. How much will the shoes cost 2 weeks after the first discount? $35

c. When will the shoes be half price? 4 wk after the first discount

d. When will the shoes cost $30? 3 wk after the first discount

e. Write an expression for the price of the shoes *w* weeks after the first discount is taken. $45 - 5w$

f. When an item is discounted to 100% off, the store donates it to charity. If the shoes don't sell, how long will they stay in the store before they are donated? Does your answer depend on the original price of the item? 10 discounts, or 9 wk after the first discount; The original price has no effect.

88 CHAPTER 2 Geometry in Three Dimensions

Additional Answers

12c. Possible answers: $36 - (s - 1)^2$; Or start with 36, and take away the area of a square with sides 1 unit shorter than the stage number. (Note: This works only for Stages 1–7.)

15. Joaquin owes his sister \$30 for taking him to a concert. He earns \$5 each week for doing chores. He promised to give his sister half his earnings every week until the \$30 is paid.

a. How much does Joaquin owe his sister after 1 week? \$27.50

b. Write an expression for how many dollars Joaquin owes his sister after w weeks. $30 - 2.5w$

c. How many weeks will it take Joaquin to pay off his debt? 12

16. Preview Biologists take water samples from a particular swamp in the beginning of spring. They estimate there are 100 mosquito larvae per square meter in the swamp. The area has had a very rainy spring, so the mosquito population is growing quickly, tripling every month.

a. How many mosquito larvae are there per square meter 1 month after the scientists first measured? 2 months after? 300, 900

b. If there are x larvae in a given month, how many are there in the next month? In the month after that? $3x$; $9x$, or 3^2x

c. How can you find the number of mosquito larvae in a square meter m months after the scientists first measured?

d. After how many months will there be more than 5,000 mosquito larvae per square meter?

e. Would this growth continue forever? Explain your answer.

16c–e. See Additional Answers.

17. Here is a shrinking pattern that starts with a square sheet of paper. Each stage is the same height as, and half as wide as, the previous stage.

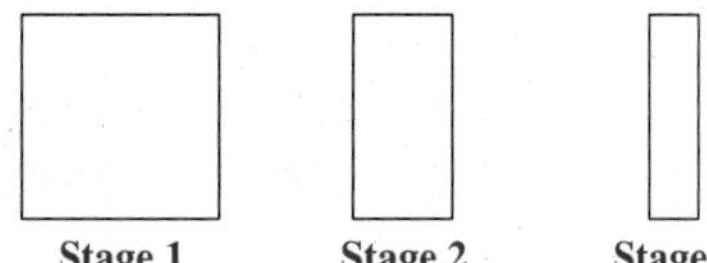

a. What happens to the area of the paper from one stage to the next?

b. What happens to the perimeter of the paper from one stage to the next?

c. Will the paper ever disappear (have area 0 units)? Explain your answer.

17a. It is cut in half.

17b. It is reduced, but not by the same amount each time. First, you subtract w (the width), then $\frac{w}{2}$ (half the original width), then $\frac{w}{4}$, and so on.

17c. No; you always leave half of the figure, so you always leave something for the next stage.

In your own words

Suppose you know that in a particular block pattern, three blocks are added from one stage to the next. How could you find the number of blocks in Stage s? What other information do you need to answer this question?

Additional Answers

16c. Multiply 100 by 3, then multiply the result by 3, and so on until you have multiplied by 3 m times.

16d. after 3 months, or between 3 and 4 months after the first measurement

16e. no; Possible explanation: the seasons change.

Assign and Assess

Quick Check

Informal Assessment
At the end of the lesson, students should be able to:

- ✔ continue a block pattern given the first three stages
- ✔ describe block patterns visually (where the blocks are placed) and numerically (how many blocks are added)
- ✔ describe block patterns with algebraic expressions

Quick Quiz

1. Consider this block pattern:

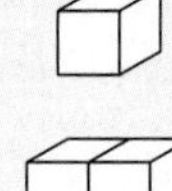

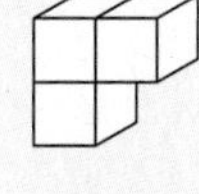

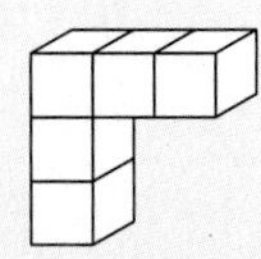

   a. How many blocks are added from one stage to the next? How are they arranged? 2; in an L-shape and one new block is added on each end

   b. Write an expression for the total number of blocks in stage s. $2s - 1$

• ***Teaching notes continued on page A383.***

18. Challenge Neeraj found that the number of blocks in Stage s of his block pattern is $s^3 + 3$.

a. How many blocks are in Stage 10 of Neeraj's pattern? 1,003

b. How many blocks does Neeraj add to go from Stage 1 to Stage 2? From Stage 2 to Stage 3? From Stage 3 to Stage 4? 7, 19, 37

c. Without calculating the number of blocks in each stage, predict how many blocks Neeraj will add to go from Stage 4 to 5 and from Stage 5 to 6. Explain how you found your answer.

Mixed Review

Rewrite each expression using exponents.

19. $t \times t \times t$ t^3 **20.** $\pi \times r \times r$ πr^2 **21.** $y \times y \times y \times y \times y$ y^5

Order each group of numbers from least to greatest.

22. $\frac{1}{3}, \frac{2}{3}, 1, \frac{5}{3}, 0$

23. $\frac{2}{6}, \frac{1}{6}, -\frac{1}{2}, -1, -\frac{3}{6}, 1$

24. $4, 0, 0.4, ^-0.04, -\frac{1}{4}, \frac{1}{4}$

25. $1\frac{3}{8}, 0.125, \frac{3}{8}, \frac{9}{8}, 0$

26. $3, 30, 0.3, 0.03, \frac{3}{10}$

27. $^-1, 10, ^-0.1, \frac{1}{5}, 0, 0.005$

Fill in the blanks to make true statements.

28. $\frac{1}{8} + \underline{\ \frac{7}{8}\ } = 1$

29. $\frac{8}{5} - \underline{\ \frac{3}{5}\ } = 1$

30. $0.5 + \underline{\ 0.5\ } = 1$

31. $0.5 + 0.25 + \underline{\ 0.25\ } = 1$

32. $\frac{9}{12} + \frac{3}{12} + \underline{\ 0\ } = 1$

33. $\frac{3}{10} + \frac{7}{10} - \underline{\ 0\ } = 1$

Find the product or quotient.

34. $156 \cdot 3$ 468

35. $12 \cdot 25$ 300

36. $52 \div 13$ 4

37. $352 \div 11$ 32

38. Kiran wants to display his collection of 30 first-class stamps from 1993 in groups of equal size. What group sizes are possible? groups of 1, 2, 3, 5, 6, 10, 15, and 30

18c. 61, 91; Possible explanation: The earlier stages had a pattern using multiples of 6. Adding 12 to 7 is 19, and adding 18 to 19 is 37. So, add 24 to 37, for 61, and add 30 to 61, for 91.

22. $0, \frac{1}{3}, \frac{2}{3}, 1, \frac{5}{3}$

23. $-1, -\frac{1}{2} = -\frac{3}{6}, \frac{1}{6}, \frac{2}{6}, 1$

24. $-\frac{1}{4}, ^-0.04, 0, 0.4, \frac{1}{4}, 4$

25. $0, 0.125, \frac{3}{8}, \frac{9}{8}, 1\frac{3}{8}$

26. $0.03, \frac{3}{10} = 0.3, 3, 30$

27. $^-1, ^-0.1, 0, 0.005, \frac{1}{5}, 10$

2.2 Visualizing and Measuring Block Structures

Objectives

- To draw front, top, and side views of block structures
- To understand the difference between regular views and engineering views
- To understand volume as the number of blocks that make up a structure

Overview (pacing: about 4 class periods)

In this lesson, students improve their visualization skills by thinking about different flat views for three-dimensional structures. This kind of visualization is important in many fields including architecture and engineering. It is also important in later mathematical study that students can think flexibly about two-dimensional objects that describe three-dimensional objects. In calculus, for example, students think about the solid created by revolving a two-dimensional object such as a line or a circle.

Advance Preparation

Make several copies of Master 7, 2-Centimeter Dot Paper; Master 9, Centimeter Graph Paper; and/or Master 10, Quarter-Inch Graph Paper for each student. They will find it much easier to record their work using them rather than plain paper. Students will need to work with the blocks throughout the lesson, actually building and manipulating the structures. Have sets of 35 blocks per pair ready each day of the lesson. Using Master 8, Building Mat, often makes identifying the different views easier because students can rotate the mats.

Lesson Planner

	Summary	Materials	On Your Own Exercises	Assessment Opportunities
Investigation 1 page T92	Students build block structures from flat views of front, top, and side. They also practice drawing views from their own structures. Students also find the relationship in pairs of views: front/back, right/left, and top/bottom.	• Master 7, (Teaching Resources, page 12) • Master 8, (Teaching Resources, page 13) • Master 9, (Teaching Resources, page 14) • Master 10, (Teaching Resources, page 15) • Cubes	Practice & Apply: 1–3 Connect & Extend: 17–19 Mixed Review: 33–56	Share & Summarize, pages T93, 93 On the Spot Assessment, page T92 Troubleshooting, page T93
Investigation 2 page T94	Students learn that the front/top/right views do not determine a unique structure. They also learn a modified version of the three-view drawing used by architects and engineers.	• Master 8 • Master 9 • Blocks	Practice & Apply: 4–5 Connect & Extend: 20–25 Mixed Review: 33–56	Share & Summarize, pages T96, 96 Troubleshooting, page T96
Investigation 3 page T97	Students practice drawing and interpreting engineering views.	• Masters 7, 8, 9, 10 • Blocks	Practice & Apply: 6–7 Connect & Extend: 26–28 Mixed Review: 33–56	Share & Summarize, pages T97, 97 Troubleshooting, page A384
Investigation 4 page T98	Students are introduced to volume as counting the cubes in a block structure and to surface area as counting exposed squares on the faces.	• Blocks	Practice & Apply: 8–16 Connect & Extend: 29–32 Mixed Review: 33–56	Share & Summarize, pages T99, 99 On the Spot Assessment, page T99 Troubleshooting, page T99 Informal Assessment, page 108 Quick Quiz, page 108

Introduce

1 Begin the lesson by having pairs of students build the structure in the introduction, preferably on Master 8, Building Mat. Ask them to think about viewing this structure from the top, left side, right side, front, back, and bottom. Thinking about what these views look like is not always easy for students. They may find it helpful to think of these structures as "collapsing" into a surface from the different views.

Students may choose any side as the "front," but they should keep the same side as the front when considering the other views. For all but the bottom view, students can move themselves or rotate the structure to see the other sides. For the bottom view, students should face the front of the structure and imagine picking it up and tipping it back to see the bottom.

2 **Explore** **Grouping: Pairs**
Students first build the block structure on Master 8, Building Mat and then they record the views using Master 7, 2-Centimeter Dot Paper, or Master 9, Centimeter Graph Paper.

For all structures, the top and bottom views are mirror images of each other, as are the front and back views, and the right and left views. For each case, the opposite view can be found by flipping the view. In this particular object, some of the views are identical because the views are symmetric. For example, below are both the right and left views. They are mirror images, or flips, of each other. But because the shape is symmetric about the dashed line shown, they are also the same.

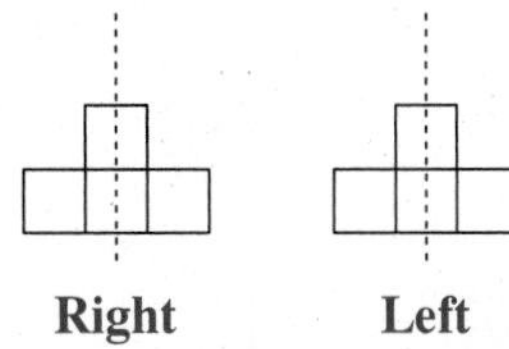

3 It's important to mention to students that when viewing this structure, they need to be facing the front to distinguish right and left views.

2.2 Visualizing and Measuring Block Structures

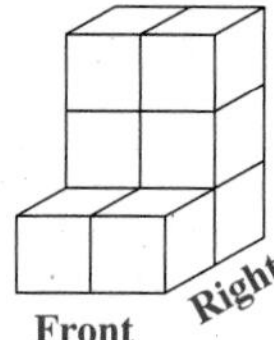

One way to describe a structure is to draw how it looks from different viewpoints. For example, here are six views that might describe the block structure at left.

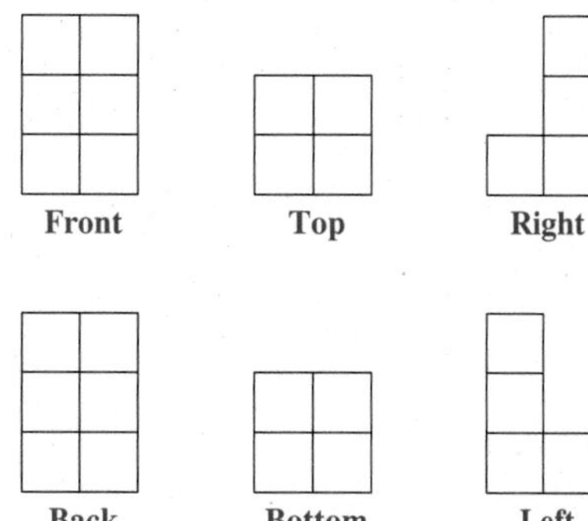

These flat views are like shadows that would be cast against a wall or a floor by the structure, but they also show the lines between the blocks. The top view is a "bird's-eye view," looking down from above. For the bottom view, imagine building the structure on a glass table and looking at it from underneath. The left and right views show how the structure looks when viewed from those sides.

1
- Have pairs of students build block structure.
- Have students think about viewing the structure from all sides.

MATERIALS
- cubes
- graph paper or dot paper

Explore

Build this block structure. Then draw the six views of it using graph paper or dot paper. If you build your structure on a sheet of paper, you can write the labels *Front, Back, Left,* and *Right* on the paper. This will make it easier for you to remember which side is which.

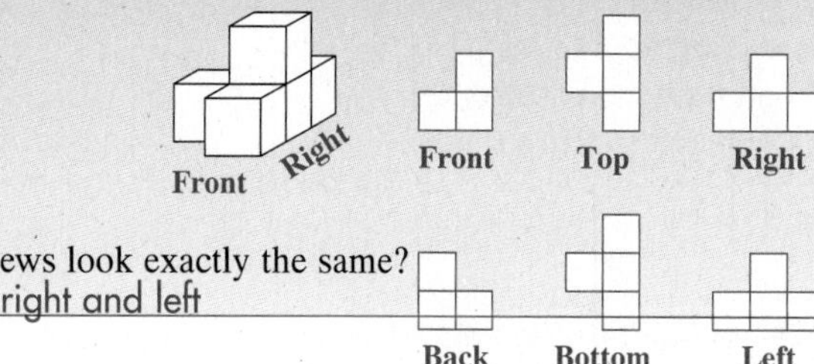

Which of your views look exactly the same?
top and bottom, right and left

2 Have students work in pairs.

3 Have students face front of structure to distinguish right and left views.

LESSON 2.2 Visualizing and Measuring Block Structures 91

Investigation 1

In this investigation, students are asked to think about the relationships between pairs of views: right/left, top/bottom, and front/back. Students will find that only three of these views—left or right, top or bottom, and front or back—are distinct because of the relationships between these pairs. In this book, we will use the top, front, and right views to describe a structure.

1 Depending on your class, you might go over the rules for a good block structure before beginning the problem sets.

2 **Problem Set A** **Grouping: Pairs**
In working through these problems, students will find that they can flip one view to find the other view in each of these pairs: front/back, top/bottom, and right/left views. To come to this conclusion, it is important that students build some "nice" structures and at least one "funny-looking," very asymmetric structure. As you observe students' work, encourage them to check "extreme" cases to see whether their conjectures hold. You may wish to have students use Master 7, 2-Centimeter Dot Paper, and Master 8, Building Mat.

On the Spot Assessment

If students build structures that are too regular and conclude that, for example, the right and left views are always the same, ask them to alter one of their structures just a little and find the right and left views again. For example, if students have structures like the one from the Explore, ask them to move the top block back one unit to make a new, less symmetric structure.

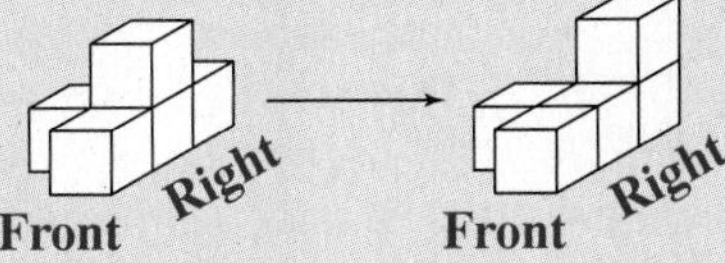

Students should notice that whenever the right view changes, so does the left. Whenever the top view changes, so does the bottom. And whenever the front view changes, so does the back. However, they do not always change in exactly the same way.

3 **Problem Set Wrap-Up** After working through Problem Set A, students should reach conclusions about the pairs of views, namely that they can flip each view to make the other view. Ask students why they think these relationships hold.

Investigation 1 Seeing All the Angles

In this lesson, you will consider only block structures in which at least one face of each block matches up with a face of another block. (Creating views like those in the Explore on page 91 can be difficult for other kinds of buildings.) Keep this in mind as you build your structures.

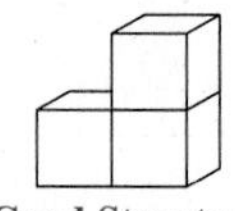
Good Structure

Not Good

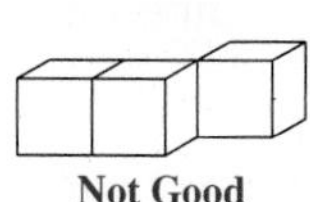
Not Good

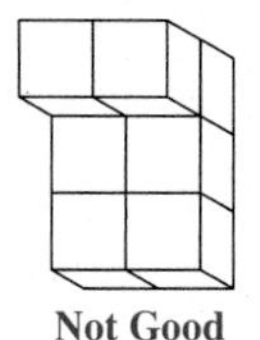
Not Good

Since you will build these structures on your desk, the laws of gravity apply. Blocks need to rest on the table or on other blocks, so you can't make a structure like the one at left.

1 You might review rules for good block structure.

MATERIALS
- cubes
- graph paper or dot paper

Problem Set A

2
- Have students work in pairs.
- Encourage students to build symmetric structures and check their conjectures.

Work with your partner to build three different block structures. Use 6 to 10 blocks for each of them, and follow the rules of good structures. Keep the structures in front of you for this set of problems.

1. First, focus on top and bottom views.
   a. For each of your structures, draw top and bottom views. Be sure to label which is which. Drawings will vary.
   b. Describe in words the relationship between the top and bottom views of a structure.
   c. Does that relationship hold for *any* block structure, or just for those you built?
2. Now focus on left and right views.
   a. For each structure, draw and label left and right views.
   b. Describe the relationship between the left and right views of a structure.
   c. Does that relationship hold for *any* block structure?
3. Finally, focus on front and back views.
   a. For each structure, draw and label front and back views.
   b. Describe the relationship between the front and back views of a structure.
   c. Does that relationship hold for *any* block structure?

1b. The bottom view is the top view flipped upside down.
1c. It holds for any structure.
2a. Drawings will vary.
2b. The right view is the left view flipped left to right.
2c. It holds for any structure.
3a. Drawings will vary.
3b. The back view is the front view flipped left to right.
3c. It holds for any structure.

3 Ask students why these relationships hold.

Problem Set B **Suggested Grouping: Individuals**
In this problem set, students are given a view of a structure and are asked to draw the opposite view. Make sure students understand that the three views shown are not for the same structure but rather for three different structures.

Students may want to build structures that fit the views. You can have students use Master 9, Centimeter Graph Paper, or Master 10, Quarter-Inch Graph Paper, to draw their views. Encourage them to try to draw the views without building and then to build a structure as a check. The point of the problem set is that you don't have to build a structure to know the other view in a pair because each image is a flip of the other.

Share & Summarize
Students should be able to explain that because the top and bottom views are flips of each other, you need to know only one of them.

The fact that three views gives you all the information you can get from these flat views may seem confusing to students. The point is that adding other views would not add any more information.

Troubleshooting The big idea of this lesson is representing three-dimensional structures in two-dimensional drawings. If students are having trouble drawing and interpreting the front/top/right views, they will have a lot of trouble in Investigation 2 with the more complicated engineering views. The good news is that all students can get better at working with these views with practice. You may want to provide some additional easy structures and have students practice drawing views. For example, the square-shaped structure below (and square-shaped structures of other sizes) have easier views to determine.

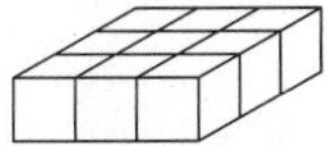

You can then complicate the structure by adding a single cube to the middle and by asking students to think about which views change and how they change.

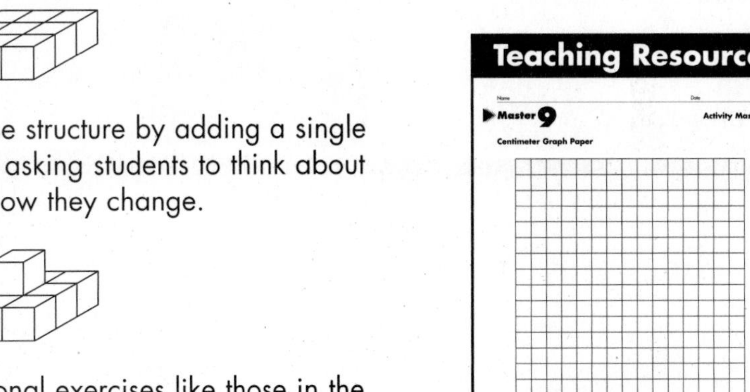

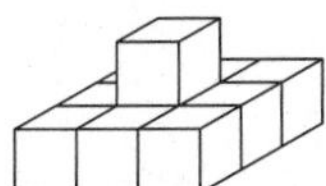

You can also create additional exercises like those in the On Your Own Exercises section, in which students are asked to match the views to a structure and to identify the views as front, top, or right.

If students have trouble seeing the relationships between the pairs of views, asking students to look at all six views in these same activities will help reinforce the important ideas.

On Your Own Exercises

Practice & Apply: 1–3
Connect & Extend: 17–19
Mixed Review: 33–56

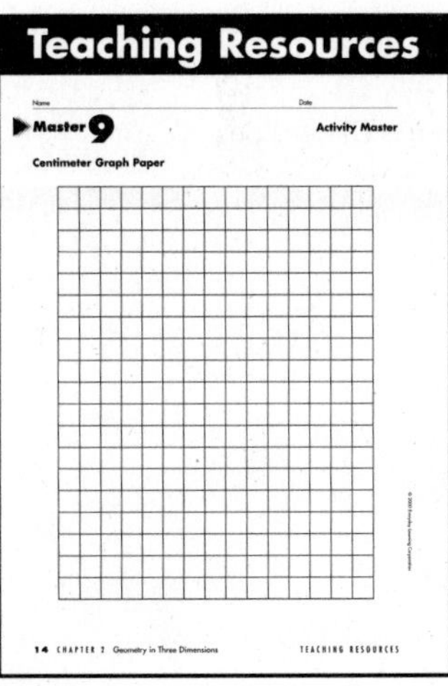

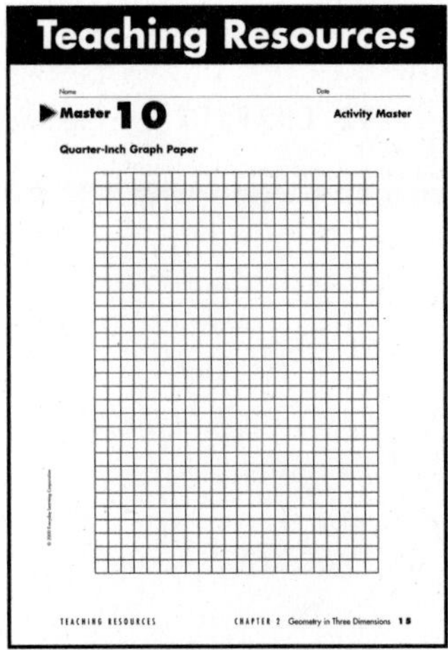

Problem Set B

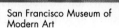

San Francisco Museum of Modern Art

Use the relationships you discovered in Problem Set A to complete these problems.

1. This is the right view of a structure. Draw the left view.

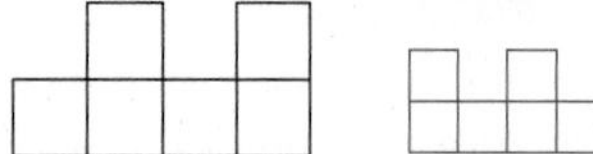

2. This is the top view of a structure. Draw the bottom view.

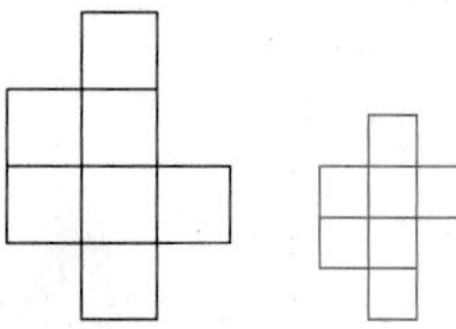

3. This is the front view of a structure. Draw the back view.

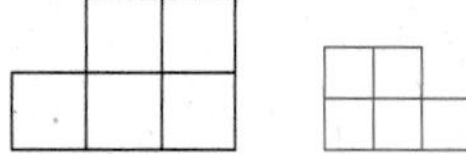

- Be sure students understand that different structures are used in each problem.
- Encourage students to draw views. Then build structures as a check.

Share & Summarize

1. No; the bottom view is just a mirror image of the top view, so it wouldn't give any new information.

1. Suppose you know the top view of a structure. Would you learn anything more about the structure from the bottom view? Explain your answer.
2. If you know the front, top, and right views of a structure, would any other view give you more information about the structure? Explain. No; each of the other views is paired with one of these views, so they wouldn't add any information.

Be sure students can explain their answers.

If necessary, provide additional structures.

Complexe des Jardins, Montreal, Quebec

Investigation 2

This investigation points out a problem in the front/top/right views that students have been working with: for some structures, you can't know what the structure is even if you know all the views. That is, more than one structure may have the same set of three views as shown in Problem 2 of Problem Set C. For example, here are eight different structures (shown as top-count views) that all have the same front, top, and side views. (And these are not all of the possibilities!)

2	2	2		2	2	2		2	2	2		2	2	2
2	2	2		1	2	2		2	1	2		2	2	1
1	1	1		1	1	1		1	1	1		1	1	1

2	2	2		2	2	2		2	2	2		2	2	2
2	0	2		1	2	1		2	1	1		1	1	2
1	1	1		1	1	1		1	1	1		1	1	1

The eight structures above share these three views:

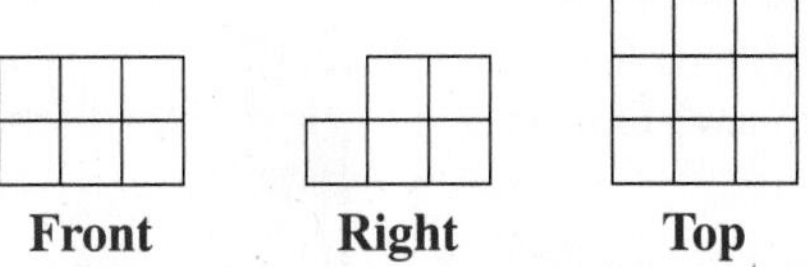

Because these views show only the "highest point" for each view, they hide how many blocks are behind or in front of others. Also, you'll notice that they can hide "holes" in the middle of the structure, making it look like there's a block when there isn't (look at the top-count view on the bottom left).

Students already have one way to describe a unique block structure: the top-count view. However, if they want to describe nonblock structures, the top-count view is less useful. Students will learn a simplified version of a new kind of drawing, which we call "engineering views" but which are more traditionally known as "orthographic views." This is the kind of drawing actually practiced by architects and engineers, and when drawn correctly, the front, top, and right views describe a unique structure. This may not be true for students' drawings. It is slightly different from the technique in Investigation 1 (and common in curricula). Most people find it more difficult to visualize and build from the three engineering views.

The intent here is not that students become proficient with the drawing technique but rather that students have some exposure to how these ideas play out in other fields.

Think & Discuss

This should be a quick discussion. Students should realize that, since they know the exact number of blocks in each stack, there is only one possible structure. This is true only because of the rules for block structures described on page 92 of the student text. If the blocks did not have to obey gravity and could hover in the air or be glued to the faces of other blocks, then the top-count view shown would not describe a unique structure. The row of 1s might be on the bottom or top level, and there would be no way to know which. If students think more than one structure is possible, you may need to revisit the rules to clarify why there can only be one.

Problem Set C Grouping: Pairs

2

In **Problem 1,** students are asked to build their own structures and draw top-count, front, top, and right views of them. They then exchange their views with a partner and ask the partner to construct a structure that matches these views. Tell students to hide their structures and top-count views from their partners so that when they exchange views it is really a test of the drawings. Students should notice that their partners, in fact, may not build the same structures as the originals. It may be helpful for students to build on the Building Mat provided on Master 8; it makes it easier to identify the different views.

In **Problem 2,** students build a structure given three views (front, right, top) and draw a top-count view of the structure. They are then asked to build another structure that fits these three views. In doing so, students discover that a front-, top- and side-view picture does not determine a unique structure.

Eight different structures that fit these three views are shown on the left side of this page. There are more possibilities. For example, the back row does not need to have all 2s.

As students work on finding the first couple of structures, they may discover "rules" that the building must follow to fit the drawings. For example:

- The front row has all 1s.
- There must be at least one 2 in the middle row.
- There must be at least one 2 in the back row.
- There must be at least a 1 in every spot, but the very middle might be 0.

• ***Teaching notes continued on page A383.***

Investigation 2 Different Views

Remember
The top-count view shows a top view of the structure and the number of blocks in each stack.

Think & Discuss

2	2	2
2	1	2
1	1	1

In many problems in this chapter, you have used top-count views to describe block structures. For this top-count view, is there more than one possible structure? no

Is there *any* top-count view that could fit more than one structure? Explain your answer. No; the blocks must sit on top of each other in stacks, and the top-count view tells how the stacks are arranged and how many blocks are in each, so there is only one possibility.

1 You may review rules for block structures.

MATERIALS
- cubes
- graph paper or dot paper

Problem Set C

You will now explore this question: Can more than one structure fit the same front, top, and right views?

2 Tell students to hide structures and top-count views from partners.

1. Working on your own, use 10 to 15 blocks to build a block structure.

a. Draw a top-count view for your structure. Drawings will vary.

b. On another sheet of paper, draw front, top, and right views. Then take your structure apart. Drawings will vary.

c. Exchange front, top, and right views with a partner, and build a structure that matches your partner's drawings. Did you build the structure your partner had in mind? (Use the top-count view to check.) Students may or may not build their partners' structures.

2. Here are three views of a block structure.

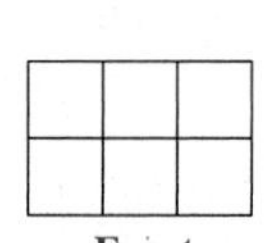

Front

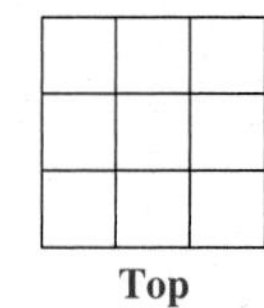

Top

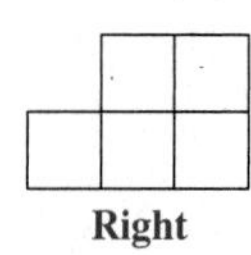

Right

a. Build a structure that fits these views. Draw a top-count view for your structure.

b. Build a different structure that fits these views, and draw a top-count view. See the answer to Part a for some possibilities.

c. Do you think there are other possible structures? Why or why not? Yes, there are many more possibilities. For example, the back row does not need to have all 2s, though it must have at least one.

3
- Have students share answers.
- Compile a master list of their suggestions.

2a. Some possible answers:

2	2	2
2	2	2
1	1	1

2	2	2
1	2	2
1	1	1

2	2	2
2	0	2
1	1	1

2	2	2
1	2	1
1	1	1

2	2	2
2	1	2
1	1	1

2	2	2
2	2	1
1	1	1

2	2	2
2	1	1
1	1	1

2	2	2
1	1	2
1	1	1

Develop

1 Discuss the usefulness of having three views of a structure. Students may mention that the information is not precise and that most structures are not made of blocks.

2 **Example** **Suggested Grouping: Pairs**
Ask students to build the example structure and to look at the three views. Discuss each of the three views and what the lines show. Rather than showing separation between blocks, the lines show different levels of the structure—that is, when blocks are at different heights or depths.

Making and interpreting these drawings can be a challenge for many students. It is important that they have a partner with whom to check their ideas as they work. The major idea is that engineering views give more information than regular views.

Although top-count views show exactly how the blocks are arranged in a block structure, they aren't really useful to engineers and architects because things in real life aren't usually made of blocks.

Creating a structure from three given views is an interesting puzzle, but if three views represent lots of different structures, they are not very useful. If you were designing a house, for instance, you would want to be very specific in your drawings so that what you imagine is what gets built.

Engineers and architects often need to make drawings of structures, but the types of drawings they make must give more precise information about a structure. The drawings you will work with next can give more information about the block structures they represent.

EXAMPLE

Remember this structure?

Below is another type of three-view drawing that describes it. This type of drawing shows the different levels of the block structure but not the lines between blocks.

Front Right

Front Top Right

The line in the front view shows that there are two different levels of blocks in the structure. In this structure, the base extends beyond the tall part.

The line in the top view shows that there are two different heights of blocks in the structure. The right view shows that the part in front is lower.

These three views together often contain more information than the front, top, and right views you have used before. We will refer to the earlier kind of views as *regular views* and the new kind as *engineering views.*

It is sometimes hard to picture a structure from just looking at the engineering views. Practice will help!

1 Discuss usefulness of having three views of a structure.

2
- You may have students work in pairs.
- Have students build structure.
- Discuss three views.

LESSON 2.2 Visualizing and Measuring Block Structures **95**

Problem Set D **Grouping: Pairs**
As a class, look at **Problem 1.** Ask the class the following questions:

> How many blocks tall is the structure? *From the front and right views, you can tell that it is 2 blocks tall at the highest point and 1 block tall in some places.*
>
> How many blocks go across the front view of the structure? *From the top and right views it looks like it is 3 blocks across.*
>
> How many blocks go along the right side of the structure? *From the top and right views, it looks like this is also 3 blocks.*

2 Write the questions and the answers to each on the board or overhead. Tell students that the final thing to figure out in **Problem 1** is where the levels are: Where is the structure one block high? Where is it two blocks high? Add these last two questions to the list on the board for student reference. Then ask students to work with their partners on **Problems 2 and 3.**

Sample Strategy Students may use this strategy to solve **Problems 1–3.**

- The three sets of engineering views show closely related structures. In each case, you get from one to the next by simply removing a block. Students may find the solution for Problem 1 and then turn it into the solution for Problem 2 by removing the center block on the top. From there, they can turn it into the solution for Problem 3 by removing the front left block on the top.

3 **Problem Set Wrap-Up** You may want to show the three solutions and have all students build the appropriate structures, especially if some pairs were struggling with interpreting the drawings. Remind students to refer to the five questions listed on the board as they do these types of problems.

Point out that these three structures have different *engineering* views but have the same *regular* front/top/right views. In fact, they were all solutions to Problem 3 in Problem Set C.

Share & Summarize
Check that students' examples for Question 1 really do show an ambiguous case. You may need to point out that not all front/top/right views fit more than one structure; only some of them have this problem.

For Question 2, we simply want students to restate the fact that the lines in the engineering drawings show you different levels and that this is useful information.

Troubleshooting If students seem to think that all regular front/top/right views give different structures, you may want to provide some simple examples where they do describe a unique structure. See the additional examples below.

Students will have a chance to practice the engineering views some more in Investigation 3, so do not be overly concerned if they are struggling with interpreting the drawings at this stage.

Additional Examples These sets of front/top/right views describe unique structures:

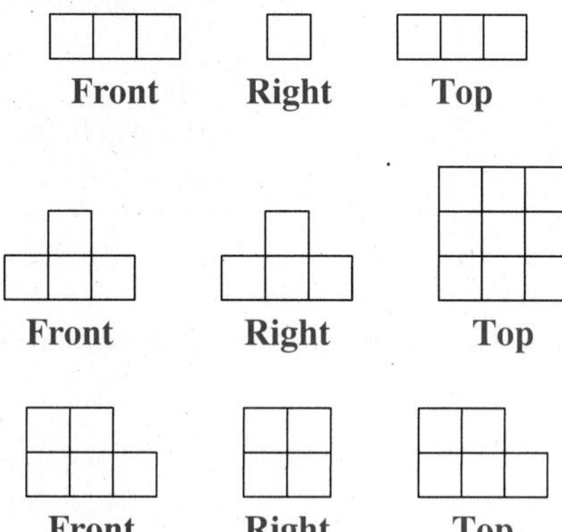

On Your Own Exercises

Practice & Apply: 4–5
Connect & Extend: 20–25
Mixed Review: 33–56

MATERIALS
- cubes
- graph paper or dot paper

Problem Set D

Build the structure described by each set of three views. Draw a top-count view to record each structure you build.

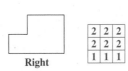

1. Front, Top, Right

2	2	2
2	2	2
1	1	1

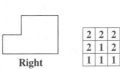

2. Front, Top, Right

2	2	2
2	1	2
1	1	1

3. Front, Top, Right

2	2	2
1	1	2
1	1	1

Just the facts

These types of views are technically known as *orthographic drawings.*

Share & Summarize

1. Can there be more than one structure with the same *regular* front, top, and right views? Explain your answer by giving an example.

2. The three structures in Problem Set D all fit the same regular front, top, and right views. How do the engineering views show the differences among the structures?

1. Yes; lots of structures have the regular views shown in Problem 2 of Problem Set C.
2. The engineering views show the different levels in the structures.

1
- Ask leading questions.
- Display questions and answers.

2 Have students work in pairs.

3
- Show solutions and have students build structures.
- Point out that all structures have same views.

4 Check that each student's Problem 1 example show an ambiguous case.

5 If necessary, provide more examples.

Investigation 3

In this investigation, students draw engineering views to match block structures. Students may use Masters 7, 8, 9, or 10 in the following problem set.

Problem Set E Grouping: Pairs

Again, it is helpful for students to work with a partner in creating these drawings because the drawings are quite challenging. We have structured the problems so that there are some easy examples first with more difficult ones to follow.

If students are having trouble creating the engineering views, you can provide some guidance. The Sample Strategies below explain how students might reason through the creation of the drawings.

Sample Strategies There are several ways students might create their drawings for **Problems 1–6:**

- If students are comfortable with the regular front/top/right views, they can draw those first. Then they can erase the lines between blocks and add the lines between levels. For **Problem 3,** this would look like:

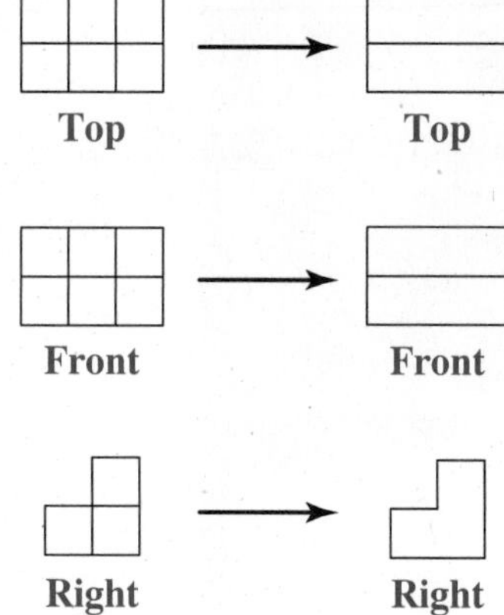

- Students might draw the overall shape of the view first. Is it a square? Rectangle? L-shape? Something else? Then they may add the lines between levels. This is similar to the other suggestion, but doesn't require first drawing the other kinds of views. For **Problem 2,** it would look like this:

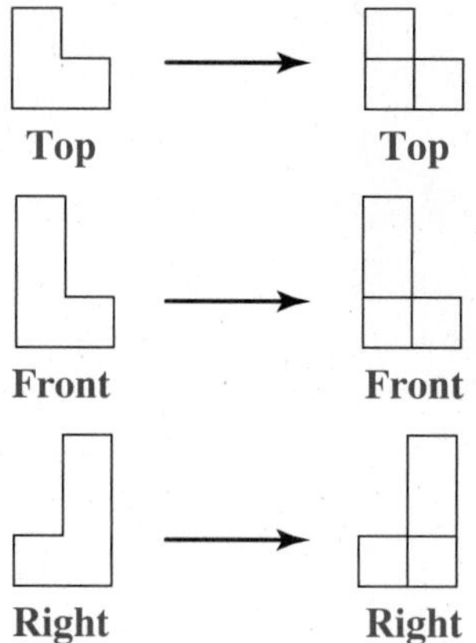

- For the top view, students can draw a top-count view and then erase the lines between blocks that have the same number. Students can then adapt this to make front-count views and right-count views to do the other views. For **Problem 4,** it would look like this:

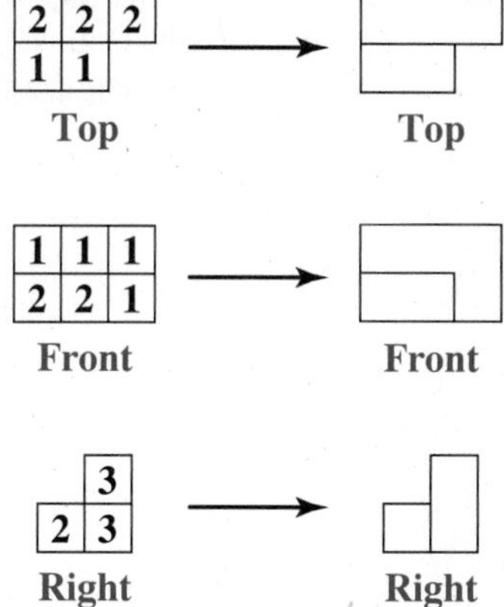

• *Teaching notes continued on page A383.*

Investigation 3 Creating Engineering Views

In Problem Set D, you learned to interpret engineering views and to show the structures they represent with top-count views. Now you will draw engineering views yourself.

MATERIALS
- cubes
- graph paper or dot paper

1\.

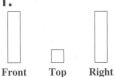

Front Top Right

2–6. See Additional Answers.

Problem Set E

Work with a partner to draw the three engineering views for each structure shown. It will probably help if you build the structures.

1\. 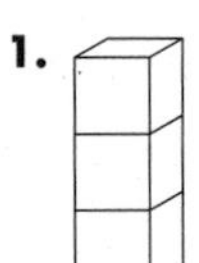

2\. 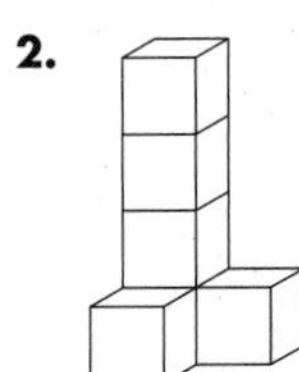

3\. 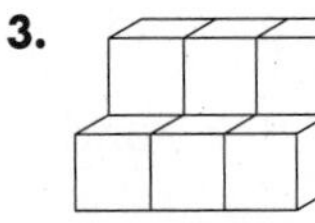

4\. 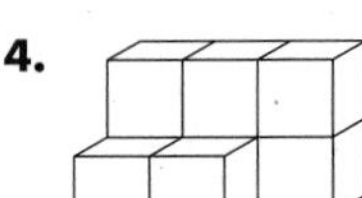

5\. 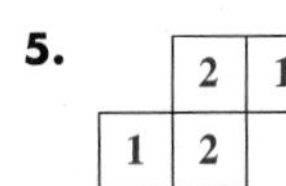

6\. 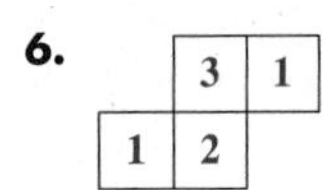

7\. Working on your own, use 10 to 15 blocks to build a block structure.

a. Draw a top-count view for your structure. Drawings will vary.

b. On another sheet of paper, draw front, top, and right engineering views. Then take your structure apart. Drawings will vary.

c. Exchange engineering views with a partner, and build a structure that matches your partner's drawings. Did you build the structure your partner had in mind? (Use the top-count view to check.)

7c. Answers will vary. Note: Confusion should arise only if a structure has a hole (a column with no blocks).

1 Have students work in pairs on Problems 1–6.

2 If necessary, provide Sample Strategies.

Share & Summarize

1\. Use 6 to 10 blocks to build a new structure. Then draw each of the following: Drawings will vary.

- the top-count view
- the regular front, top, and right views
- the engineering front, top, and right views

2\. Which do you find easier to work with: regular front, top, and right views; engineering views; or top-count views? Why? Answers will vary.

3 Be sure students are comfortable with top-count views.

Additional Answers Problem Set E

2\.

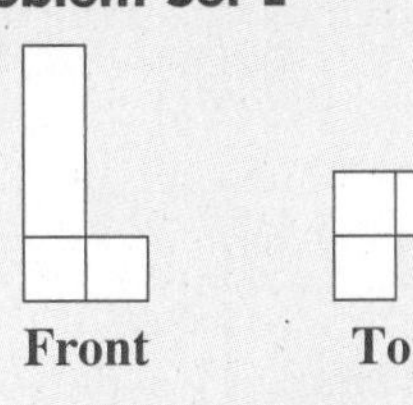

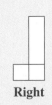

Front Top Right

3\.

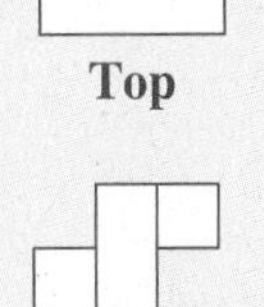

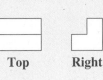

Front Top Right

4\.

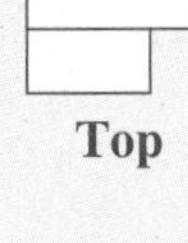

Front Top Right

5\.

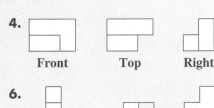

Front Top Right

6\.

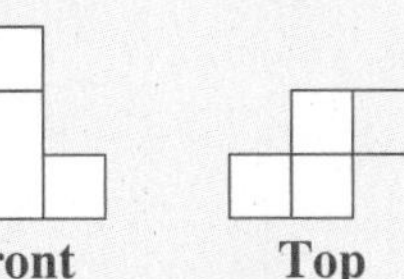

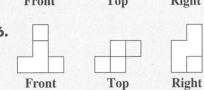

Front Top Right

LESSON 2.2 Visualizing and Measuring Block Structures 97

Investigation 4

This investigation makes the connection between block structures and the major topics in the next lesson: surface area and volume.

1 Ask students to look at the picture of the irregular shape on page 98. Ask them how many dimensions it has. How would they describe the area? Notice that we are not asking students to measure with any standard units, although centimeter units are described in the text. Counting the squares and using those squares as the unit of area is appropriate in this situation. Likewise, when they are determining volume, they can simply count the number of cubes in the three-dimensional structure.

2 Students solved area problems at the end of Lesson 1. Surface area is exactly what its name implies: the surface area of a three-dimensional object's surfaces.

3 Discuss volume by asking students to build any block structure. Ask students how they would describe the volume of this structure. Point out to students that they could think of the number of blocks as the volume. Explain that volume is measured in cubic units, and for all the structures they have built, students could simply count the blocks. Later, students will be given measurements in standard units and asked for areas and volumes. You may need to return to the blocks to talk about the difference between square units and cubic units, and relate that to specific units of measure such as cm^2 and cm^3. You may point out that the exponent 2 in cm^2 relates to area which measures a 2-dimensional surface. The exponent 3 in cm^3 refers to volume, a 3-dimensional measure.

Think & Discuss

Allow students time to read and solve the problems before discussing them as a class. Be sure students understand how surface area and volume were determined and that they use the appropriate units of measurement for each.

Investigation  Measuring Block Structures

Area, which is the space inside a two-dimensional figure, is measured in *square units.* To find the area of an irregular figure like the one shown here, you can count squares (shown with dashed lines).

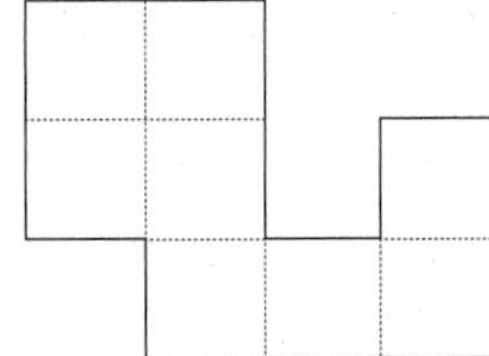

You can say that the area of this figure is 8 square units. Or, if you know the size of the squares, you can use it to state the area exactly. For example, these squares have a side length of 1 centimeter, so the area of the figure is 8 square centimeters. This can be written 8 cm^2.

VOCABULARY
surface area

The **surface area** of a three-dimensional object is the space covering the object's surface. If you could open up the object and flatten it so you could see all sides at once, the area of the flat figure would be the surface area. (Don't forget to count the bottom surface!) Surface area is also measured in square units.

VOCABULARY
volume

Volume, the space inside a three-dimensional object, is measured in *cubic units.* If the blocks you build with are each 1 cubic unit, then the volume of a block structure is equal to the number of blocks in the structure. For example, a structure made from eight blocks has a volume of 8 cubic units. If the blocks have an edge length of 1 cm, the structure's volume is 8 cm^3.

In the problems that follow, the blocks each have an edge length of 1 unit, faces of area 1 square unit, and a volume of 1 cubic unit.

Think & Discuss

What is the surface area of a single block in square units? 6 square units

If the edge lengths of a block are 2 cm, what is the block's surface area? 24 cm^2

What is the volume of the structure at right in cubic units? 2 cubic units

What is the surface area of the structure above in square units? (Remember: Count only the squares on the *outside* of the structure.) 10 square units

Remember
The volume of a one-block structure is 1 cubic unit.

1 • Have students tell how many dimensions this figure has.
• Have students describe the area of figure.

2 Discuss the meaning of surface area.

3 Discuss the meaning of volume.

Problem Set F **Suggested Grouping: Individuals**
In this problem set, students are asked to calculate the surface area and the volume of each of several 3- and 4-block structures. They are not using formulas for volume and surface area here. Students are asked to think of volume in cubic units and of surface area in square units and to find the volume and surface area by counting cubes and squares. This experience will ground students in the work they do in subsequent chapters in volume and area.

Students should quickly realize that the volume of any 4-block structure is the same regardless of how the cubes are arranged. The surface area, however, differs, and it is important that students think about the relationship here between surface area and volume. The 3-block structures all have the same surface area, but that will be true only for structures of 3 blocks or fewer. Once you have more ways to arrange the blocks, you have the option to cover more than one face (for at least one of the blocks), and you have the possibility of different surface areas.

On the Spot Assessment

If students are miscalculating the surface areas, they may be forgetting the "bottom" of the structure, the part sitting on the table. Remind students that the bottom is one of the surfaces and thus part of the surface area as well. If you have snap cubes available, you might encourage students to build with those. When students can pick up the structure from the table, it is easier for them to remember to count the squares on the bottom face.

Problem Set Wrap-Up It may come as a surprise to students that two structures can have the same volume but different surface areas. You can relate this to the fact that two two-dimensional objects may have the same area but different perimeters. For example, here are a rectangle and a square. Both have an area of 9 square units. The square has a perimeter of $4 \times 3 = 12$ units, but the rectangle has a perimeter of $(2 \times 9) + (2 \times 1) = 20$ units.

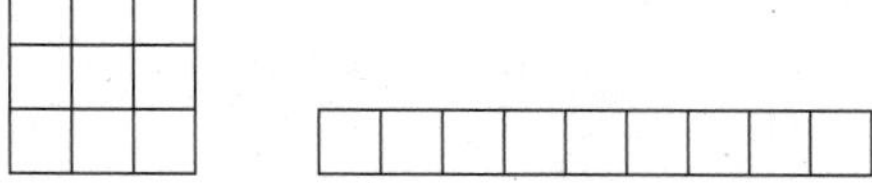

Share & Summarize

Students are asked to use the information they gathered in Problem Set D to create a structure with less surface area. With a little experimentation, students will notice that taking two or more cubes from the row and placing them on top of the others will create a structure of less surface area.

Troubleshooting Lesson 2.3 delves more deeply into surface area and volume relationships. It is not important now that students can create the structure with the least or the most surface area for a given volume. However, it is essential that students are able to find volume by counting blocks before moving on. They should also be able to find surface area by counting squares. If they seem to get the two ideas confused, you can use some of the examples below to clarify the difference. Ask students to add their own ideas to this list:

Volume	Surface area
The amount of soup in a can	The amount of aluminum used to make the can
The amount of cotton you need to stuff a teddy bear	The amount of material used to sew the outside of the teddy bear
The amount of sand used to fill a box	The amount of cardboard used to make the box

On Your Own Exercises

Practice & Apply: 8–16
Connect & Extend: 29–32
Mixed Review: 33–56

MATERIALS

- cubes
- graph paper or dot paper

Problem Set F

1 Have students work individually.

1. Find the volume and the surface area of each three-block structure.

a. 3 cubic units, 14 square units

b. 3 cubic units, 14 square units

2. Find the volume and the surface area of each four-block structure.

a. 4 cubic units, 18 square units

b. 4 cubic units, 16 square units

c. 4 cubic units, 18 square units

d. 4 cubic units, 18 square units

e. 4 cubic units, 18 square units

f. 4 cubic units, 18 square units

3. Do the structures in Problem 2 all have the same volume? Explain your answer.

4. Which of the structures in Problem 2 have the greatest surface area? Which has the least surface area?

5. Build two block structures with at least six blocks each that have the same volume but different surface areas.

a. For each structure, draw a top-count view. Drawings will vary.

b. Record the volume and the surface area of each structure. Answers will vary.

3. Yes; they are all made of four blocks, so they all have volume 4 cubic units.

4. Structures a, c, d, e, and f have the greatest surface area; Structure b has the least.

Share & Summarize

Make a block structure with the same volume as this structure, but less surface area. How did you decide how to rearrange the blocks?

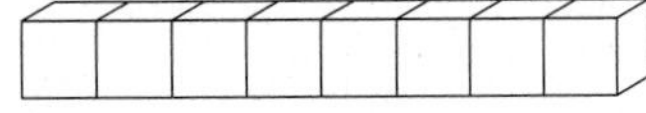

2 Be sure students can find volume by counting cubes and area by counting squares.

Possible answer: When more faces of a block touch faces of other blocks, the surface area is reduced. I rearranged them so that more faces would touch:

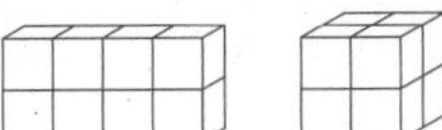

LESSON 2.2 Visualizing and Measuring Block Structures 99

On Your Own Exercises

On Your Own Exercises

Investigation 1
Practice & Apply: 1–3
Connect & Extend: 17–19

Investigation 2
Practice & Apply: 4–5
Connect & Extend: 20–25

Investigation 3
Practice & Apply: 6–7
Connect & Extend: 26–28

Investigation 4
Practice & Apply: 8–16
Connect & Extend: 29–32

Assign Anytime
Mixed Review: 33–56

Exercises 1–7:
Visualizing is the major theme of this lesson. It may be challenging to make decisions about the views without building the structures. However, it is good practice for students to picture the structure. Since much of geometry and mathematics does not deal with real objects but only with what you imagine, students need to develop this skill.

Practice & Apply

1. Here is a block structure and four views. Some of the views match the structure, but at least one does not. The top-count view is given to help you know how the blocks are arranged. For each view, write *top, front, right,* or *not possible.*

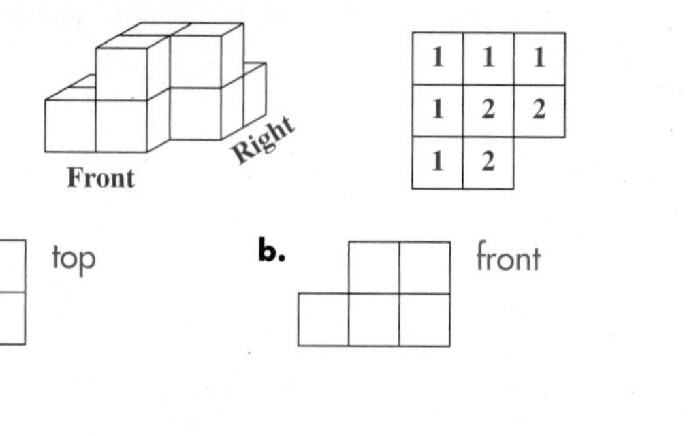

a. top

b. front

c. right

d. not possible

2. Here is a block structure and five views. Some of the views match the structure, but at least one does not. The top-count view is given to help you know how the blocks are arranged. For each view, write *top, front, right,* or *not possible.*

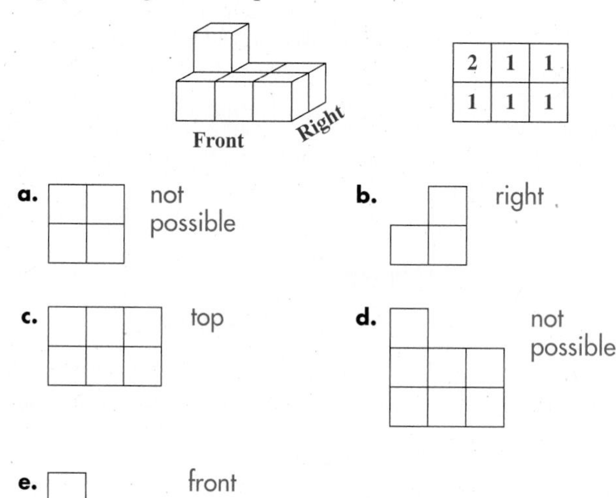

e. front

100 CHAPTER 2 Geometry in Three Dimensions

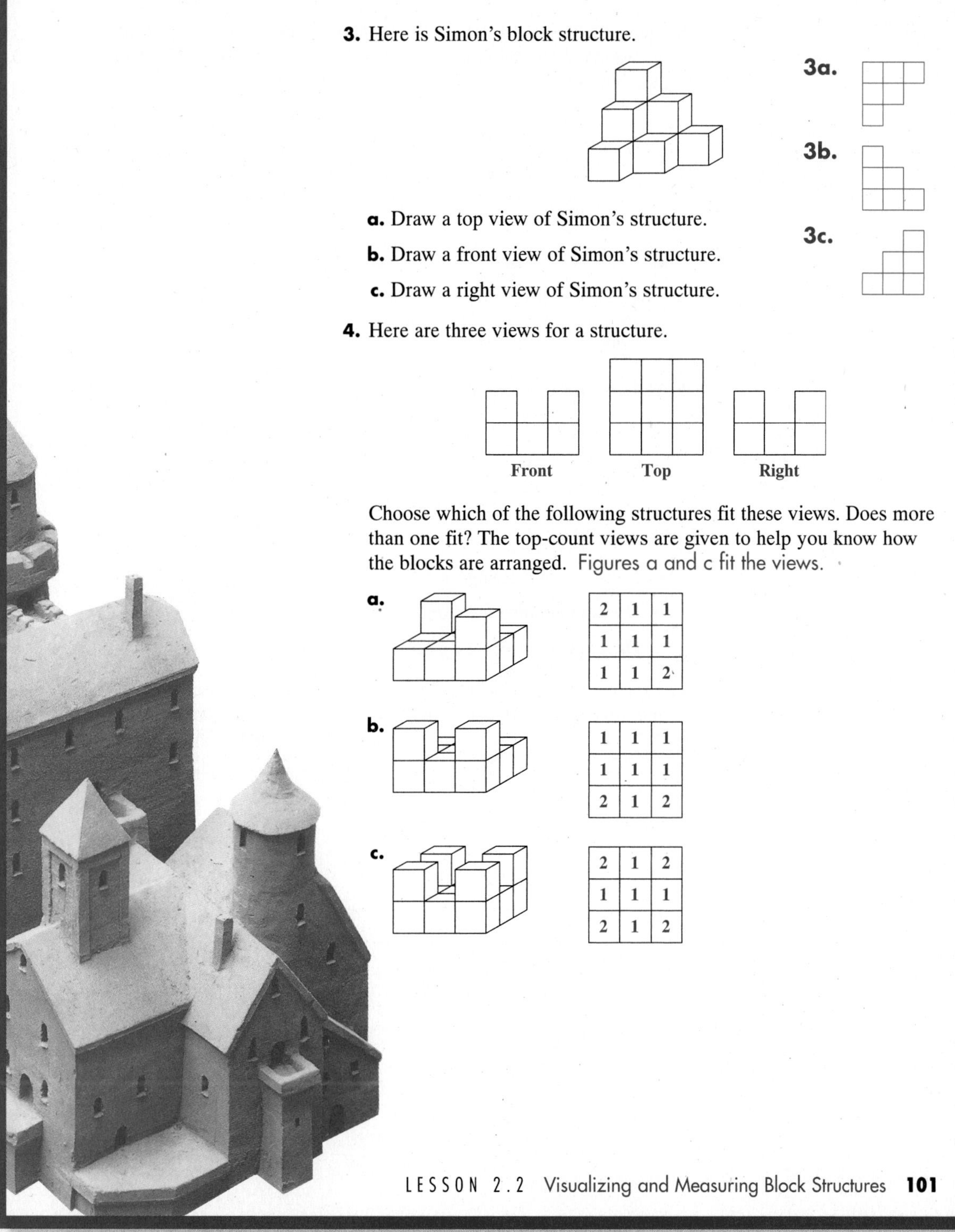

3. Here is Simon's block structure.

a. Draw a top view of Simon's structure.

b. Draw a front view of Simon's structure.

c. Draw a right view of Simon's structure.

3a.

3b.

3c.

4. Here are three views for a structure.

Choose which of the following structures fit these views. Does more than one fit? The top-count views are given to help you know how the blocks are arranged. Figures a and c fit the views.

a.

2	1	1
1	1	1
1	1	2

b.

1	1	1
1	1	1
2	1	2

c.

2	1	2
1	1	1
2	1	2

Exercise 4:
Both a and c fit the views given. In fact, several other structures work as well. On the second level, you can have blocks in the front-left and back-right corners as well, or you can have blocks in any three corners on the second level.

LESSON 2.2 Visualizing and Measuring Block Structures **101**

Exercise 5:
Using the dashed lines, the front view (b) would be like this:

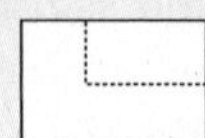

The dashed lines are correct, but not necessary. This structure cannot be confused with another, even without them. If you have discussed the use of dashed lines with your class, you might want to show them the corrected drawing.

Exercise 7:
This exercise uses the same structures as Exercise 4, but in this case only one of them (c) fits the three views given.

6a.

6b.

6c.

5. Here is a block structure and four engineering views. Some of the views match the structure, but at least one does not. For each engineering view, write *top, front, right,* or *not possible.*

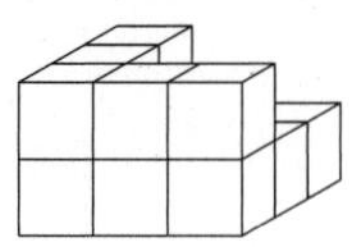

2	1	1
2	1	1
2	2	2

a. 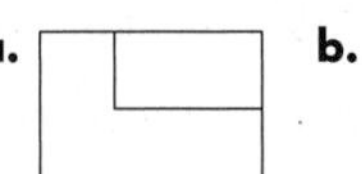 right

b. 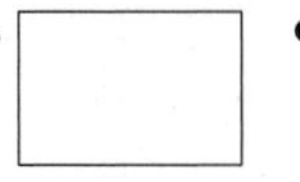 front

c. 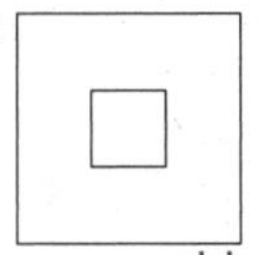 not possible

d. 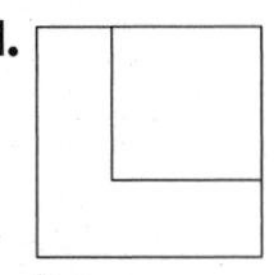 top

6. Here is Maya's block structure.

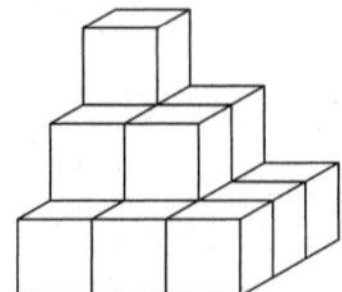

a. Draw an engineering top view of Maya's structure.

b. Draw an engineering front view of Maya's structure.

c. Draw an engineering right view of Maya's structure.

7. Here are three engineering views for a structure. Choose which of the three structures shown fit these views. Does more than one fit?

Only c fits all three views.

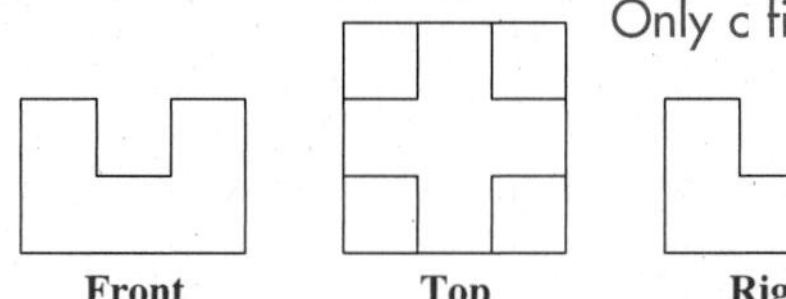

a. 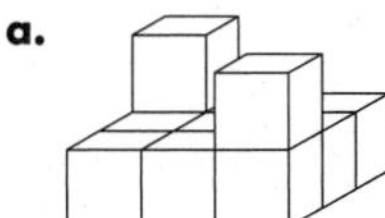

2	1	1
1	1	1
1	1	2

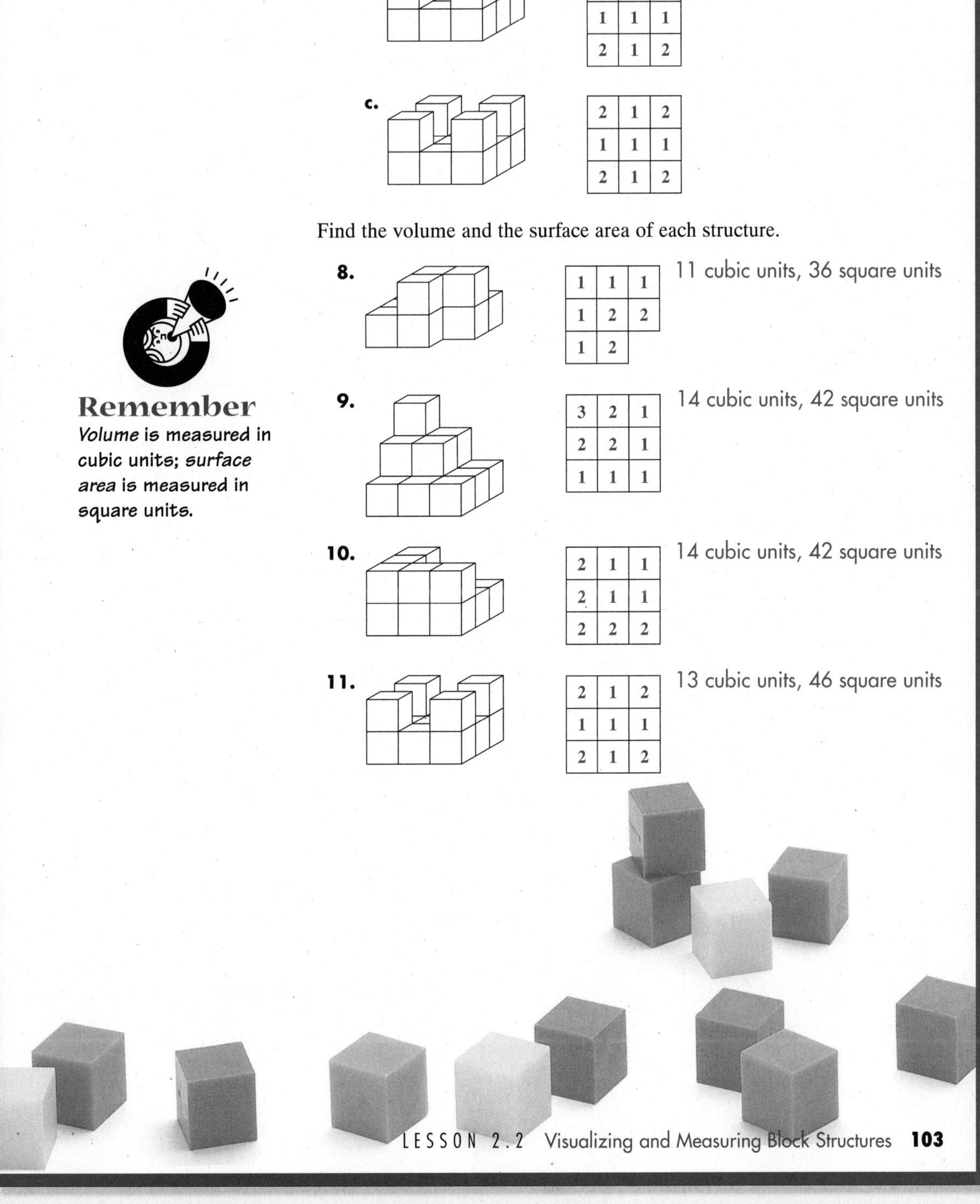

b.

1	1	1
1	1	1
2	1	2

c.

2	1	2
1	1	1
2	1	2

Find the volume and the surface area of each structure.

8.

1	1	1
1	2	2
1	2	

11 cubic units, 36 square units

Remember

Volume is measured in cubic units; *surface area* is measured in square units.

9.

3	2	1
2	2	1
1	1	1

14 cubic units, 42 square units

10.

2	1	1
2	1	1
2	2	2

14 cubic units, 42 square units

11.

2	1	2
1	1	1
2	1	2

13 cubic units, 46 square units

Exercises 8–15:
Finding volume from top-count views involves adding the numbers to find the total number of blocks used in all the stacks. Finding the surface area is more complicated; you must decide where faces are exposed by comparing the heights of stacks that are next to each other. Students may not get the right number but should be able to explain how they thought about which faces were exposed. The point is to help them develop visualization skills. Also, remind students to count the bottom of the structure in the surface area.

Below are top-count views for four block structures. Find the volume and the surface area of each structure.

12.

3	2	1
3	2	1

12 cubic units, 36 square units

13.

2	2	2
2	2	2

12 cubic units, 32 square units

14.

1	1	1	1	1	1
1	1	1	1	1	1

12 cubic units, 40 square units

15.

2	2	2
2	0	2
2	2	2

16 cubic units, 48 square units

16. Answers will vary.

16. Draw top-count views for three structures that each have a volume of 9 cubic units. Find the surface area of each structure.

Connect & Extend

17. Drawings will vary. The top view must be symmetric about a horizontal line through the center, as in this example:

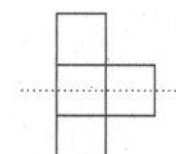

18. Answers will vary. The right view must be asymmetric about every vertical line through the figure, as in this example:

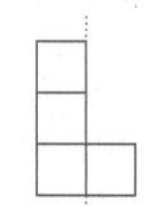

19. This is not possible; the front and back views must show the same number of squares.

17. If possible, draw a top view for a block structure so that the bottom view would be identical. If you have blocks available, you may want to build the structure.

18. If possible, draw a right view for a block structure so that the left view would *not* be identical. If you have blocks available, you may want to build the structure.

19. If possible, draw a front view of a block structure so that the back view would show a different number of squares.

Polyominoes are figures that are formed by joining squares with edges lined up exactly.

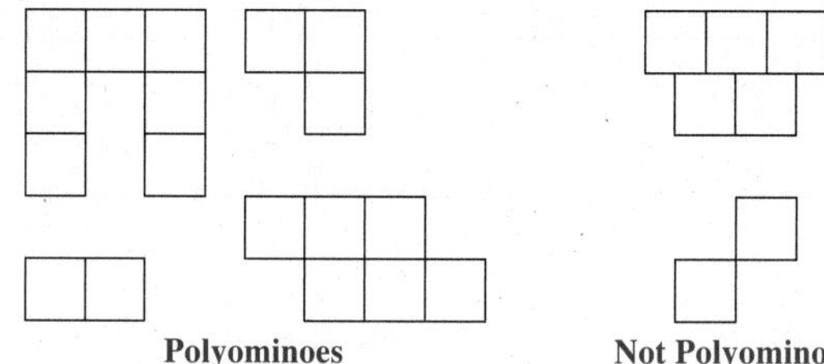

Two polyominoes are the same if you can cut them out of the paper and fit them exactly on top of each other.

104 CHAPTER 2 Geometry in Three Dimensions

20. Which of these are polyominoes? a and c

a.

b.

c.

d.

e.

21. Which of the polyominoes below are the same? a and e; b, f, and h; c and g

a.

b.

c.

d.

e.

f.

g.

h.

i.

Exercise 21:
Some students may not recognize that the figures in c and g are the same because they must flip one (out of the plane of the paper) to get the other. It is a good check whether students understand the definition of "the same."

Exercise 24:
Because you can only rotate the shapes on the screen and not flip them, students must use two of the "Z" and two of the "L" tetrominoes. This relates back to Exercise 21.

Exercise 25:
You may wish to provide students with enlarged copies of Master 9, Centimeter Graph Paper, to draw and cut out the hexominoes.

22. You have probably played the game of dominoes. In the game, dominoes are tiles that have two squares containing dots. In mathematics, *dominoes* are just polyominoes made of two squares. Considering the *mathematical* definition, how many different dominoes are there? Draw them. There is only one domino.

23. *Trominoes* are built with three squares. How many different trominoes are there? Draw them. There are two trominoes.

24. A popular computer game is played with tetrominoes (polyominoes with four squares). These pieces are used:

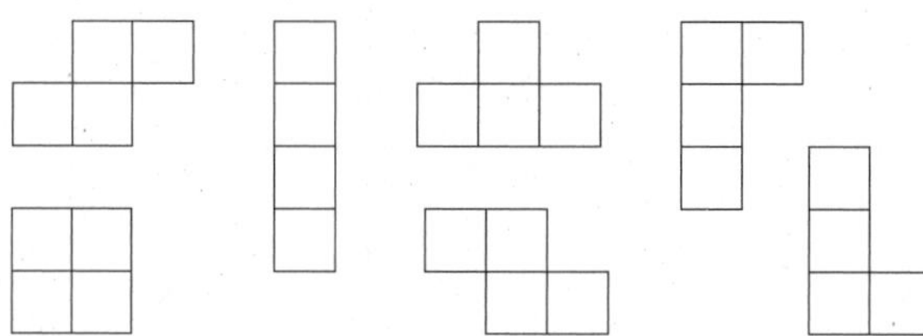

As the pieces fall from the top of the screen, you can move them left or right and rotate them clockwise and counterclockwise, trying to create solid rows (with no gaps) when the pieces land near the bottom of the screen.

a. Are all the pieces different tetrominoes, or are some of them the same?

b. Why must this game include more than one piece to represent the same tetromino?

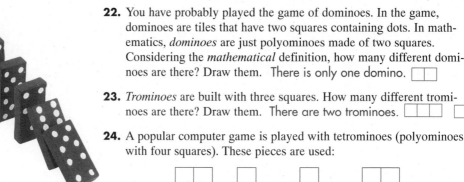

24a. Some are the same. There are two L-shapes and two Z-shapes.

24b. In the game, the pieces can only rotate, not flip, so to use all the possible variations, both versions of the L-shape and the Z-shape must be included.

25. Preview Hexominoes are built with six squares.

a. Draw at least six different hexominoes. See Additional Answers.

b. You can cut out some hexominoes along the outside and fold them along the lines on the inside to make a cube.

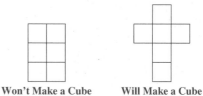

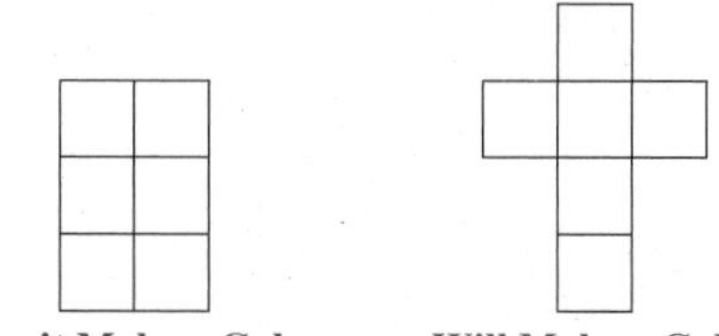

Group the hexominoes you found in Part a by whether or not they will make a cube. (You can draw them on graph paper and cut them out to test.) The hexominoes in the answer to Part a are the only ones that will fold into cubes.

In your own words

Why is it useful to be able to build structures from flat views? In what kinds of jobs would visualizing be an important skill?

Additional Answers

25a. Possible answer:

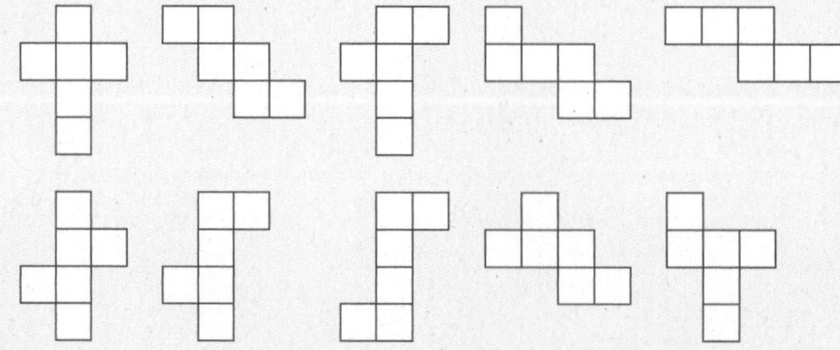

26. You can draw three engineering views for objects other than block structures. For example, here are front, top, and right views for a roll of tape.

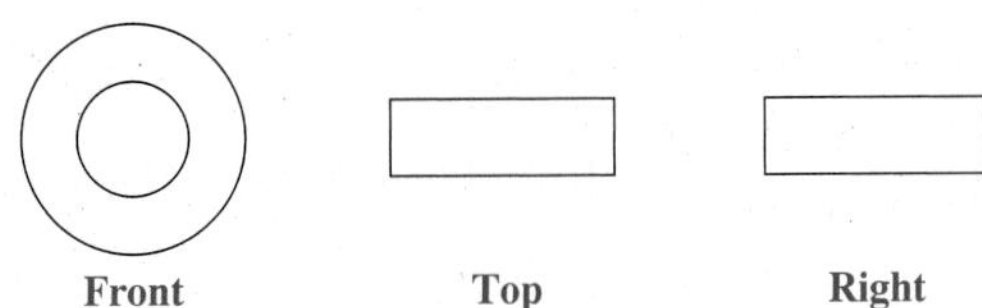

Draw front, top, and right engineering views for two other common objects. Name each object. Drawings will vary.

27. Draw front, top, and right views of a sphere. It might help to look at a ball.

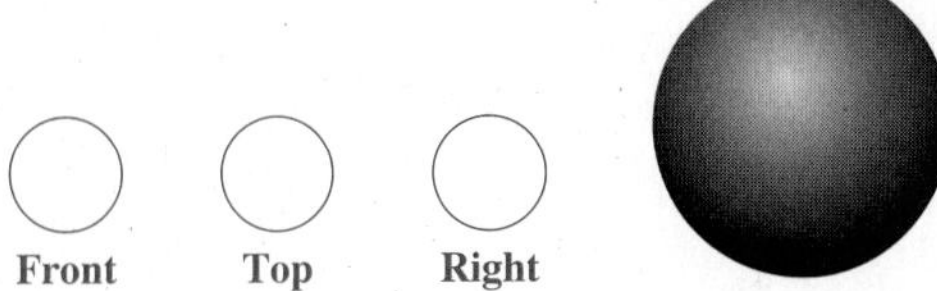

28. Some engineers draw mechanical devices, like gears. Draw front, top, and right engineering views for this simple gear.

Note: Students might choose a different view as the front view.

Preview Suppose you had a different kind of block to build with, a half cube. You could build structures like those below. Find the volume, in cubic units, of each structure.

29.  $\frac{1}{2}$

30.  1

31.  1

32. Estimate the volume of a room in your home in 1-inch blocks. Describe your method. Answers will vary.

Mixed Review

Find the indicated percentage.

33. 50% of 12 6 **34.** 12% of 50 6 **35.** 25% of 12 3

36. 12% of 25 3 **37.** 75% of 12 9 **38.** 12% of 75 9

39. Which of the following are factors of 36? 1, 2, 3, 4, 6, 9, 12, 36

1 2 3 4 5 6 7 8
9 10 11 12 13 14 24 36

Exercise 26:
Encourage students to select objects with simple geometric properties. A soft drink can is a reasonable choice but a rocking chair would be quite difficult to draw in this way.

Exercise 32:
You might want to follow up this exercise by doing the estimation for your classroom. How many blocks fit along the floor? How could we approximate it without taking the time to line them up? How many fit along the floor in the other direction? How many fit floor to ceiling? We can picture covering the floor with blocks. If we estimate 150 blocks in one direction and 120 in the other direction, then the floor would be covered (to a depth of one block high) by 18,000 blocks. To make that 100 blocks high (if that were our estimate), then the total would be $100 \times 18{,}000$ (18,000 in each of 100 levels), or 1,800,000 blocks.

Assign and Assess

Quick Check

Informal Assessment
At the end of the lesson, students should be able to:

- ✔ draw front, top, and side views of a block structure
- ✔ understand the difference between the three regular views and engineering views
- ✔ understand volume as the number of blocks that make up a structure

Quick Quiz

1. Here are front/top/right views that match several possible structures. Build and draw top-count views for three possible structures that match these views. *Answers will vary.*

Front

Top

Right

2. Here are engineering views for a structure. Draw a top-count view for this structure.

3	3	3
3	2	3
3	2	3

Front

Top

Right

The number pair "2, 10" is a *factor pair* of 20 because $2 \times 10 = 20$. For each number below, list all the factor pairs. (The factor pairs "2, 10" and "10, 2" are the same.)

40. 5 *1, 5*
41. 10 *1, 10; 2, 5*
42. 25 *1, 25; 5, 5*
43. 18 *1, 18; 2, 9; 3, 6*

Evaluate each expression.

44. $\frac{3}{7} - \frac{2}{7}$ $\frac{1}{7}$
45. $\frac{8}{7} - 1$ $\frac{1}{7}$
46. $\frac{3}{8} + \frac{4}{8} - \frac{1}{8}$ $\frac{3}{4}$
47. $\frac{1}{2} \times \frac{9}{3}$ $\frac{3}{2}$, or $1\frac{1}{2}$
48. $\frac{1}{8} \times \frac{3}{5}$ $\frac{3}{40}$
49. $\frac{4}{7} \times \frac{1}{4}$ $\frac{1}{7}$
50. $\frac{3}{5} \div \frac{1}{2}$ $\frac{6}{5}$, or $1\frac{1}{5}$
51. $\frac{1}{4} \div \frac{3}{4}$ $\frac{1}{3}$
52. $\frac{1}{8} \div \frac{3}{8}$ $\frac{1}{3}$

Sketch a graph to match each story.

53. Paul charted his height from when he was 3 until he turned 12.

54. The space shuttle was launched on Monday, orbited the planet for 10 days, and then returned to Earth.

55. Batai threw the ball into the air and watched as it rose, fell, and then hit the ground.

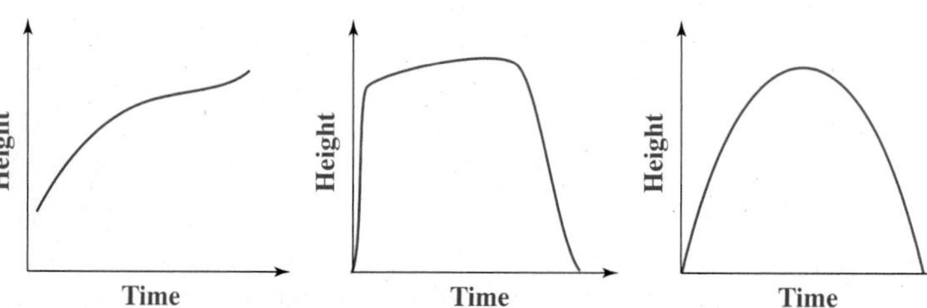

56. Write each of the numbers 1 through 35 in a diagram like the one below. If a number does not fit in any of the circles, write it outside the diagram.

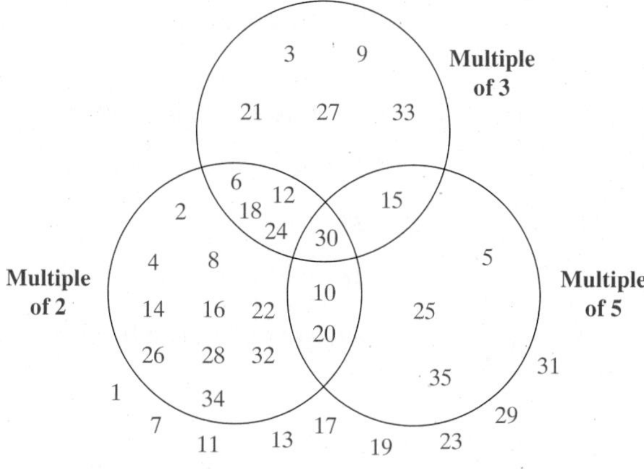

2.3 Surface Area and Volume

Objectives

- To find the volume of any prism or cylinder as *area of base times height*
- To understand that for a given volume, the cube is the rectangular prism with the minimum surface area
- To articulate some applications of surface area and volume, in particular, the relationship of surface area per unit volume and what it tells you about heat loss

Overview (pacing: about 4 class periods)

In this lesson, students explore surface area and volume relationships in geometric solids as well as some applications of these ideas to science. The notion of counting cubes to find volume is used as a way to create a formula for the volume of any prism: area of base times height, or perhaps better, area of one base times the distance between the bases. Students explore some ideas about minimizing surface area for a given volume and look at how volume and surface area affect dehydration in people.

We define cylinders simply as "like a prism, but with circles for the bases." Traditionally, prisms have polygons as their bases and parallelograms as the other sides. For our purposes, it is useful for students to think of cylinders as just like prisms, and it is important not to obscure the important ideas of the "layering" approach to volume with a vocabulary lesson in the difference between cylinder and prism.

Advance Preparation

You may wish to make several copies of Master 7, 2-Centimeter Dot Paper, for students to record their work in Investigation 1. Since students will need to work with blocks throughout the lesson, actually building and manipulating the structures, some students may need to use Master 8, Building Mat. Later, they will use the blocks as models of people. Have sets of 65 blocks for each group of 4 students ready each day of the lesson. Students will need construction paper to complete their work for the Lab Investigation.

Lesson Planner

	Summary	Materials	On Your Own Exercises	Assessment Opportunities
Investigation 1 page T110	In Problem Set A, students create rectangular prisms given a certain number of blocks. They determine structures with the minimal and maximal surface areas. In Problem Set B, students create a general formula for the volume of a rectangular prism: area of top view times height.	• Master 7 (Teaching Resources, page 12) • Master 8 (Teaching Resources, page 13) • 65 blocks for each group of 4 students	Practice & Apply 1–2 Connect & Extend: 10–11 Mixed Review: 18–32	Share & Summarize, pages T112, 112 Troubleshooting, page T112
Investigation 2 page T112	Students generalize the volume formula to include other prisms and cylinders.	• Decks of cards (optional), especially cards of different shapes • 65 blocks for each group of 4 students	Practice & Apply: 3–7 Connect & Extend: 12–15 Mixed Review: 18–32	Share & Summarize, pages T116, 116 Troubleshooting, page T116
Investigation 3 page T116	Students investigate the ratio of surface area to volume in babies and adults by using the results to explain why babies are at greater risk for dehydration.	• 65 blocks for each group of 4 students	Practice & Apply: 8–9 Connect & Extend: 16–17 Mixed Review: 18–32	Share & Summarize, pages T119, 119 On the Spot Assessment, page T118 Troubleshooting, page T119, Informal Assessment, page 128 Quick Quiz, page 128
Lab Investigation page T119	Students use their knowledge of surface area and volume to build a better soft drink can—one that will get attention.	• Construction paper		

Introduce

Begin the lesson by asking students what they know about prisms. Are there any prisms in the room? Have they used any prisms in science? If you have access to prisms from a school science lab, you may want to show them and explain that they refract light, splitting white light into all the colors of the rainbow. Because of that, the term "prism" is used more generically in science to mean anything, even a drop of water, that refracts light.

You may want to review some of the terms used to describe three-dimensional figures before discussing the Think & Discuss questions. Show students a rectangular prism and discuss the properties. Point out the relationship between the planes of the figure, noting pairs of parallel lines, perpendicular lines, and skew lines.

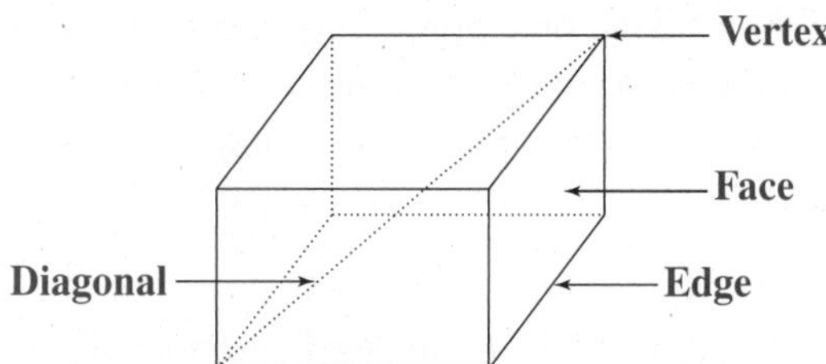

Think & Discuss

Direct students' attention to the figures at the top of page 109. As you discuss the two questions in the Think & Discuss section, compile a list of what the prisms have in common:

- two identical faces (same size and shape)
- the identical two faces are opposite and parallel
- the other faces are parallelograms

You can use this list to lead into the definition of a *prism.*

It is not necessary to focus on the bases being polygons; in fact, it will be helpful for students to think of cylinders as like prisms later in the lesson. If any part of the definition is missing (for example, if they don't say that two faces must be the same size and shape), point to a specific example in the pictures on page 109.

Students may divide the prisms into two types: those with parallelogram faces and those with rectangular faces. This is because many students do not see rectangles as a special kind of parallelogram, one with all right angles, but rather see them as two different kinds of shapes. If you notice this, you may want to take a moment to clarify the ideas. First ask students to define a parallelogram. A good definition would be something like "a quadrilateral with opposite sides parallel." Ask them whether a rectangle fits that definition. Is it a quadrilateral? Are opposite sides parallel? So, is every rectangle a parallelogram? Yes! Is every parallelogram a rectangle? No! These ideas are not essential for moving on in this lesson, but it is nice to clarify these issues when they come up.

To transition into the lesson, build two different 4-block structures in the front of the room—one that is four cubes high in a single stack and one that is two cubes high, with two layers of two cubes.

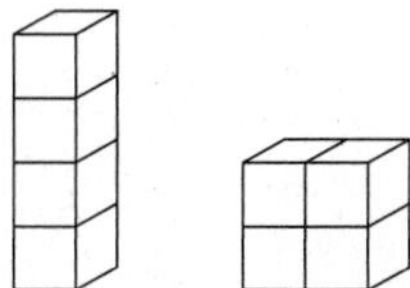

Explain to students that these are both prisms: they have the same number of blocks in every stack and a constant height measured perpendicular to the table. In other words, each structure has two identical, parallel faces in the shape of a polygon and the other faces are parallelograms.

Ask students, "What is true of the numbers in the top-count view of any prisms?" (They are all the same.)

Build another structure, using four cubes again, that is not a prism. Ask students which part of the definition is not satisfied. For example, if you use this structure

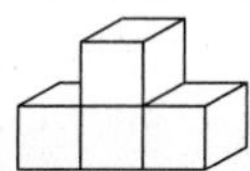

students should say that the middle stack is not the same height as the ends, so it is not a prism. Let students know that in this lesson, they will be finding easier ways to find the volumes of these prisms than by simply counting the cubes that form them.

2.3 Surface Area and Volume

These figures are *prisms.*

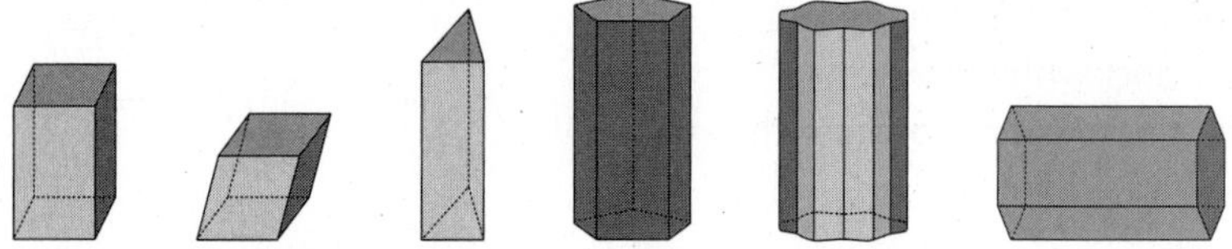

These figures are not prisms.

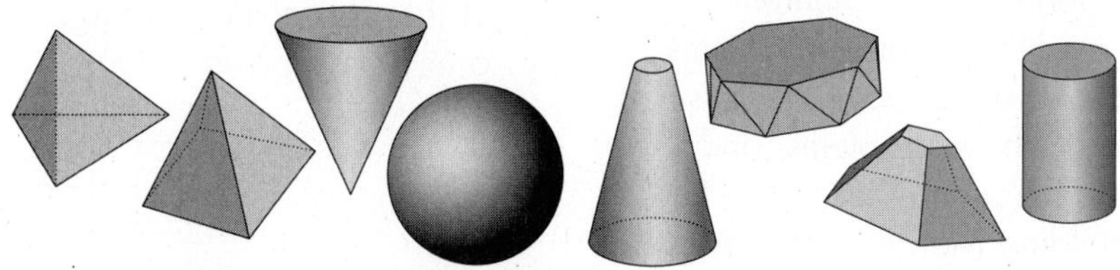

1 • Discuss and display prisms.

• Review terms used with three-dimensional figures.

Think & Discuss

What do all the prisms have in common? See ①.

How are the nonprisms different from the prisms? See ②.

① They all have two faces that are the same size and shape and parallel to each other; their other faces are parallelograms.

2 Compile a list of the common features.

VOCABULARY
prism

All **prisms** have two identical, parallel faces. These two faces are always polygons. A prism's other faces are always parallelograms.

3 Discuss parallelograms.

A prism is sometimes referred to by the shape of the two identical faces on its ends. For example, a *triangular prism* has triangular faces on its ends, and a *rectangular prism* has rectangular faces on its ends.

② All the prisms have faces, and all their faces have straight sides. Some of the nonprisms have circular faces, and the sphere doesn't have faces. Some of the nonprisms have a flat face on one end and come to a point on the opposite end; none of the prisms are like this. The sides of some of the nonprisms are triangles; all the sides of the prisms are parallelograms.

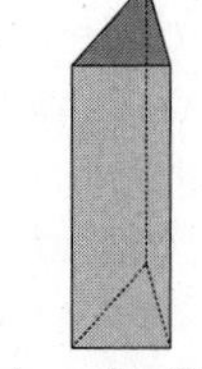

Triangular Prism

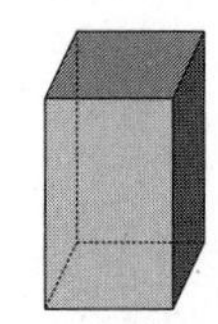

Rectangular Prism

LESSON 2.3 Surface Area and Volume **109**

Investigation 1

In this investigation, students are asked to construct different rectangular prisms given a certain number of cubes. Students then determine which of the structures have the greatest surface areas and which have the least. They also write algebraic expressions to show the volume of a prism.

Problem Set A **Suggested Grouping: Pairs**
In this problem set, students experiment with different numbers of blocks to determine which rectangular prisms have the greatest surface area and which have the least. Students should have blocks to do these problems, and they will need 20 blocks per pair. You may also wish to have students use Master 8, Building Mat, and Master 7, 2-Centimeter Dot Paper. These problems should take a relatively short amount of time to complete, since students will begin to see some patterns as they go through the problems.

Sample Strategy Students should notice that they can start with a string of blocks of the appropriate length, see that they can make a prism that is twice as wide and half as long, then three times as wide and one-third as long, and so on, until they start getting duplicates. This takes care of all the prisms that are one block high. For the 12 blocks in **Problem 2,** it looks like this:

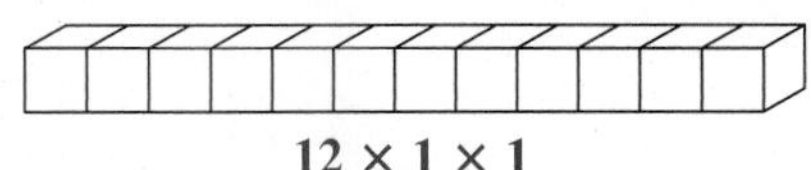

$12 \times 1 \times 1$

Break the original 12-block row in half:

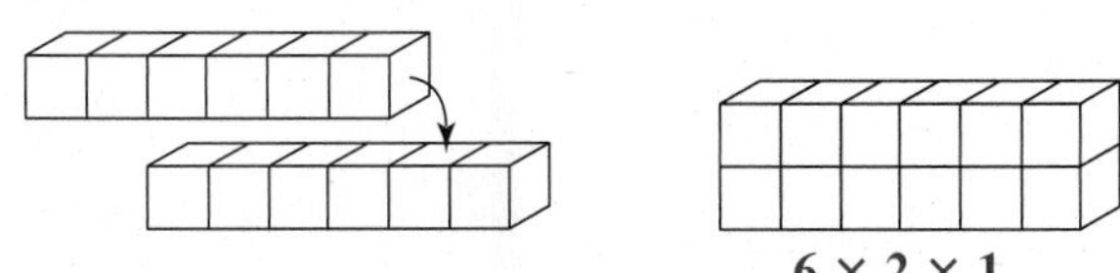

$6 \times 2 \times 1$

Break the original 12-block row into thirds:

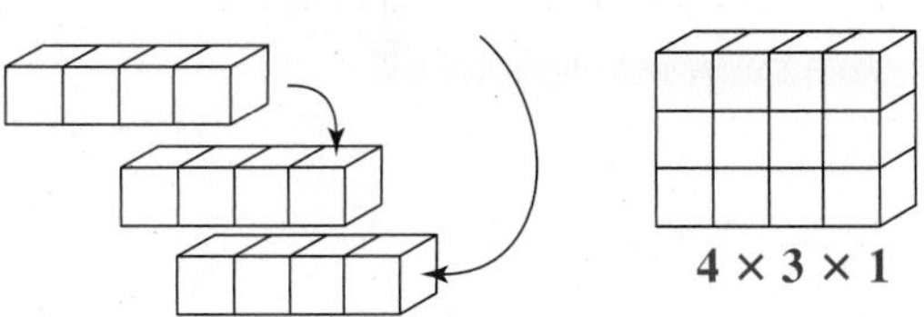

$4 \times 3 \times 1$

Break the original 12-block row into fourths:

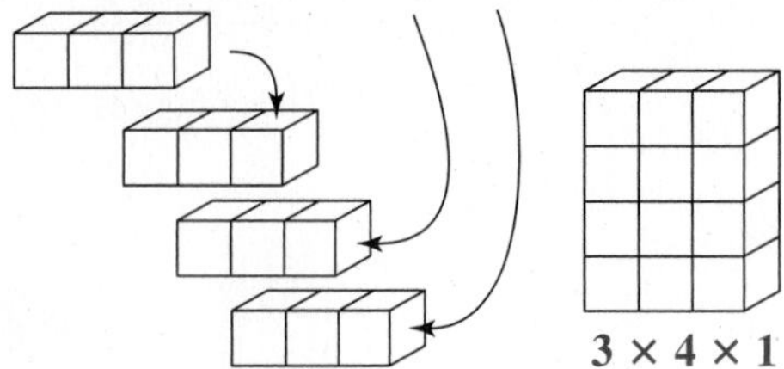

$3 \times 4 \times 1$

This is a duplicate, so we can start looking at prisms that are 2 blocks high. Have students use the results of each of the previous ones and break them in half. For the $6 \times 2 \times 1$ prism, it looks like this:

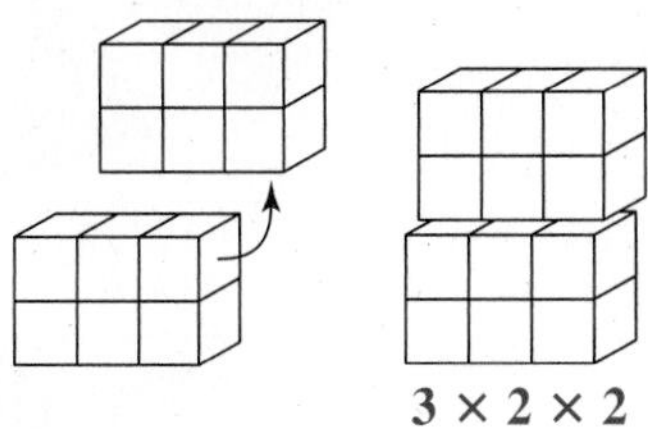

$3 \times 2 \times 2$

The others both give these same dimensions, and breaking into 3 or 4 blocks high will give duplicates as well, so we've found all the possible structures.

Starting from each of these, can students pull off half of the blocks to make one prism that is two blocks high? Three blocks high?

One interesting question that may come up is what we mean when we say two rectangular prisms are different. One useful definition is that two block prisms are the same if they have the same set of three measurements or dimensions. A $1 \times 2 \times 6$ prism is the same as a $6 \times 1 \times 2$ prism. You may want to mention the term *congruent* to describe this relationship of same size and shape. This idea will be revisited in Chapter 7 when students study similarity.

Another important mathematical idea is that if there is a finite number of possibilities, you can check them all to find the maximum and minimum surface area. Because we are working only with blocks, this is the case. If we were solving the more general problem of finding the rectangular prism with volume 12 cubic units and minimum surface area, we would find that there is an infinite number of possibilities. There is no reason the dimensions must be whole numbers, so we would need some other way to be sure.

Investigation 1 Finding Volumes of Block Structures

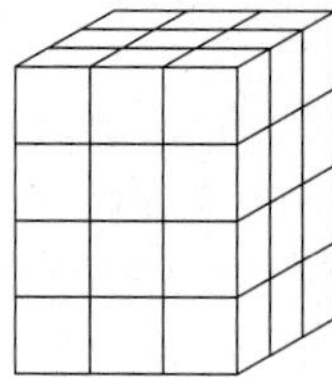

If a block structure has a constant height—that is, has the same number of blocks in every column—that structure is a prism. If the top view of such a structure is a rectangle, the structure is a rectangular prism.

MATERIALS
cubes

Problem Set A

1 Have students work in pairs.

By using its dimensions, you can describe a rectangular prism exactly. For example, a prism with edge lengths 3 units, 2 units, and 4 units is a $3 \times 2 \times 4$ prism.

1. Make all the rectangular prisms you can that contain 8 blocks.
   a. Record the dimensions, volume, and surface area of each prism you make. See below.
   b. Do the 8-block rectangular prisms all have the same volume? See below.
   c. Which of the 8-block rectangular prisms has the greatest surface area? Give its dimensions. $8 \times 1 \times 1$
   d. Which of the prisms has the least surface area? $2 \times 2 \times 2$
2. Make all the rectangular prisms you can that have a volume of 12 cubic units. See below.
   a. Record the dimensions and surface area of each prism you make.
   b. Which prism has the greatest surface area? $12 \times 1 \times 1$
   c. Which prism has the least surface area? $3 \times 2 \times 2$
3. Now find all the rectangular prisms that have a volume of 20 cubic units. Try to do it without using your blocks.
   a. Record the dimensions and surface area of each prism. See below.
   b. Which prism has the greatest surface area? $20 \times 1 \times 1$
   c. Which prism has the least surface area? $5 \times 2 \times 2$

2 After students complete Problems 1–3, discuss as a class the strategy they used to make sure they found *all* the rectangular prisms for each Problem.

1a. $8 \times 1 \times 1$: SA = 34, V = 8; $4 \times 2 \times 1$: SA = 28, V= 8; $2 \times 2 \times 2$: SA = 24, V = 8 (Note: Students may include duplicates, such as $2 \times 1 \times 4$.)

1b. yes, 8 cubic units

2a. $12 \times 1 \times 1$, SA = 50; $6 \times 2 \times 1$, SA = 40; $4 \times 3 \times 1$, SA = 38; $3 \times 2 \times 2$, SA = 32 (Note: Students may include duplicates.)

3a. $20 \times 1 \times 1$, SA = 82; $10 \times 2 \times 1$, SA = 64; $5 \times 4 \times 1$, SA = 58; $5 \times 2 \times 2$, SA = 48 (Note: Students may include duplicates.)

Problem Set B Suggested Grouping: Pairs
In this problem set, students begin with a top view and try to construct a prism from this picture. These problems motivate the concept of volume by having students think of layering cubes to produce a three-dimensional structure. As they create these structures, students begin to think of counting the number of layers and multiplying by the number of cubes in each layer—the foundation of the volume formulas.

It is important that students build these structures with cubes to reinforce this layering. Each pair will need 35 blocks.

In **Problem 3c,** as they begin to think about fractional parts of a unit height, students are introduced to the idea that the height is not necessarily an integer.

Problem Set B

MATERIALS
cubes

Remember
Your block has an edge length of 1 unit and a volume of 1 cubic unit. Each face has an area of 1 square unit.

1a. 6 cubic units
1b. 12 cubic units
2a. 6 cubic units
2b. 18 cubic units

3a. 7 cubic units
3b. 35 cubic units
3c. $\frac{7}{2}$ cubic units, or 3.5 cubic units

1 Have students work in pairs.

1. Here is a top view of a prism.

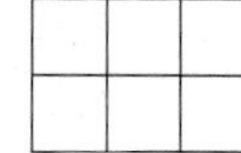

a. Build a prism 1 unit high with this top view. What is its volume?

b. Build a prism 2 units high with this top view. What is its volume?

c. What would be the volume of a prism 10 units high with this top view? 60 cubic units

d. Write an expression for the volume of a prism with this top view and height h. $6h$ cubic units

e. What is the area of this top view? 6 square units

2. Here is another top view.

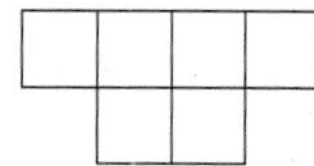

a. Build a prism 1 unit high with this top view. What is its volume?

b. Build a prism 3 units high with this top view. What is its volume?

c. Suppose you built a prism 25 units high with this top view. What would its volume be? 150 cubic units

d. Write an expression for the prism's volume, using h for height. $6h$ cubic units

e. What is the area of this top view? 6 square units

3. Here is a third top view.

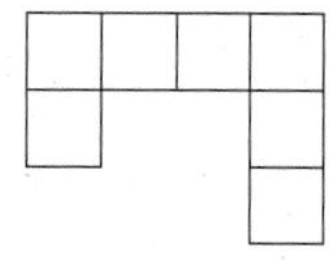

a. Build a prism 1 unit high with this top view. What is its volume?

b. Build a prism 5 units high with this top view. What is its volume?

c. Suppose you cut your blocks in half to build a structure half a unit high with this top view. What would its volume be?

Two Half Blocks

2 Ask students how to construct this structure.

d. Write an expression for the prism's volume, using h for height. $7h$ cubic units

e. What is the area of this top view? 7 square units

LESSON 2.3 Surface Area and Volume **111**

Share & Summarize

Question 1 addresses concepts from Problem Set A: The general conjecture that students should have now is that the block prism that minimizes surface area is the one most like a cube. Because we are working with only whole numbers of blocks, we cannot always make a cube. If we could, that would be the best.

For **Question 3,** students should have a general rule that is something like "area of top view times the height" or "number of squares in top view times the height."

Troubleshooting It is important that students understand this general rule before moving on to the next investigation. If students are struggling with articulating the rule, provide additional top views to work with. Ask the area of the top view, the volume for a one-cube structure, the volume for a two-cube structure, and so on. If the top view has an area of 4 squares, encourage students to write the volumes as 4×1, 4×2, and so on.

On Your Own Exercises

Practice & Apply: 1–2
Connect & Extend: 10–11
Mixed Review: 18–32

Investigation 2

In this investigation, students examine prisms that are not block structures and continue their exploration of volume. Students are introduced to prisms with triangles and parallelograms as bases, as well as to cylinders—prism-like figures. Students use the same fundamental principle of building up from the base with layers of blocks in the shapes of the bases.

Problem Set C Suggested Grouping: Pairs

In **Problem 1,** students are asked to think about a triangular base in terms of a square and should realize that the area of the base is half the area of the square. They are then asked to imagine having blocks the "right shape" that would fit this triangular base with height of one unit, the same height as the blocks they've been using.

1. To build a prism with the greatest surface area, place the blocks in a row—making a long, skinny prism. To build a prism with the least surface area, build the prism that is the most like a cube; its dimensions would be as close to one another as possible.

Share & Summarize

1. If someone gave you some blocks, how could you use all of them to build a rectangular prism with the greatest surface area? How could you use all of them to build a rectangular prism with the least surface area?

2. Suppose the top-count view of a prism contains 8 squares. What is the volume of a prism that is

   a. 1 unit high? 8 cubic units **b.** 10 units high? 80 cubic units

   c. $\frac{1}{2}$ unit high? 4 cubic units **d.** h units high? $8h$ cubic units

3. Write a general rule for finding the volume of a prism made from blocks. area of top view × height in blocks

1 Be sure students understand this rule before moving on to the next Investigation.

Investigation 2 Finding Other Volumes

Will your method for finding the volume of a prism work for prisms that are not block structures? The problems that follow will help you find out.

VOCABULARY
base

Remember that a prism has two identical, parallel faces that can be any type of polygon. These faces are called the **bases** of the prism.

Problem Set C

2 You might have students work in pairs.

1. This triangle is half of the face of one of your blocks.

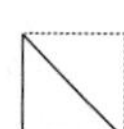

   a. What is the area of this triangle? $\frac{1}{2}$ square unit

   b. If you cut one of your blocks in half as shown here, you could build a structure 1 unit high with the triangle as its base. What would the volume of this structure be? $\frac{1}{2}$ cubic unit

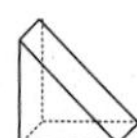

   c. If you built a structure 10 units high that had the triangle as its base, what would its volume be? 5 cubic units

Remember
Your block has an edge length of 1 unit and a volume of 1 cubic unit. Each face has an area of 1 square unit.

Develop

For the parallelogram in **Problem 2,** students should notice that the block base has the same area as the parallelogram, and thus the area is 1 square unit.

For **Problem 3,** students are given the area formula of a circle. The important realization is that the radius is 1 unit (the same as a side of the square), so the total area is π square units.

In **Problems 3 and 5,** students are asked to calculate with π. You might remind them that π represents a nonrepeating, infinite decimal. The pi key on the calculator gives a better approximation of the value than 3.14 does—but it is still an approximation.

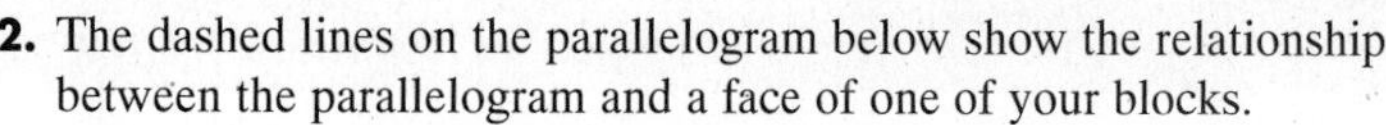

2. The dashed lines on the parallelogram below show the relationship between the parallelogram and a face of one of your blocks.

a. What is the area of the parallelogram? 1 square unit

b. If you had blocks like the one shown here, you could build a structure 2 units high that had the parallelogram as its base. What would its volume be? 2 cubic units

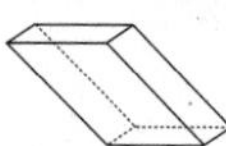

c. If you could build a structure h units high with this parallelogram as its base, what would its volume be? h cubic units

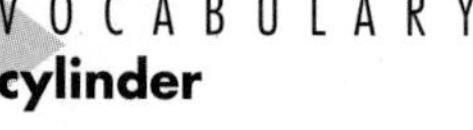

VOCABULARY
cylinder

A **cylinder** is like a prism, but its two bases are circles. These are all cylinders.

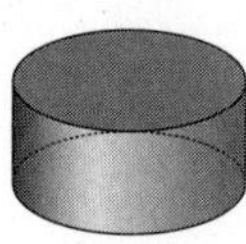

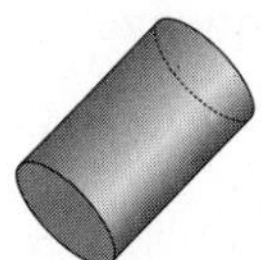

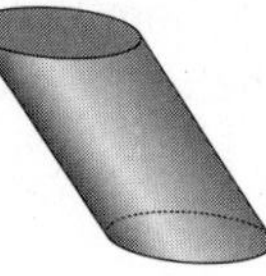

3. The dashed lines on the circle below show the relationship between the circle and a face of one of your blocks.

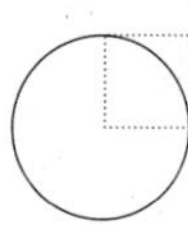

a. What is the area of the circle? π square units, or about 3.14 square units

b. If you had blocks like this one, you could build a structure 3 units high with the circle as its base. What would its volume be? 3π cubic units, or about 9.42 cubic units

c. If you could build a structure 1,000 units high with this base, what would its volume be? $1{,}000\pi$ cubic units, or about 3,142 cubic units

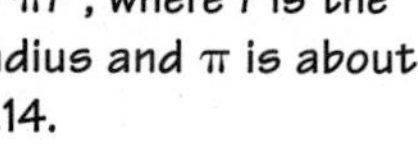

Remember
The area of a circle is πr^2, where r is the radius and π is about 3.14.

1

- Note that radius is 1 unit.
- Remind students that π is a non-repeating, infinite decimal.

LESSON 2.3 Surface Area and Volume 113

Develop

In **Problems 4 and 5,** students are given measurements for the base rather than a view of the number of units. The strategy for finding the volume should still be the same: find the area of the base and multiply by the height.

Problem Set Wrap-Up Before moving on to the next problem set, ask students to share their answers for Problems 4 and 5. Make sure that they report the volumes in cubic feet. You may need to again discuss the differences between units, square units, and cubic units.

Think & Discuss

Have students describe and test their strategies for finding the volume of a prism. Then have them explain why the same strategy will work to find the volume of a cylinder.

4. Luis drew a floor plan for a playroom.

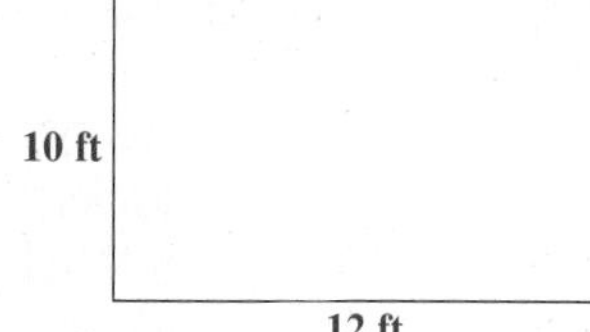

a. What is the area of the floor? 120 ft^2

b. If the playroom has 8-ft ceilings, what is its volume? 960 ft^3

c. If the playroom has 10-ft ceilings, what is its volume? 1,200 ft^3

5. Here is a design for a large oil tank.

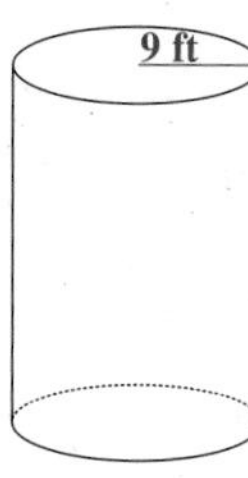

a. What is the area of the base of the tank? 81π ft^2, or about 254.5 ft^2

b. If the tank is 50 ft high, how much water will it hold (in cubic feet)? $4{,}050\pi$ ft^3, or about 12,717 ft^3

c. If the tank is h ft high, how much water will it hold? $81\pi h$ ft^3, or about $254.5h$ ft^3

Think & Discuss

Look back over your answers for Problem Set C.

- Describe a single strategy that you think will work for finding the volume of *any* prism. Test your strategy with the prisms in Problem Set C. Multiply the area of the base by the height.
- Will the same strategy work for the volume of any *cylinder*? If not, can you modify the strategy so that it *will* work? yes

1
- Have students share answers for Problems 4 and 5, using correct units of measure.
- If necessary, discuss differences between units, square units, and cubic units.

2 Have students explain why this strategy works.

Develop

Problem Set D **Suggested Grouping: Small Groups**

This problem set is designed to give students a visual, intuitive idea of why the volume formula they have discovered (area of base times height) will work even for an oblique prism.

2 First, have students look at the prisms in the upper left-hand corner of page 115. Then ask them to explain the difference between right and oblique prisms. There are different ways to state this: "In right prisms, the polygonal faces are lined up." Or, "In right prisms, the connecting faces are rectangles." Students might also notice that in a right rectangular prism, any pair of opposite faces may be used as the bases.

If you have decks of cards available, use them to demonstrate these ideas. Either give two decks to each group, or do **Problem 1** as a demonstration. Stack up one deck as a right prism. With the other deck, start with it stacked as a right prism and then push the cards so that they form an oblique prism. Ask students to answer Problems 1a–1d on their papers first, and then to share their answers with the group or the whole class. (Stacks of coasters would also work quite well.)

The notion that the two decks have the same volume because they contain the same cards (this is the "amount of stuff inside") is important for understanding volume relationships. The fact that the heights of the two decks are the same may be a little harder to see. Ask students to explain why they think the heights are the same or why they think the heights are different. If no one can express a good reason, ask some prompting questions like

> Do they have the same number of cards? *Yes.*
>
> In both decks, are the cards stacked right on top of each other, or are they arranged differently? *In both decks, they are stacked.*
>
> Are the cards thicker in one deck than the other? *No.*
>
> If you stack cards that have the same thickness but stack them a little off center, will the stack be taller than if the cards were lined up perfectly? *No.*

This type of thinking should lead students to see that the stacks are, in fact, the same height. Students can go on to **Problems 2 and 3** on their own or in small groups.

Problem Set Wrap-Up Ask several students to share their answers for Problem 3, including their explanations.

Problem Set D

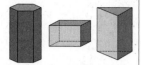

Right Prisms

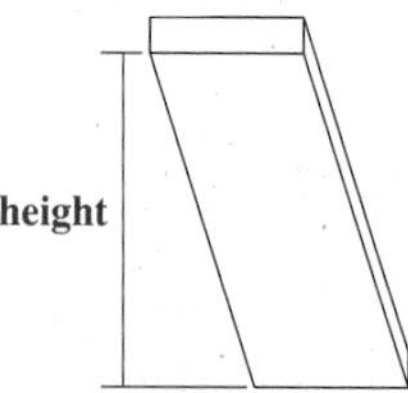
Oblique Prisms

1. See Additional Answers.

2a. 144π cm^3, or about 452.4 cm^3

2b. The same; they have the same number of cards and the cards are the same size.

2c. The same; for both decks, the base is a single card, and the cards are the same size.

2d. The same; the decks have the same number of cards and the cards are the same thickness.

3. See Additional Answers.

Some prisms, called *oblique prisms,* are slanted. However, you have only been finding the volumes of prisms with sides that are straight up and down, which are called *right prisms.*

1. This right prism has been sliced into very thin pieces, like a deck of cards. These "cards" have then been pushed into an oblique prism, but the cards themselves haven't changed.

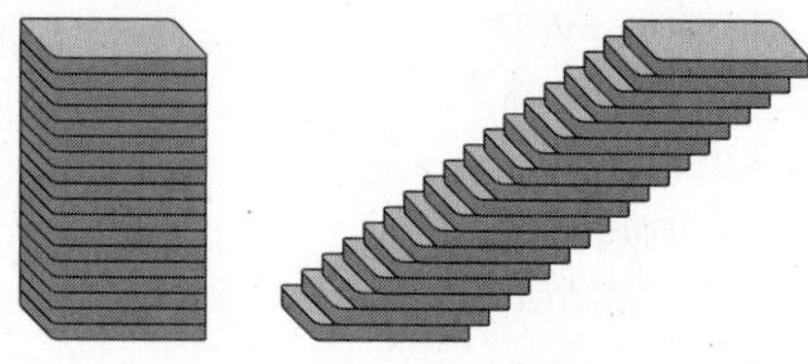

   a. If each card is 5 cm wide and 8 cm long, and the stack is 15 cm high, what is the volume of the first "deck"?

   b. Is the volume of the second deck *the same as, greater than,* or *less than* the volume of the first deck? Explain your answer.

   c. Is the base of the second deck *the same as, larger than,* or *smaller than* the base of the first deck? Explain.

   d. The diagram at left shows how to measure the height of an oblique prism. Is the height of the second deck *the same as, greater than,* or *less than* the height of the first deck? Explain.

2. Now think about a deck of circular cards.

   a. If the cards each have radius 4 cm, and the stack is 9 cm high, what is the volume of the first deck?

   b. Is the volume of the second deck *the same as, greater than,* or *less than* the volume of the first deck? Explain.

   c. Is the base of the second deck *the same as, larger than,* or *smaller than* the base of the first deck? Explain.

   d. Is the height of the second deck *the same as, greater than,* or *less than* the height of the first deck? Explain.

3. Will the formula *area of base* × *height* give you the volume of an oblique prism? Explain.

1 You might have students work in small groups.

2 Have students explain difference between right and oblique prisms.

3
- Have students answer Problem 1 individually and then share their answers before solving Problems 2 and 3.
- Be sure that students can explain why heights are the same or different.

4 Have students share their answers.

Additional Answers
Problem Set D

1a. 600 cm^3

1b. The same; they contain the same number of cards and the cards are the same size.

1c. The same; for both decks, the base is a single card, and the cards are the same size.

1d. The same; the decks have the same number of cards and the cards are the same thickness.

3. Yes; if a right prism has been pushed into an oblique prism and no parts have been added or removed from it, it will still occupy the same amount of space, that is, it will still have the same volume.

Share & Summarize

These two problems ask students to write the volume formulas for prisms based on the work they have been doing. The first asks students to generalize $V = Ah$; the second asks students to write formulas in terms of the dimensions for a rectangular solid and a cylinder. As a
1 follow-up, you may want to ask students to find the formula for the volume of a cube as a special case of the rectangular solid. You may want to put these formulas on a poster or in some other way make them a permanent, visible part of the room for later reference.

Troubleshooting If students have difficulty creating the formulas but have been successful in finding volumes with specific measurements given, lead students through an example like the one below.

2 **Additional Example** Here is a rectangular solid.

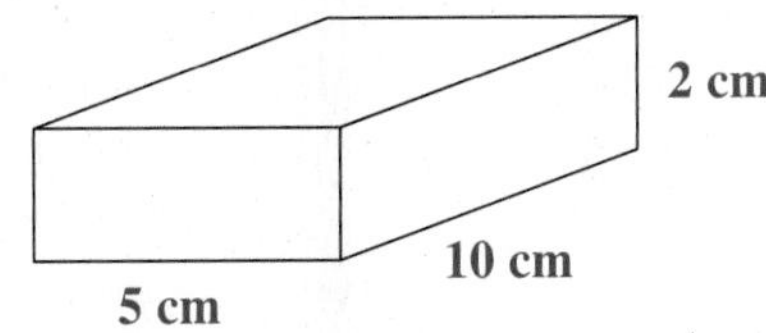

Tell students to consider the bottom surface as the base for the prism. Then ask students:

What is the area of the base? $50\ cm^2$

How did you find that area? multiplied the length and the width

Have students look back at the rectangular prism in the Share & Summarize and consider the bottom surface as the base. Then ask

What are the length and width of the base? What is the area? *l* is the length and *w* is the width; The area is *lw*.

Continue relating the dimensions in the two prisms.

In the prism with centimeter measures, what is the height? 2 cm

What is the height of the prism in the Share & Summarize? *h*

If volume is area of base times height, what is the volume of the 2-cm high prism? $100\ cm^3$

If volume is area of base times height, what is the volume of the prism in the Share & Summarize? *lwh*

You could construct a similar specific example for the cylinder, using perhaps a radius of 2 and a height of 3.

You could also ask a few students to show their formulas and explain how they found them. If the problem is one of translating words to symbols—that is, they can tell you what to multiply but have difficulty coming up with the formula in terms of *l*, *w*, and *h*—it is fine to move on. Students will have a lot more practice creating expressions and formulas later in the year. For now, they need to be able to compute volume.

On Your Own Exercises

Practice & Apply: 3–7
Connect & Extend: 12–15
Mixed Review: 18–32

Investigation 3

The major mathematical idea of this investigation is surface area per unit volume. If this is students' first exposure to ratios, it may take some time to understand that while babies have less *total* surface area, they have more surface area per unit volume. In this investigation, students will be using mathematics and science to understand why babies and adults react differently to extreme temperatures.

Many people, even adults who know mathematics fairly well, find this investigation goes against their intuitions. It is a fact that the danger to babies in locked cars, on beaches, and so on, is dehydration—not suffocation. When you dehydrate and lose all your water, you overheat. As long as you have water to sweat, your body is quite effective at cooling itself and maintaining a constant temperature. However, if you lose all that water, your temperature regulation breaks down, and you are in danger.

Begin the investigation by asking students whether they know a good reason why babies should not go in hot tubs or saunas and why it is unsafe to leave a baby in a car on a warm day. Most likely answers will be, "Babies are very sensitive" or "They might become ill." Explain that both of these situations relate to the surface area of a baby's body in relation to the volume.

• ***Teaching notes continued on page A384.***

Share & Summarize Answer

1. $V = Ah$; Volume is the amount of space in a 3D figure. Using the card prisms as an example, the amount of space is the area of a card (the base) times the height of the stack. For a real prism, use the area of the base times the height.

Share & Summarize

1. Write a formula for the volume of a prism based on the area of the base A and the height h. Explain why your formula works.
2. Write a formula for the volume of a rectangular prism, using l, w, and h. Write another formula for the volume of a cylinder, using r and h. $V = lwh$, $V = \pi r^2 h$

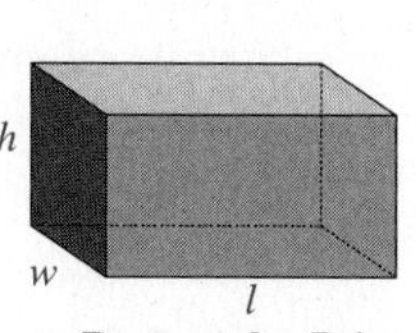

Rectangular Prism

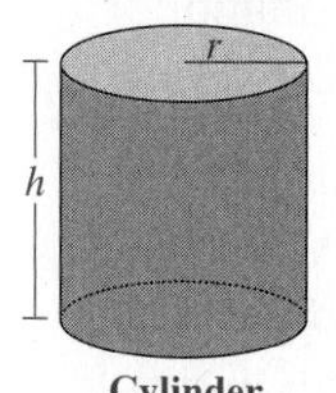

Cylinder

1 You may wish to put formulas on a poster.

2 If necessary, present Additional Example.

Investigation 3 Modeling with Block Structures

Many adults find hot tubs, saunas, steam rooms, and hot baths relaxing. In public places, though, these are off-limits to babies and young children, because children are affected much more quickly by heat than adults are. Why do you think this is true?

3 Discuss why babies should not go into hot tubs or saunas or be left in cars on a hot day.

Just the facts

Pigs don't sweat. After they roll around in mud, the mud dries and cools them. So "sweating like a pig" means not sweating at all!

Your body uses energy, in the form of calories taken from food you have eaten, to keep its temperature relatively constant. When your body grows too hot, you start to sweat. As the sweat evaporates, it carries heat away from your skin, and you feel cooler.

4
- Ask students why sweat cools a person.
- Discuss examples of keeping warm or cool as related to surface area.

Sweat is composed mostly of water and minerals. The more you sweat, the more your body cools—and the more water it loses. When your body is hot—because of the weather, because you are active, or because you are relaxing in a hot bath—you need to drink fluids to replace the water you are losing through sweat. Otherwise, you can become dehydrated and very sick. Because you sweat only through your skin, how fast you cool off—and how fast you lose water—depends on how much skin you have. That is, it depends on your surface area.

Think & Discuss

Have 8 cubes in the front of the room. Ask students to imagine building two "animals" from these 8 cubes. Can students suggest ways to build one that would cool off quickly and another that would cool off more slowly? Have students who think they can build one animal or the other come to the front of the room and build one.

Students should be able to think about this problem in relation to the other block structures they built as they were considering which had the greatest and the least surface areas. This problem gives a wonderful example of how these minimum and maximum conditions relate to a scientific phenomenon.

Sample Strategy Based on their work with rectangular prisms, some students may suggest the cube as the animal that would cool less quickly (less surface area) and the $8 \times 1 \times 1$ prism as the animal that would cool more quickly (more surface area). Some students may have noticed that the problem was not restricted to prisms (much less rectangular prisms) and create a shape like this which would cool very quickly, indeed!

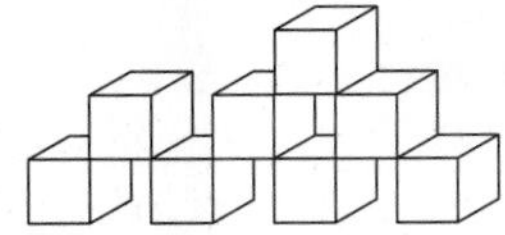

Problem Set E Suggested Grouping: Pairs

In this problem set, students are asked to use a single cube as a model for a baby. Students may find this model a bit peculiar. But try to convince students that in fact, this is a reasonable model for exploring the relationship between surface area and volume if we can find a reasonable way to model an adult with cubes. The important characteristics of the model are the relative relationships between a baby and an adult in terms of volume.

In **Problem 1,** students are asked to determine whether a $2 \times 2 \times 2$ cube, 8 times the size of the 1-cube model for the baby, is a good model for an adult. If a baby weighs 15 pounds, the adult would weigh $8 \times 15 = 120$ pounds. This is a small adult. Also adults are definitely not twice as big in every dimension as babies, and students will be asked in Problem Set F to build a better model of an adult.

In **Problems 2–4,** students are asked to compare the volume of the baby with the surface area of the baby and then to do the same for an adult. What students should discover in Problem 4 is that the ratio of surface area to volume for the baby is 6 to 1, and for an adult, 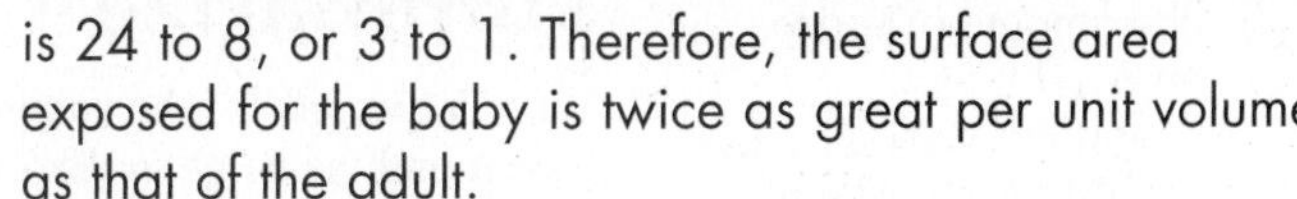is 24 to 8, or 3 to 1. Therefore, the surface area exposed for the baby is twice as great per unit volume as that of the adult.

Problem Set Wrap-Up Ask students to share their answers for Problem 4. The idea of converting $\frac{24}{8}$ to $\frac{3}{1}$ should not be new to students, but the context of getting a unit volume in the denominator is. Students may need some help thinking about equivalent fractions with 1 in the denominator. In particular, when students alter the model of the adult, the numerator may no longer be a whole number. The Example on page 118 following the problem set provides students with two ways of thinking about this: one way involves thinking of equivalent fractions; the other way involves a more visual approach, counting the exposed faces on each block. Ask students which way they like to think about surface area for each unit volume. You can also ask how to adapt each strategy if the blocks do not all have the same number of faces exposed.

For example, on a $3 \times 3 \times 3$ cube, there are 8 corner blocks with three faces exposed, 12 blocks between the corner blocks with 2 faces exposed, 6 blocks in the center of each face with one face exposed, and 1 block in the very middle with no faces exposed at all.

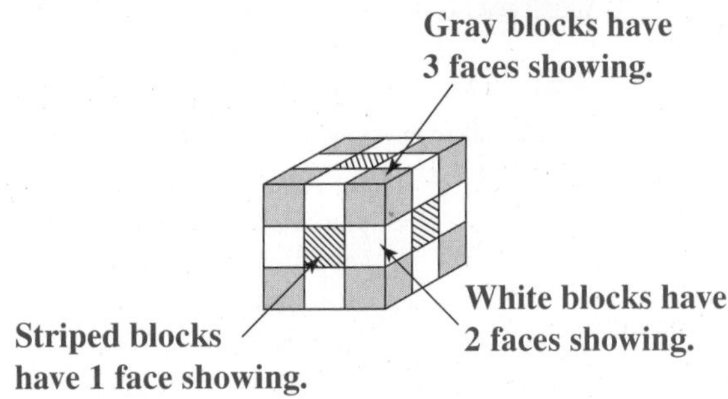

The best strategy is to count the total number of squares exposed (in this case 54) and divide by the total number of blocks (27) to find the squares per unit volume (2, in the case of the $3 \times 3 \times 3$ cube).

For the $2 \times 2 \times 2$ cube, there are literally 3 faces on each block exposed. For the $3 \times 3 \times 3$ cube, it's a kind of "average." Some blocks have more than two faces showing, some have fewer than two faces showing, but on the average they all have two faces showing. When students are comfortable with this idea, they can move on to the next problem set.

MATERIALS
cubes

Think & Discuss

Build models of two different 8-block "animals." Design them so that one would cool more quickly than the other.

Explain the reasoning you used to construct your animals. See below.

1 Have students demonstrate.

Building animals from blocks may sound silly. After all, blocks are nothing like animals. However, these models actually work quite well.

When mathematicians build a model, they ignore less-important details in order to simplify the situation they are modeling. Using blocks, you built two shapes that represented the *relative* sizes of the animals. You used the same number of blocks for each animal so that your animals had the same volume. Then you were able to compare just their surface areas.

MATERIALS
cubes

Problem Set E

2
- You may want to have students work in pairs.
- Convince students that cubes are reasonable models for the situation.

Mathematical models of a human baby and a human adult can help you make more comparisons between surface area and volume. For these problems, use a single block to model a baby and a $2 \times 2 \times 2$ cube to model an adult.

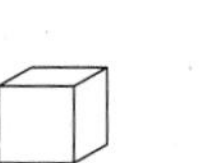
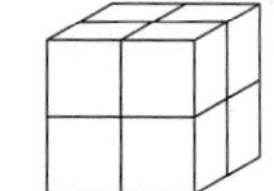

1. Given that the baby is represented by 1 block, consider whether the model for the adult is a good model.
   a. If the baby weighs 15 lb, how much does the adult weigh? Does that seem about right?
   b. Are adults really twice as large as babies in every dimension (length, width, and height)? no

1a. 8×15 lb, or 120 lb; It may be slightly less than the average adult, but it's not way off.

2. What is the volume of the model of a baby? What is its surface area? 1 cubic unit, 6 square units
3. What is the volume of the model of an adult? What is its surface area? 8 cubic units, 24 square units
4. For every 1 cubic unit of the adult's volume, how many square units of surface area are there? Is this more or less than the surface area of the baby's 1 cubic unit? 3 square units; It is less than for the baby.

Think & Discuss Answer

Possible answer: The animal with more surface area will cool more quickly, so I made one animal like a cube and the other like a snake. The snake will cool more quickly than the cube-shaped animal.

3
- Have students share answers.
- You may want to include the concepts in the Example on page 118 in your discussion on unit volume.

LESSON 2.3 Surface Area and Volume **117**

Develop

1 **Problem Set F** **Suggested Grouping: Pairs or Small Groups**

Students continue with the surface area/volume comparisons between babies and adults. First, they get some quick practice in finding surface area per unit volume. Then they improve their model of the adult and do the computations again. Students should find that, with a better model, the baby still has much more surface area per unit volume.

Sample Strategies Students may use one of these models for the adults in **Problems 2–5.**

2

- A better model for an adult would probably use about 10 cubes. Your students may not know how much an average adult weighs. You could provide that information or ask students what their assumptions are in building the model. Adults are much taller than babies, but adults are not more than twice as big around. So one "improved model" is this:

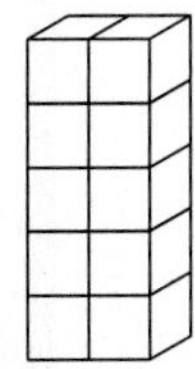

- Some students may get creative, trying to make the structures more "human-like," as in this top-view example:

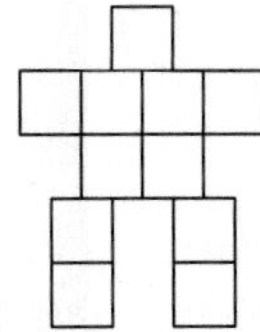

If the blocks are offset by some obvious amount like $\frac{1}{2}$ unit, this doesn't make it much harder to compute surface area, and it may go a long way toward making students feel like they have a more reasonable model.

EXAMPLE

Shaunda and Luis reasoned differently about Problem 4 in Problem Set E.

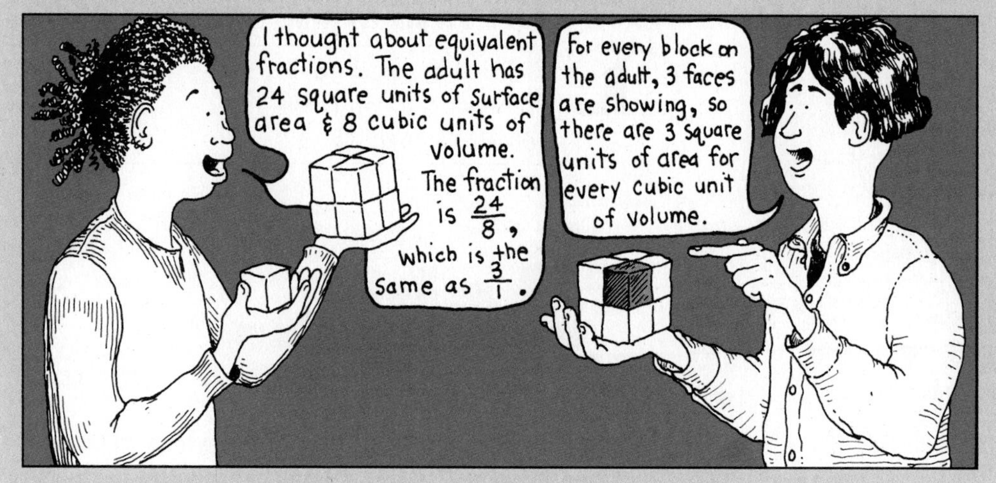

MATERIALS
cubes

Problem Set F

As you do these problems, consider both Shaunda's and Luis's reasoning.

1. For each structure, answer this question: For every 1 cubic unit of volume, how many square units of surface area are there?

a. 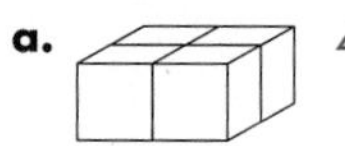 4 **b.** 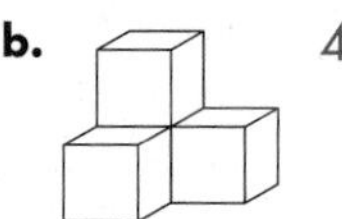 4.5 **c.** 3.5

2. Continue to use the single block as a model for a baby, but build a new block model for an adult that you think is better than a 2 × 2 × 2 cube. (It does not have to be a cube, a prism, or any other special shape, but it should be about the right size and shape compared to the model of a baby.) Draw a top-count view of your model.

3. Explain why you think your model of an adult is a better model than a 2 × 2 × 2 cube.

4. What is the volume of your adult? Possible answer: 10 cubic units

5. What is the surface area of your adult? Possible answer: 30 square units

2. Possible model:

3	3
2	2

3. Possible explanation: Heads and arms are smaller than body and legs, so the model is smaller on top. Also, adults are closer to 10 times as big, so the model uses 10 blocks.

1 You could have students work in pairs or small groups.

2 Discuss students' assumptions in building the model.

On the Spot Assessment

Watch for students who compare total surface area with volume instead of finding the equivalent fraction. You can relate this back to the ice-cream tub example described on page T116. It doesn't make sense to compare a single scoop with a big tub, but you can compare many single scoops with a big tub that has the same amount of ice cream. Similarly here, you are "scaling down" the adult to be the same size as the baby and seeing what surface area the adult would have.

Share & Summarize

These problems point out the relationship between surface area and volume for adults and babies, and ask students to justify mathematically the reason that babies dehydrate and get cold more quickly than adults. You might want to ask students if they remember any articles in the newspaper that relate to this question.

Troubleshooting If students are stuck on the idea that babies have less surface area and therefore should cool more slowly, students do not see the connection to surface area per unit volume. You might try some in-class experiments to model the situation. The problem may be that most of the examples have been things of the same volume and different surface areas (for example, the ice cream in a tub versus the same amount scooped into bowls), when what you really want is a comparison of different volumes and different surface areas.

Here is one possible experiment using plastic containers. Freeze a small chunk of ice, perhaps about the same size as the blocks you've been working with. Also freeze a larger chunk of ice, twice as big in every direction. These are in the same proportions as the first model of the baby and the adult. At the beginning of class, remove both ice chunks from the freezer and set them out. Clearly, the smaller chunk has less total surface area, but you should find that at the end of class, more of it has melted than of the larger chunk.

The ideas of surface area and volume relationships are not essential for moving on in the chapter, and students will see them again in Chapter 7. Also, students will revisit these early ideas of ratio and proportion in Chapter 8.

On Your Own Exercises

Practice & Apply: 8–9
Connect & Extend: 16–17
Mixed Review: 18–32

Lab Investigation

This investigation can be done anytime after Investigation 3. The creativity shown by students will increase if the scenario of "being slightly outrageous" for a convention is accepted by them, so extra energy expended in promoting the scenario is well spent.

Share & Summarize Answers

1. A baby has more surface area per unit volume, so it sweats its water away more quickly than an adult does.
2. A baby loses heat more quickly than an adult does because a greater percent of its skin per unit volume is exposed to the cold.

6. For every block in your adult model, how many square units of surface area are there? Possible answer: 3
7. For its size, does your adult have relatively more or less surface area than the baby has? Possible answer: It has less surface area per cubic unit than the baby but more total surface area.

Share & Summarize

1. It is not safe to leave a baby in a closed car on a hot day because it can quickly become dehydrated (lose water)—much more quickly than an adult would. Explain why this is true.
2. In chilly weather, babies get colder much more quickly than adults do, so they must be wrapped warmly. Explain why.

1 Encourage students to share news items.

2 If necessary, demonstrate with experiments.

Lab Investigation ▸ The Soft Drink Promotion

MATERIALS

materials for making models of soft drink containers

Bursting Bubbles soft drink company wants to attract attention to its products at an upcoming convention. The company normally packages its soft drinks in 350-milliliter cylindrical cans that are 15 centimeters high.

Bursting Bubbles wants to show creativity at the convention by packaging its soft drinks in new containers of different shapes. The company has commissioned you, a mathematician, to investigate some other sizes and shapes and to make a recommendation. Company representatives tell you that the new containers can be any height at all—but they must have a volume of 350 milliliters. It's now up to you to create some attention-getting containers.

The company gave the required volume in milliliters (mL). You probably already know that there are 1,000 mL in 1 liter (L). To do this problem, you also need to know that 1 milliliter has the same volume as 1 cubic centimeter.

LESSON 2.3 Surface Area and Volume 119

Develop

Make a Prediction

Based on earlier work, students should have a good sense for how things change in this situation. Without making exact calculations, they should be able to say that for a tall container, the base and hence the radius would get smaller if the volume remained the same. For a very short container, the radius of the base would have to get bigger if the container were to maintain the same volume.

Try It Out

The trial-and-error method, using a calculator for tracking down the volume, is used deliberately. Teachers report this method keeps the focus on the concept of volume and generates visual images of the shapes they are considering.

Make a Prediction

You decide to design some cylindrical containers first. As the height of the can changes, the base area must also change to keep the volume fixed at 350 milliliters.

1 Students should be able to make a fairly accurate prediction based on earlier work.

1. You could design a really tall container—even as tall as 1 m (100 cm)! To keep the volume 350 mL, would the radius of the base circle have to increase or decrease as the height of the can increased? decrease

2. Suppose you designed a very short can—even as short as 2 cm. To keep the volume 350 mL, would the radius of the base circle have to increase or decrease as the height decreased? increase

Try It Out

2 Students can use calculators to find the radius that gives a volume of 350 mL.

3. Bursting Bubble's standard cans are 15 cm high. What is the radius of the circular base of these cans? To find the radius, you can use a strategy of systematic trial and error. The table shows the volume for a base radius of 3 cm and of 2.5 cm. Use a calculator to find the radius that would give a volume of 350 mL. Keep searching until you get within 1 mL of 350 mL. Answers should be between 2.72 cm and 2.73 cm.

Base Radius (cm)	Base Area (cm^2) ($A = \pi \times r \times r$)	Volume (mL, want 350) (base area × height)
3	28.27	424.05 mL (too large)
2.5	19.635	294.525 mL (too small)

Remember
The number π, pronounced "pie" and spelled pi, is *about* 3.14. Your calculator probably has a π key to make these calculations easier.

4. Choose five heights from the table below and make your own table. Complete your table with radius values that give a volume within 1 mL of 350 mL. Possible table entries:

Height (cm)	Radius of Base Circle (cm)
1	10.56
2	7.46
3	6.09
5	4.72
10	3.34
20	2.36

Height (cm)	Radius of Base Circle (cm)
30	1.93
50	1.493
75	1.22
90	1.112
100	1.056
150	0.862

5. Were your predictions from Questions 1 and 2 correct? yes

Try It Again

In this section, students explore two other shapes for containers: spheres and cones. You might want to talk about the appeal of each. Which would be nice to drink out of? Which would grab more attention? How would the containers look on the shelves? Would the spheres keep rolling off? How would a company logo look on the container?

Access for all Learners

Extra for Experts Just as they did for cylinders, students can use trial and error to find different cones with a volume of 350 mL. Consider having students summarize their results by creating a graph of height versus radius.

Sample Strategy Some students may think to use the cylinders they found in Try It Out as a starting point for finding the size of cone-shaped containers in **Problem 6.** For each cylinder with volume 350 mL, students can make a cone with the same radius and the height three times as big, canceling the factor of $\frac{1}{3}$ in the volume equation.

On the Spot Assessment

Watch out for students who use the above strategy to solve **Problem 6** and try to make the radius three times as big as well. Since the value of the radius is squared in the equation for volume, this would give them a container bigger than the starting cylinder—nine times bigger, in fact!

When students begin working on the sphere in **Problem 7,** they should use trial and error to find the radius that works. The problem is stated in such a way ("find as many spheres as you can") that students will have to figure out for themselves that only one sphere has the appropriate volume. Since the volume depends on only the radius, a sphere with a longer radius will have more volume; a sphere with a shorter radius will have less volume. Unlike the cylinder and cone, there is no second dimension (height) to alter, compensating for a change in the radius.

What Did You Learn?

This section could be done for homework with students presenting their models the next day. Encourage creativity in the designs, and ask students to prove that their models have a volume of 350 mL. If you have access to a science lab and if the models can hold water or popcorn, you could actually test out the capacity of some models.

Tips from Teachers

Our students liked making extreme models. One group decided to use drinking straws as the shape of their cylinder. They measured the diameter of the straws, halved this to get the radius and then calculated how many straws they would need to put end to end to equal 350 mL. One straw type had a 0.25 cm radius and was 20 cm long, which meant a volume of about 4 mL per straw, hence we needed about $\frac{350}{4} = 87$ straws taped end to end to hold the 350 mL; they even tried to prove it by pouring in the contents of a can! This caused much mirth about the silliness of such a container, leading into why current designs are as they are for efficiency and ease of handling. An interesting point for me as the teacher is that we reached the desired endpoint from the "silly side of the street," rather than the serious side.

Try It Again

The committee wants you to consider other shapes, not just cylinders, that might get attention at the convention. You can think about cones, spheres, other prisms—anything you want!

Here are two shapes, with formulas for their volumes. Use this information to answer the next set of questions.

Sphere

Volume = $\frac{4}{3}\pi r^3$

Cone

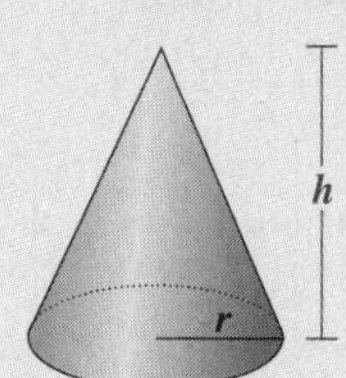

Volume = $\frac{1}{3}$ base area × height, or $\frac{1}{3}\pi r^2 h$

1 Discuss appeal of various shapes.

6. Try the cone shape first. Choose at least three heights for the cone. For each height, find the radius needed to give a cone a volume of 350 mL. Get within 1 mL of 350 mL.
7. Using the formula for the volume of a sphere, find as many spheres as you can with a volume of 350 mL.
8. Find at least two other shapes for containers with a volume of 350 mL. Answers will vary.

2 Have students use trial and error.

6. Possible answer:

Height (cm)	Radius (cm)
10	5.78
100	1.83
1	18.28

7. Only one sphere has this volume: the sphere with a radius of about 4.37 cm.

What Did You Learn?

Choose one design to present to the company.

9. Describe your design to the company, including its dimensions.
10. Explain why your design might be successful at the convention.
11. Make a model of your design to show the company.

9. Answers will vary.
10. Explanations will vary.
11. Models will vary.

3
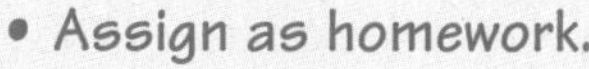

- Assign as homework.
- Have students present models and prove volumes.
- Use water or popcorn to test capacities.

LESSON 2.3 Surface Area and Volume **121**

Assign and Assess

On Your Own Exercises

On Your Own Exercises

Investigation 1
Practice & Apply: 1–2
Connect & Extend: 10–11

Investigation 2
Practice & Apply: 3–7
Connect & Extend: 12–15

Investigation 3
Practice & Apply: 8–9
Connect & Extend: 16–17

Assign Anytime
Mixed Review: 18–32

Exercise 1:
Students are asked to solve this exercise without actually building the different prisms. The real question is whether students processed the fact that when volume is unchanged, the cube has the greatest surface area and a row has the least surface area, or do they need to check all the different prisms?

Exercises 3–4:
In these exercises, students move from generic "units" (the blocks) to structures with specific measurements. Watch to be sure students report their answers in appropriate units (square units for area and cubic units for volume).

Practice & Apply

1a. $27 \times 1 \times 1$, $9 \times 3 \times 1$, $3 \times 3 \times 3$

1. Consider all the rectangular prisms that can be made with 27 blocks.

a. Give the dimensions of each prism.

b. Which of your 27-block prisms has the greatest surface area? Which has the least surface area? greatest: $27 \times 1 \times 1$; least: $3 \times 3 \times 3$

2. Think of a top view made of squares that is different from the top views you have seen so far.

a. Draw your top view. Drawings will vary.

b. Suppose you wanted to build a prism 2.5 units high with that top view. What would its volume be? See margin.

c. Write an expression for the volume of the prism, using h for height. See margin.

Remember
The formula for the area of a parallelogram is *bh*, where *b* is the base and *h* is the height.

3. Here is a parallelogram.

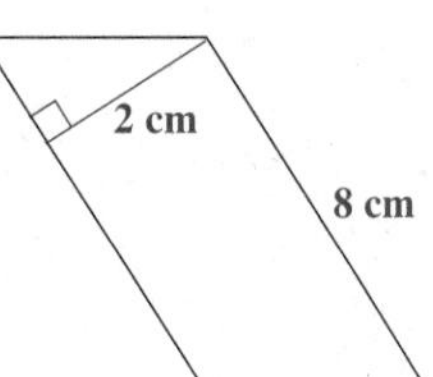

a. What is the area of the parallelogram? 16 cm^2

b. If you build a prism 1 cm high using this parallelogram as a base, what will its volume be? 16 cm^3

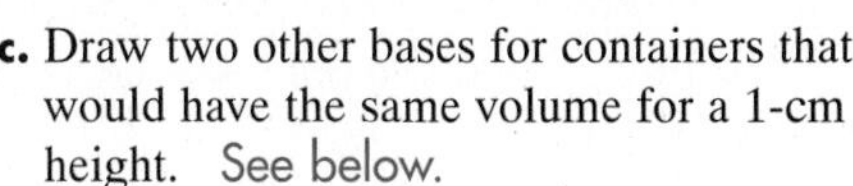

c. Draw two other bases for containers that would have the same volume for a 1-cm height. See below.

4. Six equilateral triangles are joined to form a hexagon.

2b. Answers will vary. The volume should be 2.5 times the number of squares in the top view.

2c. Answers will vary. The volume should be h times number of squares in the top view.

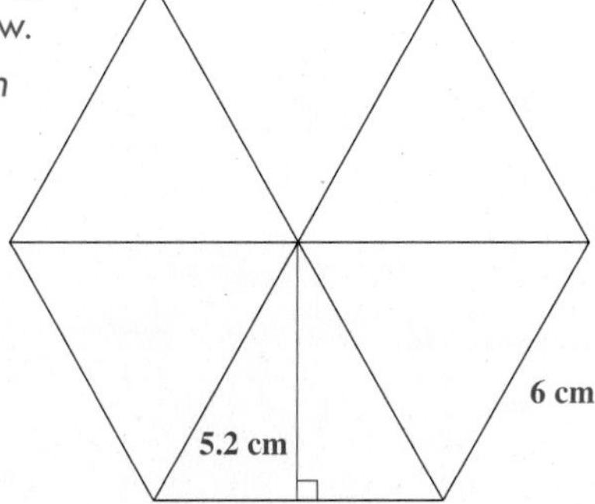

Remember
The formula for the area of a triangle is $\frac{1}{2}bh$, where *b* is the base and *h* is the height.

a. What is the area of the hexagon? Explain how you found your answer. See below.

b. If you built a prism on this base with a height of h cm, what would its volume be? $93.6h\text{ cm}^3$

3c. Possible answers: a $4\text{ cm} \times 4\text{ cm}$ square, a triangle with base 8 cm and height 4 cm, a $16\text{ cm} \times 1\text{ cm}$ rectangle

4a. Each triangle has area $\frac{1}{2}(6)(5.2)\text{ cm}^2$, or 15.6 cm^2; six triangles are 93.6 cm^2.

5. The base of a cylinder has radius r meters.

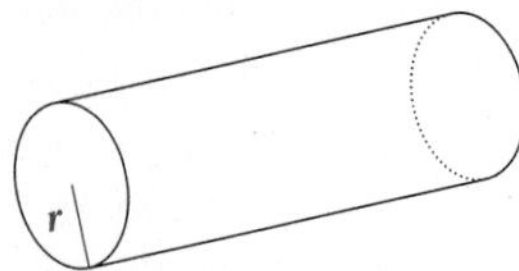

a. What is the area of the cylinder's base? πr^2 m^2

b. If the height of the cylinder is 1 m, what is its volume (in m^3)? πr^2 m^3

c. If the height is 10 m, what is the volume? $10\pi r^2$ m^3

d. What is the cylinder's volume if its height is h meters? $\pi r^2 h$ m^3

6. You can find, or at least make a good estimate of, the volume of a room in your home.

a. Draw the base (floor) of the room, and show the measurements in feet or meters. If you measured exactly, say so. If you estimated, describe how you made your estimates. Answers will vary.

b. What is the height of the room? Do you know exactly, or did you approximate it? Answers will vary.

c. What is the volume of the room?

6c. Answers will vary. For a rectangular room, the volume should be length times width times height.

7. Possible answer: a $6 \times 6 \times 10$ and a $36 \times 1 \times 10$ rectangular prism, a cylinder with radius about 3.4 cm and height about 10 cm, and any triangular prism so that $\frac{1}{2}bh$ for the triangle is 6 cm^2 and the height is 60 cm

7. Give the dimensions of four different containers that each have a volume of 360 cubic centimeters. They should not all be rectangular prisms.

8. For each structure, answer this question: For each 1 cubic unit of volume, how many square units of surface area are there?

a. 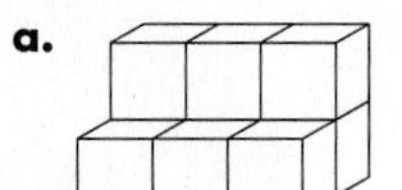 $\frac{10}{3}$, or $3\frac{1}{3}$

b. 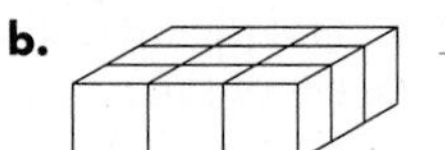 $\frac{10}{3}$, or $3\frac{1}{3}$

c. 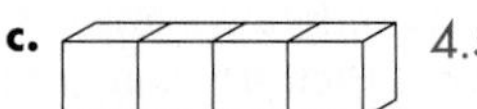 4.5

LESSON 2.3 Surface Area and Volume 123

Exercise 9:
In this exercise, students are given real data to check against the models they built. Because the data uses newborns rather than 15-pound babies, the models will be slightly off in that respect.

9. World Cultures Countries keep statistics on the average weights of newborns and adults.

a. Babies born in the United States have an average weight of 7.25 lb. Adults in the United States have an average weight of 160 lb. How heavy is an adult compared to a newborn (in other words, how many times as heavy)? about 22 times as heavy

b. If a block is your model of a newborn, how many blocks would be in your model of an adult? How would you arrange them?

9b. about 22 blocks; Arrangements will vary.

c. Babies born in the United States have an average length of 20 in. Adults in the United States have an average height of 5 ft 7 in. How tall is an adult compared to a baby (how many times as tall)? 3.35 times as tall

d. Use the information from Part c to check your answer for Part b. Now how would you arrange the blocks?

9d. Answers should include the fact that the adult should be 3 to 4 times as long in one direction.

Connect & Extend

10. Suppose you want to design five different covered boxes that each hold the same amount of sand. You want each box to hold exactly 500 cm^3.

a. Describe five different containers with this volume. Draw a top-count view of each structure, or draw the base (including the dimensions) and tell how high each structure will be.

10a. Possible dimensions: $500 \times 1 \times 1$, $50 \times 10 \times 1$, $5 \times 10 \times 10$, $25 \times 2 \times 10$, $25 \times 20 \times 1$

b. Which of your boxes has the least surface area? Is that the least surface area possible for a 500-cm^3 box?
The least surface area will be for the box that is shaped most like a cube, or $5 \times 10 \times 10$. (Or, for non-integer edge lengths, a cube approximately 7.94 cm on each edge.)

124 CHAPTER 2 Geometry in Three Dimensions

In your **own words**

Give two examples of structures with the same volume and different surface areas. Suppose you are making one of these structures for art class, and you want to paint them. Which one will need less paint? Explain.

11. A standard playing card is about 5.7 cm wide and 8.9 cm long. A stack of 52 cards—a whole deck—is about 1.5 cm high.

   a. What is the volume of a deck of cards? about 76.1 cm^3

   b. Use your answer to Part a to find the volume of a single card. about 1.46 cm^3

12. Many cereal boxes have dimensions of about 6 cm by 20 cm for the base and are about 27 cm high.

   a. What volume of cereal could this shape box hold? 3,240 cm^3

   b. Give the dimensions (in cm) of four other rectangular boxes that have this same volume. See Additional Answers.

   c. Give the dimensions of two other containers that have this same volume. They do not have to be rectangular boxes. See Additional Answers.

13. Here are three cylinders that you probably have in your house. Pick one and find its volume. See Additional Answers.

   - a penny (It is hard to measure the height of a single penny, but it's not hard to measure the height of 10 pennies and then divide.)
   - a soup can
   - a strand of spaghetti

14. Which of these containers holds the most water?

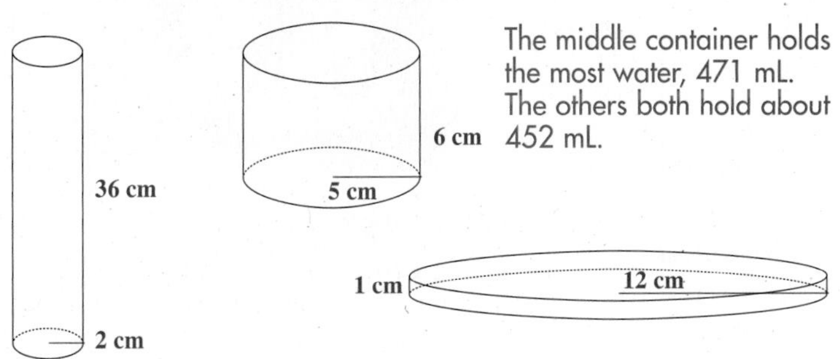

The middle container holds the most water, 471 mL. The others both hold about 452 mL.

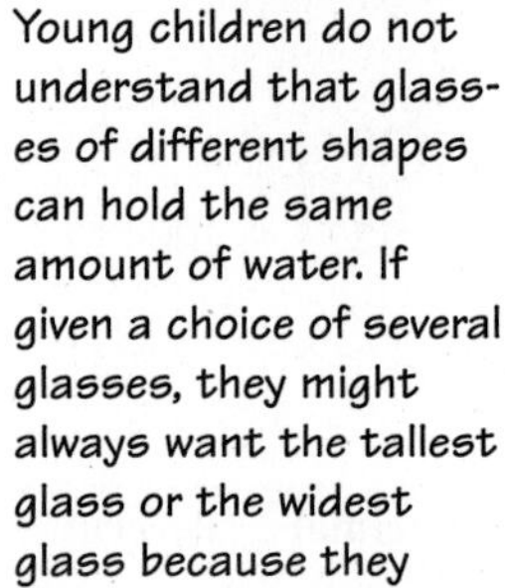

Just the facts

Young children do not understand that glasses of different shapes can hold the same amount of water. If given a choice of several glasses, they might always want the tallest glass or the widest glass because they think it holds the most.

15. Draw two glasses that look different but hold the same amount of water. Show their dimensions.
Possible answer:

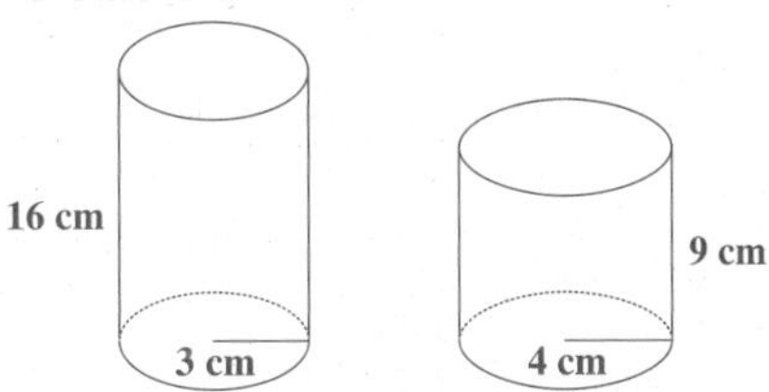

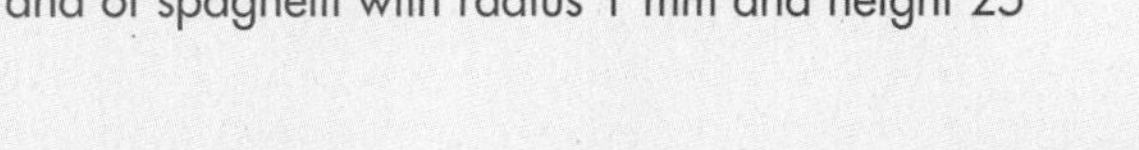

Exercise 14:
The result that the middle container holds more water may seem counter-intuitive, but if students believe their development of volume formulas, they must believe this as well.

Additional Answers

12b. Possible answer: 18 × 20 × 9, 9 × 9 × 40, 10 × 18 × 18, 3,240 × 1 × 1

12c. Possible answer: a triangular prism with base area 324 cm^2 (say, a triangle with height 18 cm and base 36 cm) and height 10 cm, and a cylinder with base area 324 cm^2 (a circle with radius about 10.16 cm) and height 10 cm

13. Possible answers: A penny has a diameter of about 2 cm (radius about 1 cm). A stack of 7 pennies is about 1 cm high. So 7 pennies form a cylinder of volume π cm^3, or about 3.14 cm^3, so the volume of a single penny is about 0.45 cm^3. Or the volume of a strand of spaghetti with radius 1 mm and height 25 cm is 0.785 cm^3.

Exercise 17 Extension: Ask students to give examples of Fechner's law in action other than the ones that are provided. What about birds in colder climates?

Just the facts

Fechner's law says that for the same or closely related species, larger animals will be found in colder climates, and smaller animals in hotter climates. For example, the polar bear is bigger than other bears, and the arctic fox is bigger than other foxes.

16. Zoe has two Alaskan malamutes, Trooper and Scooter. Scooter is Trooper's puppy.

a. Does Trooper have more or less total surface area than Scooter? more

b. Does Trooper have more or less surface area for a given unit of volume than Scooter? less

c. Which dog will cool off more quickly, Trooper or Scooter? Scooter

17. Life Science One of the plants pictured here lives in the desert and must conserve water. The other plant lives in the rain forest and does not need to conserve water. Describe how surface area and volume relationships could help you determine which plant is which.

17. The plant with the wide, flat leaf is from the wet climate. The cactus is from the dry climate; it has less surface area per unit volume, so it can retain water better.

Mixed Review

Find each fractional amount.

18. $\frac{3}{4}$ of 12 9

19. $\frac{1}{2}$ of 50 25

20. $\frac{3}{5}$ of 15 9

21. $\frac{2}{3}$ of 12 8

22. $\frac{4}{5}$ of 100 80

23. $\frac{5}{4}$ of 100 125

Complete each table.

24.

Fraction	Decimal	Percent
$\frac{1}{2}$	0.5	50%
$\frac{3}{4}$	0.75	75%
$\frac{3}{10}$	0.3	30%
$\frac{1}{4}$	0.25	25%

25.

Fraction	Decimal	Percent
$\frac{1}{2}$	0.5	50%
$\frac{1}{8}$	0.125	12.5%
$\frac{4}{5}$	0.8	80%
$\frac{1}{20}$	0.05	5%

126 CHAPTER 2 Geometry in Three Dimensions

26. If there are n blocks in each bag, write an expression for the total number of blocks. $2n + 1$

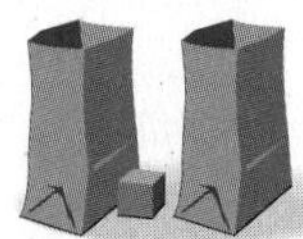

27. If there are n blocks in each bag, write an expression for the total number of blocks. $3n$

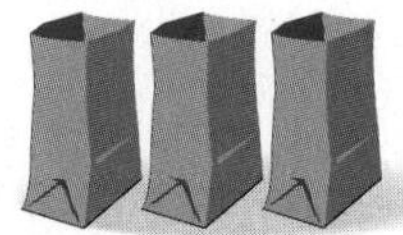

28. Complete the table.

n	0	1	2	3	10	50	101
$n + 9$	9	10	11	12	19	59	110

29. The formula for the perimeter of a rectangle is $2L + 2W$, where L is the length of the rectangle and W is the width. Find the perimeter of a rectangle with length 6 cm and width 2 cm. 16 cm

30. This table is from a game of *What's My Rule?* Find two ways of writing the rule in symbols. Choose your own variable. $3n + 3$ or $3(n + 1)$, where n is the input

In	0	1	2	3	4
Out	3	6	9	12	15

31. Probability On a scale from 0 (impossible) to 100 (very likely), rate the chances of each event happening today.

a. You do homework. Answers will vary.

b. Someone in your state has a baby. 100

c. Someone in your city has a baby. Answers will depend on the size of the city.

d. You learn to drive. Answers will vary.

e. It snows somewhere in your country. Answers will vary.

LESSON 2.3 Surface Area and Volume **127**

Assign and Assess

Quick Check

Informal Assessment
At the end of the lesson, students should be able to:

✔ find the volume of any prism or cylinder as area of base times height

✔ understand that for a given volume, the cube is the rectangular prism with the minimum surface area

✔ articulate some applications of surface area and volume, in particular, the relationship of surface area per unit volume and what it tells you about heat loss

Quick Quiz

1. A block prism has a volume of 36 cubic units.
   a. What is the least surface area it could have? 66 square units ($1 \times 1 \times 36$)
   b. What is the greatest surface area it could have? 146 square units ($3 \times 3 \times 4$)
2. Find a cylinder and a rectangular prism that have the same volume. Describe the dimensions of each object. (Hint: It may be easier to start with the cylinder.) Possible answer: Cylinder has radius 4 units and height 5 units. Volume $= 16\pi \times 5 = 80\pi$ cubic units. Prism has dimensions of $5 \times 4 \times 4\pi$.

32. Zoe wants to build a doghouse for her dogs Trooper and Scooter. She made this sketch to work from.

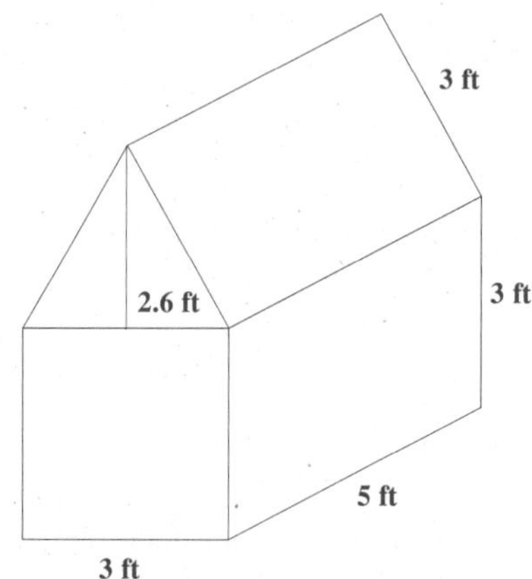

32a. 100.8

a. Zoe plans to make the doghouse out of plywood, and she wants to include a floor. How many square feet of plywood will she need?

b. The hardware store sells scrap plywood for 25¢ a square foot, in increments of 10 square feet. How much will Zoe spend on plywood? $27.50

c. Zoe plans to cut a circular door in the front of the doghouse, and then paint the outside of the house (but not the floor). If the door has a diameter of 2 ft, how much area will Zoe need to paint to give the house two coats? about 164 ft^2

d. If a small can of paint covers 30 square yards, how many cans will Zoe need to buy? 1

e. The hardware stores sells discount carpeting for $3 per square yard. How much will it cost Zoe to buy carpet for the floor of her doghouse? $5.00

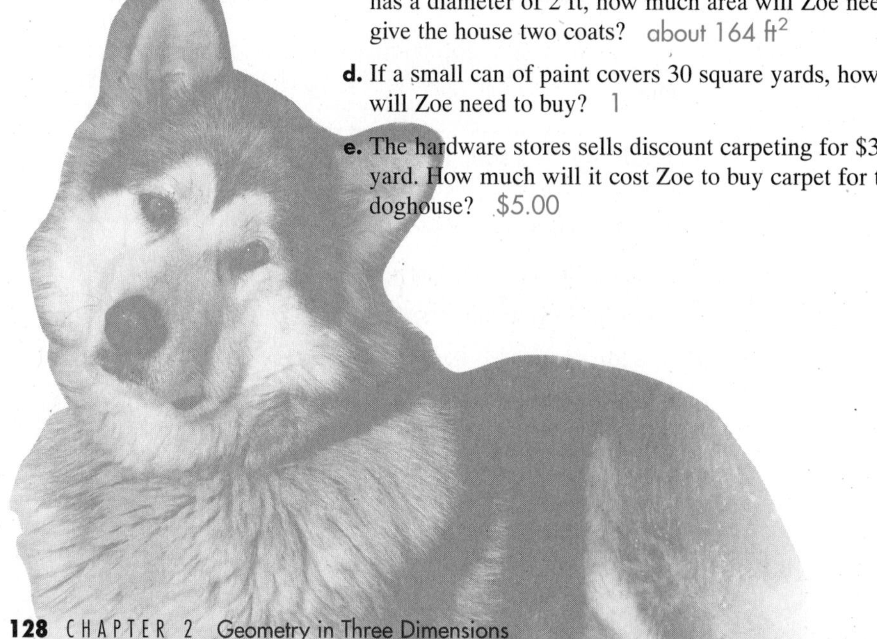

2.4 Nets and Solids

Objectives

- To decide if a given net will fold into a closed three-dimensional solid
- To create nets that will fold into given shapes
- To use information about the nets of an object to find surface area and volume

Overview (pacing: about 3 class periods)
In this lesson, students extend several major themes of the chapter. First, they learn yet another two-dimensional description of a three-dimensional object—a net that will fold into a solid. Previously students looked at front/right/top view combinations, top-count views, engineering front/right/top views, and perspective drawings of the figures. Second, students use these nets to expand their abilities to find surface areas and volumes.

Advance Preparation
Collect soft drink cans for Investigation 3. About ten cans should be plenty. Rinse the cans and completely remove tabs. Most students will need to actually cut out the shapes and fold them to decide whether they are nets or not. Prepare at least one copy of each of the following Masters for each student, enlarging the nets if necessary:

Master 11, Cube Nets I, II, and III for the Explore on page 129
Master 12, Will It Fold? I, II, and III for Problem Set A
Master 13, Nets Used to Find Volume and Surface Area, I and II for Problem Set B
Master 14, Surface Area: Net for Share & Summarize on page 134
Master 15 and 16, On Your Own Exercises

Lesson Planner

	Summary	Materials	On Your Own Exercises	Assessment Opportunities
Investigation 1 page T130	Students use nets to learn more about three-dimensional figures. They decide which measurements on a net must match up for the net to fold.	• Master 9 (Teaching Resources, page 14) • Master 11 (Teaching Resources, pages 16–18) • Master 12 (Teaching Resources, pages 19–21) • Master 15 (Teaching Resources, page 25) • Scissors • Tape	Practice & Apply: 1–4 Connect & Extend: 13–18 Mixed Review: 21–36	Share & Summarize, pages T131, 131 Troubleshooting, page T131
Investigation 2 page T131	Students use nets to find surface areas and to estimate volumes of solid objects.	• Master 13 (Teaching Resources, pages 22–23) • Master 14 (Teaching Resources, page 24) • Master 16 (Teaching Resources, page 26)	Practice & Apply: 5–8 Connect & Extend: 19 Mixed Review: 21–36	Share & Summarize, pages T134, 134 Troubleshooting, page T134
Investigation 3 page T134	Students explore whether the surface area of a soft drink can is the best (least) possible for the volume it holds. They try to find the can with the required volume but with minimal surface area.	• Soft drink cans • Rulers • Calculators	Practice & Apply: 9–12 Connect & Extend: 20 Mixed Review: 21–36	Share & Summarize, pages T135, 135 Troubleshooting, page T135 Informal Assessment, page 140 Quick Quiz, page 140

Hold up a cube prepared from the net labeled *Net* on Master 11, Cube Nets 1. Have the sides loosely taped. Take the cube and unfold it for the class, and explain to them that this flat object is called a *net.* Nets are useful tools for calculating surface area since these flat objects represent the total surface area of the figure.

Explore

You will need scissors and copies of Master 11, Cube Nets I, II, and III. Ask students to determine which of the shapes will fold up into a cube. Many students need to manipulate the shapes to answer this question— these are difficult to visualize without cutting.

After they have determined that Figure B and Figure D form nets, ask students to work in pairs to draw three other nets for a cube. Using Master 9, Centimeter Graph Paper, will make it easier for students to draw their nets.

As students are working, ask one pair of students to draw all the nets they have found so far on the board or to tape them to the board if the nets are big enough. Then ask another pair to add to that list. To tell if two nets are the same, students must check to see if they can rotate, flip, or move one net to lie exactly on top of the other.

There are 11 possibilities, all shown in the right column. The question about finding them all is not intended for in-depth class time, but you might offer it as an extra project. Tell students there are eleven and challenge them to find them all.

Access for all Learners

Extra for Experts Have students try to find all eleven nets on their own and then explain why their's is a complete list. Students may think about sorting the nets into categories of "main string" net length. For example, for a main string length of 4, ☐☐☐☐, there are only 6 nets possible. They could look at cases of length 3, and so on.

Here are the eleven possible nets:

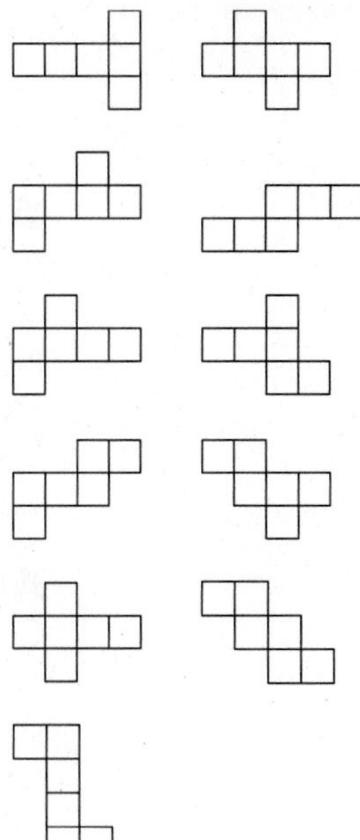

Students may notice without checking that some nets will definitely not form solids. For example, if four squares are around a single point, the shape will lie flat rather than fold up. If five or more squares are in a line, two faces will overlap and the figure will not close.

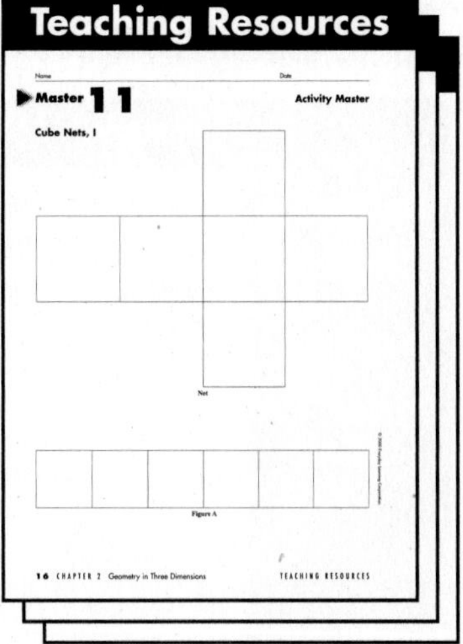

2.4 Nets and Solids

VOCABULARY
net

A **net** is a flat figure that can be folded to form a closed, three-dimensional object. Such an object is called a *solid.*

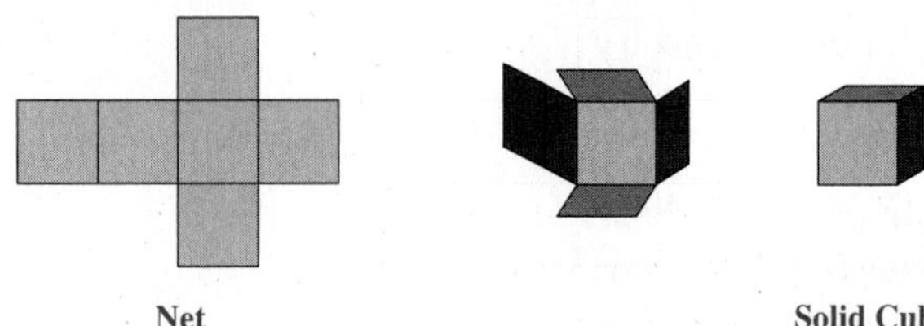

1 Unfold a cube to display the net.

MATERIALS
- scissors
- graph paper

Explore

- Which of these figures are also nets for a cube? That is, which will fold into a cube? Cut out a copy of each figure and try to fold it into a cube. B and D

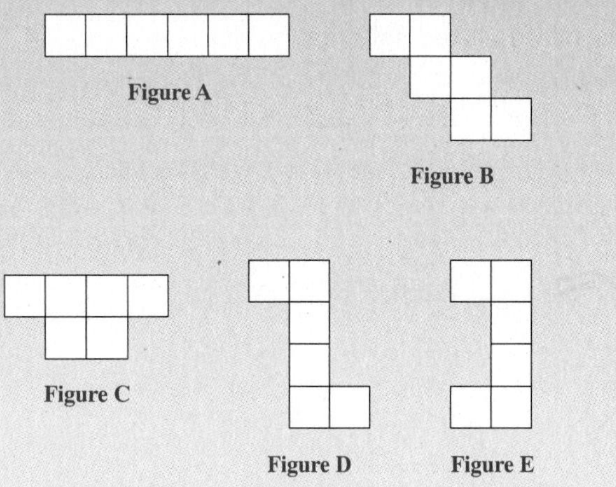

- Find and draw three other nets for a cube. See ①.

With your class, compile all the different nets for a cube that were found. How many nets are there? Do you think your class found all of them?

① Answers will vary. There are 11 nets for a cube; the other 9 are shown here.

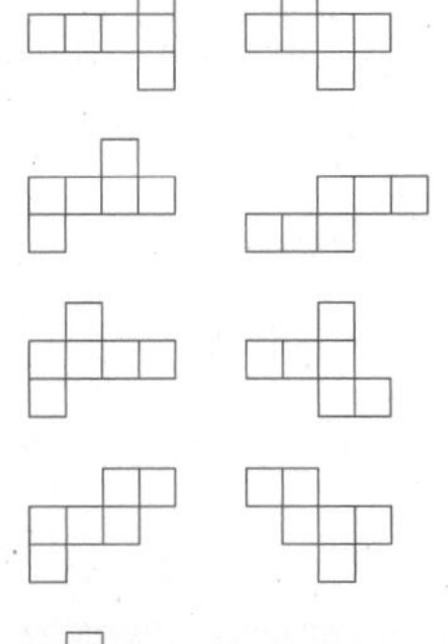

2 Have students work in pairs.

3
- Have students draw nets on board.
- You might challenge students to find 11 nets.

Investigation 1

In this investigation, students will decide whether or not certain nets will fold into a closed solid. The nets pictured on pages 130–131 can be duplicated using Master 12 so that students can cut each net out and try to fold it.

Problem Set A **Suggested Grouping: Individuals**
In this problem set, students are given several nets and are asked to determine whether the nets will form closed solids. If you do not use Master 12, Will It Fold? I, Will It Fold? II, or Will It Fold? III, encourage students to trace the nets, cut them out, and try to fold the ones that might be difficult to determine visually. Some students may need to try folding all of them.

One important lesson is that sometimes "not possible" is an acceptable answer. In this problem set, **Problems 3, 4, 6, 8, and 9** all fail to fold into a closed solid for various reasons.

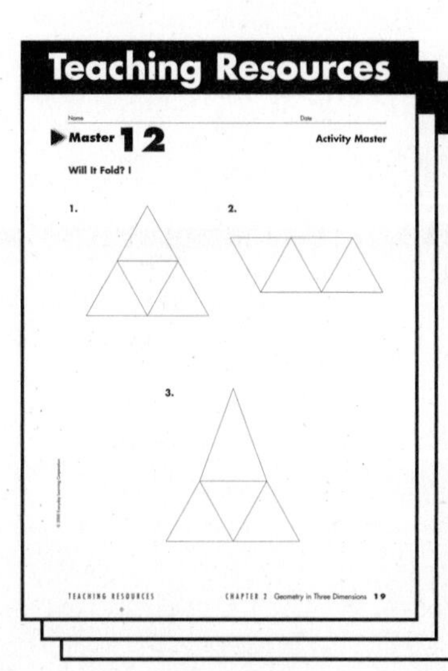

Investigation 1 Will It Fold?

For a net to form a closed solid, certain lengths have to match. For example, in the nets for cubes, the side lengths of all the squares must be the same. You will now investigate whether other nets will form closed solids. Pay close attention to the measurements that need to match.

> 1 Duplicate Master 12, so that students can cut out each net and try to fold it.

MATERIALS
scissors

Problem Set A

Decide whether each figure is a net—that is, whether it will fold into a solid. You might be able to decide just by looking at the figure. You can also cut out a copy of the figure and try to fold it. If the figure is a net, describe the shape it creates. If it isn't a net, tell what goes wrong.

1. It is a net; it makes a shape with four triangular faces.

2. It is a net; it makes a shape with four triangular faces.

3. 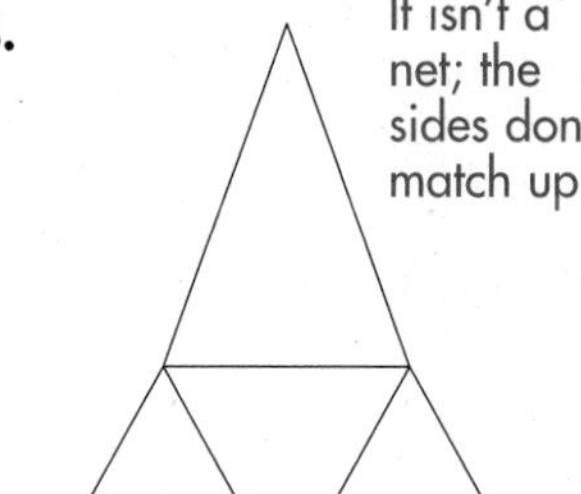

It isn't a net; the sides don't match up.

4. 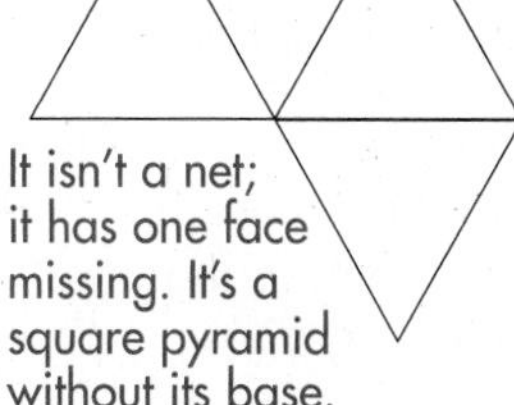

It isn't a net; it has one face missing. It's a square pyramid without its base.

5. 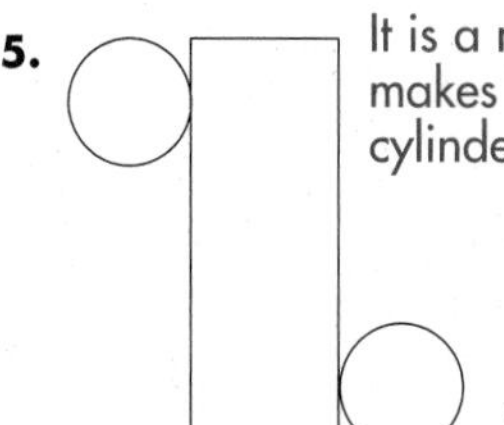

It is a net; it makes a cylinder.

6. 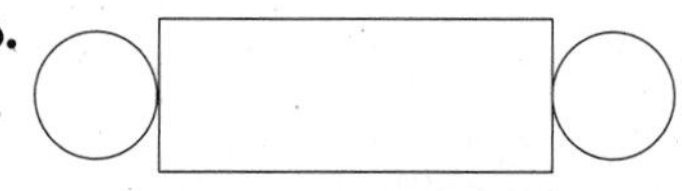

It isn't a net; the sides of the rectangle are not long enough to wrap around the circles.

Share & Summarize

Students may have trouble articulating exactly what length they mean in **Question 1.** Acceptable answers would be, "The circumference needs to be the same length as the side where the circle is attached." or "It needs to be the same length as the side that wraps around it." You may want to follow up by asking students how they could find that length. If the circle's radius is 2 cm, what is the length of that side? (This is just a review that $C = 2\pi r$; so in this case it would be 4π or about 12.6 cm.)

2 For **Question 2,** ask students what strategies they use to determine whether or not figures are actually nets. Here are some reasons that something that looks like a net won't form a solid.

- It is missing a face.
- Two faces are overlapping.
- The figure is impossible to fold. There is a vertex that won't fold out of the plane. This will happen with four squares, 6 triangles, or 3 hexagons around a central point, for example.

Troubleshooting For **Question 1,** if students have trouble saying which side they mean but can point to the side in the nets for cylinders from the problem set, that's fine. If students are not sure that the circumference needs to be the same as any particular length, you may want to revisit problems that were not nets in Problem Set A. Ask students to find their net from Problem 6 and try to fold it up. What goes wrong? (The sides of the rectangle are not long enough to "wrap around" the circle.) Similarly for Problem 8, ask students to fold the net. In this case, students may simply overlap the sides of the parallelogram to make everything fit. If so, explain that in a net, all the edges must meet exactly. What happens when you match up the edges of the parallelogram exactly? (The circles don't cover the "hole," or the sides are too long.)

On Your Own Exercises

Practice & Apply: 1–4
Connect & Extend: 13–18
Mixed Review: 21–36

Investigation 2

In this investigation, students use nets with measurements given to determine both surface area and volume for various solids. This allows students to practice the concepts that they have learned in the previous lessons. In some cases, students will be able only to estimate the volume.

To find surface area, add the area of each face of the solid. If you have the net, you can compute the area rather than "count squares." For volume, the situation is a bit trickier. Given the net of a rectangular prism, you can find the volume from the three measurements. However, the net for a square pyramid, for example, doesn't give all the information you need. You can find the area of each face but not the height of the pyramid. However, you *can* use the net to estimate volume. In the example of a square pyramid, students may estimate the volume to be $\frac{1}{2}$ of the volume of a rectangular prism with the same base and with rectangles rather than triangles as sides. The ratio is closer to $\frac{1}{3}$, and you can relate this back to the cones and cylinders; but in any case, you can get an idea for the volume:

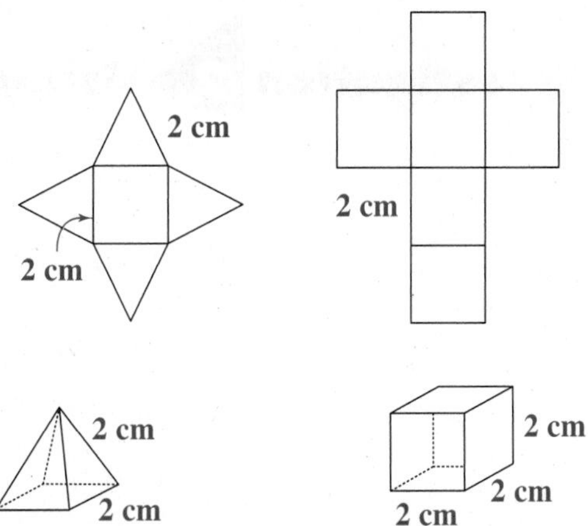

The square pyramid has about $\frac{1}{3}$ the volume of the cube, which we can compute as $2 \times 2 \times 2 = 8\ \text{cm}^3$.

You may know that there is a standard formula for surface area of prisms: $2 \times$ (area of the base) + (perimeter of the base $\times$ height). We do not develop this formula, but it may come up naturally as students work on finding surface areas. We are more concerned with the concept of surface area as "adding up the areas of the faces," whether the solid is a prism or some other object.

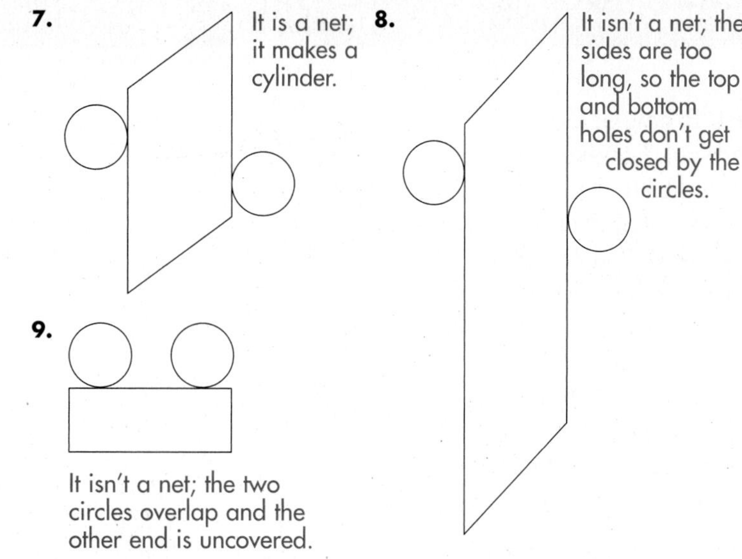

7.
It is a net; it makes a cylinder.
8.
It isn't a net; the sides are too long, so the top and bottom holes don't get closed by the circles.
9.
It isn't a net; the two circles overlap and the other end is uncovered.

Share & Summarize

1. For a net to fold into a cylinder, the circumference of the circles must be the same as what other length?

2. Draw a net for a figure different from those in Problem Set A. Explain how you know your net will fold to form a solid.

Answers will vary.

1. the sides of the parallelogram to which the circles are attached

1 Discuss with students how to find this length.

2 Have students share strategies for deciding whether or not figure are actually nets.

Investigation  Using Nets to Investigate Solids

You have calculated surface area by counting the squares on the outside of a block structure. If the faces of a solid are not squares—like the figures below—you can find the solid's surface area by adding the areas of all its faces.

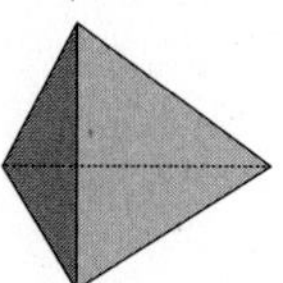  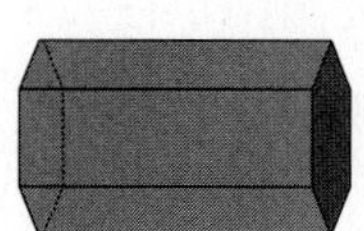

LESSON 2.4 Nets and Solids 131

Develop

1 Start the lesson by discussing the Example. Give students another, similar example to work out. For example, use the same shape but change the radius to 1 cm. How does that affect the length of the rectangle? How does it affect the surface area of the cylinder? You can give another example where the length labeled 10 cm is very small, maybe $\frac{1}{2}$ cm. Ask if that affects whether or not the cylinder will fold up. (This is just a review of the previous Share & Summarize). Have them compute the surface area changing only the value of the radius to 1 cm (69.08 cm^2). Then have them compute the surface area changing only the value of the height to $\frac{1}{2}$ cm (172.7 cm^2).

2 You can also ask students to find the volume of the cylinder shown. What is the area of the circular base? (25π cm^2) What is the height? (10 cm, the other side of the rectangle) If students have difficulty seeing that the length shown as 10 cm is really the height of the cylinder, you may want to have them trace the net, cut it out, and fold it up. When it is folded, students should place one of the circular faces on their desks and note that the segment marked 10 cm does, in fact, go from one base to the other. Since this appears to be a right cylinder, that segment is the height. Then have students calculate the volume. ($25\pi \times 10 = 250\pi$ cm^3, or 785 cm^3)

3 **Problem Set B** **Suggested Grouping: Pairs**
Students should be able to determine the surface areas and the volumes of all of the prisms. To identify the heights for the various nets, students may need to trace the net, cut it out, and fold it up. Or you can use Master 13, Nets Used to Find Volume and Surface Area I and II, which duplicates the figures in Problem Set B.

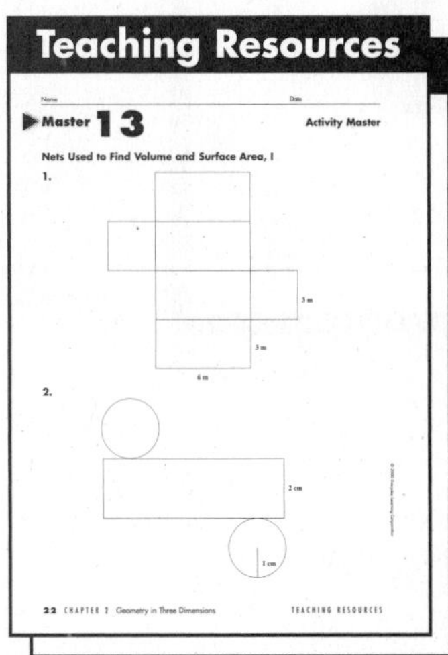

Teaching Resources

Master 13 Activity Master

Nets Used to Find Volume and Surface Area, I

1.

2.

EXAMPLE

This net folds to form a cylinder.

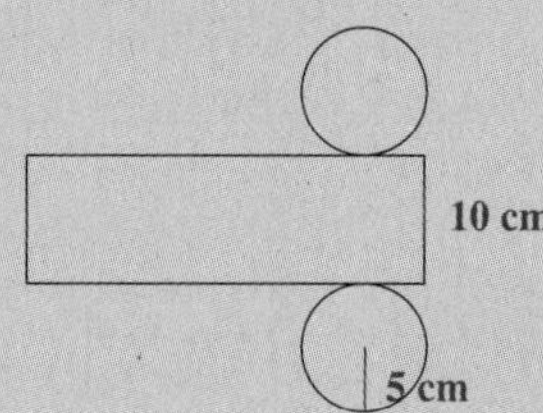

Because the net folds into a cylinder, the circles must be the same size. The area of each circle is πr^2 cm^2, or 25π cm^2. This is about 78.5 cm^2.

The length of the rectangle must be equal to the circumference of each circle, which is 10π cm, or about 31.4 cm. So the area of the rectangle is about 314 cm^2.

To find the cylinder's surface area, just add the three areas:

$$78.5 \text{ cm}^2 + 78.5 \text{ cm}^2 + 314 \text{ cm}^2 = 471 \text{ cm}^2$$

1 • Discuss the Example.
• Give students a similar example.

2 Have students find the volume of the cylinder.

3 You may have students work in pairs.

MATERIALS
scissors

Problem Set B

Each net shown will fold to form a closed solid. Use the net's measurements to find the *surface area* and *volume* of the solid. If you can't find the exact volume, approximate it. It may be helpful to cut out and fold a copy of the net.

1.

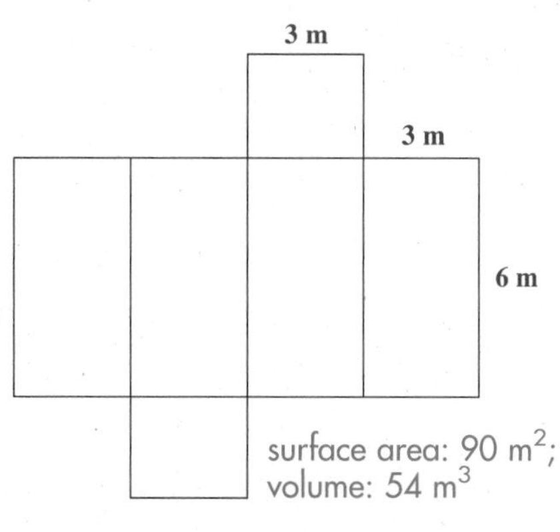

surface area: 90 m^2;
volume: 54 m^3

2.

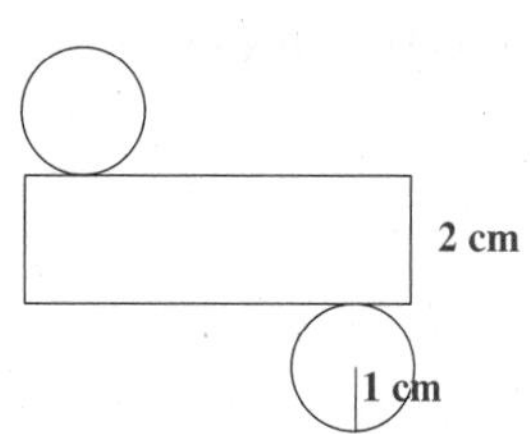

surface area: 6π cm^2, or about 18.8 cm^2;
volume: 2π cm^3, or about 6.3 cm^3

Remember
The formula for the circumference of a circle is $2\pi r$, where r is the radius; or πd, where d is the diameter.

Develop

In **Problem 5,** particularly, students may need help identifying the height of the prism, since the lateral face is shown as a parallelogram rather than as a rectangle. Cutting and folding should convince students that the height of the parallelogram is also the height of the cylinder. In fact, the parallelogram could be "dissected" into a rectangle while still part of the net, and the same cylinder would result:

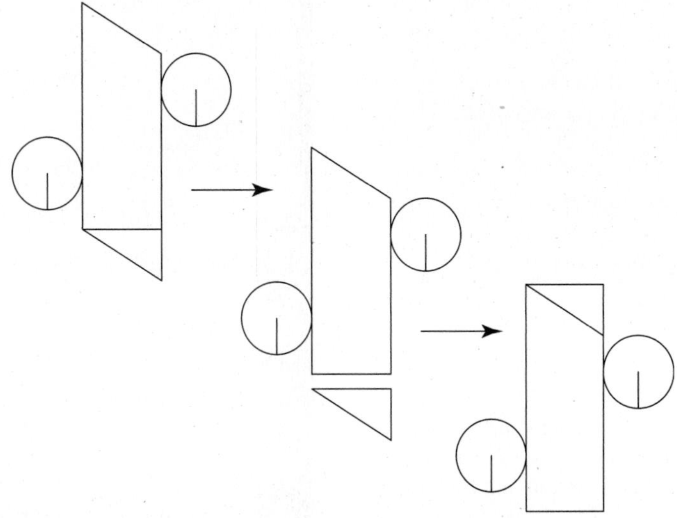

Remember

The formula for the area of a triangle is $\frac{1}{2}bh$, where b is the base and h is the height.

3.

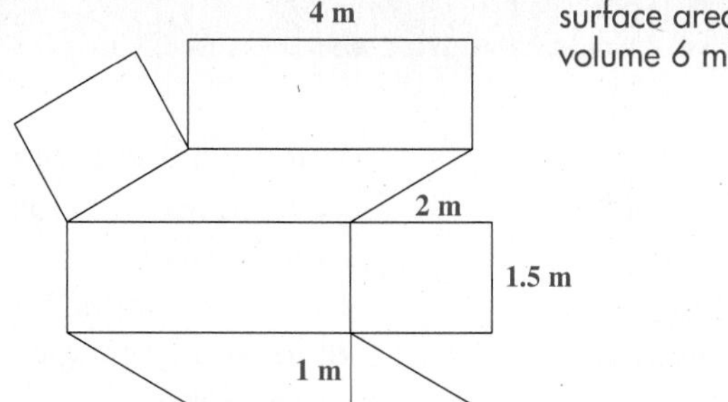

surface area 26 m^2; volume 6 m^3

4.

surface area: 48 m^2; volume: 18 m^3 (area of base triangle is 6 m^2, height is 3 m)

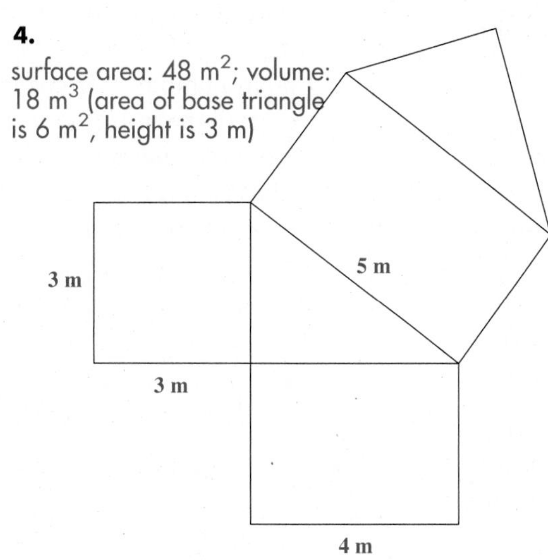

5.

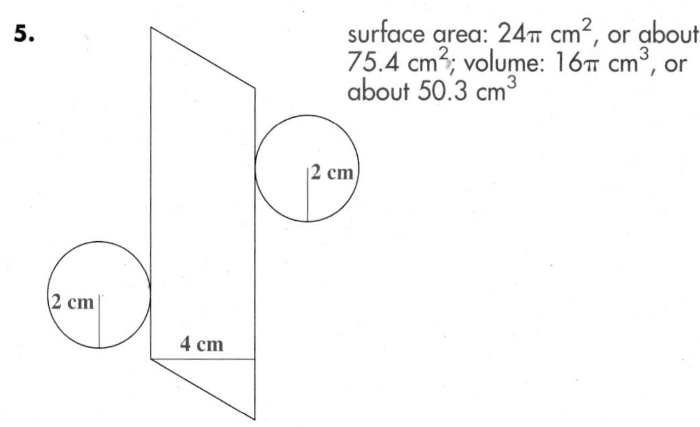

surface area: 24π cm^2, or about 75.4 cm^2; volume: 16π cm^3, or about 50.3 cm^3

1 Discuss with whole class why 4 cm is the height of the net.

LESSON 2.4 Nets and Solids **133**

Share & Summarize

The point of the first question is that the net is, exactly, the surface of a solid. So the area of the net is, exactly, the surface area of that solid. Since students have good ways for finding areas, they also have some good ways for finding surface areas.

For the second question, students need to identify the appropriate measurements, determine the measurements, and use them appropriately.

1 **Troubleshooting** If students misidentify the measurements they need, you may ask them to cut out a copy of the net and fold it. Or you may wish to use Master 14, Surface Area: Net for Share & Summarize, which provides a copy of the net for Question 2. Which measurements will help them find the area of the base? What is the height? They can even measure the folded-up solid.

If students have difficulty accurately determining the measurements, they may need help using and reading a ruler. Some quick direct instruction on these skills should solve the problem.

If students misapply the formula for volume of a prism, you may need to revisit the idea of using blocks. Relate the question of volume to "How many 1 cm^3 blocks will fill this box?" Students should mark along the base in square cm and then stack the blocks to the right height. The total number of blocks is the number in that base layer (or length times width) times the total number of layers (the height in cm).

On Your Own Exercises

Practice & Apply: 5–8
Connect & Extend: 19
Mixed Review: 21–36

In the last two investigations and in the related On Your Own Exercises, students have explored nets and the connection to surface area. In the course of their studies, students explored making nets from just one shape: just squares or just equilateral triangles. This could lead to an exploration of Platonic solids. A Platonic solid is a three-dimensional solid in which all faces are the same regular polygon and in which the same number of faces meet at each vertex. Within a given Platonic solid, all faces must be equilateral triangles, squares, or other regular polygons. With some guidance, middle school students can create the proof that there are only five possible solids meeting these requirements.

If you want to conduct this exploration of Platonic solids, you should have lots of equilateral triangles, squares, regular pentagons, regular hexagons, and regular heptagons on paper for students to cut out. They will need at least 35 triangles, 10 squares, 15 pentagons, and 3 each of the other shapes. The idea is to pick a shape and make all the possible Platonic solids with that shape as a face. One question to answer is, What is the minimum number of faces meeting at a vertex? With a little experimenting, students will see that if only two faces meet at a vertex, you can never form a closed solid. So at least three faces must meet at a vertex. Students can then try to create solids by placing 3, 4, 5, and 6 of each shape at a vertex and continuing until the solid closes. See chart on page A385.

Investigation 3

2 Ask students whether they think soft drink cans have the shape they do for a special reason. Why aren't the cans shaped like cereal boxes? And why aren't the cans short and stubby?

Ask students what factors they think companies consider when they design containers. Students might suggest shape to fit the hand, cost of materials, and so on. Certainly, they might want to consider using the minimum surface area for the volume of soda they want the can to have.

3 **Problem Set C** **Suggested Grouping: Small Groups**

You will want a soft drink can and a ruler per group for this exploration. Have students get into groups of 4. Ask each group to find the area of the base of the soft drink can in square centimeters. Ask them to measure the height in centimeters. Soft drink cans are not perfectly cylindrical, so students will have to approximate the measurements. If they do so carefully, students should come out with a volume close to the one shown on the can. If students' volumes are quite far off, they should redo their measurements with greater accuracy.

If students have difficulty finding the diameter of the can in Problem 1, suggest that they trace the can on paper, cut out the circle, and fold to find the diameter. Then students can measure the length of their folds.

• ***Teaching notes continued on page A385.***

MATERIALS

metric ruler

Share & Summarize

1. Explain how to find the surface area of a solid from the net for that solid.
2. Here is a net for a rectangular solid. Take whatever measurements you think are necessary to find the solid's *volume* and *surface area*. Explain what measurements you took and what you did with them.

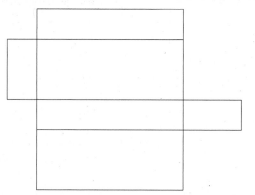

1. The solid's surface area is the same as the net's area, so just add the areas of the two-dimensional figures that make up the net.
2. To find the volume, measure length and width of a small rectangle, and length (long side) of one of the larger rectangles. Multiply those three numbers: 2 cm × 1 cm × 5 cm = 10 cm^3. To find the surface area, add the areas of all six rectangles: 5 cm^2 + 5 cm^2 + 10 cm^2 + 10 cm^2 + 2 cm^2 + 2 cm^2 = 34 cm^2.

1

- If necessary, have students cut and fold a copy of net.
- You may review measuring skills.
- You may have students review using blocks to find volume.

Investigation 3 Is Today's Soft Drink Can the Best Shape?

Bursting Bubbles soft drink company is trying to reduce their manufacturing costs in order to increase their profits. The president of the company wonders if there is a way to use less material to make a soft drink can.

How could Bursting Bubbles reduce the amount of aluminum it takes to make a can? One way is to design a can that has the minimum surface area for the volume of beverage it contains.

2 Discuss why soft drink cans have the shape they do.

MATERIALS

- 12-oz soft drink can
- metric ruler

Problem Set C

To get started, inspect a 12-oz soft drink can. Get an idea of its dimensions, volume, and surface area.

1. Find the area in square centimeters of the base of the can. (If the can you are using is indented at the bottom, assume that it isn't.)
2. Measure the can's height in centimeters. about 12.4 cm

1. The diameter of the wider part is about 6.4 cm, so the area is about 32.2 cm^2.

3 Have students work in groups of 4.

Teaching Resources

Master 14 — Activity Master

Surface Area: Net for Share & Summarize

1 Students will also need to calculate the surface area of the can. You may want to ask them to sketch the net for the can. Where is the radius of the circle in that net? Where is the height of the can? If students can correctly label the pieces of the net, they will see that they do have enough information to find the surface area.

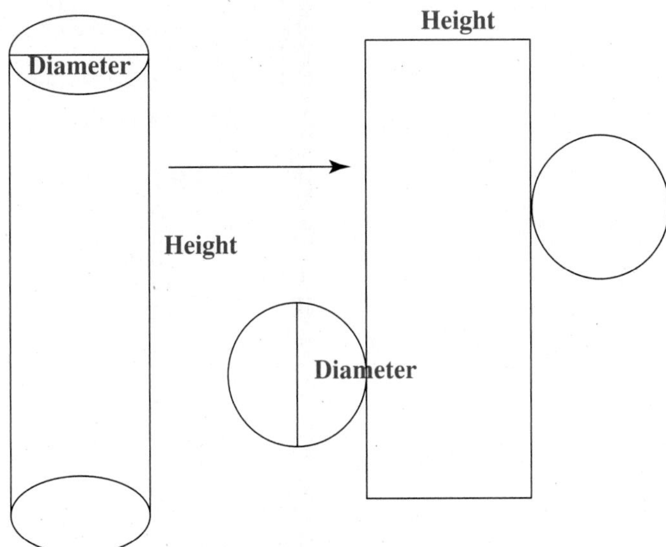

Problem Set Wrap-Up Before moving on to the next problem set, you may want to bring the whole class together and compare results. How close did each group come to the volume shown on the can? What were the individual measurements they took? Who thinks this shape gives the least surface area?

2 Problem Set D Suggested Grouping: Groups of 4

In this problem set, students use the volume they *calculated* in Problem Set C. In **Problem 1,** students use their calculated volumes to determine five other figures that have the same volume but different dimensions.

In **Problem 2,** students revisit the concept of different surface areas for the same volume.

3 As students work and find cans with the appropriate volume, each group should send a recorder to the board and add the measurements of their can to a table. Encourage students to try cans that are close in shape to the original (maybe 1 cm shorter or taller) and cans that are quite different from the original (maybe 5 cm shorter or taller).

height	radius	surface area

The table above will give the groups considerable data for answering **Problem 4,** which asks them to conjecture which can uses the least amount of material.

Finding cans of a given volume is not easy. If students have completed the Lab Investigation from Lesson 2.3, they will have some good strategies and they may even have all the data they need. If they have not, you may suggest some of the methods below.

Sample Strategies Students may use one of these strategies to solve **Problem 1:**

- Guess-check-and-improve: If a can has a height of 15 cm and a volume of 350 mL, what is the radius of the circular base? Some students may use a strategy of systematic trial and error. They will use a calculator and search until they get very close to 350 mL.

base radius (cm)	base area (sq cm) ($A = 3.14 \times r \times r$)	Volume (want 350 mL) (V = Base area · Height)
3 cm	28.26 sq cm	423.9 mL (too big)
2.5 cm	19.625 sq cm	294.375 mL (too small)

- Use the calculator and work backward: Using the same numbers as above, if V = base × height and the height is 15 cm, the base must be 23.3 cm^2. If $A = \pi r^2$ and the area is 23.3, then r^2 must be $\frac{23.3}{\pi}$, or about 7.4 cm^2. If necessary, show students how to use the square-root key to finish the calculation and to find that r is about 2.73 cm.

• ***Teaching notes continued on page A386.***

3. See Additional Answers.

4. about 313.7 cm^2; The area of each circular end is about 32.2 cm^2. The area of the surface that wraps around the can is about $12.4 \times 6.4\pi$ cm^2, or about 249.3 cm^2.

Just the facts

The first "soft drinks" were mineral waters from natural springs. As water bubbles up through the earth, it collects minerals and carbon dioxide. In the 1700s, chemists perfected a method of adding carbonation and minerals to plain water and bottling the result.

4. Possible answer: The can with the least surface area will be the one whose diameter and height are closest to being equal. The surface areas in the class table decrease until the radius is about half the height, and then they increase again.

The volume printed on the can is given in milliliters (abbreviated mL). A milliliter has the same volume as a cubic centimeter, so 1 mL = 1 cm^3.

3. Does multiplying the area of the base by the height give the volume that is printed on the can? If not, why might the measures differ?

4. What is the surface area of the can in square centimeters? How did you find it? (Hint: Imagine what a net for the can would look like.)

Problem Set D

Now consider how the can design might be changed. For these problems, use the volume you *calculated* in Problem Set C, rather than the volume printed on the can. **1–3.** See Additional Answers.

1. Design and describe five other cans that have approximately the same volume as your can. Sketch a net for each can, and record the radius of the base and the height. Include cans that are both shorter and taller than a regular soft drink can. (Hint: First choose the height of the can, and then find the radius.)

2. Calculate the surface area of each can you designed. Record your group's data on the board for the class to see.

3. Compare the surface areas of the cans you and your classmates found. Which can has the greatest surface area? Which has the least surface area?

Bursting Bubbles wants to make a can using the least amount of aluminum possible. They can't do it by evaluating every possible can, like the five you found, and choosing the best. There are too many—an infinite number!—and they could never be sure they had found the one using the *least* material.

One problem-solving strategy that mathematicians use is to gather data, as you did in Problem 1, and look for patterns in the data. For a problem like this one, they would also try to show that a particular solution is the best in a way that doesn't involve testing every case.

4. Use what you know about volume and any patterns you found in Problems 1 and 2 to recommend a can with the least possible surface area to the president of Bursting Bubbles. Describe your can completely. Explain why you believe it has the least surface area.

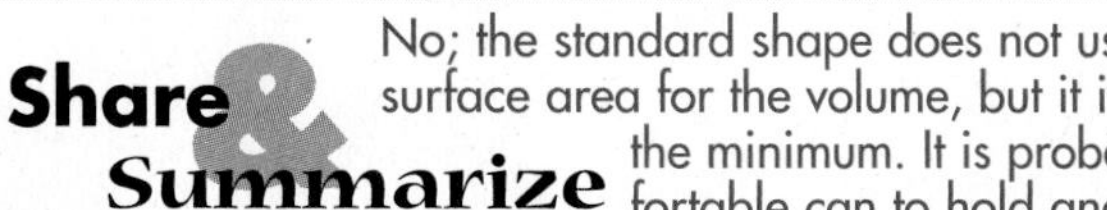

Share & Summarize

No; the standard shape does not use the minimum surface area for the volume, but it is not far from the minimum. It is probably a more comfortable can to hold and more attractive.

Does the shape of standard soft drink cans use the minimum surface area for the volume they contain? If not, what might be some reasons companies use the shape they do?

1 • In Problem 1, students need to sketch a net of the can.
• Have the whole class compare results.

2 Have students work in groups of 4.

3 Students can record their data in a table on the board.

4 Have groups report on their decision.

5 Have students share and explain answers.

Additional Answers
Problem Set C

3. Possible answer: Not quite. The formula gives about 399 mL, while the can claims 355 mL. Part of the difference may be that the can is not completely filled with liquid (carbonation takes up some of the space) and the fact that the can is not a true cylinder (its top and bottom aren't flat).

• ***Additional Answers continued on page A386.***

Assign and Assess

On Your Own Exercises

Investigation 1
Practice & Apply: 1–4
Connect & Extend: 13–18

Investigation 2
Practice & Apply: 5–8
Connect & Extend: 19

Investigation 3
Practice & Apply: 9–12
Connect & Extend: 20

Assign Anytime
Mixed Review: 21–36

Exercises 1–3 and 5–8:
These nets can be duplicated using Masters 15, On Your Own Exercises: Nets, and 16, On Your Own Exercises: Surface Area.

4. Possible answer:

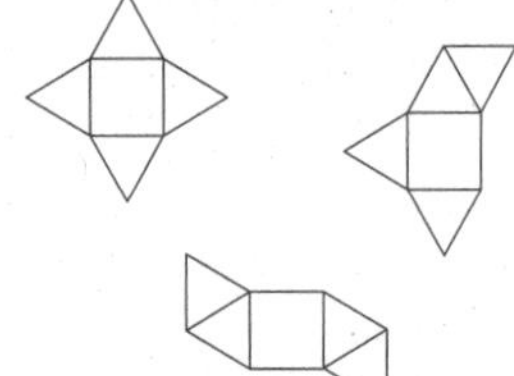

On Your Own Exercises

Practice & Apply

Decide whether each figure is a net—that is, whether it will fold into a closed solid. One way to decide is to cut out a copy of the figure and try to fold it. If the figure is a net, describe the shape it creates. If it isn't a net, tell what goes wrong.

1.

It is a net; it forms a solid with 8 triangular sides (an octahedron).

2.

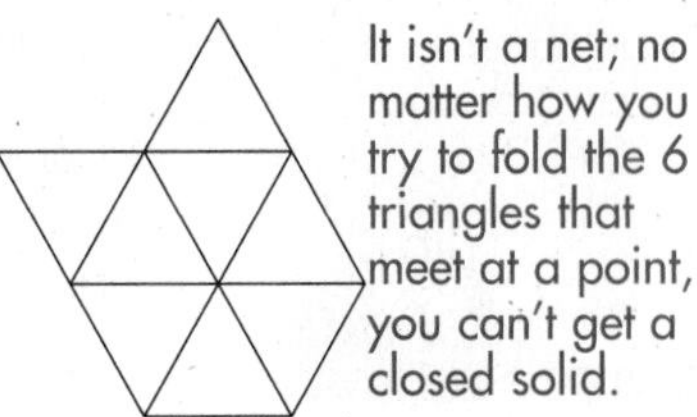

It isn't a net; no matter how you try to fold the 6 triangles that meet at a point, you can't get a closed solid.

3.

It is a net; it forms a solid with 2 parallel square faces connected by triangular faces.

4. A *square pyramid* has a square base and triangular faces that meet at a vertex. Find and draw at least three nets for a square pyramid.

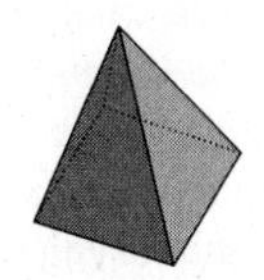

Square Pyramid

In Exercises 5–8, find the surface area of the solid that can be created from the net. Show how you found the surface area.

5. Each triangle is equilateral, with sides 5 cm and height 4.3 cm.
area of one triangle: 10.75 cm^2; total surface area: 86 cm^2

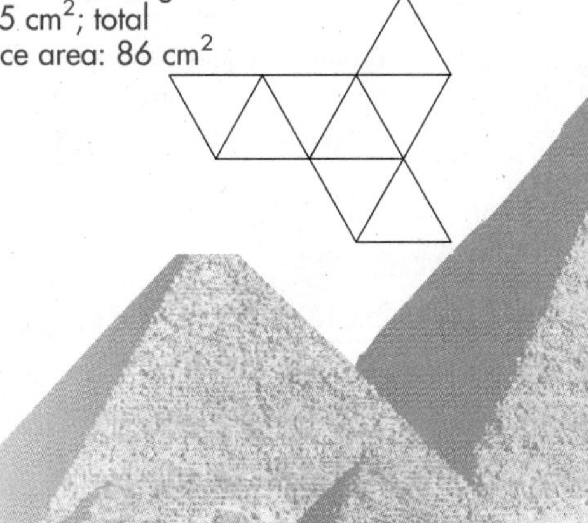

6. total area of triangles: 224 cm^2; total area of squares: 128 cm^2; total surface area: 352 cm^2

6. Each triangle is equilateral, with sides 8 cm and height 7 cm. The other shapes are squares.

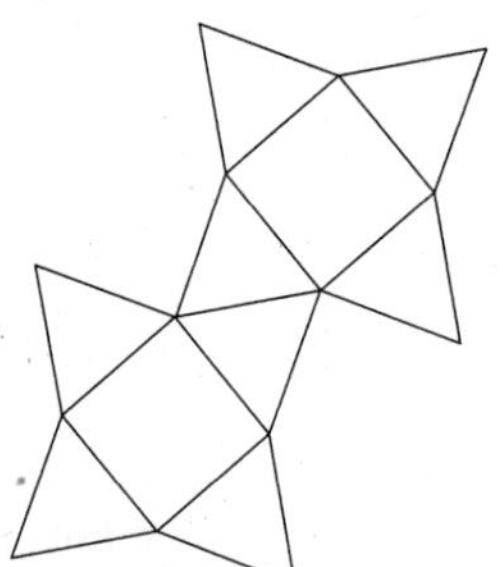

7. The radius of each circle is 2 cm. The height of the parallelogram is 2 cm.

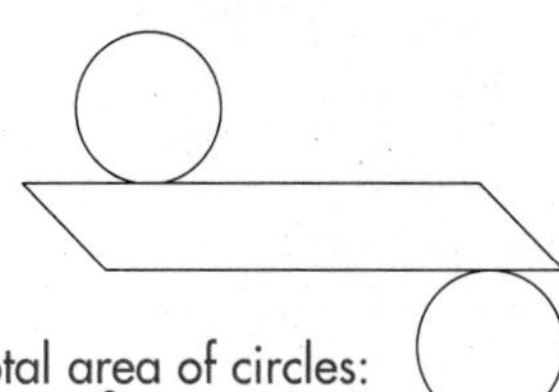

total area of circles: 8π cm^2; area of parallelogram: 8π cm^2; total surface area: 16π cm^2, or about 50.3 cm^2

8. The pentagons have side lengths of 3 cm. If you divide each pentagon into five isosceles triangles, the height of each triangle is 2 cm. The other shapes are squares.

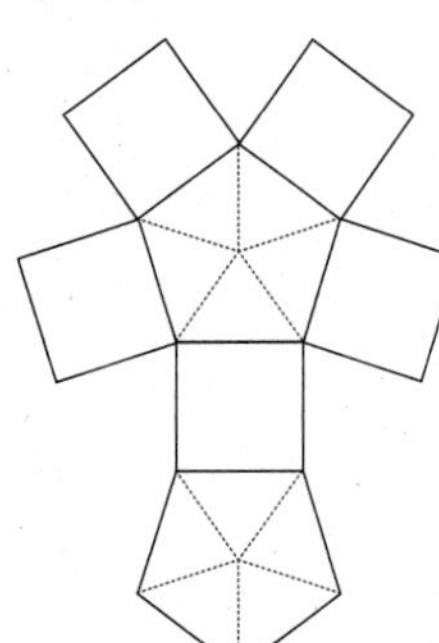

total area of pentagons: 30 cm^2; total area of squares: 45 cm^2; total surface area: 75 cm^2

9. An unopened box of tissues has length 24 cm, width 12 cm, and height 10.5 cm.

a. What is the volume of the box? 3,024 cm^3

b. What is the surface area of the box? 1,332 cm^2

10. A juice pitcher is shaped like a cylinder. It is 30 cm tall and has a base with radius 6 cm. It has a flat lid.

a. How much juice will the pitcher hold? $1{,}080\pi$ cm^3, or about 3,393 cm^3 (about 3.4 L)

b. What is the surface area of the pitcher? 432π cm^2, or about 1,357 cm^2

Exercises 5 and 11: These relate to what could be a whole day's investigation on the Platonic solids. See Teaching Notes on pages T134 and A385 for more on this topic.

Exercise 10: Students may answer in cm^3 or in mL or L. You might point out that milliliters and liters are more commonly used for liquids.

Teaching Resources

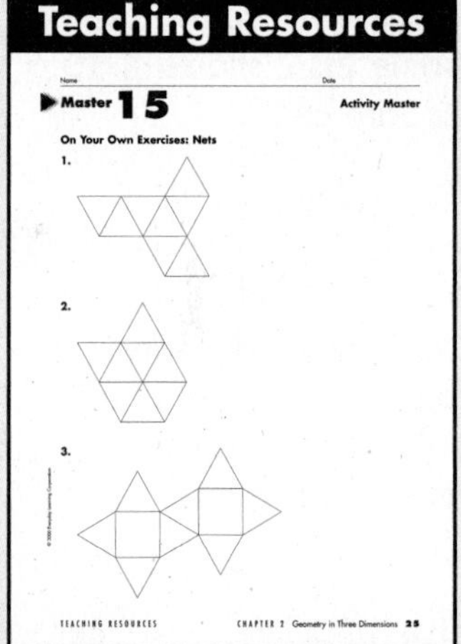

Master 15 — Activity Master

On Your Own Exercises: Nets

1.

2.

3.

TEACHING RESOURCES — CHAPTER 2 Geometry in Three Dimensions 35

Teaching Resources

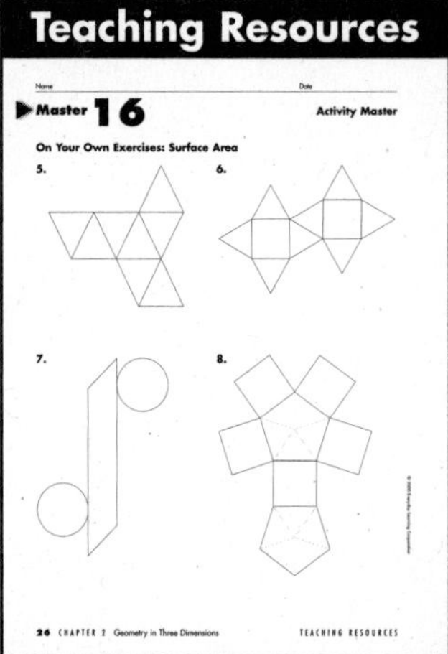

Master 16 — Activity Master

On Your Own Exercises: Surface Area

5.

6.

7.

8.

36 CHAPTER 2 Geometry in Three Dimensions — TEACHING RESOURCES

LESSON 2.4 Nets and Solids **137**

Assign and Assess

Exercise 11:
Students can find the surface area of the pyramid by finding the area of the large triangular net or by finding the area of each face and adding these areas. The dimensions of the whole triangle are given, so the surface area is $\frac{1}{2}(bh)$, which is $\frac{1}{2}(6 \cdot 5.2)$, or 15.6 square cm. If students notice that the points on each side are midpoints (or appear to be), then they can find that each triangle has a base of 3 cm and height of 2.6 cm, so each small triangle has an area of $\frac{1}{2}(3 \cdot 2.6)$ or 3.9 square cm. Since there are four triangles in the larger one, the answer comes out the same (as it should!): 15.6 square cm.

Exercise 13:
Students may note, rightly, that the label on the can actually overlaps itself a bit, so the length of the label will be a little bit more than $2\pi r$.

In your own words

Explain why nets might be useful in sewing, manufacturing, or some other profession.

12c. Nets and surface areas will vary.

12d. Answers will vary. If the object is a prism, a cylinder will work. The cylinder with the same diameter as height will have less surface area than any other cylinder or prism.

Connect & Extend

13b. $2\pi r$ and h

14. Possible net:

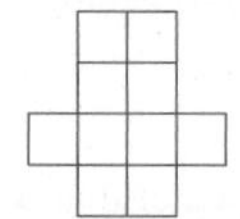

15. Possible net:

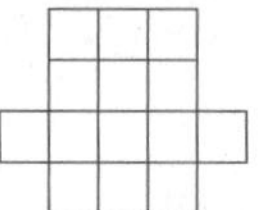

16. Possible net:

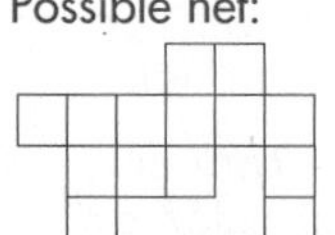

11. Challenge This net will fold into a *triangular pyramid.* Find the surface area of the pyramid, and estimate its volume. You may want to fold a copy of the net into the pyramid. surface area: about 15.6 cm^2; volume: about 3 cm^3 (See teaching notes for suggestions of strategies for estimating the volume.)

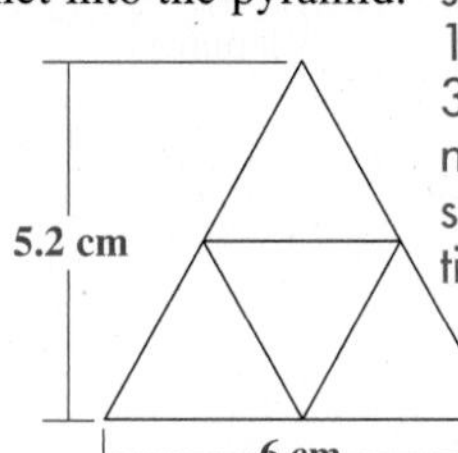

12. Choose a container in your house. You might choose a can (but not a soft drink can), a rectangular box, or some other object.

a. Draw a net for the object. Nets will vary.

b. Find the surface area and volume of the object by measuring its dimensions. Answers will vary.

c. Draw nets for three other objects with the same volume as your container, and find the surface area of each. The new objects do not have to be real containers from your home.

d. Is there a prism or cylinder with less surface area but the same volume as your container? If so, draw a net for it.

13. Imagine removing a label from a soup can.

a. What is the shape of the label? a rectangle

b. If the radius of the soup can is r and the height is h, what are the dimensions of the label?

Create a net for each box.

14.

15.

16. Challenge

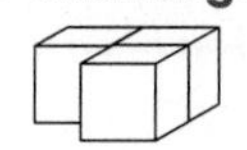

17. Challenge A cone has a circular base and a vertex some height away from that base. Make a net for a cone. See Additional Answers.

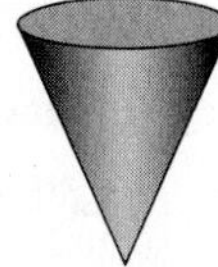

Additional Answers

17. Possible net:

Note: The net is a quarter circle with a smaller circle tangent to the curve. The radius of the quarter circle is 4 times the radius of the smaller circle. Students may not get the proportions correct.

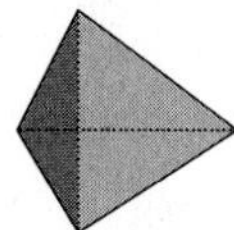

Tetrahedron

18. Possible answer: You can make a net for a solid with 8 triangular faces (an octahedron, as pictured in Exercise 1) and for a solid with 20 triangular faces (an icosahedron).

19b. $5{,}050\pi$ ft^2, or about 15,900 ft^2

20a. $3{,}000\pi$, or about 9,420

20c. 9,420 cm^3 ÷ 75.4 cm^3 = about 125 scoops

20e. surface area of single scoop: 32π cm^2, or about 100 cm^2; total surface area: about 12,500 cm^2

20f. The scooped ice cream has more surface area and would therefore melt faster.

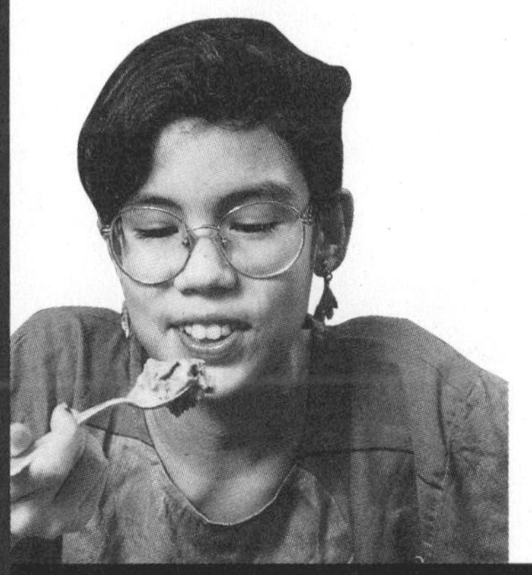

18. Challenge A *tetrahedron* is a solid with four triangular faces. You have made tetrahedrons from nets in this lesson. Nets for a tetrahedron contain only triangles. Can you make a net for another figure using only triangles? (Hint: You might try taping paper triangles together to form a new solid.)

19. A circular pond is 100 ft in diameter. In the middle of winter, the ice on the pond is 6 inches thick.

a. Think of the ice on the pond as a cylinder. What is the volume of ice? about 3,927 ft^3

b. What is the surface area of the floating cylinder of ice?

c. What would be the edge length of a cube of ice that had the same volume? about 15.8 ft

d. What would be the surface area of a cube of ice that had the same volume? about 1,493 ft^2

e. Which has greater surface area: the cylinder of ice or the cube of ice? How much more? the cylinder of ice; about 14,400 ft^2

20. Lana's Ice Cream Parlor packs ice cream into cylindrical tubs that are 20 cm in diameter and 30 cm tall.

a. How much ice cream does a tub hold?

b. Lana's Ice Cream Parlor sells ice cream in cylindrical scoops. If each scoop has base radius 2 cm and height 6 cm, what is the volume of a single scoop? 24π cm^3, or about 75.4 cm^3

c. How many scoops of ice cream are in a tub? Show how you found your answer.

d. What is the surface area of a tub? 800π cm^3, or about 2,510 cm^3

e. What is the total surface area of the ice cream from one tub *after* it has all been scooped out?

f. Which has more surface area: the ice cream in the tub or the scooped ice cream? Which would melt faster?

Exercise 14–16:
Students may find it challenging to visualize the nets for a block structure rather than for other solids they have worked with. Partly, there are other squares to confuse the picture—squares that lie in the same plane rather than folding up. Encourage students to cut out their nets and fold them to test whether they work. They may also want to distinguish the lines between blocks from the lines along which you fold by using dashed lines or heavier lines for one of them. Master 9, Centimeter Graph Paper, might help with this somewhat. If students create the nets on graph paper, then the lines of the graph paper can show the lines between blocks, and the lines students draw will be the lines of the net.

Quick Check

Informal Assessment
At the end of the lesson, students should be able to:

- ✔ decide if a given net will fold into a closed three-dimensional solid
- ✔ create nets that will fold into given shapes
- ✔ use the nets of an object to find surface area and volume

Quick Quiz

1. Draw a net for a cube that has a volume of 8 cubic cm. *Possible answer:*

2. What is the surface area of a cube with a volume of 8 cubic cm? 24 cm^2

Mixed Review

Evaluate each expression.

21. $0.6 \cdot 0.6$ 0.36 **22.** $0.3 \cdot 0.3$ 0.09 **23.** $0.02 \cdot 0.02$ 0.0004

24. $0.8 + 0.01$ 0.81 **25.** $0.8 - 0.01$ 0.79 **26.** $2 - 0.8$ 1.2

27. Complete the table.

n	0	1	2	3	5	47	100
$2n + 1$	1	3	5	7	11	95	201

Write each expression without using multiplication signs.

28. $b \times b \times b \times b$ **29.** $y \times y \times y \times 3$ **30.** $a \times a \times a \times a \times 4$

28. b^4
29. $3y^3$
30. $4a^4$

Find the value for $2k^2$ for each value of k.

31. $k = 0$ 0 **32.** $k = \frac{1}{2}$ $\frac{1}{2}$ **33.** $k = 1.2$ 2.88

Use the given expression to complete each table. Then write another expression that gives the same values.

34.

t	0	1	2	3	4	100
$2(t + 10)$	20	22	24	26	28	220

$2t + 20$

35.

r	2	3	4	5	6	100
$6(r - 2)$	0	6	12	18	24	588

$6r - 12$

36. Ecology The table lists some of the types of endangered species in the world.

a. Make a pie chart (circle graph) of these data. On each section, write the percentage each category is of the total number of species listed. Round to the nearest tenth.

b. About what percentage of the endangered species listed are mammals or birds?

c. Write three statements comparing the number of endangered fish species to the number of endangered snail species.

Species	Number Endangered
mammals	310
birds	253
fishes	79
reptiles	78
snails	16

36a. See Additional Answers.
36b. about 75.5%
36c. Possible answer: There are about 5 times as many endangered fish species as endangered snail species. There are 63 more endangered fish species than endangered snail species. There is about 1 endangered snail species for every 5 endangered fish species.

• *See Additional Answers on page A386.*

140 CHAPTER 2 Geometry in Three Dimensions

VOCABULARY
base
cylinder
net
prism
surface area
volume

MATERIALS
cubes

Chapter Summary

In this chapter, you have explored four representations of three-dimensional figures:

- top-count views
- engineering views
- regular views (front, top, and right)
- nets

You learned that volume is measured in cubic units, and that area and surface area are measured in square units. You found volume and surface area for block structures by counting cubes and counting exposed faces. You also found a formula for the volume of prisms, and a method for finding surface area by using nets.

Finally, you investigated a scientific application of surface area and volume: the relationship between surface area and volume in human beings, and what it reveals about cooling and dehydration.

Strategies and Applications

The questions in this section will help you review and apply the important ideas and strategies developed in this chapter.

Working with block patterns

1. Create your own block pattern. Answers will vary.

a. Draw top-count views for the first three stages of your pattern.

b. Describe how you arrange blocks as you build from one stage of your pattern to the next. Your description should be detailed enough that someone could use it to build any stage from the previous one.

c. Describe the number of blocks added from one stage of your pattern to the next. Write an expression for the number of blocks you add to Stage s to make Stage $s + 1$.

d. Write an expression for the total number of blocks in Stage s.

Representing three-dimensional structures

2. Use 10 blocks to create a structure. Answers will vary.

a. Draw the top-count view for your structure.

b. Draw regular front, top, and right views of your structure.

c. Draw engineering views for your structure.

3. Draw a net for the solid shown at left. See margin.

3.

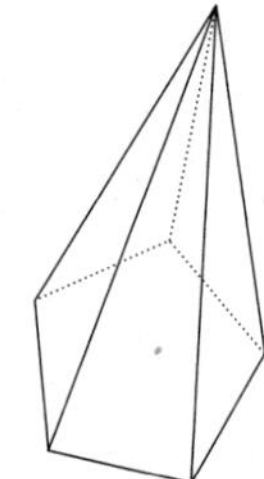

Chapter Summary
This summary helps students recall the major topics of the chapter.

Vocabulary
Students should be able to explain each of the terms listed in the vocabulary section.

Strategies and Applications
The questions in this section help students review and apply the important mathematical ideas and problem-solving strategies developed in the chapter. The questions are organized by mathematical highlight. The highlights correspond to those in "The Big Picture" chart on page 75a.

Exercise 1:
Watch for students who do not add blocks to their pattern in a predictable way.

Exercise 2:
Students draw top-count views, front/top/side views, and engineering views for their own structure.

Exercise 3:
Watch for students who draw three triangular sides rather than the five sides that are necessary for the pattern. Remind them that the number of sides depends on the number of sides of the base.

Exercise 4c:
You may wish to have your students round their estimate of the radius to the nearest hundredth. Then ask them to describe how their estimate will be affected if they round to the nearest tenth and to the nearest whole number.

Exercise 5:
If students are having trouble, encourage them to use blocks to model the different rectangular prisms.

Exercise 8:
In order to form a net, the triangles must not only be isosceles, but they must be taller than the side of the base to allow the figure to close.

Finding the volume of a solid

4. A block prism has a base 4 cm long and 3 cm wide. The prism is 5 cm tall.

a. What is the prism's volume? 60 cm^3

b. Imagine a different block prism with the same height and volume as the original prism. What are its dimensions?

4b. Possible answers:
1 cm × 12 cm × 5 cm,
2 cm × 6 cm × 5 cm

c. Imagine a cylinder with height 5 cm and the same volume as the original prism. What is the area of its base? Estimate its radius.
12 cm^2, about 1.95 cm

Finding the surface area of a solid

5. Find all the rectangular prisms you can make with 24 blocks. Try to do this without building all of them.

a. Give the dimensions of each prism.

5a. 24 × 1 × 1,
12 × 2 × 1,
8 × 3 × 1,
6 × 4 × 1,
6 × 2 × 2,
4 × 3 × 2

b. Which of your prisms has the greatest surface area? What is its surface area? 24 × 1 × 1, 98 square units

c. Which of your prisms has the least surface area? What is its surface area? 4 × 3 × 2, 52 square units

Find the surface area of each solid.

6. 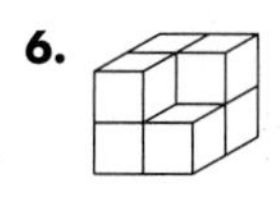 24 square units

7. 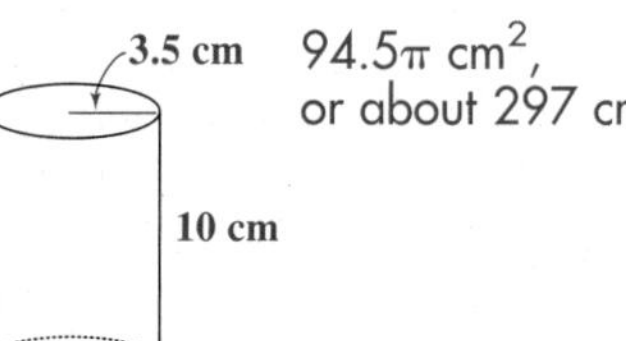

94.5π cm^2, or about 297 cm^2

Remember
An isosceles triangle has two sides of equal length.

8. The square in the figure at right has sides of length 3 cm. The triangles are isosceles, and the height of each triangle is 4 cm. Is the figure a net? In other words, does it fold up to form a closed solid? Explain how you know.

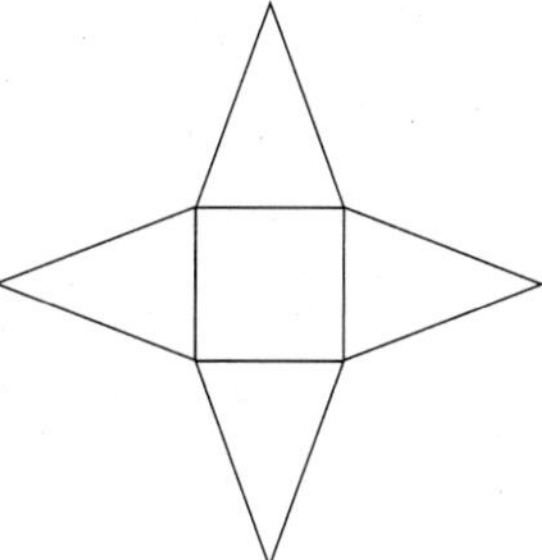

Yes; since the triangles are all isosceles and the same size, the sides will fit together.

142 CHAPTER 2 Geometry in Three Dimensions

Demonstrating Skills

In Questions 9–16, find the volume and surface area of the solid.

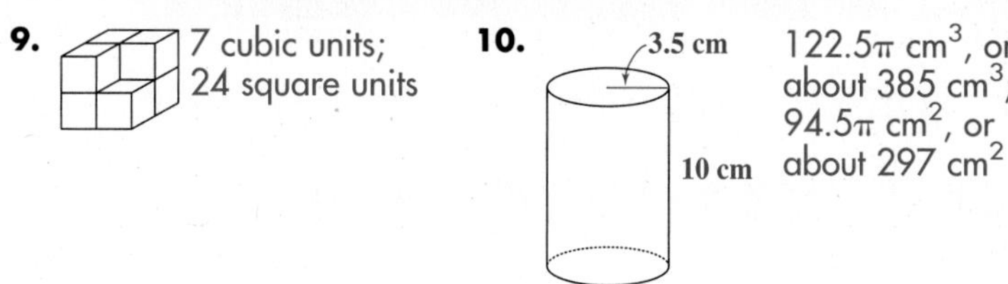

9. 7 cubic units; 24 square units

10. 122.5π cm^3, or about 385 cm^3; 94.5π cm^2, or about 297 cm^2

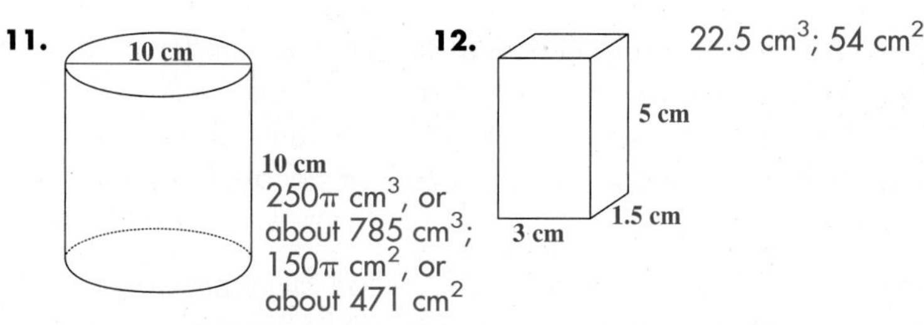

11. 250π cm^3, or about 785 cm^3; 150π cm^2, or about 471 cm^2

12. 22.5 cm^3; 54 cm^2

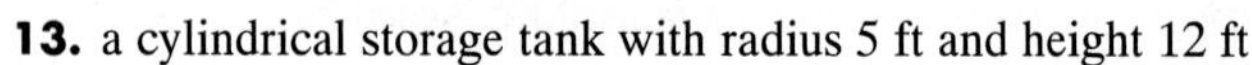

13. a cylindrical storage tank with radius 5 ft and height 12 ft
14. a cardboard box with length 2 m, width 2.5 m, and height 3 m
15. a can with height 10 cm and circumference 18 cm
16. a cube with side length 1.5 m   3.375 m^3; 13.5 m^2
17. Which of these three solids has the greatest surface area? Which has the least surface area?   greatest: the $3 \times 9 \times 5$ prism; least: the cylinder

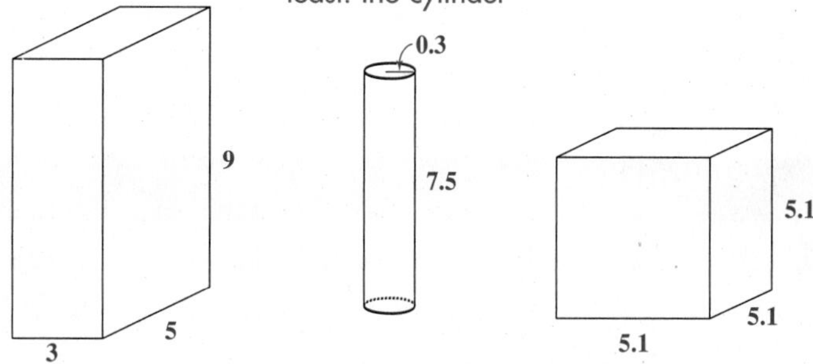

13. 300π ft^3, or about 942 ft^3; 170π ft^2, or about 534 ft^2
14. 15 m^3; 37 m^2
15. about 258 cm^3; about 232 cm^2

Remember

The circumference of a circle is $2\pi r$, where r is the radius.

Exercise 9 Extension: Ask students how the volume and the surface area of the solid change if another block is added to make the solid a cube.

Exercise 11: Watch for students who use 10 cm as the radius. Remind them that 10 cm is the diameter.

Exercise 17: Have students predict which solid will have the greatest surface area and which solid will have the least surface area before they solve the problem.

Review and Self-Assessment **143**

CHAPTER 3

Exploring Exponents

Chapter Overview

In this chapter, students use stretching and shrinking machines to help them understand the product, quotient, and powering laws of exponents: $a^b \times a^c = a^{b+c}$, $a^c \times b^c = (a \times b)^c$, $a^b \div a^c = a^{b-c}$, $a^c \div b^c = (a \div b)^c$, and $(a^b)^c = a^{b \times c}$. Students also investigate exponential increase, or growth, and exponential decrease, or decay, in both abstract and real-world situations.

After developing a sense of large numbers like a million and a billion, students work with powers of 10 and learn how to express large numbers in scientific notation. Students also investigate scientific notation on their calculators.

Chapter 3 Highlights	Links to the Past	Links to the Future
Working with stretching and shrinking machines (3.1, 3.2)	**Course 1:** Working with a machine model for fractions	**Chapter 4:** Using stretching and shrinking machines to understand negative exponents
Understanding laws of exponents (3.1, 3.2)	**Course 1:** Working with exponents in prime factorizations and geometric formulas	**Chapter 4:** Extending laws of exponents to negative exponents **Course 3:** Extending laws of exponents to fractional exponents
Identifying and working with exponential growth (3.3)	**Course 1:** Looking at doubling patterns	**Chapter 9:** Investigating exponential growth curves **Course 3:** Exploring exponential growth and decay with growth and decay rates expressed as percents
Developing a sense of large numbers (3.4)	**Elementary grades:** Developing a sense of 1 million	**Chapter 4:** Working with very small numbers
Expressing large numbers in scientific notation (3.4)	**Course 1:** Relating place value to powers of 10	**Chapter 4:** Expressing small numbers in scientific notation

Lesson Objectives	Pacing	Materials	NCTM Standards
3.1 Stretching and Shrinking Machines page 145b • To model the behavior of exponents using stretching and shrinking machines • To understand and apply the product laws of exponents	4 class periods	• Master 17 (Teaching Resources, page 29) • Master 18 (Teaching Resources, page 30)	2, 6, 7, 8
3.2 Shrinking and Super Machines page 163b • To model the behavior of exponents using stretching and shrinking machines • To understand and apply the quotient laws of exponents • To understand and apply the power of a power law of exponents	3 class periods	• Master 17	2, 6, 7, 8, 10
3.3 Growing Exponentially page 175b • To develop a sense of exponential growth and exponential decay • To describe examples of exponential increase and exponential decrease • To compare exponential growth with other kinds of growth (linear, quadratic, and so on)	2 class periods	• Master 9 (Teaching Resources, page 14)	3, 9
3.4 Describing Large Numbers page 189b • To understand the relative difference between a million and a billion • To multiply and divide numbers by powers of 10 • To write numbers using scientific notation • To use a calculator to work with numbers in scientific notation	4 class periods	• Master 17 • Rulers, quarters • Tower of Hanoi setup, 6 blocks per group	1, 2, 10

NCTM Curriculum and Evaluation Standards

1. Number and Operation
2. Patterns, Functions, and Algebra
3. Geometry and Spatial Sense
4. Measurement
5. Data Analysis, Statistics, and Probability
6. Problem Solving
7. Reasoning and Proof
8. Communication
9. Connections
10. Representation

Assessment Opportunities

Standard Assessment

Impact Mathematics offers three types of formal assessment. The Chapter 3 Review & Self-Assessment in the Student Edition serves as a self-assessment tool for students. In the Teacher's Guide, a Quick Quiz at the end of each lesson allows you to check students' understanding before moving on to the next lesson. The Assessment Resources include blackline masters for chapter and semester tests.

- **Student Edition** Chapter 3 Review and Self-Assessment, pages 213–215
- **Teacher's Guide** Quick Quizzes, pages 163, 175, 189, 212
- **Assessment Resources** Chapter 3 Test, Form A, pages 47–49; Chapter 3 Test, Form B, pages 50–52

Ongoing Assessment

Impact Mathematics provides numerous opportunities for informal assessment of your students as they work through the investigations. Share & Summarize questions help you determine whether students understand the important ideas of an investigation. If students are struggling, Troubleshooting offers tips with suggestions for helping them. On the Spot Assessment notes appear throughout the teaching notes. They give you suggestions for preventing or remedying common student errors. Assessment Checklists in the Assessment Resources book provide convenient ways to record student progress.

- **Student Edition** Share & Summarize, pages 149, 152, 156, 159, 165, 167, 171, 178, 182, 192, 195, 199, 202
- **Teacher's Guide** On the Spot Assessment, pages T147, T150, T155, T166, T171, T191, T201
  Troubleshooting, pages T149, T152, T156, T159, T165, T167, T171, T178, T182, T192, T195, T199, T202
- **Assessment Resources** Chapter 3 Assessment Checklists, pages 107–108

Alternative Assessment, Portfolios, and Journal Ideas

The alternative assessment items in *Impact Mathematics* are perfect for inclusion in student portfolios and journals. The Share & Summarize and In Your Own Words features in the Student Edition gives students a chance to write about mathematical ideas. The Performance Assessment items in the Assessment Resources book provide rich, open-ended problems, ideal for take-home or group assessment.

- **Student Edition** In Your Own Words, pages 162, 175, 187, 211
- **Assessment Resources** Chapter 3 Performance Assessment, page 53

Assessment Resources

The Assessment Resources book provides a chapter test in two equivalent forms, along with additional performance items. The performance items can be used in a variety of ways. They are ideal for take-home assessment or in-class group assessment.

- Chapter 3 Test, Form A, pages 47–49
- Chapter 3 Test, Form B, pages 50–52
- Chapter 3 Performance Assessment, page 53
- Chapter 3 Assessment Solutions, pages 54–55

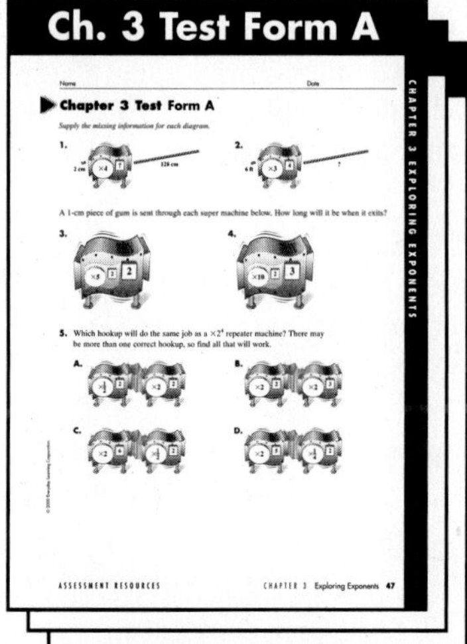

Ch. 3 Test Form A

Chapter 3 Test Form A

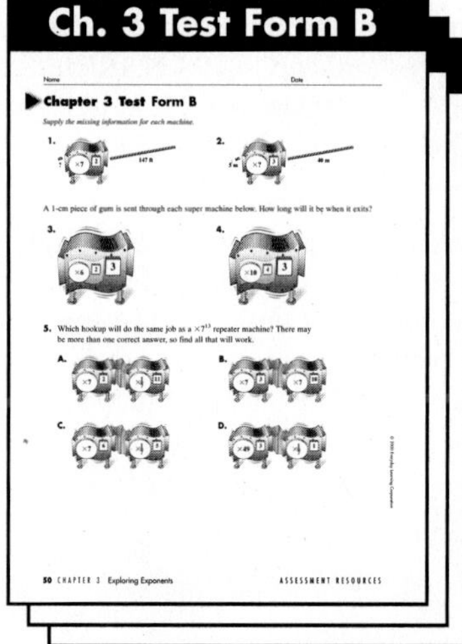

Ch. 3 Test Form B

Chapter 3 Test Form B

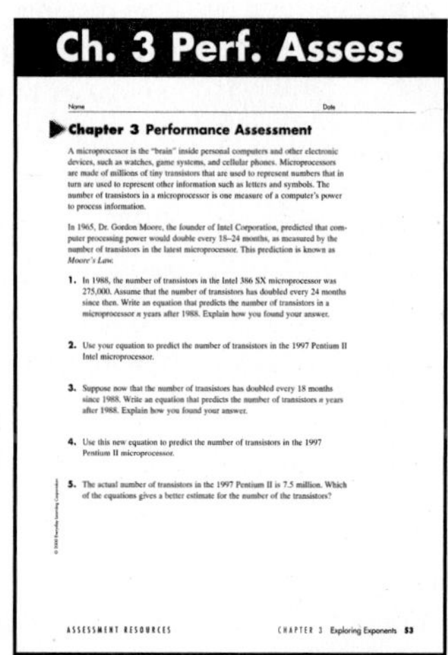

Ch. 3 Perf. Assess

Chapter 3 Performance Assessment

Additional Resources

Print	Software	Video	Web sites
Power Play by Edward J. Barbeau, Mathematical Association of America, 1997 This book is a walk through the wonderful world of numbers, enjoyable for teachers and students alike. Includes exercises and solutions. *Powers of Ten: About the Relative Size of Things in the Universe* by Philip Morrison and Phyllis Morrison, W.H. Freeman, 1994 This book takes the reader from the extremely small to the extremely vast corners of the universe, creating thirty-two scenes with different "power of ten" levels of magnification.	*Jumpstart Algebra: Easy Step by Step Approach,* Heartsoft Software, 1992 Macintosh or IBM compatible Grades 6–12 This interactive software provides beginning algebra students with practice in exponents, order of operations, polynomials, factoring. *The GO Program: New Gravity and Orbit* by Gilbert Yanow, National Aeronautics and Space Administration, Jet Propulsion Laboratory (Pasadena, CA) Macintosh compatible Grades 5–12 This program contains data for all the planets and major satellites.	*Patterns with Ten* by Nebraska Mathematics and Science Coalition, Sunburst Communications, Inc. (Pleasantville, NY) Grades 6–9 This video emphasizes the multiplication factor involved in changing units of measurement. Use of scientific notation is shown. *Using Positive Exponents,* Louisiana Educational Television Authority (Baton Rouge, LA) Grades 8, 9 Part of the POWER OF ALGEBRA series, this video uses an animated Sherlock Holmes to lead students on math adventures.	Visit the Everyday Learning Web site at **http://www.everydaylearning.com** *Mathematics Hot List* **http://sln.fi.edu/tfi/hotlist/math.html** This site contains numerous references and links to many math topics. *A Math Web site: A Learning site for Middle School Students* **http://www-personal.umd.umich.edu/~jobrown/math.html** Grades 5–8 This site contains numerous links to math activities and problems in algebra and geometry.

Introduction

The captions on the opening spread give examples of the use of scientific notation in astronomical figures and amounts of money. You might want to discuss the captions with the class, asking students to explain what each statement means. They will probably be surprised by the enormity of the numbers involved.

The "Astronomical Figures" feature describes distances in space and provides a bit of background regarding a recent mission to the planet Mars, along with the cost of the mission.

Explain to students that in this chapter they will work on many problems with large numbers and that it will be handy to learn a new way, called *scientific notation*, to express those numbers. Ask whether anyone has seen or used scientific notation in science class or elsewhere and what it looks like. If no one has, ask students how they might represent very large numbers if they didn't want to write out all the digits.

Finally, ask students to think of other contexts besides space and astronomy in which they might have to deal with very large numbers.

CHAPTER 3

Exploring Exponents

Scientists often use very large numbers. To save time and space, and to make comparing and calculating with numbers easier, they often use a shorthand notation. The shorthand uses the number 10 and an exponent. The 6 in 10^6 is an example of an exponent. In this chapter, you'll learn about exponents and many of their uses, including scientific notation.

Astronomical Figures

The distances from the sun to each of the nine planets in our solar system varies from about 35,980,000 miles to 3,666,000,000 miles! These distances are easier to write in shorthand: 3.598×10^7 and 3.666×10^9 miles. The distance from the sun to the star nearest to it, Proxima Centauri, is about 25,000,000,000,000 miles. It would be much easier for an astronomer to write 2.5×10^{13} miles.

Mars, the fourth planet in our solar system, is 1.41×10^8 miles from the sun. On July 4, 1997, The Mars *Pathfinder* from the National Aeronautics and Space Administration landed on Mars. The spacecraft put the surface rover *Sojourner* on the planet. *Sojourner* sent detailed photos back to Earth, giving us our first up-close views of our sister planet!

The Mars Pathfinder Mission was part of a NASA program with a spending limit of \$150,000,000, or 1.5×10^8 dollars.

144

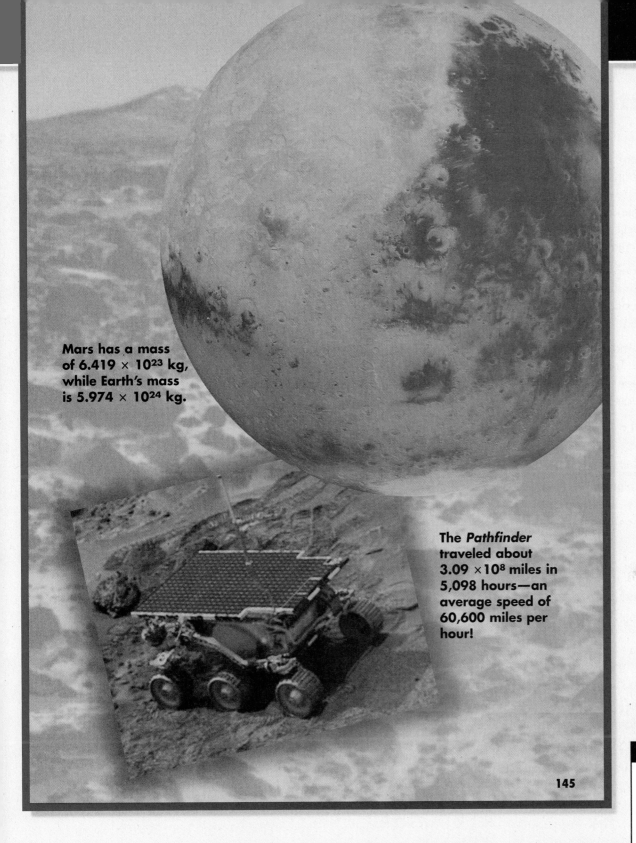

Mars has a mass of 6.419×10^{23} kg, while Earth's mass is 5.974×10^{24} kg.

The *Pathfinder* traveled about 3.09×10^8 miles in 5,098 hours—an average speed of 60,600 miles per hour!

145

Ch 3 Family Letter

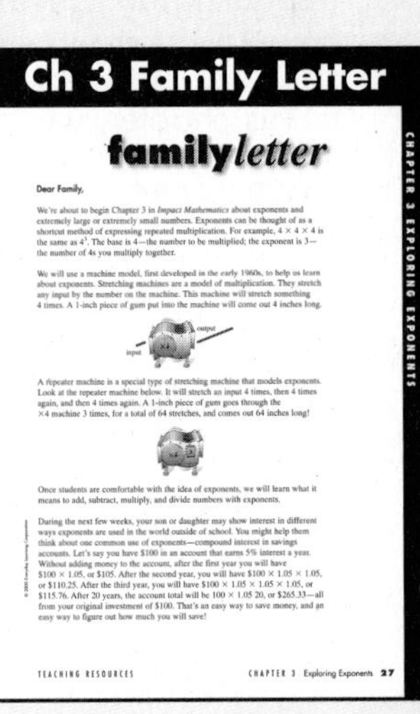

familyletter

Dear Family,

We're about to begin Chapter 3 in *Impact Mathematics* about exponents and extremely large or extremely small numbers. Exponents can be thought of as a shortcut method of expressing repeated multiplication. For example, $4 \times 4 \times 4$ is the same as 4^3. The base is 4—the number to be multiplied; the exponent is 3—the number of 4s you multiply together.

We will use a machine model, first developed in the early 1960s, to help us learn about exponents. Stretching machines are a model of multiplication. They stretch any input by the number on the machine. This machine will stretch something 4 times. A 1-inch piece of gum put into the machine will come out 4 inches long.

A repeater machine is a special type of stretching machine that models exponents. Look at the repeater machine below. It will stretch an input 4 times, then 4 times again, and then 4 times again. A 1-inch piece of gum goes through the ×4 machine 3 times, for a total of 64 stretches, and comes out 64 inches long!

Once students are comfortable with the idea of exponents, we will learn what it means to add, subtract, multiply, and divide numbers with exponents.

During the next few weeks, your son or daughter may show interest in different ways exponents are used in the world outside of school. You might help them think about one common use of exponents—compound interest in savings accounts. Let's say you have \$100 in an account that earns 5% interest a year. Without adding money to the account, after the first year you will have \$100 × 1.05, or \$105. After the second year, you will have \$100 × 1.05 × 1.05, or \$110.25. After the third year, you will have \$100 × 1.05 × 1.05 × 1.05, or \$115.76. After 20 years, the account total will be 100 × 1.05 20, or \$265.33—all from your original investment of \$100. That's an easy way to save money, and an easy way to figure out how much you will save!

CHAPTER 3 EXPLORING EXPONENTS

TEACHING RESOURCES CHAPTER 3 Exploring Exponents 27

Mathematical Background

How many is a million? How about a billion? Which is more, 100 million or 1 billion? References and comparisons to numbers like this, or even larger, are tossed around rather cavalierly in today's conversations. Chapter 3 introduces students to ways of taming extremely large numbers by using the laws of exponents. They will find out how numbers with exponents are related to numbers written in scientific notation. They will also investigate exponential growth and exponential decay by way of word problems.

Stretching and shrinking machines, introduced in Course 1 to help students think about factors, will be used in this chapter. Using the "stretching machine" as a model for multiplication, with repeated applications of the machine related to repeated multiplication, is a natural lead-in to the laws of exponents.

A nice connection to make in this chapter is the analogy between exponentiation and integer multiplication. This analogy is often encapsulated by saying: "Just as multiplying by a positive integer indicates repeated addition, so raising to a positive integer power indicates repeated multiplication."

So $na = a + a + \ldots + a$ (a is an addend n times),
and $a^n = a \cdot a \cdot \ldots \cdot a$ (a is a factor n times).

Furthermore, each of the three basic laws of exponents, all of which students will encounter in this chapter, have an exact counterpart in multiplication.

Laws of Exponents	Laws of Multiplication
$a^m a^n = a^{m+n}$	$ma + na = (m + n)a$
$(a^m)^n = a^{m \times n}$	$n(ma) = (nm)a$
$(ab)^n = a^n b^n$	$n(a + b) = na + nb$

The analogy continues. For example,

$a^0 = 1$ (1 is the identity for multiplication.)	$a \cdot 0 = 0$ (0 is the identity for addition.)
$a^{-n} = \left(\frac{1}{a}\right)^n$ ($\frac{1}{a}$ is the inverse for multiplication.)	$(^-n)a = n(^-a)$ (^-a is the inverse for addition.)

Perhaps the most difficult thing for students to remember is that exactly the same idea (repeating an operation) is expressed in very different notations for addition (na) and for multiplication (a^n).

In this chapter, we focus on the laws of exponents:

Product Laws	$a^m \cdot a^n = a^{m+n}$	$(a \cdot b)^m = a^m \cdot b^m$
Quotient Laws	$a^m \div a^n = a^{m-n}$	$(a \div b)^m = a^m \div b^m$
Power of a Power Law		$(a^m)^n = a^{m \times n}$

Students will be expected to understand and at times construct informal proofs of these laws, similar to this one: To see that $a^m \cdot a^n = a^{m+n}$, we need to count the number of a's in the expression $a^m \cdot a^n$ and to observe that there will be $m + n$ of them.

• ***Teaching notes continued on page A387.***

3.1

Stretching and Shrinking Machines

Objectives

- To model the behavior of exponents using stretching and shrinking machines
- To understand and apply the product laws of exponents

Overview (Pacing: about 4 class periods)

In this lesson, students learn exponents through a concrete model of stretching and shrinking machines. The model we use was developed by Peter Braunfeld and Max Beberman in 1963, at the University of Illinois. By hooking up stretching and shrinking machines, students can work with a model that demonstrates the laws of exponents.

If students have worked with this model before, you may want to move more quickly through Investigation 1.

Advance Preparation

You may want to make an overhead transparency of Master 17, Blank Stretching and Shrinking Machines, to use as you discuss the stretching and shrinking machines in class and of Master 18, Hookup Table to use with Problem Set A. This master includes blank versions of the stretching and shrinking machines used in this lesson. You might also provide copies of this master to students to use for their work on the problem sets and homework. Be aware that while Master 18 is referred to in the teacher's notes for Problem Set A, there are no other specific references to Master 17 in the chapter.

	Summary	Materials	On Your Own Exercises	Assessment Opportunities
Investigation 1 page T147	Students work with stretching machines. They explore a "big problem" of how to replace machines with hookups, which can lead to a review of some ideas about prime factorization.	• Master 17 (Teaching Resources, page 29) • Master 18 (Teaching Resources, page 30)	Practice & Apply: 1–8 Connect & Extend: 50–51 Mixed Review: 61–74	Share & Summarize, pages T149, 149 On the Spot Assessment, page T147 Troubleshooting, page T149
Investigation 2 page T149	Students work with stretching machines to model repeated multiplication and to begin work with exponents.	• Master 17	Practice & Apply: 9–20 Connect & Extend: 52–57 Mixed Review: 61–74	Share & Summarize, pages T152, 152 On the Spot Assessment, page T150 Troubleshooting, page T152
Investigation 3 page T152	Students use hookups of stretching machines to model the law of exponents, $r^a \times r^b = r^{a+b}$.	• Master 17	Practice & Apply: 21–33 Connect & Extend: 58 Mixed Review: 61–74	Share & Summarize, pages T156, 156 On the Spot Assessment, page T155 Troubleshooting, page T156
Investigation 4 page T156	Students use hookups of stretching machines to model the law of exponents, $r^a \times s^a = (rs)^a$. Students also explore erroneous "sum laws" to see why they do not work.	• Master 17	Practice & Apply: 34–49 Connect & Extend: 59–60 Mixed Review: 61–74	Share & Summarize, pages T159, 159 Troubleshooting, page T159 Informal Assessment, page 163 Quick Quiz, page 163

Introduce

1 Walk students through the scenario of owning a resizing factory. Draw a $\times 4$ machine on the board, and explain that any item put into the machine will come out 4 times as long. You might mention that these machines change only the length of the item.

Of course, the factory also has other stretching machines with many different stretching capabilities.

2 **Think & Discuss**
As part of a whole-class discussion, you might ask additional questions like those in the text, varying the input length and the machines:

> If you put a 3-inch carrot into a $\times 9$ machine, how long would it be when it came out? 27 in.
>
> What would this $\times 4$ machine do to a 100-inch carrot? *stretch it to 400 in.*

3.1 Stretching and Shrinking Machines

Congratulations! You are now the proud owner of a resizing factory. Your factory houses a magnificent set of machines that will stretch almost anything. Imagine the possibilities: you could stretch a 5-meter flagpole into a 10-meter flagpole, a 10-foot ladder into a 30-foot ladder, or a 10-inch gold chain into a 100-inch gold chain!

1 Introduce stretching machines.

With the ×4 machine, for example, you can put a regular stick of gum into the input slot . . .

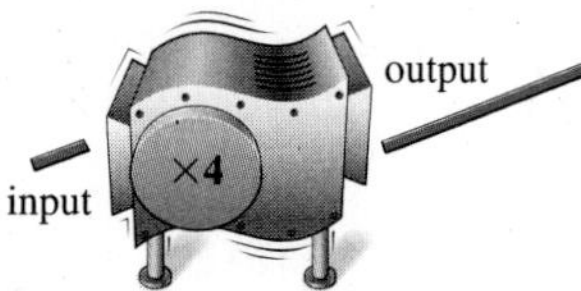

. . . and, in no time at all, a stick of gum four times as long emerges from the output slot!

Think & Discuss

2 After discussing these problems, give students additional examples.

If you put a 2-inch carrot into a ×4 machine, how long will it be when it comes out? 8 in.

2 in. ×4 ?

If you put a 3-inch crayon into a ×4 machine, how long will it be when it comes out? 12 in.

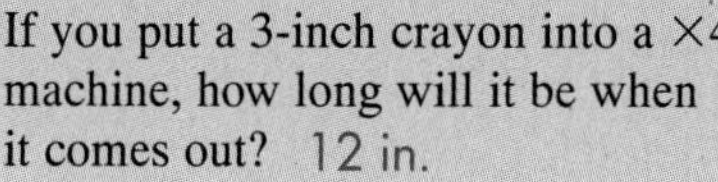

Your factory has other stretching machines as well. If you put a 5-inch piece of wire into a ×7 machine, how long will it be when it comes out? 35 in.

Investigation 1

Students should be comfortable with the machine model before beginning the problem sets in Investigation 1.

In this investigation, students practice using the model of stretching machines, including hookups (two or more machines linked together in which the output of one becomes the input of the next). The idea of a hookup is central to the concept of repeated multiplication, a concept important for the introduction of exponents.

Problem Set A **Grouping: Pairs**

This problem set gives students practice with the model of stretching machines and a few simple hookups. You may want to provide students with copies of Master 18, Hookup Table, to record their answers to Problem 5a. You could also use a transparency of this master to discuss the problem.

In **Problems 1–4,** students find hookups to replace some broken machines. This involves finding factors of the number on the original machine.

In **Problem 3,** students may find that they can use one set of hookups to find other hookups. For example, they may have learned that they could replace a ×36 with a ×2 machine and a ×18 machine. Then they may have learned that they can replace the ×18 machine with two ×3 machines and a ×2 machine. Students can substitute these three machines for the ×18 machine in the previous solution and find another way to do the work of a ×36 machine: two ×2 machines and two ×3 machines.

On the Spot Assessment

Watch for students who think that the machines add rather than multiply. Despite the ×2 on the machines, students can still be confused if they think of as ×2 as "2 longer than" rather than "2 times as long." Take advantage of each opportunity to have students say aloud the proper names of the machines, such as "times 2."

A pen went through a $\times 6$ machine and emerged 30 inches long. How long was it when it entered? 5 in.

It is stretched to a length of $8g$.

What happens if a pen of length g goes through a $\times 8$ machine?

Investigation 1 Machine Hookups

1 Be sure students are comfortable with the machine model.

As with any machine, the stretching machines at your factory occasionally break down. Fortunately, with a little ingenuity, your employees usually find a way to work around this problem.

Problem Set A

2 Have students work in pairs.

1. One day, one of the $\times 10$ machines broke down. Caroline figured out she could hook two machines together to do the same work as a $\times 10$ machine. When something is sent through this hookup, the output from the first machine becomes the input for the second.

What two machines hooked together do the same work as a $\times 10$ machine? Is there more than one arrangement of two machines that will work? a $\times 5$ and a $\times 2$, in either order

2. What stretching machine does the same work as two $\times 2$ machines hooked together? a $\times 4$ machine

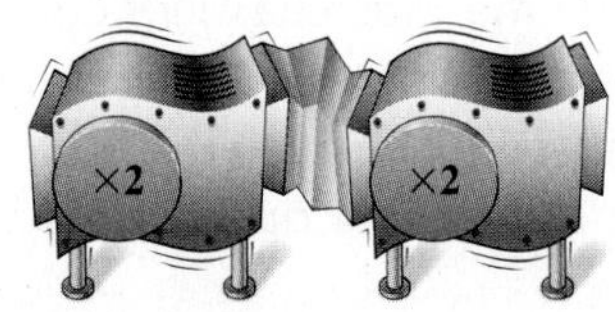

3. It was a bad day at the factory: one of the $\times 36$ machines also broke down. Describe four ways Caroline could hook together other machines to replace the $\times 36$ machine. Assume she can use any number of machines (not just two) and that several machines of each type are available. Possible answer: $\times 2 \times 18$, $\times 6 \times 6$, $\times 2 \times 3 \times 6$, $\times 2 \times 2 \times 3 \times 3$

Teaching Resources

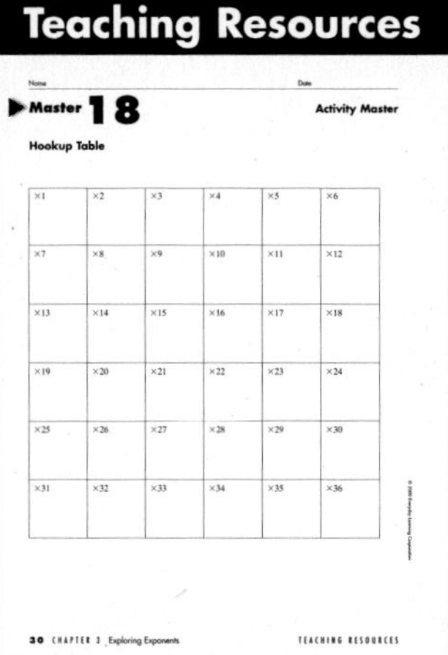

×1	×2	×3	×4	×5	×6
×7	×8	×9	×10	×11	×12
×13	×14	×15	×16	×17	×18
×19	×20	×21	×22	×23	×24
×25	×26	×27	×28	×29	×30
×31	×32	×33	×34	×35	×36

Develop

In **Problem 5,** students tackle the larger question of which machines are really necessary in the factory if you can use the same machine more than once and can hook different machines together.

In solving **Problem 5a,** students should be encouraged to use their previous work and to revise as they go along. Students may have used this technique in Problem 3 when they learned that they could replace a ×36 machine with a ×2 machine and a ×18 machine.

Problem 5 is rich; for further exploration, you could ask the questions provided in the Problem Set Wrap-Up for this problem set.

> **Tips from Teachers**
>
> Whenever our work involves finding factors of a number, I review with students the rules for divisibility by 2, 3, 4, 5, 6, 9, and 10.

Problem Set Wrap-Up It's important to bring some closure to **Problem 5** before moving on to Share & Summarize. You may want to ask some of the pairs to fill in rows of the table on the board or in an overhead
3 transparency of Master 18. Rather than have the pairs answer **Problem 5b,** you could have a whole-class discussion, having students identify the machines that cannot be replaced and making sure that every replaceable machine has been properly replaced. You may need to remind students of the term *prime number* and discuss its meaning.

Discuss with students the special nature of the ×1 machine. It cannot be replaced by any hookup; yet it is not essential because it does not change the size of any input.

Is the ×1 machine necessary? Why or why not? *No; the ×1 machine does not change anything put into it.*

The number 1 is known as the identity for multiplication. Can you explain why? *because multiplying a number by 1 does not change the number*

Can you think of the identity for addition? *0* For subtraction? *0* For division? *1*

The focus of this chapter is exponents, but if students enjoy the prime-factors work in Problem 5, you should certainly spend some time with it.

Suppose you keep all machines necessary to make the stretches from 1 to 36. Can you make 37? Explain why or why not. *No; 37 is prime, so there are no numbers less than 37 that we can multiply together to get 37.*

Are there any other stretches you can make with this set of machines? If so, give some examples.

Students should suggest any stretch that has all its prime factors less than 36. One example is 100 = 2 × 2 × 5 × 5.

Is there a biggest stretch you can make with this set of machines? Explain your answer. *Assuming you can use the machines as many times as you want, you can always make a bigger stretch than the one you have. Here's a proof: Suppose there is some biggest stretch, call it S. I can do a ×2 machine first and then do the stretch of S, for a total stretch of 2S. This is bigger than the biggest stretch, so there must not really be a biggest stretch.*

4. It was a *very* bad day at the resizing factory: in the afternoon, a ×20 machine broke down. Caroline considered hooking together a ×2 machine and a ×10 machine, but her ×10 machine was still broken. What machines might Caroline hook together to replace the ×20 machine? two ×2s and a ×5, or a ×4 and a ×5

5. You have seen that some of the machines in your factory can be replaced by "hookups" of other machines. Not every machine can be replaced, however. After all, you need some machines to build the hookups.

a. Work with your partner to figure out which of the machines—from the ×1 machine to the ×36 machine—are essential, and which are replaceable.

To do this, start with a chart of all the machines, like the one below. If a machine can be replaced by two other machines, cross it out and write a hookup that replaces it. Then see if one of the machines in your hookup can be replaced. If so, cross out that hookup, and write a new hookup with more machines. (See the ×10 and ×20 machines in the table for examples.) Continue this process until the hookups can't be "broken down" any further.

See Additional Answers.

Hookups

×1	×2	×3	×4	×5	×6
×7	×8	×9	~~×10~~ ×2×5	×11	×12
×13	×14	×15	×16	×17	×18
×19	~~×20~~ ~~×4×5~~ ×2×2×5	×21	×22	×23	×24
×25	×26	×27	×28	×29	×30
×31	×32	×33	×34	×35	×36

b. How would you describe the machines that are essential? That is, what do the numbers on the machines have in common?
The numbers on the essential machines are all prime (since ×1 isn't essential).

1 Encourage students to use work from previous problems.

2 You may want to have pairs of students fill in rows of the table on the board or an overhead transparency.

3
- Discuss Problem 5b as a whole class.
- Review the concept of prime numbers.

• ***Additional Answers on page A387.***

Share & Summarize

Students should realize that if each machine stretches $\times 10$, then the total stretch will be $\times 10 \times 10 \times 10$, or $\times 1{,}000$. For the second question, students must simply think of being unable to find a replacement hookup and relate that to the fact that 29 is a prime number.

1 **Troubleshooting** Before moving on, be sure that students fully understand the model of the stretching machine as "multiplying the length of an item by some number." If students are having trouble, you may want to create additional problems like those in Think & Discuss on page 146. Simply change the inputs and the numbers on the machines. Vary the given information so that sometimes students must determine the output, sometimes the input, and sometimes the machine, using examples such as the following:

> If you put a 2-foot baton into a $\times 6$ machine, how long will the baton be when it comes out? 12 ft
>
> What stretching machine was used to stretch a 3-inch carrot to a length of 15 inches? $\times 5$ machine
>
> How long was a stick before it entered the $\times 2$ machine if it was 14 inches long when it came out? 7 in.

Do not be overly concerned at this time if some students are having trouble identifying primes and relating them to machines that cannot be replaced. This is not the emphasis of Chapter 3.

On Your Own Exercises

Practice & Apply: 1–8
Connect & Extend: 50–51
Mixed Review: 61–74

Investigation 2

In this investigation, students relate the model of stretching machines, particularly hookups, to the concept of repeated multiplication. They are introduced to "repeater machines"—machines with exponents to signify the number of times the machine is to be applied.

Discuss the text on page 149 with the class. This text reviews the idea of using exponents to represent repeated multiplication and introduces repeater machines.

Share & Summarize

1. If a strand of fettucine is put through this hookup, how many times longer will it be when it comes out? 1,000

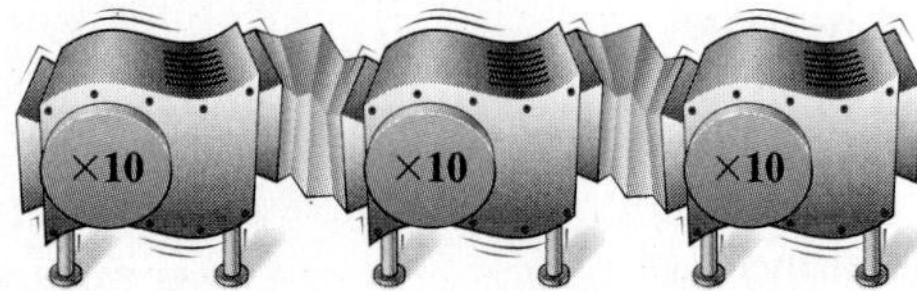

2. Why is it impossible to replace a ×29 machine with a hookup of other stretching machines?
Since 29 is prime, there are no whole numbers besides 1 and 29 that can be multiplied to get 29. So, there is no way to replace a ×29 machine with a combination that does not include ×29.

1 Make sure students understand the model of the stretching machine.

Investigation  2 Repeater Machines

2 Review exponents and introduce the repeater machines.

VOCABULARY
base
exponent
power

If you send a 1-inch piece of taffy through a ×2 machine four times, its length becomes $1 \times 2 \times 2 \times 2 \times 2 = 16$ inches. In Chapter 1, you learned that $2 \times 2 \times 2 \times 2$ can be written 2^4. The expression 2^4 is read "two to the fourth **power.**" The 2 is called the **base,** and the raised 4 is called the **exponent.**

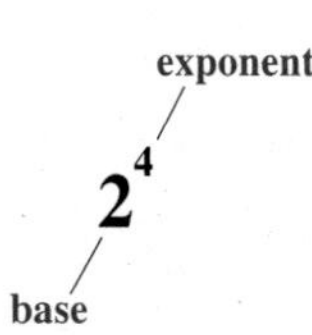

Imagine that you rig up some of the machines in your factory to automatically feed a piece of taffy through several times. You add an exponent to the machine labels to indicate the number of times each machine is applied. For example, sending a piece of taffy through a $\times 2^4$ machine is the same as putting it through a ×2 machine four times.

You call these adjusted machines *repeater* machines because they repeatedly stretch the input by the same factor. In the example above, the original machine, or *base* machine, is a ×2 machine.

LESSON 3.1 Stretching and Shrinking Machines 149

Problem Set B **Suggested Grouping: Pairs**
This problem set introduces students to the repeater machine. It includes questions about identifying the number of times the machine is applied, finding repeater machines that will stretch a given total amount, and investigating the $\times 1$ machine and 0 as an exponent.

1 For **Problems 1–3,** be sure students understand that they need to calculate the total stretch. In addition, they need to tell the number of times a machine is to be applied and to say how much the machine stretches an item each time it is applied.

On the Spot Assessment

Watch for students who confuse the notation of a repeater machine with a multiplication expression. For example, they may think of the repeater machine $\times 7^5$ in Problem 2 as repeating 7×5. Review with them the idea of hookups of the same base, pointing out that the exponent is a shortcut notation for strings of machine hookups. You might write several expressions involving exponents on the board and have students explain their meaning.

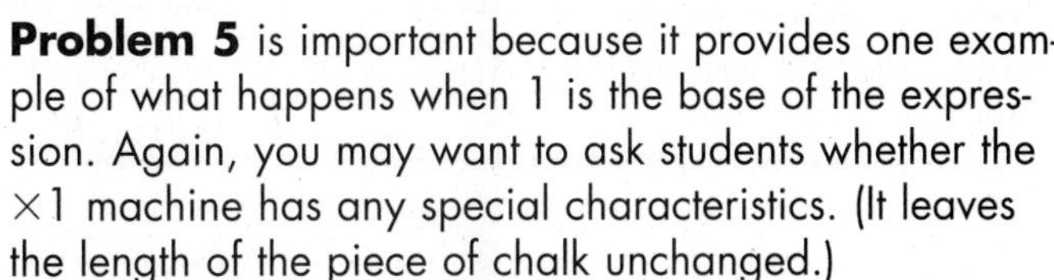

Problem 5 is important because it provides one example of what happens when 1 is the base of the expression. Again, you may want to ask students whether the $\times 1$ machine has any special characteristics. (It leaves the length of the piece of chalk unchanged.)

Problem 6 asks students to consider what an exponent of 0 might mean. Discuss the machine metaphor here. Usually it is difficult to explain why a number to the 0 power is 1. In this case, the exponent tells you how many times to use the machine. Zero means "don't use the machine at all," so it leaves the stick unchanged. We've seen that the $\times 1$ machine also leaves the stick unchanged. Then for any number n, $\times n^0$ has the same effect as $\times 1$ and $n^0 = 1$.

About the Mathematics

It is more accurate to say that "any *nonzero* number to the 0 power is 1," since 0^0 is usually considered undefined. If we look at the function $f(x) = x^0$ and plug in 0 for x, we should expect to get $f(0) = 1$, since $f(x)$ is 1 for every other number. However, if we look at the function $g(x) = 0^x$ and plug in 0 for x, we might expect to get $g(0) = 0$, since $g(x)$ is 0 for every other number. There is no right way to reconcile this dilemma, so 0^0 is left undefined. This subtlety should not be problematic for students, since we do not have an x^0 machine and never ask them to find 0^0.

For further discussion, you may want to ask students to find 0^0 on their calculators and discuss the result.

Problem Set Wrap-Up Before moving on, make sure students understand the meaning of the $\times 1$ machine and 0 as an exponent.

If students explored the problem about "replaceable" machines from Investigation 1, they should have noticed that the $\times 1$ machine cannot be replaced. But since every item stretched by $\times 1$ remains unchanged, there is no need for such a machine. Similar reasoning tells us that any power of a $\times 1$ machine is the same as the $\times 1$ machine itself, since $1^x = 1$ for any number x.

The fact that any nonzero number to the 0 power is 1 will be revisited throughout this chapter, but it is important for students to be able to connect this fact to the model of machines. If students can think of the 0 exponent as meaning "don't apply the machine at all," then they should have no trouble understanding why n^0 is the same as 1.

4 Discuss the $\times\frac{1}{2}$ machine mentioned on the bottom of page 150. Make sure students understand that this machine multiplies the length of a segment by $\frac{1}{2}$, *shrinking* it to half its length.

You might ask students to give examples of other shrinking machines—machines with fractional multipliers—and to explain how these machines would change the length of an input.

Problem Set B

For each repeater machine, tell how many times the base machine is applied and how much the total stretch is.

1.

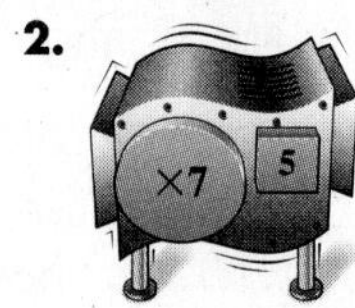

2.

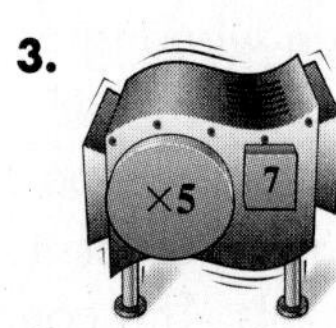

3.

1. applied 2 times; stretched 10,000 times
2. applied 5 times; stretched 16,807 times
3. applied 7 times; stretched 78,125 times
4. Possible answer: $\times 8^2$, $\times 4^3$, $\times 2^6$
5. Nothing; the chalk comes out the same length it went in.

6a. Nothing; the chalk comes out the same length it went in.

6b. 1

4. Find three repeater machines that will do the same work as a ×64 machine. Draw them, or describe them using exponents.

5. Surinam played a joke on Jeff by giving him this machine to run. What will it do to a 2-inch-long piece of chalk?

6. In a repeater machine with 0 as an exponent, the base machine is applied 0 times.

a. What do these machines do to a piece of chalk?

b. What do you think the value of 6^0 is?

Evaluate each expression without using a calculator.

7. 7^0 1 **8.** 2^5 32 **9.** 4^2 16 **10.** 3^3 27

Peter found a $\times\frac{1}{2}$ machine in a corner of the factory. He wasn't sure what it would do, so he experimented with some licorice. This is what he found.

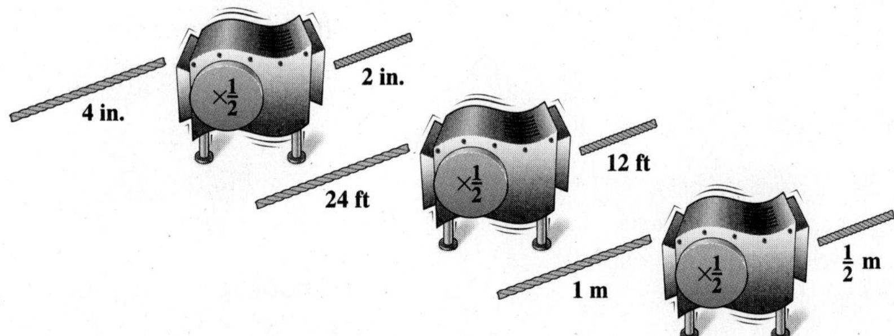

1 Be sure students calculate the total stretch for each machine.

2 Discuss special characteristics of a ×1 machine.

3 Relate the 0 exponent to the ×1 machine.

4 Discuss the $\times\frac{1}{2}$ machine.

Develop

Problem Set C **Suggested Grouping: Individuals**
This problem set gives students practice working with machines with fractional multipliers, which actually shrink the input items. The shrinking model will be used again later in this chapter and again in Chapter 4, when students look at negative exponents. The concept is introduced here so that students can think about rational numbers raised to powers. This is an area that is traditionally difficult for students; but with the model of a machine, the effect of $\left(\frac{1}{3}\right)^2$ as in **Problem 3** should be more easily understood.

Problems 3–5 ask students to think about raising a fraction to a power. If students are having difficulty, ask them to think of the intermediate stages in the process: After the first $\times\frac{1}{3}$ machine, a 1-inch stick is a $\frac{1}{3}$-inch stick; after the second $\times\frac{1}{3}$ machine, the $\frac{1}{3}$-inch stick is $\frac{1}{3}$ as long as when it went in, that is, $\frac{1}{3} \times \frac{1}{3}$, or $\frac{1}{9}$, inch long.

Access for All Learners

Extra Help Some students may benefit from a physical model of raising a fraction to an exponent. Start with a whole piece of paper, tear it in half, throw one half away, and ask,

What size is the paper now? $\frac{1}{2}$ ***sheet***

Now tear the $\frac{1}{2}$ sheet in half, and throw one half away. Ask,

What size is the paper now? $\frac{1}{4}$ ***sheet***

If students have trouble finding the correct fraction, have them keep a whole sheet handy for comparison. If 4 pieces like the remaining part will cover the whole sheet of paper, then the last torn piece must represent $\frac{1}{4}$.

Connect tearing paper in half to putting a stick through the $\times\frac{1}{2}$ machine. Putting the stick through the machine once provides the same result as tearing the paper the first time. If the exponent of the fraction is 2, the result is the same as tearing the paper 2 times; if the exponent of the fraction is 3, the result is the same as tearing the paper 3 times; and so on.

For **Problems 6–8,** students look at hookups of stretching machines and their "reciprocal" shrinking machines. For example, $\times 2$ and $\times\frac{1}{2}$ and $\times 3$ and $\times\frac{1}{3}$.

Sample Strategies Here are some ways students might think about **Problems 6–8.**

- Students may see that they can pair up stretches and shrinks, ignoring those that match and just looking at how many are "left over." The ones left over will be just shrinks or just stretches, but not both. For example, in Problem 6, there are three stretches and two shrinks.

Pairing the stretches and shrinks leaves one stretch.

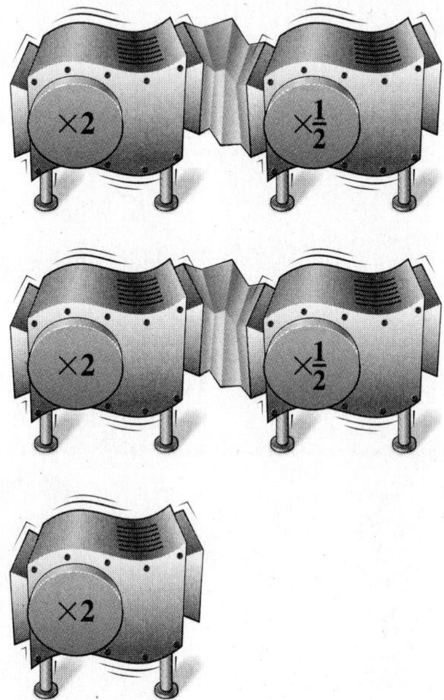

So the hookup is the same as a $\times 2$ machine. In symbols, $2^3 \times \left(\frac{1}{2}\right)^2 = 2$.

- Students may think of the hookups of fractions with the same factor repeated several times in the numerator and the denominator. So, in Problem 6, $(2)^3 \times \left(\frac{1}{2}\right)^2$ can be thought of as a fraction with two factors of 2 in the denominator and three factors of 2 in the numerator.

For centuries Native Americans chewed the sap, called *chicle*, of the sapodilla tree. Settlers took up the habit, and in the late 1800s chewing gum began to be made commercially from chicle, sugar, and flavorings.

The pot contains chicle, which must be boiled before it is ready to chew.

Each piece of licorice was compressed to half its original length. Peter decided this was a *shrinking* machine.

Problem Set C

Try a shrinking machine for yourself.

1. If a foot-long sandwich is put into the machine below, how many inches long will it be when it emerges? 4 in.

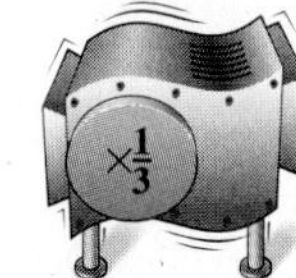

2a. They stay the same length.

2b. They shrink to $\frac{1}{8}$ in.

Like stretching machines, shrinking machines can be used in hookups and repeater machines.

2. What happens when 1-inch gummy worms are sent through these hookups? See above.

a.

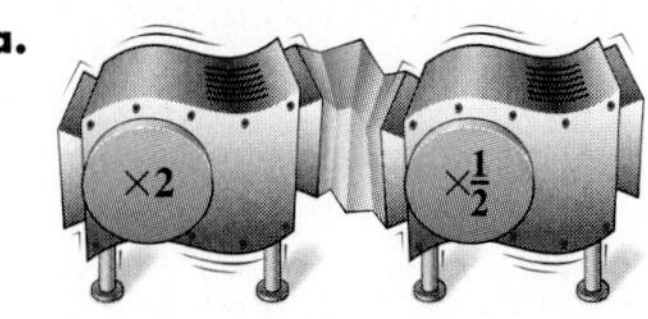

b.

3. Evan put a 1-inch stick of gum through a $\left(\times\frac{1}{3}\right)^2$ machine. How long was the stick when it came out? $\frac{1}{9}$ in.

4. This stick of gum came out of a $\times\left(\frac{1}{2}\right)^2$ machine. Without measuring, estimate the length of the input stick in inches. Explain how you found your answer. It may be helpful if you copy this stick onto your paper. about 5 in.; A $\times\left(\frac{1}{2}\right)^2$ machine shrinks a stick to $\frac{1}{4}$ its length, so the original stick must have been 4 times the length of this stick, which is about 1.25 in.

5. Sam had a 1-inch piece of gum. He put it through this repeater machine, and it came out $\frac{1}{100{,}000}$ in. long. What is the missing exponent? 5

Find a single repeater machine that will do the same job as the given hookup.

6. a $\times 2^3$ machine followed by a $\times\left(\frac{1}{2}\right)^2$ machine $\times 2$

7. a $\times 2^4$ machine followed by a $\times\left(\frac{1}{2}\right)^2$ machine $\times 2^2$

8. a $\times 5^{99}$ machine followed by a $\times\left(\frac{1}{5}\right)^{100}$ machine $\times\frac{1}{5}$

1 Review raising numbers, particularly fractions, to a power.

2 Students may use various strategies.

LESSON 3.1 Stretching and Shrinking Machines 151

Share & Summarize

These questions ask students to work with some of the main ideas of this investigation: 0 as an exponent, a fraction repeater machine, and a hookup of a fraction machine and a whole-number machine.

It is important for students to have a thorough understanding of repeater machines and hookups. Investigations 3 and 4 and Lesson 3.2 develop laws of exponents based on these models.

The concept of a number to the 0 power will be explored again later, but if you want to present an alternative way to think about this idea here, you might consider showing a table of powers.

10^4	10,000
10^3	1,000
10^2	100
10^1	10
10^0	1

If we look at the table beginning with 10^4, we see that the value in the right column is $\frac{1}{10}$ the output above it. The last item on the left in the table would be 10^0 and on the right would be $\frac{1}{10}$ of 10, or 1. You can continue this argument to include negative exponents as well; this material is covered in Chapter 4.

Troubleshooting If students are having trouble with the concepts presented in this investigation or if you feel they need additional examples, provide a simple hookup of two $\times 3$ machines and two $\times\frac{1}{3}$ machines and ask students to put a stick through each machine, one at a time. Then rearrange the machines so that each $\times 3$ machine is followed by a $\times\frac{1}{3}$ machine; students will be able to see the "canceling-out" effect immediately.

On Your Own Exercises

Practice & Apply: 9–20
Connect & Extend: 52–57
Mixed Review: 61–74

Investigation 3

In this investigation, students develop a product law of exponents: $r^a \times r^b = r^{a+b}$. They gain an understanding of this law by creating hookups of repeater machines and then considering a single machine that will do the same work. Students begin the investigation with the machine model and then move on to numerical examples.

Have students read about Evan's mistake of sending a 1-inch noodle through the $\times 2^3$ machine instead of through the $\times 2^5$ machine. Discuss the options presented by coworkers in the cartoon.

Evaluate each expression without using a calculator.

9. $\left(\frac{1}{2}\right)^5$ $\frac{1}{32}$ **10.** $\left(\frac{1}{4}\right)^2$ $\frac{1}{16}$ **11.** $\left(\frac{1}{3}\right)^3$ $\frac{1}{27}$ **12.** $\left(\frac{1}{7}\right)^0$ 1

Share & Summarize

1. If you put a 2-inch toothpick through this machine, how long will it be when it comes out? 2 in.

2. A 1-inch-long beetle crawled into a repeater machine and emerged $\frac{1}{16}$ in. long. What repeater machine did it go through? Is there more than one possibility?

2. There are two possibilities: $\times\left(\frac{1}{4}\right)^2$ and $\times\left(\frac{1}{2}\right)^4$.

3. What single repeater machine does the same work as a $\times 3^5$ machine followed by a $\times\left(\frac{1}{3}\right)^3$ machine? $\times 3^2$

1 Be sure students understand repeater machines and hookups.

2 Give students additional examples.

Investigation 3 Strings of Machines

Evan's supervisor asked him to stretch a 1-inch noodle into a 32-inch noodle. Evan intended to send the noodle through a $\times 2^5$ machine, but he accidentally put it through a $\times 2^3$ machine. His coworkers had several suggestions for how he could fix his mistake.

3 Discuss the cartoon and the suggested solutions.

Develop

Think & Discuss

Ask students which worker's solution will correct Evan's mistake. The following are possible explanations for why the methods work.

Everett's suggestion: The $\times\left(\frac{1}{2}\right)^3$ machine halves the noodle's length 3 times, returning it to its original length. Then Evan can put the noodle through the machine originally intended.

Ana's suggestion: He doubled the noodle's length only 3 times, but he meant to double it 5 times. The $\times 2^2$ machine doubles the length 2 additional times.

Jon's suggestion: The $\times 2^3$ machine doubles the noodle's length 3 more times for a total of 6 times. Sending the result through the $\times\frac{1}{2}$ machine halves the length once, so the noodle comes out doubled 5 times.

Bev's suggestion will work, of course, but then you've wasted one noodle.

Some may not readily see that Everett's solution—sending it through a $\times\left(\frac{1}{2}\right)^3$ machine and then a $\times 2^5$ machine—will work. It is important that this method is understood by the whole class, since it reviews the material they learned in Investigation 2. Jon's solution—sending the noodle through the $\times 2^3$ machine and then through a $\times\frac{1}{2}$ machine—also reviews material in Investigation 2.

After students are convinced that Everett's and Jon's suggestions work, focus the discussion on Ana's solution. Ask students whether it's true that $2^3 \times 2^2 = 2^5$, and to explain how to prove this using machines.

Sample Strategies There are several strategies students might use in their "proofs."

- Students might first describe what happens to the 1-inch noodle as it passes through the $\times 2^3$ machine and then calculate what happens to the resulting 8-inch noodle as it goes through the $\times 2^2$ machine. Then students can compare how the result relates to that of a $\times 2^5$ machine.
- Students might also compute $2^5 = 32$ and $2^3 = 8$ and then determine that a $\times 4$ machine is needed to complete the task. A $\times 4$ machine does the same work as a $\times 2^2$ machine, so Ana's suggestion is correct.
- Students may understand the model and say that 2^5 means using the $\times 2$ machine 5 times. If using the $\times 2^3$ machine is the same as using the $\times 2$ machine 3 times, then students need to use the $\times 2$ machine only twice more. That would be the same as using a $\times 2^2$ machine.

Example

Read through the Example with the class. Ask students whether they agree with Evan's logic. Then ask,

> What single machine will do the same thing as a hookup of two $\times 3^2$ machines? *a $\times 3^4$ machine or a $\times 81$ machine*

Problem Set D Suggested Grouping: Individuals

In this problem set, students think about the results of repeater machine hookups.

Students may struggle with **Problem 4** because it involves variable exponents. You might suggest that they think of y as a certain number in this situation, so they see that they will be doubling the exponent as a result of the hookup. If students understand the rule of "adding exponents," then they should be able to apply it even in this situation.

Problem 4 is worth discussing with the whole class, since it brings up a problem that students often stumble over: What does it mean to have a variable in the exponent?

Think & Discuss

Will all the suggestions work? Why or why not?
They will all work. See the teaching notes for possible explanations.

1 Discuss why the suggestions do or do not work.

Evan's mistake wasn't so terrible after all, because he figured out how to find single repeater machines that do the same work as some hookups.

2 Discuss the Example.

EXAMPLE

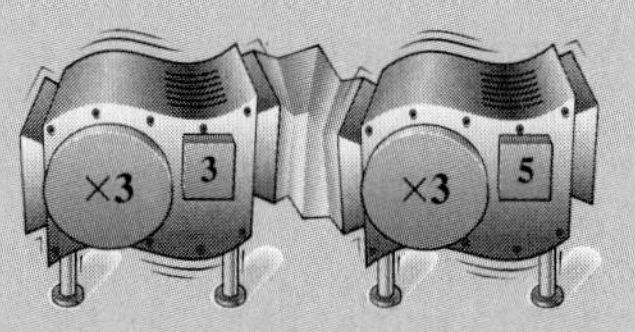

Evan found a single machine for this hookup. He reasoned like this: "The first machine tripled the noodle's length 3 times. The second machine took that output and tripled *its* length 5 times. So, the original noodle's length was tripled $3 + 5$ times, or 8 times in all. That means a $\times 3^8$ machine would do the same thing."

Problem Set D

Follow Evan's reasoning to find a single repeater machine that will do the same work as each hookup.

1. 

$\times 2^9$

2. 

$\times 100^{12}$

3. 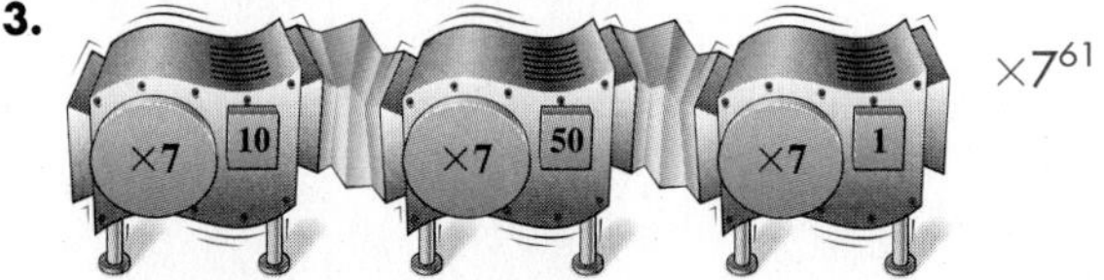

$\times 7^{61}$

4. 

$\times 3^{y+y}$, or $\times 3^{2y}$

3 You might suggest that students think of y as a certain number.

LESSON 3.1 Stretching and Shrinking Machines 153

Develop

Example

Refer students to the cartoon explaining one way to think about $2^{20} \times 2^5$. They should notice that these numeric expressions behave in the same way as the repeater machines.

Explain to students that Neeraj's "discovery" is one of the *product laws of exponents.* Write the law on the board, or refer students to it in their books.

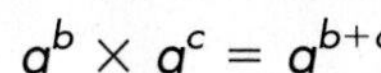

$$a^b \times a^c = a^{b+c}$$

Make sure students understand that to apply the law, the bases—represented by the letter *a* in the law's statement—must be the same in all the expressions being multiplied.

You have seen that a hookup of repeater machines with the same base can be replaced by a single repeater machine. Similarly, when you multiply exponential expressions with the same base, you can replace them with a single expression.

EXAMPLE

Neeraj thought about how he could rewrite the expression $2^{20} \times 2^5$.

Neeraj's idea is one of the *product laws of exponents,* which can be expressed like this:

Multiplying Expressions with the Same Base

$$a^b \times a^c = a^{b+c}$$

Actually, this law can be used with more than two expressions. As long as the bases are the same, to find the product you can add the exponents and use the same base. For example:

$$\begin{aligned} 3^2 \times 3^3 \times 3^{10} &= 3^{2+3+10} \\ &= 3^{15} \end{aligned}$$

1 • Discuss the cartoon.

• Explain that Neeraj's "discovery" is a product law of exponents.

2 Be sure students understand that the bases in this product law must be the same.

Problem Set E **Suggested Grouping: Individuals or Pairs**
Students now move from the machine model to numbers with exponents. There are some machine-related problems, as well, to ensure that students continue to think about the model. Also, the problems require students to decide whether the product law they have learned applies or not. Not all of the expressions they are given can be rewritten.

On the **Spot Assessment**

In **Problems 1–6,** watch for students who think that the bases should be multiplied. For example, some students may think that in Problem 2, $2^5 \times 2^4 = 4^9$. This confusion is easily addressed if students return to thinking about machines. Lead them step-by-step through the process of putting a 1-inch stick through each $\times 2$ machine. They should see that these machines would never become $\times 4$ machines.

Problems 1 and **3** are worth special mention, since they provide examples of terms in which the exponent 1 is not written.

Sample Strategies **Problem 5** includes 2^0. Students may approach this in one of two ways.

- They may remember that any *nonzero* number raised to the 0 power is simply 1, so the answer must be 1×2^3, or 2^3.
- Alternatively, they may simply apply the product law to find $2^0 \times 2^3 = 2^{0+3} = 2^3$.

Both strategies are appropriate. You may want to ask students to explain their thinking for this problem, reminding them that there is more than one way to determine the answer. This will further solidify the idea that 2^0 is 1.

Problems 13 and **15** include numbers whose base is a decimal. If students seem puzzled by this, ask them to think of this as a fraction machine, the same way they thought of a $\times\frac{1}{2}$ machine.

Problem Set Wrap-Up Discuss **Problems 18–23** before moving on. Be sure that students are able to rewrite the expressions both when the expressions contain variables and when they do not. If students are struggling with this idea, they should not yet begin Problem Set F. For these students, you may need to make up several more practice problems like these.

- $6^4 \times 6^3$ (6^7)
- $2 \times 2 \times 2 \times 2$ (2^4)
- $x^5 \times x^3$ (x^8)
- $3^2 \times 3^3$ (3^5)
- $n^a \times n^b$ (n^{a+b})

If students are comfortable with these ideas, they are ready to tackle more difficult simplification problems.

Example
Review the Example after the problem set with the class, so students see how to multiply expressions with coefficients. Although this problem could be constructed using the machine analogy, it may be more obvious to students in the numerical form. You may need to review the commutative and associative properties of multiplication.

Make sure students understand the point made in the Remember feature: $ab^n = a \times b^n$, not $(a \times b)^n$.

Problem Set E

Rewrite each expression as a power of 2. It may help to think of the expressions as hookups of ×2 machines.

1. 2×2 2^2 **2.** $2^5 \times 2^4$ 2^9 **3.** $2^{10} \times 2$ 2^{11}

4. $2^{10} \times 2^{10}$ 2^{20} **5.** $2^0 \times 2^3$ 2^3 **6.** $2^m \times 2^n$ 2^{m+n}

For each hookup, determine whether there is a single repeater machine that will do the same work. If so, describe or draw it.

7. $\times 7^5$
8. $\times (0.5)^5$
9. not possible
10. $\times 12^5$

7.

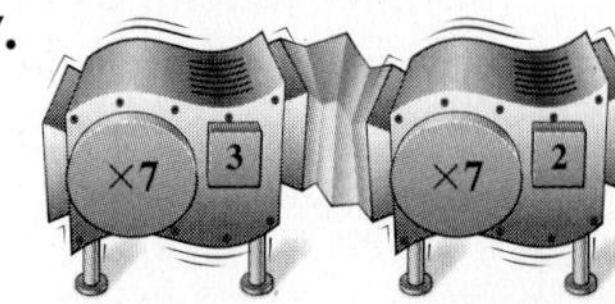

8.

9.

10.

11.

not possible

Tell what number should replace the question mark to make each statement true.

12. $5 \times 5 \times 5 = ?^3$ 5   **13.** $2.7^{10} \times 2.7^? = 2.7^{12}$ 2

14. $\left(\frac{1}{5}\right)^4 \times \left(\frac{1}{5}\right)^6 = \left(\frac{1}{5}\right)^?$ 10   **15.** $1.2^? \times 1.2^2 = 1.2^2$ 0

16. $\frac{2}{3} \times ? = \left(\frac{2}{3}\right)^2$ $\frac{2}{3}$ **17.** $a^{20} \times a^5 = a^?$ 25

If possible, rewrite each expression using a single base. For example, $6^2 \times 6^3$ can be rewritten 6^5.

18. $3^3 \times 3^3 \times 3^4$ 3^{10} **19.** $2^5 \times 5^2$ not possible   **20.** $4 \times 4 \times 4$ 4^3

21. $4x^3 \times y^2$ not possible   **22.** $4^4 \times 2^2$ 4^5 or 2^{10} **23.** $a^n \times a^m$ a^{n+m}

When you simplify algebraic expressions involving exponents, it's important to keep the *order of the operations* in mind.

Remember

By the order of operations, $2b^3$ means $2 \times b^3$, not $(2 \times b)^3$.

EXAMPLE

$2b^3 \times 5b^2 = 2 \times b^3 \times 5 \times b^2 = 2 \times 5 \times b^3 \times b^2 = 10b^5$

1 You may have students work in pairs.

2 For Problems 1 and 3, remind students that $x^1 = x$.

3 Give students more practice problems if necessary.

4 Review with students the commutative and associative properties of multiplication.

LESSON 3.1 Stretching and Shrinking Machines 155

Problem Set F **Suggested Grouping: Pairs**
It is probably best for students to work in pairs on these more challenging problems.

The best strategy for solving these problems is the one presented in the Example: Rearrange the factors so that the coefficients are together and the variables are together. Then combine the coefficients using multiplication. Finally, combine the variables using the product law of exponents.

Share & Summarize

For **Question 2,** it is fine if students continue to use the machine model to explain their thinking. Other students may want to use the shortcut technique presented in the Example.

Troubleshooting If students have trouble with the Share & Summarize questions, have them think about or rephrase the questions in terms of machines. *If you have two repeater machines with the same base number but with different exponents (different number of repetitions), how can you replace them with a single machine?* When students can answer the general questions in terms of the machines, reexplain the connection between the machines and exponential notation.

On Your Own Exercises

Practice & Apply: 21–33
Connect & Extend: 58
Mixed Review: 61–74

Investigation 4

In this investigation, students develop a second product law of exponents, $r^a \times s^a = (r \times s)^a$. Students gain an understanding of this law as they create hookups of repeater machines and then consider a single machine that will do the same work. They begin the investigation with the machine model and then move on to numerical examples.

Problem Set G **Suggested Grouping: Pairs**
Students explore hookups of stretching machines with the same exponents and different bases.

Problem Set F

Simplify each expression.

1. $2b \times 2b$ $4b^2$ or $(2b)^2$
2. $5z^2 \times 6z^2$ $30z^4$
3. $5a^2 \times 3a^4$ $15a^6$
4. $z^2 \times 2z^3 \times 6z^2$ $12z^7$

1 You may have students work in pairs.

Share & Summarize

1. Find a single repeater machine to do the same work as this hookup. $\times 5^9$

2. In your own words, write the rule that lets you figure out the missing exponent in equations like $3^3 \times 3^{16} = 3^?$ and $r^{15} \times r^? = r^{23}$.

2. Possible answer: When you multiply a number raised to a power by the same number raised to a power, the result is the same number raised to the sum of the two powers.

2 If students have trouble, have them rephrase questions in terms of machines.

Investigation 4 More Strings of Machines

Combining expressions that have the same base can make products much easier to understand. Do you think you can simplify products that *don't* have the same base?

Problem Set G

3 You may have students work in pairs.

1. Caroline has an order from a golf course designer to put palm trees through a $\times 2^3$ machine and then through a $\times 3^3$ machine. She thinks she can do the job with a single repeater machine. What single repeater machine should she use? $\times 6^3$

2. Caroline also needs to stretch some pine trees to 10^2 times their original lengths, but her $\times 10$ machine is still broken and someone is using the $\times 10^2$ machine. Find a hookup of two repeater machines that will

Develop

1 It may be difficult for students to know how to approach **Problem 2.** Encourage them to think about a machine hookup that will do the same thing as a $\times 10$ machine. They may use the fact that the hookup of the $\times 2$ machine and the $\times 5$ machine will do the work of a $\times 10$ machine and see that they can they could combine these two machines and then hook them up again.

This is the equivalent of a $\times\ 10^2$ machine, but it is not a hookup of 2 repeater machines as pictured. Of course, when you multiply, the order of factors doesn't matter. So $2 \times 5 \times 2 \times 5$ is the same as $2 \times 2 \times 5 \times 5$. In machines, we have,

The two $\times 2$ machines can be replaced by a $\times 2^2$ machine, and the two $\times 5$ machines can be replaced by a $\times 5^2$ machine. As with the numerical expression, order doesn't matter; so $\times 5^2$ and $\times 2^2$ works just as well.

Access for All Learners

Early Finishers Ask students to look again at Problem Set D, **Problem 4,** where they determined that the answer is 3^{2y}. In Problem Set G, **Problem 6,** students will probably say that the answer is 9^y. Ask students whether the two answers are the same and to justify their responses. This relates to the power of a power law students will learn later. In fact, $3^{2y} = (3^2)^y = 9^y$.

Example

With the whole class, discuss Maya's strategy for combining machines and the corresponding product law of exponents on the top of the next page. Ask,

> How is Maya's strategy different from Neeraj's rule—the previous product law of exponents?

Students should understand that in Neeraj's rule, the bases have to be the same but the exponents can be different. Maya's strategy involves combining machines in which the bases are different and the exponents are the same.

do the same work as a $\times 10^2$ machine. To get started, think about the hookup you could use to replace the $\times 10$ machine. $\times 2^2 \times 5^2$

1 Encourage students to "break up" and regroup machines.

For each hookup, find a single repeater machine to do the same work.

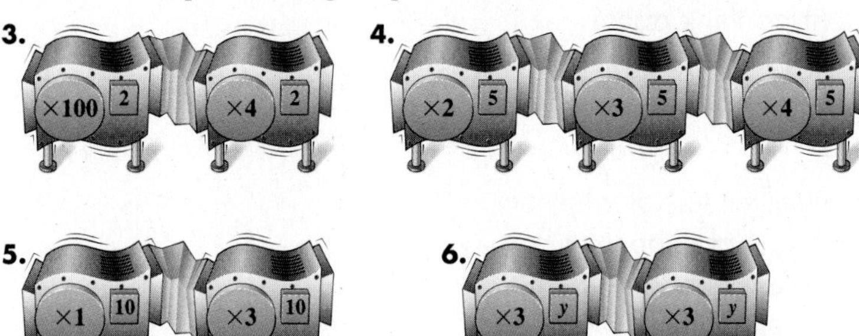

3. $\times 400^2$
4. $\times 24^5$
5. $\times 3^{10}$
6. $\times 9^y$ or $\times 3^{2y}$

You can use the same kind of thinking you used in the problems above to multiply expressions with the same exponent.

EXAMPLE

Maya multiplied $4^2 \times 3^2$ by thinking about stretching machines.

2 Discuss Maya's strategy.

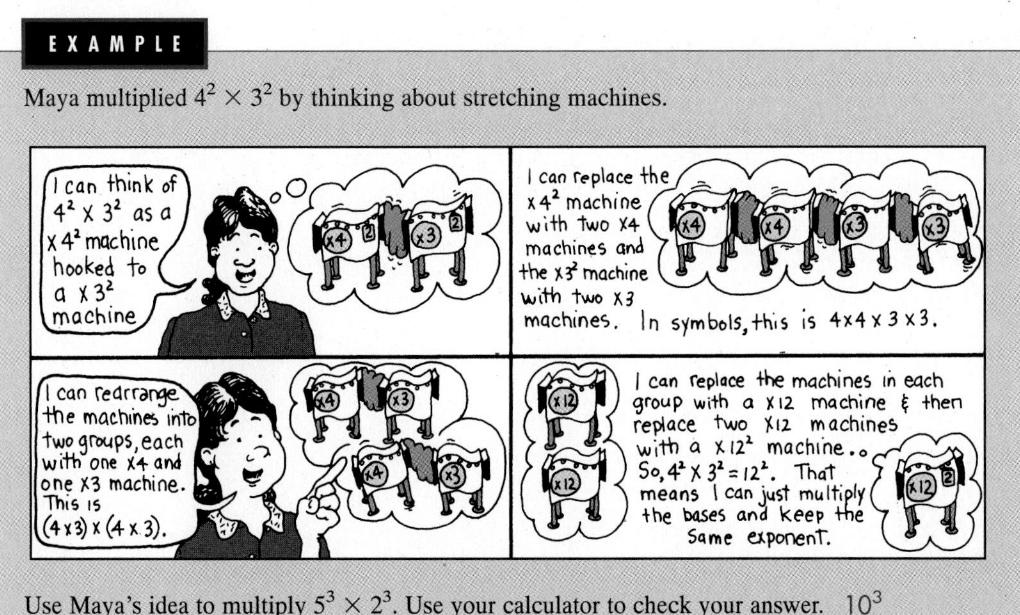

I can think of 4² X 3² as a X 4² machine hooked to a X 3² machine
I can replace the X 4² machine with two X4 machines and the X3² machine with two X3 machines. In symbols, this is 4x4 x 3 x 3.
I can rearrange the machines into two groups, each with one X4 and one X3 machine. This is (4 x 3) x (4 x 3).
I can replace the machines in each group with a X12 machine & then replace two X12 machines with a X 12² machine. So, 4² X 3² = 12². That means I can just multiply the bases and keep the same exponent.

Use Maya's idea to multiply $5^3 \times 2^3$. Use your calculator to check your answer. 10^3

LESSON 3.1 Stretching and Shrinking Machines 157

Develop

Problem Set H **Suggested Grouping: Pairs**
In this problem set, students concentrate on numbers with exponents. There are some machine-related problems as well to ensure that students continue to think about the model.

For **Problems 1–11,** ask students to think about whether the new product law applies before they solve each problem. Not all of the expressions in this problem set can be rewritten.

Problems 12–15 provide an excellent test of whether students are properly applying the law of exponents $a^c \times b^c = (a \times b)^c$. As you circulate around the room, you might ask students to explain their thinking for solving these problems.

Maya's idea is another *product law of exponents.*

Multiplying Expressions with the Same Exponents
$a^c \times b^c = (a \times b)^c$

You can use this law with more than two expressions. If the exponents are the same, multiply the expressions by multiplying the bases and using the same exponent. For example, $2^8 \times 3^8 \times 7^8 = (2 \times 3 \times 7)^8 = 42^8$.

Problem Set H

1 • You may have students work in pairs.

• Ask students if new product law applies.

Rewrite each expression using a single exponent. For example, $2^3 \times 3^3$ can be rewritten 6^3.

1. $100^2 \times 3^2$ 300^2

2. $10^{20} \times 25^{20}$ 250^{20}

3. $5^{100} \times 5^{100} \times 2^{100}$ 50^{100}

4. $\left(\frac{1}{3}\right)^a \times \left(\frac{1}{5}\right)^a$ $\left(\frac{1}{15}\right)^a$

5. $1{,}000^5 \times 3^5$ $3{,}000^5$

6. $x^2 \times y^2$ $(xy)^2$

For each hookup, determine whether there is a single repeater machine that will do the same work. If so, describe it.

7. $\times 1^3$, or $\times 1$

8. $\times\left(\frac{1}{6}\right)^2$

9. not possible

10. 40^2

7.

8.

9.

10.

11.

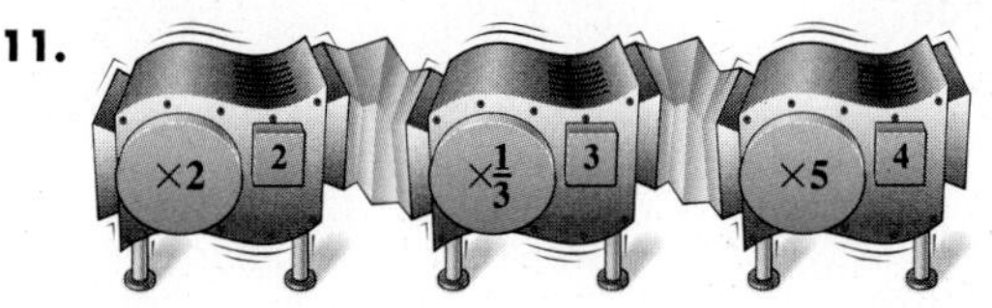

not possible

Tell what number should replace the question mark to make each statement true.

2 Ask students to explain their thinking.

12. $100^? \times 3^2 = 300^2$ 2

13. $4^{20} \times 25^{20} = ?^{20}$ 100

14. $5^{100} \times \left(\frac{1}{2}\right)^{100} = ?^{100}$ $\frac{5}{2}$

15. $\left(\frac{1}{3}\right)^3 \times \left(\frac{1}{5}\right)^3 = \left(\frac{1}{15}\right)^?$ 3

You have worked with the product laws of exponents. Do you think there are similar laws for sums of exponential expressions? You will explore this question in the next problem set.

Develop

Problem Set I **Suggested Grouping: Small groups**
These problems are important because they address common confusions. Because of the close relationship between the laws of exponents and analogous laws for repeated addition, students often think they can simplify sums of numbers written with exponents. (See Mathematical Background on page 145a for details.)

For **Problems 1 and 2,** students can calculate the right side and the left side and see whether the two results are equal. For example, $2^3 = 8$, $2^4 = 16$. The sum is 24. But $2^7 = 128$, which is not equal to 24.

1 If students answer Problems 1 and 2 correctly, they should have little trouble determining that the statements in **Problems 3 and 4** are not true. In fact, counterexamples are given in Problems 1 and 2, respectively.

Ask students for their answers for Problems 3 and 4. Most students will correctly answer "no" to both of these questions. You might then challenge them by presenting an example for which the statement *is* true.

> If I let both a and b be 1, then I get $2^1 + 2^1 = 4$, which is 2^2. How can this be? You told me $2^a + 2^b$ is not equal to 2^{a+b}.

Help students realize that this is only a special instance. Unless the statement is true for *all* values of a and b, the statement cannot be considered a rule.

For Problem 4, ask students whether there is a special instance for which $a^2 + b^2 = (a + b)^2$. This statement is true when $a = 0$ or $b = 0$. But again, unless the statement is true for all values of a and b, the statement is not a rule.

Share & Summarize

For these questions, it is fine if students continue to use the machine model to explain their thinking. Hopefully, other students will want to use the shortcut techniques available in the product laws of exponents.

Help students articulate the difference between the two product laws of exponents. For example, one law applies when the bases are the same but the exponents are different; the other law applies when the bases are different but the exponents are the same. Ask students which law should be used when the bases are the same and the exponents are also the same, as in $3^y \times 3^y$. A reasonable answer is that either law may be used. It's not correct to say "use them both," since after you use one law, the other will no longer apply to the simplified expression.

Troubleshooting If students have trouble with the Share & Summarize questions, have them rephrase the questions in terms of machines. *If you have two repeater machines with different base numbers but with the same exponents (number of repetitions), how can you replace them with a single machine?* When students can answer the general questions in terms of the machines, reexplain the connection between the machines and exponential notation.

On Your Own Exercises

Practice & Apply: 34–49
Connect & Extend: 59–60
Mixed Review: 61–74

Problem Set I

Determine whether each statement is true or false, and explain how you decided.

1. $2^3 + 2^4 = 2^7$
2. $3^2 + 5^2 = 8^2$
3. From your answers to Problems 1 and 2, do you think $2^a + 2^b = 2^{a+b}$ for any numbers a and b? no
4. From your answers to Problems 1 and 2, do you think $a^2 + b^2 = (a + b)^2$ for any numbers a and b? no

Problem Set I Answers

1. false; $2^3 + 2^4 = 8 + 16 = 24$, and $2^7 = 128$
2. false; $3^2 + 5^2 = 9 + 25 = 34$, and $8^2 = 64$

1 Without using the term, students are informally introduced to the use of counterexamples.

Share & Summarize

1. In your own words, write the rule that lets you find the missing base in equations like $3^{30} \times 2^{30} = ?^{30}$ and $5^{15} \times ?^{15} = 100^{15}$.

Find the missing numbers.

2. $15^3 \times 4^3 = ?^3$ 60
3. $3^7 \times 3^? = 3^{12}$ 5
4. $\left(\frac{2}{5}\right)^{12} \times \left(\frac{2}{5}\right)^3 = \left(\frac{2}{5}\right)^?$ 15
5. $2^2 \times ?^2 = 18^2$ 9
6. You have seen two product laws for working with exponents. Explain how you know when to use each rule.

Product Laws

$$a^b \times a^c = a^{b+c}$$
$$a^c \times b^c = (a \times b)^c$$

Share & Summarize Answers

1. Possible answer: When one base raised to a power is multiplied by another base raised to the same power, the product is equal to the product of the two original bases raised to that power.

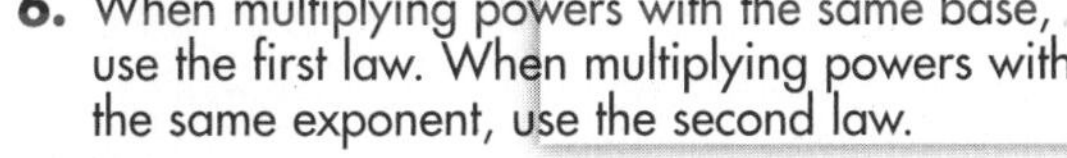

6. When multiplying powers with the same base, use the first law. When multiplying powers with the same exponent, use the second law.

2
- Help students articulate the difference between the two product laws for exponents.
- Encourage struggling students to rephrase questions in terms of machines.

Assign and Assess

On Your Own Exercises

Investigation 1
Practice & Apply: 1–8
Connect & Extend: 50–51

Investigation 2
Practice & Apply: 9–17
Connect & Extend: 52–57

Investigation 3
Practice & Apply: 18–37
Connect & Extend: 58

Investigation 4
Practice & Apply: 38–49
Connect & Extend: 59–60

Assign Anytime
Mixed Review: 61–74

Exercise 5 Extension: Ask students to list on the board all possible hookups for a ×100 machine. Remind them that changing the order of a set of machines or factors does not constitute a new hookup.

Exercises 12–20: Make sure students do not use a calculator to evaluate these expressions; the goal is to have students become familiar with exponents.

On Your Own Exercises

Practice & Apply

1. Possible answers: $\times 1$ or $\times 3^0$
2. $\times 5$
3. 5-ft output
4. 3-cm input

Supply the missing information for each diagram.

1. 5 cm → ? → 5 cm

2. 3 in. → ? → 15 in.

3. 1.25 ft → ×4 → ?

4. ? → ×4 → ×3 → 36 cm

If possible, find a hookup that will do the same work as the given stretching machine. Do not use ×1 machines.

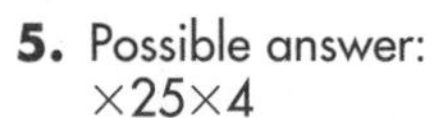

5. Possible answer: $\times 25 \times 4$
6. Possible answer: $\times 3 \times 33$
7. not possible
8. Possible answer: $\times 11 \times 101$

5. ×100 **6.** ×99

7. ×37

8. ×1,111

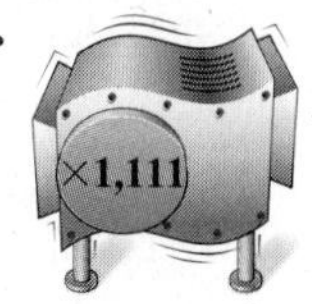

9. Find two repeater machines that will do the same work as a ×81 machine. $\times 9^2$, $\times 3^4$

10. Find a repeater machine that will do the same work as a $\times\frac{1}{8}$ machine. $\times\left(\frac{1}{2}\right)^3$

11. about 1 cm; a $\times 3^2$ machine stretches a stick to 9 times its length, so the original stick must have been $\frac{1}{9}$ this length, which is about 9 cm.

11. This stick of gum exited a $\times 3^2$ machine. Without measuring, estimate the length of the input stick in centimeters. Explain how you found your answer.

Evaluate each expression without using your calculator.

12. 6^2 36 **13.** 9^2 81 **14.** $\left(\frac{1}{3}\right)^3$ $\frac{1}{27}$

15. 3×2^3 24 **16.** 8^1 8 **17.** x^1 x

Do each calculation in your head. (Hint: Think about stretching and shrinking machines.)

18. $\left(\frac{1}{3}\right)^5(3)^5$ 1 **19.** $(4)^6\left(\frac{1}{4}\right)^6$ 1 **20.** $\left(\frac{1}{10}\right)^7(10)^8$ 10

160 CHAPTER 3 Exploring Exponents

If possible, find a repeater machine to do the same work as each hookup.

21. not possible

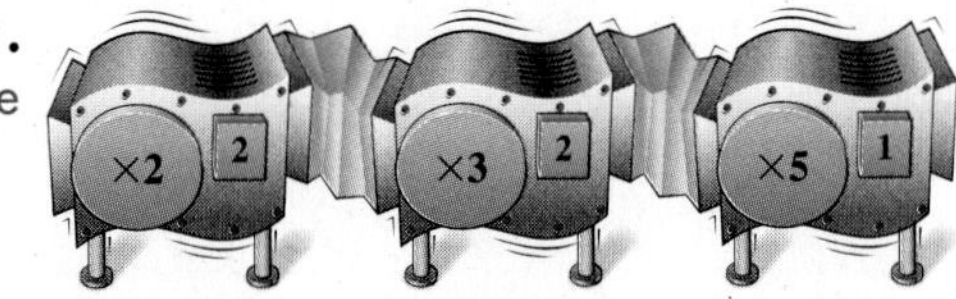

22. $\times 5^4$

23. $\times 10^{10}$

24. not possible

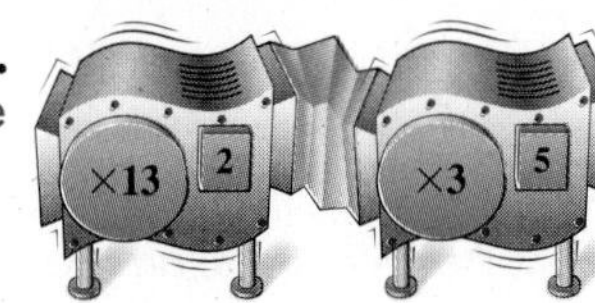

If possible, rewrite each expression using a single base.

26. not possible
27. not possible

25. $6^4 \times 6^2$ 6^6 **26.** $4^{10} \times 5^3$ **27.** $1.1^{100} \times 1.2^{101}$

28. $7^{10} \times 7^k$ 7^{10+k} **29.** $4^n \times 4^m$ 4^{n+m} **30.** $a^{20} \times a^5$ a^{25}

Simplify each expression.

31. $3c \times 5c$ $15c^2$ **32.** $10z^2 \times z^2$ $10z^4$ **33.** $2a^3 \times 10a$ $20a^4$

If possible, find a repeater machine to do the same work as each hookup.

34. not possible

35. 15^2

36. $\times 10^{10}$

37. not possible

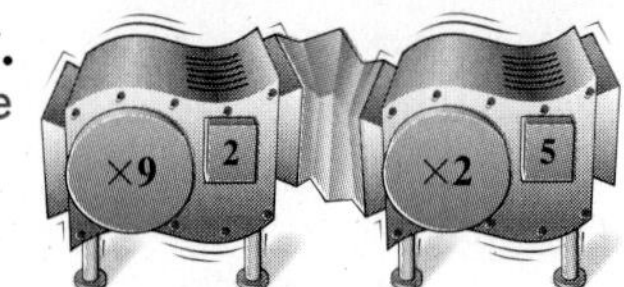

If possible, rewrite each expression using a single base and a single exponent.

44. not possible
47. not possible

38. $2^3 \times \left(\frac{1}{3}\right)^3$ $\left(\frac{2}{3}\right)^3$ **39.** $4^0 \times 5^2$ 5^2 **40.** $1^{100} \times 5^2$ 5^2

41. $3^9 \times \left(\frac{1}{3}\right)^7$ 3^2 **42.** $\left(\frac{1}{2}\right)^2 \times \left(\frac{1}{5}\right)^2$ $\left(\frac{1}{10}\right)^2$ **43.** $6^4 \times 2^4$ 12^4

44. $4^{10} + 1^{10}$ **45.** $x^{10} \times x^8$ x^{18} **46.** $4^n \times 100^n$ 400^n

47. $a^{20} + a^5$ **48.** $a^4 \times b^4$ $(ab)^4$ **49.** $n^a \times m^a$ $(nm)^a$

Exercise 15:
Students may incorrectly multiply 3 × 2 first and then raise the product to the third power. You may want to go over this exercise in class and review order of operations. Students also need to be reminded that although the exponent of 3 is not indicated, the exponent is 1; 3 is the same as 3^1.

Exercises 25–33 and 38–49:
Many students will benefit from creating and referring to a brief summary that lists all the key rules for simplifying expressions with exponents, along with a numerical example of each rule. Be sure students' lists include ×0, ×1, the two product laws of exponents, and an example with coefficients. This kind of list is also a great study aid.

Exercises 25–30:
Students use the law $r^a \times r^b = r^{a+b}$. You may want to go over one of these in class to be sure students are applying this law correctly. Watch for students who find a way to simplify the expressions that don't have the same base.

Exercises 31–33:
Students use the law $r^a \times r^b = r^{a+b}$, but remind them to multiply the coefficients independently of the variables.

LESSON 3.1 Stretching and Shrinking Machines **161**

Assign and Assess

Exercise 58:
Make sure students know how to enter these expressions with exponents into their calculators. Watch for students who get wrong answers by switching the base and exponent. This exercise reinforces the fact that for n not equal to 0, n^0 is 1.

Exercise 60a:
If students have trouble, suggest they start with the original needle and follow it through each machine. When the 1-inch needle goes through the first machine, its length becomes 3 inches; when it goes through the second machine, its length becomes 9 inches, and so on. Students should discover that, in fact, the needles will be different lengths, that is, 3^5 is *not* equal to 5^3.

Exercise 60b:
Students may see this as a difficult exercise at first. But, in fact, they have seen the example that works ($2^4 = 4^2$).

Connect & Extend

50. A ×4 machine can be replaced by a hookup of two ×2 machines.

A ×8 machine can be replaced by a hookup of three ×2 machines.

50b. No; if you multiply two 2s, then three 2s, then four 2s, and so on, you get 4, 8, 16, 32, 64, 128. You never get 100.

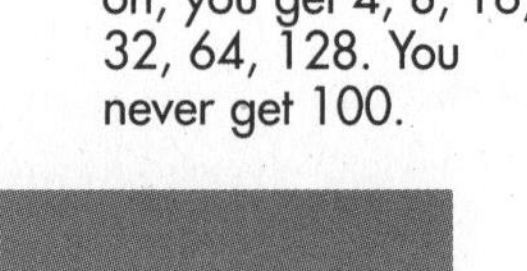

a. Find three other machines that can be replaced by hookups of ×2 machines. Possible answer: ×16, ×32, ×64

b. Can a ×100 machine be replaced by a hookup of ×2 machines? Explain.

c. Find three machines that can be replaced with hookups of ×5 machines. Possible answer: ×25, ×125, ×625

In your own words

Choose one of the product laws of exponents and explain it so a fifth grader could understand. Use stretching and shrinking machines in your explanation if you wish.

51. The left column of the chart lists the lengths of input pieces of ribbon. Stretching machines are listed across the top. The other entries are the outputs for sending the input ribbon from that row through the machine from that column. Copy and complete the chart.

Input Length	Machine ×2	×10	×1	×5
$\frac{1}{2}$	1	5	$\frac{1}{2}$	$\frac{5}{2}$
3	6	30	3	15
7	14	70	7	35

52. The left column of the chart lists the lengths of input chains of gold. Repeater machines are listed across the top. The other entries are the outputs you get when you send the input chain from that row through the repeater machine from that column. Copy and complete the chart.

Input Length	Repeater Machine $\times 2^3$	$\times 3^3$	$\times 5^2$	$\times 2^2$
5	40	135	125	20
2	16	54	50	8
6	48	162	150	24

162 CHAPTER 3 Exploring Exponents

53. 59,049
54. 28,561
55. 2,744
56. 30.25
57. 0.32768

Remember

The only factors of a prime number are the number itself and 1. The *prime factorization* of a number expresses the number as a product of prime numbers: $12 = 2 \times 2 \times 3$.

Mixed Review

62. $\frac{23}{18}$, or $1\frac{5}{18}$
63. $\frac{7}{5}$, or $1\frac{2}{5}$
64. $3\frac{17}{84}$
65. $\frac{399}{16}$, or $24\frac{15}{16}$
66. 0.2066
67. 0.00108
68. $3\frac{43}{63}$
69. 0.538
70. 0.0005
71. false; $2x + 6$

Evaluate each expression.

53. 3^{10} **54.** 13^4 **55.** 14^3 **56.** 5.5^2 **57.** 0.8^5

58. Use your calculator to evaluate each expression.

a. 3^0 1 **b.** 100^0 1 **c.** $\left(\frac{1}{2}\right)^0$ 1

d. Try to explain your answers from Parts a–c using the idea of repeater machines. See Additional Answers.

59. You can use exponents to write prime factorizations in a shorter form. For example, $36 = 2 \times 2 \times 3 \times 3 = 2^2 \times 3^2$. Write the prime factorization of each number using exponents.

a. 27 3^3 **b.** 12 $2^2 \times 3$ **c.** 100 $2^2 \times 5^2$ **d.** 999 $3^3 \times 37$

60. Peter has a 1-inch sewing needle. He says that putting the needle through a $\times 3$ machine five times will have the same effect as putting it through a $\times 5$ machine three times. Caroline says the needles will turn out different lengths.

a. Who is right? Explain how you know. See below.

b. In Part a you compared 3^5 and 5^3. Are there *any* two different numbers, a and b, for which $a^b = b^a$? Your calculator may help you. $a = 2, b = 4$

61. This is an input/output table from a game of *What's My Rule?* Find two ways of writing the rule in symbols. Possible answer: $4n + 2$, $2(2n + 1)$

Input	0	1	2	3	4
Output	2	6	10	14	18

Evaluate each expression.

62. $\frac{1}{2} + \frac{1}{9} + \frac{2}{3}$ **63.** $\frac{3}{5} \times 2\frac{1}{3}$ **64.** $3\frac{2}{7} - \frac{1}{12}$

65. $7\frac{1}{8} \div \frac{2}{7}$ **66.** $0.217 - 0.0104$ **67.** 0.27×0.004

68. $\frac{1}{9} + 3\frac{4}{7}$ **69.** $0.982 - 0.444$ **70.** 0.5×0.001

Tell whether each equation is true. If it is not true, rewrite the expression to the right of the equal sign to make it true.

71. $2(x + 3) = 2x + 3$ **72.** $2(x + 9) = 2x + 18$ true

73. $3(2x + 1) = 2x + 3$ false; $6x + 3$ **74.** $15x - 95 = 5(3x - 19)$ true

60a. Caroline; $1 \times 3 \times 3 \times 3 \times 3 \times 3 = 243$ and $1 \times 5 \times 5 \times 5 = 125$.

Quick Check

Informal Assessment

Students should be able to

✔ model the behavior of exponents using stretching and shrinking machines

✔ understand and apply the product laws of exponents

Quick Quiz

Fill in the missing input, machine, or output in each situation.

1. 30 in.

2. 2 cm

3. ×4 machine

Rewrite each of the following as simply as you can using laws of exponents.

4. $2^n \times 2$ 2^{n+1}
5. $25^n \times 4^n$ 100^n
6. $b^n \times b^0$ b^n
7. $12^5 \times \left(\frac{1}{3}\right)^5$ 4^5
8. $3x^2 \times 4x^3$ $12x^5$

Additional Answers

58d. Possible answer: If a repeater machine has an exponent of 0, it will stretch an input by the base number 0 times, so the length of the input won't change. This is the same thing that happens when you put something through a $\times 1$ machine.

Teacher Notes

3.2

Shrinking and Super Machines

Objectives

- To model the behavior of exponents using stretching and shrinking machines
- To understand and apply the quotient laws of exponents
- To understand and apply the power of a power law of exponents

Overview (Pacing: about 3 class periods)

In this lesson, we continue using the stretching and shrinking model to think about division of numbers with exponents. In addition to learning about the quotient laws of exponents, students explore the power of a power law of exponents.

The problems and activities throughout this lesson involve only nonnegative exponents. In Chapter 4, students explore negative numbers and negative exponents in depth.

Advance Preparation

You may want to make an overhead transparency of Master 17, Blank Stretching and Shrinking Machines, to use as you discuss the stretching and shrinking machines in class. This master includes blank versions of the stretching and shrinking machines used in this lesson. You might also provide copies of this master to students to use for their work on the problem sets and homework.

Lesson Planner

	Summary	Materials	On Your Own Choices	Assessment Opportunities
Investigation 1 page T164	Students are introduced to the new division machines as machines that "undo" the multiplication machines with the same base.	• Master 17 (Teaching Resources, page 29)	Practice & Apply: 1–9 Connect & Extend: 36–37 Mixed Review: 73–83	Share & Summarize, pages T165, 165 Troubleshooting, page T165
Investigation 2 page T166	Students use shrinking machines to model the law of exponents $\frac{r^a}{r^b} = r^{a-b}$.	• Master 17	Practice & Apply: 10–18 Connect & Extend: 38–45 Mixed Review: 73–83	Share & Summarize, pages T167, 167 On the Spot Assessment, page T166 Troubleshooting, page T167
Investigation 3 page T168	Students use super machines to model and work with the power of a power law of exponents $(r^a)^b = r^{a \times b}$.	• Master 17	Practice & Apply: 19–35 Connect & Extend: 46–72 Mixed Review: 73–83	Share & Summarize, pages T171, 171 On the Spot Assessment, page T171 Troubleshooting, page T171 Informal Assessment, page 174 Quick Quiz, page 175

Introduce

The whole-number division machines are introduced as shrinking machines. However, keep in mind that a machine with division by a proper fraction will *not* shrink the input but will increase it.

1 Introduce students to the new division machines. Suggest to students that they can think about a $\div m$ machine as a machine that *undoes* the work of a $\times m$ machine. For example, a $\times 3$ machine triples the length of a stick, and a $\div 3$ machine returns the stick to its original length. A $\times\frac{1}{3}$ machine also undoes the work of a $\times 3$ machine; but in this lesson, we want to concentrate on the division machines.

Ask students to imagine that the resizing factory has other machines that add to or subtract from the length of an item. For example, a $+7$ machine would need to follow a -7 machine in order to restore the input item to its original length. You might ask about "undoing" other operations as well:

> How could you undo a $+5$ machine? use a -5 machine
>
> How could you undo a -199 machine? use a $+199$ machine

You can also relate undoing to the backtracking strategy of solving equations. As you backtrack, you really think about "undoing" the indicated operations one at a time.

Any two operations that undo each other are called *inverse* operations. The idea of inverses is important throughout mathematics, and students get a good taste of inverses in the early part of this lesson.

Think & Discuss

Students are already familiar with the four $\times$ machines, and the $\div 10$ and $\div 2$ machines should not cause much confusion.

However, the $\div\frac{1}{2}$ machine and the $\div\frac{1}{10}$ machine may cause a bit of discussion. Early student reaction may be that the stick that comes out is $\frac{1}{2}$ as long. Tell students to remember, though, that the $\div\frac{1}{2}$ machine must *undo* the $\times\frac{1}{2}$ machine.

Ask students what happens if you put a 2-inch stick through the $\times\frac{1}{2}$ machine. Students should say the stick will come out 1 inch long. If you put that stick through the $\div\frac{1}{2}$ machine, it should undo the first machine, and the output should be a 2-inch stick. Ask students what $\div\frac{1}{2}$ does. Hopefully, they will reply that it does the same thing as $\times 2$!

Students have already studied multiplication and division of fractions in Course 1; but these are always tricky topics, and it wouldn't hurt to spend some time on other examples. Replace the eight machines given with four others like them, perhaps $\times 5$, $\div 5$, $\times\frac{1}{5}$, $\div\frac{1}{5}$, $\times 3$, $\div 3$, $\times\frac{1}{3}$, and $\div\frac{1}{3}$. Have students give the output for each machine when a meter stick travels through it.

Tips
from **Teachers**

When students experience difficulty with the concept of dividing by a fraction less than 1, I have them refer to an inch ruler and determine, for instance, how many half inches are in 3 inches, how many fourth inches are in 2 inches, and so on. This exercise helps to reinforce the notion that dividing a whole number by a fraction less than 1 results in a quotient greater than the whole number.

You may want to prepare copies of Master 17, Blank Stretching and Shrinking Machines, for extra practice of the problems in this lesson.

Investigation 1

In this investigation, students work with division machines and with repeater versions of them. They also put these machines in hookups with $\times$ machines.

Problem Set A **Suggested Grouping: Pairs**
This problem set gives students practice with the division-machine model and introduces exponents to division machines as well.

Problems 1–4 provide practice with the basic shrinker or division machines.

Be sure students note that **Problems 1–5** ask for answers in inches.

3.2 Shrinking and Super Machines

Peter arrived at the resizing factory one day to find a whole new set of machines. Instead of × symbols, the machines had ÷ symbols. Peter's supervisor explained that the factory was getting more orders for shrinking things. So, the factory purchased a new type of shrinking machine that uses whole numbers instead of fractions. For example, a ÷2 machine divides the length of whatever enters the machine by 2.

1 • Introduce division machines.

• Review the concept of "undoing" operations.

Think & Discuss

How long will a meterstick be after traveling through each machine?

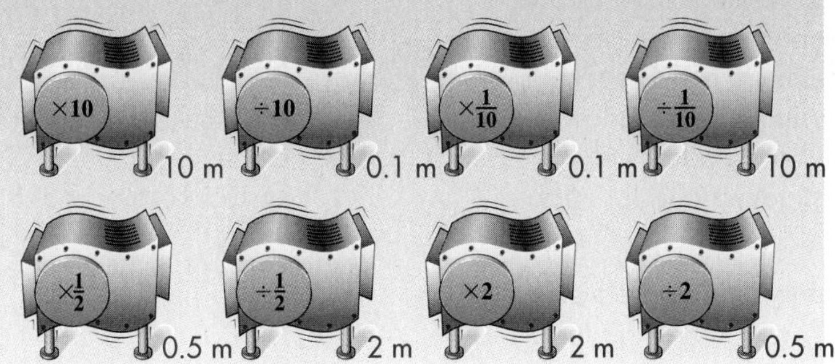

2 Discuss the machines, focusing on the $\div\frac{1}{10}$ and $\div\frac{1}{2}$ machines.

Investigation  A New Shrinking Machine

The new shrinking machines can be hooked to other shrinking machines and to stretching machines.

3 You may have students work in pairs.

Problem Set A

If a yardstick is put into each machine, how many inches long will it be when it comes out?

1. 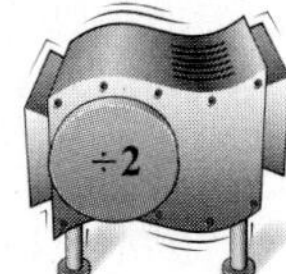

2. 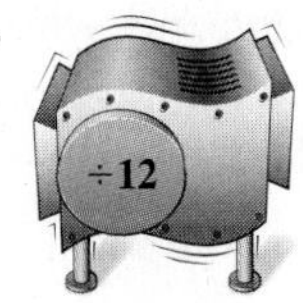

3. ÷12

1. 12 in.
2. 18 in.
3. 3 in.

Develop

Problem 5 is more difficult than Problems 1–4; it might help students to think of this machine as one that undoes a $\times 0.1$ machine.

In **Problems 6–8,** students work for the first time with repeater machines that perform division. They may need to go back to basics, thinking about what a repeater machine does. They may need to think of the $\div 2^3$ machine, for example, as one that divides by 2, then divides by 2 again, and then divides by 2 a third time.

1 In **Problems 9–12,** students look at hookups of repeater $\times 3$ machines and $\div 3$ machines. If students struggle, encourage them to break up the machines and pair up machines that undo one another. Some students may prefer to think of a $\div 3$ machine as a $\times \frac{1}{3}$ machine and solve some of the problems using a product law of exponents learned earlier. This sets the stage nicely for the quotient laws in the next investigation and for negative exponents in Chapter 4.

Problem Set Wrap-Up If students seem to be having trouble with the division machines, you may want to bring the class together to share solutions before moving on to the Share & Summarize questions.

Make sure students understand that the division machines with proper-fraction bases are stretching machines, just like the multiplication machines with whole-number bases.

Share & Summarize

It is certainly possible to solve **Question 1** without using division machines. The goal is for students to find both fraction-multiplication and division machines that work. Have students work on the question independently and then share their answers so that students who focused on the division machines, for example, are reminded of the similarities to the multiplication machines.

Question 2 asks students to find a repeater machine to "cancel" the $\div 5^4$ and leave an additional $\times 25$. Students must recognize that $25 = 5^2$ in order to answer the question.

3 **Troubleshooting** If students come up with only multiplication machines for the first question, you may want to ask them to find division machines that work.

Additional Examples You may want to use additional examples that require hookups of machines. Ask students to give answers with division machines.

- Draw a repeater machine that will shrink a 1-inch stick to $\frac{9}{16}$ of its original size. *Possible answer:* $\div\left(\frac{4}{3}\right)^2$
- Draw a repeater machine that will shrink a stick to $\frac{4}{25}$ of its original size. *Possible answer:* $\div\left(\frac{5}{2}\right)^2$
- Find two division machines that will make a stick 4 times as long. *Possible answer:* $\div\frac{1}{2}$ *and* $\div\frac{1}{2}$ *machines*

On Your Own Exercises

Practice & Apply: 1–9
Connect & Extend: 36–37
Mixed Review: 73–83

4. 9 in.
5. 360 in.

4.

5.

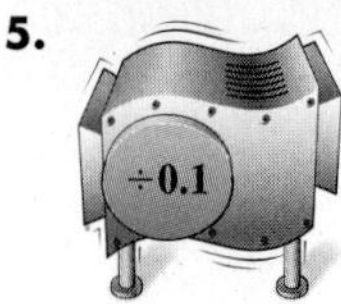

Some of the new shrinking machines are rigged up to make repeater machines. If a yardstick is put into each repeater machine, how many inches long will it be when it exits?

6. 4 in.
7. 9 in.
8. 4.5 in.

6.

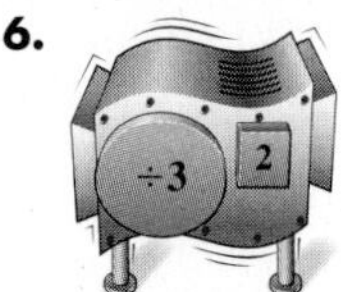

7.

8.

9. If a 1-inch paper clip is put through this hookup, what will its final length be? 9 in.

Find a single repeater machine to do the same work as each hookup.

10. $\times 3^3$
11. $\times 3^5$

10.

11.

12.

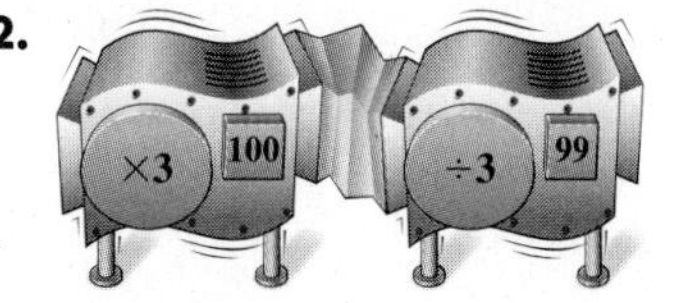

$\times 3^1$

Share & Summarize

1. Possible answers: $\div 2^4$, $\div 4^2$, $\times\left(\frac{1}{2}\right)^4$, $\times\left(\frac{1}{4}\right)^2$
2. $\times 5^6$

1. Find two repeater machines that will shrink a 1-inch gummy worm to $\frac{1}{16}$ of an inch.

2. A 1-inch gummy worm was sent through this hookup and emerged 25 inches long. What is the first machine in the hookup?

1 For Problems 9–12, encourage students to break up and pair machines that undo each other.

2 For Problems 9–12, have students share solutions.

3 Have students find both multiplication and division machines.

4 Give students additional examples.

LESSON 3.2 Shrinking and Super Machines 165

Investigation 2

In this investigation, students use division machines to develop two quotient laws of exponents. These laws are counterparts to the product laws from Lesson 3.1, and that connection should be made clear to students.

Example

Begin by walking students through the example in which Shaunda thinks about hookups of × and ÷ machines that have the same base. If students have worked with multiplying and dividing numbers written as fractions, you may want to write something like this on the board:

$$\frac{3^5}{3^3} = \frac{\not{3} \times \not{3} \times \not{3} \times 3 \times 3}{\not{3} \times \not{3} \times \not{3}}$$

Three of the 3s in the numerator "cancel" the 3s in the denominator. We are left with just 3×3, or 3^2, in the numerator. Be sure to relate the canceling to the "undoing" of the machines: each ÷3 machine undoes a ×3 machine, so each pair has the same effect as a ×1 machine.

Problem Set B **Suggested Grouping: Pairs**
Students are asked to apply the quotient law to a set of expressions written in exponential form.

> On the **Spot Assessment**
>
> Look for students who do division problems such as $\frac{2^a}{2^b}$ by "canceling out" the bases to get $\frac{1^a}{1^b}$. Students will be less likely to do this if they think of translating these problems into machine language.

Problem Set Wrap-Up Ask students to share their answers for **Problems 10–17.** In particular, ask whether anyone found a way to simplify **Problem 12, 14, or 17.** If so, take some time to find out what those students did, and have the class discuss it. If not, move on to the Example on page 167.

Investigation 2 Dividing and Exponents

The machine model can help you divide exponential expressions.

EXAMPLE

Here's how Shaunda thought about $3^5 \div 3^3$.

Shaunda had discovered one of the *quotient laws of exponents.*

Dividing Expressions with the Same Base

$$a^b \div a^c = a^{b-c}$$

$$\frac{a^b}{a^c} = a^{b-c}$$

1 • Walk students through the Example.

• Write the expression as a fraction without exponents and relate "canceling" to "undoing."

Problem Set B

2 You may have students work in pairs.

Write each expression as a power of 2.9.

1. $2.9^5 \div 2.9^3$ 2.9^2
2. $2.9^{10} \div 2.9^6$ 2.9^4
3. $2.9^{13} \div 2.9^{12}$
4. $2.9^{13} \div 2.9^{11}$ 2.9^2
5. $2.9^{25} \div 2.9^{25}$
6. $2.9^8 \div 2.9^3$ 2.9^5

Evaluate each expression without using your calculator.

7. $2^3 \div 2^3$ 1
8. $2^{10} \div 2^{10}$ 1
9. $2^{15} \div 2^{15}$ 1

If possible, rewrite each expression using a single base.

10. $5^5 \div 5^2$ 5^3
11. $3^4 \div 3^2$ 3^2
12. $2^5 \div 3^4$
13. $3^2 \div 3^0$
14. $2^8 \div 3^2$
15. $a^{10} \div a$ a^9
16. $a^n \div a^m$
17. $a^n \div b^m$

3 Have students share answers and discuss strategies.

3. 2.9^1, or 2.9
5. 2.9^0, or 1
12. not possible
13. 3^2
14. not possible
16. a^{n-m}
17. not possible

Develop

Example

Discuss the Example with the whole class. Ask students whether they prefer writing the expression as $\left(\frac{2}{3}\right)^2$ or as $\frac{4}{9}$. Both forms are useful. Explain that the form $\left(\frac{a}{b}\right)^c$ is useful because it is much easier to simplify a fraction—divide both numerator and denominator by any common factors *before* the fraction is raised to a power. For example, $\left(\frac{6}{8}\right)^3 = \left(\frac{3}{4}\right)^3 = \frac{27}{64}$. We know $\left(\frac{6}{8}\right)^3 = \frac{216}{512}$, but it is not obvious that $\frac{216}{512} = \frac{27}{64}$.

Review the quotient law of exponents given after the cartoon. This law applies to expressions with the same exponent. It is parallel to the second product law of exponents.

Problem Set C Suggested Grouping: Individuals

This short problem set asks students to apply the two quotient laws. **Problems 7 and 8** ask students to justify why it is possible to divide the bases when the exponents are the same. If a student questions why they should assume that $b \neq 0$, you might ask what would happen if $b = 0$. They should know that division by 0 is undefined.

If students are having difficulty with the general argument for Problems 7 and 8, encourage them to substitute numbers for the variables. For example, in Problem 8, substitute 2 for a, 5 for b, and 3 for c. Then $\frac{2^3}{5^3} = \frac{2 \times 2 \times 2}{5 \times 5 \times 5} = \left(\frac{2}{5}\right)\left(\frac{2}{5}\right)\left(\frac{2}{5}\right) = \left(\frac{2}{5}\right)^3$. Then replace 2, 5, and 3 by a, b, and c. The final step is to assure students that there is nothing special about the numbers chosen. *Any* exponent will work as long as it is the same for the two bases.

Additional Examples To provide students more practice with general arguments and the laws of exponents, ask them to "prove" any of the four laws below. Students have seen arguments for the first three laws listed here but not general arguments with variables.

$$a^b \times a^c = a^{b+c}$$

$$a^c \times b^c = (ab)^c$$

$$a^b \div a^c = a^{b-c}$$

$$a^c \div b^c = (a \div b)^c$$

If students are confused by the general arguments but can articulate and apply the rules correctly, that's fine. Throughout the year, there will be more opportunities for building these abstract arguments.

Share & Summarize

This question asks students to articulate the first quotient law. The second law is not covered, since the most recent problem was a general proof of the second quotient law. It is essential that students are able to explain that the difference between the two exponents on the left must be the same as the exponent on the right.

Troubleshooting It is not essential for students to have a *complete* understanding of the quotient laws because some confusion about dividing numbers with exponents will not hinder progress through the other material. The rest of the chapter focuses on exponential growth, powers of 10, and scientific notation. Students should be able to reason through division of numbers with exponents, however. They will have some opportunity to revisit the quotient laws in Chapter 4, where the laws will be extended to include negative exponents.

On Your Own Exercises

Practice & Apply: 10–18
Connect & Extend: 38–45
Mixed Review: 73–83

Though you may not be able to rewrite an expression using a single base, there may sometimes still be a way to simplify the expression.

EXAMPLE

Kate wondered if it would be possible to simplify an expression like $2^2 \div 3^2$. Simon and Jin Lee tried to help her decide.

I got $(\frac{2}{3})^2$.
But the quotient law talks only about expressions with the same base.
I think Simon's right. Think about what $2^2 \div 3^2$ means. 2^2 is 4 and 3^2 is 9, So you get $\frac{4}{9}$!
Is that the same as $(\frac{2}{3})^2$?
Sure! When you multiply fractions, you multiply the two numerators and the two denominators. So $(\frac{2}{3})^2 = \frac{2}{3} \times \frac{2}{3} = \frac{2 \times 2}{3 \times 3}$ which is $\frac{4}{9}$!

This led the class to discuss another quotient law of exponents.

Dividing Expressions with the Same Exponent

$$a^c \div b^c = (a \div b)^c$$

$$\frac{a^c}{b^c} = \left(\frac{a}{b}\right)^c$$

Problem Set C

Write each expression in the form c^m. The variable c can be a fraction or a whole number.

1. $2^2 \div 5^2$ $\left(\frac{2}{5}\right)^2$ **2.** $5^6 \div 5^2$ 5^4 **3.** $a^2 \div 2^2$ $\left(\frac{a}{2}\right)^2$

4. $a^9 \div b^9$ $\left(\frac{a}{b}\right)^9$ **5.** $3^7 \div 3^4$ 3^3 **6.** $x^n \div y^n$ $\left(\frac{x}{y}\right)^n$

7. Prove It! Show that $\frac{a^3}{b^3} = \left(\frac{a}{b}\right)^3$, for $b \neq 0$. Hint: Write a^3 and b^3 as products of a's and b's, and regroup the quotient into a string of $\left(\frac{a}{b}\right)$'s.

8. Do you think $\frac{a^c}{b^c} = \left(\frac{a}{b}\right)^c$ for $b \neq 0$ and any value of c? Explain.

7. $\frac{a^3}{b^3} = \frac{a \times a \times a}{b \times b \times b} = \frac{a}{b} \times \frac{a}{b} \times \frac{a}{b} = \left(\frac{a}{b}\right)^3$

8. yes; Possible explanation: If $c > 0$, you can always rewrite and regroup like I did for Problem 7; you get $\frac{a}{b}$ multiplied by itself c times. If $c = 0$, you get $\frac{a^0}{b^0} = \frac{1}{1} = 1 = \left(\frac{a}{b}\right)^0$.

Share & Summarize

In your own words, write the rule that lets you find the missing exponent in equations like $5^{16} \div 5^8 = 5^?$ and $r^? \div r^{10} = r^5$. See ①.

① When you divide a base raised to a power by the same base raised to a power, the result is the base raised to the difference of the powers.

1 Discuss the Example, stressing both expressions.

2 Review this quotient law of exponents, noting that exponents are the same.

3
- Have students explain why b cannot equal 0.
- Encourage students who are struggling to substitute numbers for variables.

4 Be sure that students can articulate the first quotient law of exponents.

Investigation 3

This investigation takes the machine metaphor to a new level: repeaters of repeater machines. This is simply to make a point about, and to give students a visual image of, the power of a power law: $(r^a)^b = r^{ab}$.

1 Have the students read the text in the beginning of the investigation, and ask them to describe what a super machine really does, given the manufacturer's instructions. Some students may think about the super machine this way: "It's a repeater machine of repeater machines!" In fact, this is a good explanation.

2 **Think & Discuss**

Students should be able to calculate what happens to the 1-inch stick in stages. After the first time through a $\times 2^3$ machine, the stick is 8 inches long. After feeding the 8-inch stick through a $\times 2^3$ machine, we get a stick that is $8 \times 2 \times 2 \times 2$, or 64, inches long.

Sample Strategies Students may approach the second question in several different ways.

- They might think about sending the 1-inch stick through a $\times 2$ machine, then sending the output through a $\times 2$ machine, and so on, counting how many machines are needed to output a 64-inch stick.
- Other students may relate to problems they have already solved, determining which power of 2 equals 64.
- Still others may use the laws of exponents from Lesson 3.1 and simply say that $2^3 \times 2^3$ is 2^6 because you add the exponents.

It is important for students to understand the need for parentheses in writing "powers of powers" in order for them to communicate clearly in their mathematical writing. Ask,

> In what ways might $2^{3\ 2}$ be confusing?
>
> How do parentheses clear up the confusion?

Finally, to help students understand the hookup for the super $\times(4^2)^3$ machine, reproduce the following diagram of the machines, without the numbers filled in, on the board or on the overhead. Then have students tell you how to fill in the numbers.

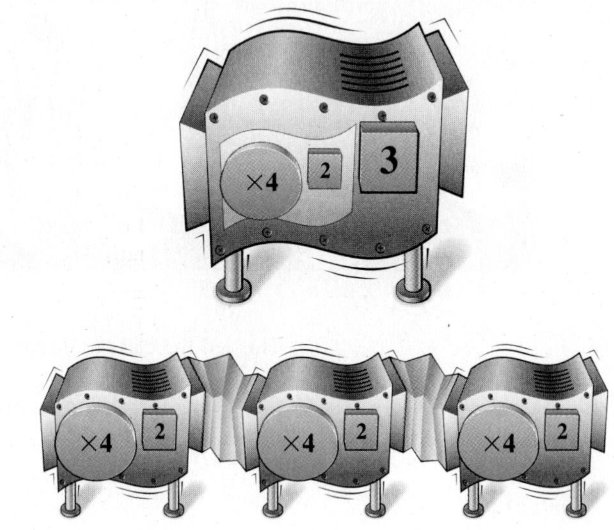

Investigation  Super Machines

Your resizing factory is such a success, you decide to order a shipment of *super machines.* Here's one of the new machines.

Peter was excited to try the machine, but he wasn't sure what it would do. He found this diagram in the manufacturer's instructions:

1 Introduce the idea of super machines.

Just the facts

Improperly discarded chewing gum can be a litter nightmare. Schools and businesses spend thousands of dollars every year cleaning chewing gum from floors, carpets, and furniture.

Think & Discuss

If Peter puts a 1-inch stick of gum through the super machine above, how long will it be when it comes out? 64 in.

How many times would Peter need to apply a $\times 2$ machine to do the same work as this new super machine? 6

Peter used the shorthand notation $\times(2^3)^2$ to describe this super machine. Why is this shorthand better than $\times 2^{3\ 2}$? See ①.

Describe or draw a hookup of three repeater machines that will do the same work as a $\times(4^2)^3$ machine. Possible answer: $\times 4^2 \times 4^2 \times 4^2$

① $\times 2^{3\ 2}$ could be confused with $\times 2^{32}$.

2
- Review the questions in class, discussing multiple strategies for the second question.
- Make sure students understand the need for parentheses.

Develop

Problem Set D **Suggested Grouping: Pairs**
Problems 1–4 ask students to think about outputs of super machines. **Problem 5** asks them to show the hookups that the super machines represent. Some students might find it helpful to think about the hookups of repeater machines first. For example, they may, for the first machine in Problem 1, think about hooking up two 5^2 machines together to come up with a final answer of $5^2 \times 5^2 = 625$.

For **Problem 3,** ask students to think about the simplest machine that could replace the machine given in order to help them recognize the "easy" problems and use shortcuts. Sometimes students think exceptional numbers, like 1^n and a^0, are tricky; but understanding how to work with these special quantities is important.

In **Problem 6,** students may need to think first of equal factors of 81: $81 = 9 \times 9$, and $9 = 3^2$. Therefore, one super machine is $\times(3^2)^2$.

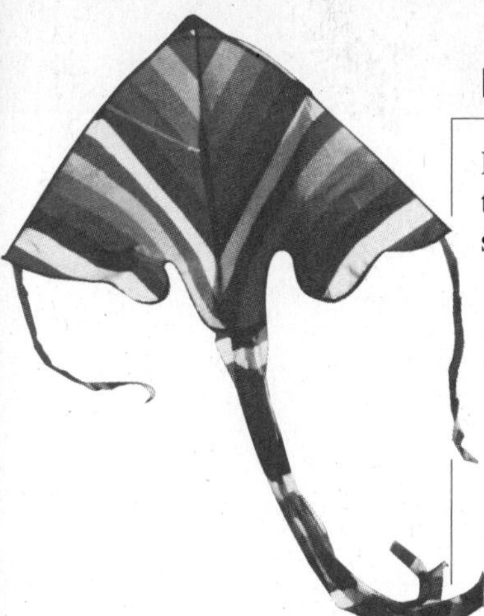

Problem Set D

Hannah has an order from a kite maker who wants to stretch different types of kite string. If a 1-inch piece of kite string is sent through each super machine, how long will it be when it exits?

1.

2.

3.

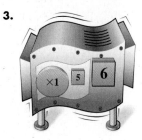

4.

1. 5^4 in., or 625 in.
2. 2^{10} in., or 1,024 in.
3. 1^{30} in., or 1 in.
4. See below.
5. See below.

5. For each super machine in Problems 1–4, describe or draw a hookup of two or more repeater machines that would do the same work.

6. Describe a super machine that will stretch a 1-inch strand of kite string to 81 inches. Do not use 1 for either exponent.

Possible answer:
$\times(3^2)^2$

7. Consider the expression $(4^3)^2$.

a. Draw a super machine that represents this expression.

b. How many times would you need to apply a $\times 4^3$ machine to do the same work as your super machine? 2

c. How many times would you need to apply a $\times 4$ machine to do the same work as your super machine? 6

7a.

4. 10^{15} in., or 1,000,000,000,000,000 in.

5. Possible answers: $\times 5^2 \times 5^2$, $\times 2^5 \times 2^5$, $\times 1^5 \times 1^5 \times 1^5 \times 1^5 \times 1^5 \times 1^5$, $\times 10^3 \times 10^3 \times 10^3 \times 10^3 \times 10^3$

1 You may have students work in pairs.

2 For Problem 3, ask students for the simplest replacement machine.

3 Have students find equal factors of 81.

LESSON 3.2 Shrinking and Super Machines **169**

Develop

1 **Example**

Refer students to the Example, which explains how Maya thought about $\times(4^3)^2$. Describe the power of a power law and how it relates to the super machine and to repeated multiplication. For $\times(4^3)^2$, you can remind them that the outer exponent 2 indicates "multiply what's in the parentheses by itself." So we have $4^3 \times 4^3$. We can break this down even further, as Maya did: each 4^3 is really $4 \times 4 \times 4$, and $(4 \times 4 \times 4) \times (4 \times 4 \times 4) = 4 \times 4 \times 4 \times 4 \times 4 \times 4$.

Discuss the power of a power law of exponents, which is given in the box at the bottom of page 170. It might be helpful for students to work through Maya's strategy a few times with other super machines, for example, $(3^4)^2$, $(5^3)^2$, $(7^2)^3$.

The expressions represented by the super machines can be simplified.

EXAMPLE

In Problem 7, Zoe added the exponents and decided it would take five $\times 4$ machines to do the same work as the $\times(4^3)^2$ super machine. Maya thought the answer was six. She drew a diagram to explain her thinking to Zoe.

Maya's diagram convinced Zoe she should have multiplied the exponents rather than adding them. The diagram shows that $(4^3)^2 = 4^{3 \times 2} = 4^6$.

The diagram Maya used demonstrates an example of the *power of a power law of exponents.*

Raising a Power to a Power

$$(a^b)^c = a^{b \times c}$$

1 Discuss the Example.

2
- Discuss the power of a power law of exponents.
- Have students work through other examples.

Develop

Problem Set E **Suggested Grouping: Individuals** Students now move from the machine model to numbers with exponents. These problems provide a good check on whether students understand how to use the power of a power law.

Problem 6 includes 0 as an exponent. Students should note right away that the number in parentheses, 2^0, is 1, since it is a number raised to the 0 power, and, therefore, give the answer as 1^5, or 1. Other students might choose to apply the law and just multiply the exponents.

2 For **Problems 8 and 9,** remind students of the importance of using parentheses within these power of a power expressions. Some calculators evaluate 2^2^3 as 2^8 rather than 2^6 if parentheses are not included. That is, the calculator evaluates 2^2^3 rather than (2^2)^3, so it's better to use parentheses just to be sure.

If students have trouble with **Problem 11,** ask them to think about the numerator and the denominator in terms of machines. Ask whether there is a way to think about the 4^3 machine in terms of $\times 2$ machines. Students might work backward from the law of exponents and respond that $4^3 = (2^2)^3 = 2^6$.

On the **Spot Assessment**

In **Problem 11,** watch for students who are tempted to treat the bases as the fraction $\frac{2}{4}$ and change the problem to $\frac{1^7}{2^3}$. Explain that to change $\frac{2}{4}$ to $\frac{1}{2}$, the exponents of 2 and 4 must match. For example, $\frac{4^5}{6^5} = \left(\frac{4}{6}\right)^5 = \left(\frac{2}{3}\right)^5$, according to the quotient law of exponents.

In **Problem 14,** some students may be tempted to add bases or exponents and get $2^7 + 2^7 = 4^7$ or $2^7 + 2^7 = 2^{14}$. Ask those students to try to verify their answers with calculators. They will not get the results they expected, so students should start thinking about proper use of the appropriate exponent law. If we think of 2^7 as "some number," then we have two of that number or 2×2^7. By one of the product laws of exponents, this is 2^8.

Share & Summarize

Have students work on **Questions 1–6** individually as you circulate around the room to see whether students understand the questions. At this point, students should feel confident answering these questions.

Ask students to work individually to write their answers to **Question 7** and then share their answers with a partner. Encourage students to draw machines or to use symbolic notation to describe the differences.

Troubleshooting Questions 1, 3, and 4 illustrate classic mistakes that students make and should be assessed carefully. If students are having difficulty with these questions, ask them to draw a picture of each situation and to describe what is happening in terms of machines.

On Your Own Exercises

Practice & Apply: 19–35
Connect & Extend: 46–72
Mixed Review: 73–83

Problem Set E

Write each expression as a power of 2.

1. $(2^4)^2$ 2^8
2. $(2^2)^3$ 2^6
3. $(2^4)^3$ 2^{12}
4. $(2^2)^2$ 2^4
5. $(2^1)^7$ 2^7
6. $(2^0)^5$ 2^0

Tell what number should replace the question mark to make each statement true.

7. $4 = 2^?$ 2
8. $4^? = (2^2)^3$ 3
9. $4^4 = (?^2)^4$ 2
10. $2^3 \times 4^? = 2^{13}$ 5
11. $2^7 \div 4^3 = 2^?$ 1
12. $?^3 \div 2^3 = 2^3$ 4
13. $8^2 = 2^?$ 6
14. $2^7 + 2^7 = 2^?$ (Be careful!) 8
15. Use a calculator to check your answers for Problems 1–14. To evaluate an expression like $(2^4)^2$, use parentheses and push the exponent key twice. To find $(2^4)^2$, you could use the following keystrokes:

[(] 2 [^] 4 [)] [^] 2

or

[(] 2 [y^x] 4 [)] [y^x] 2

Share & Summarize

Tell whether each equation is true or false. If an equation is false, rewrite the expression to the right of the equal sign to make it true.

1. $3^5 \times 3^3 = 3^{15}$ false, 3^8
2. $(2^5)^0 = 1$ true
3. $(a^3)^4 = a^7$ false, a^{12}
4. $a^{30} \div a^2 = a^{15}$ false, a^{28}
5. $(a^5)^3 = a^{15}$ true
6. $a^4 \times a^3 = a^7$ true
7. Explain the difference between $(a^b)^c$ and $a^b \times a^c$. Refer to stretching and shrinking machines if they help you explain.

Possible answer: $(a^b)^c$ means "do $\times a^b$ c times." $a^b \times a^c$ means "do $\times a$ b times and then do $\times a$ c times."

1 Have students work individually.

2
- Remind students of the importance of parentheses.
- If students struggle with Problem 11, suggest that they think about machines.

3
- Circulate to make sure students understand.
- Encourage students to draw pictures if they have difficulty.

LESSON 3.2 Shrinking and Super Machines 171

On Your Own Exercises

On Your Own Exercises

Investigation 1
Practice & Apply: 1–9
Connect & Extend: 36–37

Investigation 2
Practice & Apply: 10–18
Connect & Extend: 38–45

Investigation 3
Practice & Apply: 19–35
Connect & Extend: 46–72

Assign Anytime
Mixed Review: 73–83

Exercises 8 and 9: These problems challenge students to estimate input sticks given an output and the machine. Some students will find this more challenging than calculating the lengths with numbers.

Practice & Apply

1. 1 in.
2. 6 in.
3. 120 in.
4. 4 in.
5. 3 in.

6. $\times 2^3$
7. $\times 7^6$

A 12-inch ruler is put through each machine. Find its exit length.

1. ÷12

2.

3.

4. ÷3

5.

Find a single repeater machine that will do the same work as the given hookup.

6.

7.

8. This pencil emerged from a ÷3 machine. Estimate the length of the output in inches. Then find the length of the input pencil. 6 in.

9. This pencil came out of a $\div \frac{1}{2}$ machine. Estimate the length of the output in inches. Then find the length of the input pencil. 1 in.

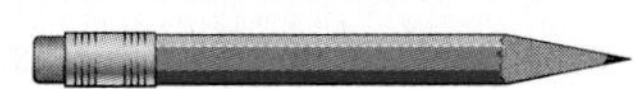

Write each expression using a single base and a single exponent.

10. $2.7^{10} \div 2.7$ 2.7^9

11. $0.2^{10} \div 0.2^{10}$ 0.2^0

12. $a^{20} \div a^5$ a^{15}

13. $\frac{s^{100}}{s}$ s^{99}

14. $\frac{a^n}{a^m}$ a^{n-m}

15. $r^2 \div 5^2$ $\left(\frac{r}{5}\right)^2$

Write each expression as simply as you can.

16. $5a^4 \div 5a^4$ 1

17. $\frac{12z^2}{6z^2}$ 2

18. $\frac{15a^3}{5a^3}$ 3

172 CHAPTER 3 Exploring Exponents

19. Caroline was working with this super machine.

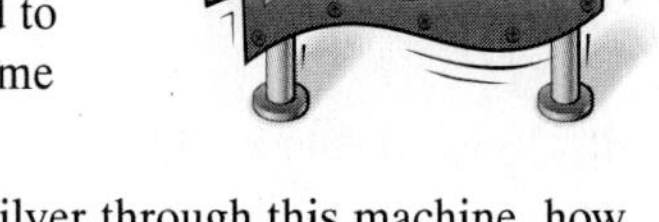

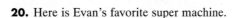

a. How many times would Caroline need to apply a $\times 3^3$ machine to do the same work as this super machine? 3

b. How many times would she need to apply a $\times 3$ machine to do the same work as this machine? 9

c. If Caroline puts a 1-inch bar of silver through this machine, how long will it be when it exits? 19,683 in.

20. Here is Evan's favorite super machine.

a. How many times would Evan need to apply a $\times 10^3$ machine to do the same work as this super machine? 2

b. How many times would he need to apply a $\times 10$ machine to do the same work? 6

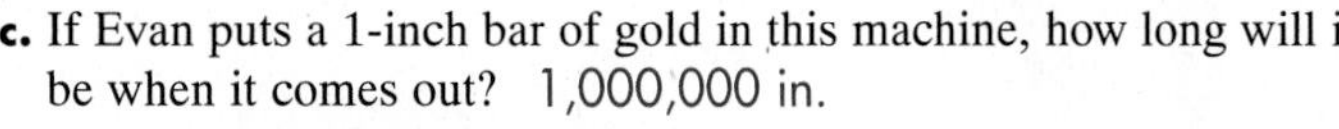

c. If Evan puts a 1-inch bar of gold in this machine, how long will it be when it comes out? 1,000,000 in.

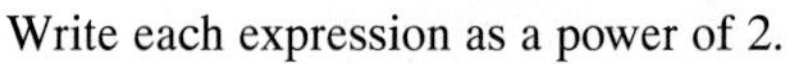

Write each expression as a power of 2.

21. $(4^2)^3$ 2^{12} **22.** $2^4 \div 4^2$ 2^0 **23.** $2^3 \div 2^3$ 2^0

Write each expression using a single base and a single exponent.

24. $(0.5^2)^2$ **25.** $(2.5^9)^0$ **26.** $(1.9^5)^3$ **27.** $(p^{25})^4$

28. $(p^4)^{25}$ **29.** $(5^n)^2$ **30.** $(5^2)^n$ **31.** $(4n)^3$

32. $(3^2)^3$ **33.** $(5^2)^2$ **34.** $(99^1)^5$ **35.** $(100^0)^5$

24. 0.5^4
25. 2.5^0
26. 1.9^{15}
27. p^{100}
28. p^{100}
29. 5^{2n}
30. 5^{2n}
31. correct as is
32. 3^6
33. 5^4
34. 99^5
35. 100^0

Connect & Extend

36. Describe a hookup of repeater machines that will shrink a traffic ticket to $\frac{16}{27}$ of its original length.

36. Possible answers: $\times 2^4 \div 3^3$, $\times 4^2 \div 3^3$

37. Which one of these is not equal to the others? $\frac{1}{8}$

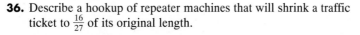

$\left(\frac{1}{4}\right)^2$ $\left(\frac{1}{2}\right)^4$ $\frac{1}{8}$ 6.25% $\frac{625}{10,000}$

Preview Write each expression in the form $\frac{1}{5^n}$.

38. $5^4 \div 5^{10}$ $\frac{1}{5^6}$ **39.** $5^4 \div 5^{14}$ $\frac{1}{5^{10}}$ **40.** $5^{10} \div 5^{20}$ $\frac{1}{5^{10}}$

Exercises 20c and 46: These are worth going over in class, since they require students to think about numbers that multiply to one million. This previews their study of powers of 10 later in the chapter. If students are having trouble thinking about the exercise, ask them what two equal numbers multiply to one million. They should respond, $1{,}000 \times 1{,}000$. Then ask them whether they can write 1,000 as a power of 10. This should help them with the solution $(10^3)^2$. You can then ask them whether this is the same as $(10^2)^3$.

Exercises 38–40: These exercises preview work with negative exponents.

Exercises 52–66: These problems ask students to pull together all of the laws of exponents they have learned and practice them, deciding for each expression which is the appropriate law to use. Students will have more practice with this in Chapter 4.

Exercises 67–72: Review these exercises in class. If students have difficulty, ask them to regroup the expressions to make computation easier. For example, in Exercise 67, students can rewrite the expression as $m^3m^5 \times n^5n^2$.

Exercise 73: You may need to remind students how to find the volume of a cylinder, $V = \pi r^2h$.

Quick Check

Informal Assessment

Students should be able to

- ✔ model the behavior of exponents using stretching and shrinking machines
- ✔ understand and apply the quotient laws of exponents
- ✔ understand and apply the power of a power law of exponents

Your factory has received a special order to stretch a 1-inch bar of gold to *over* 1,000 inches. In Exercises 41–45, give the exponent of the repeater machine that would get the job done. If it is not possible to do the work with the given base machine, say so.

41.

42.

43.

44.

45. ÷2

41. any number > 9
42. any number > 3
43. any number > 6
44. any number > 9
45. any number < $^-9$ (Note: Students will likely say it's not possible.)
46. Possible answer: $(10^2)^3$, $(10^3)^2$

46. Preview Describe two super machines that would stretch a bar of gold to one million times its original length.

Remember
5,280 feet = 1 mile

Preview A 1-inch bar of titanium is put through each super machine. How long will it emerge? Give your answers in inches, feet, and miles.

47.

48.

49.

50.

47. 1,000 in.; 83.3 ft; 0.016 mi
48. 1,000,000 in.; 83,333.3 ft; 15.8 mi
49. 1,000,000,000 in.; 83,333,333.3 ft; 15,782.8 mi
50. 1,000,000,000,000 in.; 83,333,333,333.3 ft; 15,782,828.3 mi

51. How long will the bar of copper be when it exits this hookup? 300 in.

174 CHAPTER 3 Exploring Exponents

In your own words

Choose one of the laws of exponents and explain the law so a fifth grader could understand it. You can refer to stretching and shrinking machines if they help you explain.

52–73. See Additional Answers.

Rewrite each expression using a single base or a single exponent, if possible. For example, $3^7 \div 5^7$ can be rewritten $\left(\frac{3}{5}\right)^7$. You will have to decide which exponent laws to apply. Here are the laws you have seen so far.

Product Laws	Quotient Laws	Power of a Power Law
$a^b \times a^c = a^{b+c}$	$a^b \div a^c = a^{b-c}$	$(a^b)^c = a^{b \times c}$
$a^c \times b^c = (a \times b)^c$	$a^c \div b^c = (a \div b)^c$	

52. $7^5 \div 3^5$ **53.** $7^5 \times 5^7$ **54.** $s^{100} \times s$

55. $1{,}000^{14} \div 2^{14}$ **56.** $6^5 \div 6^2$ **57.** $100^{100} \div 25^{25}$

58. $(2^0)^3$ **59.** $10^2 \times \left(\frac{1}{2}\right)^2$ **60.** $6^b \times 6^b$

61. $(x^2)^x$ **62.** $d^2 \times d^0$ **63.** $10^p \div 5^p$

64. $a^n \times a^m$ **65.** $(4x)^2 \div x^2$ **66.** $(10^2)^3 \div 10^2$

Challenge Use what you know about exponents to write each expression in a simpler form.

67. $m^3n^5 \times m^5n^2$ **68.** $a^3b^4c \times 2ab^3c^2$ **69.** $14^p \div 7^{2p}$

70. $2y^3z \times (6yz^4)^2$ **71.** $\frac{x^2yz^3}{x^3y^2z}$ **72.** $\frac{15m^3n^2}{60k^3m^4n^2}$

73. Geometry Consider this cylinder.

a. Find the volume of this cylinder.

b. Find the volume of a cylinder with the same height as this cylinder and twice the radius.

c. Find the volume of a cylinder with the same radius as this cylinder and twice the height.

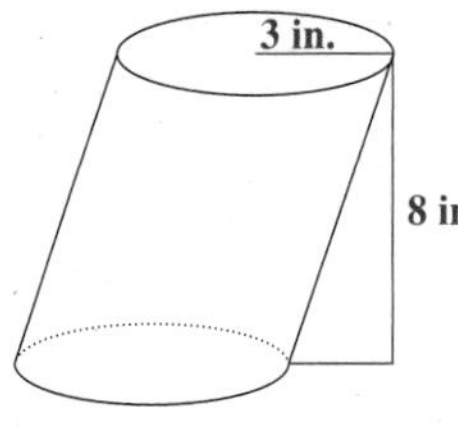

Mixed Review

Order each set of numbers from least to greatest.

74. $4, 2, -\frac{1}{2}, 0, -4$ **75.** $-30, 30, 3, -3, 0$

76. $200, -500, -50, 20, 2, -5$ **77.** $0.001, 0.1, -0.1, -1, -0.001$

Algebra Solve each equation for a.

78. $5a - 3a = 19$ **79.** $7a - 3a = a$ **80.** $a - 5 = 1.5a - 6$

81. Use a factor tree to find the prime factors of 75.

82. Use a factor tree to find the prime factors of 72.

83. Use a factor tree to find the prime factors of 100.

81–83. See Additional Answers.

74. $-4, -\frac{1}{2}, 0, 2, 4$
75. $-30, -3, 0, 3, 30$
76. $-500, -50, -5, 2, 20, 200$
77. $-1, -0.1, -0.001, 0.001, 0.1$
78. 9.5
79. 0
80. 2

Quick Quiz

Fill in the missing input, machine, or output.

1. 3 cm

2. ÷5

3. ×2

4. 10,000 cm

Rewrite these as simply as you can using rules of exponents.

5. $2^4 \div 2^1$	2^3
6. $7^n \div 2$	$7^n \div 2$
7. $25^n \times 4^n$	100^n
8. $(4^3)^n$	4^{3n}
9. $24^{10} \times \left(\frac{1}{3}\right)^{10}$	8^{10}

Additional Answers

52. $\left(\frac{7}{3}\right)^5$ **53.** not possible **54.** s^{101} **55.** 500^{14} **56.** 6^3

57. not possible **58.** 2^0 **59.** 5^2 **60.** 36^b or 6^{2b} **61.** x^{2x}

62. d^2 **63.** 2^p **64.** a^{n+m} **65.** 4^2 **66.** 10^4

67. m^8n^7 **68.** $2a^4b^7c^3$ **69.** $\left(\frac{2}{7}\right)^p$ **70.** $72y^5z^9$ **71.** $\frac{z^2}{xy}$

72. $\frac{1}{4k^3m}$ **73a.** 72π in^3, or about 226.2 in^3

• ***Additional Answers continued on page A388.***

Teacher Notes

3.3 Growing Exponentially

Objectives

- To develop a sense of exponential growth and exponential decay
- To describe examples of exponential increase and exponential decrease
- To compare exponential growth with other kinds of growth (linear, quadratic, and so on)

Overview (Pacing: about 2 class periods)

In this short lesson, students gain a sense for exponential growth functions and how they differ from other functions. In particular, they compare $2x$ with x^2 and 2^x and then compare $3x$ with x^3 and 3^x.

Advance Preparation

You may want to make an overhead transparency of Master 9, Centimeter Graph Paper, to show graphs of quadratic and exponential equations. Students will need graph paper or copies of this master to plot points in Problem Set A.

	Summary	Materials	On Your Own Exercises	Assessment Opportunities
Investigation 1 page T176	Students compare $2x$ with 2^x and x^2 by using tables and decide which expression best matches a described situation. Similarly, they compare $3x$ with 3^x and x^3.	• Master 9 (Teaching Resources, page 14)	Practice & Apply: 1–4 Connect & Extend: 7 Mixed Review: 21–32	Share & Summarize, pages T178, 178 Troubleshooting, page T178
Investigation 2 page T179	Students see examples of exponential growth and decay and answer questions using the formula for exponential growth.		Practice & Apply: 5–6 Connect & Extend: 8–20 Mixed Review: 21–32	Share & Summarize, pages T182, 182 Troubleshooting, page T182 Informal Assessment, page 188 Quick Quiz, page 189

1 Read the opening paragraphs with students, and then move directly into Explore.

Explore

2 It is helpful to model this exponential growth with a quick demonstration. Have one student come to the front of the room. Explain that on day 1, this student tells a funny joke to two other students. Have two more students come to the front of the room and stand in a row behind the first student. Now explain that on day 2, each of these two students tells the joke to two new people. Ask students,

> How many people are hearing the joke for the first time on day 2? 4

Then have four students come to the front of the room and stand in a row behind the row of two students. Make sure that students understand that for this to work, they must always tell the joke to *new* people. (This is not so trivial in real life; it becomes harder and harder to achieve, as the number of people who already know the joke becomes a greater and greater portion of the entire population.) Now ask:

> How many new people will hear the joke for the first time on day 3? 8

Have eight students come to the front of the room and ask,

> How many people will hear the joke for the first time on the day 4? 16

Point out to students that these numbers grow very quickly and that after the third round, many of the students in the class, if not all, had been called to the front of the room.

3 Have students sit down, and then ask them to try to figure out on which day about 1,000 people will hear the joke for the first time. They can use a guess-check-and-improve strategy, trying greater and greater powers of 2, or they might continue the doubling process until they reach 1,024. You might want to put a table like the following on the board to show how the powers of 2 are involved in this problem.

Day	Number of People	Power of 2
1	2	2^1
2	4	2^2
3	8	2^3
.	.	.
.	.	.
.	.	.
9	512	2^9
10	1,024	2^{10}

Students should recognize that the day number is the same as the power of 2. Ask,

> How many people will hear the joke on day 20? $2^{20} = 1{,}048{,}576$

Ask students to figure out how many days it would take for everyone in the school to hear the joke. Be sure students understand that to answer this question, they need to add the number of students in each stage.

Investigation 1

Students compare $2x$, 2^x, and x^2 with tables, deciding which best matches a described situation. Similarly, they compare $3x$, 3^x, and x^3.

3.3 Growing Exponentially

Have you ever heard someone say, "It's growing exponentially"? People use this expression to describe things that grow very rapidly.

In this lesson, you will develop a more precise meaning of *exponential growth.* You'll also investigate what it means to decrease, or decay, exponentially.

1 Read the opening paragraphs with students.

Explore

Suppose you make up a funny joke one evening. The next day, you tell it to two classmates. The day after that, your two classmates each tell it to two people. Everyone who hears the joke tells two new people the next day.

How many new people will hear the joke on the fourth day after you made it up? 16

On which day will more than 1,000 new people hear the joke? the 10th

If the joke was told only to people in your school, how many days would it take for everyone in your school to hear it?
Answers will vary, depending on school size.

2 Use students to model this situation.

3
- Have students figure out the answers to the last two questions.
- Make sure students realize that the last question requires adding the numbers at each stage.

The number of students who hear the joke for the first time doubles each day. *Repeated doubling* is one type of exponential growth. In the next two investigations, you will look at other situations in which things grow exponentially.

Investigation  1 Telling the Difference

The expressions 2^x, $2x$, and x^2 look similar—they all include the number 2 and the variable x—but they have very different meanings. The same is true of 3^x, $3x$, and x^3. Looking at tables and graphs for these expressions will help you discover just how different they are.

Problem Set A **Grouping: Pairs**
Students should work with partners to compare the two tables. The idea of matching the table to the rule "doubling every week" should not be new to students. The terminology may be confusing, since $2x$ is "doubling x," but here we are not doubling the input (the week number) but rather doubling the previous output. Students also may be confused because both tables indicate that the number of flies doubles between weeks 1 and 2. If students are unsure of the correct answer, ask them whether the number of flies determined by each rule doubles between weeks 5 and 6.

You may want to make an overhead transparency of Master 9, Centimeter Graph Paper, to display the graphs for Problem 7. You may want to supply students with copies of this master or graph paper, as well.

Problem 7 is important because this may be one of the few times students have seen a quadratic or an exponential curve. This is a good time to point out that the graph of an equation is linear only when the exponents of the variable are 1, as in $y = 2x$.

Problem Set Wrap-Up You may want to wrap up by focusing a short discussion around **Problem 6.** The striking difference between the two answers at week 10 shows how much more quickly 2^x grows. Noting this difference will help students with Share & Summarize, as well as with Investigation 2.

Problem Set A

Just the facts

The fruit fly is one of the world's most studied animals. Because it reproduces so rapidly, it is ideal for many scientific experiments.

1 Have students work in pairs.

Ms. Nisonoff brought two fruit flies to her biology class. She told her students that the flies would reproduce, and that the population of flies would double every week. Luis and Zoe wanted to figure out how many flies there would be each week.

Luis made this table:

Week	1	2	3	4	5
Flies	2	4	6	8	10

Zoe made this table:

Week	1	2	3	4	5
Flies	2	4	8	16	32

1. Whose table is correct? That is, whose table shows the fruit fly population doubling every week? Zoe's
2. How do the fly-population values in the incorrect table change each week? They increase by 2.
3. Complete this table to compare the expressions $2x$, 2^x, and x^2.

x	0	1	2	3	4	5
$2x$	0	2	4	6	8	10
2^x	1	2	4	8	16	32
x^2	0	1	4	9	16	25

4. As x increases from 0 to 5, which expression's values increase most quickly? 2^x
5. Which expression describes Luis's table? Which describes Zoe's table? $2x$, 2^x
6. How many flies does the expression for Luis's table predict there will be in Week 10? How many flies will there actually be (assuming none of the flies die)? 20; 1,024
7. Use your table from Problem 3 to plot the points for each set of ordered pairs—$(x, 2x)$, $(x, 2^x)$, and (x, x^2)—on one set of axes. If you can, use a different color for each set of points to help you remember which is which. How are the graphs similar? How are they different?

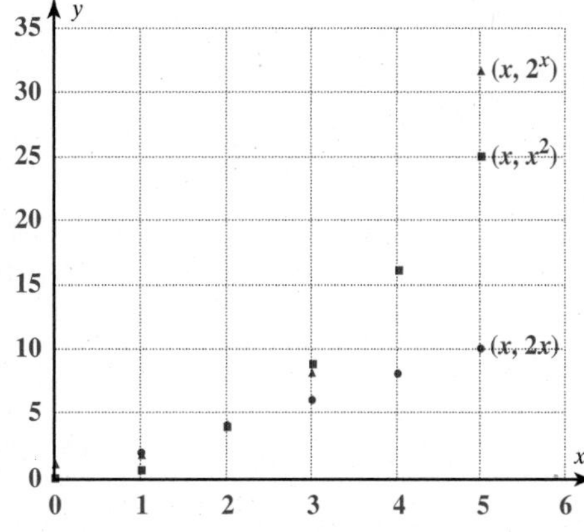

7. Possible answer: All the graphs have the point (2, 4). The graph for the $(x, 2x)$ points lie on a line; both of the other two graphs lie on a curve. The curve for the $(x, 2^x)$ points becomes very steep as x increases.

2 Wrap up the problem set by discussing Problem 6.

LESSON 3.3 Growing Exponentially 177

Problem Set B **Suggested Grouping: Pairs or Individuals**

This problem set is similar to Problem Set A, so you may want students to continue working in pairs. However, because the ideas in the two problem sets are similar, this may be a good time for individual processing of the ideas.

In this problem set, students compare tables for $3x$, 3^x, and x^3, deciding which correctly calculates the volume of a cube. Students know, of course, that the volume of a cube is computed with x^3 where x is the length of an edge. The point is to match the correct table of values to the expression x^3.

Share & Summarize

For **Question 1,** students should be able to articulate that although $2x$ and 2^x are equal at the two values $x = 1$ and $x = 2$, 2^x grows much more quickly than $2x$ does. They may also point out that although both of these are "doubling" expressions, they double different quantities: $2x$ doubles the value of x and 2^x doubles each previous output. Later in the lesson, we refer to the expression $2x$ as having a constant *difference* between terms, while the exponential expression 2^x has a constant *factor* or *ratio* between terms.

Looking at the overall behavior of the rules, 4^x grows fastest. However, if students look only at small values of x ($0 \leq x \leq 3$), they may be misled and think that x^4 grows fastest. It might be worthwhile to have students look at graphs of the different relationships for the sake of comparison.

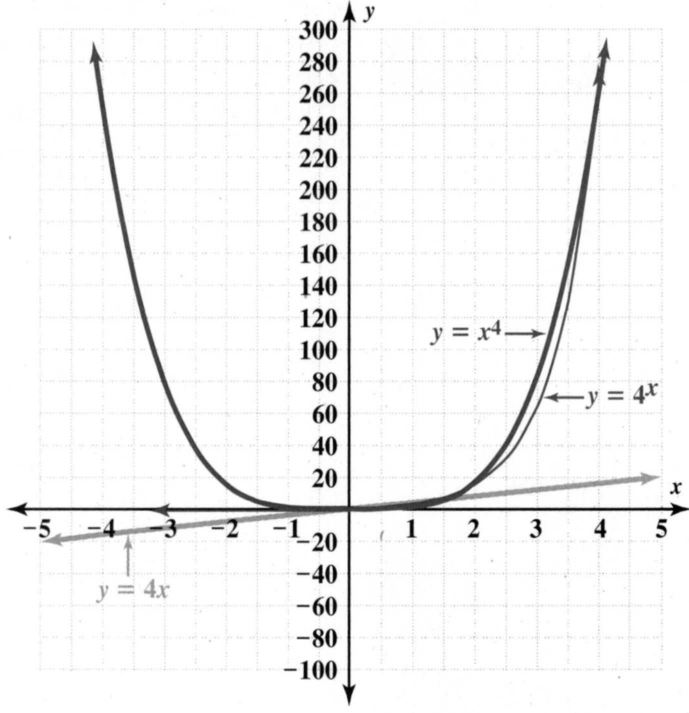

After the two curves intersect at $(4, 4^4)$, they do not intersect again, as neither of them turns. So, $y = 4^x$ remains above $y = x^4$.

Troubleshooting If students are not convinced that exponential functions with bases greater than 1 grow much more quickly than polynomial functions (comparing x^n with nx and n^x, where n is some whole number greater than 1 and x is the variable), you might want to engage them in an activity like this: First, have students tell you where x^n and n^x are equal; use a specific value such as 7 for n. You can even ask them to prove that the expressions will be equal at $x = n$. In the case of $n = 7$, you get 7^7 when you substitute into both expressions. Then have students use calculators to check what happens at the next value of x. For greater values of x, the important thing to understand is that for 7^x, they are multiplying together many more numbers (x of them) than for x^7 (only 7 of them, no matter what x is).

On Your Own Exercises

Practice & Apply: 1–4
Connect & Extend: 7
Mixed Review: 21–32

Problem Set B

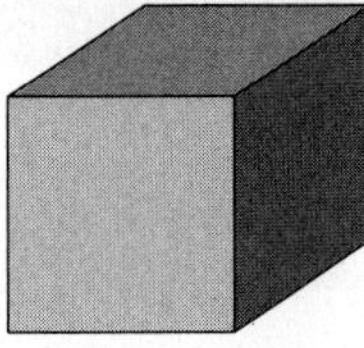

Kate and Darnell made tables to show the relationship between the edge length and the volume of a cube.

Remember
The formula for the volume of a cube with edge length x is $V = x^3$.

Kate made this table:

Edge Length	1	2	3	4	5
Volume	3	9	27	81	243

Darnell made this table:

Edge Length	1	2	3	4	5
Volume	1	8	27	64	125

1. Whose table shows the correct volumes? Darnell's
2. Complete this table to compare the expressions $3x$, 3^x, and x^3.

x	0	1	2	3	4	5
$3x$	0	3	6	9	12	15
3^x	1	3	9	27	81	243
x^3	0	1	8	27	64	125

3. As x increases from 0 to 5, which expression's values increase most quickly? 3^x
4. Which expression describes Kate's table? Which describes Darnell's table? 3^x, x^3
5. Look at the values in the table for 3^x. Describe in words how to get from one value to the next. multiply by 3
6. Look at the values in the table for $3x$. Describe in words how to get from one value to the next. add 3

Share & Summarize

1. Compare the way the values of $2x$ change as x increases to the way the values of 2^x change as x increases.
2. Consider the expressions $4x$, 4^x, and x^4. Without making a table, predict which expression's values grow the fastest as x increases. 4^x

1. Possible answer: In the tables, $2x$ increases by the same amount each time: 2 is added to it each time. 2^x increases faster than $2x$ does for large values of x.

1 You may have students work in pairs or as individuals.

2 Be sure students can articulate that 2^x grows more quickly than $2x$ does.

3
- You might have students look at graphs of the three expressions.
- Have students verify results by substituting a number for x.

Investigation 2

In this investigation, students see one example of exponential growth, or increase (the number of grains of rice on a chessboard), and one of exponential decay, or decrease (the height of a bouncing ball). This is not the first time they have seen a fraction raised to a power, but it may be the first time they have really thought about what something like $\left(\frac{1}{2}\right)^n$ means.

Discuss the two tables and be sure students understand the difference between a constant rate of growth, as in the comics table, and an increasing rate of growth, as in the fruit-fly table.

Think & Discuss

You may want to explain to students the difference between the growths of numbers determined by $3x$ and 3^x by using the argument given here: For $3x$, as x is increased by 1, the term is increased by 3×1, or 3. This means that each new term is *3 more than* the previous term; so the terms of $3x$ increase by 3 each time. For 3^x, as x is increased by 1, the term is increased by another *factor of 3*; so instead of adding 3 to get the next term, we multiply the previous term by 3.

Investigation  2 Exponential Increase and Decrease

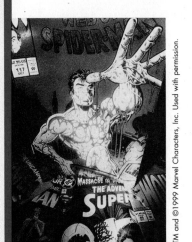

Suppose you buy four comic books each week. The table shows how your comic book collection would grow.

Weeks	1	2	3	4	5	6
Comics	4	8	12	16	20	24

Since you add the same number of comics each week, your collection grows at a *constant rate.* You add 4 comics each week, so the number of comics in your collection after x weeks can be expressed as $4x$.

Now consider the fruit fly population from Problem Set A.

Weeks	1	2	3	4	5	6
Flies	2	4	8	16	32	64

The fly population grows at an *increasing rate*. That is, the number of flies added is greater each week. In fact, the total number of flies is multiplied by 2 each week.

VOCABULARY
exponential increase
exponential growth

Quantities that are repeatedly multiplied by a number greater than 1 are said to grow exponentially, or to show **exponential increase,** or **exponential growth.** The number of flies after x weeks can be expressed as 2^x.

Think & Discuss

Look back at your tables from Investigation 1.

The values of $2x$ and $3x$ grow at a constant rate. How do the values of $2x$ and $3x$ change each time x increases by 1? How is the change related to the expression? See ①.

① The values of $2x$ increase by 2, and the values of $3x$ increase by 3. The amount of increase is the number that x is multiplied by.

The values of the expression 3^x grow exponentially. How do the values of 3^x change each time x increases by 1? How is the change related to the expression?
The values of 3^x are multiplied by 3. This is related to the 3 in the expression. Each time x increases by 1, the number of 3s being multiplied increases by 1.

1
- Discuss the two tables.
- Be sure students understand the difference between constant and increasing rates of growth.

2
Explain difference between growths of $3x$ and 3^x.

LESSON 3.3 Growing Exponentially 179

Problem Set C **Suggested Grouping: Pairs**
This story of the ruler and the rice is a famous one and appears in many curricula. The surprising number of rice grains on the twentieth square, which is less than a third of the 64 squares, illustrates the great rapidity with which a quantity grows exponentially.

2 Students may need help solving **Problem 4** because it requires two steps: dividing the number of grains on a square by 250 and then multiplying by 5. You might ask students how this two-step process can be simplified to one step. (Divide by 50.)

In **Problem 6,** students are asked to find the number of grains in the 64th square. For any power of 2 beyond 2^{33}, most calculators will produce an answer in scientific notation. Ask students whether they can explain the notation in the calculator display. Do not be concerned if no one can, and tell the class that they will learn what the notation means in Lesson 3.4. You can revisit this problem once they have an understanding of scientific notation.

Just the facts

Rice, the staple food of millions of people in Asia and eaten around the world, is actually a grain harvested from a plant in the grass family.

Problem Set C

In an ancient legend, a ruler offers one of his subjects a reward in return for a favor. For the reward, the subject requests that the ruler place 2 grains of rice on the first square of a chessboard, 4 grains on the second square, 8 on the third, and so on, doubling the number of grains of rice on each square.

The ruler thinks this wouldn't take much rice, so he agrees to the request.

1. Copy and complete the table to show the number of grains of rice on the first six squares of the chessboard.

Square	1	2	3	4	5	6
Grains of Rice	2	4	8	16	32	64

2. Which expression describes the number of grains on Square x? 2^x

x^2 $\quad$ 2^x $\quad$ $2x$

3. Use the expression to find the number of grains on Square 7, Square 10, and Square 20. 128; 1,024; 1,048,576

4. For one type of uncooked, long-grain rice, 250 grains of rice have a volume of about 5 cm^3. What would be the volume of rice on Square 5? On Square 7? On Square 10? 0.64 cm^3, 2.56 cm^3, 20.48 cm^3

5. When the ruler saw there were about 20 cm^3 of rice on Square 10, he assumed there would be 40 cm^2 on Square 20. Is he correct? Is he even close? How many cubic centimeters of rice will actually be on Square 20? He is wrong. There will be about 20,972 cm^3.

6. The number of grains of rice on the last square is 2^{64}. Use your calculator to find this value. What do you think your calculator's answer means? 1.8447 19; Explanations will depend on the calculator used.

The value of 2^{64} is too large for calculators to display normally, so they use a special notation, which you will learn about in Lesson 3.4.

1 You may have students work in pairs.

2 Help students solve in two steps.

3 Have students try to explain the calculator display.

Develop

Problem Set D Suggested Grouping: Pairs
This problem set is similar to Problem Set C, but it deals
with exponential decay rather than exponential growth.
There are some subtle points here that may trouble
2 students. If the situation is correct, then the ball never
stops bouncing. Ask questions such as the following:

> Is it realistic that the ball will never stop bouncing?
>
> What causes a ball to stop rather than continue with smaller and smaller bounces?

Students may suggest that someone grabs the ball, that the bounce is so small that we just don't notice, that something else (hitting a wall, for example) causes it to stop, and so on. In fact, this is an imperfect model of a bouncing ball. While it matches the real behavior for several bounces, the model eventually falters. Students have seen this aspect of models, for example, in their block models of babies and adults in Chapter 2. Mathematical models are meant to be convenient and easy to work with; as a result, they are by nature imperfect.

In Problem Set C, the number of grains of rice on each square grows exponentially—it is multiplied by 2 each time. In Problem Set D, you will look at a different kind of exponential change.

Problem Set D

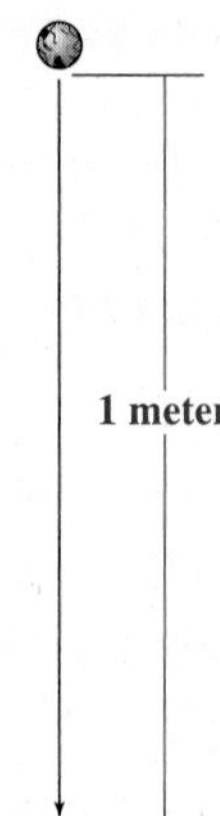

Imagine that a superball is dropped onto concrete from a height of 1 meter and is allowed to bounce repeatedly. Suppose the height of each bounce is 0.8 times the height of the previous bounce. (To understand how the height changes, you can imagine sending a stick of gum through a ×0.8 machine repeatedly.)

1 You may have students work in pairs.

Remember
1 m = 100 cm

1. How high does the ball rise on the first bounce? 0.8 m, or 80 cm
2. How high does the ball rise on the second bounce? 0.64 m, or 64 cm
3. How high does the ball rise on the third bounce? 0.512 m, or 51.2 cm
4. Complete the table to show how the ball's height in centimeters changes with each bounce.

Initial Height	100	100
1st Bounce Height	100×0.8	100×0.8^1
2nd Bounce Height	$100 \times 0.8 \times 0.8$	100×0.8^2
3rd Bounce Height	$100 \times 0.8 \times 0.8 \times 0.8$	100×0.8^3
4th Bounce Height	$100 \times 0.8 \times 0.8 \times 0.8 \times 0.8$	100×0.8^4
10th Bounce Height	$100 \times 0.8 \times 0.8 \times 0.8 \times 0.8 \times 0.8 \times 0.8 \times 0.8 \times 0.8 \times 0.8 \times 0.8$	100×0.8^{10}

5. How high does the ball rise on the 10th bounce? about 11 cm
6. How many times do you think the ball will bounce before coming to rest? Answers will vary.
7. Use the pattern in the right column of your table to write an expression for the ball's height on the nth bounce. 100×0.8^n
8. Assuming the ball continues to bounce, use your expression to find the height of the ball on the 100th bounce. Does your answer surprise you?

2 Ask questions about the limitations of the model.

8. about 0.00000002 cm; Possible answer: Yes; I thought the ball would have stopped bouncing by then.

LESSON 3.3 Growing Exponentially 181

Develop

To help students conceptualize the differences between exponential growth and exponential decay, have them determine the values for 2^n, 1^n, and $\left(\frac{1}{2}\right)^n$ for $n = 1, 2, 3, 4,$ and 5. The value of 2^n *increases* from 2 to 32, 1^n *remains constant* at 1, and $\left(\frac{1}{2}\right)^n$ *decreases* from $\frac{1}{2}$ to $\frac{1}{32}$.

Share & Summarize

Question 1 asks students to explain exponential growth. The main idea is that when something doubles at each stage, it grows much more quickly than something that simply doubles the input number.

In **Questions 2 and 3,** students again explore the ideas of exponential decay and exponential growth. They should have at least a general idea that with exponential decay, the numbers get smaller and smaller, but never disappear entirely, and that with exponential growth, the numbers continue to grow larger and larger.

2 **Troubleshooting** If students are having trouble with either exponential growth or exponential decay, you may choose to work with one of the additional examples below. If the problem is in dealing with very large or very small numbers, it is fine to proceed. Students will work more with that in upcoming lessons. At this point, it is important that students be able to write and use expressions with a number raised to a power, particularly those with a variable as the exponent.

Additional Examples A good example of exponential growth involves the awarding of a lottery prize as described here.

Billy won a local lottery which offered him a choice of three payment methods, with the winnings to be distributed over a period of 25 years.

Method 1 He could receive $1,000 the first year, $2,000 the second year, $3,000 the third year, and so on, getting $1,000 more each year.

Method 2 He could receive $100 the first year, $400 the second year, $900 the third year, and so on, each year getting 100 times the square of the year number (1, 2, 3, . . .), or $100y^2$.

Method 3 He could receive $1 the first year, $2 the second year, $4 the third year, $8 the fourth year, and so on, each year getting twice what he got the year before.

Which payment method should Billy choose and why?

Students may answer right away that the third payment method is the best, because all the work in this lesson was about how quickly exponential functions grow. Or they may be fooled by the small starting amount into thinking that one of the other two methods is better. In any case, actually finding the totals—which requires not just finding the individual values for an exponential relationship, but also summing the series—is a nice exercise.

Students might also raise the question of Billy's age and his life expectancy. If he were 70 when he won the lottery, the linear method (first choice) or quadratic method (second choice) might be more lucrative.

You might ask follow-up questions such as these:

- For how many years does the first rule give the greatest totals? *13 years*
- For how many years does the second rule give the greatest totals? *17 years*
- What is one example of a rule that would give you an even greater total than the three rules presented here? *He could receive $1 the first year, $3 the second year, $9 the third year, $27 the fourth year, and so on, each year getting three times what he got the year before.*

To illustrate exponential decay, present the model of car depreciation.

Suppose four different types of cars have annual depreciation rates of 15%, 12%, 10%, and 8%, respectively. Which car depreciates most quickly? *the one with a 15% rate*

Which car depreciates least quickly? *the one with an 8% rate*

To help students answer these questions, have them construct a table of values like the one below, assuming that the original value of each car is $10,000. Be sure they understand that the value of each car is 100% minus the depreciation rate.

Number of Years (t)	1	2	3	4	5
Value at 15% Rate: $\$10,000 \times (0.85)^t$					
Value at 12% Rate: $\$10,000 \times (0.88)^t$					
Value at 10% Rate: $\$10,000 \times (0.90)^t$					
Value at 8% Rate: $\$10,000 \times (0.92)^t$					

• ***Teaching Notes continued on page A388.***

VOCABULARY
exponential decrease
exponential decay

In both the bouncing-ball problem and the rice problem, a quantity is repeatedly multiplied by the same factor. For the ball problem, however, the factor is 0.8, which is between 0 and 1. This means the bounce height gets smaller with each bounce. This type of exponential change is called **exponential decrease,** or **exponential decay.**

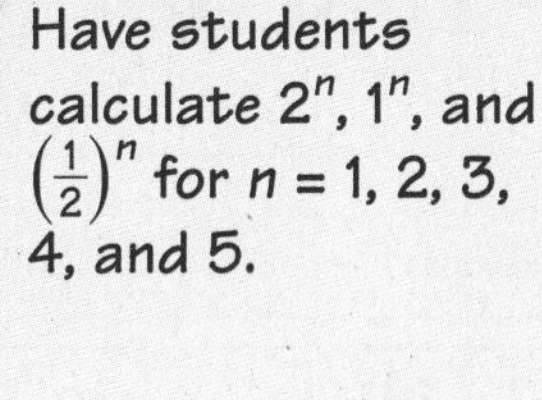

Have students calculate 2^n, 1^n, and $\left(\frac{1}{2}\right)^n$ for $n = 1, 2, 3, 4,$ and 5.

Share & Summarize

1. Briefly explain why the amount of rice on each square of the chessboard grows so rapidly.
2. As n increases, what happens to the value of $\left(\frac{1}{5}\right)^n$? It decreases.
3. As n increases, what happens to the value of 5^n? It increases.

1. Because the number of grains on each square is doubled, more and more rice is added each time.

2 Give students additional examples.

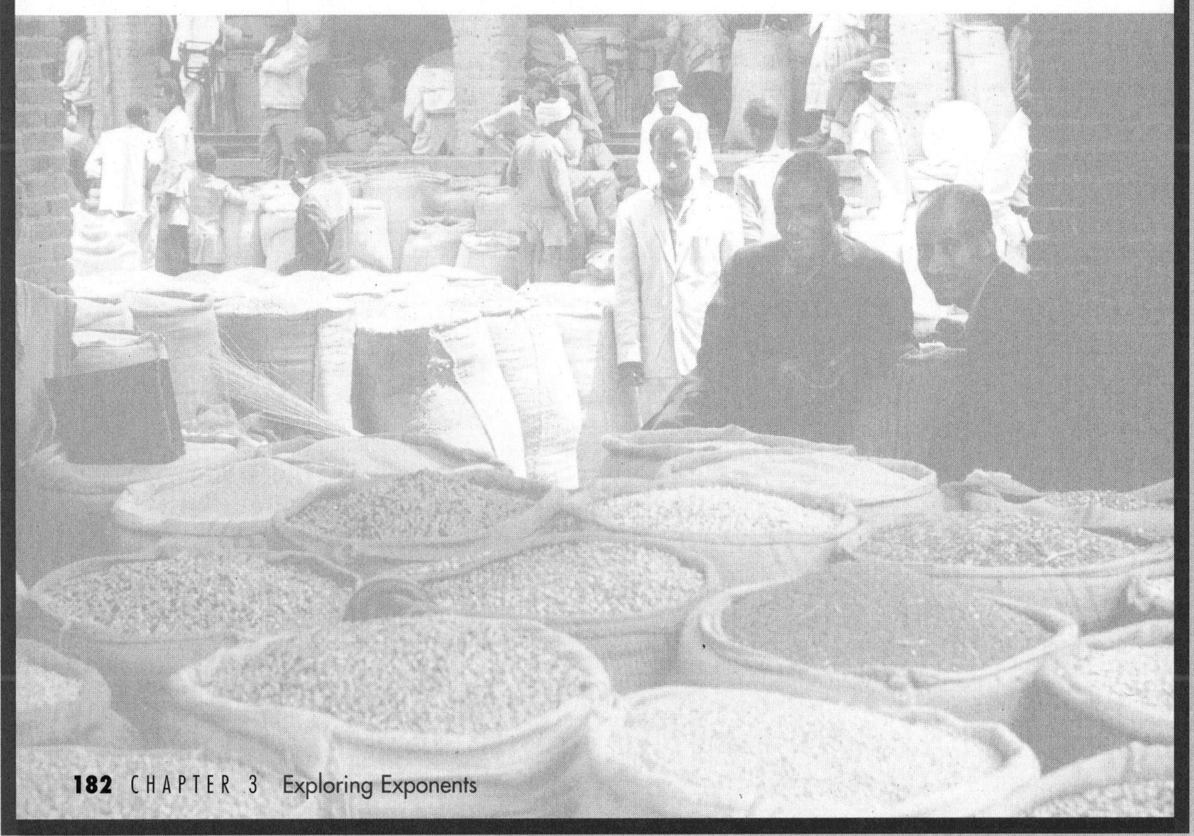

Teacher Notes

On Your Own Exercises

1. The rows of this table represent the expressions 4^x, x^4, and $4x$. Copy the table. Fill in the first column with the correct expressions, and then fill in the missing entries.

x	0	1	2	3	4	5	6
4^x	1	4	16	64	256	1,024	4,096
$4x$	0	4	8	12	16	20	24
x^4	0	1	16	81	256	625	1,296

2. For a science experiment, Jinny put a single bacterium in a dish and placed it in a warm environment. Each day at noon, she counted the number of bacteria in the dish. She made this table from her data:

Day	0	1	2	3
Bacteria	1	4	16	64

a. How do the bacteria population values change each day? They are multiplied by 4.

Jinny repeated her experiment, beginning with 1 bacterium. She wanted to see if she could get the number of bacteria to triple each day by lowering the temperature of the environment. She predicted the number of bacteria in the dish with this table:

Day, d	0	1	2	3
Bacteria, b	1	3	6	9

b. Which expression describes her table: $b = 3d$, $b = d^3$, or $b = 3^d$? $b = 3d$

c. Is the table correct? If not, which expression should Jinny have used? no; $b = 3^d$

3. It's the first day of camp, and 242 campers are outside the gates waiting to enter. The head counselor wants to welcome each camper personally, but she doesn't have enough time. At 9:00 A.M., she welcomes two campers and leads them into camp. This takes 10 minutes.

Now the camp has three people: the head counselor and the two campers. The three return to the gate, and each welcomes two more campers into the camp. This round of welcomes—for six new campers this time—also takes 10 minutes.

a. How many people are in the camp after this second round of welcomes? 9

b. At what time will all of these people be ready to welcome another round of campers? 9:20

On Your Own Exercises

Investigation 1
Practice & Apply: 1–4
Connect & Extend: 7–12

Investigation 2
Practice & Apply: 5–6
Connect & Extend: 13–20

Assign Anytime
Mixed Review: 21–32

Exercise 1:
This exercise is similar to the questions in Share & Summarize in Investigation 1, but here students are asked to identify the expressions 4^x, $4x$, and x^4 based on some data points and then to complete a table.

Exercise 3:
This rather lengthy exercise requires students to complete a table and figure out how numbers are growing and to then use that growth pattern to make predictions.

Exercise 5: Students must think about what exponents mean (repeated multiplication) and distinguish that from repeated addition.

c. With every round, each person in the camp welcomes two new campers into camp. After the third round of welcomes, how many people will be in the camp? What time will it be then? 27; 9:30

d. Copy and complete the table.

Welcome Rounds, n	0	1	2	3	4	5	6	7	8
Time at End of Round	9:00	9:10	9:20	9:30	9:40	9:50	10:00	10:10	10:20
People in Camp, p	1	3	9	27	81	243	729	2,187	6,561

3g. 3^n; Possible explanation: The number of welcome rounds is the number of times 3 is a factor.

3h. 7 rounds, 9 rounds

3i. yes; 1 million campers would be welcomed by 11:10

e. At what time will all 242 campers have been welcomed into camp? (Don't forget about the head counselor!) 9:50

f. Look at the last row in your table. By what number do you multiply to get from one entry to the next? 3

g. Which expression describes the total number of people in the camp after n rounds: 3^n, $3n$, or n^3? Explain your choice.

h. Use your expression from Part g to find the number of welcome rounds that would be required to bring at least 1,000 campers into camp and to bring at least 10,000 campers into camp.

i. Lunch is served at noon. Could a million campers be welcomed before lunch? (Ignore the fact that it would be very chaotic!)

Just the facts

Duckweed is a small water plant that grows very quickly during the summer.

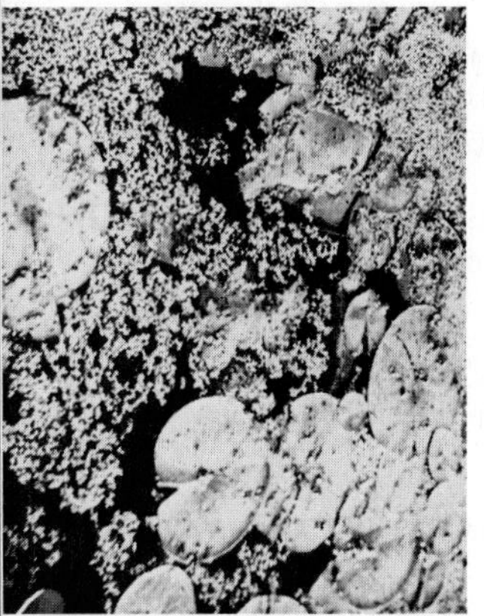

4. Match the given expression with the situation it describes.

$3p$ $\qquad$ p^2 $\qquad$ 2^p

a. area of the squares in a series, with side length p for the square at Stage p $\quad p^2$

b. a population of bacteria that doubles every hour $\quad 2^p$

c. a stamp collection to which 3 stamps are added each week $\quad 3p$

5. A botanist recorded the number of duckweed plants in a pond at the same time each week.

Week, w	0	1	2	3	4
Plants, d	32	48	72	108	162

a. Look at the second row of the table. By what number do you multiply each value to get the next value? 1.5

b. Predict the number of plants in the fifth week. 243

c. Which expression describes the number of plants in the pond after w weeks? 32×1.5^w

32×1.5^w $\qquad$ $1.5w + 32$ $\qquad$ $w^2 + 32$

184 CHAPTER 3 Exploring Exponents

6. Start with a scrap sheet of paper. Tear it in half and throw half away. Then tear the piece you have left in half and throw half away. Once again, tear the piece you have left in half and throw half away.

   a. What fraction of the original piece is left after the first tear? After the second tear? $\frac{1}{2}$, $\frac{1}{4}$

   b. Make a table showing the number of tears and the fraction of the paper left. See Additional Answers.

   c. Look at the second row of your table. By what number do you multiply each value to get the next value? $\frac{1}{2}$

   d. Write an expression for the fraction of the paper left after t tears.

   e. If you continue this process, will the paper ever disappear? Why or why not?

6d. $\frac{1}{2^t}$

6e. By the model, I will always have half of the previous piece, but at some point the pieces will be too small for me to tear.

Connect & Extend

7. **Preview** You can evaluate the expression 2^x for negative values of x. This table is filled in for x values from 0 to 5.

x	−5	−4	−3	−2	−1	0	1	2	3	4	5
2^x	$\frac{1}{32}$	$\frac{1}{16}$	$\frac{1}{8}$	$\frac{1}{4}$	$\frac{1}{2}$	1	2	4	8	16	32

   a. How do the 2^x values change as you move from *right to left*?

   b. Use the pattern you described in Part a to complete the table.

Tell whether each expression represents exponential growth, exponential decay, or neither.

8. 3.2^x **9.** $3x^2$ **10.** $32x$ **11.** $\left(\frac{3}{2}\right)^x$ **12.** $\left(\frac{2}{3}\right)^x$

Tell whether each sentence describes exponential growth, exponential decay, or neither. Explain how you decided.

13. Each time a tennis ball is used, its pressure is $\frac{999}{1,000}$ what it was after the previous use.

14. Each year the quantity of detergent in a liter of groundwater near an industrial area is expected to increase by 0.05 gram.

15. A star becomes twice as bright every 10 years.

16. It is predicted that the membership in a club will increase by 20 people each month.

17. The number of tickets sold in a national lottery is expected to increase 1.2 times each year.
Exponential growth; the number of tickets is repeatedly multiplied by 1.2.

7a. Each value is half the value to its right.
8. exponential growth
9. neither
10. neither
11. exponential growth
12. exponential decay
13–16. See Additional Answers.

Exercise 6:
This exercise involves some sophisticated ideas. To begin with, the notion of limit—central to calculus—is part of the answer to **Part e.** Can you ever make the piece of paper totally disappear? No, but you can make it as close to nothing as you want by ripping it enough times. Students may challenge you on this. Since you're talking about physical paper, in fact, you *can't* continue the tearing process indefinitely. This shows that *limit* is a mathematical concept, not a real-world concept.

Exercise 7:
Students will see more about negative numbers, including their use as exponents, in Chapter 4.

Exercises 8–12:
These exercises provide a quick test of whether students recognize exponential expressions that represent exponential growth or exponential decay.

Additional Answers

6b.

Tears	0	1	2	3	4	5	6
Fraction Left	1	$\frac{1}{2}$	$\frac{1}{4}$	$\frac{1}{8}$	$\frac{1}{16}$	$\frac{1}{32}$	$\frac{1}{64}$

13. Exponential decay; the pressure is repeatedly multiplied by $\frac{999}{1,000}$, a number less than 1.
14. Neither; a constant number, 0.05, is repeatedly added, so this is constant change.
15. Exponential growth; the brightness is repeatedly doubled.
16. Neither; a constant number is added each year, so this is constant change.

LESSON 3.3 Growing Exponentially 185

Exercise 18: Even if students are not familiar with percent increase, they should be able to tackle this exercise using the fact that each year's population is 1.14 times the previous year's population. One thing to watch for is when students report "fractions of a whale" in their populations. Working just with the numbers, students discover that there will be 454.86 whales after the two years. This number makes no sense, given the context; 455 is a more sensible answer. In fact, any answer is an approximation, since the growth is exponential only in the statistical sense. If the total number of whales turns out to be 453 rather than 455, that doesn't mean the model is wrong.

18a. 399

18b. about 455

18c. $350 \times 1.14 \times 1.14 \times 1.14 \times 1.14 \times 1.14 \times 1.14 \times 1.14 \times 1.14 \times 1.14 \times 1.14 \times 1.14 \times 1.14$

18. Ecology "Whale Numbers up 12% a Year" was a headline in a 1993 Australian newspaper. A 13-year study had found that the humpback whale population off the coast of Australia was increasing significantly. The actual data suggested the increase was closer to 14%! This means that the population each year was 1.14 times the previous year's population.

a. When the study began in 1981, the humpback whale population was 350. If the population grew to 1.14 times this number in the next year, what was the humpback whale population in 1982?

b. What would you expect the whale population was in 1983?

c. Complete the table to show how the population grew each year.

1981: Year 0	350	350
1982: Year 1	350×1.14	350×1.14^1
1983: Year 2	$350 \times 1.14 \times 1.14$	350×1.14^2
1984: Year 3	$350 \times 1.14 \times 1.14 \times 1.14$	350×1.14^3
1985: Year 4	$350 \times 1.14 \times 1.14 \times 1.14 \times 1.14$	350×1.14^4
1993: Year 12	See margin.	350×1.14^{12}

d. Write an expression for the number of whales x years after the study began in 1981. 350×1.14^x

e. How long did it take the whale population to double from 350? 6 years

186 CHAPTER 3 Exploring Exponents

In your own words

Describe the difference in the way 4^x and $4x$ grow. In your description, tell which expression grows exponentially, and explain how you could tell from a table of values.

19. Challenge A ball of Malaysian rubber, displayed in a museum of science and technology, rolled off the 1.25-meter-high display table and onto the floor. It bounced, rose to a height of 0.75 meter, and was caught at the top of its bounce.

a. What fraction of the original height was the bounce height of the ball? 0.6, or $\frac{3}{5}$

b. Assume each bounce height is a fixed fraction of the previous bounce height. Suppose the ball falls off the table again and is not caught. Write an expression for the height of the bounce, in centimeters, after n bounces. 125×0.6^n

c. Darnell wondered whether he would have been able to slide his hand between the ball and the floor on the 10th bounce. Would he have been able to? Explain. See below.

d. Suppose the same ball fell from a 2-meter-high shelf. Would Darnell have been able to fit his hand between the ball and the floor on the 10th bounce? Explain.
No; the height would be 200×0.6^{10} cm, or about 1.2 cm.

Remember
An *equilateral triangle* has three sides of the same length.

20a. from the inside out, 2 cm, 4 cm, 8 cm, 16 cm

20. This drawing was created by first drawing a large equilateral triangle. A second equilateral triangle was drawn inside the first by connecting the midpoints of its sides. The same process was used to draw a third triangle inside the second, and so on. The sides of each triangle are half as long as the sides of the previous triangle.

a. If the sides of the smallest triangle are 1 cm long, what are the side lengths of the other triangles?

b. What is the length of the blue spiral in the drawing? 18 cm

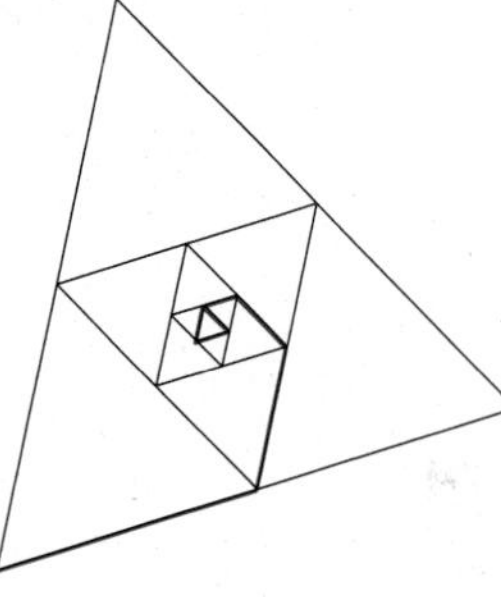

Mixed Review

21. Each expression below is equal to one of the other expressions. Find the matching pairs. a and d, b and h, c and i, e and j, f and g

a. 2^5	**b.** $c \times c \times c$	**c.** 2×5
d. $2 \cdot 2 \cdot 2 \cdot 2 \cdot 2$	**e.** $c + c + c$	**f.** 5^2
g. 5×5	**h.** c^3	**i.** $5 + 5$
j. $3c$		

19c. The ball would bounce to about 0.76 cm, not high enough to get a hand underneath.

Exercise 19:
You may want to ask students to talk about how they decided whether a hand would fit between the ball and the floor. Did they measure their own hands? Did they make reasonable guesses about the size of a hand? Or did the number come out so big or so small that they felt it was obvious?

Exercise 20:
This problem shows exponential growth in a geometric context.

Quick Check

Informal Assessment

Students should be able to

- ✔ develop a sense of exponential growth and exponential decay
- ✔ describe examples of exponential increase and exponential decrease
- ✔ compare exponential growth with other kinds of growth (linear, quadratic, and so on)

22. Suppose you flip a coin two times.

a. What is the probability you will get two heads? Two tails? $\frac{1}{4}, \frac{1}{4}$

b. What is the probability you will get one head and one tail? $\frac{1}{2}$

23. Earth Science A middle school class in Florida conjectured that the temperature in coastal areas varies less dramatically than it does inland. They gathered the data shown in the table.

Average Temperature on First Day of the Month

Month	Coastal Temperature, °F (St. Augustine)	Inland Temperature, °F (Lakeland)
January	59	63
February	58	62
March	60	65
April	66	70
May	72	75
June	77	79
July	81	82
August	81	82
September	80	81
October	76	79
November	69	70
December	61	63

Source: Southeast Regional Climate Center Home Page, *water.dnr.state.sc.us/climate/sercc/*.

a. On a graph like the one shown, plot the points for coastal temperatures in one color and those for inland temperatures in another.

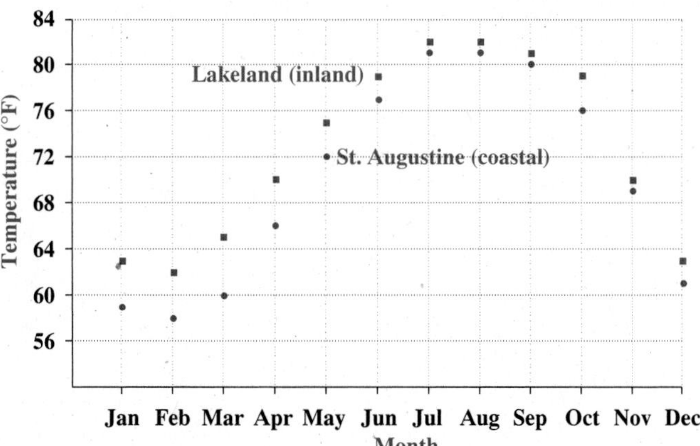

188 CHAPTER 3 Exploring Exponents

23b. St. Augustine: 81°F and 58°F; Lakeland: 82°F and 62°F

23c. Possible answer: No; the difference in the range of temperatures is not very great.

24a. Stage 1 to Stage 2: 1 square; Stage 2 to Stage 3: 2 squares; Stage 3 to Stage 4: 1 square; Stage 4 to Stage 5: 2 squares

24b. When s is odd, 1 square is placed on top of the column, which is centered where the original two squares meet. When s is even, 2 squares are added—1 on either end of the bottom row of squares.

24c. Stage 1: 2; Stage 2: 3, Stage 3: 5; Stage 4: 6; Stage 5: 8

24d. 11, 15

b. What are the highest and lowest temperatures shown for Saint Augustine? For Lakeland?

c. Does the information for these two cities support the idea that coastal temperatures vary more dramatically than inland temperatures? Explain.

24. Consider this pattern of squares.

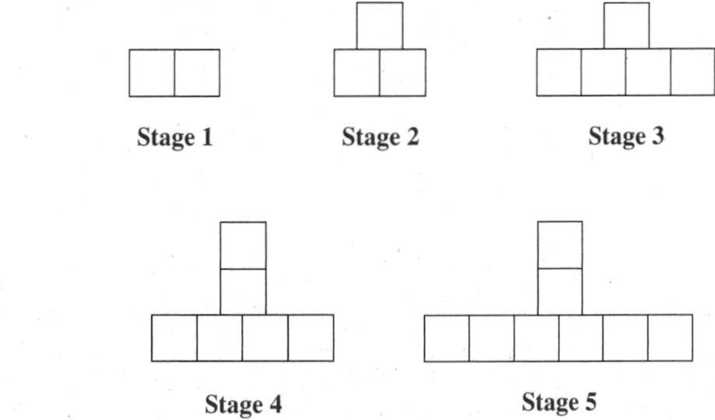

a. For the part of the pattern shown, how many squares are added from each stage to the next?

b. How many squares are added to go from Stage s to Stage $s + 1$? Where are the squares placed? (Hint: Consider two cases, when s is even and when s is odd.)

c. How many squares in all are in each stage shown?

d. How many squares will be needed to make Stage 7? Stage 10?

e. What stage has 20 squares? 13

Simplify each expression.

25. $\frac{1}{3} \div \frac{2}{3}$ $\frac{1}{2}$

26. $\frac{7}{5} \div \frac{5}{7}$ $\frac{49}{25}$

27. $\frac{7}{5} \div \frac{7}{5}$ 1

28. $\frac{1}{8} \div \frac{1}{4}$ $\frac{1}{2}$

Fill in each blank to make a true statement.

29. $0.25 + \underline{0.75} = 1$

30. $0.6 + 0.15 + \underline{0.25} = 1$

31. $0.05 + \underline{0.95} = 1$

32. $\frac{3}{10} + \frac{9}{10} - \underline{\frac{1}{5}} = 1$

Quick Quiz

Tell whether each expression represents exponential growth, exponential decay, or neither.

1. $10x$ neither
2. $\left(\frac{1}{10}\right)^x$ decay
3. 10^x growth
4. $\frac{1}{10} \cdot x$ neither
5. x^{10} neither
6. Describe a situation in which a quantity increases at an exponential rate. Possible answer: Jo gets 1¢ allowance one week, 2¢ the next, 4¢ the next, 8¢ the next, and so on.

LESSON 3.3 Growing Exponentially **189**

Teacher Notes

3.4 Describing Large Numbers

Objectives

- To understand the relative difference between a million and a billion
- To multiply and divide numbers by powers of 10
- To write numbers using scientific notation
- To use a calculator to work with numbers in scientific notation

Overview (Pacing: about 4 class periods)

This lesson presents students with some useful ways of dealing with large numbers. First, students get a sense of the difference between millions and billions. Then, they learn ways to represent large numbers by using powers of 10 and scientific notation. They practice using scientific notation correctly, sometimes with the help of a calculator.

A second emphasis is on the importance of the precision of large numbers. When someone says "3 million years old," students should know this is not an exact age but a good approximation. Similarly, they should understand why it makes little sense to add two numbers like 3.2×10^{25} and 6.8×10^{10}. The second is so much smaller than the first that the "sum" would not be a significant increase over the first number.

Advance Preparation

Have quarters ready for Investigation 1. For small-group work, you will need about 20 quarters per group. Chips or other disks about the size of a quarter will also work, but be sure to adjust the answers to match the actual diameter and thickness of the disks. Have blocks ready for the Lab Investigation.

You may want to make an overhead transparency and several copies of Master 17.

	Summary	Materials	On Your Own Exercises	Assessment Opportunities
Investigation 1 page T191	Students calculate characteristics of a million quarters: how high they will stack, how far they will reach, and how much area they will cover.	• Rulers • 20 quarters	Practice & Apply: 1–7 Connect & Extend: 39–42 Mixed Review: 63–81	Share & Summarize, pages T192, 192 On the Spot Assessment, page T191 Troubleshooting, page T192
Investigation 2 page T192	Students use powers of 10 to represent numbers. Students multiply and divide numbers by powers of 10.	• Master 17 (Teaching Resources, page 29)	Practice & Apply: 8–22 Connect & Extend: 43–57 Mixed Review: 63–81	Share & Summarize, pages T195, 195 Troubleshooting, page T195
Investigation 3 page T196	Students convert between numbers in scientific notation and standard notation. Students rewrite numbers using scientific notation.		Practice & Apply: 23–33 Connect & Extend: 58–59 Mixed Review: 63–81	Share & Summarize, pages T199, 199 Troubleshooting, page T199
Investigation 4 page T200	Students use their calculators to explore contexts in which they use numbers expressed in scientific notation.		Practice & Apply: 34–38 Connect & Extend: 60–62 Mixed Review: 63–81	Share & Summarize, pages T202, 202 On the Spot Assessment, page T201 Troubleshooting, page T202 Informal Assessment, page 212 Quick Quiz, pages 212
Lab Investigation page T203	Students investigate the Tower of Hanoi problem. They learn that the time it takes to move the disks grows exponentially with the number of disks.	• Tower of Hanoi setup, 6 blocks per group		

Introduce

Ask students to tell you some benchmarks for a million and a billion. For further discussion you might ask the following questions:

> Which is closer to the number of people in China, 1 million or 1 billion? 1 billion
>
> Which is closer to the number of people in Nashville, Tennessee, 1 million or 1 billion? 1 million
>
> Which is closer to the amount of money you will earn in your lifetime? 1 million is closer than 1 billion for most of us.
>
> Which is closer to the area of the United States, 1 million or 1 billion square miles? 1 million

Think & Discuss

Allow students a few minutes to read and enjoy the cartoons before discussing what makes them funny.

For the first cartoon, students will see that a billion is *already* real money and that it is the scale of federal spending that makes the quote funny—and a little frightening.

For the second, the fact that a student is relieved that the destruction is a billion years away (which, indeed, is a lot more than a million years) is funny because a million years is already an extremely long time compared to a human's lifetime. Over the lifetime of a planet, however, a million years is not such a long period of time.

The third cartoon shows the lack of number sense of many people in the world—even doctors! "99% safe" and "1 in a million chance something will go wrong" provide very different statistics. The first is 10,000 times as likely as the second.

Finally, the last cartoon addresses the precision of large numbers. "A million" rarely means exactly a million, but rather "close to a million." You might ask students to give a reasonable age range for a rock that is labeled "1 million years old."

3.4 Describing Large Numbers

Can you imagine what a million quarters look like? If you stacked a million quarters, how high would they reach? How long is a million seconds? How old is someone who has been alive a billion seconds?

In this lesson, you will explore these questions, and you will learn a new way of writing and working with very large numbers.

Think & Discuss

What is funny about each of these cartoons? See teaching notes.

1 Ask students for benchmarks for a million and a billion.

2 Allow students time to study these cartoons before discussing them.

Investigation 1

In this investigation, students gain a better sense of big numbers, including the fact that a million and a billion are quite different. "Order of magnitude" is important in mathematics, and too few people understand it.

1 **Think & Discuss**

These questions should be fairly familiar to students, but it is worth taking a few minutes to discuss them.

2 **Problem Set A** **Suggested Grouping: Small Groups**

Before students convert the age from a million seconds to years, months, or days, ask them to guess what the answer will be. You can either write several guesses on the board or have students write down their guesses on slips of paper that you collect. If students don't know what to guess, offer some benchmarks. Ask:

> Who thinks he or she is more than a million seconds old?
>
> Who thinks humans don't live that long?

Students should use calculators to figure out exactly how old a million seconds is.

If students are working in groups, stop the class after most groups have finished working on **Problem 1** and ask for several volunteers to give their answers and explain their calculations.

Students may be tempted to answer Problem 1 in years, getting a value of about 0.031. Encourage them to answer in whatever unit gives them a sense for the age.

On the Spot Assessment

In going from seconds to minutes, students may incorrectly multiply by 60 instead of divide by 60. Ask students to use common sense to decide whether the answer is reasonable. For example:

> If the amount of time is the same, would you expect the number of seconds to be more or less than the number of minutes? *more*
>
> If you multiply by 60, is the product greater or less? *greater*

Before students work on **Problem 2,** which asks them to figure out how long 1 billion seconds is, again ask students to make a guess. You may be surprised to find their guesses—"a month" and "a year"—are not at all close. This shows that they are thinking additively ("a billion is like a few million") rather than multiplicatively. To many people, a billion and a million are both big numbers, so if a million seconds is not that long, then a billion seconds must not be that long either.

For Problem 2, give students the option of doing the calculations individually or in small groups. You might also ask students whether any of them found a shortcut method for determining the answer to Problem 2. If no one suggests the following method, you may want to point it out: Since a billion is 1,000 times a million, you can simply take the converted value of a million seconds, multiply by 1,000, and divide by 365 to get an answer for a billion seconds expressed in years.

Problem Set B **Suggested Grouping: Small Groups**

Students will need about 20 quarters per group. This is quite a few quarters, so you might just have each group measure the diameter and the thickness of one quarter and use those measurements. Or you might tell students that 16 quarters stacked are about 1 inch high. If students use disks other than quarters, be sure to adjust answers accordingly.

3 As students work, encourage them to check that their answers make sense. When converting inches to feet, you should always get a smaller number, about $\frac{1}{10}$ as much. When converting feet to miles, you again get a smaller number because you are converting to a larger unit and it takes fewer of them to cover the same distance. A foot is about $\frac{1}{5{,}000}$ as long as a mile. These approximate benchmarks are easy for students to use when checking to see whether their answers are reasonable.

On the Spot Assessment

Watch for students who multiply rather than divide when converting inches to feet and feet to miles. Have them use common sense to determine whether their calculations are reasonable.

• *Teaching notes continued on page A388.*

Investigation  1 Millions and Billions

It's difficult to understand just how large 1 million and 1 billion are. It helps to think about these numbers in contexts that you can imagine. The problems in this investigation will help you get a better sense of the size of a million and a billion.

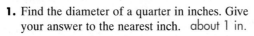

Think & Discuss

How many zeroes follow the 1 in 1 million? 6

How many zeroes follow the 1 in 1 billion? 9

How many millions are in 1 billion? 1,000

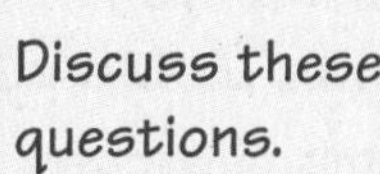

1 Discuss these questions.

Problem Set A

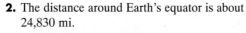

1. about $11\frac{1}{2}$ days
2. about 31 years $8\frac{1}{2}$ months

1. How old is someone who has been alive 1 million seconds?
2. How old is someone who has been alive 1 billion seconds?

2
- Have students guess the answers before they begin working.
- After they finish Problem 1, have students make another guess for Problem 2.

MATERIALS
a quarter

Problem Set B

1. Find the diameter of a quarter in inches. Give your answer to the nearest inch. about 1 in.
2. The distance around Earth's equator is about 24,830 mi.
   a. If you lined up 1 million quarters end to end, how far would they reach? Give your answer in miles. about 15.8 mi
   b. Would they reach around the equator? If not, how many quarters *would* you need to reach around the equator?
3. How many quarters do you need to make a stack 1 in. high? 16
4. The average distance from Earth to the moon is 238,855 mi.
   a. If you stacked 1 million quarters, how high would they reach?
   b. Would they reach the moon? If not, how many quarters *would* you need to reach the moon? Estimate your answer without using a calculator, and explain how you found your answer.
   No; 1 million quarters forms a stack about a mile high, so you would need about 238,855 × 1,000,000 = about 239,000,000,000 quarters.

2b. See Additional Answers.

3 Encourage students to check whether their answers are reasonable.

Remember
5,280 ft = 1 mi

4a. about 5,208 ft, or about 1 mi

Additional Answers

2b. no; about $1{,}000{,}000 \times \frac{24{,}830}{15.8}$ = about 1,570,000,000 quarters

LESSON 3.4 Describing Large Numbers 191

Develop

Sample Strategies The unit conversion is more complicated for **Problem 5.** In this problem, students have to deal with square feet rather than linear feet. Here are some strategies students might use.

- They might convert all measurements to inches before starting and thus use 1,080 inches for 90 feet.
- Students might compute the area of the infield in terms of quarters. The area in square feet is 90^2, so students have to find the number of quarters needed to cover a square foot. A square foot of quarters would have 12 quarters along each side, and 144 quarters would cover one square foot. Then students should multiply 144 by 90^2 to see whether a million quarters are enough. $144 \times 90^2 = 1{,}166{,}400$, so a million quarters is not quite enough.

2 **Additional Example** Work with your students to describe other distances that are the same as the length of a million quarters. For example, a million quarters laid end to end reach almost 16 miles. That's about a 20-minute drive on the highway. Maybe it is the distance from your town to another town. Similarly, a million quarters form a tower a mile high. That's the elevation (above sea level) of Denver!

Share & Summarize

Question 1 asks students to do a computation similar to that in Problem Set B but for a greater distance. You may want to have students work on this individually and then share their answers with partners. Consider asking students to read their answers aloud to check their understanding of larger numbers.

Question 2 asks students why people make mistakes with large numbers. There are certainly many reasonable answers. Some may say that both numbers are so big that the difference between them is confusing. Others may say that people are not careful with what they say. Or others may say that people have trouble deciding whether to add or to multiply; they think of a billion as more like "a few million" rather than "a thousand million."

Troubleshooting For students who are still struggling with the concepts of this lesson, consider using one or more of the activities below to help them envision a million:

- It is hard to gather a million objects, but your class could try over the course of the year. Instead of actually gathering a million items, you might feel it is sufficient for the class to figure out what they would have to do to accomplish the task. For example, if each of 25 students brings in 222 pennies on each of the 180 days of school, they would be only 1,000 pennies short of 1 million: $25 \times 222 \times 180 = 999{,}000$.
- Another way to picture a million is to use centimeter cubes. Find or create a box with 1-meter edges and put a few centimeter cubes inside. Students can then "see" what 1 million cubes would look like, as 1 million centimeter cubes would exactly fill the box. Ask students to prove this by computing the volume of the box.
- Challenge students or groups to write the numbers 1–1,000,000 on sheets of paper. If they write one number per second and work around the clock, it will take 11.5 days. The task is so great as to be practically impossible, and few students will persist after a day or two.

On Your Own Exercises

Practice & Apply: 1–7
Connect & Extend: 39–42
Mixed Review: 63–81

Investigation 2

In this investigation, students use stretching and shrinking machines to work with powers of 10. You may want to start with a short discussion about why so many things are described in powers of 10. For example, in talking about money, we often give amounts in terms of how many billion: "The deficit is around 5.4 billion dollars" or "The number of people in the world is around 6.2 billion." The reasons are varied. Below are some that students might offer:

- Our number system is based on 10s, so people are familiar with what powers of 10 means.
- Our money system is based on 10s, with 10 pennies in a dime and 10 dimes in a dollar.
- The metric system is based on 10s, so measurement conversions are pretty easy when dealing with powers of 10.
- It's easy to multiply and divide with powers of 10.

5. no; Possible explanation: 1,000 quarters extend about 83 ft, so 1 million quarters will cover a square measuring 83 ft on a side.

5. A baseball diamond is a square, 90 ft on each side. Would 1 million quarters cover a baseball diamond if you spread them out? Explain how you found your answer.

Hint: Think of 1 million quarters forming a square with 1,000 quarters on each side. Since quarters are round, they don't fit together exactly. Don't worry about the extra space left uncovered.

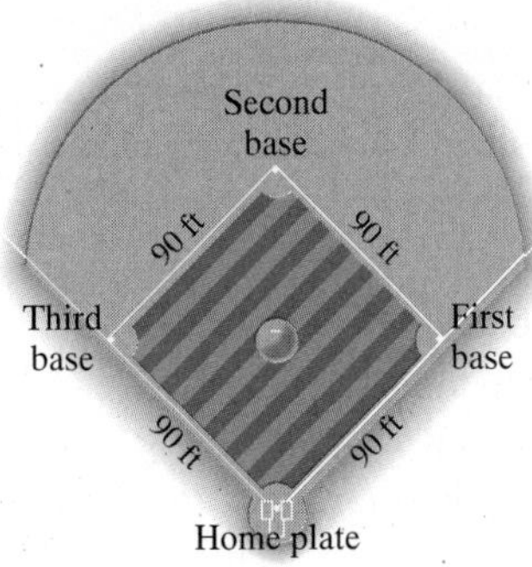

1 Discuss Sample Strategies.

2 Have students describe other distances equal to length of a million quarters.

Share & Summarize

1. The average distance from Earth to the sun is about 93,000,000 miles. How many quarters would you need to stack for the pile to reach the sun? See below.

2. Why do you think many people don't understand the difference between a million and a billion? Answers will vary.

3 Have student read answers aloud.

4 Present other activities to illustrate a million.

Investigation 2 Powers of 10

In Investigation 1, you investigated 1 million and 1 billion. Both of these numbers can be expressed as powers of 10.

$$1 \text{ million} = 1{,}000{,}000 = 10^6$$

$$1 \text{ billion} = 1{,}000{,}000{,}000 = 10^9$$

5 Discuss why so many things are described in powers of 10.

Share & Summarize Answer

1. Since 1 million quarters form a stack about a mile high, about $93{,}000{,}000 \times 1{,}000{,}000 =$ about 93,000,000,000,000 quarters would be needed.

Think & Discuss

Since students should be familiar with the stretching machines introduced in Lesson 3.1, this material can be discussed rather quickly.

1 When discussing the first group of machines, ask students to explain how to use the exponent to predict the length of the streamer. They may refer to the relationship between the exponent and the number of zeros or the number of decimal places moved in the length of the output streamer. For example, in the second machine, the output streamer must have 3 zeros because the exponent is 3 ($2 \times 10^3 = 2{,}000$). In the fourth machine, the decimal place had to be moved 6 places because the exponent is 6 ($1.25 \times 10^6 = 1{,}250{,}000$).

2 Have students try to generalize a rule for determining the length of an output streamer, given the input length and the exponent. They may suggest the "counting zeros" technique but have trouble stating the relationship for situations involving decimals, such as that in the fourth machine. If so, review how to multiply decimals by powers of 10. Since Problem Set C includes problems with both whole numbers and decimals, you may wish to provide several more examples that have decimal input numbers such as 2.35 inches.

For the second group of machines, students will need to work backward, as they are given the beginning and ending lengths and must determine the exponent. Of course, the relationship between the exponent and the number of zeros or decimal places moved is the same as for the first group of machines.

3 Again, have students try to generalize a rule for determining the exponent, given the input and output lengths. They should be able to use the same logic that helped them generalize a rule for the first group of machines.

It is often useful to talk about large numbers in terms of powers of 10. Imagining $\times 10$ repeater machines can help you get used to working with such powers.

Think & Discuss

Your resizing factory is so successful, you plan a celebration for all your employees. To make decorations, you send pieces of colored party streamers through stretching machines.

1 Ask students to explain how to use the exponent to predict the length.

Find the length of the streamer that exits each machine. Give your answers in centimeters.

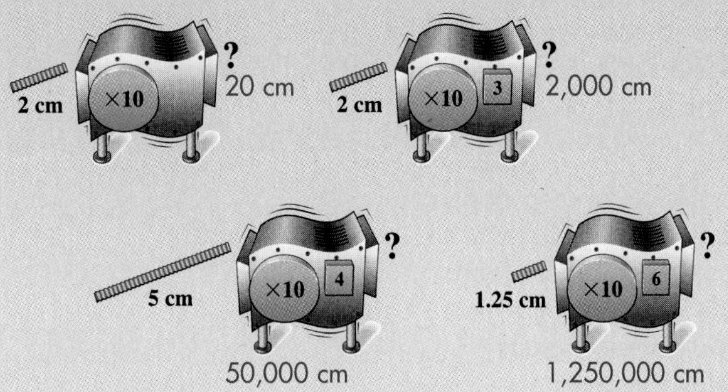

If you know the length of the input streamer and the exponent on the $\times 10$ repeater machine, how can you find the length of the output streamer? See ①.

2 Have students generalize a rule for determining the length of an output streamer, given the input length and the exponent.

Find the exponent of each repeater machine. (Note: The output streamer is not drawn to scale.)

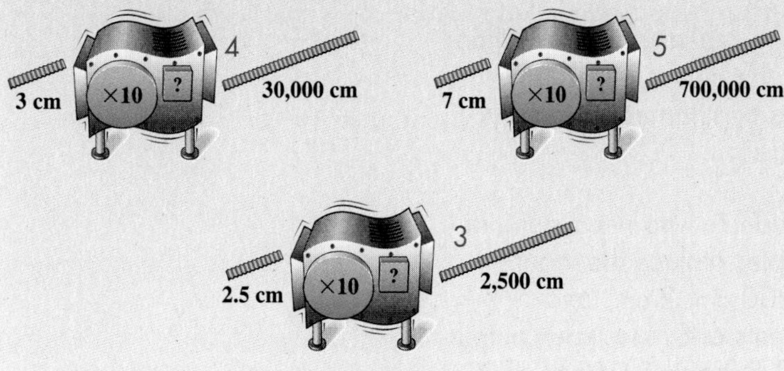

If you know the length of the input and output streamers, how can you find the exponent of the $\times 10$ repeater machine? See ②.

3 Have students generalize a rule for determining the exponent, given the input and output lengths.

Just the facts

Here are some other big numbers.

10^{12}	trillion
10^{15}	quadrillion
10^{18}	quintillion
10^{21}	sextillion
10^{24}	septillion
10^{27}	octillion
10^{30}	nonillion

① Possible answer: If the input length is a whole number, add a number of zeros equal to the exponent. If the input length is a decimal number, move the decimal point to the right the number of places equal to the exponent.

② Possible answer: If the input length is a whole number, count the number of zeros added to the input length to get the output length. The number of added zeros is the exponent. If the input length is a decimal, then count the places the decimal moved to the right to get from the input length to the output length. That number is the exponent.

LESSON 3.4 Describing Large Numbers 193

Problem Set C **Suggested Grouping: Pairs**
Because our number system is a base-10 system, students should recognize how convenient it is to multiply with powers of 10. Multiplying by powers of 10 changes the position, or place value, of the digits, but does not change the digits or their order. Students may be familiar with these ideas but may need practice using them in the context of the stretching machines.

Problem 1 is particularly interesting because it illustrates the true *magnitude of change* caused by repeated applications of a ×10 machine. Help students to realize that the input straw was only $\frac{1}{100}$ the length of the output straw.

For **Problems 3–11,** students should be able to apply the generalizations they discussed in Think & Discuss. Be sure that they can state why these generalizations work. That is, "adding zeros" (with whole numbers) and "moving the decimal point" (with decimals) really means "multiplying by a power of 10." Have students note that these problems cover all three types of situations—finding output lengths, finding exponents, and finding input lengths.

Call attention to the fact that Problem 6 involves different units of measure. You might ask,

> How can you determine the repeater number when the input is in meters and the output is in kilometers? *Change the meters to kilometers or the kilometers to meters first.*

Additional Examples For students who need additional practice, you can, for example, replace the input lengths in Problems 3–5 with 200 cm, 2 cm, and 0.8 cm, respectively. For Problems 6–8, use input/output values of 14 cm and 14 m, 50.5 ft and 5,050 ft, and 23.9 ft and 239,000 ft, respectively. For Problems 9–11, use a 10^5 machine and an output of 34,000 cm, a 10^6 machine and an output of 480 m, and a 10^8 machine and an output of 25,000 mi.

Problem Set C

1. about 0.12 cm; A $\times 10^2$ machine stretches a straw to 100 times its original size. This straw is about 12 cm, and the input straw must have been $\frac{1}{100}$ of this length.
3. 1,500 cm, or 1.5 m
4. 1,500,000 cm, or 15,000 m, or 15 km

1. This party straw exited a $\times 10^2$ machine. Without measuring, estimate the length of the input straw in centimeters. It may be helpful if you copy the straw onto your paper. Explain how you found your answer.

2. This straw went into a $\times 10$ machine. Without measuring, estimate the length of the output straw in centimeters. about 15 cm

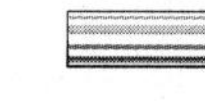

Find the length of each output straw.

3.

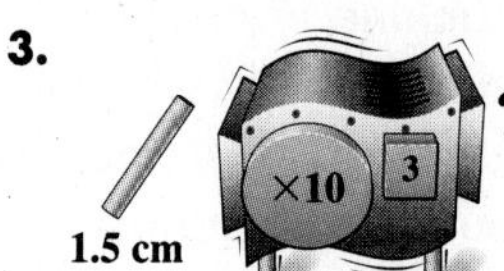

4.

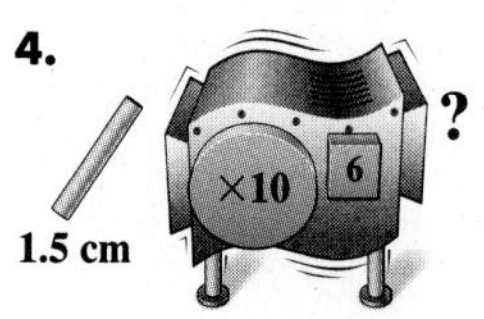

5.

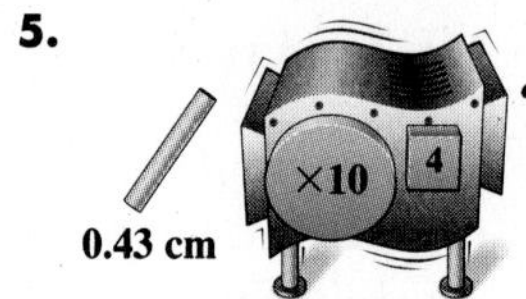

4,300 cm, or 43 m

Find each exponent.

6. 3

7. 2

8. 5

Find the length of each input straw.

9. 2 cm

10.

0.07 cm, or 0.7 mm

1 You may have students work in pairs.

2 Be sure students know why generalizations work.

3 In Problem 6, note different units of measure.

4 Give students additional examples.

As preparation for Problem Set D, you may want to show the example that follows Problem 11 and have students write numerical expressions corresponding to several of the problems in Problem Set C.

Problem Set D **Suggested Grouping: Pairs**
This problem set provides a few numerical practice problems for students. The idea of a number times a power of 10 is a nice lead-in to the next investigation, which focuses on scientific notation.

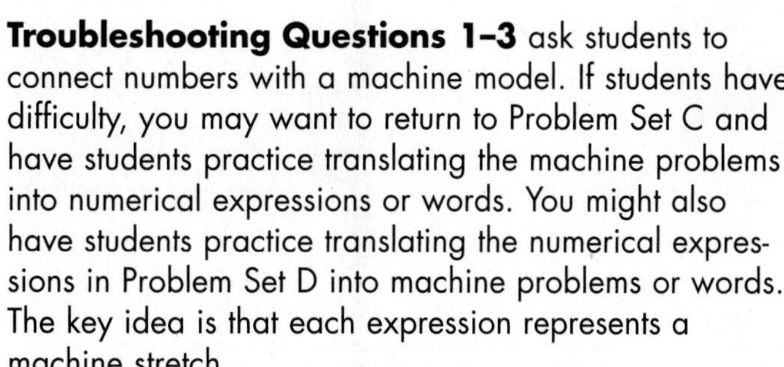

Access for All Learners

Extra Help If students have difficulty with these problems, you may want to encourage them to create "machine stories" for them. That is, they should translate the numerical expressions into machine situations, which they then describe to their partner. For instance, "$6 \times 10^N = 600$" can be translated into "I took a 6-inch stick and put it through a 10 repeater machine. It came out 600 inches long, so the exponent (or exponents) on the machine must have been . . . ."

Share & Summarize

These questions connect the first two investigations: thinking about which repeater machines stretch things to 1 million and 1 billion times their original size. In addition, we emphasize the size difference by asking students what repeater machine stretches a million into a billion.

3 **Troubleshooting Questions 1–3** ask students to connect numbers with a machine model. If students have difficulty, you may want to return to Problem Set C and have students practice translating the machine problems into numerical expressions or words. You might also have students practice translating the numerical expressions in Problem Set D into machine problems or words. The key idea is that each expression represents a machine stretch.

If students do not answer Question 3 correctly, you may want to spend some time reviewing different ways to compare a million and a billion. Students may remember from Investigation 1 that to get from a million to a billion, you must multiply by 1,000. This means sending the stick through a $\times 1{,}000$ machine. Ask,

What power of 10 is 1,000? 3rd

Alternately, students might prefer using laws of exponents. If you consider turning a 1-million-inch stick into a 1-billion-inch stick, the following reasoning works: 1 million is 10^6 and 1 billion is 10^9. So we want to know what repeater machine will give an output of 10^9 for an input of 10^6. By one of the product laws of exponents, we see that the machine must be a $\times 10^3$ machine, since $10^6 \times 10^3 = 10^{6+3} = 10^9$.

This machine must work the same way for a 2.3-million-inch stick. Exactly why this is true will become clear as students learn about numbers written in scientific notation, but their experience with the machine model so far should have convinced them that it will work.

On Your Own Exercises

Practice & Apply: 8–22
Connect & Extend: 43–57
Mixed Review: 63–81

11.

4.5 mi

In Problem Set D, you will work with expressions involving powers of 10. As you work, it may help to think of repeater machines. For example, you could use this machine to think about 5×10^3.

Problem Set D

Find each product.

1. 8×10^5
2. 18.6×10^8
3. $9,258 \times 10^4$

Find the value of N in each equation.

4. $6 \times 10^N = 600$ 2
5. $8.6 \times 10^N = 86,000$ 4
6. $54 \times 10^N = 5,400,000$ 5
7. $2,854 \times 10^N = 285,400$ 2
8. $N \times 10^2 = 800$ 8
9. $N \times 10^3 = 47,000$ 47
10. $N \times 10^6 = 54,800,000$ 54.8
11. $N \times 10^4 = 3,958$ 0.3958
12. $85 \times 10^4 = N$ 850,000
13. $9.8 \times N = 9,800,000$
14. $0.00427 \times 10^N = 42.7$ 4
15. $N \times 10^{11} = 24,985,000,000$ 0.24985

1. 800,000
2. 1,860,000,000
3. 92,580,000
13. 1,000,000, or 10^6

Just the facts

The longest gum-wrapper chain on record was 18,721 feet long and took more than 30 years to complete.

Source: *Guinness Book of World Records*. New York: Bantam Books, 1998.

Share & Summarize

1. What repeater machine would stretch a 6-inch gum-wrapper chain to 6 million inches? $\times 10^6$
2. What repeater machine would stretch a 3-inch gum-wrapper chain to 3 billion inches? $\times 10^9$
3. What repeater machine would stretch a 2.3-million-inch gum-wrapper chain to 2.3 billion inches? $\times 10^3$

1 Have students write numerical expressions for Set C.

2 You may have students work in pairs.

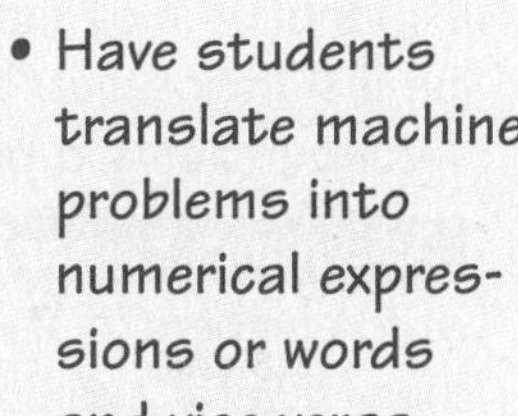

3
- Have students translate machine problems into numerical expressions or words and vice versa.
- For Question 3, review different ways to compare a million to a billion.

Investigation 3

Scientific notation is a convention that makes it easy to communicate the values of numbers. For convenience and because of limited display space, calculators use scientific notation to display very large and very small numbers. In this investigation, we concentrate on very large numbers; students will learn about very small numbers, using negative powers of 10, in Chapter 4.

1 Talk students through the introduction to scientific notation.

Example

2 Be sure that students understand that the three expressions do indeed equal 5,878,000,000,000. They may need to be reminded of their work in Problem Set D. You might ask them to think about why a large number might be written in a more compact form.

3 After discussing the Example, use the third expression to present the concept of scientific notation. Explain that the first factor of the product is a number that has exactly one nonzero digit to the left of its decimal place. This explanation may make more sense than explaining that the first factor must be at least 1 but less than 10. The second factor is a power of 10.

Additional Examples When you introduce how to write numbers in scientific notation, you may want to show several examples, such as

- 52.67×10^3 *incorrect; 5.267×10^4*
- 0.349×10^8 *incorrect; 3.49×10^7*
- 8×10^2 *correct*
- 5.1×10^3 *correct*
- $8{,}304 \times 10$ *incorrect; 8.304×10^4*

Ask students to identify which are in scientific notation and which are not. These problems occur in the text, but it is helpful to students to process the definition before tackling problems on their own. This is truly a case where students must learn something—how numbers are represented in scientific notation—rather than where they must figure out something.

Access for All Learners

Extra for Experts You may want to point out that this is not the only convention for working with large numbers. Engineers use a variation on scientific notation, in which the first factor is between 1 and 1,000 rather than between 1 and 10, and the power of 10 is a multiple of 3, that is, 10^3, 10^6, 10^9, and so on.

Investigation 3 Scientific Notation

Powers of 10 give us an easy way to express very large and very small numbers without writing a lot of zeros. This is useful in many fields, such as economics, engineering, computer science, and other areas of science. For example, astronomers need to describe great distances—like the distances between planets, stars, and galaxies. Chemists often need to describe small measurements—like the sizes of molecules, atoms, and quarks.

In this investigation, you will focus on a method for expressing large numbers. In Chapter 4, you will see how this method can be used to express small numbers, as well.

The Centaurus system includes Alpha Centauri, the star—other than our own sun—that is closest to Earth.

EXAMPLE

Astronomical distances are often expressed in light-years. For example, the Centaurus star system is 4.3 light-years from Earth. A *light-year* is the distance light travels in one year. One light-year is approximately 5,878,000,000,000 miles.

There are lots of ways to express the number of miles in a light-year as the product of a number and a power of 10. Here are three.

$5{,}878 \times 10^9 \qquad 58.78 \times 10^{11} \qquad 5.878 \times 10^{12}$

Can you explain why each of these three expressions equals 5,878,000,000,000?

VOCABULARY
scientific notation

The third expression above is written in scientific notation. A number is in **scientific notation** when it is expressed as the product of a number greater than or equal to 1 but less than 10, and a power of 10.

at least 1 but less than 10 — a power of 10

$$\mathbf{5.878 \times 10^{12}}$$

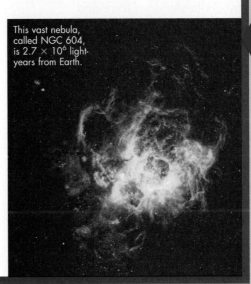

This vast nebula, called NGC 604, is 2.7×10^6 light-years from Earth.

1 Talk students through this paragraph.

2 Be sure students understand that these expressions are equal.

3
- Explain *scientific notation.*
- Show additional examples.

Develop

1 Discuss the examples shown in the chart on the top of page 197. This chart helps students make the connection between the machine model, scientific notation, and standard notation.

2 At this point, you may want to ask students why they think the scientific-notation convention exists.

Think & Discuss

3 Because the numbers written in standard notation are not aligned, students will need to count the digits, or places, in order to compare the numbers. You may want to review with students how to compare whole numbers with the same number of digits and whole numbers with a different number of digits. For numbers that have the same number of digits, if the first digits are the same, compare the second digits; if the second digits are the same, compare the third digits; and so on. If the numbers have a different number of digits, the one with more digits is greater.

Students should recognize that numbers written in scientific notation are much easier to compare.

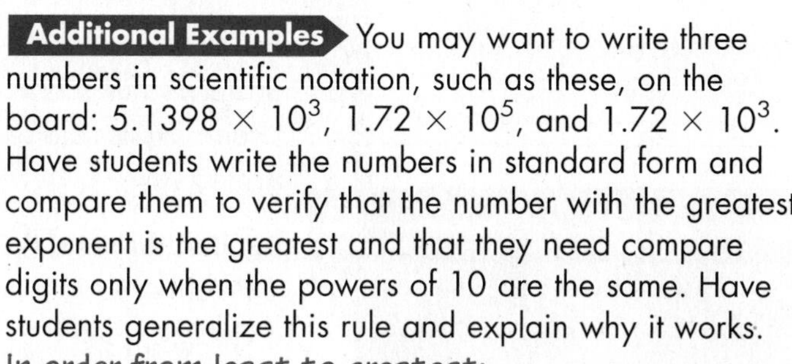

4 **Additional Examples** You may want to write three numbers in scientific notation, such as these, on the board: 5.1398×10^3, 1.72×10^5, and 1.72×10^3. Have students write the numbers in standard form and compare them to verify that the number with the greatest exponent is the greatest and that they need compare digits only when the powers of 10 are the same. Have students generalize this rule and explain why it works. *In order from least to greatest:*

- 1.72×10^3 (1,720)
- 5.1398×10^3 (5,139.8)
- 1.72×10^5 (172,000)

You may need to review several times that a number in scientific notation is a product of two factors: one factor is a number at least 1 but less than 10, and the other factor is a power of 10.

You might follow up this discussion by giving two numbers in scientific notation with the same exponents and different number factors, such as 5.5×10^{15} and 9.75×10^{15}. Ask,

> How can you compare these two numbers?

In this case, students need only compare number factors.

Then give two numbers in scientific notation with different exponents and different number factors, such as 3.498×10^4 and 1.002×10^{15}. Ask,

> How can you compare these two numbers?

In this case, students need to compare only the exponents.

The chart lists the outputs of some repeater machines in scientific and standard notation.

Machine	Scientific Notation	Standard Notation	Example of Number
3 ×10 2	3×10^2	300	length of a football field in feet
6.5 ×10 7	6.5×10^7	65,000,000	years since dinosaurs became extinct
2.528 ×10 13	2.528×10^{13}	25,280,000,000,000	distance from Earth to Centaurus star system in miles

Scientific notation can help you compare the sizes of numbers.

Think & Discuss

① 242,000,000,000,000,000,000; Since all the numbers are whole numbers, the number with the most digits is greatest.

Here are three numbers written in standard notation.

74,580,000,000,000,000,000

8,395,000,000,000,000,000

242,000,000,000,000,000,000

- Which number is greatest? How do you know? See ① above.
- Which number is least? How do you know? See ② below.

Here are three numbers written in scientific notation.

3.723×10^{15} 9.259×10^{25} 4.2×10^{19}

- Which number is greatest? How do you know? 9.259×10^{25}; The number with the greatest exponent is greatest.
- Which number is least? How do you know? 3.723×10^{15}; The number with the least exponent is least.

② 8,395,000,000,000,000,000; Since all the numbers are whole numbers, the number with the fewest digits is least.

1 Discuss examples.

2 Ask why scientific-notation convention exists.

3 Review comparison of whole numbers.

4
- Show Additional Examples.
- Have students generalize a rule.

LESSON 3.4 Describing Large Numbers 197

Problem Set E **Suggested Grouping: Small Groups**

Because students often find scientific notation tricky at first, encourage them to work in small groups to solve these problems.

Students practice recognizing numbers written in scientific notation and translating between standard notation and scientific notation. The last problem uses a context for which scientific notation is truly necessary: comparing distances from the different planets to the sun.

Students will get more practice changing numbers from standard notation into scientific notation in the next problem set. For now, they will probably think about how many places to the left they have to move the decimal point to get a single digit before it and then making the exponent of the 10 equal to that number. In a sense, they undo the strategy for translating a number into standard notation.

2 **Problem Set Wrap-Up** Have students share the methods they used for **Problems 9–14.** You can direct the discussion by asking,

> How do you take a number written in standard notation and rewrite it in scientific notation?

If someone describes the "moving the decimal point" strategy, take advantage of that moment to talk about what moving the decimal point to the left does to a number. Then ask,

> How does 6.2 compare to 62? It is $\frac{1}{10}$ as much.
>
> How does 0.05 compare to 5? It is $\frac{1}{100}$ as much.
>
> What computation are you really doing when you move the decimal point one place to the left? dividing by 10 Two places to the left? dividing by 100 Three places to the left? dividing by 1,000
>
> How can you get back to the original value of a number if you divide it by 10? multiply by 10 Divide it by 100? multiply by 100 Divide it by 1,000? multiply by 1,000

Then have students try to generalize a strategy for writing a number in scientific notation. Their rules should include the idea that the number of 10s by which you multiply, that is, the exponent of 10, is equal to the number of places you moved the decimal point.

Problem Set E

Tell whether each number is written correctly in scientific notation. For those that are not written correctly, describe what is incorrect.

1. 6.4535×10^{52} correct
2. 41×10^3
3. 0.4×10^6
4. 1×10^1 correct

2. 41 is not between 1 and 10
3. 0.4 is not between 1 and 10

Write each number in standard notation.

5. 1.28×10^6 1,280,000
6. 9.03×10^5 903,000
7. 6.02×10^{23} See below.
8. 5.7×10^8 570,000,000

Write each number in scientific notation.

9. 850 8.5×10^2
10. 7 thousand 7×10^3
11. 10,400,000 1.04×10^7
12. 659,000 6.59×10^5
13. 83 million 8.3×10^7
14. 27 billion 2.7×10^{10}
15. The table shows the average distance from each planet in our solar system to the sun.

Planet	Distance from Sun (km) Standard Notation	Distance from Sun (km) Scientific Notation
Earth	149,600,000	1.496×10^8
Jupiter	778,300,000	7.783×10^8
Mars	227,900,000	2.279×10^8
Mercury	57,900,000	5.79×10^7
Neptune	4,497,000,000	4.497×10^9
Pluto	5,900,000,000	5.9×10^9
Saturn	1,427,000,000	1.427×10^9
Uranus	2,870,000,000	2.87×10^9
Venus	108,200,000	1.082×10^8

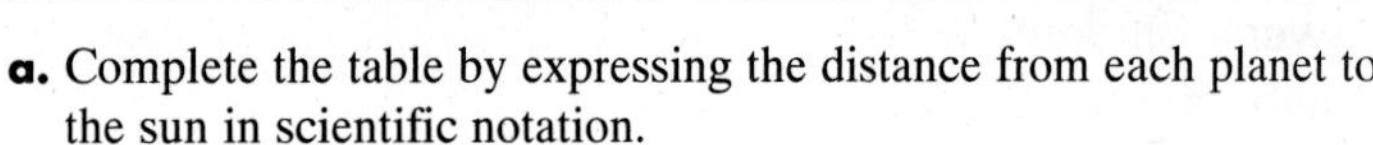

a. Complete the table by expressing the distance from each planet to the sun in scientific notation.

b. Order the planets from closest to the sun to farthest from the sun. Mercury, Venus, Earth, Mars, Jupiter, Saturn, Uranus, Neptune, Pluto

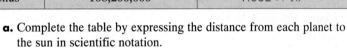

7. 602,000,000,000,000,000,000,000

Just the facts

Pluto's orbit is unusual. Pluto is sometimes closer to the sun than its neighbor Neptune is, as it was from January 1979 to February 1999.

1 You may have students work in small groups.

2 Have students share and generalize strategies.

Develop

Discuss the text preceding the Example on page 199.

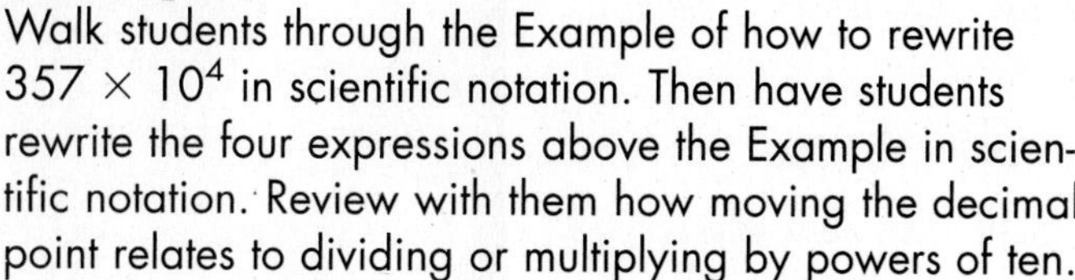

Example
Walk students through the Example of how to rewrite 357×10^4 in scientific notation. Then have students rewrite the four expressions above the Example in scientific notation. Review with them how moving the decimal point relates to dividing or multiplying by powers of ten.

Problem Set F **Suggested Grouping: Pairs**
Students practice rewriting a few numbers in scientific notation. If your students seem to have a good handle on the ideas, you may want to use these problems as an assessment of how individual students are doing. First, do students recognize scientific notation when it is written correctly, as in **Problem 4**? Second, do they understand how to convert a number given as a number times a power of ten into scientific notation?

Access for All Learners

Extra Help If your students are struggling with scientific notation, allowing them to work in pairs will help them solidify their understanding. Encourage pairs to take different roles for each problem. The first person may rewrite the number in scientific notation; the second person may check it against the example to see that the steps make sense. For the next problem, have them alternate roles.

Share & Summarize
Ask for volunteers to share their answers. Students will have more practice working with numbers in scientific notation and rewriting numbers that are not written correctly. The main goal of this investigation is that students can recognize whether or not a number is written correctly in scientific notation.

Troubleshooting If students do not correctly describe a number written in scientific notation, it is not necessary at this point to drill the definition and ask students to identify examples and nonexamples of it. Rather, keep it in mind as you move through Investigation 4, which focuses on using the calculator with numbers written in scientific notation. Periodically ask students,

> Is the answer written in scientific notation? How do you know?

On Your Own Exercises

Practice & Apply: 23–33
Connect & Extend: 58–59
Mixed Review: 63–81

Just the facts

Here are some really big numbers.

10^{45} quattuordecillion
10^{57} octadecillion
10^{60} novemdecillion
10^{63} vigintillion
10^{100} googol

Scientific notation is useful for ordering numbers only if the convention is followed properly—that is, if the first part of the number is between 1 and 10. Otherwise, the power of 10 may not tell you which number is greatest.

1 Discuss this text.

The expressions below show the same number written in four ways as the product of a number and a power of 10. However, none of these expressions is in scientific notation. If you compare these numbers by looking at the powers of 10, you might not realize that they are all equal.

$0.0357 \times 10^8 \qquad 35.7 \times 10^5 \qquad 3{,}570 \times 10^3 \qquad 357{,}000 \times 10^1$

You can change numbers like these into scientific notation without changing them into standard form first.

EXAMPLE

Write 357×10^4 in scientific notation.

You can change 357 to a number between 1 and 10 by dividing it by 100. To compensate, you need to multiply by 100, or 10^2.

$$\begin{aligned} 357 \times 10^4 &= \tfrac{357}{100} \times 100 \times 10^4 \\ &= 3.57 \times 10^2 \times 10^4 \\ &= 3.57 \times 10^6 \end{aligned}$$

2
- Walk students through the Example.
- Have students rewrite expressions above the Example in scientific notation.
- Review multiplying and dividing by powers of 10.

Problem Set F

Write each number in scientific notation.

1. 13×10^2 1.3×10^3
2. 0.932×10^3 9.32×10^2
3. 461×10^4 4.61×10^6
4. 5.9×10^5 5.9×10^5
5. 98.6×10^9 9.86×10^{10}
6. 197×10^6 1.97×10^8

3 You may have students work in pairs.

Share & Summarize

How can you tell whether a number greater than 1 is written in scientific notation? If it is written as a number, greater than 1 but less than 10, times a power of 10, it's in scientific notation.

4 Ask for volunteers to share their answers.

LESSON 3.4 Describing Large Numbers 199

Develop

Investigation 4

Students learn how to use calculators to work with numbers in scientific notation. This involves both entering the numbers correctly and interpreting the display when an answer is given in scientific notation.

1 Remind students of the "rice on the chessboard" problem from Lesson 3.3, Problem Set C, and ask whether they remember about how many grains of rice were on the last square (2^{64}).

Think & Discuss

Have students find 2^{40} on their calculators and tell what the display is. Their response should be 1.09951 E 12 (or a similar decimal with more or fewer digits, depending on their calculators). Ask,

> Does that mean there were 1.09951 grains of rice on the last square?

Students should realize that since the second square had 2 grains and the amount was doubled at each stage, 1.09951 cannot be correct.

Have the class recall how they found the number of grains of rice on each square of the checkerboard with repeated doubling or by finding a power of 2. Then tell students your calculator display for 2^{33} is 8,589,934,592, and write this number on the board. Next ask them to find 2^{34} by hand by doubling your calculator display for 2^{33}. Write the answer, 17,179,869,184, on the board. Finally, tell them that your calculator display for 2^{34} is 1.717986918 E 10, and write this number on the board. Ask:

> Do you see any relationship between the last two numbers I wrote? What do you think the 10 means in the last number?

Suggest that students think of the last number, 1.717986918 E 10, as a number in scientific notation, with the decimal as the number factor and the 10 as the exponent. Have them write this number in standard notation and compare it with the second number, which they calculated by hand. The two numbers are identical, except for the last digit! This should help to convince them of the validity of the calculator display.

For further verification, students can use their own calculators to find successive powers of 2 until their calculators switch from standard notation to scientific notation, and then they can follow the steps outlined above.

Then ask students to find both the power of 2 that would be on the 64th square (2^{64}) and its value on their calculators. Ask a student to write the answer on the board: 2^{64} = 1.84467 E 19 (again depending on the calculator).

At this point, discuss with students that calculators vary in the way they display exponents. In the example above, "E 19" has replaced "$\times 10^{19}$." The 19 still represents the power of 10. Students may need to mentally reinsert "$\times$ 10."

Investigation 4 Scientific Notation on Your Calculator

In Lesson 3.3 you worked on a problem about a ruler who had to place rice on the squares of a chessboard as a reward for one of his subjects. The first square had 2 grains of rice, and every square after that had twice as many as the previous square.

The table describes the number of grains of rice on each square.

Square	Number of Grains (as a product)	Number of Grains (as a power of 2)
1	1×2	2^1
2	$1 \times 2 \times 2$	2^2
3	$1 \times 2 \times 2 \times 2$	2^3
4	$1 \times 2 \times 2 \times 2 \times 2$	2^4
5	$1 \times 2 \times 2 \times 2 \times 2 \times 2$	2^5
6	$1 \times 2 \times 2 \times 2 \times 2 \times 2 \times 2$	2^6
7	$1 \times 2 \times 2 \times 2 \times 2 \times 2 \times 2 \times 2$	2^7

Think & Discuss

There are 2^{40} grains of rice on Square 40. Evaluate this number on your calculator. What does the calculator display? What do you think this means? See ①.

① 1.09951 12; Explanations will vary. (Note: Calculator displays will vary in the number of decimal places displayed and the notation used to indicate the power of 10.)

Numbers too large to fit in a calculator's display are expressed in scientific notation. Different calculators show scientific notation in different ways. When you entered 2^{40}, you may have seen one of these displays:

1.09951E12 | 1.09951E+12 | 1.09951 12

All of these represent 1.09951×10^{12}. When you read the display, you need to mentally insert the "$\times$ 10."

If you continued the table, what power of 2 would represent the number of grains of rice on Square 64, the last square on the chessboard? 2^{64}

Use your calculator to find the number of grains of rice on Square 64. Give your answer in scientific notation. 1.84467×10^{19}

1
- Remind students of the "rice on the chessboard" problem.
- Ask students how many grains of rice were on the last square.

2
- Ask students about the calculator display for 2^{40}.
- Discuss the calculator displays for 2^{33} and 2^{34}.

3
- Ask a volunteer to write the answer on board.
- Discuss differences in calculator displays.

Develop

Problem Set G **Suggested Grouping: Individuals**
In this problem set, students use calculators to work with numbers that have more than 10 digits. On most calculators, a number with more than 10 digits will automatically be displayed in scientific notation. After students complete **Problem 5,** check their understanding by asking them to explain why numbers are easier to compare when all are written in scientific notation.

> On the **Spot Assessment**
>
> In **Problem 6,** watch for students who are not sure that they need to multiply. Ask questions such as,
>
> Will light travel farther in a day than in a second?
>
> By using common sense, students should see the need to multiply.
>
> Also watch for students who miss intermediate steps. Students may not think to multiply by 60 to find the distance in a minute and by 60 again to find the distance in an hour but may simply multiply by only 24.

If students had trouble with the unit equivalences or intermediate steps in **Problem 6,** you may want to walk through the problem with the whole class.

Additional Examples If students are having trouble understanding the display on their calculators, you may want to engage them in an activity in which they can actually watch the display switch from standard to scientific notation. On their calculators, have students enter the items from the first column of the table below. After each new input, have students record the number displayed.

Key Presses	Calculator Display
10 [×] 10 [ENTER]	100
[×] 10 [ENTER]	1000
[×] 10 [ENTER]	
[×] 10 [ENTER]	
[×] 10 [ENTER]	
[×] 10 [ENTER]	
[×] 10 [ENTER]	
[×] 10 [ENTER]	
[×] 10 [ENTER]	
[×] 10 [ENTER]	

Students should continue the pattern until the display switches to scientific notation, usually at the tenth "[×] 10 [ENTER]."

They can continue entering the "[×] 10 [ENTER]" to try to find the greatest number their calculator can display. Usually, the calculator displays an error message for a number greater than 10^{99}. Of course, this does not mean that 1×10^{99} is the greatest number the calculator can display, but that $9.99999999 \times 10^{99}$ is the greatest number the calculator can handle. The number of 9s will depend on the maximum number of characters the calculator can display.

To lead into the next problem set, tell students that if they wanted to compute with the value of a light-year—for example, if they wanted to figure out how many miles are in 5 light-years—they would need to know how to enter the value of a light-year into their calculators. Walk students through the steps of entering numbers in scientific notation using the example in the text of 2.4×10^{12}.

Problem Set H **Suggested Grouping: Pairs**
Students enter numbers in scientific notation and compute with them, including adding, subtracting, multiplying, and dividing. Students should work individually on **Problems 1–3** and then pair up for **Problem 4,** in which they explore the relative difference between two very large numbers written in scientific notation.

Problem Set Wrap-Up A wrap-up of this problem set is essential so that students don't come away with misunderstandings from Problem 4. Ask the class,

> How can it be that the sum of two numbers is one of those numbers?

The point to make is that these numbers are very large and that there is a notion of relative difference. That is, if you have a billion of something and take 1 away, most people would still say you have a billion rather than saying you have 999,999,999. In fact, it was unlikely you had *exactly* 1 billion to begin with, but rather you had something close to 1 billion. So subtracting a very small number essentially has no effect.

Of course, what constitutes a "large number" or a "small number" depends on the problem at hand. Most people would consider 8.5×10^{20} a large number, but when it is added to 1.43×10^{45} as in Problem 4b, 8.5×10^{20} is so small as to be nearly insignificant.

Problem Set G

Use your calculator to evaluate each expression. Give your answers in scientific notation.

1. 3^{28} **2.** 4.05^{21} **3.** 7.95^{12} **4.** 12^{12}

5. It would be difficult to order the numbers in Problems 1–4 as they are given. It should be much easier now that you've written them in scientific notation. List the four numbers from least to greatest.

6. Light travels at a speed of about 186,000 miles per second.

a. How many miles does light travel in a day? 1.60704×10^{10}

b. How many miles does light travel in a year? 5.865696×10^{12}

When the result of a calculation is a very large number, your calculator automatically displays it in scientific notation. You can also enter numbers into your calculator in scientific notation. Different calculators use different keys, but common ones are [EXP], [EE], and [10^x].

For example, to enter 2.4×10^{12}, press

2.4 [EXP] 12 or 2.4 [EE] 12 or 2.4 [10^x] 12

Just the facts

A day is the time it takes for one rotation of a planet; a year is the time it takes for a planet to make one revolution around the sun. On Jupiter, a day is about 10 Earth hours long, and a year is about 12 Earth years.

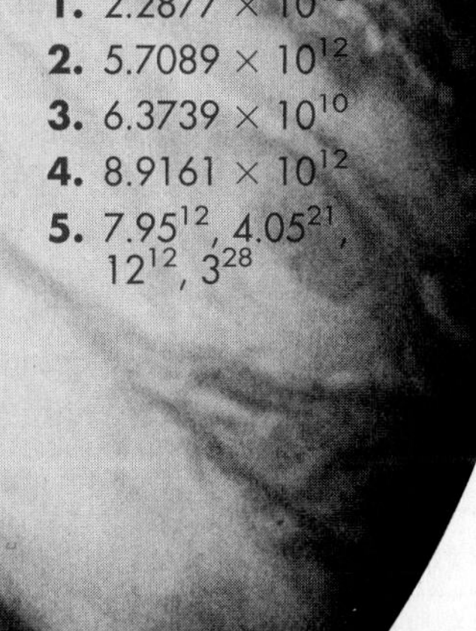

Problem Set G Answers

1. 2.2877×10^{13}
2. 5.7089×10^{12}
3. 6.3739×10^{10}
4. 8.9161×10^{12}
5. 7.95^{12}, 4.05^{21}, 12^{12}, 3^{28}

Problem Set H

Estimate the value of each expression, and then use your calculator to evaluate it. Give your answers in scientific notation.

1. $5.2 \times 10^{15} + 3.5 \times 10^{15}$ 8.7×10^{15}

2. $(6.5 \times 10^{18}) \times (1.8 \times 10^{15})$ 1.17×10^{34}

3. $(8.443 \times 10^{18}) \div 2$ 4.2215×10^{18}

4. Estimate the value of each expression, and then use your calculator to evaluate it. Give your answers in scientific notation.

a. $6 \times 10^{12} + 7 \times 10^{4}$ 6×10^{12}

b. $8.5 \times 10^{20} + 1.43 \times 10^{45}$ 1.43×10^{45}

c. $4.92 \times 10^{22} - 9.3 \times 10^{5}$ 4.92×10^{22}

d. How do your results in Parts a–c compare to the numbers that were added or subtracted? See below.

e. Write the numbers in Part a in standard notation and then add them. How does your result compare to the result you found in Part a? If the answers are different, try to explain why.

4d. In each case, the result is equal to one of the original numbers.

4e. 6,000,000,070,000; The answers are different. One of the numbers being added or subtracted is so small relative to the other number that it affects only decimal places that aren't shown on the display.

1
- You may have students work individually.
- Use Problem 5 to check understanding.
- You might walk through Problem 6 as a class.

2 Walk students through entering numbers on their calculators.

3 Have students work alone on Problems 1–3 and then pair up for Problem 4.

4 Review the key ideas of Problem 4.

Develop

Problem Set I **Suggested Grouping: Pairs**
This problem set asks students to use their calculators and their new skills of entering and interpreting numbers written in scientific notation to answer the question posed about the number of "worthwhile" books still existing in 1945. **Problems 1–3** walk students through some necessary assumptions and the intermediate steps.

If you wish to have students find the assumptions on their own, you might turn this problem set into a class mini-project and have groups of students gather various parts of the data. Ask students to,

1. Go to a local library and ask the librarian how many books are in the library. If he or she does not know, then estimate the number of books in the library by determining the number of bookshelves, the number of individual shelves per bookshelf, and the number of books per shelf. Depending on the size of the library, students might have to make intermediate estimates, such as the number of bookshelves in a room and the number of rooms housing books. *30 books per bookshelf × 7 shelves per bookshelf × 50 bookshelves = 10,500 books*

2. Randomly select several books from several different sections of the library and find the total number of pages. Make a good estimate for the average number of pages in a book in the library. *total number of pages in the 5 books chosen: 103, 227, 92, 151, 177; average = 150 pages per book*

3. Survey each of the books in Part 2 to find how many lines are on a page of text. Make a good estimate for the average number of lines per page in a book. *total number of lines on a page of text in 5 pages chosen: 50, 61, 48, 58, 63; average = 56 lines per page*

4. Count the characters in a single line of text in each book. Be sure to include spaces and punctuation marks. Make a good estimate for the average number of characters in a line of text in a book. *total number of characters on a single line of text: 54, 39, 51, 55, 56; average = 51 characters per line*

5. Use these estimates to find the approximate amount of disk space necessary to hold all the information in all of the books in the library. Compare this to the amount of disk space available in computers sold in local stores or advertised in the newspaper. Determine the number of computers needed to hold all this information. *from above: $10{,}500 \times 150 \times 56 \times 51 = 4.4982 \times 10^9$ total characters; bytes; 4.4982×10^9 bytes $\div 1 \times 10^9 \approx$ 4.5 gigabytes; on average, computers can hold about 6–8 gigabytes of information. So, one computer is all that is necessary to hold 4.5 gigabytes.*

Share & Summarize
Students should realize that calculators cannot have an "infinite display"; there is some limit to the number of digits that can be shown. Scientific notation makes it easier for people to compare very large numbers and for machines to display them. The calculator display does not have to show all the places because it shows the *number* of places. The number that follows the E or the space is the number of places, the exponent of 10.

Question 2 is key: When you deal with very large and very small numbers it is important to think about both significant digits (not in the formal sense, but in the sense that 6.25 billion is rarely an exact reporting of a number, whether it refers to dollars, miles, or anything else) and relative size.

Troubleshooting If students have difficulty with the Share & Summarize questions, they are probably still unsure about the whole notion of scientific notation. It would be appropriate to spend some time going back over the basic ideas. Emphasize,

- Scientific notation is a convention that makes it easier for scientists to talk to each other about quantities represented by big numbers.
- There are only two rules about how the number is written: the number factor is between 1 and 10 (that is, it has one digit before the decimal point) and the other factor is a power of 10.
- Calculators display numbers in scientific notation for your convenience and because the display space is limited.

On Your Own Exercises

Practice & Apply: 34–38
Connect & Extend: 60–62
Mixed Review: 63–81

Problem Set I

In 1945 a librarian at Harvard University estimated that there were 10 million books of "worthwhile" printed material. Suppose you wanted to enter all this printed material into a computer for storage.

Use your calculator to solve the following problems. When appropriate, record your answers in scientific notation. Make these assumptions as you work:

- The average book is 500 pages long.
- The average page holds 40 lines of text.
- The average line holds 80 characters.

1. How many characters are on one page of an average book? 3,200

2. How many characters are in the average book? 1,600,000, or 1.6×10^6

3. How many characters were in all the "worthwhile" books in 1945?

4. One *byte* of computer disk space stores about one character of text. A *gigabyte* of computer disk space is 1×10^9 bytes, so a gigabyte can store about 1×10^9 characters. How many gigabytes are needed to store all the "worthwhile" books from 1945? 16,000

Just the facts

Near the end of 1998, the U.S. Library of Congress held more than twice the number of books considered "worthwhile" in 1945. It also had about 3.5 million sound recordings.

Problem Set I Answer

3. 1.6×10^{13}

1
- You may have students work in pairs.
- You might turn the problem set into a class project.

Share & Summarize

1. Explain, in a way that a fifth grader could understand, why a calculator sometimes displays numbers in scientific notation. See ①.

2. Explain why sometimes when you add two numbers in scientific notation on your calculator, the result is just the greater of the two numbers.

One of the numbers being added is so small relative to the other number that it affects only decimal places that aren't shown on the display.

① Some numbers are too big to display on a calculator screen. Calculators use this special notation as a way to write big numbers so they take less space.

2 If students have trouble, review the basics of scientific notation.

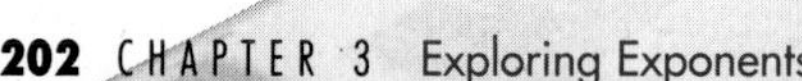

Suggested Grouping: Small Groups

Materials and Preparation

Each group will need 6 blocks labeled 1, 2, 3, 4, 5, and 6.

This very rich puzzle has many layers of opportunity for the teacher. In this investigation, students first solve an intriguing puzzle: How do you move all the disks from one spike to another, following the rules laid out in the description of the problem?

From there, students find how the number of moves depends on the number of disks they must move. Each time a disk is added, the number of moves is twice the previous number of moves plus 1. This is a slightly more complicated form of exponential growth than what they saw in Lesson 3.2.

The general formula, which students will need help discovering, represents the number of moves needed to move d disks from one spike to another: $2^d - 1$. The support will have to come in at least two places: helping students find the most efficient algorithm for moving the disks and then expressing the numerical pattern they find in the table they create.

Discuss the introductory text about the legend behind the Tower of Hanoi puzzle.

Make a Prediction

2 Students will probably not have a good sense for this pattern; it is not a simple exponential function. Remind students not to draw conclusions about the pattern too soon. If they come up with 1 move for 1 disk and 3 moves for 2 disks, they may extend (incorrectly) and think about odd numbers. Or they may automatically be looking for exponential growth because of the placement of the Lab Investigation in this chapter, and think that it grows like 3^x. Once students solve the first three problems and see that moving 2 disks requires 2 moves more than moving 1 disk and that moving 3 disks requires 4 moves more than moving 3 disks, students may begin thinking in terms of 2s or powers of 2.

In any case, part of the fun of this investigation is the multiple layers of the puzzle: deciding how to move the disks, then identifying the growth, and finally applying that to the original lesson.

Encourage students to move somewhat quickly through these problems in order to get some initial ideas but not to puzzle about them too long. At some point, be sure students have figured out that they may move a disk back onto Spike A. Of course, they still may move only one disk at a time, and they may not put a larger disk on top of a smaller one.

Lab Investigation ▶ The Tower of Hanoi

MATERIALS
6 cubes, labeled 1, 2, 3, 4, 5, and 6

1 Discuss the legend behind the puzzle.

The Tower of Hanoi is a famous puzzle invented in 1883 by Edouard Lucas, a French mathematician. Lucas based the puzzle on this legend:

At the beginning of time, the priests in a Hindu temple were given three golden spikes. On one of the spikes, 64 golden disks were stacked, each one slightly smaller than the one below it.

The priests were assigned the task of moving all the disks to one of the other spikes while being careful to follow these rules:

- *Move only one disk at a time.*
- *Never put a larger disk on top of a smaller disk.*

When the priests completed the task, the temple would crumble and the world would vanish.

Just the facts
The Tower of Hanoi is sometimes called the *End of the World* puzzle.

In this lab, you will figure out how long it would take the priests to move all the disks from one spike to another. We will start by assuming the disks are so large and heavy that the priests can move only one disk per minute.

Make a Prediction

2 Remind students not to draw conclusions about the pattern too soon.

Imagine that the spikes are labeled A, B, and C and that the disks start out on Spike A. Since it can be overwhelming to think about moving all 64 disks, it may help to first consider a much simpler puzzle.

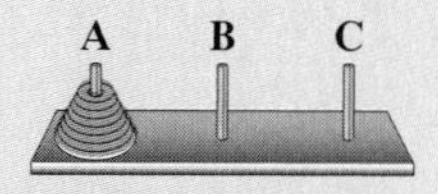

1. Suppose the puzzle started with only 1 disk on Spike A. How long would it take to move the disk to Spike B? 1 min
2. Suppose the puzzle started with 2 disks on Spike A. How long would it take to move both disks to Spike B? What would the moves be?
3. Try again with 3 disks. How long would it take? What would the moves be?

Remember
A disk cannot be placed on top of a smaller disk.

2, 3. See Additional Answers.

Additional Answers

2. 3 min; Move the top disk to C, then move the second disk to B, and then move the disk on C to B.

3. 7 min; Move the top disk to C, then move the second disk to B, and then move the disk on C to B. Now move the third disk to C. Move the top disk on B to A, move the second disk to C, and finally move the disk on A to C.

Try It Out

Students model the puzzle by using cubes and try to create an algorithm for moving disks from one spike to another, following the Tower of Hanoi rules.

One strategy for solving the problem of how to move the disks is, of course, try to solve a simpler problem.

Students can move two disks to another spike this way: Suppose we want to move them to Spike B. Move disk 1 to Spike C, disk 2 to Spike B, and then disk 1 on top of disk 2.

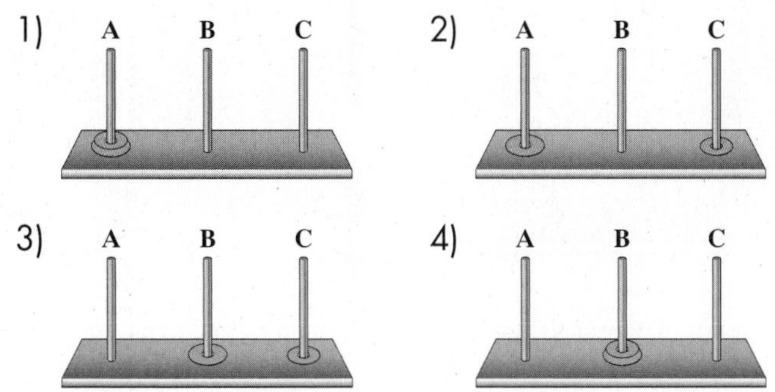

To move three disks to Spike B, move disks 1 and 2 to Spike C following the strategy above; then move disk 3 to Spike B. Finally, move disk 1 back to Spike A, disk 2 to Spike B, and then disk 1 to Spike B.

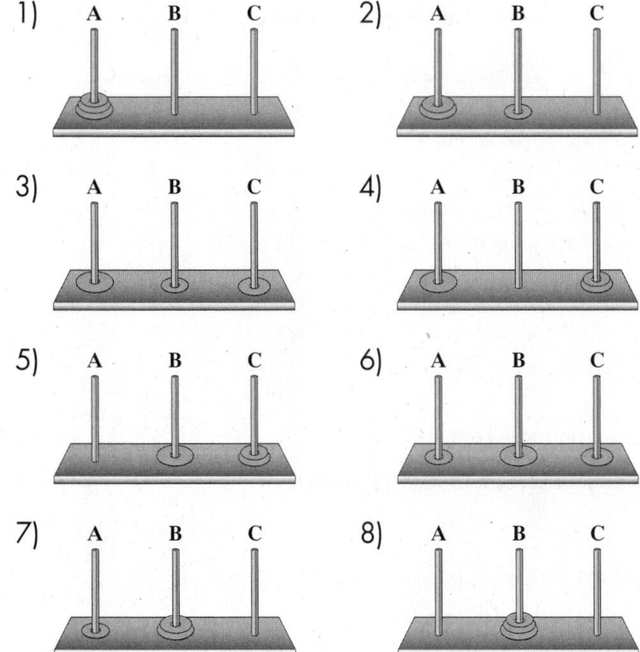

The reasoning can continue to any number of disks: Move $(d - 1)$ disks to Spike B, move the bottom disk to Spike C, and then move the $(d - 1)$ disks to Spike C.

Before moving on to counting the number of moves, it's important that all of the groups have the general strategy of how to move the disks. It's also helpful if you can help them articulate how the number of moves grows.

Many students will see that the number of moves is double the previous number of moves plus 1. If it takes 3 moves to move 2 disks, it will take $2 \times 3 + 1$ moves to move 3 disks (move 2, move 1, move 2).

Try It Again

After solving the puzzle of how to move the disks, students search for a relationship between the number of disks and number of moves required. It's fine if students work through the tables in **Questions 6 and 8** using the "double and add 1" rule on the outputs.

4. Predictions will vary. Each time a disk is added, the time is double the previous time, plus 1 min.

5. Predictions will vary. The correct answer is $2^{64} - 1$ min, or about 1.84×10^{19} min.

4. Predict how the total time required to solve the puzzle will change each time you increase the number of disks by 1.

5. Predict how long it would take to move all 64 disks. Write down your prediction so you can refer to it later.

Try It Out

Luckily, you don't need 64 golden disks to try the Tower of Hanoi puzzle. You can model it with some simple equipment. Your puzzle will have 5 "disks," rather than 64. You'll need a blank sheet of paper and five blocks, labeled 1, 2, 3, 4, and 5.

Label your paper with the letters A, B, and C as shown. Stack the blocks in numerical order, with 5 on the bottom, next to the A.

To solve the puzzle, you need to move all the blocks to another position—either B or C—following these rules:

- Move only one block at a time.
- Never put a larger number on a smaller number.

This is not an easy puzzle. To solve it, you might want to start with a puzzle using only 2 or 3 blocks. As you explore, look for a *systematic* way to move all the blocks to a new position.

Try It Again

6. Solve the puzzle again for towers of 1, 2, 3, 4, and 5 blocks. This time, count the number of moves it takes you to solve each puzzle. Record your data in a table.

Tower Height	1	2	3	4	5
Number of Moves	1	3	7	15	31

7. Describe any patterns you see that might help you make predictions about how many moves it would take for larger towers. See below.

8. Use your pattern to fill in a table like the one below. Then use a sixth cube to test your prediction for a tower of height 6.

Tower Height	6	7	8	9	10
Number of Moves	63	127	255	511	1,023

7. Possible answers: The number of moves for a tower is twice the number for the previous tower (the tower with one less disk), plus 1. *Or* the number of moves required to solve a puzzle of height $n + 1$ is the number required for height n, plus 2^n. *Or* the number of moves required for a tower of height n is $2^n - 1$.

1 Have students model the puzzle by using cubes.

2
- Be sure students know how to move disks (blocks).
- Help students articulate how number of moves grows.

Question 9 asks students to come up with an algebraic expression between the number of disks and the number of moves. This is not easy for students to generalize, so you may want to solve this problem as a whole class. Some students may recognize that all the numbers are odd but that the answer is not "the odd numbers." If no one notices that they are all 1 less than a power of 2, you may need to lead them down that road. Here's one way to do it. Ask students,

> Since each number is twice the previous number of moves plus 1, is the growth pattern more like $2x$, x^2, or 2^x?

From Lesson 3.2, they should realize that 2^x models double at each stage. But clearly these numbers are not exact powers of 2.

Copy the table in the text onto an overhead transparency or a blackboard, and add a third row for powers of 2.

2

Tower Height	1	2	3	4	5
Number of Moves	1	3	7	15	31
2^d	2 (2^1)	4 (2^2)	8 (2^3)	16 (2^4)	32 (2^5)

Have students help you fill in the powers of 2, and ask whether they see a relationship between the powers of 2 and the numbers in the "number of moves" row. They should notice that the number of moves is always 1 less than the corresponding power of 2. If the class can articulate that much, then help them write the expression $2^d - 1$.

Back to the Legend

Students finally have all the pieces they need to solve the puzzle of the legend: How long after the priests start this process will the world end? The answer is $2^{64} - 1$ minutes, which they must convert to years (or even centuries or millennia, if you wish) to get a sense of what that means.

Certainly once they have the expression or rule, students can plug that into their calculators to find the solution in scientific notation. If a scientific calculator is available, it will produce a display of 1.8446744 E 19 when 2^{64} is entered.

Dividing this number by 60, by 24, and by 365 gives 3.50965×10^{13} years. Written out on the board as 35,096,500,000,000, this number is rather impressive, particularly when you realize that the age of the planet Earth thus far is estimated by some scientists to be about 5 billion, or 5,000,000,000, years.

There are also some nice methods for estimating the magnitude of this time, if you want to work on those skills with your students.

If you work your way up to 64 disks in stages, 20 disks take $2^{20} - 1$, or 1,048,575, moves. If we round that to 1 million, then 21 disks will take about 2 million moves, 22 disks will take about 4 million moves, and so on. So with a base unit that every 20 disks increase the total by a factor of 1 million, then 40 disks can be seen to be approximately a million million.

Height	Moves
20	a million: 1,000,000
40	a million million: 1,000,000,000,000
60	a million million million: 1,000,000,000,000,000,000

Doubling last number for 61, again for 62, again for 63, and once more for 64, we have an estimate of 16 followed by 18 zeros. This can be divided by 60 to convert the final estimate into hours, by 24 for days, and by 365 for years.

What Did You Learn?

Questions 13–15 are intended as homework for students to process and then to share what they have learned. Question 14 asks students to put the length of time into context. Some students may realize that since the priests supposedly started at the beginning of time, they need to take the time from then to now into account. There are many estimates for the age of the universe. Most astronomers estimate the age between 10 and 20 billion years; 12 to 15 billion seems to be the most commonly accepted estimate. Biblical scholars who base their estimates on the number of generations discussed in the Bible usually place the age at around 6,000 years. Regardless of what students may use, the Hindu priests have at least several dozen billion years left to finish moving the disks.

9. Write an expression for the number of moves it would take to solve the puzzle for a tower of height t. (Hint: Add 1 to each entry in the second row of your table for Question 6, and then look at the pattern again.) $2^t - 1$

1 You may want to solve Question 9 as a whole class.

Back to the Legend

10. Assume the priests move one disk per minute. Figure out how long it would take them to solve the puzzle for the heights shown in the table below. Report the times in appropriate units. (After a while, minutes are not very useful.)

Tower Height	1	2	3	4	5	6	7	8	9	10
Number of Moves	1	3	7	15	31	63	127	255	511	1,023
Time	1 min	3 min	7 min	15 min	31 min	1 hr 3 min	2 hr 7 min	4 hr 15 min	8 hr 31 min	17 hr 3 min

2 Discuss table with related powers of 2.

11. $2^{64} - 1$ min = about 1.845×10^{19} min = about 3.510×10^{13} yr

11. How long would it take the priests to move all 64 disks? Give your answer in years. How does your answer compare to your prediction in Question 5?

12. You are able to move blocks at a much faster pace than one per minute. What if the disks the priests used were smaller and lighter, so they could also work faster?

a. If the priests move one disk per second, how long would it take them to finish? about 5.850×10^{11} yr

b. If they move 10 disks per second, how long would it take them to finish? about 5.850×10^{10} yr

What Did You Learn?

3
- Assign as homework.
- Have students share answers.

13, 14. See below.

13. When you move a piece in the Tower of Hanoi puzzle, you often have two choices of where to place it. Explain how you decide which move to make.

14. Suppose the legend is true and the priests can move pieces at the incredible rate of 10 per second. Do you think they are likely to finish the puzzle, causing the world to end, in your lifetime? Explain.

15. Write a newspaper article about the Tower of Hanoi puzzle. You might mention the legend and the time it takes to move the disks for towers of different heights. Articles will vary.

13. Possible answer: If one of the piles has a smaller disk on top, there's no choice. If the disk I'm moving is smallest and the number of pieces in the pile I am moving from is odd, I move the top disk to the pile I want it to end on. If the number of disks in the pile I am moving from is even, I move the top disk to the pile I don't want it to end on.

14. Possible answer: No; even at this fast rate, it will be a very long time before they finish. (See teaching notes for more information.)

LESSON 3.4 Describing Large Numbers 205

On Your Own Exercises

On Your Own Exercises

Investigation 1
Practice & Apply: 1–7
Connect & Extend: 39–42

Investigation 2
Practice & Apply: 8–22
Connect & Extend: 43–57

Investigation 3
Practice & Apply: 23–33
Connect & Extend: 58–59

Investigation 4
Practice & Apply: 34–38
Connect & Extend: 60–62

Assign Anytime
Mixed Review: 63–81

Exercise 1:
Another way to picture a million is to show a meter stick. One thousand meters contain 1 thousand thousand, or 1 million, millimeters.

Exercise 2:
This is a nice problem to discuss in class. You can save some calculation time by realizing that 16 quarters will take up about 1 cubic inch (1 inch in diameter by about 1 inch high). So, $\frac{1{,}000{,}000}{16}$, or 62,500, is the approximate number of cubic inches they will fill. Then you just have to convert the refrigerator's volume to cubic inches. 20 cubic feet is $20 \times (12 \times 12 \times 12)$, or 34,560, cubic inches.

Practice & Apply

1. How many millimeters are in a kilometer? 1 million

2. In this exercise, you will think about the volume of 1 million quarters.

   a. Imagine a box that has dimensions of 1 inch on each edge. What is the volume of the box? 1 in.^{3}

   b. Now imagine putting a stack of quarters in the box. How many quarters would fit in the box? (Notice that there will be some empty space because the quarters are round instead of square. For this exercise, don't worry about the extra space.) 16

   c. How many quarters would fit in a cubic foot of space? Explain. (Hint: Think carefully about the number of cubic inches in a cubic foot. It is not 12.)

   d. Would 1 million quarters fill your refrigerator? (If you can't measure your refrigerator, use 20 ft^3 as an estimate of the volume.)

3. In this exercise, you will figure out how far you would walk if you took 1 million steps and if you took 1 billion steps.

   a. Measure or estimate the length of a single step you take.

   b. If you took 1 million steps, about how far would you walk? Give your answer in miles. between 379 mi and 568 mi

   c. If you took 1 billion steps, about how far would you walk? Give your answer in miles. between 379,000 mi and 568,000 mi

   d. Do you think you will walk 1 million steps in your lifetime? What about 1 billion steps? Explain your answers.

Supply each missing value. For Exercises 6 and 7, give the answer in kilometers.

4.

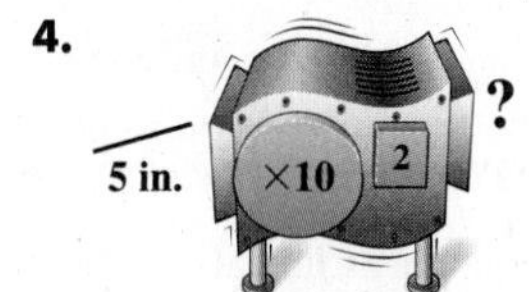

5.

6.

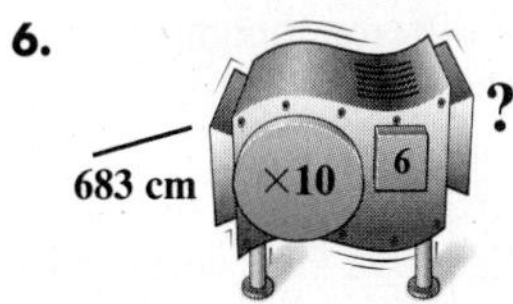

7.

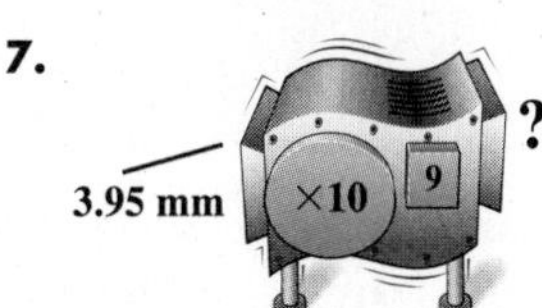

2c, 2d. See below.

3a. Answers will vary. An average stride is between 2 ft and 3 ft.

3d. Possible answer: I may walk 1 million steps, but I won't walk 1 billion. If I walk 5 mi a week, or 260 mi a year, for 60 yr, I'll walk 15,600 mi in my lifetime. This is somewhere between 27 million and 41 million steps. To walk 1 billion steps, I would have to walk 24 to 37 times as many miles, or between 120 mi and 185 mi every week for 60 yr.

4. 500 in.

5. 1,900,000 ft

6. 6,830 km

7. 3,950 km

2c. There are 1,728 in.^{3} in 1 ft^3, so $16 \times 1{,}728 = 27{,}648$ quarters fit in 1 ft^3.

2d. Answer for a 20-ft^3 refrigerator: Yes; 1 million quarters would fill a refrigerator ($20 \times 27{,}648 = 552{,}960$), with lots of quarters left over.

Find each product.

8. 4×10^3 4,000 **9.** 62×10^4 620,000 **10.** 15.8×10^2 1,580

Find each exponent.

11. 2

12. 4

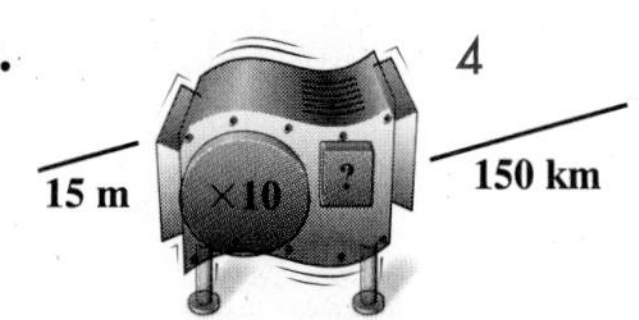

Find the value of N in each equation.

13. $8 \times 10^N = 80$ 1 **14.** $53 \times 10^N = 5{,}300$ 2

15. $9.9 \times 10^N = 99{,}000$ 4

Find the length of each input.

16. 0.125 in.

17. 2.8 m

18. 0.007545 km

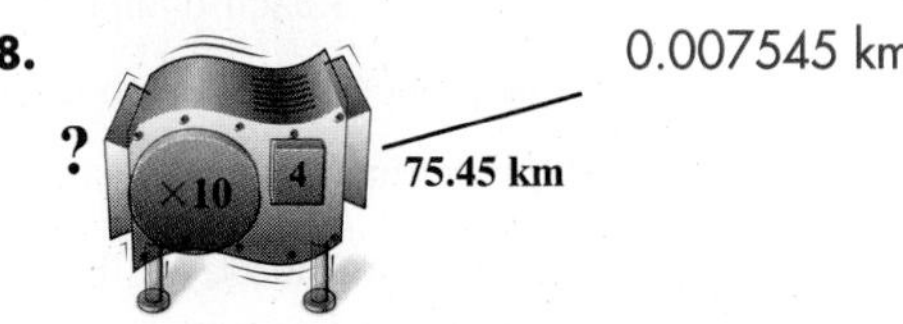

Find the value of N in each equation.

19. $N \times 10^2 = 900$ 9 **20.** $523 \times N = 52{,}300$ 10^2

21. $0.0614 \times N = 6.14$ 10^2 **22.** $N \times 10^6 = 39{,}650{,}000$ 39.65

Write each number in standard notation.

23. 8×10^1 80 **24.** 5×10^3 5,000

25. 7.5×10^2 750 **26.** 3.54×10^8 354,000,000

Exercise 3:
Students may not know the lengths of their paces, but they should be able to make a reasonable estimate of 1–2 feet per step. The goal is to relate what they have learned, especially lengths of time related to 1 million seconds and 1 billion seconds, and to realize it is unlikely, though possible, that anyone will take a billion steps in a lifetime. Student responses may include some of the following reasoning: A reasonable estimate is that it takes 1 second to take a step. If this is the case, walking 1 million steps would be equivalent to walking for 11 straight days. Over a lifetime, most people probably do walk that much. A billion steps, however, would be equivalent to walking for more than 30 years without a break. It is possible that someone who lived a long time and spent a lot of time walking could accomplish that, but most people would not.

Exercises 8–26:
These problems provide practice for multiplying by powers of 10.

Write each number in scientific notation.

27. 300 3×10^2 **28.** ten thousand 1×10^4

29. 158,000 1.58×10^5 **30.** 8,350,000,000 8.35×10^9

31. 183 billion 1.83×10^{11} **32.** 421,938,000,000,000 4.21938×10^{14}

33. Astronomy The table shows the mass of the planets in our solar system and of the sun and the moon.

Just the facts

Venus is the brightest planet in our solar system. It can often be seen in the morning and at night, and is sometimes called the Morning Star or the Evening Star.

Celestial Body	Mass (kg) Standard Notation	Mass (kg) Scientific Notation
Sun	1,990,000,000,000,000,000,000,000,000,000	1.99×10^{30}
Mercury	330,000,000,000,000,000,000,000	3.30×10^{23}
Venus	4,870,000,000,000,000,000,000,000	4.87×10^{24}
Earth	5,970,000,000,000,000,000,000,000	5.97×10^{24}
Mars	642,000,000,000,000,000,000,000	6.42×10^{23}
Jupiter	1,900,000,000,000,000,000,000,000,000	1.90×10^{27}
Saturn	568,000,000,000,000,000,000,000,000	5.68×10^{26}
Uranus	86,800,000,000,000,000,000,000,000	8.68×10^{25}
Neptune	102,000,000,000,000,000,000,000,000	1.02×10^{26}
Pluto	12,700,000,000,000,000,000,000	1.27×10^{22}
Moon	73,500,000,000,000,000,000,000	7.35×10^{22}

33a. See table.
33b. Pluto, the moon, Mercury, Mars, Venus, Earth, Uranus, Neptune, Saturn, Jupiter

a. Write the mass of each planet and the moon in scientific notation.

b. Order the planets and the moon by mass, from least to greatest.

c. Which planet has about the same mass as Earth? Venus

34. Refer to the table of masses in Exercise 33. Find how many times greater the mass of Earth is than the mass of each body.

a. Mercury 18 times **b.** Venus 1.23 times **c.** Mars 9.30 times

d. Pluto 470 times **e.** the moon 81.2 times

35. Refer to the table of masses in Exercise 33. Find how many times greater the mass of each body is than the mass of Earth.

a. the sun **b.** Jupiter 318 times **c.** Saturn 95.1 times

d. Uranus **e.** Neptune 17.1 times

35a. 3.33×10^5 times
35d. 14.5 times

208 CHAPTER 3 Exploring Exponents

Estimate the value of each expression. Then use your calculator to evaluate it. Give your answers in scientific notation.

36. $7.35 \times 10^{22} - 1.33 \times 10^{21}$ 7.217×10^{22}

37. $6.42 \times 10^{45} + 4.55 \times 10^{45}$ 1.097×10^{46}

38. $6.02 \times 10^{23} \times 15$ 9.03×10^{24}

39. Economics In this exercise, you will investigate what you could buy if you had \$1 million. To answer these questions, it might help to look at advertisements in the newspaper.

a. How many cars could you buy? Tell how much you are assuming each car costs. Possible answer: 50 cars at \$20,000 each

b. How many houses could you buy? Tell how much you are assuming each house costs.

39b. Possible answer: 10 houses at \$100,000 each

c. Make a shopping list of several items that total about \$1 million. Give the price of each item. Lists will vary.

40. Astronomy The average distance from Earth to the sun is 93,000,000 miles. How many of you, stacked on top of yourself, would it take to reach to the sun? Explain how you found your answer. See below.

Remember
12 in. = 1 ft
5,280 ft = 1 mi

41. How many dollars is 1 million quarters? 250,000

42. Count the number of times your heart beats in 1 minute.

a. At your current heart rate, approximately how many times has your heart beaten since your birth? Answers will vary.

b. How many times will your heart have beaten when you reach age 20? Answers will vary.

c. How many times will your heart have beaten when you reach age 80? Answers will vary.

43. A dollar bill is approximately 15.7 cm long.

a. How long would one thousand dollar bills laid end to end be? 157 m

b. How long would one million dollar bills laid end to end be? 157 km

c. The distance from Earth to the sun is about 1.5×10^8 km. How many dollar bills, taped together end to end, would it take to reach the sun? about 9.55×10^{11}

40. Possible answer: I am about 5 ft 3 in. tall, or 5.25 ft. It would take $5{,}280 \div 5.25$ = about 1,000 of me reach 1 mi, so it would take $93{,}000{,}000 \times 1{,}000 = 93{,}000{,}000{,}000$ of me to reach the sun.

Exercises 36–38:
You may want to go over these exercises with the whole class. Consider discussing a shortcut using the laws of exponents to solve Exercise 37. In Exercise 38, some students may multiply 6.02 by 15 to get 90.30×10^{23} and then rewrite the answer in proper scientific notation.

Exercise 39:
This exercise helps students get a sense for what a million dollars will buy. Why is it that lottery winners could spend all of their winnings within a few years? It's not that hard to do. You can ask the question, "If you had a million dollars, what would you do with it? How long would it last?" It's also a nice comparison with someone who has billions of dollars. That is really a *lot* more money.

Exercises 40–43:
Ask students which of these exercises they found particularly interesting. Ask them to explain why and how they solved the problem.

Assign and Assess

Exercises 52–57: These exercises preview the work students will do in Chapter 4 on negative exponents.

Find the length of each output.

44. 400 in. **45.** 84,000 ft

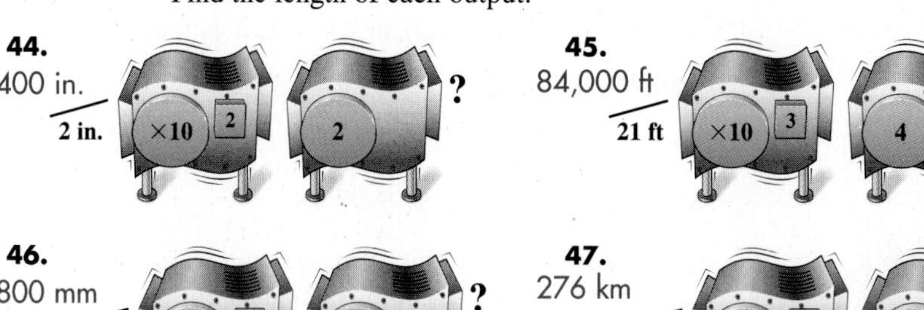

46. 800 mm **47.** 276 km

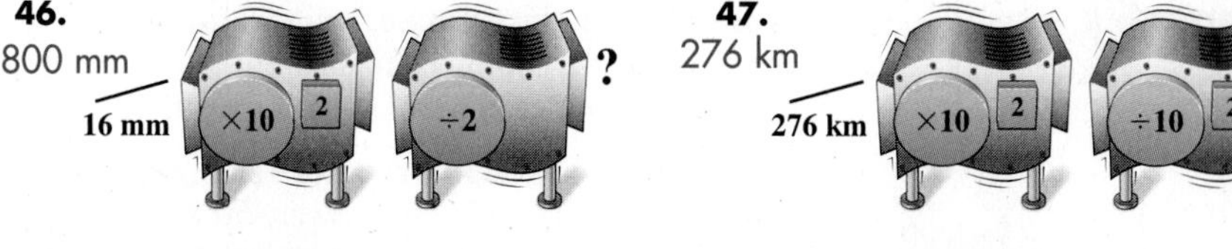

48. 2 in. **49.** 0.5 in.

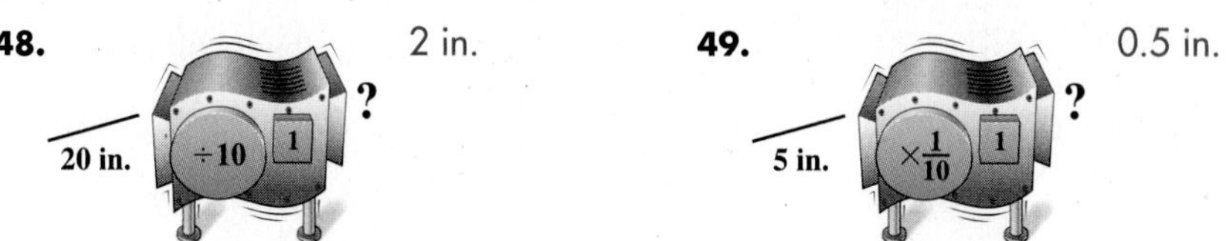

50. 3 in. **51.** 0.0005 in.

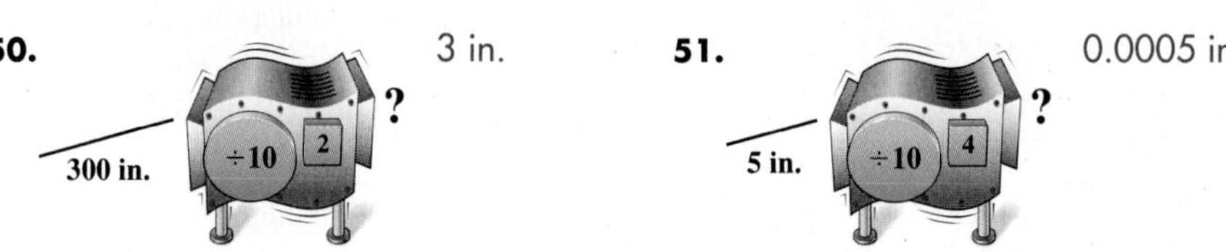

Find the value of N in each equation.

52. $N \times \frac{1}{10^2} = 8$ **53.** $N \times \frac{1}{10^4} = 12$ **54.** $N \times \frac{1}{10^6} = 4.927$

55. $17 \div 10^1 = N$ **56.** $128.4 \div 10^3 = N$ **57.** $714 \div 10^8 = N$

58. List these numbers from least to greatest.

a quarter of a billion	2.5×10^7	two thousand million
10^9	half a million	10^5

59. **Geometry** Suppose you arranged 10^3 1-cm cubes into a large cube.

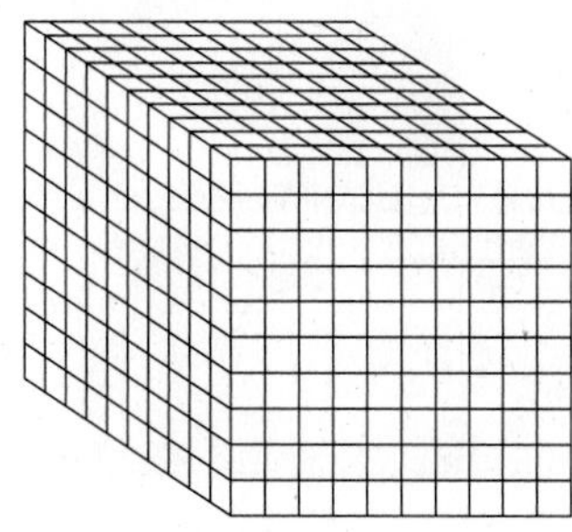

a. What is the length of an edge of the cube, in centimeters? 10

b. What is the volume of the cube, in cubic centimeters? 1,000, or 10^3

52. 800
53. 120,000
54. 4,927,000
55. 1.7
56. 0.1284
57. 0.00000714
58. 10^5, half a million, 2.5×10^7, a quarter of a billion, 10^9, two thousand million

210 CHAPTER 3 Exploring Exponents

In your own words

Explain why scientific notation is a useful way to write very large numbers.

Now suppose you arranged 10^6 1-cm cubes into a large cube.

c. What is the edge length of the new cube, in centimeters? What is the volume of the new cube, in cubic centimeters? 100, 10^6

d. What is the volume of the new cube, in cubic meters? What is the volume of the first large cube, in cubic meters? 1, 0.001

e. What is the area of a face of the new cube, in square centimeters?

59e. 10,000

60. Geometry Suppose you stacked 10^6 2-cm cubes into a tower. Part of the tower is shown here. What would be the height of the tower in meters? 2×10^4

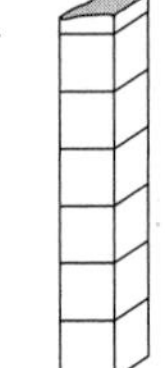

61. Preview Fill in the exponents below. (Hint: Fill in the exponents you know first. Then fill in the others by continuing the pattern.)

$5{,}000 = 5 \times 10^?$ 3
$500 = 5 \times 10^?$ 2
$50 = 5 \times 10^?$ 1
$5 = 5 \times 10^?$ 0
$0.5 = 5 \times 10^?$ −1
$0.05 = 5 \times 10^?$ −2

62b. About $139,000,000 in $1 bills will fill one freight car, so about 40,250 freight cars will be needed. $13.9 billion in $100 bills will fill a freight car, so about 403 freight cars would be needed.

Just the facts

You can find out today's estimated federal deficit at *www.brillig.com/debt_clock/* and the current U.S. population at *www.census.gov/cgi-bin/popclock.*

62. On December 10, 1998, the U.S. federal deficit was $5.5949 trillion, or $\$5.5949 \times 10^{12}$.

a. If the government could pay back $1 million each year, and the deficit did not increase, how long would it take to pay off the entire deficit? 5.5949 million years

b. A typical railway freight car measures 3 m × 4 m × 12 m. A dollar bill is approximately 15.7 cm long and 6.6 cm wide. A stack of 100 dollar bills is 1 cm high. How many freight cars would it take to carry the 1998 U.S. federal deficit in $1 bills? In $100 bills (a $100 bill is the same size as a $1 bill)? See above.

c. On December 10, 1998, the estimated population of the United States was 271,143,000. Imagine that every person in the country gave the government $1 each minute. How many times would you pay $1 during your math class? During a day (24 hours)? How long would it take to pay off the deficit? See below.

d. Invent another example to illustrate the size of the federal deficit. Examples will vary.

62c. Answers will vary depending on length of class; 1,440 times; 20,634 min, or 14.33 days

Exercise 62:
You may want to spend some time discussing this exercise in class. These kinds of comparisons are common in the media, and it would be interesting to discuss which ones are most powerful to the students and why. What did students choose as their models? Which ones give you a better sense for the magnitude of the debt—ones in which you think about your share of the debt or geometric ones in which you think about the number of dollar bills?

Quick Check

Informal Assessment

Students should be able to

- ✔ understand the relative difference between a million and a billion
- ✔ multiply and divide numbers by powers of 10
- ✔ write numbers using scientific notation
- ✔ use a calculator to work with numbers in scientific notation

Quick Quiz

Rewrite each number in standard notation.

1. 438×10^6 438,000,000
2. $\left(\frac{6}{10}\right)^2$ 0.36

Write each number in scientific notation.

3. 45,000,000 4.5×10^7
4. 239.4 2.394×10^2

Suppose you save $100 each month beginning now but stuff it in your mattress so you don't earn interest.

5. How old would you be by the time you saved 1 million dollars? Answers will vary, but should be more than 800 years.
6. How old will you be when you will have saved 1 billion dollars? Answers will vary, but should be more than 800,000 years.

Mixed Review

63. A block structure and its top engineering view are shown. What are the volume and surface area of this structure? 8 cubic units, 34 square units

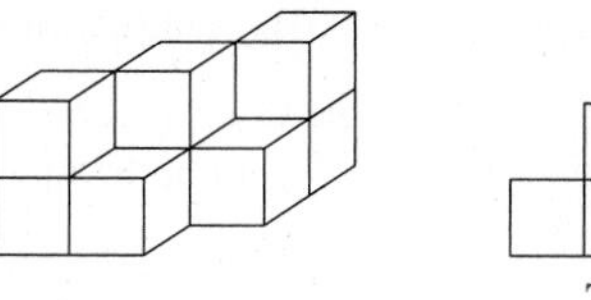

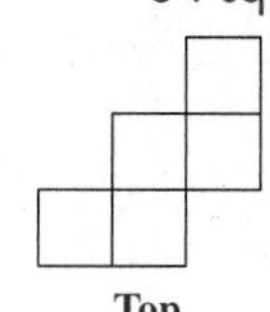

Top

64. Here is the top-count view of a block structure. What are the structure's volume and surface area? 16 cubic units, 48 square units

2	2	2	2
2	1	1	2
	1	1	

Decide whether each equation is true. If an equation is not true, rewrite the right side to make it true.

65. $(y + 1) \times 7 \doteq 7y + 7$

66. $(y - 1) \times 8 = y - 8$

67. $(3 + y) \times 7 = 3 \times 7 + y \times 7$

68. $2(4b + 1) = 8b + 2$

69. $2(4b + 4) = 8b + 4$

70. $1.5(A + 9) = 1.5A + 9.5$

Order each set of numbers from least to greatest.

71. $^{-}25, {}^{-}42, {}^{-}12, {}^{-}10$

72. $0, 5, {}^{-}5, {}^{-}2, {}^{-}2.5$

73. If a point on a graph has 0 as its x-coordinate, what do you know about the point's location? It is on the y-axis.

74. What does the graph of all points with 3 as their y-coordinate look like? a horizontal line 3 units above the x-axis

75. Name a point that lies to the right and above point (1, 3).

Answers:

65. true
66. false, $8y - 8$
67. true
68. true
69. false, $8b + 8$
70. false, $1.5A + 13.5$
71. $^{-}42, {}^{-}25, {}^{-}12, {}^{-}10$
72. $^{-}5, {}^{-}2.5, {}^{-}2, 0, 5$
75. any point for which $x > 1$ and $y > 3$

Evaluate each expression.

76. 0.25×0.4 0.1

77. 0.25×4 1

78. 0.25×0.1 0.025

79. 0.04×0.04 0.0016

80. 0.02×4 0.08

81. 0.2×0.7 0.14

7. Will one billion dollar bills fit in your mattress? Explain any assumptions you make and show your work. Answers will vary, but students will probably say no.

212 CHAPTER 3 Exploring Exponents

Chapter Summary

VOCABULARY
base
exponent
exponential decay
exponential decrease
exponential growth
exponential increase
power
scientific notation

In this chapter, stretching and shrinking machines helped you understand the laws of exponents.

Product Laws	Quotient Laws	Power of a Power Law
$a^b \times a^c = a^{b+c}$	$a^b \div a^c = a^{b-c}$	$(a^b)^c = a^{b \times c}$
$a^c \times b^c = (a \times b)^c$	$a^c \div b^c = (a \div b)^c$	

You looked at quantities that grow exponentially, and investigated how exponential and constant growth differ. You explored situations in which quantities decrease exponentially. You learned how to recognize exponential growth and decay in tables, expressions, and written descriptions.

You worked on problems that helped you develop a sense of large numbers like a million and a billion. You learned about powers of 10, and you found that sometimes it is useful to express large numbers in scientific notation.

Strategies and Applications

The questions in this section will help you review and apply the important ideas and strategies developed in this chapter.

Working with stretching and shrinking machines

Supply the missing information for each diagram.

1. ? → ×6 → 42 ft

2. 4 cm → ×3, ? → 36 cm

1. 7 ft
2. 2

3. 12.9 m → ×10, 5 → ?

4. 24 in. → $\times\frac{1}{10}$, 2 → ?

3. 1,290,000 m
4. 0.24 in.

If a 1-cm stick of gum is sent through each super machine, how long will it be when it exits?

5.

6. ×3, 2, 4

5. 2^{12} cm, or 4,096 cm
6. 3^8 cm, or 6,561 cm

Chapter Summary
This summary helps students recall the major topics of the chapter.

Vocabulary
Students should be able to explain each of the terms listed in the vocabulary section.

Strategies and Applications
The questions in this section help students review and apply the important mathematical ideas and problem-solving strategies developed in the chapter.

The questions are organized by mathematical highlight. The highlights correspond to those in "The Big Picture" chart on page T143a.

Exercise 2: Watch for students who may not recognize that the question mark takes the place of the exponent in the repeater machine. Some may think of 3 × 3, rather than the correct solution of 3^2.

Exercise 4: Make sure students understand that the decimal should move to the left when multiplying by powers of $\frac{1}{10}$.

Review and Self-Assessment 213

Exercise 10: Students may come up with a variety of responses to this question. Some will note that if you multiply a by itself b times, and divide a by itself c times the inverse operations cancel each other out, leaving $(b - c)$ a's.

Others may think about the machine model, where every $\times a$ is "undone" by a $\div a$, leaving $(b - c)$ $\times a$'s. Some may accompany these explanations with a picture that shows how the operations undo each other.

Exercise 11: This may be challenging for students. Some may want to start with a problem that they know has an answer of 1, using exponents, such as $2^4 \div 2^4$. Since the numerator and denominator are the same, the answer must be 1. But using the division law of exponents, we know that $2^4 \div 2^4 = 2^{4-4} = 2^0$, and therefore $2^0 = 1$. [Refer to the answer to this question for another explanation using machines.]

Exercise 12: Students may make the mistake of thinking that x^2 is an exponential rule since it contains an exponent. Ask students to complete the table for x^2. As they move from one value in the table to the next, that is, 0, 1, 4, 9, 16, 25, are they multiplying by a constant number? Students should notice that for x^2, there is not a constant ratio between terms.

7. $\times 6^9$
8. $\times 0.5^4$

Find a single repeater machine to do the same work as each hookup.

7. **8.**

9. How long will the gummy worm be when it exits this hookup? Give your answer in meters. 80 m

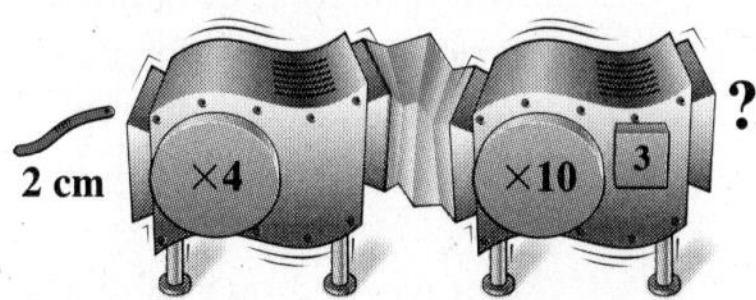

Understanding the laws of exponents

10, 11. See Additional Answers.

10. Explain why $a^b \div a^c = a^{b-c}$. You can refer to stretching and shrinking machines if they help you explain.

11. Explain why $2^0 = 1$. You can refer to stretching and shrinking machines if they help you explain.

Identifying and working with exponential growth

12. The table shows the values of several expressions containing x.

x	0	1	2	3	4	5
$3x$	0	3	6	9	12	15
2^x	1	2	4	8	16	32
x^2	0	1	4	9	16	25

a. Complete the table.

b. Which expression grows at a constant rate? Explain.

c. Which expression grows exponentially? Explain.

12b. $3x$; Each time x increases by 1, a constant amount (3) is added to $3x$.

12c. 2^x; Each time x increases by 1, 2^x is multiplied by the same number (2).

13. It is said that some Swiss banks are still holding the funds of people who died in the collapse of the Hapsburg Empire in Europe. The accounts keep growing, but no one has come forward to claim the fortunes. Suppose someone invested \$100 in a Swiss bank in 1798, and that the account earned 7% interest each year. This means that the amount each year is 1.07 times the amount the previous year.

a. How much money is in the account at the end of the first year? \$107

b. How much money is in the account at the end of the second year? \$114.49

Additional Answers

10. Possible answer: If you put a stick through a $\times a^b$ machine and then through a $\div a^c$ machine, each $\div a$ shrink cancels a $\times a$ stretch, leaving $(b - c)$ stretches.

11. Possible answer: A $\times 2^0$ machine doubles the length of a stick 0 times. In other words, it doesn't change the length. This is the same as putting the stick through a $\times 1$ machine.

c. Copy and complete the table to show how the account grows for the first four years after it is opened.

Year after 1798	Amount
0 (1798)	100
1	100×1.07^1
2	$100 \times 1.07 \times 1.07 = 100 \times 1.07^2$
3	$100 \times 1.07 \times 1.07 \times 1.07 = 100 \times 1.07^3$
4	$100 \times 1.07 \times 1.07 \times 1.07 \times 1.07 = 100 \times 1.07^4$

13d. 100×1.07^n

d. Write an expression for the amount in the account after *n* years.

e. How much money was in the account in 1998, 200 years after it was opened? \$75,293,162.17

Developing a sense of large numbers

14. What repeater machine will stretch a stick 1 million miles long into a stick 1 billion miles long? $\times 10^3$

15. Which is worth more: a billion \$1 bills, or a 100 million \$1 bills? a billion \$1 bills

Expressing large numbers in scientific notation

16. Explain how to write a large number in scientific notation. Use an example to demonstrate your method.

17. Explain how to write $1{,}234 \times 10^9$ in scientific notation.

16. See Additional Answers.

17. Divide 1,234 by 1,000 to get 1.234. To compensate, multiply 10^9 by 1,000, or 10^3, to get 10^{12}. The number in scientific notation is 1.234×10^{12}.

Demonstrating Skills

Rewrite each expression in exponential notation.

18. $3^2 \times 27$ 3^5 **19.** $3 \times d \times d \times d \times 2 \times d$ $6d^4$

Write each expression in the form 4^c.

20. $\frac{4^5}{4^3}$ 4^2 **21.** $4^5 \times 4^7$ **22.** $(4^3)^5$ **23.** 4×4^7 **24.** $\frac{4^6}{4^6}$

21. 4^{12}
22. 4^{15}
23. 4^8
24. 4^0

Find the value of N in each equation.

25. $3.56 \times 10^N = 356$ 2 **26.** $N \times 10^5 = 6{,}541$ 0.06541

27. $0.23 \times 10^3 = N$ 230 **28.** $N \times \frac{1}{10^5} = 0.34$ 34,000

Write each number in scientific notation.

29. 123,000 **30.** 57,700,000 **31.** 45×10^6

29. 1.23×10^5
30. 5.77×10^7
31. 4.5×10^7

Exercise 15: This may be counter-intuitive for students, since 100 million dollar bills may sound like it is more money than a billion dollar bills. Watch for students who have difficulty multiplying 100 times 1 million. Ask them to do the multiplication in exponential form, as well, if they are having difficulty.

Exercise 18: Students need to convert 27 to 3^3 before they multiply by 3^2.

Exercises 26–28: Ask students if they can tell just by looking at the problems whether the decimal will move to the right or to the left.

Exercises 29–31: Watch for common mistakes. Make sure that students are moving the decimal point correctly to equalize the powers of 10. You might ask them to be sure they have the same number they started with after they change the power of 10.

Additional Answers

16. Possible answer: Imagine there is a decimal point at the right end of the number. Move the decimal to the left until you have a number between 1 and 10. Multiply this number by 10 raised to the number of decimal places you moved. For the number 336,000,000, you move the decimal 8 places to get 3.36, so the number in scientific notation is 3.36×10^8.

Review and Self-Assessment **215**

CHAPTER 4

Working with Signed Numbers

Chapter Overview

The chapter begins with a Lab Investigation to introduce addition and subtraction with signed numbers. Students play a game that is a prelude to the "walking the number line" model. As students develop their understanding of signed numbers, they move from the concrete model to a more abstract level of thinking in Investigation 2. Students build on this understanding as they learn how to multiply and divide with signed numbers. Graphing on the coordinate plane is introduced, and students learn how to calculate lengths on a coordinate graph using the Pythagorean theorem and the distance formula. Finally, students learn to evaluate expressions involving negative exponents.

Chapter 4 Highlights	Links to the Past	Links to the Future
Adding and subtracting with signed numbers (4.1)	**Course 1:** Understanding the concept of negative numbers	**Chapter 6 and Course 3:** Adding and subtracting with negative numbers in the context of algebra
Multiplying and dividing with signed numbers (4.2)	**Course 1:** Understanding the concept of negative numbers	**Chapter 6 and Course 3:** Multiplying an dividing with negative numbers in the context of algebra **Grade 8:** Solving problems involving negative percent change
Working with points in all four quadrants (4.3)	**Course 1:** Graphing in the first quadrant	**Chapter 5, Chapter 9, and Course 3:** Graphing in four quadrants as a way to represent information
Calculating lengths using the Pythagorean Theorem and the distance formula (4.4)	**Grade 6:** Using the Pythagorean Theorem	**Course 3:** Exploring how scaling figures on the coordinate plane affects lengths
Evaluating expressions involving negative exponents (4.5)	**Chapter 3:** Evaluating fractional expressions with exponents in the denominator	**Course 3:** Reviewing negative exponents and using scientific notation to represent very small numbers

Lesson Objectives	Pacing	Materials	NCTM Standards
4.1 Adding and Subtracting with Negative Numbers page 217b • To add and subtract signed numbers • To use number sense when working with signed numbers • To predict the sign of a sum or difference involving negative and positive numbers	5 class periods (6 class periods with Lab)	• Master 19, or a copy of the Captain's Game Plank • Master 20 • Master 21 • Master 22 • Master 23 • Master 24 • Blank sheets of paper • Paper arrow • Direction cube with 3 faces labeled *Ship* and 3 faces labeled *Shark* • Walking cube with faces labeled *F1, F2, F3, B1, B2,* and *B3*	1, 2, 4, 6, 7, 9
4.2 Multiplying and Dividing with Negative Numbers page 241b • To multiply and divide with signed numbers • To predict the sign of a product or quotient involving signed numbers • To develop number sense with signed numbers	3 class periods		1, 2, 4, 5, 6, 9
4.3 Plotting Points in Four Quadrants page 253b • To create and interpret four-quadrant graphs • To use the distinguishing characteristics of points in the four quadrants and on the two axes to analyze graphs • To think more flexibly about operations with signed numbers	3 class periods	• Master 25 • Master 26 • Blue, black, or red pens or pencils	1, 2, 3, 4, 6, 9
4.4 Finding Distances page 267b • To understand a variety of ways to compare lengths of line segments on a graph • To apply the Pythagorean theorem or distance formula when finding lengths of line segments on a graph • To describe how the Pythagorean theorem and distance formula are related	2 class periods	• Master 25 or graph paper	1, 2, 3, 4, 5, 6, 9
4.5 Negative Numbers as Exponents page 279b • To relate negative exponents to both multiplication by fractions and repeated division • To evaluate simple expressions with negative exponents • To apply laws of exponents to expressions with negative exponents • To write numbers in scientific notation with negative exponents	3 class periods		1, 2, 4, 6, 9

NCTM Curriculum and Evaluation Standards

1. Number and Operation
2. Patterns, Functions, and Algebra
3. Geometry and Spatial Sense
4. Measurement
5. Data Analysis, Statistics, and Probability
6. Problem Solving
7. Reasoning and Proof
8. Communication
9. Connections
10. Representation

Assessment Opportunities

Standard Assessment

Impact Mathematics offers three types of formal assessment. The Chapter 4 Review & Self-Assessment in the Student Edition serves as a self-assessment tool for students. In the Teacher's Guide, a Quick Quiz at the end of each lesson allows you to check students' understanding before moving to the next lesson. The Assessment Resources include blackline masters for chapter and semester tests.

- **Student Edition** Chapter 4 Review & Self-Assessment, pages 293–297
- **Teacher's Guide** Quick Quizzes, pages 241, 253, 267, 279, and 292
- **Assessment Resources** Chapter 4 Test, Form A, pages 57–61; Chapter 4 Test, Form B, pages 62–66

Ongoing Assessment

Impact Mathematics provides numerous opportunities for informal assessment of your students as they work through the investigations. Share & Summarize questions help you determine whether students understand the important ideas of an investigation. If students are struggling, Troubleshooting tips provide suggestions for helping them. On the Spot Assessment notes appear throughout the teaching notes. They give you suggestions for preventing or remedying common student errors. Assessment Forms in the Assessment Resources provide convenient ways to record student progress.

- **Student Edition** Share & Summarize, pages 227, 230, 233, 235, 244, 247, 249, 258, 262, 263, 272, 275, 284, 285, 287
- **Teacher's Guide** On the Spot Assessment, pages T225, T228, T233, T244, T246, T247, T255, T260, T274, T275, T281, T283, T285, T286
  Troubleshooting, pages T227, T230, T233, T235, T244, T247, T249, T258, T262, T263, T272, T275, T284, T285, T287
- **Assessment Resources** Chapter 4 Assessment Checklists, pages 109–110

Alternative Assessment, Portfolios, and Journal Ideas

The alternative assessment items in *Impact Mathematics* are perfect for inclusion in student portfolios and journals. The In Your Own Words feature in the Student Edition gives students a chance to write about mathematical ideas. The Performance Assessment items in the Assessment Resources provide rich, open-ended problems, ideal for take-home assessment.

- **Student Edition** In Your Own Words, pages 240, 250, 266, 276, 291
- **Assessment Resources** Chapter 4 Performance Assessment, pages 67–68

Assessment Resources

The Assessment Resources provide a chapter test in two equivalent forms, along with additional performance items. The performance items can be used in a variety of ways. They are ideal for take-home assessment or in-class assessment.

- Chapter 4 Test, Form A, pages 57–61
- Chapter 4 Test, Form B, pages 62–66
- Chapter 4 Performance Assessment, pages 67–68
- Chapter 4 Assessment Solutions, pages 69–72

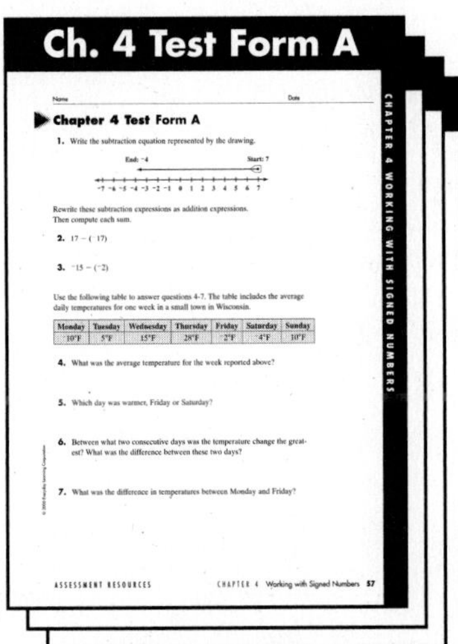
Ch. 4 Test Form A

Name Date

Chapter 4 Test Form A

1. Write the subtraction equation represented by the drawing.

Rewrite these subtraction expressions as addition expressions. Then compute each sum.

2. $17 - (^{-}17)$

3. $^{-}15 - (^{-}2)$

Use the following table to answer questions 4-7. The table includes the average daily temperatures for one week in a small town in Wisconsin.

Monday	Tuesday	Wednesday	Thursday	Friday	Saturday	Sunday
10°F	5°F	15°F	28°F	$^{-}2$°F	$^{-}4$°F	10°F

4. What was the average temperature for the week reported above?

5. Which day was warmer, Friday or Saturday?

6. Between what two consecutive days was the temperature change the greatest? What was the difference between these two days?

7. What was the difference in temperatures between Monday and Friday?

CHAPTER 4 WORKING WITH SIGNED NUMBERS

ASSESSMENT RESOURCES CHAPTER 4 Working with Signed Numbers 57

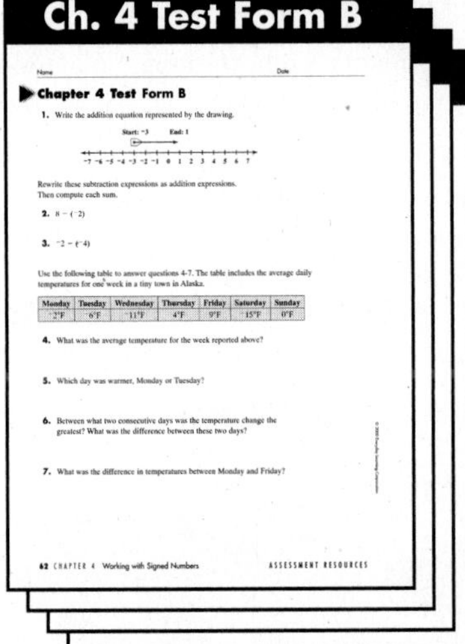
Ch. 4 Test Form B

Name Date

Chapter 4 Test Form B

1. Write the addition equation represented by the drawing.

Rewrite these subtraction expressions as addition expressions. Then compute each sum.

2. $8 - (^{-}2)$

3. $^{-}2 - (^{-}4)$

Use the following table to answer questions 4-7. The table includes the average daily temperatures for one week in a tiny town in Alaska.

Monday	Tuesday	Wednesday	Thursday	Friday	Saturday	Sunday
$^{-}2$°F	$^{-}6$°F	$^{-}11$°F	4°F	9°F	$^{-}15$°F	0°F

4. What was the average temperature for the week reported above?

5. Which day was warmer, Monday or Tuesday?

6. Between what two consecutive days was the temperature change the greatest? What was the difference between these two days?

7. What was the difference in temperatures between Monday and Friday?

62 CHAPTER 4 Working with Signed Numbers ASSESSMENT RESOURCES

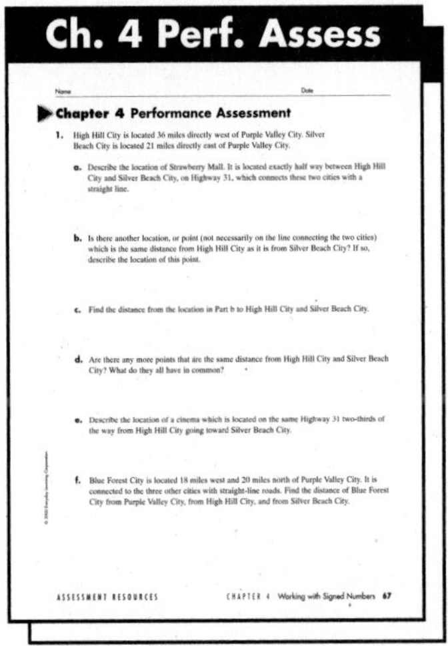
Ch. 4 Perf. Assess

Name Date

Chapter 4 Performance Assessment

1. High Hill City is located 36 miles directly west of Purple Valley City. Silver Beach City is located 21 miles directly east of Purple Valley City.

   a. Describe the location of Strawberry Mall. It is located exactly half way between High Hill City and Silver Beach City, on Highway 31, which connects these two cities with a straight line.

   b. Is there another location, or point (not necessarily on the line connecting the two cities) which is the same distance from High Hill City as it is from Silver Beach City? If so, describe the location of this point.

   c. Find the distance from the location in Part b to High Hill City and Silver Beach City.

   d. Are there any more points that are the same distance from High Hill City and Silver Beach City? What do they all have in common?

   e. Describe the location of a cinema which is located on the same Highway 31 two-thirds of the way from High Hill City going toward Silver Beach City.

   f. Blue Forest City is located 18 miles west and 20 miles north of Purple Valley City. It is connected to the three other cities with straight-line roads. Find the distance of Blue Forest City from Purple Valley City, from High Hill City, and from Silver Beach City.

ASSESSMENT RESOURCES CHAPTER 4 Working with Signed Numbers 67

Additional Resources

Print	Software	Video	Web sites
Operations on Integers by Julie King and Peter Rasmussen, Curriculum Press, 1990 This student workbook, the first in a series of ten workbooks, uses simple language and provides clear examples with traditional exercises that reinforce concepts. It focuses on general operations with integers. *Middle School Mathematics with Color Tiles* by William J. Masalski, Scott Resources, 1994 This teacher resource contains activities that use one-inch square tiles to explore mathematical concepts, including operations on integers.	*In the Neighborhood: Fundamental Operations & Elementary Algebraic Expressions,* Critical Thinking Books & Software IBM compatible This is a game individuals, small groups, or the whole class can play against the computer or themselves. Skills range from simple addition to all four operations with both positive and negative exponents. *Math Blaster Knowledge Adventure* This software reviews addition, subtraction, multiplication, and division of positive and negative numbers.	*Integers,* GPN (Lincoln, NE), 1996 This video is part of the MATH VANTAGE series developed by the Nebraska Mathematics and Science Coalition. It presents positive and negative numbers as key elements needed to communicate ideas in a variety of fields. *Operations on Signed Numbers,* Education Video Resources, 1993 This tutorial video is part of the MATH MADE EASY: FUNDAMENTALS OF PRE-ALGEBRA series. In the video, students are introduced to absolute value, operations with signed numbers, and the order of algebraic operations as well as other algebraic topics.	Visit the Everyday Learning Web site at **http://www.everydaylearning.com** *Windows to the Universe* **http://windows.ivv.nasa.gov/** This site provides information about earth and space sciences. You can access data on negative temperatures on planets and other places in space. *Public Debt Online* **http://www.publicdebt.treas.gov/** This site provides background information on the United States public debt and current figures on the United States debt.

Introduction
Before having students read the chapter opener, you might engage the students in a discussion about how they would measure elevation. How would you compare the elevation of Mt. Rainier and Mt. Everest? Clearly, there is a need for some kind of elevation scale. Once the need for a scale is established, you and your students can discuss where to set the 0 mark on the scale. If there were a point on Earth with the lowest elevation, it might make sense to measure elevation of other points from that point.

However, if a place were discovered with an elevation lower than the point thought to have the lowest elevation, then this new place would have an elevation less than 0. Thus, an elevation scale *must* involve negative numbers, so it becomes necessary to look for a natural, intuitive place from which to measure elevation. The level of the ocean intuitively makes sense since it is the breakpoint between land and water.

CHAPTER 4

Working with Signed Numbers

What do temperatures, elevations, and golf scores have in common? They all involve signed numbers. In this chapter, you will learn how to work with signed numbers that appear in sums, differences, products, quotients, exponents, and graphs.

Soaring to New Heights

How high is the highest mountain? How deep is the deepest part of the ocean? How are height and depth measured?

We call height and depth *elevation,* and we measure elevation from sea level, the average level of the ocean. Parts of the world that are at sea level have an elevation of 0. Denver, the "mile-high" city, is approximately 1 mile above sea level; its elevation is approximately 1 mile. Death Valley, shown in the background, is 282 feet below sea level; we say that its elevation is $^{-}282$ feet.

Mt. Everest, situated in the Himalayas of Nepal, is the highest point on Earth. It has an elevation of 29,028 feet.

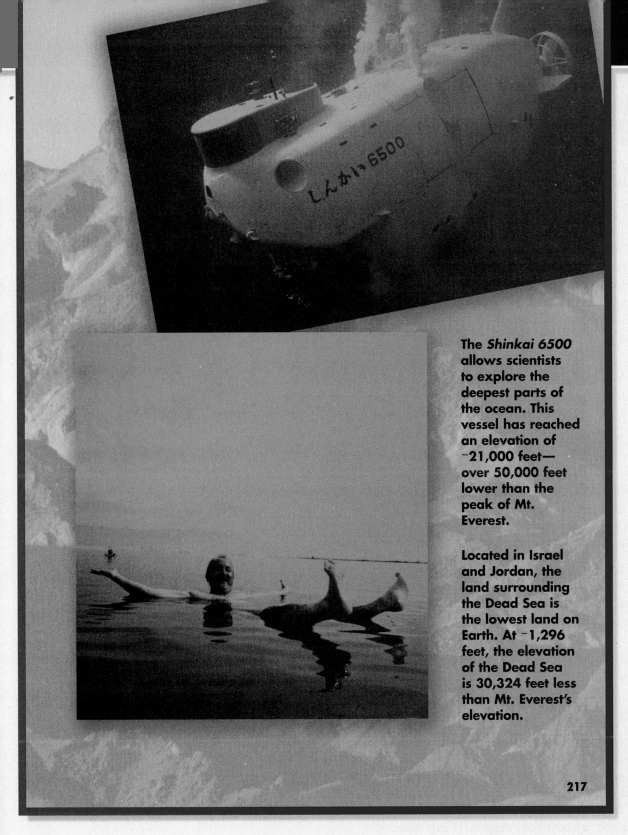

The *Shinkai 6500* allows scientists to explore the deepest parts of the ocean. This vessel has reached an elevation of $^-21,000$ feet—over 50,000 feet lower than the peak of Mt. Everest.

Located in Israel and Jordan, the land surrounding the Dead Sea is the lowest land on Earth. At $^-1,296$ feet, the elevation of the Dead Sea is 30,324 feet less than Mt. Everest's elevation.

After engaging the students in a discussion about measuring elevation, have students read the chapter opener. Some seas like the Dead Sea are at elevations below sea level, so the term seems contradictory. Emphasize that sea level is really the average level of the oceans. Your students might be interested in knowing the elevation of your town or city, so you might want to have that information on hand for the discussion.

You might ask your students some questions about the opening spread. It previews some of the topics in the chapter. For example, what is the difference in elevation between the Dead Sea and the deepest point in the ocean that the *Shinkai 6500* has reached? Asking these kind of questions can help students begin thinking about negative numbers and help you assess their understanding of negative numbers.

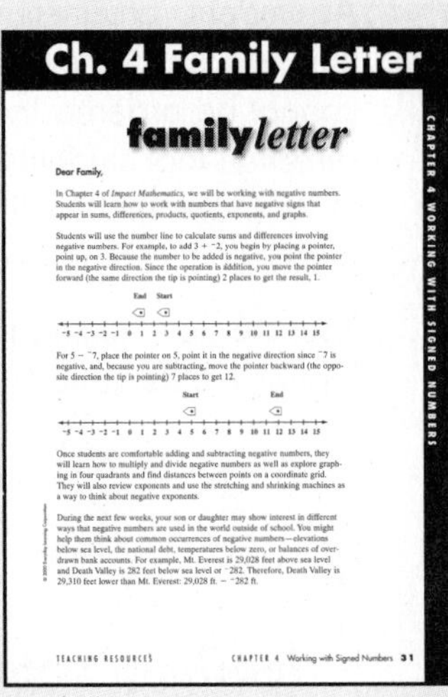

Ch. 4 Family Letter

family*letter*

CHAPTER 4 WORKING WITH SIGNED NUMBERS

Dear Family,

In Chapter 4 of *Impact Mathematics*, we will be working with negative numbers. Students will learn how to work with numbers that have negative signs that appear in sums, differences, products, quotients, exponents, and graphs.

Students will use the number line to calculate sums and differences involving negative numbers. For example, to add $3 + {}^-2$, you begin by placing a pointer, point up, on 3. Because the number to be added is negative, you point the pointer in the negative direction. Since the operation is addition, you move the pointer forward (the same direction the tip is pointing) 2 places to get the result, 1.

For $5 - {}^-7$, place the pointer on 5, point it in the negative direction since $^-7$ is negative, and, because you are subtracting, move the pointer backward (the opposite direction the tip is pointing) 7 places to get 12.

Once students are comfortable adding and subtracting negative numbers, they will learn how to multiply and divide negative numbers as well as explore graphing in four quadrants and find distances between points on a coordinate grid. They will also review exponents and use the stretching and shrinking machines as a way to think about negative exponents.

During the next few weeks, your son or daughter may show interest in different ways that negative numbers are used in the world outside of school. You might help them think about common occurrences of negative numbers—elevations below sea level, the national debt, temperatures below zero, or balances of overdrawn bank accounts. For example, Mt. Everest is 29,028 feet above sea level and Death Valley is 282 feet below sea level or $^-282$. Therefore, Death Valley is 29,310 feet lower than Mt. Everest: 29,028 ft. $-$ $^-282$ ft.

TEACHING RESOURCES CHAPTER 4 Working with Signed Numbers **31**

Mathematical Background

This chapter explores two important mathematical territories: the arithmetic of signed numbers and finding distance using the Pythagorean theorem.

For many people, signed-number arithmetic is a problem area. Though the rules of signed-number arithmetic are sometimes hard to state in words, the patterns make sense once the concept of signed numbers is clear.

Until we encounter signed numbers for the first time, we have a sense of numbers meaning "how much" there is of something: how much money, how much weight, how much time. Negative numbers can also be thought of that way—how much debt, for example. The idea that a debt is "negative money" can sometimes help students think about signed-number arithmetic, but it may be a subtle idea.

Here's the subtlety. We say that $^{-}5$ *is less than* $^{-}2$, because negative 5 is to the left of negative 2 on the number line. But if we are relating negative numbers to debts, we also say (correctly) that $^{-}5$ represents a *greater* debt. How can $^{-}5$ be both less than and greater than $^{-}2$?

Sometimes we need to think about the *magnitude* of a number (also called the *absolute value* of the number, or how far the number is from zero) independently from the "direction" of that distance. We encounter this distinction in real life. Distance from the surface of the Earth (in the air or down a mine shaft) is positive, but altitude or elevation includes direction and can be positive or negative. In fact, distance, including the "distance" a number is from 0, is always positive. Speed is independent of direction; velocity includes direction.

When we think of greater and lesser debts, we are looking only at the magnitude of the debt and ignoring the fact that it is all debt (all "negative"). When we think of bank balances, we must keep track of sign as well as magnitude, in order to know whether the balance is positive or negative.

When we say that $^{-}5 < {}^{-}2$ or that $5 > {}^{-}20$, we are talking about order on a number line. The set of all real numbers (numbers like $^{-}\frac{3}{8}$, 2π, $4\frac{2}{3}$, 43.618, $^{-}0.00001$, 1.27×10^{-23}, 0, $^{-}12$, and so on) has a property called *order* that makes such comparisons possible. All numbers on the number line are real numbers; all real numbers are points on the number line.

As students progress into more advanced mathematics and physics in high school, they will encounter other numbers (complex numbers, for example, and vectors) that *cannot* be ordered the way the real numbers can. But the ideas of *magnitude* and *direction* that students are learning right now will hold for these new numbers as well; in fact, arithmetic with these new numbers will be very similar to arithmetic with signed numbers in that it takes into account both magnitude and direction.

You are now setting the foundation both for keeping bank balances straight and for higher mathematics!

• ***Teaching notes continued on page A389.***

4.1

Adding and Subtracting with Negative Numbers

Objectives

- To add and subtract signed numbers
- To use number sense when working with signed numbers
- To predict the sign of a sum or difference involving negative and positive numbers

Overview (pacing: about 5 class periods)

Students begin this lesson by "walking the number line" to learn how to compute sums of signed numbers. They go on to identify several equivalent operations and then solve simple inequalities on an intuitive level. The lesson closes by having students predict the sign of sums and differences of positive and negative numbers. Students should not use calculators while they are learning how to add and subtract signed numbers. After they have completed this chapter, they can use a calculator.

Advance Preparation

You will need Master 19, Captain's Game Plank, Master 20, Plank Table, as well as several sheets of blank paper. You will also need a direction cube with three faces labeled *Ship* and three faces labeled *Shark,* and a walking cube with faces labeled *F1, F2, F3, B1, B2,* and *B3* to use in the Lab Investigation. You will need Masters 21, 22, 23, and 24, which are different types of number lines, to use in Investigations 1–2.

	Summary	Materials	On Your Own Exercises	Assessment Opportunities
Lab Investigation page T220	The lab investigation gives students a kinesthetic experience similar to walking on the number line that allows them to begin to think about adding and subtracting with signed numbers on an informal level.	• Master 19 (Teaching Resources, page 33) • Master 20 (Teaching Resources, page 34) • Several blank sheets of paper • Paper arrow • Direction cube with 3 labeled faces • Walking cube with labeled faces		
Investigation 1 page T222	Students are introduced to the "walking the number line" model for adding and subtracting with signed numbers. Students create number line pictures to represent the "walking the number line" model.	• Master 21 (Teaching Resources, page 35) • Master 22 (Teaching Resources, page 36) • Master 23 (Teaching Resources, page 37)	Practice & Apply: 1–25 Connect & Extend: 38–39 Mixed Review: 62–82	Share & Summarize, pages T227, 227 On the Spot Assessment, page T225 Troubleshooting, page T227
Investigation 2 page T228	Students use the number line pictures to discover two sets of equivalent operations.	• Master 23 • Master 24 (Teaching Resources, pages 38–40)	Practice & Apply: 26–32 Connect & Extend: 40–41 Mixed Review: 62–82	Share & Summarize, pages T230, 230 On the Spot Assessment, page T228 Troubleshooting, page T230
Investigation 3 page T231	Students solve problems set in contexts that require they add and subtract with negative numbers. Students then solve simple inequalities using intuitive methods that require a firm understanding of adding and subtracting with signed numbers.		Practice & Apply: 33–34 Connect & Extend: 42–56 Mixed Review: 62–82	Share & Summarize, pages T233, 233 On the Spot Assessment, page T233 Troubleshooting, page T233
Investigation 4 page T234	Students predict the sign of sums and differences involving signed numbers. For example, they discover that the sum of two negatives is always negative, while the sum of a negative and a positive can be negative, positive, or zero.		Practice & Apply: 35–37 Connect & Extend: 57–61 Mixed Review: 62–82	Share & Summarize, pages T235, 235 Troubleshooting, page T235 Informal Assessment, page 241 Quick Quiz, page 241

Introduce

1 Discuss negative numbers with students to assess their knowledge and experience with this topic. Have students give examples of how they might use negative numbers in their daily lives. Students may mention low elevations, cold temperatures, debt, and percent change.

Have students read the top cartoon. You may want to have students use Zoe's reasoning to tell how to locate other negative numbers on a number line.

2 Then have students read the bottom cartoon. Some students may need to review the definition of *opposite.* Bring out the idea that opposites are on opposite sides of zero. They are the same distance from zero on a number line. Encourage these students to give examples of other opposite numbers.

3 Review the definition of *absolute value.* Students should remember that absolute value is the distance from zero on a number line. Ask students why we use the term *opposite* to describe pairs of positive and negative numbers with the same absolute value.

4.1

Adding and Subtracting with Negative Numbers

You have probably seen negative numbers used in many situations. Golf scores below par, elevations below sea level, temperatures below 0°, and balances of overdrawn bank accounts can all be described with negative numbers.

Zoe and Darnell have different ways of thinking about negative numbers.

Zoe and Darnell both used positive numbers when they thought about negative numbers. Zoe actually used the *absolute value* of $^{-}4$. Since $^{-}4$ and 4 are both four units from 0, both have absolute value 4.

1
- **Discuss the meaning of *negative numbers* with entire class.**
- **Have students give other examples of negative numbers.**

2
Review the meaning of *opposite.*

3
Review the meaning of *absolute value.*

Develop

Think & Discuss
Pose the Think & Discuss questions to the whole class. Students will use these concepts as they work with negative numbers in this lesson.

If students are having difficulty answering the second question—writing numbers with the fewest number of negative signs—you might suggest that they use Darnell's thinking to help them understand and remember these concepts.

In the third question, students must make a general statement about the relationship between the number of negative signs in front of a numeral and the associated number's sign.

If students have difficulty understanding how to determine whether ^-x is positive or negative, ask them to test a few cases. Be sure they test positive and negative numbers. You might want to encourage students to read ^-x as *the opposite of* x instead of as *negative* x to reinforce the idea that ^-x is not always negative.

In the last two problems, students relate the value of x to the absolute value of x. Discuss students' explanations for why each is true. Some students may think that the last statement is false since the absolute value of any number is a positive number. Have them think about a specific number, such as $^-5$, then think $^-(^-5) = 5$. After listening to students' explanations, encourage them to provide examples to show that the explanations are true.

To show the absolute value of a number, draw a vertical segment on each side of the number.

$$|4| = 4 \qquad |^{-}4| = 4$$

Remember

The absolute value of a number is its distance from 0 on the number line.

① If the number of negative signs is even, the number is positive. If the number of negative signs is odd, the number is negative.

② You have to know whether x is negative or positive; ^{-}x has the opposite sign.

③ Possible answer: $|x|$ is the distance of x from 0 on the number line. If x is positive, this is just x units.

Think & Discuss

These questions will help you review some important ideas about negative numbers.

- Order these numbers from least to greatest: $^{-}5$, $^{-}3.5$, $^{-}0.25$, 0, 1.75, 4, 4.2

  4 $\quad$ $^{-}5$ $\quad$ 0 $\quad$ $^{-}3.5$ $\quad$ 4.2 $\quad$ $^{-}0.25$ $\quad$ 1.75

- Express each number using the fewest negative signs possible.

  $^{-}(^{-}2)$ 2 $\qquad$ $^{-}(^{-}(^{-}(^{-}(7))))$ 7 $\qquad$ $^{-}(^{-}(^{-}5.5))$ $^{-}5.5$

- How can you tell whether a number is positive or negative by counting how many negative signs it has? See ①.

- How can you tell whether ^{-}x is positive or negative? See ②.

- Explain why the following is true: See ③.

  If x is positive, then $|x| = x$.

- Tell for what numbers the following is true: for $x \leq 0$.

  If x is negative, then $|x| = {}^{-}x$.

1 Work through the Think & Discuss questions with the whole class.

2 Have students use Darnell's thinking.

3 Have students give examples to support their answers.

In this lesson, you will expand your understanding of negative numbers by learning how to add and subtract negative and positive numbers. Throughout the lesson, do your calculations without a calculator. This will help you better understand why the operations work the way they do.

Golf scores below par are given as negative numbers.

LESSON 4.1 Adding and Subtracting with Negative Numbers 219

1 **Suggested Grouping: Pairs**

Materials and Preparation

2 Each pair of students should have the following materials:

- one direction cube with three faces labeled *Ship* and three faces labeled *Sharks*
- one walking cube with sides labeled *F1, F2, F3, B1, B2, B3*
- several sheets of blank paper
- a paper arrow
- a plank, as described below

If you want students to physically "walk the plank," you need to set up a plank for each pair of students on the floor of your classroom, the floor of an open space in your school, or on the ground outside. You can make planks with masking tape or chalk, but all planks must have lines at 1 foot intervals. If lack of space does not permit you to do this, each pair of partners can play the game using Master 19, a copy of *The Captain's Game* Plank gameboard. As students play the game, they can use Master 20, Plank Table, to record their results.

This activity foreshadows the "walking the number line" model students will use as they learn how to add and subtract signed numbers in subsequent investigations of this lesson. It is meant to give students an intuitive, informal feel for moving on a number line without referring to either signed numbers or the number line.

In this activity, students first play a game in which they roll two cubes. They use the information on the cubes to decide whether to face the ship end or the shark end of the plank gameboard and to move forward and backward a given number of spaces. The game ends when they move off the plank. This movement connects to movement on a number line.

The "walking the number line" model in subsequent investigations has students move pointers on a number line to show addition and subtraction. Instead of facing sharks or the ship as in this activity, students face the positive direction or the negative direction of the number line in the model. Just as students move forward or backward in this game, they move forward or backward when they use the model. So if the sharks represent the negative end of the number line and the ship represents the positive end of the number line, then we have the following relationships between the two models:

- facing the ship and moving forward is equivalent to adding a positive number
- facing the ship and moving backward is equivalent to subtracting a positive number
- facing the sharks and moving forward is equivalent to adding a negative number
- facing the sharks and moving backward is equivalent to subtracting a negative number

Thus, structurally, *The Captain's Game* is equivalent to the model students will be using to add and subtract signed numbers. This structure, however, does not need to be presented to students.

The game was designed to encourage some of the thinking that students will need as they begin adding and subtracting signed numbers. For example, if students see that facing the sharks and moving backward (subtracting a negative) has the same result as facing the ship and moving forward (adding a positive), they have made an important connection. Both movements put them in a more advantageous position—farther away from the shark-infested waters. This is introduced more formally in Investigation 2 as students discover that subtracting a negative number is equivalent to adding the opposite of the negative number.

In addition to giving students an informal look at adding and subtracting with signed numbers, this activity has students think about probability concepts and data collection. Although the probability involved in finding an exact correlation between the length of the plank and the average number of moves in a game is very complex, students can observe and explain the simpler fact that as the length of the plank increases, so does the average number of moves necessary to complete one game. Furthermore, there are ample opportunities to discuss data collection with students as discussed in the Check Your Prediction section in this Investigation.

• ***Teaching notes continued on page A390.***

Lab Investigation ▶ Walking the Plank

Imagine that you are on the crew of a pirate ship commanded by a very generous captain. He has decided to give victims who must walk the plank a chance to survive. He has formulated a game he can play with his victims, but he's asked your help in testing and revising the game.

The Captain's Game

The captain has set up an 8-foot plank that extends from the ship toward the water. He has drawn lines on the plank at intervals of 1 foot.

MATERIALS
- a copy of the plank
- several blank sheets of paper
- a paper arrow

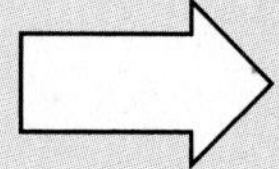

- a direction cube with 3 faces labeled *Ship* and 3 labeled *Shark*
- a walking cube with faces labeled *F1, F2, F3, B1, B2,* and *B3*

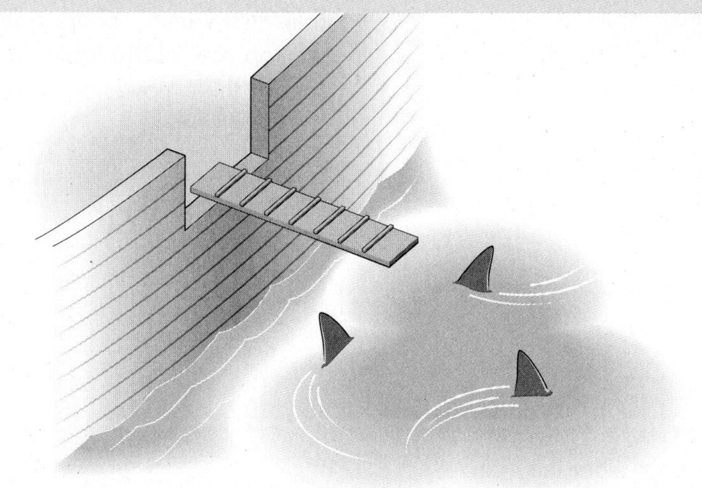

The victim starts by standing in the center of the plank, with 4 feet in front of him or her and 4 feet behind him or her. To decide where the victim should move, the captain rolls two cubes, a *direction* cube and a *walking* cube.

Direction Cube If the captain rolls *Ship,* the victim faces the ship. If he rolls *Shark,* the victim faces the sharks in the water.

Walking Cube If the captain rolls *F1, F2,* or *F3,* the victim must walk forward 1, 2, or 3 steps. If he rolls *B1, B2,* or *B3,* the victim must walk backward 1, 2, or 3 steps.

The captain continues to roll the cubes until the victim walks off the edge of the plank—either into the shark-infested water or onto the safety of the ship's deck.

1
- Discuss *The Captain's Game* with the whole class.
- Students work in pairs as they play this game.

2
Ask students what materials they think they will need.

Teaching Resources

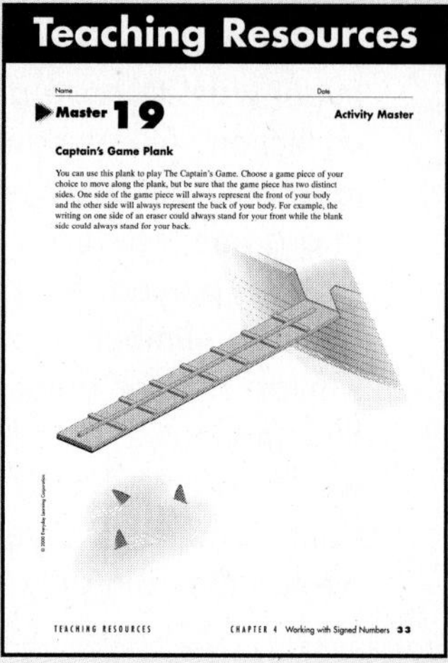

Develop

Try It Out

Students work in pairs as they play the game. Each person should be the captain and the victim at least once.

On the Spot Assessment

Watch for students who count each roll of the two number cubes as two moves instead of one move. Make sure students understand that when the text asks them to keep track of the number of times the cubes are rolled, it means the number of times the pair of cubes are rolled. They should also understand that when the book refers to the number of moves, it is referring to the number of times the victim moves. For each move, the captain rolls two number cubes. Students will need this information as they work on **Problems 1–7.**

Make a Prediction

Students' answers to **Problem 3** will vary because the ideal number of moves is entirely subjective. However, it is important that students are clear about what they consider to be an ideal number of moves, because their answers to Problems 4 and 6 will depend on this number. Once students have set their ideal number of moves, they must reason mathematically to determine the length of the plank that will generate that ideal number of moves.

You may wish to highlight that there is an element of industrial design involved in designing games. All designers need to experiment with elements of their games to make the game as enjoyable as possible. Often mathematics assists designers in making choices about these elements.

Check Your Prediction

Before students begin this part of the investigation, you might want to have a class discussion about data collection. Ask students how many games they needed to play to get a sense of the average number of moves in a game. Emphasize the idea that the more games that are played, the more accurate the estimate of the average number of moves will be. Students may recall a similar, simpler situation involving probabilities and coin flips in Course 1. In that situation, students found that if we flip a coin 1,000 times, we get a more accurate estimate of the theoretical probabilities than we get if we flip the coin only 10 times. They discovered that the greater the number of trials, the greater the likelihood of getting closer to the theoretical probability.

Alternatively, you could use technology to help you generate a large number of cases: you may be able to program the results of the rolls into a graphing calculator or a computer and create a simulation of the activity.

Encourage students to complete the table in **Problem 6** as they test their games. If students are satisfied with their first version of the game, they will only complete the top row of the table. You may wish to have students record their moves on Master 20, Plank Table.

Teaching Resources

Master 20 — Activity Master

Plank Table

Plank Length	Number of Moves Game 1	Game 2	Game 3	Average Number of Moves

Try It Out Answers will vary.

Play the game with a partner using a drawing of the plank and a paper arrow. Take turns playing the roles of the captain and the victim. For each game, keep track of the number of times the cubes are rolled before the victim falls to the sharks or reaches safety. Then answer the questions.

1. Did the victim in each game make it to the ship, or was he or she forced to jump into the water?
2. How many moves did it take to complete each game?

Make a Prediction Answers will vary.

The captain is thinking about changing the length of the plank and would like some advice on how long it should be. If the plank is too short, games won't last long enough to entertain him. If the plank is too long, he will become bored with the game. Your challenge is to decide on a plank length that results in an interesting game that is not too short or too long.

3. To keep the game interesting, what do you think the ideal number of moves should be?
4. How long do you think the plank should be so that the average number of moves is about the right number?

Check Your Prediction Answers will vary.

One way to check your prediction in Question 4 is to collect data. Play at least three games with the plank length you specified. Record the number of moves for each game, and then find the average number of moves for all the games you played.

5. Is the average number of moves close to the number you specified in Question 3?
6. If the plank length you predicted is too long or too short, adjust it. Play the game at least three times with the new length. Continue adjusting the plank length until the average number of moves for a particular length is about what you recommended in Question 3.

You might put the results of your games in a table like this:

Plank Length	Number of Moves Game 1	Game 2	Game 3	Average Number of Moves

1 Have students work in pairs.

2 Make a prediction about ideal plank length.

3 Have students check their predictions.

LESSON 4.1 Adding and Subtracting with Negative Numbers 221

Develop

What Did You Learn?

In **Problem 7,** students are given a move and determine what was rolled by the number cubes.

In **Problem 8,** most students will report that a good game needs a 10–14 foot-long plank. However the focus should be on students' justifications for their recommendations, not on the recommended length of the plank. Look to see that students use the data collected in the investigation to justify their recommendation.

Investigation 1

In this investigation, students are introduced to the "walking the number line" model. This model helps students learn how to add and subtract signed numbers. After familiarizing themselves with the model, students make drawings of their number-line walks. They also begin to solve more challenging problems requiring the addition and subtraction of signed numbers.

The student text suggests that students "walk the number line" with a pointer and a small number line. The model is introduced with this assumption. If you have the space and resources, you might want to have students *physically* walk the number line before using the paper models. You can create number lines using masking tape or sidewalk chalk on the floor in an open space in your school or outside. Then students can actually "walk the number line" themselves. You will need to adapt the opening materials accordingly.

If you choose to have students make smaller number lines and pointers, you can have them draw and cut out the materials. If you select this option, encourage students to make their number lines and pointers as large as possible. You may want to give each student a copy of Master 21, Number Line and Pointer. This master has a number line that extends from $^{-}9$ to 9 and a pointer that students can cut out. You can enlarge the master to make it easier for students to work with.

Review with students how to show the addition and subtraction of two positive numbers on a number line. Tell them that they can use a similar method to add and subtract negative numbers.

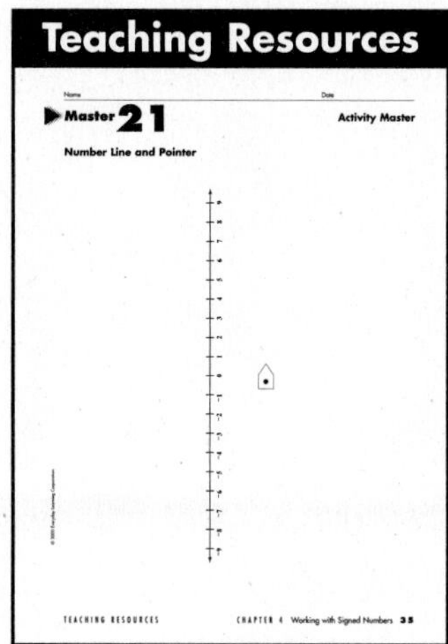

What Did You Learn?

7. Ship, F2 or Shark, B2

7. In one round of the game, the victim moved two steps in the direction of the ship. What might the captain have rolled when he rolled the two cubes? List as many possibilities as you can.

8. Write a letter to the captain giving him your recommendation. Include the following in your letter: Letters will vary.

- The number of moves you think is ideal
- How long the plank should be
- How you know that this plank length will give your ideal number of moves

1
- Have students work in pairs.
- Volunteers can share their letters with entire class.

Investigation 1 Walking the Number Line

2 Review the number-line models for adding and subtracting positive numbers.

In earlier grades, you may have learned to add and subtract positive numbers on the number line. For example, to find $2 + 3$, you start at 2 and move three spaces to the right. The number on which you end, 5, is the sum.

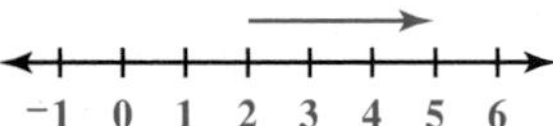

To find $6 - 4$, start at 6 and move four spaces to the left.

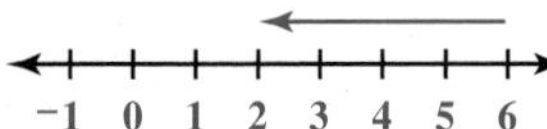

Develop

Read through the directions for using the model to find sums with your students. Go over the use of the number line to find $3 + {}^{-}2$. If you are using human-size number lines, adapt the directions accordingly. In this case, the student's body becomes the pointer, so he or she faces the way the pointer would point on the paper model.

For example, if the number being added is negative, students face the negative direction. Students walk in the direction the pointer in the paper model would move.

In a similar way, you can "walk the number line" to calculate sums and differences involving negative numbers.

Before you can walk the number line, you need to create a large number line that goes from $^{-}9$ to 9, and a pointer that looks like the one below.

Once you have created your number line and pointer, you are ready to walk the number line. Here's how to find the solution to $3 + {}^{-}2$ by using your number line.

- Place your pointer, point up, on 3.

- Look at the number being added. Since it is *negative,* point your pointer in the *negative direction* (to the left).

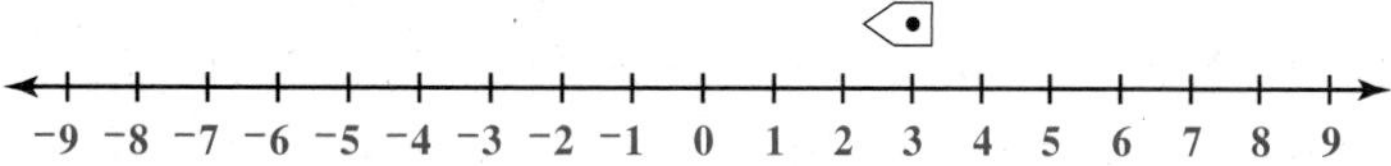

- Now look at the operation. Since it is *addition,* move the pointer *forward* (in the direction the pointer is facing) two spaces. The pointer ends on 1, which means the answer is 1. The complete addition equation for this sum is $3 + {}^{-}2 = 1$.

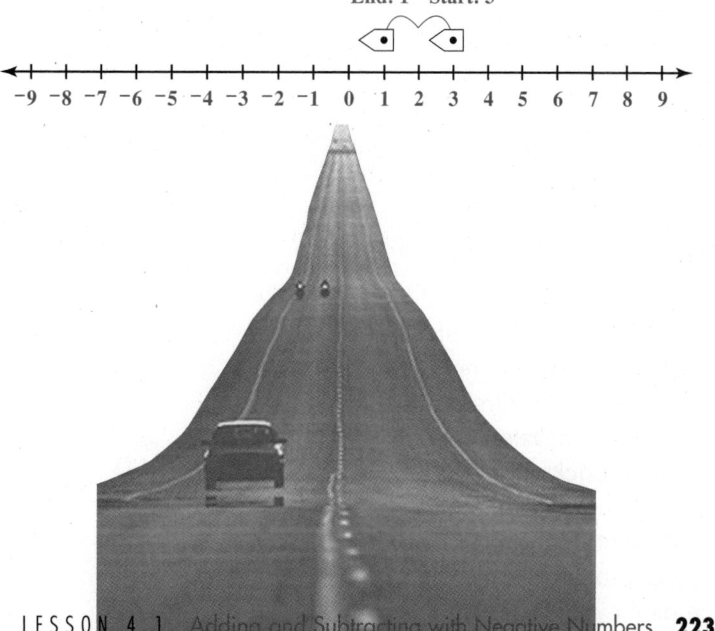

1 Introduce students to "walking the number-line models" involving positive and negative numbers.

2 Make sure students understand that the pointer faces left if the number being added is negative.

LESSON 4.1 Adding and Subtracting with Negative Numbers 223

Develop

Use your version of the model to walk students through the steps for subtracting signed numbers. You may want to have students show each step on their models as you discuss each step.

Additional Example You may wish to use the model to show how to find the sum or difference of two positive numbers. This will encourage students to build on their experience with subtraction and number lines and may help them reinforce what is being shown by the model. Then have the class practice using the model to find these sums and differences.

$4 + {}^-1$ 3

${}^-2 + 3$ 1

${}^-2 + {}^-3$ ${}^-5$

$4 - {}^-1$ 5

${}^-2 - 3$ ${}^-5$

${}^-2 - {}^-3$ 1

To avoid confusion later, you may want to point out that moving backward does not always mean moving to the left. Remind students that they must look at the direction the pointer is pointed in and move in the opposite direction. Emphasize that if the pointer is pointing in the positive direction, to the right, and students are asked to move backward, they will move to the left. If, however, the pointer is pointing in the negative direction, to the left, and students are asked to move backward, they will move to the right.

Review the rules for walking the number line given at the bottom of page 224. Be sure students know that the sign of the number being added determines which direction the pointer will face and that the operation determines whether the pointer moves forward or backward. You may want to write these rules onto a chart. You can display the chart to reinforce students' learning and to help them as they use the model to solve problems. This will give students a handy reference as they learn to use the model.

Here's how you would find the solution to $^{-}2 - 6$.

- Place your pointer, point up, on $^{-}2$.

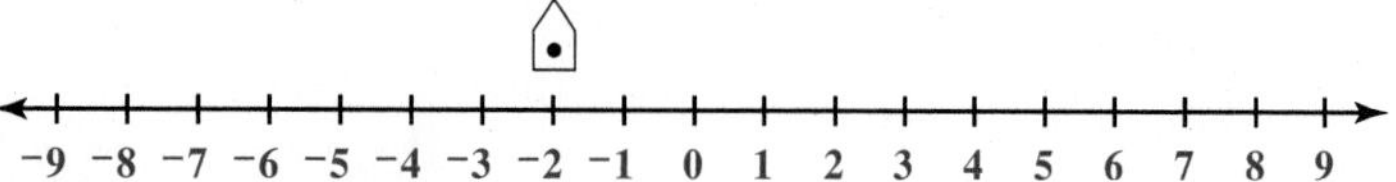

- Look at the number being subtracted. Since it is *positive,* point your pointer in the *positive direction* (to the right).

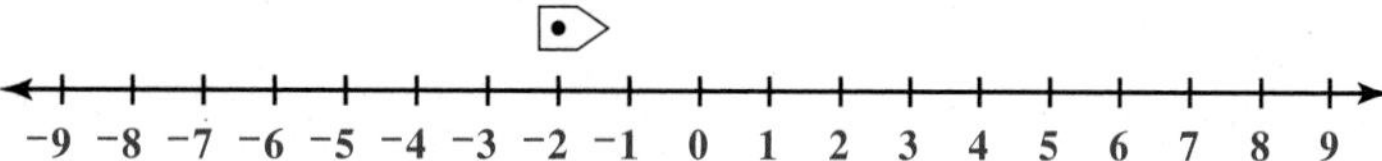

- Now look at the operation. Since it is *subtraction,* move the pointer *backward* (opposite the direction the pointer is facing) six spaces. The answer is $^{-}8$. The complete subtraction equation for this difference is $^{-}2 - 6 = {}^{-}8$.

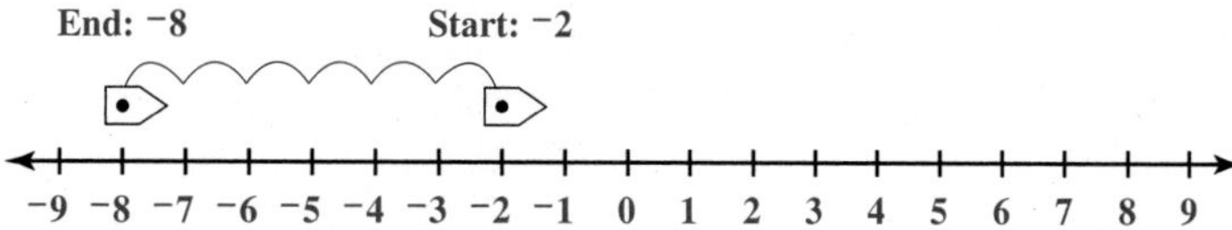

1 • Be sure students understand pointer faces right if number being added is positive.

• Ask students why they need to move the pointer backward.

When you walk the number line, the sign of the number being added or subtracted determines the direction the pointer faces.

- If the number is positive, point the pointer in the positive direction.
- If the number is negative, point the pointer in the negative direction.

2 Review the rules for walking the number-line.

The operation determines the direction to move the pointer.

- If the operation is addition, move the pointer forward, in the direction it is pointing.

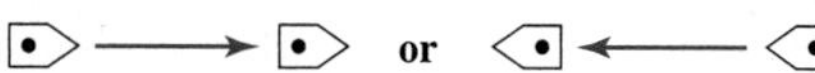

- If the operation is subtraction, move the pointer backward, opposite the direction it is pointing.

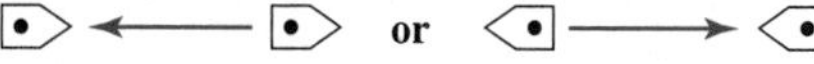

Develop

Think & Discuss

Students are asked to explain how to use a number line to find $5 + {}^{-}3$. Each picture represents one step. You may want to guide their answers by asking questions such as these:

> Why is the pointer at 5 in the first picture? *5 is the first addend.*
>
> Why does the pointer face left in the second picture? *The number to be added is negative, so the pointer faces in the negative direction.*
>
> Why did the pointer move forwards in the third picture? *The operation is addition, so the arrow moves in the direction it is pointing.*

Problem Set A **Suggested Grouping: Pairs**

In this problem set, students use the "walking the number line" model to find sums and differences. After they practice the model using whole numbers, students experience adding and subtracting with nonintegers. Since it is difficult to precisely locate nonintegers on the number line, students are forced to begin forming a more abstract notion of movement on the number line. Instead of counting a whole number of steps to move from one integer to another, students must be more aware of where they are on the number line at all times and must think about what is going on. After practicing with the model, students apply their skills to solve problems relating to situations.

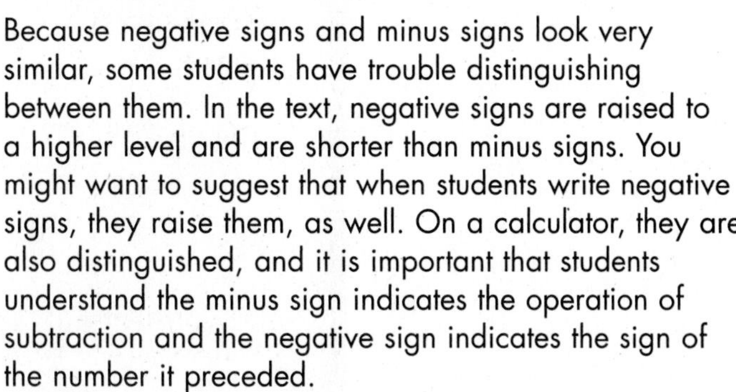

Because negative signs and minus signs look very similar, some students have trouble distinguishing between them. In the text, negative signs are raised to a higher level and are shorter than minus signs. You might want to suggest that when students write negative signs, they raise them, as well. On a calculator, they are also distinguished, and it is important that students understand the minus sign indicates the operation of subtraction and the negative sign indicates the sign of the number it preceded.

In **Problems 1–4,** students are asked to describe the steps they use to walk the number line to ensure that they understand the model. If students are still confused, you may want to have them describe their steps in Problems 5–8.

On the Spot Assessment

In **Problems 1–4,** watch for students who mix up the rules for "walking the number line." Some students will think that the sign of the number being added or subtracted dictates whether you move forward or backward instead of determining the direction of the pointer. Similarly, they will think that the operation determines the direction of the pointer, not whether you move forward or backward. Actually, the model can work with this interpretation as well, and some may find it makes more sense. That's fine.

This can be hard to spot because students who mix up the rules still get the correct answer. Students who do this will still find the correct sum because they are acting out an equivalent operation. For example, if a problem asks them to add a negative and they reverse the rules, they are in essence acting out subtracting the opposite of the negative.

Have students struggling with finding fractions and decimals on the number line in **Problems 5–8** break down the number-line movement into steps. Have them place their pointer on the first number in the exercise and then move the whole number of steps. Ask them to look at the whole-number part of the decimal or fraction and move that number of spaces. Then have them look at the fractional part of the decimal or fraction and move that number of spaces. You can make this process more detailed by having students move one space at a time.

The limits for **Problem 9** were purposefully extended so that students would have experience using the number-line model to show subtraction of integers that are more than 9 units from zero. Students will need to use a number line that extends at least from $^{-}15$ to $^{-}8$. Some students won't need to create a physical number line but will be able to imagine a number line with a larger range. For students who want to use a number line, you can use Master 22, Blank Number Lines and Pointer, which contains several copies of number lines with no number labels.

Sample Strategies Here are some ways students might think of **Problem 9:**

- Some students may use the "walking the number line" model.
- Other students may draw a picture of a thermometer or a vertical number line and then count the 7 spaces from $^{-}15$ to $^{-}8$ to find the change in temperature.

• ***Teaching notes continued on page A390.***

Think & Discuss

The number lines below show the steps for finding $5 + {}^{-}3$. Explain each step.

Start pointer at 5.

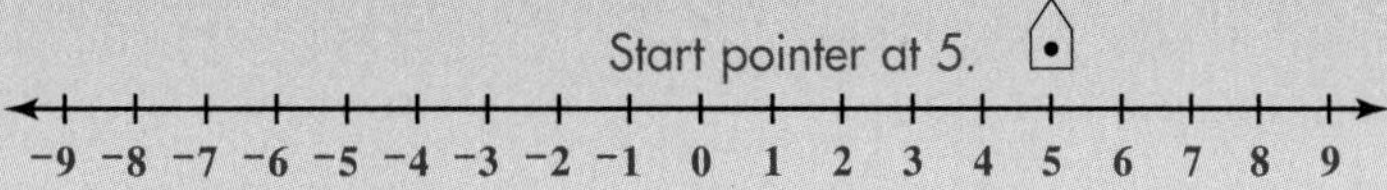

The number to be added is negative, so turn the pointer in the negative direction.

−9 −8 −7 −6 −5 −4 −3 −2 −1 0 1 2 3 4 5 6 7 8 9

The operation is addition, so move the pointer in the direction it's pointing.

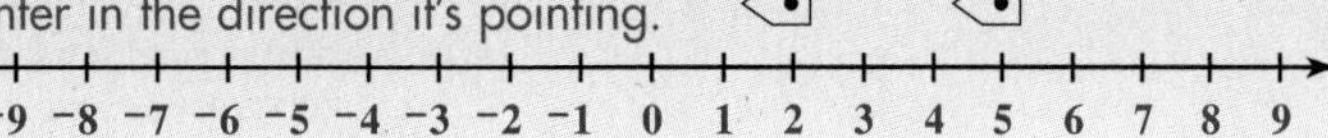

1 • Discuss answers.

• Review the rules on page 224.

Now you will have an opportunity to compute some sums and differences with the number line.

MATERIALS
number line and pointer

Problem Set A

2 Have students work in pairs.

For Problems 1–4, walk the number line to find each sum or difference. Describe your steps in words. Be sure to include the following in your descriptions:

- Where on the number line you start
- The direction the pointer is facing
- Whether you move forward or backward and how far you move
- The point on the number line at which you end (the answer)
- The complete equation that represents your moves on the number line

1. $5 + {}^{-}2$ **2.** ${}^{-}4 + {}^{-}3$ **3.** $3 - {}^{-}2$ **4.** ${}^{-}8 - {}^{-}2$

Find each sum or difference by walking the number line.

5. $3 + {}^{-}5.25$ **6.** $5 - 6\frac{1}{3}$ **7.** ${}^{-}6 - 2.23$ **8.** ${}^{-}\frac{2}{3} - {}^{-}1\frac{1}{3}$

9. When Brynn woke up one morning, the temperature was ${}^{-}15$°F. By noon the temperature had risen 7°F. What was the temperature at noon? ${}^{-}8$°F

10. Colleen was hiking in Death Valley, parts of which are at elevations below sea level. She began her hike at an elevation of 300 feet and hiked down 450 feet. At what elevation did she end her hike? ${}^{-}150$ ft, or 150 ft below sea level

1–4. See Additional Answers.
5. ${}^{-}2.25$
6. ${}^{-}1\frac{1}{3}$
7. ${}^{-}8.23$
8. $\frac{2}{3}$

3 Help students distinguish between minus signs and negative signs.

4 Discuss students' strategies for solving each problem.

Additional Answers

1. start 5, point left, move forward 2, end 3; $5 + {}^{-}2 = 3$
2. start ${}^{-}4$, point left, move forward 3, end ${}^{-}7$; ${}^{-}4 + {}^{-}3 = {}^{-}7$
3. start 3, point left, move back 2, end 5; $3 - {}^{-}2 = 5$
4. start ${}^{-}8$, point left, move back 2, end ${}^{-}6$; ${}^{-}8 - {}^{-}2 = {}^{-}6$

Teaching Resources

Master 22 — Activity Master — Blank Number Lines and Pointer

Develop

You may want to tell students that since it is impractical to always carry around the materials to walk a number line, there is a way to draw a picture of the model. They can then use their drawings to add and subtract signed numbers.

You may want to have students who are having difficulty following the steps in the Example below to first show each step on their number line models. They can compare how their model looks with the drawing in the text, on the board, or on an overhead.

1 **Example**
Walk students through the steps on how to make a drawing to show $^-3 - {}^-7$. You may want to draw a number line on the board as you ask questions such as these:

> Where will you first draw the pointer? $^-3$ since it is the number being subtracted from
>
> Which direction will the pointer face? Why? The number to be subtracted is negative, so the pointer faces in the negative direction.
>
> Will the pointer move forward or backward? Explain. Backward because we are subtracting
>
> How many spaces did the pointer move? 7
>
> Why do we use the arrow? Where does it start and end? The arrow shows the direction of the movement. It starts on $^-3$, the number being subtracted from, and ends 7 marks to the right on 4.

Label the number line with *Start:* $^-3$ and *end: 4.* Then ask students to give the difference of $^-3 - {}^-7$. 4

Emphasize that labeling the starting and ending points is important for two reasons. First, it helps to make number-line pictures even clearer. While it does not seem difficult to read the number line when the starting and ending points are integers, it is almost impossible to identify numbers exactly on the number line that are not integers. Second, it foreshadows work with number-line pictures that students will do in Investigation 2.

Be sure students understand that the drawing shows exactly what would happen if students were to use the physical "walk the number line" model.

You may want students to work through some of the additional examples before assigning Problem Set B.

Additional Example There are 12 distinct kinds of sums and differences involving signed numbers. You may wish to use one or more of these problems as the basis for a classroom discussion or as additional individual work. Make sure that if you give students extra problems to work, you give them a sampling of the 12 kinds of problems. Duplicate combinations are included to allow for the possibility of positive and negative answers.

$^-2 + 5$	**3**	Neg + Pos (answer is positive)
$^-6 + 1$	**-5**	Neg + Pos (answer is negative)
$^-7 - 2$	**-9**	Neg − Pos (answer is always negative)
$^-3 + {}^-5$	**-8**	Neg + Neg (answer is always negative)
$^-5 - {}^-8$	**3**	Neg − Neg (answer is positive)
$^-3 - {}^-1$	**-2**	Neg − Neg (answer is negative)
$6 + {}^-3$	**3**	Pos + Neg (answer is positive)
$3 + {}^-9$	**-6**	Pos + Neg (answer is negative)
$7 - {}^-1$	**8**	Pos − Neg (answer is always positive)
$2 + 6$	**8**	Pos + Pos (answer is always positive)
$6 - 2$	**4**	Pos − Pos (answer is positive)
$3 - 8$	**-5**	Pos − Pos (answer is negative)

You can make drawings to record your moves on the number line. Once you get comfortable walking the number line, you may be able to add and subtract just by making a drawing. Your drawings can show very easily the steps you take to find a sum or a difference.

1 Discuss Example with entire class.

EXAMPLE

Make a drawing to record the moves required to find ${}^-3 - {}^-7$.

First, draw a pointer over ${}^-3$. Since the number being subtracted is negative, draw the pointer so that it is facing to the left. Make sure the dot on the pointer is directly over ${}^-3$.

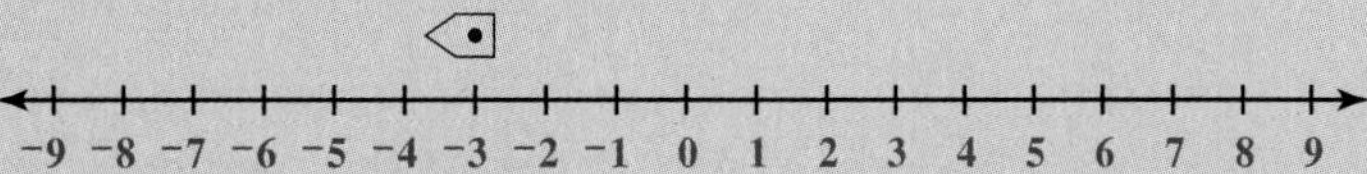

Since you are subtracting ${}^-7$, you need to move backward seven spaces. Draw an arrow from the pointer to the ending number.

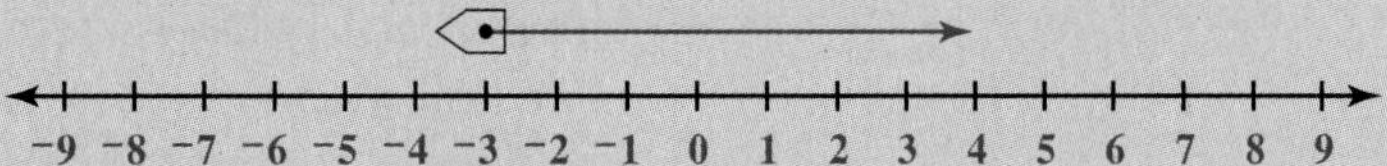

Finish your drawing by adding some labels. Write *Start* and the number where you started above the pointer. Write *End* and the number where you ended above the arrowhead. Adding labels is especially important when you find sums and differences involving fractions and decimals, because it is hard to show the numbers precisely on the number line.

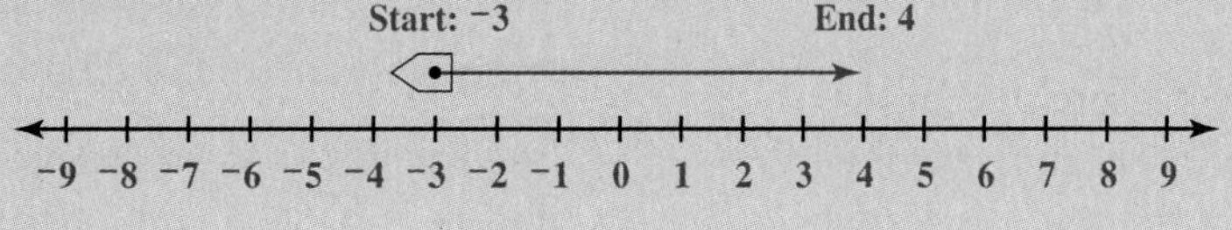

Notice that the final number-line drawing captures all your moves: It shows the number at which you began, the direction of your pointer, whether you moved forward or backward, how far you moved, and your ending number.

2 You may wish to work through the Additional Example problems on page T226.

Develop

Problem Set B Suggested Grouping: Individuals
To save time when students are creating number-line pictures, you can use copies of Master 23, 6 Number Lines, which has blank number lines with numbers extending from $^-9$ to 9.

In **Problems 1–6,** students draw number-line pictures to compute sums and differences. These are all variations of the Example.

On the **Spot Assessment**

In **Problems 1–6,** watch for students who create a number-line picture where one endpoint is the first number in the sum or difference while the other endpoint is the second number in the sum or difference. For example, for Problem 1, some students may be tempted to draw a number-line picture with endpoints $^-3$ and $^-2$. Students who make this error are confused by the model and are not thinking through the walking process as they create their picture. To help them, you might suggest they get out their pointer and act out the sum or difference using rules laid out in Investigation 1 before drawing a number-line picture.

In **Problems 7–9,** students reverse the process of creating a number-line picture. They must analyze a number-line picture and decide what equation is shown by the drawing.

Access for all **Learners**

For Early Finishers Have students who finish early find the 12 kinds of problems involving signed numbers. You may want to get them started by suggesting they add two positive numbers. Once students have found the 12 kinds of problems, have them give an example of each.

Share & Summarize
In this Share & Summarize, students practice creating and interpreting number-line pictures. You might ask students to think about what all of the addition number-line pictures have in common and what all of the subtraction number-line pictures have in common. Students may find that all the addition pictures show arrows extending from the arrow's point while subtraction pictures show the arrow extending from the back of the arrow.

Troubleshooting Students should be able to use the "walking the number line" model without serious problems. Although they will be able to use the physical model throughout the remainder of the lesson, it is hoped that they will have internalized the model to a large degree by the end of this investigation. In order for them to be at that point by the end of the lesson, it is important that students are comfortable with the model by the time they reach the end of this investigation.

If students are still uncomfortable with the model and if having them physically walk the number line does not help, you might want to consider introducing a different model. One model that has been quite successful involves representing positive numbers with cubes or chips of one color—like red, and negative numbers with cubes of another color—like blue. Using this model, addition of signed numbers is done by combining the appropriate number of cubes of the appropriate color. For example, to add $^-8$ and 3, combine 8 blue cubes and 3 red cubes. Then cancel, or match, red and blue cubes to form *zero pairs*. Since each pair of red and blue cubes represents 1 and $^-1$, their sum is zero. To compute $^-8 + 3$, cancel out three pairs of red and blue cubes leaving 5 blue cubes. Blue cubes represent negative numbers, so the answer is $^-5$.

Subtraction in the cube model works in a similar way. To find $a - b$, start with cubes representing number a and then remove cubes that represent number b. Keep in mind that different colors of cubes are not interchangeable since each color has a different value. If a and b are different signs or if the absolute value of b is larger than the absolute value of a, you must add in some of the *zero pairs* of cubes so that you have enough cubes to take away. For example, to subtract $^-3$ from 5, start with 5 red cubes. To subtract $^-3$, you need to take away 3 blue cubes, but you don't have any. To overcome this obstacle, add 3 pairs of red and blue cubes to the pile of 5 red cubes. Adding a pair of cubes is like adding 1 and $^-1$—it doesn't affect the value of the pile. The new pile of 8 red cubes and 3 blue cubes has a value of 5. To complete the problem, take away the 3 blue cubes. There are 8 red cubes left, so $5 - {^-3} = 8$.

On Your Own Exercises

Practice & Apply: 1–25
Connect & Extend: 38–39
Mixed Review: 62–82

Problem Set B

Walk the number line to compute each sum or difference, and record your steps by making a number-line drawing. Write the complete addition or subtraction equation next to the drawing.

1. $^-3 + {^-2}$
2. $5 - 8$
3. $^-5 - {^-2}$
4. $^-5 + 7$
5. $2 + {^-7.2}$
6. $2\frac{2}{3} - {^-6\frac{1}{3}}$

3, 4. See below.
5, 6. See Additional Answers.

1. End: −5 Start: −3 $^-3 + {^-2} = {^-5}$

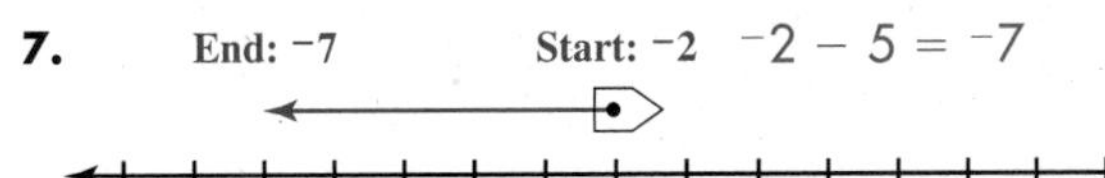

2. End: −3 $5 - 8 = {^-3}$ Start: 5

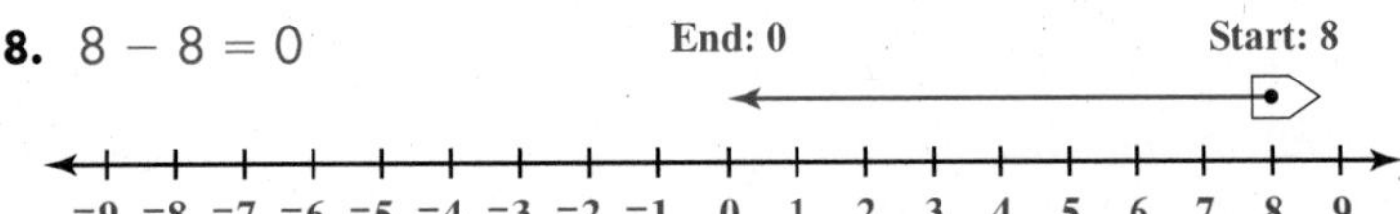

Write the addition or subtraction equation represented by each drawing.

7. End: −7 Start: −2 $^-2 - 5 = {^-7}$

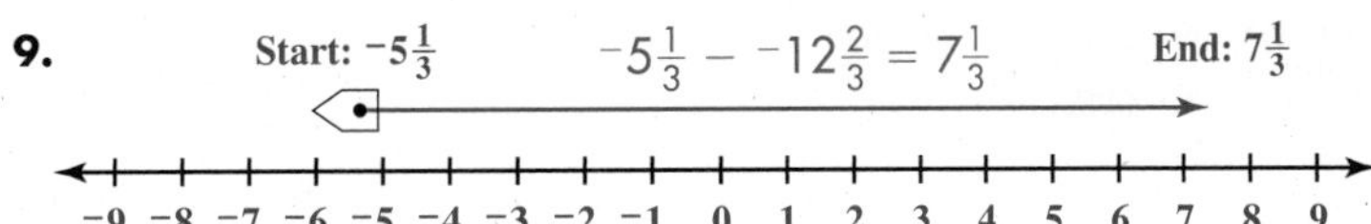

8. $8 - 8 = 0$ End: 0 Start: 8

−9 −8 −7 −6 −5 −4 −3 −2 −1 0 1 2 3 4 5 6 7 8 9

9. Start: $^-5\frac{1}{3}$ $^-5\frac{1}{3} - {^-12\frac{2}{3}} = 7\frac{1}{3}$ End: $7\frac{1}{3}$

−9 −8 −7 −6 −5 −4 −3 −2 −1 0 1 2 3 4 5 6 7 8 9

Share & Summarize

Write one addition equation and one subtraction equation. On a separate sheet of paper, make a number-line drawing for each.

Trade drawings with your partner, and write equations that match your partner's drawings. Check with your partner to make sure the equations match the drawings.

3. Start: −5 End: −3 $^-5 - {^-2} = {^-3}$

−8 −7 −6 −5 −4 −3 −2 −1 0

4. Start: −5 $^-5 + 7 = 2$ End: 2

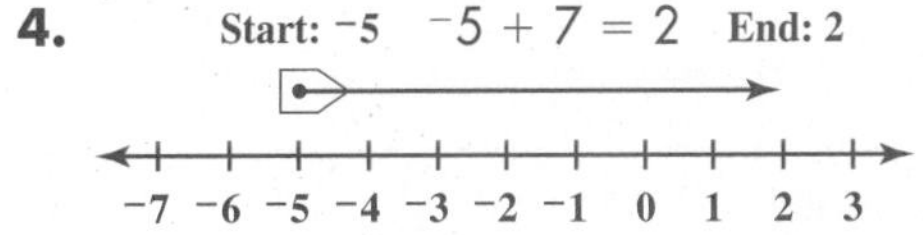

1 Have students work individually on these problems.

2 Students draw number-line pictures.

3 Students reverse the process of drawing a number-line picture.

4
- Ask partners what addition number-line pictures have in common.
- What do subtraction number-line pictures have in common?
- How are addition and subtraction number-line pictures different? The same?

Teaching Resources

Master 23 Activity Master
6 Number Lines

Additional Answers Problem Set B

5. $2 + {^-7.2} = {^-5.2}$

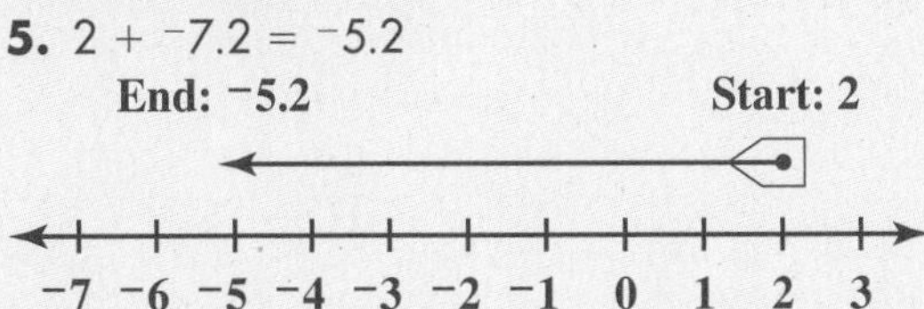

6. $2\frac{2}{3} - {^-6\frac{1}{3}} = 9$

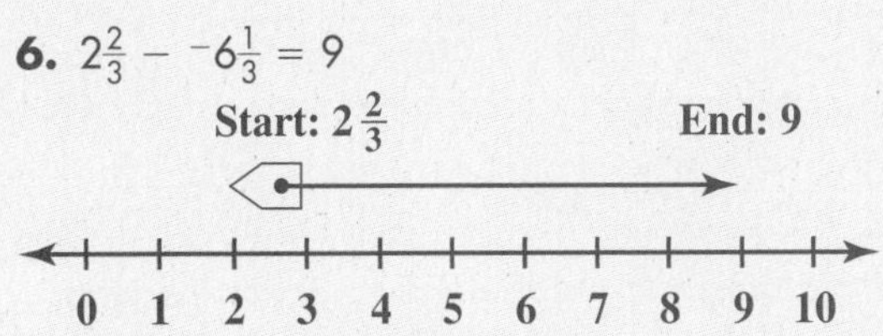

Investigation 2

In this investigation, students continue to use a number line as they formalize what they might have already observed: adding a negative is equivalent to subtracting the opposite of the negative (or a positive), and subtracting a negative is equivalent to adding the opposite of the negative (or a positive).

Think & Discuss

You may want to use an overhead and draw the two number lines or have students draw the number lines on the board as you discuss the problem.

Problem Set C Suggested Grouping: Pairs

You may wish to have students use copies of Master 24, Number Lines I, Number Lines II, and Number Lines III, to record their answers to this problem set. The master pages have two number lines with the starting and ending points labeled for each problem. Students draw in the picture of the pointer and the arrow and write the corresponding addition and subtraction equation for each number line.

On the Spot Assessment

Watch for students who think that they should add or subtract the two endpoint numbers to find the sum or difference. For example, some students might think that **Problem 1** represents the equation $5 - 2 = 3$ or $2 - 5 = {}^{-}3$. Students who are doing this are not thinking through the model correctly. You might suggest that these students do one or more of these things.

1. Review the rules for "walking the number line" set out in Investigation 1.
2. Draw the pointer and the arrow *before* writing the equation represented by the picture. Sometimes it is easier to create equations that represent pictures than it is to create pictures that represent equations.
3. Physically act out the model.

Teaching Resources

Master 24 Activity Master

Number Lines, I

Investigation  Equivalent Operations

1 Discuss the two equations that match the drawing.

2 You may have students use Master 24 to record answers.

You have practiced writing addition and subtraction equations to match number-line drawings. For each complete number-line drawing, there is only one equation that matches.

But what if a number-line drawing shows only the starting and ending values, and not the pointer or the arrow?

Think & Discuss See Additional Answers.

What number-line drawings start at $^-3$ and end at 2?

Start: $^-3$ **End:** 2

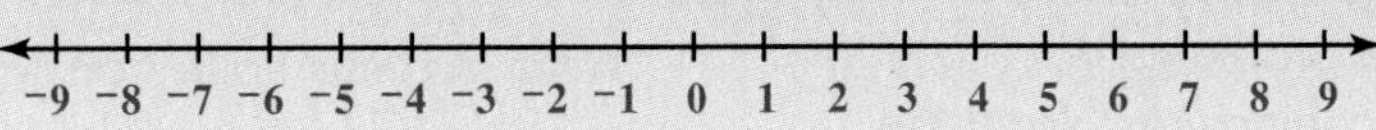

What equation does each number-line drawing represent?

In Problem Set C, you will use number-line drawings to explore the relationship between addition and subtraction.

Problem Set C

In Problems 1–6, make two copies of the number line. Complete one to represent an addition equation and the other to represent a subtraction equation. Write the equations your drawings represent.

1. **End:** 2 **Start:** 5

−9 −8 −7 −6 −5 −4 −3 −2 −1 0 1 2 3 4 5 6 7 8 9

2. **Start:** $^-7$ **End:** $^-3$

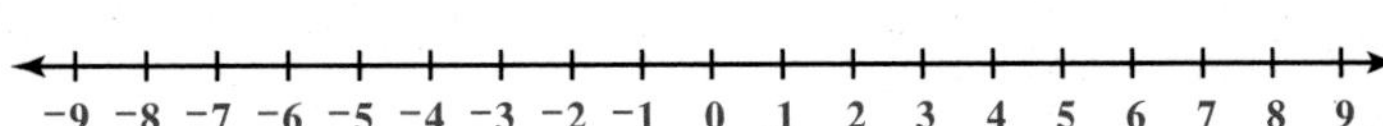

1. $5 + {}^-3 = 2$

1 2 3 4 5 6 7

$5 - 3 = 2$

1 2 3 4 5 6 7

2.

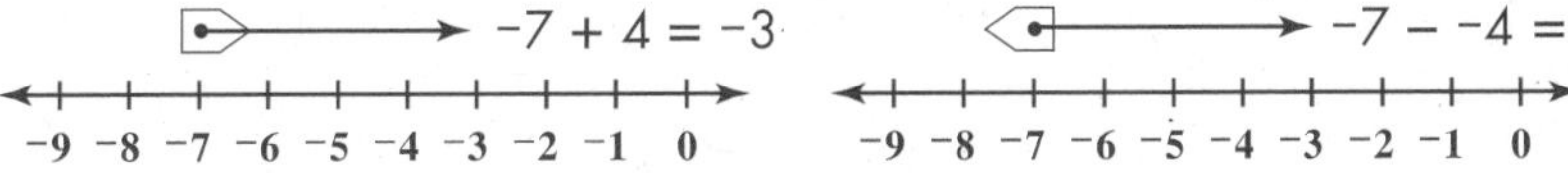

• ***Additional answers on page A390.***

Develop

Problem Set Wrap-Up Have volunteers share the equations they wrote for **Problems 1–6.** If any students had difficulty drawing the number lines, you may want volunteers to reproduce their drawings on the board or an overhead projector. Students should understand that when "walking the number line," there are two ways to move from a start number to an end number. They should be able to describe these moves for any two pairs of numbers before progressing to the Think & Discuss questions in the next section.

Think & Discuss

The Problem Set Wrap-Up provided a natural transition into this section. Ideally, as students describe their thoughts about the movements in the problems in Problem Set C, they make informal conjectures about the equivalency of adding a positive and subtracting a negative and subtracting a positive and adding a negative. The questions in this section should help them make their conjectures more explicit and formalize their understanding of the pairs of equivalent operations.

About the Mathematics

Technically speaking there are infinitely many equations that can describe the movement from one point to another on a number line. For example, **Problem 1** can be described by these equations: $5 - 3 = 2$; $5 - - {}^{-}3 = 2$; $5 - - - - {}^{-}3 = 2$, and so on. However, if you think only about the movement of the pointer, there are exactly two ways to move from any given point to any other given point. If the movement is to the right—that is, the starting point is to the left of the ending point—then you can point to the right and move forward or point to the left and move backward. If the movement is to the left—that is, the starting point is to the right of the ending point—then you can point to the left and move forward or point to the right and move backward.

Once students understand the two sets of equivalent moves, you can discuss the implications for sums and differences of signed numbers.

Guide the discussion of the two ways to move on the number line into a discussion of the operations used in the two equations. Have students compare the two equations they wrote for Problem 3 in Problem Set C. They should note that in one case they added ${}^{-}4$ and in the other they subtracted 4. When the inverse operation is used, the sign of the number added or subtracted changes. Tell students that since you started with the same number and found the same answer after adding or subtracting, the operations are *equivalent.*

After students have translated the equivalent moves, you might ask them some questions like the following one which asks them to use equivalent operations:

> How can I use operations to describe how to move from 3 to ${}^{-}8$? *Add ${}^{-}11$ or subtract 11.*

Students should have a sufficient understanding of equivalent operations to answer the questions in Problem Set D.

3. $3 + {}^-4 = {}^-1$

3 − 4 = −1

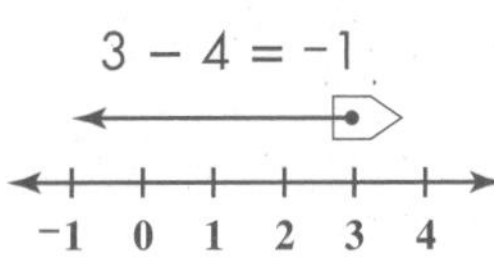

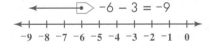

4, 5. See below.

6. See Additional Answers.

3. End: −1 Start: 3

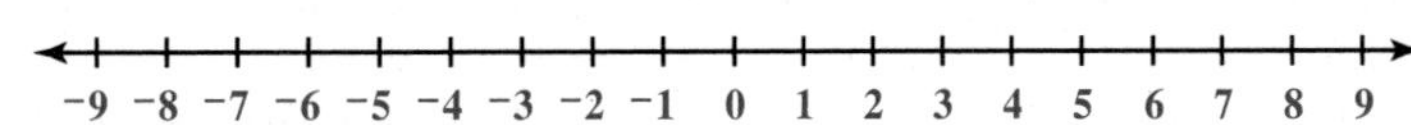

4. End: −9 Start: −6

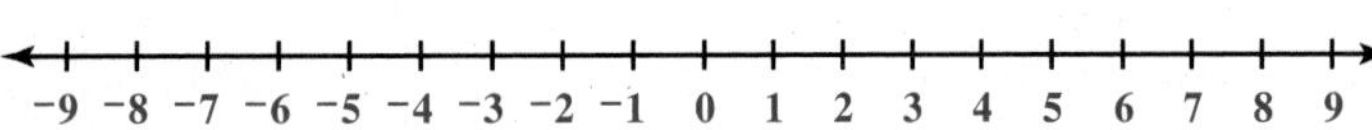

5. Start: 5.25 End: 7.75

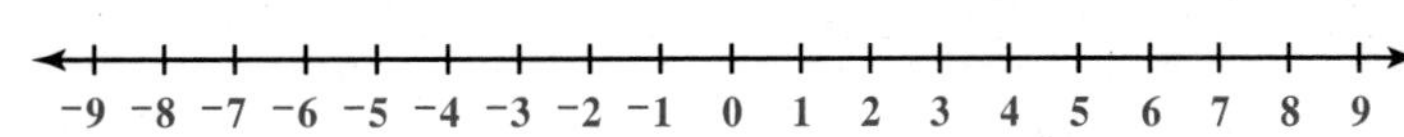

6. Start: $-3\frac{1}{3}$ End: $2\frac{1}{2}$

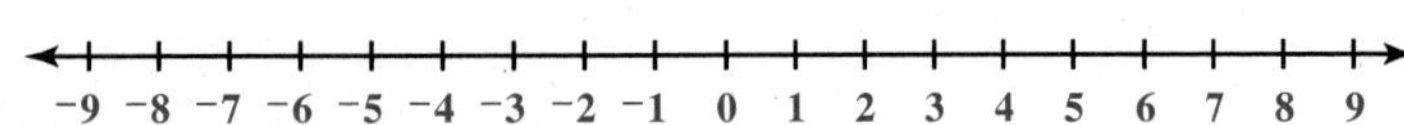

Think & Discuss Answers

① You can point the pointer toward the end point and move forward, or you can point it away from the end point and move backward.

② facing the positive direction and moving backward

③ facing the negative direction and moving backward

Think & Discuss

Describe the two ways you can move from a start point to an end point when you walk the number line. See ①.

What other move on the number line accomplishes the same thing as facing the negative direction and moving forward? See ②.

What other move accomplishes the same thing as facing the positive direction and moving forward? See ③.

In Problem Set C, you wrote two equations that started and ended at the same place on the number line. Since you started with the same number and found the same result after adding or subtracting, you're really doing *equivalent* operations.

4. $-6 + {}^-3 = -9$

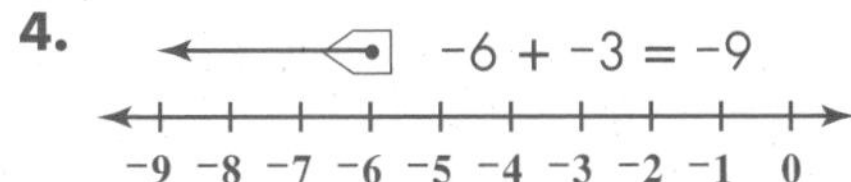

$-6 - 3 = -9$

5. $5.25 + 2.5 = 7.75$

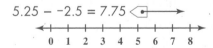

$5.25 - {}^-2.5 = 7.75$

1 Remind students to write two equations for each number line.

2
- Discuss the meaning of *equivalent*.
- Ask why students think these two equations are equivalent.

Additional Answers Problem Set C

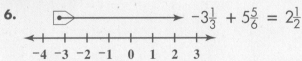

6. $-3\frac{1}{3} + 5\frac{5}{6} = 2\frac{1}{2}$

$-3\frac{1}{3} - {}^-5\frac{5}{6} = 2\frac{1}{2}$

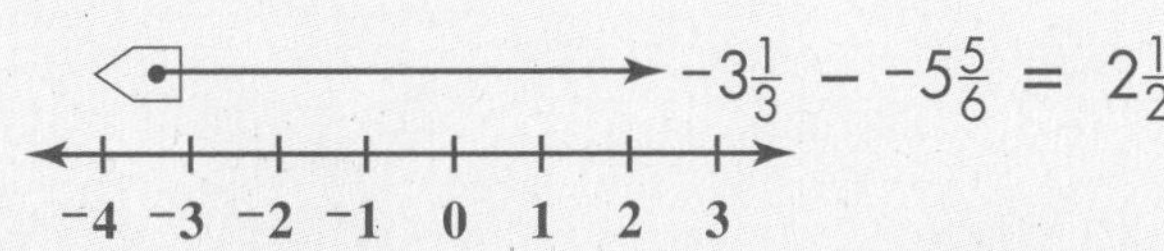

LESSON 4.1 Adding and Subtracting with Negative Numbers 229

Develop

Problem Set D **Suggested Grouping: Pairs**
This problem set asks students to write equivalent equations and solve problems. You may want to have Master 24 available for students who want to use a number line to write and solve problems. Students will need to think about scale when solving Problems 5 and 6.

In **Problems 1–4,** students find the sum or difference, write their answer as an equation, and then write an equivalent equation.

1 **Problems 5 and 6** are meant to help students make sense of equivalent equations in a problem-solving context.

2 **Sample Strategy** Students may use one of these strategies to solve **Problem 6:**

- Some students subtract the starting elevation, $^{-}600$ feet, from the ending elevation, 92 feet. These students would use this equation to solve the problem: $92 - {}^{-}600 = 692$.
- Other students will use reasoning to break apart the problem. They will add the change in elevation from $^{-}600$ feet to sea level, or 600 feet, and the change in elevation from sea level to 92 feet, or 92 feet. These students would use this equation to solve the problem: $600 + 92 = 692$.

Problem Set Wrap-Up You might want to have students share their thinking about **Problems 5 and 6.** Discussing strategies and seeing the equivalent operations in context can help students understand them better.

3 **Share & Summarize**
Students might fill in the blanks for **Questions 1–4** in a variety of ways. For example, in **Question 1,** some will complete the sentence as "Adding a negative is equivalent to subtracting a positive." Others will be more precise and write "Adding a negative is equivalent to subtracting the opposite of the negative." Regardless of how they frame the rule, all students should have a clear understanding of the two equivalent sets of operations.

You might want to have a whole-class discussion of students' answers to **Question 5.** This will give the whole class an opportunity to see several approaches to understanding these equivalencies.

Troubleshooting Students who are struggling with using signed numbers to solve problems may benefit from doing addition problems such as the two below. In these problems, equivalencies arise naturally from the context and wording of the problem.

1. Before the onset of an ice storm, the temperature outside was 7°C. After the ice storm, the temperature was $^{-}6$°C. By how much did the temperature go down? *13 degrees*
2. Raji is taking a test with 5 questions on it. For every correct answer, she gets 4 points, and for every incorrect answer, she gets $^{-}2$ points. If she gets 1 correct answer and 1 incorrect answer, what is her score on the test? 2

You may also want to explain equivalencies in terms of another model, such as the model with cubes of two colors as discussed in the Troubleshooting section of Investigation 1.

On Your Own Exercises

Practice & Apply: 26–32
Connect & Extend: 40–41
Mixed Review: 62–82

Problem Set D

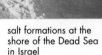

salt formations at the shore of the Dead Sea in Israel

Compute each difference, and write your answer in the form of a subtraction equation. Then write an addition equation that is equivalent to the subtraction equation.

1. $2 - 5$ $2 - 5 = ^-3$, $2 + ^-5 = ^-3$

2. $^-2 - ^-3.2$ $^-2 - ^-3.2 = 1.2$, $^-2 + 3.2 = 1.2$

Compute each sum, and write your answer in the form of an addition equation. Then write an equivalent subtraction equation.

3. $^-6 + ^-5$ $^-6 + ^-5 = ^-11$, $^-6 - 5 = ^-11$

4. $^-1 + 7\frac{1}{4}$ $^-1 + 7\frac{1}{4} = 6\frac{1}{4}$, $^-1 - ^-7\frac{1}{4} = 6\frac{1}{4}$

In Problems 5 and 6, write an addition or a subtraction equation that gives the answer to the question. Explain how your equation fits the situation.

5. When Simon went to sleep, the temperature outside was $^-2$°F. The temperature dropped 12°F overnight. What was the temperature when Simon woke up?

5. $^-2 - 12 = ^-14$ or $^-2 + ^-12 = ^-14$; See teaching notes for possible strategies.

6. Challenge Johanna was hiking near the Dead Sea. She began her hike at an elevation of $^-600$ feet and ended the day at 92 feet. What was the change in her elevation?
$^-600 + 692 = 92$ or $^-600 - ^-692 = 692$;
See teaching notes for possible strategies.

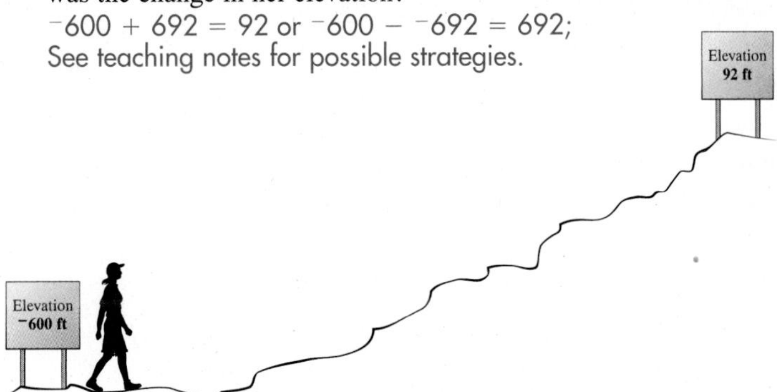

1 Students need to think about scale.

2 Discuss strategies.

Share & Summarize

Complete each sentence. The first is done for you.

1. Adding a negative is equivalent to subtracting a positive.

2. Subtracting a negative is equivalent to adding a positive.

3. Adding a positive is equivalent to subtracting a negative

4. Subtracting a positive is equivalent to adding a negative.

5. Using the number line or anything else you want, explain why the statements above are true. See Additional Answers.

3 Have students complete sentences individually before initiating class discussion.

Additional Answers
Share & Summarize

5. Possible answer: When you add a negative on the number line, you direct the pointer in the negative direction and move forward. This is a move to the left. When you subtract a positive, you direct the pointer in the positive direction and move backward. This is also a move to the left.

When you add a positive, you direct the pointer in the positive direction and move forward. This is a move to the right. When you subtract a negative number, you direct the pointer in the negative direction and move backward. This is also a move to the right.

Investigation 3

In this investigation, students practice adding and subtracting signed numbers first in situational contexts and then in a mathematical context. Students are encouraged to think more deeply about the structure of the number line and how it relates to addition and subtraction of signed numbers.

Problem Set E **Suggested Grouping: Individual**
In this problem set, students are encouraged to move away from using a physical number line to using their prior experience with number lines to solve these problems. To facilitate this transition, none of the problems in this problem set requires students to use a number line or draw a number-line picture. Allow those students who still want to use number-line pictures to do so. You may want to provide these students with Master 24, Number Lines I. Since the problems focus on temperature, you may want to have students use vertical number lines. This can ease the transition to using the four quadrants of the coordinate plane in Lesson 3.

In **Problems 1 and 2,** students use a formula to convert temperatures between Celsius and Kelvin scales. For Problem 1, students need to solve the equation $K = {}^{-}269 + 273$. For Problem 2, students need to solve the equation $1 = C + 273$.

Sample Strategy **Problem 3** is an example of how equivalent operations can be used to solve a problem. Students may use one of these strategies to solve Problem 3.

- Some students will use an algorithm to subtract the lowest temperature from the highest temperature. For example, these students will solve Part a by computing this difference: $136 - {}^{-}130$.
- Other students will solve the problem by thinking about the range in two sections: the section below zero and the section above zero. For example, these students will solve Part a by computing this sum: $130 + 136$.

Investigation  Taking It Further

Several occupations require adding and subtracting positive and negative numbers. In this investigation, you will apply what you've learned to solve some chemistry and astronomy problems. Then you will look at inequalities involving positive and negative numbers.

1 Students practice adding and subtracting positive and negative numbers in situational contexts.

Problem Set E

Temperature is usually recorded in degrees Celsius (°C) or degrees Fahrenheit (°F), but scientists often use a third scale, the Kelvin scale. The Kelvin unit is simply "kelvins," and Kelvin temperatures are abbreviated with a K. So, a temperature of 5 kelvins is written 5 K.

You can use this formula to convert a Celsius temperature, C, to a Kelvin temperature, K:

$$K = C + 273$$

2
- Discuss the meaning of the formula.
- Be sure students can use the formula before assigning problems to be worked individually.

1. Helium is usually a gas, but if it gets cold enough, it will become a liquid. The temperature at which a substance changes from gas to liquid (or from liquid to gas) is called its *boiling point.* The boiling point of helium is $^{-}269$°C. What is the boiling point of helium on the Kelvin scale? 4 K

2. If it gets even colder, helium will actually freeze into a solid. The freezing point of helium—the temperature at which it changes from liquid to solid—is 1 K. What is the freezing point of helium in degrees Celsius? $^{-}272$°C

3. Earth and its moon are about the same distance from the sun, so they receive about the same amount of heat-generating sunlight. You might expect their temperatures to be about the same, but this is not the case. Earth's temperature ranges from $^{-}130$°F to 136°F, while the moon's temperature ranges from $^{-}280$°F to 212°F.

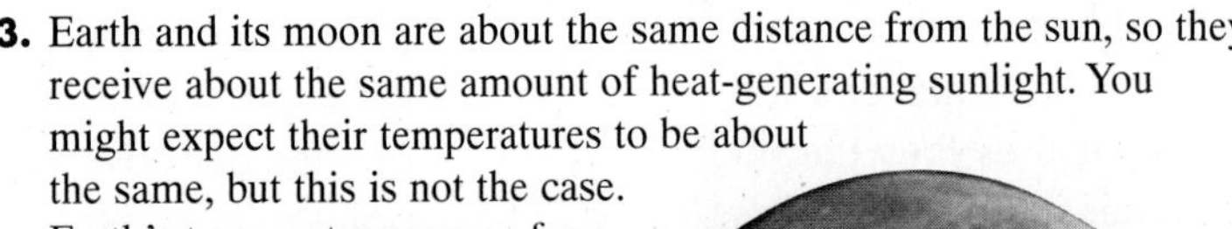

3 Discuss strategies for solving Problem 3.

   a. What is the difference between the extremes of Earth's temperature? 266°F

   b. What is the difference between the extremes of the moon's temperature? 492°F

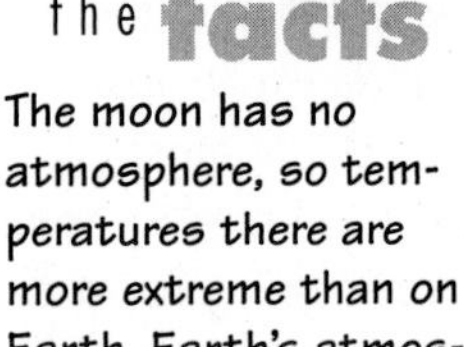

Just the facts

The moon has no atmosphere, so temperatures there are more extreme than on Earth. Earth's atmosphere shields us from some of the sun's heat during the day. At night, it traps the warm air and keeps the planet from growing too cold.

LESSON 4.1 Adding and Subtracting with Negative Numbers 231

Problem Set F **Suggested Grouping: Pairs**
This problem set was designed to take students' thinking about adding signed numbers to a higher level, using inequalities and the number line. Since this is the first time that students have used inequalities in this course, you may need to do a brief review of the definition and use of inequalities. At this point in the curriculum, it is not important that students master solving simple inequalities like the ones they solve in this problem set. They will have additional opportunities to solve inequalities later in this course and again in Course 3.

In **Problems 1–3,** students use number sense to conclude that the sum of two opposites is zero.

In **Problems 4–7,** students explore inequalities by finding missing addends that will result in a sum that is less than zero. Problem 7 provides the starting point for solving the inequality in Problem 9.

Problem 8 asks students to generalize what they did for Problems 4–7. This helps prepare students for predicting signs of sums and differences in the Investigation 4.

Students solve the inequality in **Problem 9** that was first set up in Problem 7. Suggest that students look for similarities in the three number-line pictures they created for Part a to help them find the values in Part b.

2 **Sample Strategy** Students may use one of these strategies to solve **Problem 9b:**

- Students may generalize their answers from the first part of this problem. Since $^-3 + 3 = 0$, then it follows that adding any number less than 3 will result in a sum that is less than zero.
- Students may use the commutative property and visualize the expression as $x + 3$ on the number line. These students will imagine the pointer and arrow as a single entity, or unit, representing + 3, as shown below.

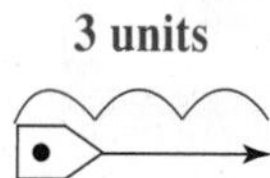

Students should realize that the only values of x that make $x + 3 < 0$ true are the values for which the arrow is on a point less than zero. As students visualize moving the unit on the number line, it soon becomes obvious that the arrow is on points less than zero only when the pointer is on points that are less than $^-3$.

- Some students will visualize the expression as $3 + x$ on a number line. This picture will have the pointer based at 3, moving in the direction the pointer is pointing. Because the sign of x is not known, we do not know which direction the pointer should point or how far the pointer should move. The two possible number-line pictures that describe $3 + x$ are the following:

Negative *x*:

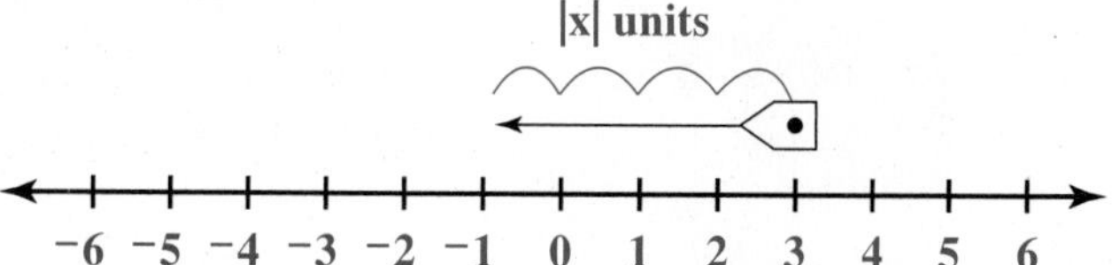

Positive *x*:

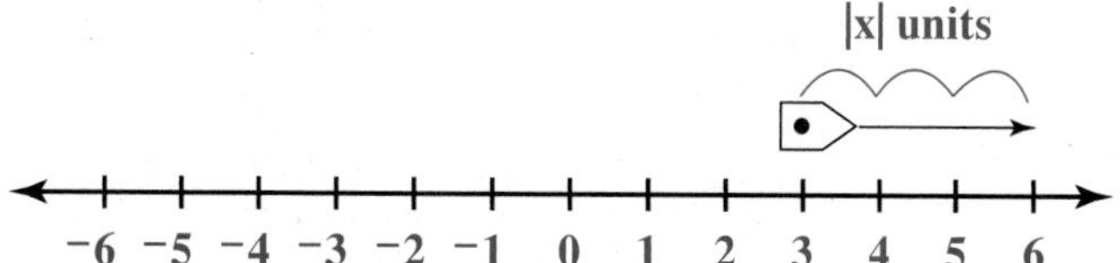

Unlike the representation for $x + 3$, what varies in these pictures is not the placement of the arrow and pointer but how far the arrow extends from the pointer. It is immediately clear that x cannot be positive since no matter how small x is, the second number-line picture *always* lands on a positive number. Once that is clear, students must figure out how to use the first number-line picture to come up with an answer. Since we are looking for a sum less than zero, the arrow must land on a value less than zero. The length of the arrow must be more than 3, so x must be less than $^-3$.

Note that for now, when you express solutions to inequalities, you probably should *not* use the standard number-line notation in which you shade parts of the number-line that are solutions to the inequality. Because the other number-line notation is similar, students may confuse the two if both are introduced in the same lesson. For example, it is not recommended that you use this notation to express the solution $x < {}^-3$:

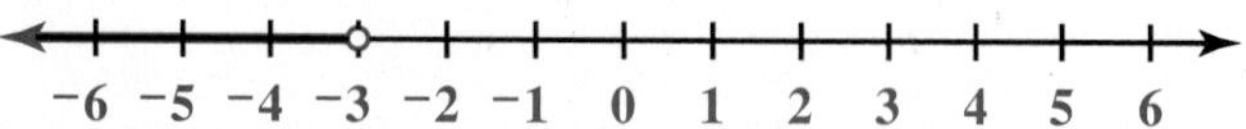

Students will have opportunities to work with the notation in later investigations.

• ***Teaching notes continued on page A390.***

In the next two problem sets, you will add and subtract with negative numbers as you solve inequalities.

Problem Set F

Tell what number you could put in each blank to make a sum of 0.

1. $3 + \underline{^-3}$

2. $^-7.2 + \underline{7.2}$

3. Look at your answers to Problems 1 and 2.

a. If you have a positive number, what number could you add to it to get a sum of 0? the opposite of the number

b. If you have a negative number, what number could you add to it to get a sum of 0? the opposite of the number

Give one number you could put in each blank to make a sum less than 0.

4. $^-6 +$ ___ Answer must be less than 6.

5. $^-4.3 +$ ___ Answer must be less than 4.3.

6. $\frac{1}{2} +$ ___ Answer must be less than $^-\frac{1}{2}$.

7. $3 +$ ___ Answer must be less than $^-3$.

8. In Problems 4–7, how did you figure out what number to put in the blank?

9. In Problem 1, you found a number that gives a sum of 0 when it is added to 3. This is the same as solving the *equation* $3 + x = 0$. In Problem 7, you found a number that gives a sum less than 0 when it is added to 3. To solve the *inequality* $3 + x < 0$, though, it isn't enough to find a single number.

a. Find three more solutions of the inequality $3 + x < 0$. Draw a number-line picture for each sum. Answers will vary.

b. Describe *all* the x values that are solutions of $3 + x < 0$. It may help to think about walking the number line. any number less than $^-3$

10. Now think about what you might do if you wanted to solve an inequality related to each of Problems 4–6.

a. What number could you add to a given positive number to get a sum less than 0? any number less than its opposite

b. What number could you add to a given negative number to get a sum less than 0? any number less than its opposite

8. Possible answer: I found the number that was 1 less than the number that would make the sum 0 (the opposite of the number).

Remember

An *inequality* is a mathematical statement that one quantity is greater than or less than another. Inequalities use these symbols:

$>$ greater than
$<$ less than
$\geq$ greater than or equal to
$\leq$ less than or equal to

1
- Students work in pairs to solve simple inequalities in mathematical contexts.
- Review the meaning of *inequality* and the symbols that can be used.

2 Discuss strategies.

Problem Set G **Suggested Grouping: Pairs**
In this problem set, students extend their thinking to include subtraction of signed numbers. They use inequalities and number lines in their explorations. The problems in the problem set mirror those in Problem Set F, so the difficulties your students faced while solving those problems may reoccur as they work though these problems. As was suggested in the prior problem set, it is not important for students to master solving simple inequalities at this time.

In **Problems 1–3,** students use number sense to determine that any number, positive or negative, subtracted from itself is zero. This should be intuitive for most students.

In **Problems 4–7,** students continue their exploration of inequalities by finding a number that can be subtracted from a given number to have a difference that is greater than zero.

> On the **Spot Assessment**
>
> In **Problems 4–7,** watch for students who solve for a difference less than zero. Most students who make this error will not have read the directions carefully. Similar problems in Problem Set F ask students to find sums less than zero, so some students may assume that since the problems are similar they should find a difference less than zero here.
>
> Other students may not be clear on the meaning of greater than and less than. Review these concepts with these students.

Problem 9 requires students to build on their explorations in Problem 7 to solve an inequality. If students have difficulty solving Problem 7, it is unlikely that they will be able to solve this problem.

In **Problem 10,** students relate their findings to the data in Problems 4–6 to generalize how to find a difference greater than zero.

Problem Set Wrap-Up Have students share their answers and strategies for solving Problem 9. Learning how others thought through the problem may help students solidify their understanding of inequalities. It may also promote a discussion on how to solve a subtraction inequality when looking for a difference greater than zero.

Share & Summarize
Students use what they have learned in their work on Problem Sets F and G to tell whether a sum or a difference is positive or negative. Although students have not been asked similar questions, they should be able to answer these questions. Encourage students to share their answers to **Question 5** with the class. Some students will use number lines or inequalities to support their answers. Other may use number sense.

Students should be comfortable with their explanations in order to continue to Investigation 4. They are asked to review their answers to these questions as they begin that investigation.

Troubleshooting Do not worry if students are not facile with solving inequalities. They will briefly touch on solving inequalities again in Investigation 3 of Lesson 3, and they will delve into solution strategies in more depth later in this course and again in Course 3. The purpose of this investigation is to get students to think creatively and flexibly about operations with signed numbers using a number line, and inequalities are a good context in which to do this.

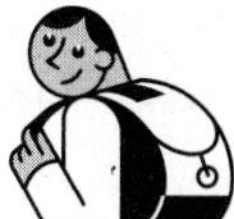

On Your Own Exercises

Practice & Apply: 33–34
Connect & Extend: 42–56
Mixed Review: 62–82

Problem Set G

Tell what number you could put in each blank to make a difference of 0.

1. $\frac{2}{3} - \underline{\frac{2}{3}}$ 2. $^-3 - \underline{^-3}$

3. Look at your answers to Problems 1 and 2.

   a. If you have a positive number, what number could you subtract from it to get a difference of 0? the number itself

   b. If you have a negative number, what number could you subtract from it to get a difference of 0? the number itself

Give one number you could put in each blank to make a difference greater than 0.

4. 7 − ___ 5. $^-2.4$ − ___ 6. $\frac{3}{4}$ − ___ 7. 5 − ___

8. In Problems 4–7, how did you figure out what number to put in the blank?

9. In Problem 7, you found a number that, when subtracted from 5, gives a difference greater than 0. That is, you found one solution of the inequality $5 - x > 0$.

   a. Find three more solutions of the inequality $5 - x > 0$. Draw a number-line picture for each difference. Answers will vary.

   b. Describe all the solutions of the inequality $5 - x > 0$. It might help to use a number-line picture. any number less than 5

10. Now think about what you might do if you wanted to solve an inequality related to each of Problems 4–6.

   a. What number could you subtract from a given positive number to get a difference greater than 0?

   b. What number could you subtract from a given negative number to get a difference greater than 0? any number less than the original number

4. Answer must be less than 7.
5. Answer must be less than $^-2.4$.
6. Answer must be less than $\frac{3}{4}$.
7. Answer must be less than 5.
8. Possible answer: I found the number that was 1 less than the number that would make the difference 0 (the opposite of the number).
10a. any number less than the original number

Have students work in pairs.

Encourage students to share strategies after completing Problem 9.

Share & Summarize

See Additional Answers.

Without doing the calculation, tell whether each sum or difference is positive or negative, and explain how you know.

1. $^-25 + 36$ 2. $^-53 - {}^-14$ 3. $45 - 87$ 4. $123 - {}^-220$

5. Choose two of Questions 1 through 4. Find the sum or difference, and explain your steps so that someone who is not in your class could understand them. You may refer to the number-line model or another method that makes sense to you.

Ask students to share answers with the class.

Additional Answers Share & Summarize

1. Positive; starting at $^-25$ and moving to the right more than 25 units gives a sum greater than 0.
2. Negative; starting at $^-53$ and moving to the right less than 53 units gives a sum less than 0.
3. Negative; starting at 45 and moving to the left more than 45 units gives a sum less than 0.
4. Positive; starting at 123 and moving to the right moves me even farther from 0 in the positive direction.
5. Possible answer: For $45 - 87 = {}^-42$, think about starting at 45 on the number line. Subtracting 87 means you move to the left 87 units. After 45 units, you're at 0, and you still have to move another 42 units to the left, so you end at $^-42$.

Investigation 4

In this investigation, students pull together what they have learned in the previous investigations as they look for rules of thumb for predicting the signs of the sums and differences of signed numbers. This investigation reinforces students' understanding of how to add and subtract signed numbers. Students develop proof techniques as they construct elementary proofs to support their opinions.

Discuss the opening paragraph with students. Tell students that they will be able to develop and test their strategies during this investigation.

Problem Set H Suggested Grouping: Individual These three problems set up the investigation by getting students to begin thinking about what signs are possible when working with particular sums and differences involving signed numbers. While it is possible to make up a sum and a difference for the first two problems, it is impossible for the third problem. This impossibility motivates the need to determine the sign of various combinations of positive and negative numbers in sums and differences. This is the focus of the remainder of the investigation.

Problem Set Wrap-Up Have individuals share their answers in small groups and reach a consensus about the details that should be included in their explanations. They can share their final solutions with the class.

Discuss the eight ways positive and negative numbers can be combined to add and subtract. Tell them that in the next problem set they will classify these combinations by looking at the sign of the answer.

Problem Set I Suggested Grouping: Pairs Students classify the sums and differences of combinations of negative and/or positive numbers as always positive, always negative, or sometimes positive, sometimes negative, and sometimes zero. At this point, the students have done enough work with "walking the number line" and addition and subtraction to be able to use the model to explain their reasoning and justify their answers, a first step toward proof.

In **Problems 1, 3, 6, and 7,** the sums or differences are either always negative or always positive. Students may use the number-line model or another strategy to show that sums or differences of particular signs are impossible.

For **Problems 2, 4, 5, and 8,** the sums and differences are sometimes negative, sometimes positive, and sometimes zero. The proof is straightforward since students need only one example of numbers whose sum or difference is positive, one example where the sum or difference is negative, and one example where it is zero.

4 **Sample Strategy** Students may use one of these strategies to find the answers to **Problems 1–8.**

- Students might use equations to prove their answers. This strategy is the most successful in Problems 2, 4, 5, and 8 where the sums or differences can be positive, negative, or zero. Following is an example of the kind of proof you can expect for Problem 2 from a student using this strategy.

  The sum of a positive number and a negative number is sometimes positive, sometimes negative, and sometimes zero. I know this because I found three sums of positive and negative numbers where one of the sums is positive, one is negative, and the other is zero.

  $$3 + {}^{-}1 = 2$$

  $$3 + {}^{-}3 = 0$$

  $$3 + {}^{-}5 = {}^{-}2$$

- They might "walk the number line" to prove their result. Following is an example of the kind of proof you can expect for Problem 6 from a student using this strategy.

  Whenever you subtract a positive number from a negative number, you get a negative number. This is because when you do this on the number line, you start with your pointer on a negative number, point it to the right, and move backward. That means you move to the left of the negative numbers. All numbers to the left of negative numbers are negative, so you must land on a negative answer.

• ***Teaching notes continued on page A391.***

Investigation 4 Predicting Signs of Sums and Differences

Look back over your answers to the Share & Summarize on the previous page. Can you always use your strategy to predict whether a sum will be positive or negative? If you can, you have a way to check that sums and differences you calculate have the correct sign.

Problem Set H

1. If possible, give an example in which the sum of a positive number and a negative number is negative. If it is not possible, explain why.
2. If possible, give an example in which the difference between two negative numbers is positive. If it is not possible, explain why.
3. If possible, give an example in which the sum of two negative numbers is positive. If it is not possible, explain why.

1. Answers will vary. The positive number must be less than the absolute value of the negative number.

2. Answers will vary. Using the form $a - b = c$, if $a > b$, then c is positive.

3. not possible; Possible explanation: When you add two negative numbers on the number line, you start to the left of 0, direct the pointer in the negative direction (to the left), and then move forward (to the left). This will always result in another number to the left of 0, which must be negative.

1 Have students complete problems individually before sharing answers in small groups.

Positive and negative numbers can be combined in sums and differences in eight ways:

- positive + positive
- positive + negative
- negative + negative
- negative + positive
- positive − positive
- positive − negative
- negative − negative
- negative − positive

You will now explore each of these combinations.

2 Discuss ways positive and negative numbers can be combined to add or subtract.

Problem Set I

3 Have students work in pairs.

Figure out whether the sums or differences in each category are

- always negative
- always positive
- sometimes positive, sometimes negative, and sometimes 0

Explain how you know you are right.

1. positive + positive
2. positive + negative
3. negative + negative
4. negative + positive
5. positive − positive
6. negative − positive
7. positive − negative
8. negative − negative

1–8. See Additional Answers.

4 Discuss strategies used to find answers to Problems 1–8.

Additional Answers
Problem Set I

1. always positive; Possible explanation: On the number line, you start to the right of 0 and move farther to the right, so the answer will be to the right of 0.
2. sometimes positive, sometimes negative, and sometimes 0; Possible explanation: These three examples show the three possibilities: $3 + {}^{-}2 = 1$, $3 + {}^{-}5 = {}^{-}3$, $3 + {}^{-}3 = 0$.
3. always negative; Possible explanation: On the number line, you start to the left of 0 and move farther to the left, so the answer will be to the left of 0.

• ***Additional Answers continued on page A391.***

In **Problem 9,** students use their answers to Problems 1–8 to look at the combinations that are sometimes negative, sometimes positive, and sometimes zero. In **Part b,** students choose one of these combinations and find the conditions that produce a positive answer, a negative answer, and a zero answer. You may want to ask different pairs of students to choose different combinations of numbers and report their findings to the class. This way you can be sure that all possibilities are investigated. This concept of classifying sums and differences will be revisited in a different context in Investigation 3 of Lesson 3.

Problem Set Wrap-Up Have a pair of students relate their finding from **Problem 9b.** This will allow all students to learn how to determine if a sum or difference will be positive, negative, or zero.

Share & Summarize

These questions require that students process some of the relationships in the investigation in reverse order. They are given the sign of a sum or difference and asked to determine the sign of the two numbers being added or subtracted. After completing the questions individually, have students share answers as a whole class.

Troubleshooting This investigation provides the only opportunity for students to focus on classifying signs of sums and differences of signed numbers. It is not crucial that rules developed in Problem Set I be memorized, but it is important that students understand why the rules work. If students are having difficulty understanding the rules, you might act out the eight cases on the number line or use another model, such as the model with cubes of two colors introduced in the Troubleshooting section of Investigation 2.

Students will briefly revisit the relationships in this investigation in Investigation 3 of Lesson 3. There they will use a 4-quadrant coordinate grid to create a visual representation of some of the relationships examined in this investigation.

On Your Own Exercises

Practice & Apply: 35–37
Connect & Extend: 57–61
Mixed Review: 62–82

9. Look at your work from Problems 1–8. See below.

a. Which combinations produce sums or differences that are sometimes negative, sometimes positive, and sometimes 0?

b. Choose one of the combinations from Part a. Figure out how you can tell—without doing the calculation—whether a given sum or difference involving that combination will produce a negative number, a positive number, or 0.

1 Use answers to Problems 1–8 to help solve Problem 9.

2 Discuss questions as a whole class.

Share & Summarize

1. The sum of two numbers is less than 0.

a. Could both numbers be negative? If so, give an example. If not, explain why not. yes; Possible example: $^-1 + ^-1 = ^-2$

b. Could both numbers be positive? If so, give an example. If not, explain why not.

c. Could one number be negative and one positive? If so, give an example. If not, explain why not.

2. The difference between two numbers is greater than 0.

a. Could both numbers be positive? If so, give an example. If not, explain why not. yes; Possible example: $9 - 3 = 6$

b. Could both numbers be negative? If so, give an example. If not, explain why not. yes; Possible example: $^-8 - ^-12 = 4$

c. Could one number be negative and one positive? If so, give an example. If not, explain why not. yes; Possible example: $6 - ^-4 = 10$

1b. No; the sum of two positives is always positive.

1c. yes; Possible example: $^-3 + 1 = ^-2$

Problem Set I Answers

9a. positive + negative, negative + positive, positive − positive, negative − negative

9b. Possible answers:
positive + negative and negative + positive: If the positive number is greater than the absolute value of the negative number, the sum will be positive. If the absolute value of the negative number is greater than the positive number, the sum will be negative. If the absolute value of the negative number equals the positive number, the sum will be 0.
positive − positive and negative − negative: If the first number is greater, the difference will be positive. If the second number is greater, the difference will be negative. If the numbers are equal, the difference will be 0.

LESSON 4.1 Adding and Subtracting with Negative Numbers 235

On Your Own Exercises

On Your Own Exercises

Investigation 1
Practice & Apply: 1–25
Connect & Extend: 38–39

Investigation 2
Practice & Apply: 26–32
Connect & Extend: 40–41

Investigation 3
Practice & Apply: 33–34
Connect & Extend: 42–56

Investigation 4
Practice & Apply: 35–37
Connect & Extend: 57–61

Assign Anytime
Mixed Review: 62–82

Exercises 1–3:
Make sure that students explain how to find the answers, and that they do not just write the equations.

Exercises 16, 17, 19, 21–23:
These problems preview solving equations with signed numbers.

Practice & Apply

In Exercises 1–3, walk the number line to find each sum or difference. Describe your steps in words. Include the following in your descriptions:

- Where on the number line you start
- The direction the pointer is facing
- Whether you move forward or backward and how far you move
- The point on the number line at which you end (the answer)
- The complete addition or subtraction equation

1. $^-8 + 5$ **2.** $8 + {}^-4$ **3.** $3 - {}^-5$

1. start $^-8$, point right, move forward 5, end $^-3$; $^-8 + 5 = {}^-3$
2. start 8, point left, move forward 4, end 4; $8 + {}^-4 = 4$
3. start 3, point left, move back 5, end 8; $3 - {}^-5 = 8$

Walk the number line to compute each sum or difference.

4. $^-6 - 3$ $^-9$

5. $^-2 + {}^-4$ $^-6$

6. $2 + {}^-11$ $^-9$

7. $^-9 - {}^-5$ $^-4$

8. $4 - 9$ $^-5$

9. $^-6 + 14$ 8

10. $^-5 - {}^-11$ 6

11. $^-3.5 - 2.2$ $^-5.7$

12. $2\frac{1}{5} - {}^-3\frac{2}{5}$ $5\frac{3}{5}$

13. $^-8.25 + 1.75$ $^-6.5$

14. $^-\frac{13}{2} - {}^-\frac{13}{4}$ $^-\frac{13}{4}$

15. $4.9 - {}^-3.2$ 8.1

Walk the number line to compute each sum or difference, and record your steps by making a number-line drawing. Write the complete addition or subtraction equation next to the drawing.

16–21. See Additional Answers.

16. $^-2 + {}^-7$

17. $6 - {}^-2$

18. $5 - 7$

19. $^-3 + 11$

20. $2.2 - 1.4$

21. $^-5\frac{1}{3} + 2\frac{5}{6}$

In Exercises 22–25, write the addition or subtraction equation represented by the drawing.

22. End: $^-6$ Start: $^-3$ $^-3 - 3 = {}^-6$

−9 −8 −7 −6 −5 −4 −3 −2 −1 0 1 2 3 4 5 6 7 8 9

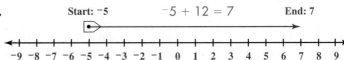

23. Start: $^-5$ $^-5 + 12 = 7$ End: 7

−9 −8 −7 −6 −5 −4 −3 −2 −1 0 1 2 3 4 5 6 7 8 9

Additional Answers

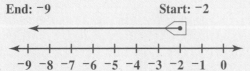

16. $^-2 + {}^-7 = {}^-9$

End: −9 Start: −2

−9 −8 −7 −6 −5 −4 −3 −2 −1 0

17. $6 - {}^-2 = 8$

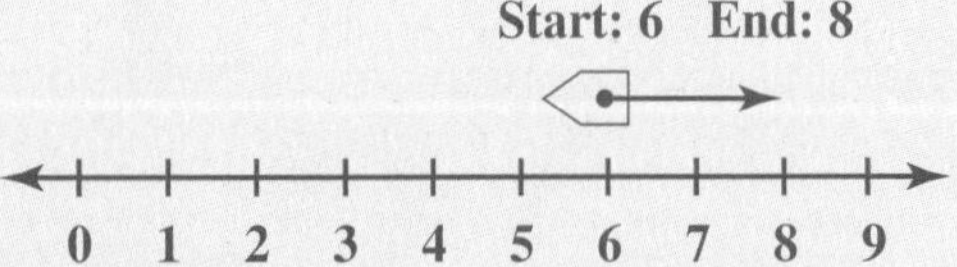

• *Additional Answers continued on page A391.*

236 CHAPTER 4 Working with Signed Numbers

24. Start: −5 $^-5 - {}^-9 = 4$ End: 4

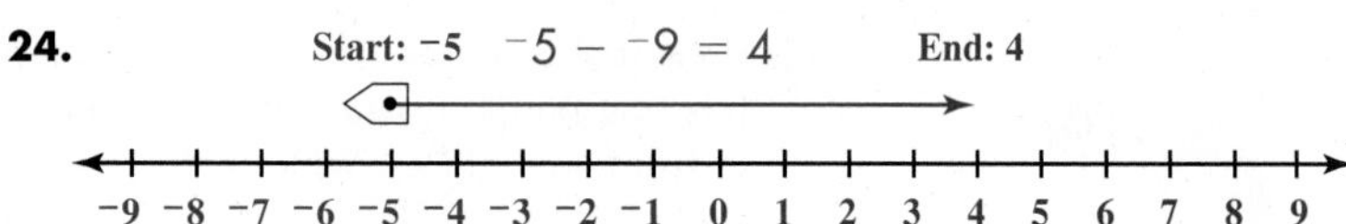

25. $2 - 11 = {}^-9$

End: −9 Start: 2

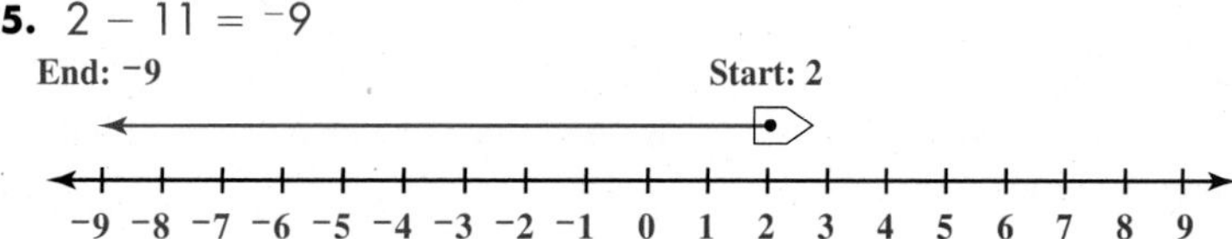

26. Possible answer: $^-3$ and $^-5$, 1 and $^-9$, $^-11$ and 3

26. The sum of two numbers is $^-8$. What could the numbers be? Give three possibilities.

Write an addition equation and a subtraction equation that each number-line picture could describe. You might want to make a drawing.

27. Start: −7 $^-7 + 16 = 9, {}^-7 - {}^-16 = 9$ End: 9

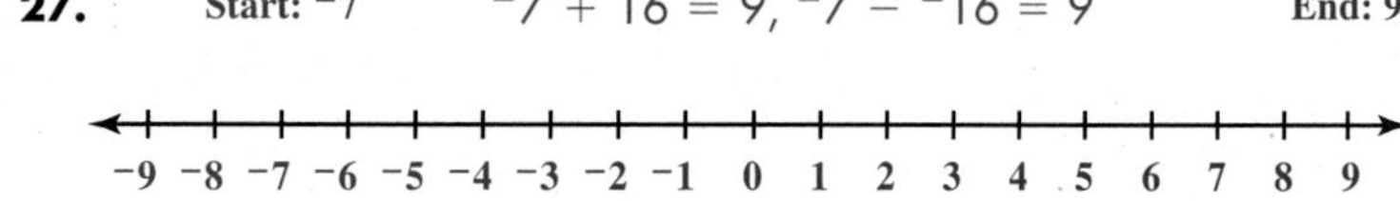

28. End: $-3\frac{3}{7}$ Start: $2\frac{1}{7}$ $2\frac{1}{7} + {}^-5\frac{4}{7} = {}^-3\frac{3}{7}$, $2\frac{1}{7} - 5\frac{4}{7} = {}^-3\frac{3}{7}$

−9 −8 −7 −6 −5 −4 −3 −2 −1 0 1 2 3 4 5 6 7 8 9

Compute each difference, and write your answer in the form of a subtraction equation. Then write an equivalent addition equation.

29. $25.2 - {}^-3.4$ $25.2 - {}^-3.4 = 28.6, 25.2 + 3.4 = 28.6$

30. $^-43 - 18$ $^-43 - 18 = {}^-61, {}^-43 + {}^-18 = {}^-61$

Compute each sum, and write your answer in the form of an addition equation. Then write an equivalent subtraction equation.

31. $^-6 + {}^-9$ $^-6 + {}^-9 = {}^-15, {}^-6 - 9 = {}^-15$

32. $^-21.8 + 17.4$ $^-21.8 + 17.4 = {}^-4.4, {}^-21.8 - {}^-17.4 = {}^-4.4$

LESSON 4.1 Adding and Subtracting with Negative Numbers 237

Assign and Assess

Exercises 38–39:
Make sure that students explain how they know their answers are correct. Otherwise, they might solve the problems by evaluating the expressions and that would defeat the purpose of the problems.

Exercise 40:
Ask students to look at the table and describe what they would do to find the average.

Remember
The formula for converting Celsius temperatures to Kelvin temperatures is $K = C + 273$.

34a. Answers will vary.
34b. Answers will vary.
34c. all values greater than $^-5$
35. not possible; Possible explanation: Subtracting a negative number is the same as adding a positive number, and the sum of two positive numbers can't be negative.
36a. no; Possible explanation: The sum of two negative numbers is always negative.

33. Physical Science At room temperature, mercury is a liquid. The freezing point of mercury—the point at which it turns from liquid to solid—is $^-39$°C. What is the freezing point of mercury on the Kelvin scale? 234 K

34. Algebra In this problem, you will solve this inequality: $^-5 - y < 0$.

a. Find three positive values of y that make the inequality true.

b. Find three negative values of y that make the inequality true.

c. Describe *all* the values of y that make the inequality true.

35. If possible, give an example in which a negative number is subtracted from a positive number and the result is negative. If it is not possible, explain why.

36. The sum of two numbers is greater than 0.

a. Could both numbers be negative? If so, give an example. If not, explain why not.

b. Could both numbers be positive? If so, give an example. If not, explain why not. yes; Possible example: $2 + 2 = 4$

c. Could one number be negative and one positive? If so, give an example. If not, explain why not. yes; Possible example: $^-3 + 5 = 2$

37. The difference between two numbers is less than 0.

a. Could both numbers be positive? If so, give an example. If not, explain why not. yes; Possible example: $2 - 5 = {}^-3$

b. Could both numbers be negative? If so, give an example. If not, explain why not. yes; Possible example: $^-5 - {}^-2 = {}^-3$

c. Could one number be negative and one positive? If so, give an example. If not, explain why not. yes; Possible example: $^-5 - 3 = {}^-8$

Connect & Extend

38, 39. See Additional Answers.

Do each computation by walking the number line. Explain each step you take.

38. $3 + {}^-4 + {}^-2 - 5$

39. $^-2 - 9 + 2 - 4 - {}^-15$

40. Statistics The chart shows the high temperature, in degrees Fahrenheit, for the first 10 days of the year in a small Alaskan town. What is the average of these temperatures? 1.1°F

Date	1/1	1/2	1/3	1/4	1/5	1/6	1/7	1/8	1/9	1/10
Temp (°F)	3	1	13	5	2	2	$^-4$	$^-7$	$^-2$	$^-2$

Additional Answers

38. $^-8$; Put the pointer on 3, facing the negative direction. Move forward 4 spaces to $^-1$. Move forward 2 more spaces to $^-3$. Direct the pointer in the positive direction and move backward 5 spaces to $^-8$.

39. 2; Put the pointer on $^-2$, facing the positive direction. Move backward 9 spaces to $^-11$. Then move forward 2 spaces to $^-9$. Then move backward 4 spaces to $^-13$. Turn the pointer in the negative direction and move backward 15 spaces to 2.

41. Luis said, "If you add $^{-}3$ to my sister's age, you will get my age." Luis is 12. How old is his sister? 15

Without calculating each sum or difference, figure out whether it is less than 0, greater than 0, or equal to 0.

42. less than 0
43. greater than 0
44. less than 0

42. $^{-}8 - 9$ **43.** $^{-}3 - {}^{-}\pi$ **44.** $^{-}78 + 2^6$

45. Copy and complete the flowchart.

$9 \xrightarrow{\times 3} 27 \xrightarrow{-20} 7$

46. *Integers* are whole numbers and their opposites: . . . , $^{-}3$, $^{-}2$, $^{-}1$, 0, 1, 2, 3, ... The sum of two negative integers is $^{-}6$.

46a. $^{-}1$ and $^{-}5$, $^{-}2$ and $^{-}4$, $^{-}3$ and $^{-}3$

a. What could the integers be? List all the possibilities.

b. Find two more pairs of negative numbers (not integers) whose sum is $^{-}6$. Possible answer: $^{-}4.2 + {}^{-}1.8$, $^{-}\frac{2}{7} + {}^{-}5\frac{5}{7}$

50. no; Possible example: $|^{-}1 + 2| \neq |^{-}1| + |2|$

Algebra Use the distributive property to rewrite each expression as simply as you can.

47. $6x - {}^{-}2x$ $8x$ **48.** $3z - 5z$ $^{-}2z$ **49.** $7x + {}^{-}2x$ $5x$

50. Prove It! Maya thinks that for all values of x and y, this equation is true:

$$|x + y| = |x| + |y|$$

For example, if x is $^{-}5$ and y is $^{-}6$, the two sides of the equation become

$$|x + y| = |^{-}5 + {}^{-}6| = |^{-}11| = 11$$

and

$$|x| + |y| = |^{-}5| + |^{-}6| = 5 + 6 = 11$$

Is Maya right? If so, explain why. If not, give an example of values for x and y such that $|x + y| \neq |x| + |y|$.

Remember

The absolute value of a number—its distance from 0—is represented with vertical lines: $|5| = 5$ because 5 is 5 units from 0, and $|^{-}7| = 7$ because $^{-}7$ is 7 units from 0.

51. Choose a number, and write down both the number and its opposite.

a. What happens when you add the two numbers? Their sum is 0.

b. Will the same thing happen when you add *any* number to its opposite? Explain why or why not.
yes; Possible explanation: Adding a number and its opposite is equivalent to subtracting the number from itself, which always has a result of 0.

Exercise 46b Extension:
There are several extension questions you could ask that are algebraic in nature, such as, How many pairs of negative integers have a sum of $^{-}7$? $^{-}8$? $^{-}9$?

Exercise 50 Extension:
Once students have determined that $|x + y| \neq |x| + |y|$, the obvious question is this "If $|x + y| \neq |x| + |y|$, what is the relationship between $|x + y|$ and $|x| + |y|$? Is one greater than the other? Is one greater than or equal to the other? Is there no relationship?" It turns out that $|x + y| \leq |x| + |y|$. You can prove this by thinking about cases: How do you show the inequality holds if x and y are negative? What if x is positive and y is negative? What if x is negative and y is positive? What if x and y are both positive? The inequality $|x + y| \leq |x| + |y|$ is known as the Triangle Inequality.

LESSON 4.1 Adding and Subtracting with Negative Numbers 239

Exercise 56: You may wish to have students who are having difficulty thinking and computing with fractions first determine the integer between $^-\frac{1}{2}$ and $^-1\frac{1}{2}$ ($^-1$) and work from that number. Then the students can use mental math or draw number lines to find the missing numbers.

Exercises 62–73: You may wish to review the laws of exponents with your students before assigning them problems.

Exercise 80: Watch for students who first compute 2 + 5 + 2 to get 9 miles as the distance Jing runs on the first Saturday, and then add 9 more miles to the 1st Saturday's 9 miles to get 18 miles (9 + 9 = 18 miles) and then continue this pattern by adding 9 miles each week to the previous week's total (9 + 9 + 9 = 27 miles). Encourage students to reread the problem. Then ask them how many miles long the ride around the park is. Some students will find that making a table helps organize the information and makes their task easier.

In your own words

Write a letter to a student a year younger than you. In the letter, explain how to subtract a negative number from another negative number. Include examples of problems in your letter.

61b. sometimes positive, sometimes negative, and sometimes 0; Possible explanation: The sum of two positive numbers is another positive. If you add that positive sum to a negative number, the sum may be positive, negative, or 0.

Algebra Solve each equation by using backtracking or another method.

52. $x + {}^-9 = 1.5$ 10.5 **53.** $y - 3 = {}^-0.5$ 2.5 **54.** $3 - x = 8.4$ $^-5.4$

55. What values of y make each inequality true?

a. $2 + y < 0$ any value less than $^-2$

b. $^-10 < 2 + y$ any value greater than $^-12$

c. $^-10 < 2 + y$ and $2 + y < 0$ any value between $^-2$ and $^-12$

56. Copy each problem, and fill in the blank with a number that gives a sum between $^-1\frac{1}{2}$ and $^-\frac{1}{2}$. See Additional Answers.

a. 10 + ___ **b.** $^-1.2$ + ___

c. $^-2$ + ___ **d.** $^-84$ + ___

e. In Parts a–d, what did you need to do to make the answer be between $^-1\frac{1}{2}$ and $^-\frac{1}{2}$?

Algebra Without solving each equation, determine whether the value of x is less than 0, equal to 0, or greater than 0.

57. $x - 3 = {}^-5$ less than 0 **58.** $^-x + 3 = 5$ less than 0

59. $4 - x = 9$ less than 0 **60.** $x - 3 = 12$ greater than 0

61. In this exercise, you will investigate the possible results for the sum of two positive numbers and a negative number.

a. Choose two positive numbers and one negative number. Is their sum positive, negative, or 0? Answers will vary.

b. Suppose you repeat Part a with different numbers. Will the sum be always positive; always negative, or sometimes positive, sometimes negative, and sometimes 0? How do you know?

Mixed Review

If possible, rewrite each expression using the laws of exponents.

62. $y^2 \times y^6$ y^8 **63.** $a^n \times a^n$ a^{2n}

64. $2b \times 3b^2$ $6b^3$ **65.** $4^5 \times 9^5$ 36^5

66. $5a^4 \times 5a^4$ $25a^8$ **67.** $a^{100} \times b^{100}$ $(ab)^{100}$

68. $(1.1^2)^4$ 1.1^8 **69.** $(0.9^4)^3$ 0.9^{12}

70. $(a^3)^4$ a^{12} **71.** $(a^4)^0$ a^0, or 1

72. $(x^2)^3$ x^6 **73.** $(3^n)^m$ 3^{nm}

Additional Answers

56a. Answers will vary; any number between $^-10\frac{1}{2}$ and $^-11\frac{1}{2}$ will work.

56b. Answers will vary; any number between $^-0.3$ and 0.7 will work.

56c. Answers will vary; any number between 0.5 and 1.5 will work.

56d. Answers will vary; any number between 82.5 and 83.5 will work.

56e. Possible answer: I know that $^-1$ is between $^-1\frac{1}{2}$ and $^-\frac{1}{2}$, so I found a number that made each sum equal to $^-1$.

Find each product.

74. $6 \times \frac{1}{10^2}$ 0.06

75. $35{,}900 \times \frac{1}{10^3}$ 35.9

76. $564{,}890 \times \frac{1}{10^2}$ 5,648.9

77. $90{,}500 \times 10^4$ 905,000,000

Copy and complete each flowchart.

78. 12 —(+ 3)→ 15 —(× 2)→ 30

79. 2.5 —(+ 5)→ 7.5 —(÷ 1.5)→ 5

80. On the first Saturday of her new weekend exercise plan, Jen bikes 2 miles to the park, 5 miles around the park on Perimeter Path, and then 2 miles back home. She plans to gradually build her workout by adding one loop on Perimeter Path each Saturday.

a. On which Saturday will Jen ride more than 25 miles? See below.

b. After the first month on her new plan (four Saturdays), what average distance will Jen have ridden each Saturday? Show how you found your answer. $(9 + 14 + 19 + 24) \div 4 = 16.5$ mi

c. How many more miles will Jen ride on the sixth Saturday than on the first Saturday? $34 - 9 = 25$ mi

d. Jen doesn't want to ride more than 50 miles in a day. After which Saturday will she stop increasing the distance she rides? What will be the distance she rides on that Saturday? See below.

Complete each table.

81.

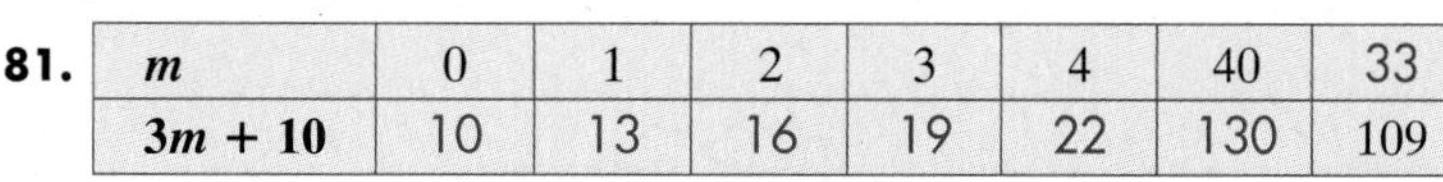

m	0	1	2	3	4	40	33
$3m + 10$	10	13	16	19	22	130	109

82.

t	1	2	4	8	11	25	31
$4t - 4$	0	4	12	28	40	96	120

80a. the fifth Saturday $(5 \cdot 5 + 4 = 29$ mi$)$

80d. the ninth Saturday, $5 \cdot 9 + 4 = 49$ mi

Quick Check

Informal Assessment

At the end of the lesson, students should be able to

- ✔ add and subtract signed numbers
- ✔ use number sense when working with signed numbers
- ✔ predict the sign of a sum or difference involving negative and positive numbers

Quick Quiz

1. Find the average of these seven numbers: $-2, -1, 0, 15, -3, 1, -4$. $\frac{6}{7}$

2. Use the "walking the number line" model to explain why adding a negative number is equivalent to subtracting the positive of that number. Possible answer: In both cases you move the same number of units to the left. When you add a negative number on the number line, you direct the pointer in the negative direction and move forward. This is a move to the left. When you subtract a positive of that number, you direct the pointer in the positive direction and move backward. This is also a move to the left.

3. Will the following sums and differences be a) always negative, b) always positive, or c) sometimes negative, sometimes positive, and sometimes zero? How can you tell?

   a. Negative number minus positive number a

   b. Negative number plus positive number c

   c. Negative number plus negative number a

Teacher Notes

4.2 Multiplying and Dividing with Negative Numbers

Objectives

- To multiply and divide with signed numbers
- To predict the sign of a product or quotient involving signed numbers
- To develop number sense with signed numbers

Overview (pacing: about 3 class periods)

In this lesson, students learn how to multiply and divide with negative numbers. Students build on their understanding of addition and subtraction of signed numbers and study patterns in computation to learn rules for multiplying and dividing with signed numbers. Students should not use calculators in this lesson unless otherwise indicated.

Advance Preparation

There are no extra materials to gather before teaching this lesson.

	Summary	Materials	On Your Own Exercises	Assessment Opportunities
Investigation 1 page T243	Students learn rules for multiplying negative and positive numbers by thinking of multiplication as repeated addition. Students then use these rules in both mathematical and situational contexts.		Practice & Apply: 1–6 Connect & Extend: 29–31 Mixed Review: 51–65	Share & Summarize, pages T244, 244 On the Spot Assessment, page T244 Troubleshooting, page T244
Investigation 2 page T245	Students learn rules for multiplying two negative numbers by examining patterns in products involving positive and negative numbers. Students then use these rules in mathematical and situational contexts.		Practice & Apply: 7–20 Connect & Extend: 32–41 Mixed Review: 51–65	Share & Summarize, pages T247, 247 On the Spot Assessment, pages T246, T247 Troubleshooting, page T247
Investigation 3 page T248	Students derive rules for dividing with signed numbers from their rules for multiplying with signed numbers. Students then use these rules in both mathematical and situational contexts.		Practice & Apply: 21–28 Connect & Extend: 42–50 Mixed Review: 51–65	Share & Summarize, pages T249, 249 Troubleshooting, page T249 Informal Assessment, page 252 Quick Quiz, page 253

Introduce

You might want to introduce multiplication and division of negative numbers by brainstorming with your class situations when it would be helpful to be able to multiply or divide signed numbers. Ask students to describe instances when they might want to multiply 4 and 2. Students' examples may include counting-type situations, such as finding the number of pens in 4 packages of 2 pens each or measurement situations such as finding the total length of four 2-foot boards. Repeat for $5 \times {}^{-}3$. Students may suggest situations such as the total yardage of 5 football plays with a 3-yard loss in each play or 5 hours with the temperature decreasing 3 degrees in each.

Explore

This Explore was designed to motivate students by illustrating the need for knowing how to multiply signed numbers. While students are able to solve the problem using skills learned in Lesson 1, it is tedious to do so.

Have students read the Explore and work the problem. You may want to have students work in pairs. When they have completed their work, discuss their answers and the strategies that students used to solve the problem. Students may use one of these strategies:

- Some students will approach the problem mechanically and compute the sum of the thirty numbers before dividing by 30.
- Some will multiply the number of days for each positive temperature by the positive temperature, then add these totals to the daily negative lows for all days with negative temperatures, and divide the sum by 30.
- Others will compute the sum of the positive temperatures separately from the negative temperatures, then add the two sums and divide the result by 30.

Regardless of the approach, students should recognize that knowing how to multiply signed numbers would make finding the average low temperature immensely easier. This may increase both students' understanding of why it is important to learn how to multiply signed numbers and their desire to learn this skill.

4.2 Multiplying and Dividing with Negative Numbers

In this lesson, you will use what you have learned about addition and subtraction of signed numbers to help you understand how to multiply and divide them.

1 Encourage students to describe situations where they might need to multiply or divide signed numbers.

This solar-powered weather instrument records data at Matanuska Glacier in Alaska.

Explore

2 Have pairs of students complete the Explore.

The table lists the lowest temperatures in degrees Celsius for each day during the month of November at a weather station in Alaska.

The first row lists the different low temperatures, and the second row tells the number of days in November with each daily low temperature. For example, the first column indicates that the low temperature was $^{-}4$°C two days during the month.

Daily Low Temperature (°C)	$^{-}4$	$^{-}3$	$^{-}2$	$^{-}1$	0	1	2	3	4
Days at This Temperature	2	1	2	4	2	3	6	6	4

Use what you learned in Lesson 4.1 to find the average low temperature during the month of November. 1°C

How did you compute the average? See ①.

① Possible answer: I added all the daily low temperatures ($^{-}4 + {}^{-}4 + {}^{-}3 + {}^{-}2 + {}^{-}2 + \ldots$) and divided by the number of days (30). (See teaching notes for other strategies.)

3 Discuss strategies with the whole class.

If you calculated the total of the temperatures by using only addition, you probably found the problem rather tedious. In this lesson, you will learn how to multiply and divide with negative numbers so you can solve problems like this one quickly and efficiently. Again, try to do the calculations without a calculator. This will help you understand why the operations work the way they do.

Investigation 1

In this investigation, students learn to multiply a positive and a negative number, a skill that would have simplified their work on the previous Explore problem. Students first calculate the product of two integers. Then they find products where at least one factor is a fraction or a decimal before using their new skill to solve problems in context.

Some students might benefit from a review of the concept of multiplication as repeated addition. It is essential that students understand this concept so that they can work on Problem Set A.

Problem Set A **Suggested Grouping: Pairs**
Students use repeated addition to multiply a negative and a positive number. You may want to have students write the expressions to show a positive number times a negative number so this strategy makes more sense. For example, in **Problem 2,** students rewrite $^-3 \times 2$ as $2 \times {}^-3$. Then they can think of 2 groups of $^-3$, or $^-3 + {}^-3$. Some students will want to "walk the number line" to compute these products. "Walking the number line" can be a helpful way to reinforce the concept of multiplication as groupings of numbers.

Problem Set Wrap-Up Be sure that all students have recorded the correct answers to these six computations. They will look for patterns in these products in the next section.

Think & Discuss
In this Think & Discuss, students begin to formalize the rules for multiplying positive and negative numbers. Ask students to look for patterns in the six computations they completed in the prior problem set. Most students will notice that the product of a positive number and a negative number is always negative. Encourage them to use this pattern to find a shortcut for performing the multiplication. Although they may use a less precise vocabulary, students should determine that they can find the product of a positive number and a negative number by multiplying their absolute values and placing a negative sign in front of the product.

About the Mathematics

The formal proof that the rules for multiplying signed numbers rely on are the definition of opposite and the distributive property. It states that if a and b are real numbers, then we want to show that $a \times {}^-b$ and $^-a \times b$ are equal to $^-(a \times b)$. We examine the first case, $a \times {}^-b$. The proof for the second case is similar. Start by adding $a \times b$ to $a \times {}^-b$. We can see that $a \times b + a \times ({}^-b) = a \times (b + {}^-b) = a \times 0 = 0$. If the sum of $a \times b$ and $a \times {}^-b$ is equal to zero, they must be opposites. So, $a \times {}^-b = {}^-(a \times b)$, as we wanted to prove.

This proof is included only to help you understand the underpinnings of the rules for multiplying with signed numbers. You probably should *not* share the proof with the class.

Problem Set B **Suggested Grouping: Pairs**
Students use multiplication rules to find the product of a negative number and a positive number. These problems help students develop number sense. They also give students experience with multiplying negative and positive numbers when at least one factor is not an integer.

In **Problems 1–4,** one number is a fraction. In **Problems 9 and 10,** both numbers are fractions. You may want to encourage students to write their answers in lowest terms.

Sample Strategies Students may use one of these strategies to find the product in **Problem 6:**

- Some students may rewrite the mixed number as an improper fraction and then multiply. These students will find $\frac{3}{2} \times {}^-20$.
- Other students may use the distributive property. These students will find $(1 \times {}^-20) + (\frac{1}{2} \times {}^-20)$. They may be able to use mental math to find the answer.

Problem Set Wrap-Up You may want to have a whole-class discussion about the strategies that students used to find the products. Students may use mental math to find many of the products. They may convert a fraction to a decimal or vice versa. For example, in Problem 5, some students may think that $0.25 = \frac{1}{4}$, and $\frac{1}{4}$ of 12 is 3 and then place the negative sign. Students may use the distributive property to solve some problems. They may also use shortcuts when multiplying two fractions.

Investigation  The Product of a Positive and a Negative

When you first learned to multiply positive numbers, you thought of multiplication as repeated addition. For example, the product of 3 and 5 can be thought of as three 5s, or 5 + 5 + 5. It can also be thought of as five 3s, or 3 + 3 + 3 + 3 + 3.

Problem Set A

Use the way of thinking described above to calculate each product.

1. $2 \times {}^{-}8$ ${}^{-}16$
2. ${}^{-}3 \times 2$ ${}^{-}6$
3. ${}^{-}5 \times 4$ ${}^{-}20$
4. $3 \times {}^{-}7.5$ ${}^{-}22.5$
5. ${}^{-}5\frac{1}{3} \times 3$ ${}^{-}16$
6. ${}^{-}1 \times 6$ ${}^{-}6$

1 Encourage partners to use repeated addition to find the answers.

Think & Discuss

Look for patterns in your computations in Problem Set A.

Can you see a shortcut you could use to compute the product of a positive and a negative number? See ①.

Use your shortcut to find each product.

$2 \times {}^{-}45$ ${}^{-}90$ ${}^{-}32 \times 11$ ${}^{-}352$

① Possible answer: Multiply the numbers as if they were both positive, and put a negative sign in front of the result.

2 Encourage students to use patterns to find a shortcut for multiplying a positive and a negative number.

Problem Set B

Now you will investigate products in which the positive number is a fraction or a decimal.

1. $\frac{1}{2} \times {}^{-}10$ ${}^{-}5$
2. $\frac{1}{3} \times {}^{-}9$ ${}^{-}3$
3. $\frac{2}{3} \times {}^{-}9$ ${}^{-}6$
4. $\frac{4}{5} \times {}^{-}15$ ${}^{-}12$
5. ${}^{-}12 \times 0.25$ ${}^{-}3$
6. $1\frac{1}{2} \times {}^{-}20$ ${}^{-}30$
7. ${}^{-}5 \times 1.2$ ${}^{-}6$
8. $3.2 \times {}^{-}1.1$ ${}^{-}3.52$
9. $-\frac{2}{3} \times \frac{3}{8}$ $-\frac{6}{24}$, or $-\frac{1}{4}$
10. $\frac{1}{7} \times -\frac{14}{3}$ $-\frac{14}{21}$, or $-\frac{2}{3}$

3
- Have partners decide which products will have a negative sign.
- Students gain experience with multiplying positive and negative numbers when at least one factor is not an integer.

Multiplying with negative numbers can help you solve some interesting problems. Use what you learned in Problem Sets A and B to complete Problem Set C.

LESSON 4.2 Multiplying and Dividing with Negative Numbers 243

Problem Set C **Suggested Grouping: Pairs**
This problem set provides students with opportunities to use their rule for multiplying positive and negative numbers in mathematical and situational contexts.

2 **Sample Strategies** Some students may use one of these strategies to solve **Problem 1b.**

- Some students will find the distance the diver has descended and then convert that measurement to an elevation. They will multiply the distance the diver descends per minute by the number of minutes she has been diving. After five minutes, the diver will have dived 50 × 5, or 250 feet. Since she is 250 feet deeper than when she began at 0 elevation, she must be at an elevation of $^-250$ feet.
- Others will approach the problem more algorithmically and consider the change in elevation. These students will think that for every minute, the diver's elevation changes by $^-50$ feet. After 5 minutes, her elevation is at $^-50 \times 5$, or $^-250$ feet.

Problem 4 should help students make sense of the rules for multiplying signed numbers. If students can think of a situational context in which it makes sense that $3 \times {}^-8 = {}^-24$, they will have a better understanding of the rule for multiplying signed numbers.

Problem 5 provides an open-ended approach. Students are given the product of two numbers and asked to find the two numbers. This problem requires combinatoric thinking as students find all possible combinations of integers that have a product of $^-14$.

On the Spot Assessment

In **Problem 5a,** watch for students who forget that the expressions $^-1 \times 14$ and $1 \times (^-14)$ have a product of $^-14$. Some students may need to be reminded that both 1 and $^-1$ are integers.

Sample Strategies Students may use one of these strategies to solve **Problem 5b:**

- Some students will derive their factor pairs from other factor pairs.
  1. Some students might multiply one factor by 2 and divide the other factor by 2. For example, given the factor pair $1 \times (^-14)$, students might multiply 1 by $\frac{1}{2}$ and multiply $^-14$ by 2 to get new factors of $\frac{1}{2} \times (^-28)$. The product of these factors is also equal to $^-14$.
  2. Other students may think about patterns when multiplying decimals. They will use these patterns to find other factor pairs. For example, they may write: $14 \times 1 = 14$
     $140 \times 0.1 = 14$
     $1400 \times 0.01 = 14$ and so on.
- Other students may use guess-check-and-improve.

Problem Set Wrap-Up You might want to highlight the strategies students use to solve Problem 1 and Problem 5b. In **Problem 1,** both strategies in the Sample Strategies sections are valuable. Understanding these strategies may help students make better sense of the rules for multiplying signed numbers.

Students may increase their number sense by listening to classmates' strategies for solving **Problem 5b.**

Share & Summarize

The Share & Summarize asks students to formalize a rule they have most likely internalized throughout the investigation. Students will revisit this rule in Investigation 3 of Lesson 3, when they create a visual representation of rules for predicting signs of products and quotients involving signed numbers.

Tips from Teachers

I post a piece of chart paper in my classroom where my class and I keep track of the rules for multiplying and dividing signed numbers. Each time we learn a new rule, we add it to the list. We keep track of rules for how to multiply and divide with signed numbers and how to predict the sign of products and quotients of signed numbers.

On Your Own Exercises

Practice & Apply: 1–6
Connect & Extend: 29–31
Mixed Review: 51–65

Problem Set C

You might want to use a calculator to help you answer Problems 1 and 2.

1. A diver jumps into the ocean from a boat. She starts at an elevation of 0 feet, and her elevation decreases 50 feet every minute.

a. What is her elevation after 1 min? $^{-}50$ ft

b. What is her elevation after 5 min? $^{-}250$ ft

c. What is her elevation after n min? $^{-}50n$ ft

In Lesson 4.1, you learned about the Kelvin temperature scale. Kelvin and Celsius temperatures are related according to the formula $K = C + 273$.

You also know that you can convert Celsius temperatures to Fahrenheit temperatures with the formula $F = \frac{9}{5}C + 32$, where C is the temperature in degrees Celsius and F is the temperature in degrees Fahrenheit.

2. Temperatures on Mercury—the planet closest to our sun—range from $^{-}173$°C to 427°C. Convert these temperatures to find the range of temperatures on Mercury in degrees Fahrenheit. $^{-}279.4$°F to 800.6°F

3. *Absolute zero,* 0 K, is theoretically the coldest anything in our universe can ever be. How many degrees Fahrenheit is absolute zero? $^{-}459.4$°F

4. Make up a word problem that requires calculating $3 \times {}^{-}8$.

5. The product of two integers is $^{-}14$. (Remember: The *integers* are the whole numbers and their opposites: . . . , $^{-}3$, $^{-}2$, $^{-}1$, 0, 1, 2, 3, ...)

a. What could the integers be? List all the possibilities. See below.

b. Find three more pairs of numbers—not necessarily integers—that have a product of $^{-}14$. Possible answer: 0.1 and $^{-}140$, $-\frac{1}{2}$ and 28, 5 and $^{-}2.8$

Solve each equation.

6. $3x = {}^{-}6$ $^{-}2$

7. $^{-}2y = 12$ $^{-}6$

8. $4x + 15 = 3$ $^{-}3$

Just the facts

The maximum depth recommended for recreational scuba diving is generally 130 feet. Beyond that depth, divers need special training and equipment to keep themselves safe from the effects of pressure.

4. Possible problem: The low temperature Monday was 0°C. The low temperature decreased by 8°C each day for the next three days. What was the low temperature on Thursday?

1 Have students work in pairs.

2 Have students discuss their strategies for solving Problem 1b.

3 Have students discuss their strategies for solving Problem 5b.

Share & Summarize

Is the product of a positive number and a negative number

- always negative?
- always positive?
- sometimes positive, sometimes negative, and sometimes 0?

always negative

5a. 1 and $^{-}14$, $^{-}1$ and 14, 2 and $^{-}7$, $^{-}2$ and 7

Investigation 2

In this investigation, students learn how to multiply two negative numbers.

Problem Set D **Suggested Grouping: Individuals**
Students observe patterns in the products of a positive and a negative number. They continue the pattern to multiply two negative numbers. Students then use a calculator to check the multiplication and verify that the pattern is correct.

In **Problem 2,** students see that as the positive factor decreases by 1, the product increases by 3. Students may explain this pattern by thinking that each decrease in the positive factor is taking away $^{-}3$, so each product will increase by 3. Understanding this connection helps students make sense of the rule for multiplying two negative numbers.

In **Problem 4,** it might be easier for some students to discover the pattern if they write all 10 products in order in one column, beginning with **Problem 1a** and ending with **Problem 3e.**

Problem Set Wrap-Up Have students share their observations about the patterns formed by the exercises in this problem set. Be sure that all students are aware of the pattern in the products before continuing. Students will use this observation in the next part of this investigation.

Think & Discuss

In Problem Set D, students observed the effects of multiplying two negative numbers. They are now asked to use that observation to make a conjecture about what the rule states. They also make sense of the rule.

Most students will say that the product of two negative numbers is equal to the product of the opposites of the negative numbers, although they may use a different vocabulary. Once students have identified the correct rule, have the class test the rule by finding the products of $^{-}5 \times {}^{-}7$ *35,* $^{-}10 \times {}^{-}90$ *900,* $^{-}2 \times {}^{-}4.4$ *8.8* and $^{-}1.2 \times {}^{-}7$ *8.4.* Then have them use a calculator to check their answers.

Investigation 2 The Product of Two Negatives

In Investigation 1, you used addition to figure out how to multiply a negative number by a positive number. You can't use that strategy with two negative numbers, because you can't add a negative number of times! However, the pattern in products of a positive number and a negative number can help you figure out how to multiply two negative numbers.

1 Students study patterns to help them multiply two negative numbers.

Problem Set D

1. Find each product.
   a. $^-3 \times 4$ $^-12$
   b. $^-3 \times 3$ $^-9$
   c. $^-3 \times 2$ $^-6$
   d. $^-3 \times 1$ $^-3$
   e. $^-3 \times 0$ 0
2. In Problem 1, what happens to the product from one part to the next? Why?

   2. The product increases by 3 because each time the number being multiplied by $^-3$ decreases by 1; the product includes one fewer "group" of $^-3$.
3. Now use your calculator to compute these products.
   a. $^-3 \times {^-1}$ 3
   b. $^-3 \times {^-2}$ 6
   c. $^-3 \times {^-3}$ 9
   d. $^-3 \times {^-4}$ 12
   e. $^-3 \times {^-5}$ 15
4. Did the pattern you observed in Problem 2 continue? yes

Think & Discuss

Look for patterns in your computations in Problem Set D. What do you think the rule is for finding the product of *any* two negative numbers? Possible answer: The product is equal to the product of the opposites of the negative numbers.

Use your rule to find each product. Check your results with your calculator.

$^-5 \times {^-7}$ 35 $^-10 \times {^-90}$ 900 $^-2 \times {^-4.4}$ 8.8 $^-1.2 \times {^-7}$ 8.4

2 • Discuss the rule.
• Test the rule by finding the products.

LESSON 4.2 Multiplying and Dividing with Negative Numbers 245

Develop

You may want to review the four ways to combine positive and negative numbers and the sign of their products before students complete Problem Set E.

positive × positive	answer: positive
positive × negative	answer: negative
negative × positive	answer: negative
negative × negative	answer: positive

2

Problem Set E **Suggested Grouping: Pairs**
In this problem set, students practice multiplying two negative numbers in mathematical contexts. The first two problems give students an opportunity to reverse the process they have been doing. Instead of calculating products of given numbers, students are given products and must determine the multiplier and multiplicand. In the last three problems, students solve equations.

On the **Spot Assessment**

Watch for students who forget to count negative numbers and 1 and $^{-}1$ as integers in **Problems 1 and 2.**

In **Problems 4 and 5,** students solve equations with two operations. Remind students to keep in mind the order of operations as they solve for x.

Access for all Learners

Extra for Experts If your class is interested in problems like **Problems 1 and 2,** there are a number of extension questions that they could examine. Every number has a certain number of factor pairs that produce that number. In Problem 1, students found that 12 has 6 factor pairs. Have students examine the relationship between a product and how many factor pairs have that product. Some relationships students may find are that prime numbers always have 2 pairs, squares of prime numbers always have 3 pairs, and square numbers in general have an odd number of factor pairs.

Problem Set Wrap-Up You may wish to have students discuss how they solve the equations in **Problems 3–5.** Some students may look for missing factors in Problem 3. They may ask $^{-}4$ times what number equals 12. Others students may use backtracking or draw a flowchart.

Example

Discuss the convention for notation of exponents and negative numbers. Students already know that the placement of parentheses can change the value of an expression. Explain how the placement of the parentheses can affect the value of a negative number and an exponent.

Walk students through the Example, stressing how the order of operations can be used to evaluate the expression. To help students differentiate between $(^{-}2)^4$ and $^{-}2^4$, encourage students to read $^{-}2^4$ as the opposite of 2^4, not as negative 2^4. You may also want the whole class to work through some additional examples.

Additional Examples

Notation	Meaning	Calculation
$(^{-}5)^2$	$^{-}5$ squared	$^{-}5 \cdot {}^{-}5 = 25$
$^{-}5^2$	square 5, then take the opposite	$^{-}(5 \cdot 5) = {}^{-}25$
$(^{-}3)^3$	$^{-}3$ cubed	$^{-}3 \cdot {}^{-}3 \cdot {}^{-}3 = {}^{-}27$
$^{-}3^3$	cube 3, then take the opposite	$^{-}(3 \cdot 3 \cdot 3) = {}^{-}27$

There are four ways to combine positive and negative numbers in products:

- positive × positive
- positive × negative
- negative × positive
- negative × negative

You now know how to multiply each combination, and what kind of results to expect.

1 Review the four ways to combine positive and negative numbers in products.

Problem Set E

If you know the result of a multiplication, can you figure out what the factors might have been? Try these problems.

2 Students reverse the process they have been doing.

1. The product of two integers is 12. What could the integers be? List all the possibilities.

1. 1 and 12, $^-1$ and $^-12$, 2 and 6, $^-2$ and $^-6$, 3 and 4, $^-3$ and $^-4$

2. The product of *three* integers is 12. What could the integers be? List all the possibilities.

2. 1, 1, and 12; 1, $^-1$, and $^-12$; $^-1$, $^-1$, and 12; 1, 2, and 6; 1, $^-2$, and $^-6$; $^-1$, 2, and $^-6$; $^-1$, $^-2$, and 6; 1, 3, and 4; 1, $^-3$, and $^-4$; $^-1$, 3, and $^-4$; $^-1$, $^-3$, and 4; 2, 2, and 3; 2, $^-2$, and $^-3$; $^-2$, $^-2$, and 3

Solve each equation.

3 Review order of operations.

3. $^-4x = 12$ $^-3$

4. $^-3x + 5 = 11$ $^-2$

5. $3 - 4x = {}^-17$ 5

When you use exponents to indicate repeated multiplication of a negative number, you need to be careful about notation. Put the negative number *inside* the parentheses, and put the exponent *outside* the parentheses.

4 After discussing the Example, have the class work through the Additional Examples on page T246.

EXAMPLE

Calculate $(^-2)^4$ and $^-2^4$.

Notation	Meaning	Calculation
$(^-2)^4$	$^-2$ to the fourth power	$^-2 \cdot {}^-2 \cdot {}^-2 \cdot {}^-2 = 16$
$^-2^4$	the opposite of 2^4	$^-(2 \cdot 2 \cdot 2 \cdot 2) = {}^-16$

Develop

Problem Set F **Suggested Grouping: Pairs**
Students practice computing with signed numbers and exponents. They are required to think algebraically as they come up with a rule for determining whether any given power of $^-2$ will be positive or negative. Then they solve equations with two answers.

> On the **Spot Assessment**
>
> **In Problems 1–4,** watch for students who confuse the meanings of parentheses in negative numbers with exponents. The similarity of Problems 1 and 2 and of Problems 3 and 4 can help catch this error early. Have students write out the calculation for each problem. For example, in Problem 1, $(^-3)^2 = {^-3} \cdot {^-3} = 9$.

It may be hard for some students to articulate their thinking in **Problem 11.** Many students will say that every other number in the pattern is positive. Push these students to pinpoint a concise description of the pattern. You can check their understanding by asking questions such as:

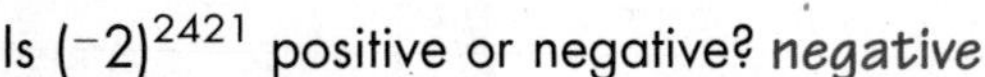

Is $(^-2)^{2421}$ positive or negative? *negative*

2 **Problem 12** represents the first time students have had to think about more than one solution to an equation. These equations have both positive and negative solutions. You might want to point out to the class that now that they can operate with signed numbers, they should look for solutions to equations that are negative, positive, and zero.

3

Share & Summarize

Question 1 asks students to formalize the rule they have been internalizing throughout the investigation. As was mentioned previously, this rule will show up again in Investigation 3 of Lesson 3, where students create a visual representation of operations with signed numbers on the coordinate plane.

Question 2 asks students to make a generalization about taking signed numbers to positive integer powers. They should be able to use thinking similar to that used in Problem 4 of Problem Set F, but at a more general level here.

Troubleshooting The reason a negative number times a negative number is equal to a positive number is very difficult to understand, even for most adults. As long as students know the rule well and can see how this definition might have grown out of the pattern developed in multiplying negatives and positives, you should not be concerned if students do not completely understand why this rule works.

On Your Own Exercises

Practice & Apply: 7–20
Connect & Extend: 32–41
Mixed Review: 51–65

Problem Set F

Evaluate each expression.

1. $(^-3)^2$ 9
2. $^-3^2$ $^-9$
3. $^-4^2$ $^-16$
4. $(^-4)^2$ 16
5. $(^-2)^1$ $^-2$
6. $(^-2)^2$ 4
7. $(^-2)^3$ $^-8$
8. $(^-2)^4$ 16
9. $(^-2)^5$ $^-32$
10. $(^-2)^6$ 64
11. Look for patterns in your answers to Problems 5–10.
    a. For what values of n is $(^-2)^n$ positive? even values
    b. For what values of n is $(^-2)^n$ negative? odd values
12. Simon said the solution of $x^2 = 16$ is 4. Luis said there is another solution. Is Luis correct? If so, find the other solution.

Solve each equation. Be careful: Each equation has two solutions.

13. $x^2 = 36$ 6 or $^-6$
14. $x^2 = \frac{1}{36}$ $\frac{1}{6}$ or $^-\frac{1}{6}$

Share & Summarize Answer

2b. negative; Possible explanation: An odd exponent means the base will be multiplied an odd number of times. Grouping in pairs will leave one factor by itself. The pairs will each multiply to give a positive number, and then multiplying by the extra factor makes the entire product negative.

12. Luis is correct. The other solution is $^-4$.

Share & Summarize

1. Is the product of two negative numbers always positive
   - always negative?
   - always positive?
   - sometimes positive, sometimes negative, and sometimes 0?
2. Consider the expression $(^-3)^m$.
   a. If m is an even number, is $(^-3)^m$ positive or negative? How can you tell?
   b. If m is an odd number, is $(^-3)^m$ positive or negative? How can you tell? See above.

2a. positive; Possible explanation: An even exponent means the base will be multiplied an even number of times. That means there will be pairs of factors whose product is positive, so the entire product will be positive.

1 Have pairs of students find answers to the first ten problems and then look for a pattern in their answers for Problems 5–10.

2 Students find two solutions to an equation.

3 After students complete questions individually, discuss each question with the whole class.

Investigation 3

In this investigation, students learn how to divide with signed numbers. Since division rules are derived from their work with multiplying with negative numbers in previous investigations, we spend only one investigation on developing rules for dividing with signed numbers.

Tell students that the numbers they have used in this lesson are *rational numbers.* That is, each number can be written as a quotient of two integers, with a divisor not equal to 0. All other numbers are *irrational numbers.*

Terminating and *repeating decimals* are rational numbers. Students should remember that a terminating decimal ends, and that they can easily convert a terminating decimal to a fraction by using place values. For example, $0.75 = \frac{75}{100}$. They can then divide the numerator and denominator by the same number to write the fraction in lowest terms: $\frac{75}{100} \div \frac{25}{25} = \frac{3}{4}$, so $0.75 = \frac{3}{4}$.

A repeating decimal repeats a pattern of digits, such as the 6 in $0.\overline{6}$ and 21 in $0.\overline{21}$. The repeating digits are designated by drawing a bar over the digits.

Students should also recognize that the value of π they used when calculating areas and circumferences of circles cannot be written as a terminating or repeating decimal, so π is not a rational number.

After students read the cartoon, you might want to walk students through a few examples of how Kate's thinking can be used to solve division problems with negative numbers.

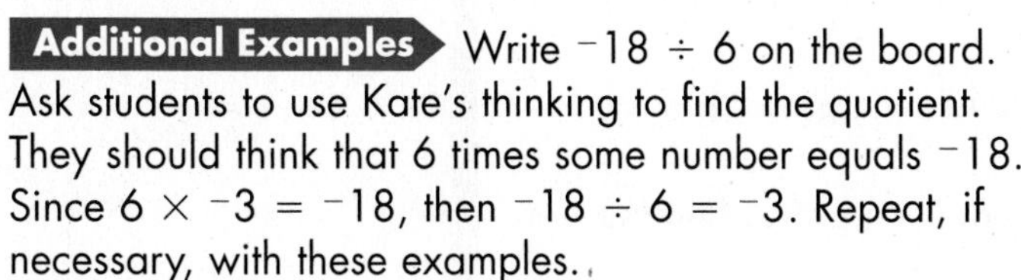

1 **Additional Examples** Write $^-18 \div 6$ on the board. Ask students to use Kate's thinking to find the quotient. They should think that 6 times some number equals $^-18$. Since $6 \times {}^-3 = {}^-18$, then $^-18 \div 6 = {}^-3$. Repeat, if necessary, with these examples.

1. $^-10 \div {}^-5$ 2
2. $12 \div {}^-3$ $^-4$

2 **Problem Set G** **Suggested Grouping: Pairs**
In this problem set, students learn how to divide with signed numbers by transforming division problems into multiplication problems.

Access for all Learners

Extra Help In this problem set, some students may have difficulty using Kate's method to find the quotients that are fractions or decimals. Since the point of solving these problems is to understand division and to find patterns in the quotients, allow these students to use Kate's methods to solve these problems with whole-number quotients. They show the same patterns as the problems in the text.

1. $^-42 \div 6$ $^-7$
2. $^-15 \div {}^-5$ 3
3. $21 \div {}^-3$ $^-7$
4. $\frac{-8}{-4}$ 2
5. $\frac{-16}{4}$ $^-4$
6. $\frac{12}{-2}$ $^-6$
7. $^-35 \div {}^-7$ 5
8. $\frac{-9}{-9}$ 1

Problem Set Wrap-Up Be sure that students have the correct answers for all problems so that they can look for patterns in the following Think & Discuss section.

Think & Discuss

Students use the patterns they observe in their calculations in Problem Set G to conjecture about the rule for dividing signed numbers. Some students may benefit from grouping like problems. They may want to circle problems with one negative number or write like problems in one column on their paper. This will help these students to focus on the relevant problems when looking for the patterns.

Students should find these two shortcuts for finding quotients:

1. When one number is negative, divide the absolute value of the numbers and place a negative sign in front of the quotient.
2. When both numbers are negative, divide the absolute values of the numbers. The result is a positive number.

Have students use their shortcuts to complete the division exercises in this section of the text.

Investigation 3 Dividing with Negative Numbers

You can solve any division problem by thinking about a corresponding multiplication problem. Look at how Kate solves 30 ÷ 5.

Problem Set G

Use Kate's method to solve each division problem.

1. $21 \div {}^{-}3$ $^{-}7$

2. ${}^{-}64 \div {}^{-}2$ 32

3. ${}^{-}24 \div 48$ $^{-}0.5$, or $-\frac{1}{2}$

4. ${}^{-}2 \div {}^{-}32$ $\frac{1}{16}$, or 0.0625

5. $-\frac{6}{5}$ $^{-}1.2$, or $-1\frac{1}{5}$

6. $\frac{9}{{}^{-}27}$ $-\frac{1}{3}$, or $^{-}0.33$

7. ${}^{-}2.16 \div {}^{-}54$ 0.04

8. $\frac{{}^{-}3}{{}^{-}0.3}$ 10

Think & Discuss

Look for patterns in your computations in Problem Set G.

- Can you see a shortcut for computing a quotient when exactly one of the numbers is negative? Possible answer: Divide the absolute values of the numbers, and put a negative sign in front of the result.
- Can you see a shortcut for computing the quotient of two negative numbers? Possible answer: Divide the absolute values of the numbers.

Use your shortcut to find each quotient.

$44 \div {}^{-}2.2$ $^{-}20$ $-\frac{7}{3}$ $^{-}2.33$, or $-2\frac{1}{3}$ ${}^{-}56 \div {}^{-}2$ 28

1 Use Kate's thinking to solve the Additional Examples on page T248 as a class.

2 Have students work in pairs to solve each problem.

3 Discuss the two shortcuts for finding quotients.

Problem Set H **Suggested Grouping: Pairs**
Students practice dividing signed numbers in situational contexts. They also backtrack to solve equations.

The scuba setting in **Problems 1–2** was first introduced in Problem Set C. These problems can be solved using strategies similar to the ones used in that problem set. Students can consider the distance of the dive and solve the problems without using negative numbers. They could consider the elevations and use negative numbers to solve the problem. You can help students make sense of the rules for dividing with signed numbers by comparing the two sets of strategies for each problem.

Sample Strategy **Problem 3** is similar in nature to the fifth problem in Problem Set C and invites a similar kind of approach. Students may use one of these strategies to solve this problem:

- Some students will come up with one pair of numbers whose quotient is $^-4$ and then derive the other pairs from the first pair. For example, students might see that $^-4$ divided by 1 is equal to $^-4$. They might then multiply each factor by the same number and find these number pairs: $^-8$ divided by 2; 12 divided by $^-3$, and so on.
- Other students may think of basic facts with a quotient of 4 and use rules to place the negative sign in the dividend or divisor to find a negative quotient.

In **Problems 4–7** students backtrack to solve equations. You may want to remind students that they can substitute their answer for *x* in the equations and simplify their expression to check their answers.

3

Share & Summarize
Although these Share & Summarize questions look similar to the ones in Investigations 1 and 2, they are different because they ask students to justify their answers. You might want to have several members of the class explain to the whole group their thinking for these two questions.

Troubleshooting Students should leave this investigation feeling fairly comfortable about dividing with signed numbers. Although they will have plenty of opportunities in subsequent investigations to practice what they have learned in various mathematical contexts, this is their main opportunity to focus on the operation and try to make sense of it. If students are having difficulty understanding how division works, you might try to explain the rules by having them think of division problems of the form $n \div m$ as $n \times \frac{1}{m}$.

On Your Own Exercises

Practice & Apply: 21–28
Connect & Extend: 42–50
Mixed Review: 51–65

Just the facts

Water exerts pressure on a scuba diver—the deeper the diver, the greater the pressure. Divers are trained to make the pressure in the body's air spaces—the lungs, sinuses, and ears—equal to the outside water pressure.

Problem Set H

1. Suppose a scuba diver begins his dive at an elevation of 0 feet. During the dive, his elevation changes at a constant rate of $^-2$ feet per second. How long will it take for him to reach an elevation of $^-300$ feet? 150 s, or 2.5 min

2. The Marianas Trench, south of Guam, contains the deepest known spot in the world. This spot, called Challenger Deep, has an elevation of $^-36{,}198$ feet. Suppose a deep-sea diver entered the ocean above this spot. She started at an elevation of 0 feet and moved at a constant rate of $^-50$ feet per minute. If the diver were able to go deep in the ocean without being affected by the pressure, and her tank contained enough air, how long would it take her to reach the bottom of Challenger Deep? 723.96 min, or slightly more than 12 h

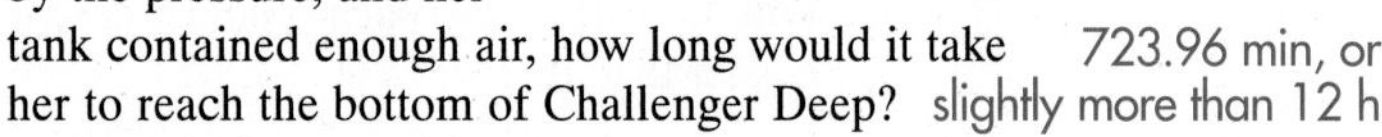

3. Write four division problems with a quotient of $^-4$. Possible answer: $20 \div {^-5}$, $^-16 \div 4$, $12 \div {^-3}$, $24 \div {^-6}$

Solve each equation.

4. $\frac{30}{x} = {^-15}$ $^-2$
5. $\frac{x}{-4} = 20$ $^-80$
6. $-\frac{x}{6} + 1 = \frac{4}{3}$ $^-2$
7. $\frac{6}{x} + 5 = 3$ $^-3$

Share & Summarize

See Additional Answers.

1. When you divide a positive number by a negative number, is the result always negative; always positive; or sometimes positive, sometimes negative, and sometimes 0? Explain how you know.
2. When you divide a negative number by a positive number, is the result always negative; always positive; or sometimes positive, sometimes negative, and sometimes 0? Explain how you know.
3. When you divide a negative number by a negative number, is the result always negative; always positive; or sometimes positive, sometimes negative, and sometimes 0? Explain how you know.

1 Have students work in pairs.

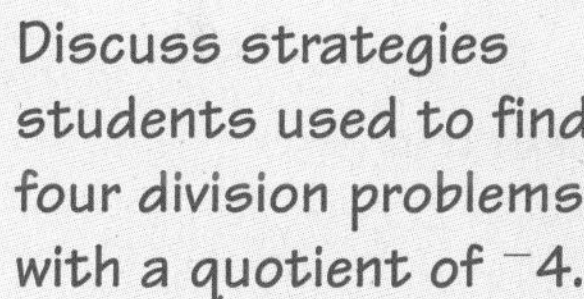

2 Discuss strategies students used to find four division problems with a quotient of $^-4$.

3
- Have individual students write answers to each question.
- Encourage volunteers to explain how they know the answers are right.

Additional Answers
Share & Summarize

1. always negative; Possible explanation: The result is the number you need to multiply the negative number by to get the positive number. This cannot be positive, because a positive times a negative is negative. It cannot be 0, because 0 times a negative number is 0.
2. always negative; Possible explanation: The result is the number you need to multiply the positive number by to get the negative number. This cannot be positive, because a positive times a positive is positive. It cannot be 0, because the product of 0 and a positive number is 0.
3. always positive; Possible explanation: The result is the number you need to multiply one of the negative numbers by to get the other. This cannot be negative, because a negative times a negative is positive. It cannot be 0, because the product of 0 and a negative number is 0.

LESSON 4.2 Multiplying and Dividing with Negative Numbers 249

On Your Own Exercises

On Your Own Exercises

Investigation 1
Practice & Apply: 1–6
Connect & Extend: 29–31

Investigation 2
Practice & Apply: 7–20
Connect & Extend: 32–41

Investigation 3
Practice & Apply: 21–28
Connect & Extend: 42–50

Assign Anytime
Mixed Review: 51–65

Exercise 4:
Students need to use the order of operations to evaluate the expression.

Exercise 25 Extension:
You may want to share the three possible answers given to show that three equations that are multiples of one another are equivalent, even when the multiple is $^-1$.

Practice & Apply

5a. 1 and $^-15$, $^-1$ and 15, 3 and $^-5$, $^-3$ and 5

5b. Possible answer: $^-45$ and $\frac{1}{3}$, 1.5 and $^-10$, $-\frac{3}{5}$ and 25

Compute each product or sum.

1. $^-3 \times 52$ $^-156$

2. $6.2 \times {}^-5$ $^-31$

3. $^-0.62 \times 5$ $^-3.1$

4. $^-2 \times 4 + 3 \times {}^-4$ $^-20$

5. The product of two integers is $^-15$.

a. What could the integers be? List all the possibilities.

b. Find three more pairs of numbers—not necessarily integers—with a product of $^-15$.

6. Solve $^-3x + 4 = 13$. $^-3$

Compute each product.

7. $^-3 \cdot {}^-32$ 96

8. $-\frac{1}{2} \cdot {}^-35$ 17.5

9. $^-5 \cdot {}^-0.7$ 3.5

10. $^-2.5 \cdot {}^-7$ 17.5

11. $^-2^5 \cdot {}^-3$ 96

12. $^-3 \cdot {}^-5^3$ 375

13. $^-3 \cdot ({}^-5)^3$ 375

14. $^-3^2 \cdot ({}^-3)^2$ $^-81$

Without calculating each product, determine whether it is less than 0 or greater than 0.

15. $3 \times {}^-2$ less than 0

16. 3×2 greater than 0

17. $^-3 \times 2$ less than 0

18. $^-3 \times {}^-2$ greater than 0

19. The product of two integers is 9. What could the integers be? List all the possibilities. 3 and 3, $^-3$ and $^-3$, $^-1$ and $^-9$, 1 and 9

20. Solve $^-5y + 13 = 3$. 2

Find each quotient.

21. $^-3 \div 2.5$ $^-1.2$

22. $^-3 \div {}^-25$ 0.12

23. $45 \div {}^-360$ $^-0.125$, or $-\frac{1}{8}$

24. $\frac{^-45}{^-90}$ 0.5, or $\frac{1}{2}$

25. One number divided by a *negative* number is 0.467. What could the two numbers be? Think of three possibilities and write them as division equations. Possible answer: $^-467 \div {}^-1{,}000$; $^-46.7 \div {}^-100$; $^-4.67 \div {}^-10$

Solve each equation.

26. $\frac{x}{^-3} + 4 = 6$ $^-6$

27. $\frac{x}{8} - 2.5 = {}^-3$ $^-4$

28. $-\frac{12}{x} + 45 = 49$ $^-3$

In your own words

Write a letter to a student a year younger than you. In the letter, explain how to divide a negative number by another negative number. Include example problems in your letter.

Connect & Extend

29. As a parachutist descends into Death Valley, her elevation decreases 15 feet every second. Five seconds before she lands, she is at an elevation of $^{-}127$ feet. What is the elevation of the place she lands? $^{-}202$

30. Physical Science When it is cold outside and the wind is blowing, it feels colder than it would at the same temperature without any wind. Scientists call the temperature that it feels outside the *windchill.*

For example, if the temperature outside is 20°F and the wind speed is 20 mph, the equivalent windchill temperature is about $^{-}10$°F. That means that even though the thermometer reads 20°F, it *feels* as cold as it would if you were in no wind at $^{-}10$°F.

Here's how meteorologists calculate windchill. The variable s represents wind speed in mph, and t represents actual temperature in °F.

$$\text{windchill} = 0.0817(3.71\sqrt{s} + 5.81 - \tfrac{s}{4})(t - 91.4) + 91.4$$

This formula works when wind speeds are between 4 mph and 45 mph.

a. If the wind blows at 20 mph and the temperature is $^{-}5$°F, what is the windchill? about $^{-}46$°F

b. If the wind blows at 30 mph and the temperature is $^{-}10$°F, what is the windchill? about $^{-}63$°F

c. Challenge If the wind blows at 25 mph and the windchill is $^{-}60$°F, what is the actual temperature? about $^{-}11$°F

31. Zoe said, "I'm thinking of a number. When I multiply my number by $^{-}2$ and subtract 4, I get $^{-}16$." What is Zoe's number? 6

Without calculating, predict whether each product is less than 0, equal to 0, or greater than 0.

32. $(^{-}4)^3 \cdot (^{-}2)^2$

33. $(^{-}3)^5 \cdot (^{-}6)^3$

34. $(^{-}1)^5 \cdot 5^2$

35. $(^{-}2)^2 \cdot (^{-}972)^{90}$

36. $^{-}45^2 \cdot (^{-}35)^5$

37. $(^{-}2)^n \cdot (^{-}5)^n$

Challenge If possible, solve each equation. If it is not possible, explain why.

38. $y^3 = {}^{-}8$ $^{-}2$

39. $x^2 = {}^{-}9$

Describe the values of b that make each inequality true.

40. $3b < 0$ b must be less than 0.

41. $3(b - 2) < 0$ b must be less than 2.

32. less than 0
33. greater than 0
34. less than 0
35. greater than 0
36. greater than 0
37. greater than 0
39. Not possible; no real number multiplied by itself yields a negative number.

Exercise 30:
Although the calculation of windchill is messy and involved, students should be able to do it with the help of a calculator.

Exercises 32–36:
Make sure that students explain how they figured out their answers for this question. Otherwise, students might compute the products to get their answers, and that would defeat the purpose of the problem.

Assign and Assess

Exercises 45–46:
Watch for students who divide $^{-}21$ by 10 in Exercise 45 and by 5 in Exercise 46. Review the meaning of average with these students.

Exercise 64 Extension:
Ask students to compare the answers for each part. About how many times greater was the volume of the cylinder when its radius was doubled? About how many times larger was the volume of the cylinder when its height was doubled? Find the volume of 3 other cylinders and do the same to their radii and heights. Check to see whether this is always true.

Quick Check

Informal Assessment
At the end of the lesson, students should be able to

✔ multiply and divide with signed numbers

✔ predict the sign of a product or quotient involving signed numbers

✔ demonstrate number sense with signed numbers

---

42. less than $^{-}1$
43. between 0 and 1
44. less than $^{-}1$
45. Answers will vary. The sum of the temperatures must be $^{-}210$°F.
46. Answers will vary. The sum of the temperatures must be $^{-}105$°F.

Without calculating, determine whether the quotient in Exercises 42–44 is less than $^{-}1$, between $^{-}1$ and 0, between 0 and 1, or greater than 1.

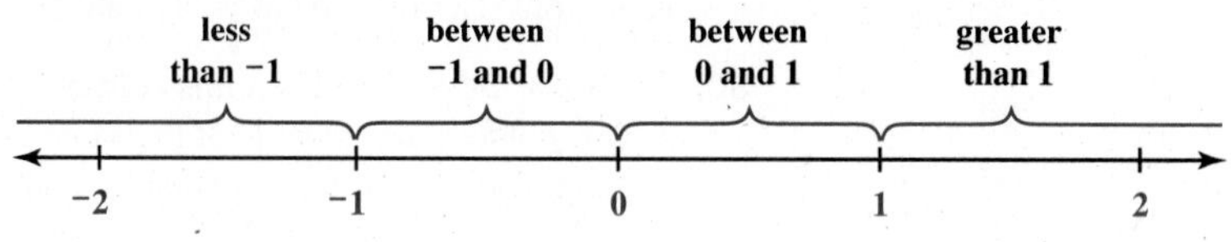

42. $1 \div {}^{-}\frac{3}{5}$ **43.** $\frac{^{-}555.233}{^{-}5{,}552}$ **44.** $78.3636 \div {}^{-}25.33$

45. The average of 10 temperatures is $^{-}21$°F. What could the temperatures be?

46. The average of 5 temperatures is $^{-}21$°F. What could the temperatures be?

Solve each equation. Be careful: Each equation has two solutions.

47. $\left(\frac{1}{y}\right)^2 = \frac{1}{9}$ 3 or $^{-}3$

48. $y^2 = \frac{1}{9}$ $\frac{1}{3}$ or $^{-}\frac{1}{3}$

Challenge Solve each equation.

49. $\left(\frac{1}{z}\right)^2 = 16$ $\frac{1}{4}$ or $^{-}\frac{1}{4}$ **50.** $^{-}\frac{5}{x} + 4 = 2$ $\frac{5}{2}$

Mixed Review

51. 0.0375
52. 0.0625
53. 0.005
54. 0.0005
55. 0.25
56. 25

Evaluate each expression.

51. $0.125 \cdot 0.3$ **52.** $0.125 \cdot 0.5$ **53.** $0.125 \cdot 0.04$

54. $0.125 \cdot 0.004$ **55.** $0.125 \cdot 2$ **56.** $0.125 \cdot 200$

Lehie drew the following flowcharts. For each flowchart, tell what equation Lehie was trying to solve. Then, copy and complete the flowchart.

57. (2) —× 16→ (32) —− 4→ (28) $16n - 4 = 28$

58. (3) —+ 6→ (9) —× 2→ (18) $2(n + 6) = 18$

59. (75) —− 5→ (70) —÷ 2→ (35) $(n - 5) \div 2 = 35$

252 CHAPTER 4 Working with Signed Numbers

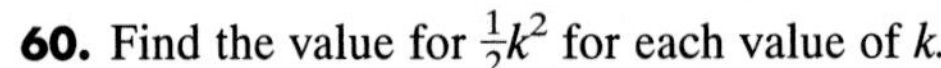

60. Find the value for $\frac{1}{2}k^2$ for each value of k.

a. 0 0 **b.** $\frac{1}{2}$ $\frac{1}{8}$ **c.** 1.2 0.72 **d.** 4 8

61. Find the value for $10m^2$ for each value of m.

a. 0 0 **b.** $\frac{1}{2}$ $2\frac{1}{2}$ **c.** 1.2 14.4 **d.** 4 160

62. Find the value for $3p^2 + 10$ for each value of p.

a. 0 10 **b.** $\frac{1}{2}$ $10\frac{3}{4}$ **c.** 1.2 14.32 **d.** 4 58

63. A calculator costs $14 and requires three batteries that are not included in the price of the calculator.

a. Suppose each battery costs b dollars. Write an expression for the total cost of the calculator and batteries.

b. What is the total cost if each battery is $.89? $16.67

63a. $14 + 3b$, where b is the cost of a battery

64. Geometry Consider this cylinder.

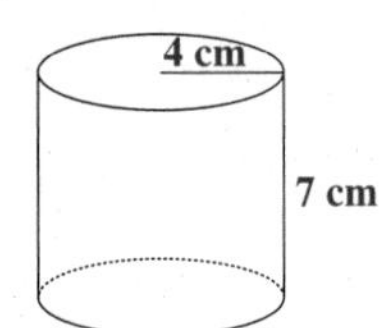

a. Find the volume of the cylinder.

b. Find the volume of a cylinder with a radius twice the length of this cylinder's radius.

c. Find the volume of a cylinder that is twice as high as this cylinder.

64a. 112π cm^3, or about 352 cm^3

64b. 448π cm^3, or about 1,407 cm^3

64c. 224π cm^3, or about 704 cm^3

65. Probability Sherina bought two dozen superballs to give out at her birthday party, and she put them in a bag. A third of the superballs were blue, 25% were striped, an eighth were hot pink, and the rest were made to glow in the dark.

a. Ken arrived first, and Sherina asked him to reach into the bag without looking and take a ball. What is the probability that Ken's ball will glow in the dark? $\frac{7}{24}$

b. Ken picked a blue ball. Ally arrived next and said she hoped to pick hot pink. What is the probability she will get her wish? $\frac{3}{23}$

c. Ally didn't get what she'd wanted, but Kiran, who picked next, did get hot pink. What was the probability of this happening? $\frac{3}{22}$

d. Kiran traded with Ally for her striped superball. Miki picked next, hoping for a glow-in-the-dark ball. What is the probability of her choosing one? $\frac{7}{21}$, or $\frac{1}{3}$

Quick Quiz

1. Explain how to divide two negative numbers. How do you know your rule works? Possible answer: Divide the absolute values of the numbers. I can multiply to check the rule. The result is the number you need to multiply one of the negative numbers by to get the other. This cannot be negative, because a negative number times a negative number is a positive number. It cannot be 0, because the product of 0 and a negative number is 0.

2. Will $^-3 \times (^-6) + 2 \times 5 - 25 \times (^-62)$ be greater than zero, equal to zero, or less than zero? Explain how you know. It will be greater than zero. Possible explanation: Take each part of the expression. The product of two negative numbers will be a positive number. The product of two positive numbers will be a positive number. The product of a positive number and a negative number will be a negative number. However, when you subtract a negative number, it is like adding the opposite number, or a positive number. The sum of the three positive numbers will be a positive number.

LESSON 4.2 Multiplying and Dividing with Negative Numbers **253**

Teacher Notes

4.3

Plotting Points in Four Quadrants

Objectives

- To create and interpret four-quadrant graphs
- To use the distinguishing characteristics of points in the four quadrants and on the two axes to analyze graphs
- To think more flexibly about operations with signed numbers

Overview (pacing: about 3 class periods)

Now that students know how to operate with signed numbers, they can examine relationships between quantities that are sometimes negative. The coordinate plane is one important way relationships can be represented. In this lesson, students learn how to plot points and interpret graphs in four quadrants and then use coordinate planes to reinforce their understanding of operating with signed numbers. This lesson forms a bridge between Lessons 1 and 2 where students compute with negative numbers and Lesson 4 where students find distances on a four-quadrant graph. Unless otherwise indicated, students should not use calculators in this lesson.

Advance Preparation

You may wish to use Master 25, 10 by 10 Grids, any time when students are asked to graph points on an empty grid. Master 26, Grid for *Undersea Search* Game, provides grids with axes that extend from $^-3$ to 3 that students can use while playing *Undersea Search* in Investigation 1.

	Summary	Materials	On Your Own Exercises	Assessment Opportunities
Investigation 1 page T255	Students learn how to plot points in four quadrants and get to know the coordinate plane.	• Master 25 (Teaching Resources, page 41) • Master 26 (Teaching Resources, page 42)	Practice & Apply: 1–2 Connect & Extend: 6 Mixed Review: 11–20	Share & Summarize, pages T258, 258 On the Spot Assessment, page T255 Troubleshooting, page T258
Investigation 2 page T259	Students explore characteristics of points in the coordinate plane and use the graph to solve problems involving the relationship between two quantities that are sometimes negative.		Practice & Apply: 3–4 Connect & Extend: 7–8 Mixed Review: 11–20	Share & Summarize, pages T262, 262 On the Spot Assessment, page T260 Troubleshooting, page T262
Investigation 3 page T262	Students color in the coordinate plane to create a visual representation of what they learned in Lessons 1 and 2 about operating with signed numbers.	• Master 25 • Blue, black, and red pens or pencils	Practice & Apply: 5 Connect & Extend: 9–10 Mixed Review: 11–20	Share & Summarize, pages T263, 263 Troubleshooting, page T263 Informal Assessment, page 267 Quick Quiz, page 267

Introduce

Tell students that they can use what they learned about signed numbers to do a number of more sophisticated things. In this lesson, they will look at signed numbers on a graph.

Some students may benefit from a quick review of graphs before working on the Think & Discuss questions. These students may not recall which axis is the *x*-axis and which is the *y*-axis or how to use coordinates to name a point on the graph.

You might have to use the graph on page 254 to initiate a short discussion with students about how graphs help us understand the relationship between two quantities better. Emphasize that the visual nature of graphs often helps us spot patterns more easily.

2

Think & Discuss

Discuss the questions in this section. Be sure that students can read and interpret the graph. Students will rely on these skills as they expand their graphing abilities to using four-quadrant graphs.

4.3 Plotting Points in Four Quadrants

1 Review the meaning of the x-axis and y-axis.

Making a graph is a useful way to represent the relationship between two quantities. For example, during a two-week snorkeling vacation, Deane timed how long he could hold his breath under water. The graph shows his maximum breath-holding time each day.

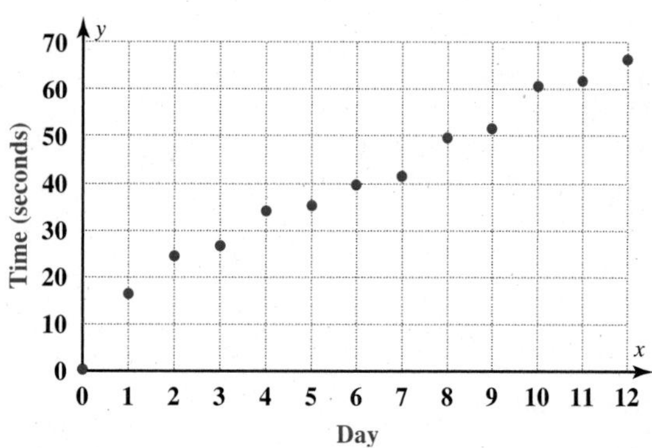

2 Review how to use coordinates to name a point on a graph.

Think & Discuss

Choose two points on the graph, and give their coordinates. Explain what the coordinates tell you about Deane's breath-holding time.

Possible answer: (1, 17) tells me that on the first day of his vacation, Deane could hold his breath for only 17 s. (12, 67) tells me that by the end of his vacation, he could hold his breath for over a minute.

How long could Deane hold his breath at the end of his sixth day of practicing? How did you find your answer from the graph?

40 s; On the *x*-axis, find day 6. Go up to the point on the graph, and see how high that point is on the *y*-axis.

In the graph above, both quantities—day and time—are always positive. What if one or both of the quantities you want to graph are sometimes negative?

For example, suppose you wanted to investigate the relationship between month of the year and average temperature in a very cold place, like Antarctica. How would you plot points for the months that have average temperatures below 0?

Investigation 1

In this investigation, students learn how to plot points on a coordinate plane.

It might help students to think about the *x*- and *y*-axes as the intersection of two number lines. You may want to elaborate on this concept in class and ask students to give the coordinates of the intersection.

Have students look at the two grids on page 255. Ask them to compare the two grids. Among their observations, students should note that the smaller one-quadrant grid is like the upper right-hand part of the larger four-quadrant grid and that the larger grid includes negative numbers.

Think & Discuss

The rule for plotting points with negative coordinates should be fairly easy for students to understand. You might want to have students share what they think the rule is for plotting points. Make sure that students' explanations state how to plot points in any of the four quadrants and on both of the axes.

Once students have correctly identified the rule, they can practice using it in Problem Set A. You may want to post the rule on chart paper in your classroom for students to refer to while they are still familiarizing themselves with the coordinate plane.

Problem Set A Suggested Grouping: Pairs

Problems 1 and 2 give students practice plotting and interpreting plots. You may want to have students plot their points for Problem 1 on Master 25, 10 by 10 Grids, which has an empty grid with darkened axes and unnumbered grid lines.

On the Spot Assessment

Watch for students who mix up the *x*- and *y*-coordinates in **Problems 1 and 2.** You may want to help these students remember that *x*-coordinates always come before *y*-coordinates by thinking of the alphabet and remembering that *x* comes before *y*. Remind them that the *x*-axis is horizontal and the *y*-axis is vertical.

Teaching Resources

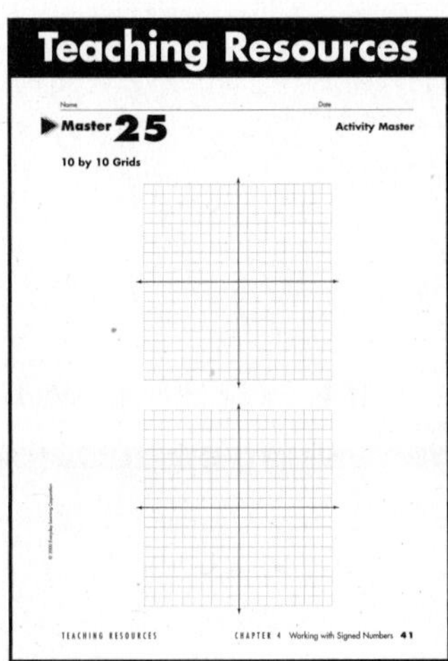

Investigation 1 Plotting Points with Negative Coordinates

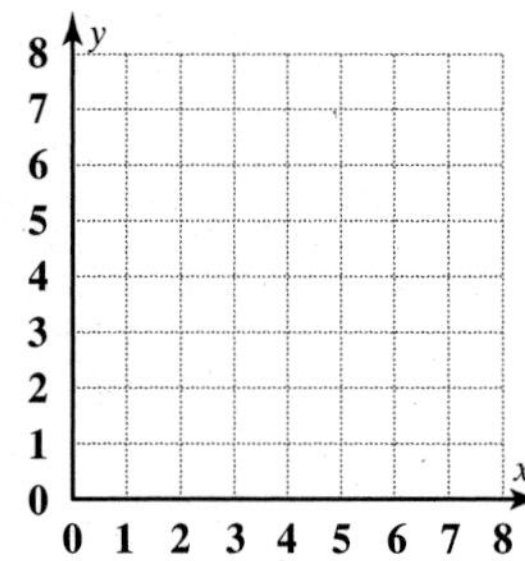

You know how to plot points on a coordinate grid that looks like the one at left. The *x*-axis of the grid is a horizontal number line, and the *y*-axis is a vertical number line.

In the graphs you have worked with so far, the number lines included only numbers greater than or equal to 0. But if they are extended to include negative numbers, the coordinate grid will look something like this:

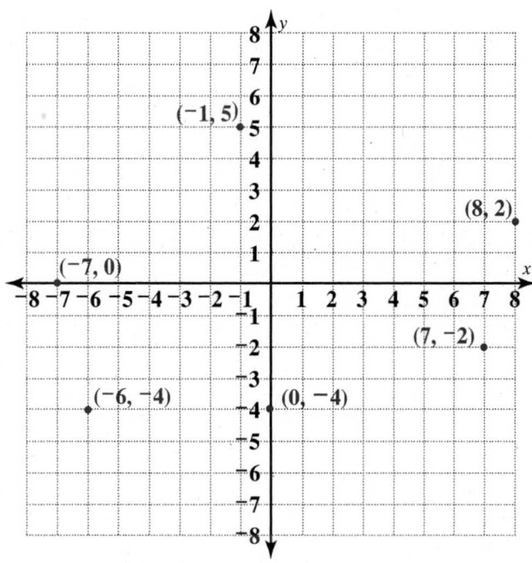

Using a grid like this, you can plot points with negative coordinates.

1\.

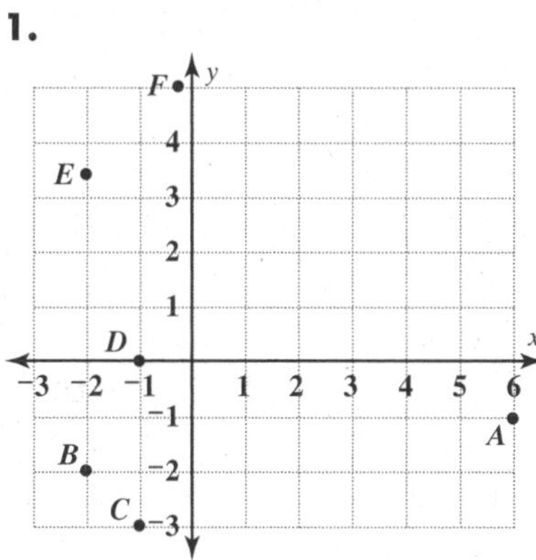

1 Students learn how to plot points on a coordinate plane.

Think & Discuss

Shaunda plotted six points on the grid above. See if you can figure out the procedure she used to plot the points. Possible answer: Move right or left to the value of the first coordinate (right if positive, left if negative), and then move up or down to the value of the second coordinate (up if positive, down if negative).

2 Students identify the rule for plotting points.

MATERIALS
graph paper

Problem Set A

3 Partners practice plotting points.

1. Plot Points *A*–*F* on the same coordinate grid. Label each point with its letter. See above.

   Point *A*: (6, −1) Point *B*: (−2, −2) Point *C*: (−1, −3)

   Point *D*: (−1, 0) Point *E*: (−2, 3.5) Point *F*: $(-\frac{3}{5}, 5)$

LESSON 4.3 Plotting Points in Four Quadrants 255

Develop

Problem 3 gives students an opportunity to use a higher level thinking skill, interpreting a graph. Data for Problem 3 were taken from a Web site containing background information on the Gulkana Glacier basin in Alaska. Visit the Web site at www.ak.water.usgs.gov/glaciology/gulkana/met//index.html to learn more about this and other Alaskan glaciers.

Access for all Learners

Extra for Experts Have students go to the Glacier Web site, www.ak.water.usgs.gov/glaciology to collect temperature data for the glacier of their choice. Have them choose a way to record the data. Most students will either list the data or make a table. Then have them graph the data on a coordinate grid. You may want to display the graphs so students can compare the temperatures from different times of the year.

Problem Set Wrap-Up You may want to discuss the graph in **Problem 3.** Some students may not understand why all four quadrants of the graph are not shown. They may also need to be reminded of what the broken line between 0 and 9 on the *x*-axis means. Neither of these concerns should affect students' ability to answer the questions unless they cannot read the labels on the graph and move on the graph from the origin to the point to find the coordinates.

2. $G(^-3, 7)$; $H(6, ^-2)$; $I(^-5, ^-6)$; $J(^-2, 0)$; $K(4.4, ^-7.8)$; $L(0, ^-3\frac{1}{3})$

2. Give the coordinates of each point plotted on this grid.

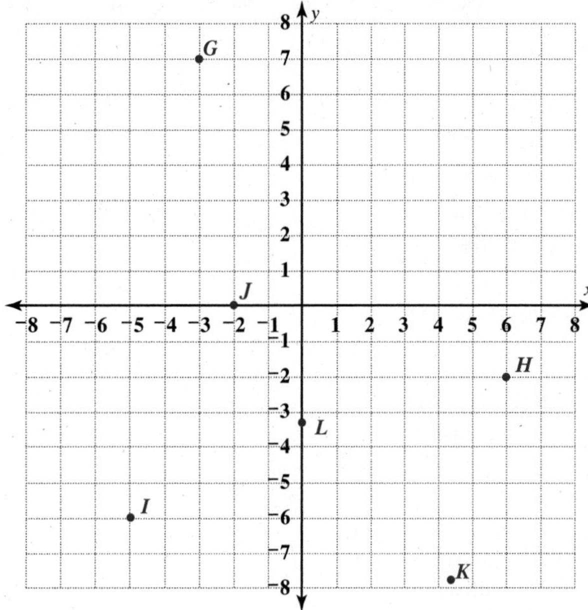

3. The graph shows daily average temperatures at the Gulkana Glacier basin in Alaska, from September 9 to September 18, 1998.

Students interpret the graph.

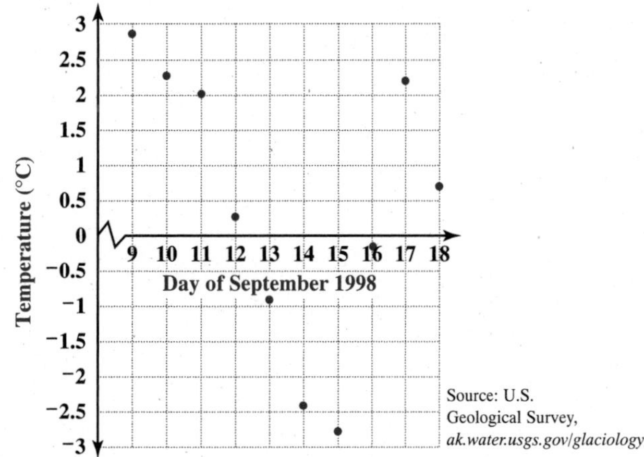

- Discuss the graph with the whole class.
- Ask students why all four quadrants are not shown.
- Remind students of the meaning of the broken line between 0 and 9 on the x-axis.

a. What was the lowest of these temperatures? about $^-2.8$°C

b. On which day was the temperature lowest? September 15

c. What was the highest of these temperatures? about 2.8°C

d. On which day was the temperature highest? September 9

Develop

Problem Set B **Grouping: Pairs**

Most of the time for this problem set will be spent playing *Undersea Search*. Playing the game gives students practice plotting points and identifying the coordinates of points on the coordinate plane. It also helps familiarize students with the structure of the coordinate plane. In order to save time, use Master 26, Grid for *Undersea Search* Game, which contains two grids whose axes extend from $^-3$ to 3.

Make sure that when students bury their treasure, they don't enlarge or shrink the pictures of the coral reef and the buried treasure. Within each picture, each X should be one unit apart on the grid.

Problems 1–3 on page 258 get students to begin thinking about the structure of the coordinate plane.

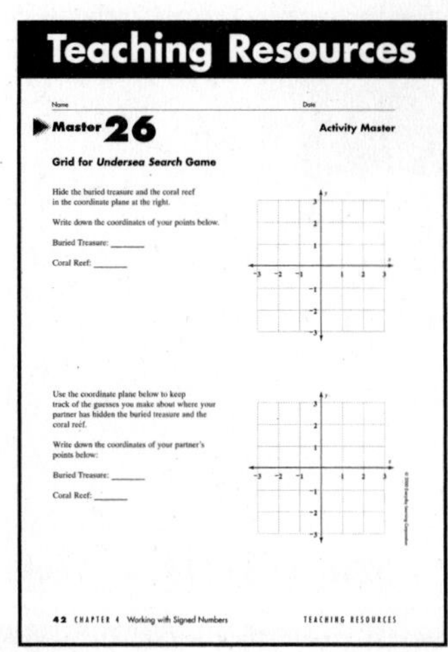

Teaching Resources

Name Date

Master 26 Activity Master

Grid for *Undersea Search* Game

Hide the buried treasure and the coral reef in the coordinate plane at the right.

Write down the coordinates of your points below.

Buried Treasure: ______

Coral Reef: ______

Use the coordinate plane below to keep track of the guesses you make about where your partner has hidden the buried treasure and the coral reef.

Write down the coordinates of your partner's points below:

Buried Treasure: ______

Coral Reef: ______

42 CHAPTER 4 Working with Signed Numbers TEACHING RESOURCES

The game you will now play will give you practice locating points on a coordinate grid.

MATERIALS
coordinate grids with x-axis and y-axis from $^{-}3$ to 3

Problem Set B

In the *Undersea Search* game, you and your partner will hide items from each other on a coordinate grid. To win the game, you need to find your partner's hidden items before he or she finds yours.

Each player will need two coordinate grids with x- and y-axes that range from $^{-}3$ to 3. Think of each grid as a map of part of the ocean floor. During the game, you will be hiding a buried treasure and a coral reef on one of your grids.

The grid below shows one way you could hide the items.

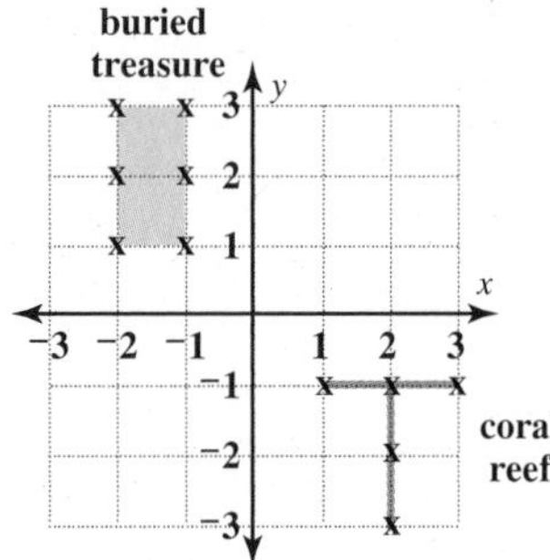

You can bury the items anywhere on the grid, but they must have the shapes shown above.

- The buried treasure must be a rectangle with two Xs along one side and three along the other.
- The coral reef must be a T-shape made from five Xs.

The Xs must all be placed where grid lines intersect. The buried treasure and the reef can't overlap, so they can't share points on your map.

1

- Students learn to play the *Undersea Search* game as a class.
- Partners play game following rules on page 258.

LESSON 4.3 Plotting Points in Four Quadrants 257

Develop

Share & Summarize
Having learned the rule for plotting points and used it to solve problems and do activities, students have an opportunity in this Share & Summarize to articulate the rule.

Troubleshooting Students will have plenty of opportunities in the remainder of the lesson to plot and interpret points. For students having extreme difficulty with these concepts, you might create a large coordinate grid on the floor of an empty space in your school and have students physically "walk the coordinate plane." The kinesthetic experience of moving from the origin to various points on the plane can be very helpful for many students.

On Your Own Exercises

Practice & Apply: 1–2
Connect & Extend: 6
Mixed Review: 11–20

Here's how you play the game.

- *Hide the buried treasure and the coral reef.* Start with one of your grids. Without showing your partner, use Xs to mark the places you want to hide the buried treasure and the coral reef. Make sure you put all your Xs where grid lines intersect.
- *Search the sea.* You and your partner take turns calling out the coordinates of points, trying to guess where the other has hidden the items.

  If your partner calls out a point where you have hidden something, say "X marks the spot." If your partner calls out any other point, say "Sorry, nothing there."

  Use your blank grid to keep track of your guesses. If you guess a point where your partner has hidden something, put an X on that point. If you guess a point where nothing is hidden, circle the point so you know not to guess it again.
- *Victory at sea.* The first person to guess all the points for both hidden items wins.

Play *Undersea Search* with your partner at least once, and then answer the questions.

1. Suppose your partner said "X marks the spot" when you guessed these points: ($^-3$, 1), ($^-3$, 2), and ($^-2$, 2). Can you tell whether you have found the buried treasure or the coral reef? Why or why not?
2. Suppose your partner said "X marks the spot" when you guessed these points: ($^-2$, $^-2$), ($^-3$, 0), and ($^-1$, 0). Can you tell whether you have found the buried treasure or the coral reef? Why or why not?
3. Suppose you have already found the coral reef, and you know that part of the buried treasure is at these points: (1, $^-2$), (0, $^-2$), and ($^-1$, $^-2$). What could be the coordinates of the other three points that make up the buried treasure? Name as many possibilities as you can.

1. No; the upside-down L configuration of the points could be part of either item, or they could be points from both items.

2. It could be the coral reef or parts of both items; the points are too far apart to be the buried treasure alone.

3. (1, $^-1$), (0, $^-1$), and ($^-1$, $^-1$); or (1, $^-3$), (0, $^-3$), and ($^-1$, $^-3$)

Share & Summarize

Write a letter to a student a grade below you explaining how to plot points with negative coordinates on a coordinate grid.

Possible answer: To plot a point, move left or right to the value of the first coordinate. Then move up or down to the value of the second coordinate.

1 Students verbalize the rule for plotting points with negative coordinates.

Investigation 2

In this investigation, students practice pattern-seeking and classifying skills while simultaneously reinforcing their understanding of the coordinate plane. They discover distinguishing characteristics of points in each quadrant and on each axis as they analyze and create graphs.

1 Direct students' attention to the coordinate plane on page 259. Define *quadrant* and explain the use of Roman numerals to identify quadrants. Be sure students understand that the points on the axes are not in any quadrant.

Problem Set C **Suggested Grouping: Pairs**
Students look for patterns in the signs of the coordinates in each quadrant and on each axis. They can use patterns to quickly identify the quadrant a point lies in without plotting the point.

Investigation 2 Parts of the Coordinate Plane

VOCABULARY
quadrant

The x- and y-axes divide the coordinate plane into four sections called **quadrants.** The quadrants are numbered with roman numerals as shown below. Points on the axes are not in any of the quadrants.

1 Discuss the quadrants on the coordinate grid.

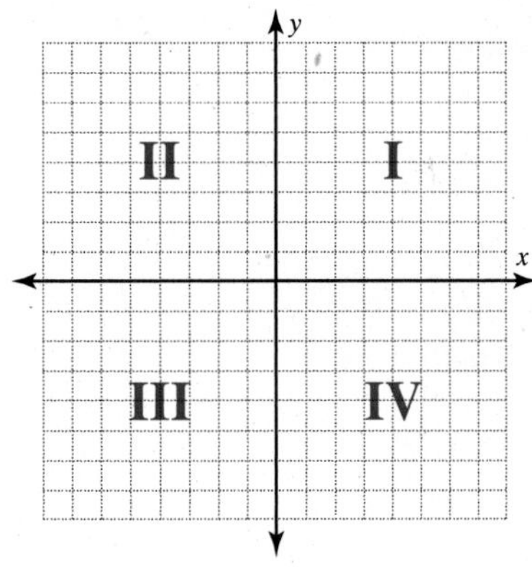

Problem Set C

2 • Partners answer the questions and look for patterns.
• Discuss answers with whole class.

Points A through R are plotted on the grid.

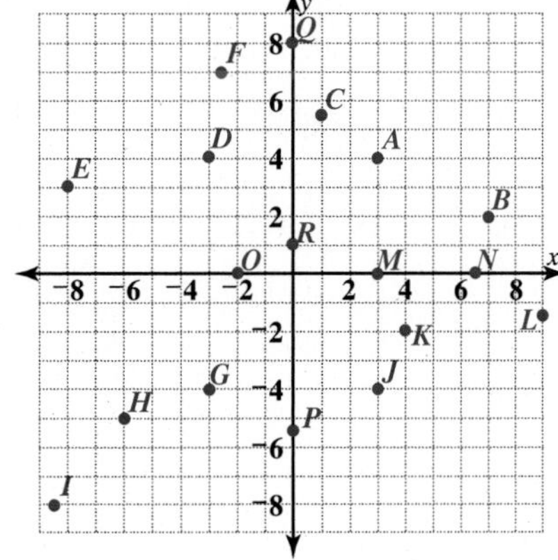

1. Look at the points in Quadrant I.

a. Record the coordinates of each point in Quadrant I.

b. What do you notice about the signs of the coordinates of each point?

c. If someone gives you the coordinates of a point, how can you tell whether it is in Quadrant I without plotting the point?

1a. (3, 4), (7, 2), (1, $5\frac{1}{2}$)

1b. Both are positive.

1c. If both coordinates are positive, it is in Quadrant I.

LESSON 4.3 Plotting Points in Four Quadrants 259

On the Spot Assessment

In **Problems 1–6,** watch for students having difficulty discovering the distinguishing characteristics of points in quadrants and on axes. Have them find the coordinates of more points. Repeating the process of naming points in the same region can help students get a sense of what actions stay the same each time they graph a point in a particular region of the graph.

You can also ask students to classify larger regions of the graph. For example, you might ask them what distinguishes all points above the *x*-axis. Then have students tell how the regions are defined. You might ask a question such as this:

> If the fourth quadrant is below the *x*-axis and to the right of the *y*-axis, what does that say about the coordinates of points in the fourth quadrant? **They have a positive *x*-coordinate and a negative *y*-coordinate.**

2b. The x-coordinates are negative, and the y-coordinates are positive.

2c. If the x-coordinate is negative and the y-coordinate is positive, the point is in Quadrant II.

3b. Both are negative.

3c. If both coordinates are negative, the point is in Quadrant III.

4b. The x-coordinates are positive, and the y-coordinates are negative.

4c. If the x-coordinate is positive and the y-coordinate is negative, the point is in Quadrant IV.

5c. If the y-coordinate is 0, the point is on the x-axis.

6c. If the x-coordinate is 0, the point is on the y-axis.

Just the facts

The word *quadrant* comes from a Latin word meaning "four." *Quadrille*, a French dance for four couples; *quart*, one-fourth of a gallon; and *quadrilateral*, a geometrical figure with four sides, are all related to the Latin word.

2. Look at the points in Quadrant II.

a. Record the coordinates of each point. $(^-3, 4)$, $(^-8, 3)$, $(^-2\frac{1}{2}, 7)$

b. What do you notice about the signs of the coordinates of each point?

c. If someone gives you the coordinates of a point, how can you tell whether it is in Quadrant II without plotting the point?

3. Look at the points in Quadrant III.

a. Record the coordinates of each point. $(^-3, ^-4)$, $(^-6, ^-5)$, $(^-8\frac{1}{2}, ^-8)$

b. What do you notice about the signs of these coordinates?

c. If someone gives you the coordinates of a point, how can you tell whether it is in Quadrant III without plotting the point?

4. Look at the points in Quadrant IV.

a. Record the coordinates of each point. $(3, ^-4)$, $(4, ^-2)$, $(9, ^-1\frac{1}{2})$

b. What do you notice about the signs of these coordinates?

c. If someone gives you the coordinates of a point, how can you tell whether it is in Quadrant IV without plotting the point?

5. Look at the points on the x-axis.

a. Record the coordinates of each point. $(3, 0)$, $(6.5, 0)$, $(^-2, 0)$

b. What do these coordinates have in common? The y-coordinates are 0.

c. If someone gives you the coordinates of a point, how can you tell whether it is on the x-axis without plotting the point?

6. Look at the points on the y-axis.

a. Record the coordinates of each point. $(0, 8)$, $(0, 1)$, $(0, ^-5\frac{1}{2})$

b. What do these coordinates have in common? The x-coordinates are 0.

c. If someone gives you the coordinates of a point, how can you tell whether it is on the y-axis without plotting the point?

Problem Set Wrap-Up You may want to give students an opportunity to prove that their conclusions are accurate by naming two coordinates and asking students where the point would lie on the coordinate plane.

Problem Set D **Suggested Grouping: Pairs**
In this problem set, students analyze graphs to solve problems involving signed numbers. Students should be in pairs for this problem set so they can see multiple-solution strategies. Because it is difficult to read the exact coordinates of some points on a graph, accept student answers that approximate those supplied here.

Most students will answer questions in **Problems 1–4** by looking at the graph. Each problem asks students to focus on a quadrant of the graph and determine values of °C and °F shown in that part of that graph.

Sample Strategies **Problem 5** can also be answered using the graph. Students may use one of these strategies to solve this problem.

- Some students may look at the coordinates of various points on the graph until they find a point where the *x*-coordinate and the *y*-coordinate are the same.
- Other students will use guess-check-and-improve.

You will now use what you've learned about the signs of the coordinates in each quadrant.

Problem Set D

Recall that the formula for converting between the Celsius and Fahrenheit temperature scales is

$$F = 1.8C + 32$$

where F is the temperature in degrees Fahrenheit and C is the temperature in degrees Celsius.

The graph of this equation is shown below. Celsius temperatures are on the horizontal axis, and Fahrenheit temperatures are on the vertical axis.

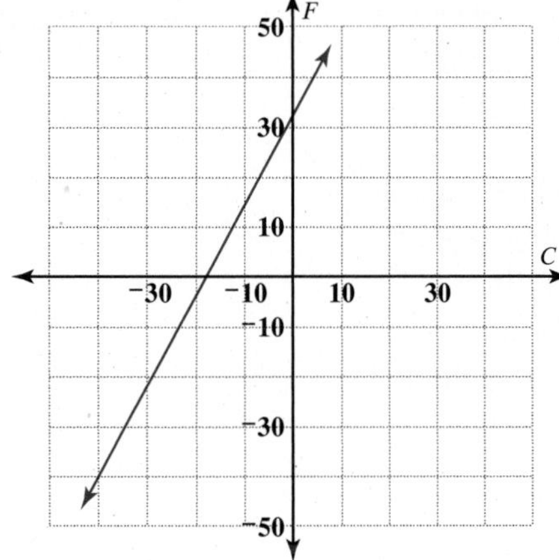

Use the graph to answer the questions.

1. Are Celsius and Fahrenheit temperatures ever both positive? If so, for which Celsius temperatures? If this never happens, explain how you know. yes; temperatures greater than 0°C
2. Are Celsius and Fahrenheit temperatures ever both negative? If so, for which Celsius temperatures? If this never happens, explain how you know. yes; temperatures less than about ⁻18°C
3. Are Fahrenheit temperatures ever positive when Celsius temperatures are negative? If so, for which Celsius temperatures? If this never happens, explain how you know.
4. Are Fahrenheit temperatures ever negative when Celsius temperatures are positive? If so, for which Celsius temperatures? If this never happens, explain how you know.
5. **Challenge** Is the Celsius temperature ever equal to the Fahrenheit temperature? If so, for which temperature? Explain how you know.

Just the facts

The Fahrenheit temperature scale was introduced by Gabriel Daniel Fahrenheit, a German-born Dutch instrument maker, in about 1720. The Celsius scale was proposed by Anders Celsius, a Swedish astronomer, in 1742.

3. yes; for temperatures between about ⁻18°C and 0°C
4. No; the graph does not pass through Quadrant IV.
5. yes; ⁻40°; The graph shows that (⁻40, ⁻40) is the only place where the x- and y-coordinates are equal.

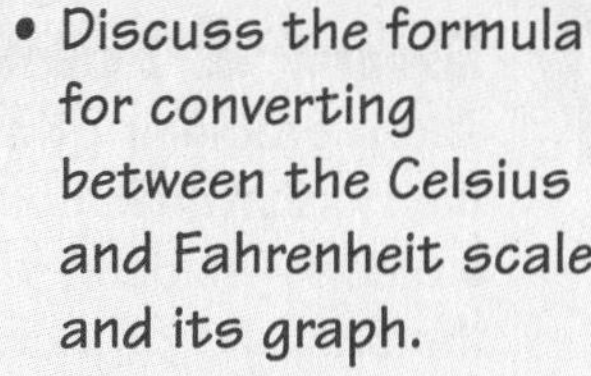

1
- Discuss the formula for converting between the Celsius and Fahrenheit scale and its graph.
- Have pairs of students work the problems.

2 Discuss Sample Strategies.

LESSON 4.3 Plotting Points in Four Quadrants 261

Share & Summarize

These problems give students an opportunity to apply their discoveries from Problem Set C. In **Problem 1b,** watch for students who forget that (0, 0) is on both of the axes. As an extension question, you might ask students whether there are any other points that are on more than one axis. They should recognize that there are none.

Troubleshooting Some students may still be having difficulty understanding the distinguishing characteristics of coordinates of points on the coordinate plane. You might have them work with a large coordinate plane that you set up on the floor of an open space in your school, as was suggested in the Troubleshooting section of the previous investigation. Ask students what sets of moves they must make to move to each of the four quadrants. For example, if they start at (0, 0) and want to move to the third quadrant, they must move to the left and move down. That corresponds to a negative *x*-coordinate and a negative *y*-coordinate.

On Your Own Exercises

Practice & Apply: 3–4
Connect & Extend: 7–8
Mixed Review: 11–20

Investigation 3

In this investigation, students do not work with the coordinate plane in a traditional way. They color points on the coordinate plane to represent various operations. In so doing, students get practice matching points to coordinates while simultaneously creating an interesting visual representation of what students learned in Lessons 1 and 2 about operating with signed numbers.

Students will need graph paper and pencils in three colors for this investigation. The instructions assume the three colors are red, blue, and black, but, of course, any three colors can be used. You may want to have students use Master 25, 10 by 10 Grids, to color in their coordinate planes.

Problem Set E Grouping: Small Groups

Before breaking the class into small groups, you might want to spend a little time walking students through the process of coloring points for a few points in different quadrants and axes.

Some students will need help deciding which points each group member should pick. This is a good opportunity to discuss methods to use when seeking patterns and the importance of testing points from all over the coordinate plane.

Share & Summarize

1a. Quadrant III
1b. x- and y-axes
1c. Quadrant IV
1d. x-axis

1. Without plotting each point, determine in which quadrant or on which axis or axes it lies.
   a. $(^-5, ^-2)$
   b. $(0, 0)$
   c. $(3, ^-\frac{2}{7})$
   d. $(^-35, 0)$
2. In general, if you are given the coordinates of a point, how can you tell which part of the coordinate plane the point is in without plotting it? You might organize your ideas in a chart with these headings: See Additional Answers.

x-coordinate	y-coordinate	Part of Coordinate Plane

1 • After students complete the questions, discuss the answers as a whole class.

• Remind students that (0, 0) is on both of the axes.

• Encourage a volunteer to organize the ideas in a chart on the chalkboard.

Investigation  Representing Operations on the Coordinate Plane

You can color points on the coordinate plane to create a representation of sums, differences, products, and quotients of signed numbers.

MATERIALS
- graph paper
- blue, black, and red pens or pencils

Problem Set E

Each member of your group will choose six points on the coordinate plane and color them according to these rules:

- *If the product of the coordinates is positive, color the point red.*
- *If the product of the coordinates is negative, color the point blue.*
- *If the product of the coordinates is 0, color the point black.*

When all the points are colored, you will look for a pattern.

1. Decide with your group which six points each member will color. Choose points in all four quadrants and on the axes, so you will get a good idea of the overall pattern. Each member of your group should plot his or her points, in the appropriate color, on the same coordinate grid. Graphs will vary.
2. What patterns do you notice in the colors of the points?
   Points in Quadrants I and III are red, points in Quadrants II and IV are blue, and points on the axes are black.

2 • Students work in small groups.

• Discuss the process of coloring points with the whole class.

Additional Answers 2.

x-coordinate	y-coordinate	Part of Coordinate Plane
positive	positive	Quadrant I
positive	negative	Quadrant IV
negative	positive	Quadrant II
negative	negative	Quadrant III
0	anything	y-axis
0	0	origin
anything	0	x-axis

Make sure that students form a good argument for **Problem 4** that adequately supports their answer to Problem 3. Many students will be tempted to justify their answer by saying that their data supports their pattern. However, they need to convince you that every point in the first and third quadrants must be red, while every point in the second and fourth must be blue and the axes must be black. They can use facts they learned in Lesson 2 to support these claims.

Tips from Teachers

I pass out overhead transparencies with empty coordinate grids to each group. If each group records its findings for **Problem 3** on a transparency, I can combine the transparencies from the class and overlay them with one another to see the data collected by the whole class at once.

Problem Set Wrap-Up You may want students to share their grids from Problem 3 and their justifications from Problem 4. This will allow them to see how others approached the problem before attempting a similar, but more complex problem in the next problem set.

Problem Set F **Suggested Grouping: Small Groups**

All of the teaching notes for Problem Set E apply also to Problem Set F. However, it should be noted that the relationship being represented in Problem Set F is significantly more complicated than the one in the prior problem set. In Problem Set E, the rules students remember for multiplication and division of signed numbers are simple: positive × positive = positive; positive × negative = negative; negative × negative = positive. These translate into a straightforward coloring of the coordinate plane because a separate rule applies to each quadrant of the coordinate plane.

Rules for adding with signed numbers are more complicated. While the sum of two positives is always positive and the sum of two negatives is always negative, the sum of a positive and a negative is sometimes positive, sometimes negative, and sometimes zero. Coloring in the coordinate plane for this problem set forces students to figure out more precisely when the sum of a negative and a positive will be negative, when it will be positive, and when it will be zero.

Share & Summarize

Students are asked to interpret their colored coordinate planes in order to shed light on operations with signed numbers. Because the problems are difficult, you might want to have several students share their thinking on this question with the entire class. Students will benefit from hearing multiple answers.

Troubleshooting Students will not come across colored coordinate planes like this later on in mathematics, so do not worry about students who are having difficulty constructing and interpreting these graphs. It is important that students be able to think flexibly about operations with signed numbers on the coordinate plane. You might want to act out the investigation on a large coordinate grid with students who are struggling.

On Your Own Exercises

Practice & Apply: 5
Connect & Extend: 9–10
Mixed Review: 11–20

3.
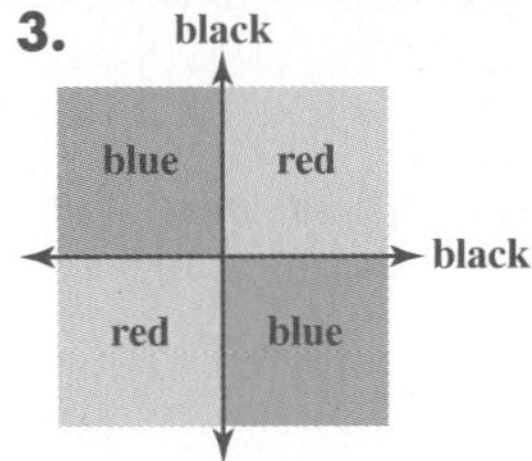

3. Imagine what the grid would look like if *every* point on it was colored. On a new coordinate grid, color *every* point red, blue, or black according to the rules above. Then compare your grid with the others in your group.

4. How do you know you colored the coordinate plane correctly? See Additional Answers.

In Problem Set E, you represented multiplication on a coordinate grid. In Problem Set F, you will look at addition.

MATERIALS
- graph paper
- blue, black, and red pens or pencils

5. Points where the y-coordinate is the opposite of x-coordinate are black. These points form a diagonal line from the upper left to the lower right. Points above the line are red, and points below it are blue.

Problem Set F

You will now color the points on the coordinate plane according to this set of rules:

- *If the sum of the coordinates is positive, color the point red.*
- *If the sum of the coordinates is negative, color the point blue.*
- *If the sum of the coordinates is 0, color the point black.*

1. Start with a new coordinate grid. Find at least 10 points that should be black, and color them. Be sure to check each quadrant. Graphs will vary.
2. Find some points that should be red, and color them. Again, check each quadrant. Graphs will vary.
3. Find some points that should be blue, and color them. Graphs will vary.
4. Now use the new coloring rules to plot all the points you plotted in Problem Set E, if you haven't already. Graphs will vary.
5. What patterns do you notice in the colors of the points?
6. Imagine coloring *every* point on the coordinate plane. On a new grid, color *every* point red, blue, or black according to the rules above. See Additional Answers.

1 Students work in small groups on the problems.

2 Review the rules for multiplication and division of signed numbers.

Share & Summarize Answers

1. Possible answer: The product is 0 for points in which one or both of the coordinates are 0. These points are on the x- and y-axes.
2. Possible answer: The sum of a number and its opposite is 0, so the black line passes through points where the coordinates have the same numbers but opposite signs.

Share & Summarize

In the grids you colored in Problem Sets E and F, the black lines form boundaries between red and blue sections.

1. For the grid in Problem Set E, explain why the black lines are located where they are.
2. For the grid in Problem Set F, explain why the black lines are located where they are.

3 Encourage students to share their thinking for Questions 1 and 2 with the entire class.

Additional Answers
Problem Set E

4. Points in Quadrant I are red because both coordinates are positive and products of two positive numbers are positive. Points in Quadrant III are also red because both coordinates are negative and products of two negative numbers are positive. Points in Quadrants II and IV are blue because they have one positive coordinate and one negative coordinate and products of a negative and a positive number are negative. Points on the axes are black because they have one coordinate equal to 0 and products of 0 and other numbers are 0.

Problem Set F

6.
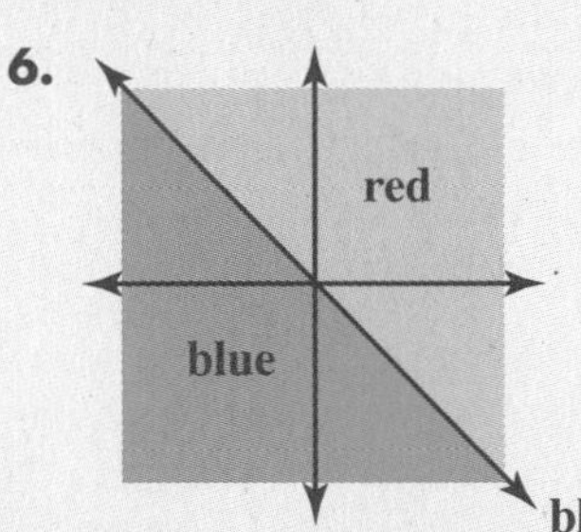

LESSON 4.3 Plotting Points in Four Quadrants 263

On Your Own Exercises

On Your Own Exercises

Investigation 1
Practice & Apply: 1–2
Connect & Extend: 6

Investigation 2
Practice & Apply: 3–4
Connect & Extend: 7–8

Investigation 3
Practice & Apply: 5
Connect & Extend: 9–10

Assign Anytime
Mixed Review: 11–20

Exercises 1, 5–10: You may want to encourage students to work on these problems using the empty coordinate grids on Master 25.

1.

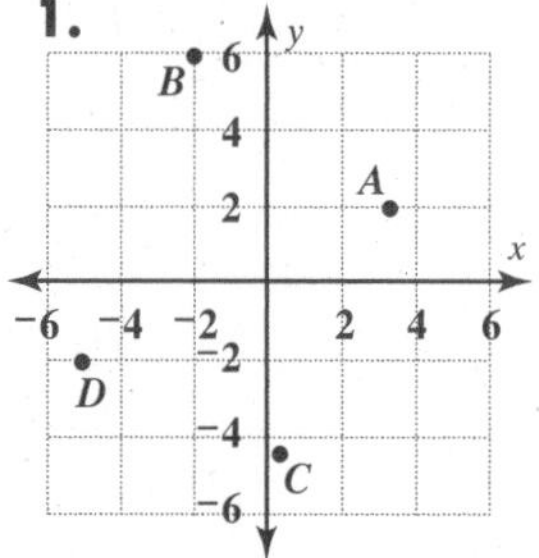

3a. yes; for temperatures greater than 0°C

3b. No; Kelvin temperature cannot be negative.

3c. yes; for temperatures less than 273°C

3d. No; Kelvin temperature cannot be negative.

Just the facts

The Kelvin scale is named for the Scottish physicist who first proposed an absolute temperature scale, William Thomson—also known by his British title, Baron of Kelvin.

1. Plot these points on a coordinate plane. Label each point with its letter.

$A\ (3\frac{2}{5}, 2)$ $B\ (^-2, 6)$ $C\ (0.4, ^-4.4)$ $D\ (^-5, ^-2)$

2. Find the coordinates of Points J through O. $J\ (^-4, ^-3)$; $K\ (0, ^-5)$; $L\ (1, ^-3)$; $M\ (^-7.5, 0)$; $N\ (^-2, 4)$; $O\ (^-5, \frac{1}{3})$

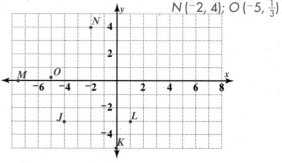

3. Physical Science The graph of the Celsius-Kelvin conversion formula, $K = C + 273$, is shown below.

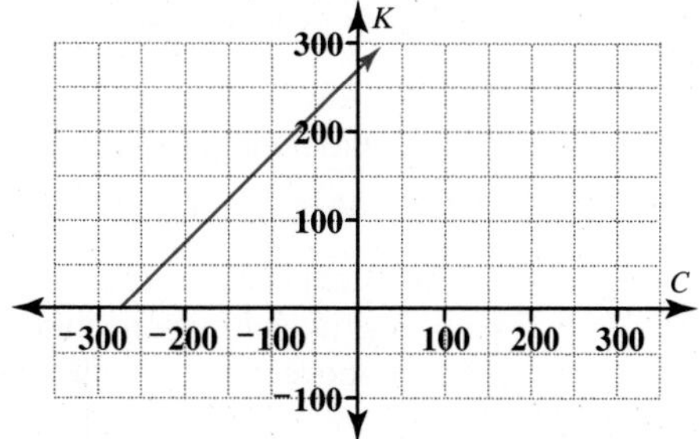

Use the graph or the equation to answer the questions.

a. Are Kelvin and Celsius temperatures ever both positive? If so, for which Celsius temperatures? If this never happens, explain how you know.

b. Are Kelvin and Celsius temperatures ever both negative? If so, for which Celsius temperatures? If this never happens, explain how you know.

c. Are Kelvin temperatures ever positive when Celsius temperatures are negative? If so, for which Celsius temperatures? If this never happens, explain how you know.

d. Are Kelvin temperatures ever negative when Celsius temperatures are positive? If so, for which Celsius temperatures? If this never happens, explain how you know.

4a. x-axis
4b. y-axis
4c. Quadrant IV
4d. Quadrant I
4e. Quadrant III
4f. Quadrant II
5. See Additional Answers.

4. Without plotting each point, tell in which quadrant or on which axis it lies.

a. (2, 0) **b.** (0, $^-24$) **c.** (35, $^-23$)
d. (3, 5) **e.** ($^-2$, $^-2$) **f.** ($^-52$, 5)

5. Challenge In this problem, you will color a coordinate plane to show the signs of differences.

a. Create a coordinate plane in which you color a point (c, d) red if $c - d$ is positive and blue if it is negative. If $c - d$ is 0, color the point black. Shade the plane to show what it would look like if you colored *every* point red, blue, or black.

b. Now create a coordinate plane in which you color a point (c, d) red if $d - c$ is positive and blue if it is negative. If $d - c$ is 0, color the point black. Shade the plane to show what it would look like if you colored *every* point red, blue, or black.

c. How are the two coordinate planes similar? How are they different? Why are they similar and different in these ways?

Connect & Extend

6. See Additional Answers.

6. Astronomy The average surface temperatures of the planets in our solar system are related to their average distances from the sun.

Planet	Distance from Sun (millions of miles)	Surface Temperature (°F)
Mercury	36	662
Venus	67	860
Earth	93	68
Mars	142	$^-9$
Jupiter	483	$^-184$
Saturn	888	$^-292$
Uranus	1,784	$^-346$
Neptune	2,799	$^-364$
Pluto	3,674	$^-382$

a. Create a graph with distance from the sun on the x-axis and average surface temperature on the y-axis. Plot the nine points listed in the table.

b. Generally speaking, how does temperature change as you move farther from the sun?

c. Why do you think the relationship you noticed in Part b happens?

d. Which planet or planets don't fit the general pattern? Why might a planet not follow the pattern?

Exercise 5:
Some students will be able to derive their answer to 5b from their answer to 5a since $c - d = ^-(d - c)$. Since many students may not use this strategy, you might want to draw their attention to the similarity between their answers to 5a and 5b and ask them why the relationship holds.

Exercise 6:
You might want to spend some time discussing students' graphs. Generally, we would expect planets farther away from the sun to be cooler than planets closer to the sun. However, many factors can affect temperature, so sometimes this is not the case. For example, as students learned in Lesson 1, Investigation 3, even though the moon and Earth are about the same distance from the sun, the moon experiences more extreme temperatures because it does not have an atmosphere. Venus is an outlier on the students' graphs because Venus experiences an extreme version of the "greenhouse effect." Conditions on Venus make it hard for heat to escape; thus it has unexpectedly high temperatures.

Additional Answers

5a.

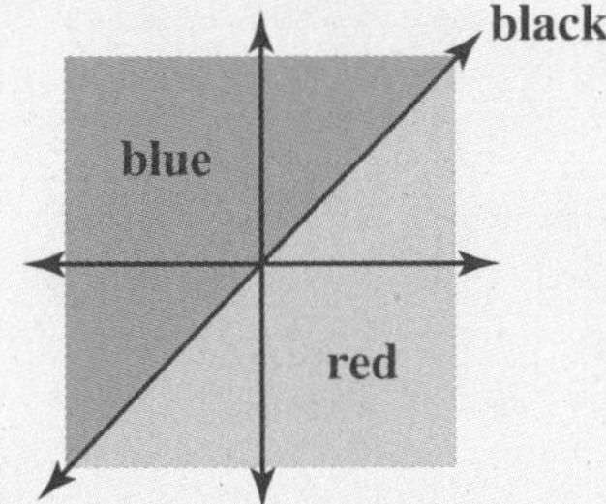

5b.

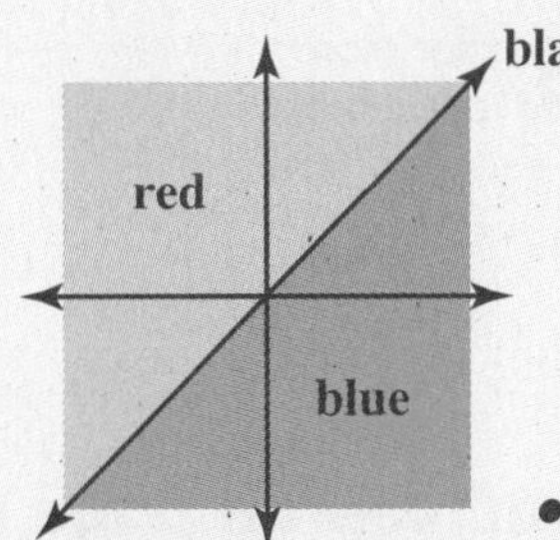

• Additional Answers continued on page A391.

Assign and Assess

Exercise 9:
In Lessons 1 and 2, students solved several inequalities. The structure of this problem suggests another way of finding solutions to inequalities. You might want to point this out to students and have them use the colored-in graphs to verify for themselves that they correctly solved the inequalities they worked on in Lessons 1 and 2.

Exercise 10 Extension:
Because this is the first problem in this chapter that asks students to think about dividing by zero, it might be a good opportunity to discuss why division by zero is undefined. You could do this by examining patterns. For example, what is the value of $\frac{1}{x}$ when x gets very close to zero? Be sure to include numbers on both sides (positive and negative) of zero. Or think about it this way: $10 \div 2 = 5$ because $5 \times 2 = 10$. $8 \div 4 = 2$ because $2 \times 4 = 8$. Now suppose $5 \div 0 = q$. Then $0 \times q = 5$. But zero times anything is always zero, so $0 \times q = 5$ is impossible.

In your own words

Give one example of a problem in which you would use a coordinate plane with four quadrants to help you solve the problem. In what way would the coordinate plane help you solve the problem?

7a. Three; a line can go through Quadrants III, II, and I; III, IV, and I; II, III, and IV; or II, I, and IV.

8. Quadrants I and II and the origin; x can be any number, and y must be positive or 0.

9–10. See Additional Answers.

7. Think about straight lines on the coordinate plane. You might draw a coordinate plane and experiment with lines to answer these questions.

a. What is the greatest number of quadrants a straight line can go through? Explain. See margin.

b. What is the least number of quadrants a straight line can go through? 0, if it is on an axis

8. If you plotted all points for which the y-coordinate is the square of the x-coordinate, in which quadrants or on which axes would the points lie? Explain how you know your answer is correct. See margin.

9. In this exercise, you will use the coordinate plane you colored for Problem Set F to help solve the inequality $x + 5 < 0$.

a. Look at all the points on the coordinate plane you made in Problem Set F with a y-coordinate of 5. Of these points, which are red? Which are blue? Which are black?

b. When is the sum of 5 and another number less than 0?

c. For which values of x is $x + 5 < 0$?

10. Challenge In Problem Set E, you colored points on a coordinate plane to represent the sign of the products of coordinates. What about the quotients? Suppose you colored a coordinate plane so that point (c, d) is red if $c \div d$ is positive, blue if $c \div d$ is negative, black if $c \div d$ is 0, and green if it is impossible to calculate $c \div d$.

a. Shade a coordinate plane to show what it would look like if you colored *every* point red, blue, black, or green.

b. Compare your coordinate plane to the one you made in Problem 3 of Problem Set F. How are they similar and different? Why?

Mixed Review

Evaluate each expression.

11. $4.5 \cdot 90.02$ 405.09

12. $3.45 \div 0.5$ 6.9

13. $0.034 \cdot 3.2 \cdot \frac{1}{2}$ 0.0544

14, 15. See Additional Answers.

14. Draw a flowchart for this rule: *output* $= 2n + 4$. Use it to find the output for the input 8.

15. Draw a flowchart for this rule: *output* $= 7n + 9$. Use it to find the output for the input 20.

16. Draw a flowchart for this rule: *output* $= \frac{n-13}{12}$. Use it to find the output for the input 73.

$n \xrightarrow{-13} n - 13 \xrightarrow{\div 12} \frac{n-13}{12}$, 5

Additional Answers

9a. red: points whose x-coordinate is greater than $^-5$; blue: points whose x-coordinate is less than $^-5$; black: the point $(^-5, 5)$

9b. when the other number is less than $^-5$

9c. x values less than $^-5$

10a.

blue	red
red	blue

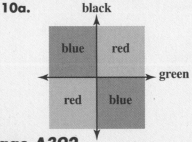

black (y-axis); green (x-axis)

• *Additional Answers continued on page A392.*

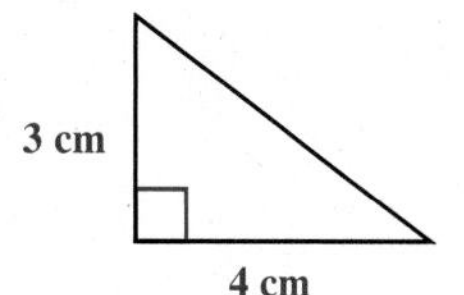

17. Geometry Consider the triangle at left.

a. What is the area of the triangle? 6 cm^2

b. Suppose you use this triangle as the base of a prism 1 cm high. What would the prism's volume be? 6 cm^3

c. Draw another triangular base that would produce a 1-cm-high prism with this volume.

d. Suppose you use the triangle to make a prism 4 cm high. What would the prism's volume be? 24 cm^3

e. Suppose you use the triangle to make a prism h cm high. What would the prism's volume be? $6h$ cm^3

17c. Possible base:

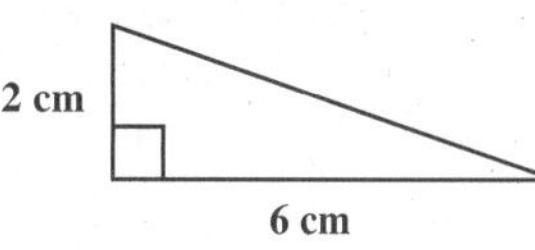

18. From the following list, find all the pairs of fractions with a sum of 1.

$\frac{15}{21}$ $\frac{10}{25}$ $\frac{8}{14}$ $\frac{1}{6}$ $\frac{2}{7}$ $\frac{3}{7}$ $\frac{3}{6}$ $\frac{10}{12}$ $\frac{3}{5}$ $\frac{1}{2}$

18. $\frac{15}{21}$ and $\frac{2}{7}$, $\frac{10}{25}$ and $\frac{3}{5}$, $\frac{8}{14}$ and $\frac{3}{7}$, $\frac{1}{6}$ and $\frac{10}{12}$, $\frac{3}{6}$ and $\frac{1}{2}$

19. At top speed, Chet the cheetah can run about 60 mph for short distances. At this speed, how far can Chet run in 40 seconds? $\frac{2}{3}$ mi

20. Statistics Doug surveyed the students in his English class about how many siblings (brothers or sisters) they had. The pictograph shows his results.

a. How many students did Doug survey? 36

b. What are the mean, median, and mode of Doug's data?

20b. mean: 1.42; median: 1; mode: 1

c. How many siblings do the students in Doug's English class have in all? 51

d. If you choose a student at random from Doug's English class, what is the probability the student has exactly three siblings? $\frac{2}{36}$, or $\frac{1}{18}$

e. If you choose a student at random from Doug's English class, what is the probability the student has more than two siblings? $\frac{4}{36}$, or $\frac{1}{9}$

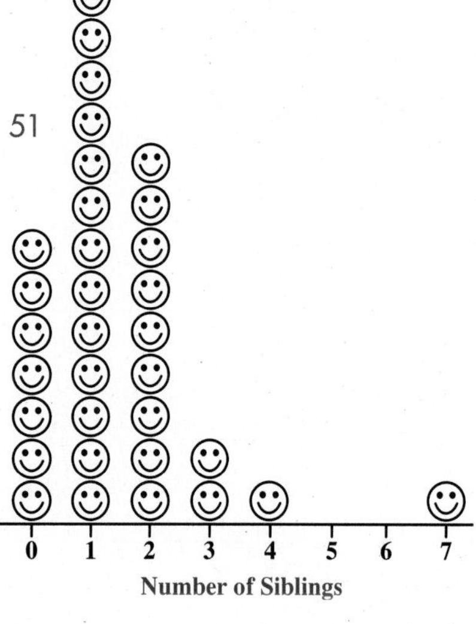

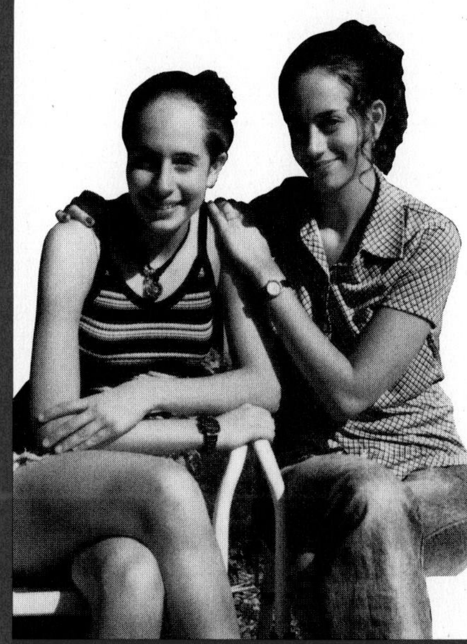

Exercise 18: Encourage students to change all fractions to lowest terms before attempting to find matching pairs that are equal to 1.

Exercise 20: Before assigning this question, you may wish to review the meaning of *mean, median,* and *mode* with your students.

Quick Check

Informal Assessment

At the end of the lesson, students should be able to

✔ create and interpret four-quadrant graphs

✔ use the distinguishing characteristics of points in the four quadrants and on the two axes to analyze graphs

✔ think more flexibly about operations with signed numbers

Quick Quiz

See page A392.

LESSON 4.3 Plotting Points in Four Quadrants 267

Teacher Notes

4.4 Finding Distances

Objectives

- To understand a variety of ways to compare lengths of line segments on a graph
- To apply either the Pythagorean theorem or distance formula when finding lengths of line segments on a graph
- To describe how the Pythagorean theorem and distance formula are related

Overview (pacing: about 2 class periods)

In this lesson, students develop both informal and formal methods for comparing and calculating lengths using coordinates on a graph. They review the Pythagorean theorem and use it to develop the distance formula. The emphasis in this lesson is on relating visual models to symbolic notation.

Advance Preparation

If students are having difficulty finding the length of a segment that is not shown on a graph, you may wish to have them create a visual image on graph paper or have them use Master 25, 10 by 10 Grids.

	Summary	Materials	On Your Own Exercises	Assessment Opportunities
Investigation 1 page T269	Students develop informal methods for comparing lengths of line segments on a graph. They review the Pythagorean theorem and use it to find the length of a segment on a grid.	• Master 25 (Teaching Resources, page 41) or graph paper	Practice and Apply: 1–6 Connect and Extend: 12–13 Mixed Review: 16–29	Share & Summarize, pages T272, 272 Troubleshooting, page T272
Investigation 2 page T273	Students use the Pythagorean theorem to develop the distance formula. They then use the distance formula to find the lengths of line segments on a coordinate grid.		Practice and Apply: 7–11 Connect and Extend: 14–15 Mixed Review: 16–29	Share & Summarize, pages T275, 275 On the Spot Assessment, pages T274, T275 Troubleshooting, page T275 Informal Assessment, page 279 Quick Quiz, page 279

Introduce

Ask students what they picture when they hear about an archaeological site or dig. Depending on your students' language ability, you may need to describe it as a place where scientists uncover very old objects that have been buried in the ground for many years. Explain that archaeologists frequently make a map of the area they are digging up by creating a grid on the ground with string. This gives them a way to describe the location of different objects that they find.

Explore

Make sure students understand what is shown by the grid. Then give them time to estimate the length of each section of wall and the distance from the toy to the corner of the building. Some students may use a ruler and then use a scale factor to convert their answer to feet or inches. Other students may just estimate the distance based on the information in the problem.

Students need to save their estimates for use later in the lesson.

As a class, discuss students' estimates and have them explain how they arrived at their estimates. Explain that in this lesson, they will learn some ways to make more accurate measurements of these distances.

4.4 Finding Distances

When pilots chart courses, they use maps with grids similar to the coordinate grids you have been working with. When archaeologists set up a dig, they create a grid on the ground with string so they can record the locations of the objects they find. Pilots and archaeologists often use their grids to find the distance between two locations. In this lesson, you will learn how to find distances between points on a coordinate grid.

1 Discuss what an archaeological site is.

Explore

Dr. Diggemup is working on an archeological dig. He has used string to lay out a grid on the ground. The lines of his grid are 1 foot apart.

So far, Dr. Diggemup has unearthed sections of two walls and an object he thinks might have been a toy. He drew this diagram to show the location of these objects on his grid. He labeled the corner of the walls (0, 0).

wall
wall
(0, 0)
toy?

- Estimate the lengths of the wall sections. Estimates will vary.
- What are the coordinates of the toy? $(^-3, ^-4)$
- Estimate the distance from the toy to the corner where the walls meet. Save your estimate so you can refer to it later in this lesson. Estimates will vary.

2 Discuss the Explore.

3
- Students estimate lengths and find coordinates.
- Discuss students' estimates with the entire class.

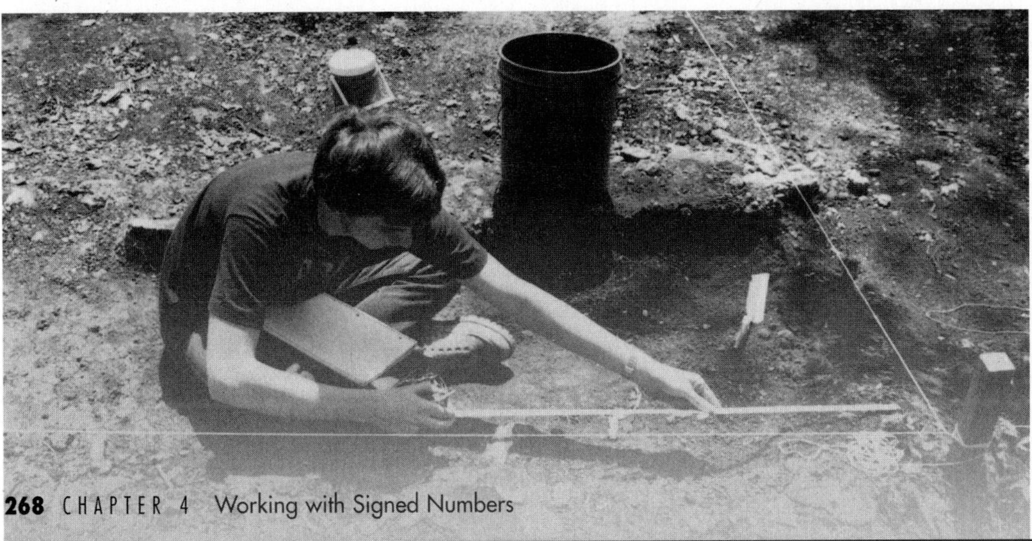

Investigation 1

Students learn an informal method for making comparisons of the lengths of different line segments on a graph by counting the horizontal and vertical units between two points. Then they find a more accurate measure using the Pythagorean theorem.

Think & Discuss

Walk students through both parts of this section. In the first part, students compare line segments that have one endpoint in common and whose other endpoints lie along the same vertical line. Since the longest segment is easy to determine visually, students may need some encouragement to find a way of explaining how to determine the length. Give them time to explore the diagram. Then have them count the number of horizontal units and vertical units for each segment and compare their results. Students should conclude that when line segments span the same number of horizontal units, the longer segment will span a greater number of vertical units. You may want to have students turn their books 90° counterclockwise to prove that the reverse is also true—when line segments span the same number of vertical units, the longer segment will span a greater number of horizontal units.

In the second part, students compare line segments that share no common endpoints by looking at the horizontal and vertical distances spanned. Students should understand that when line segments span the same number of horizontal units and the same number of vertical units, they are the same length. Students should recognize that this is an informal way to compare lengths on a grid and that the comparison only works when either the horizontal or vertical spans are the same.

Some students may need help understanding the units of measure on a graph. You may want to tell students that distances on a coordinate plane aren't usually measured in inches or centimeters. Instead, they are usually measured in terms of the number of units.

Investigation  The Pythagorean Theorem

Sometimes estimates like the ones you made for the lengths of the wall segments are all you really need. But there are times when you need a more accurate—or even exact—measurement. In this investigation, you will learn a way to find measurements like this one by using two side lengths in a triangle to calculate the third.

Think & Discuss

Four line segments are drawn on the grid. Without measuring, determine which is the longest. Explain how you know it is the longest.

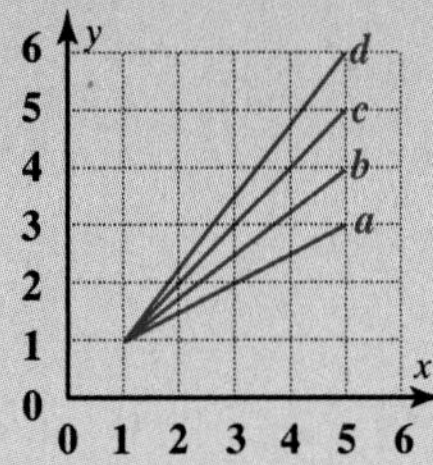

Segment *d*. Some students may just visually compare the segments; others may notice the horizontal distance between the endpoints is the same for all the segments, but the vertical distance is greatest for Segment *d*.

Without measuring, determine which segments below are the same length. Explain how you know.

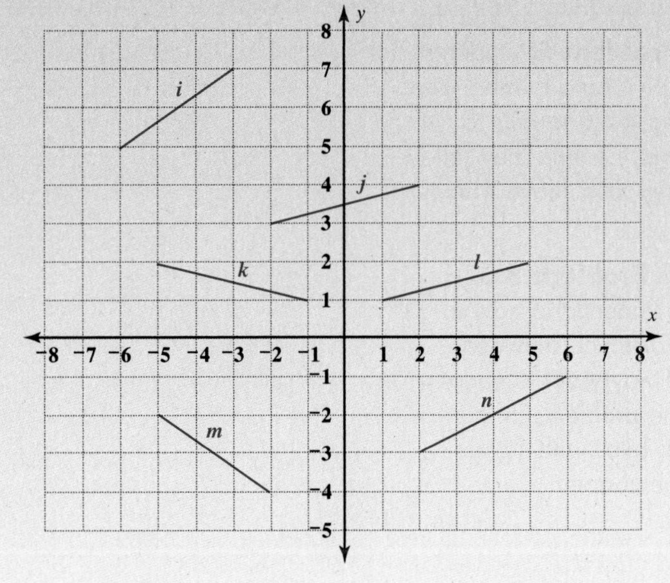

Segments *j*, *k*, and *l* are the same length, and Segments *i* and *m* are the same length. The horizontal and vertical distances spanned by the segments are the same.

1

- Discuss each graph with the whole class.
- Have students verbalize that when line segments span the same number of horizontal units, the longer segment will span a greater number of vertical units.

Develop

Problem Set A **Suggested Grouping: Whole Class**

These problems focus students on the horizontal and vertical units spanned between two points. This prepares them to think about the legs of a right triangle.

Problems 1–4 ask students to describe how to move when given the coordinates of the endpoints of line segments. The segments are shown on a coordinate grid.

In **Problems 5–7,** students are given the coordinates of two points and asked to describe how they would move from one endpoint to the next. These segments are not shown on a coordinate grid.

Sample Strategies Students may use one of these strategies to solve **Problems 5–7:**

- Some students may find the points on the coordinate grid that is shown and physically count the number of units moved horizontally and vertically.
- Other students may use number sense and their knowledge of number lines and graphing to find the units moved. For example, in **Problem 5,** students may think that $^-4$ is to the left of 4 on a number line. They move 4 units to 0 and then 4 more units to $^-4$, for a total movement of 8 units to the left. They follow a similar process to find that they must move 4 units up from 7 to reach 11.

Problem Set Wrap-Up Discuss **Problem 8** as a whole class. Be sure that students understand how to calculate the horizontal and vertical distance between points without counting units. You may want to encourage students to rework some of the problems in this problem set using the computation rules with signed numbers they learned earlier in the chapter.

Problem Set A

The segments described in Problems 1–4 are drawn on the grid. For each segment, tell how many units left or right and how many units up or down you must move to get from the first endpoint to the second.

1. left 3, down 8
2. left 4, down 2

1. Segment j: (1, 6) to ($^-2$, $^-2$)

2. Segment k: (3, $^-4$) to ($^-1$, $^-6$)

3. Segment l: ($^-2$, 5) to (1, $^-3$) right 3, down 8

4. Segment m: (8, $^-5$) to (0, $^-8$) left 8, down 3

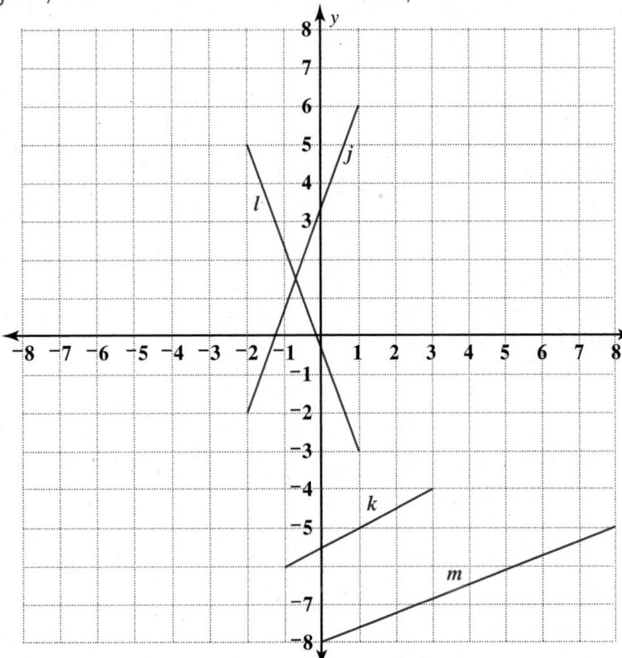

In Problems 5 and 6, the endpoints of a segment are given. Without drawing the segments, figure out how many units left or right and how many units up or down you must move to get from the first endpoint to the second.

5. (4, 7) to ($^-4$, 11) left 8, up 4

6. (9, 5) to (1, 2) left 8, down 3

7. Consider the segment with endpoints ($^-3$, $^-4$) and (3, $^-2$).

a. How many units left or right do you need to move to get from the first endpoint to the second? right 6

b. How many units up or down do you need to move to get from the first endpoint to the second? up 2

8. How can you find the horizontal and vertical distances between endpoints of a segment without counting?

8. The horizontal distance is the difference between the x-coordinates. The vertical distance is the difference between the y-coordinates.

1 Use these problems as a whole-class activity.

2 Have students describe the strategies they used to solve Problems 5–7.

Develop

You may want to discuss the cartoon by recreating the grid and pottery shards at (1, 2) and (3, 5) on the board or on an overhead. You can draw the segment connecting the two points and show how to construct a triangle by moving 2 units to the right and 3 units up. Review which segments are the legs and which is the hypotenuse.

1 Review the Pythagorean theorem with students. Tell them that they can use this theorem to find the distance between any two points on a coordinate grid.

2 **Example**

Demonstrate or have a volunteer demonstrate how to use the Pythagorean theorem to find the distance between the pottery shards at (1, 2) and (3, 5). For this lesson, students can give their answers as unsimplified radicals and/or decimal approximations.

However, students should be able to determine between which two integers their answers lie without using a calculator. After students use the formula to find that $c^2 = 13$ and $c = \sqrt{13}$, encourage them to look at the easiest option first—think if there is any integer squared that equals 13. Since there is none, ask students to approximate their answer by finding two consecutive integers that, when squared, are numbers greater than and less than 13. In this Example, the length of the hypotenuse will be between 3 and 4 since $3^2 = 9$ and $4^2 = 16$ and 13 falls between 9 and 16. The Additional Example below can provide further practice in this skill. They will learn to simplify radicals in Course 3.

Additional Example You may wish to have students find the length of a line segment that has endpoints at ($^-2$, $^-2$) and (1, 6). If you prefer not to draw a grid, this is line j on page 270. Using the Pythagorean theorem, students will find that

$$3^2 + 8^2 = j^2$$

$$9 + 64 = j^2$$

$$73 = j^2, \text{ so } j \approx 8.54$$

Remember Dr. Diggemup and his archaeological dig? One day, he found pieces of broken pottery at (1, 2) and at (3, 5) on his grid, but he did not record the distance between them. As his assistant Luisa looks at his notes, she has an idea. She draws dashed line segments to form a right triangle.

Remember
The hypotenuse of a right triangle is the side opposite the right angle. The other two sides are the legs.

The Pythagorean Theorem states that, in a right triangle with legs of lengths a and b and a hypotenuse of length c, $a^2 + b^2 = c^2$.

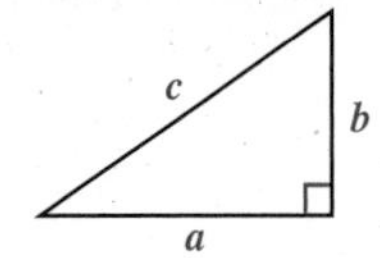

You can use the Pythagorean Theorem to find the distance between any two points on a coordinate grid.

EXAMPLE

The locations of the pieces of pottery Dr. Diggemup found are indicated on the grid. Find the distance between them.

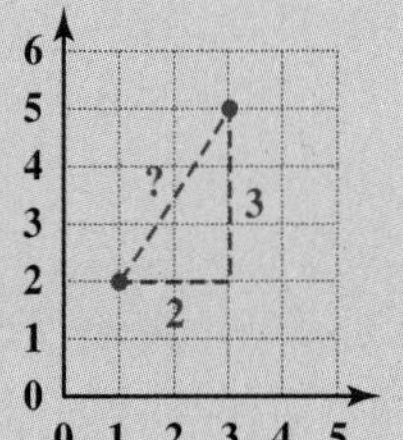

The legs of the right triangle have lengths 2 feet and 3 feet. Use the Pythagorean Theorem to find the length of the hypotenuse.

$$a^2 + b^2 = c^2$$
$$2^2 + 3^2 = c^2$$
$$4 + 9 = c^2$$
$$13 = c^2$$

The length of the hypotenuse is $\sqrt{13}$ feet, or about 3.6 feet. So, the pottery fragments are about 3.6 feet apart.

1 Review the Pythagorean theorem with the class.

2 After discussing the Example, you may want to use the Additional Example on page T271 to extend the discussion.

Develop

Problem Set B **Suggested Grouping: Pairs or Individual**

Students use the Pythagorean Theorem to find missing side lengths and lengths of segments on a coordinate grid.

Problems 1–5 review the Pythagorean Theorem. Students find the length of a hypotenuse when given the lengths of two legs, and they find the length of a leg when given the lengths of one leg and the hypotenuse.

In **Problems 6 and 7**, students apply the Pythagorean Theorem to find distances on a grid.

Access for all Learners

Extra Help Students having difficulty using the Pythagorean Theorem to find the distance on a grid in **Problem 6** may find it helpful to copy the grid and actually draw a triangle before finding the distance. Encourage them to write the length of each leg of the triangle next to the segment. You may want these students to use tracing paper or a transparency to make sure that they have copied the segments accurately.

Share & Summarize

Students share their thinking about **Problem 7a** from Problem Set B with a partner. Giving students a chance to verbalize their thoughts prepares them to write down the steps for solving the problem. After students write down the steps, you may want them to trade papers with another group and try to follow that group's steps to find the distance between points, such as (0, 0) and ($^-4$, 3). They should find that the distance is 5 units.

Students may find it helpful to save their explanations. They may like to refer to the steps in the next investigation.

Troubleshooting Students need to understand how to apply the Pythagorean theorem before starting the next investigation. If they need more practice applying it, you can have them work through the following problems.

1. Practice using the Pythagorean theorem to find the missing sides (a and b are the legs of a right triangle and c is the hypotenuse).
   a. $a = 5, b = 6$ *about 7.81*
   b. $a = 2, b = 9$ *about 9.22*
   c. $b = 6, c = 10$ *8*
   d. $a = 12, c = 25$ *about 21.93*
2. Find the lengths of these line segments:
   a. Line segment from (2, $^-1$) to ($^-4$, 5) *about 8.49*
   b. Line segment from (1, 2) to ($^-5$, $^-3$) *about 7.81*
   c. Line segment from (1, $^-3$) to (4, $^-1$) *about 3.61*

On Your Own Exercises

Practice & Apply: 1–6
Connect & Extend: 12–13
Mixed Review: 16–29

5a. Possible answer: Square the lengths of each of the other two sides, add the results, and take the square root of the sum.

5b. Possible answer: Subtract the square of the leg from the square of the hypotenuse, and take the square root of the result.

Problem Set B

Use the Pythagorean Theorem to find each missing side length.

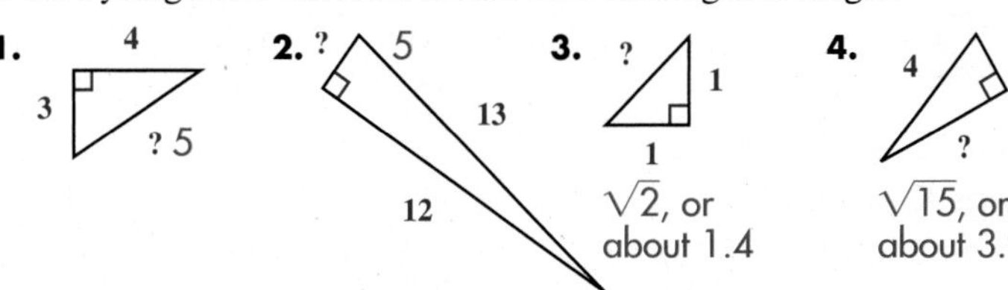

5. You will now explain the Pythagorean Theorem in your own words.
   a. How do you use the Pythagorean Theorem to find the length of the hypotenuse if you know the lengths of the other two sides?
   b. If you know the lengths of the hypotenuse and one leg, how can you use the Pythagorean Theorem to find the other leg's length?
6. Use the methods you described in Problem 5 to find the length of each segment on the grid shown at left.
7. Dr. Diggemup's assistant Luisa uncovered one end of a farm tool at $(4, {}^{-}1)$ and the other end at $(9, {}^{-}4)$.
   a. How many units long is the farm tool? $\sqrt{34}$, or about 5.83
   b. Remember that the grid lines are 1 foot apart. What is the actual length of the tool? about 5.8 ft

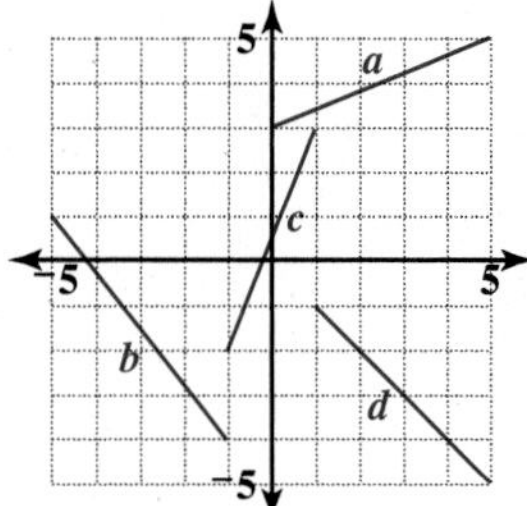

6. a: $\sqrt{29}$, or about 5.39; b: $\sqrt{41}$, or about 6.40; c: $\sqrt{29}$, or about 5.39; d: $\sqrt{32}$, or about 5.66

Share & Summarize

Explain to another student how you did Part a of Problem 7. Then work together to write steps for using the Pythagorean Theorem to find the distance between *any* two points on the coordinate plane. Your steps should be clear enough that someone else could follow them.
See Additional Answers.

1 Students can work individually or in pairs to solve these problems.

2 Students work with a partner as they write steps for using the Pythagorean theorem.

Additional Answers
Share & Summarize

Draw a right triangle by drawing a horizontal segment from one of the points and a vertical segment from the other, so that the two segments connect. Connect the two points to form the hypotenuse. Subtract the x-coordinates to find the length of the horizontal leg. Subtract the y-coordinates to find the length of the vertical leg. Square each length, and add the squares. The length of the hypotenuse is the square root of the sum, and that length is the distance between the points.

Investigation 2

Students learn that the distance formula is related to the Pythagorean theorem. They match steps for using the Pythagorean theorem to the symbolic notation to find the distance formula.

Problem Set C **Suggested Grouping: Individuals and Whole Class**

This problem set draws a parallel between the steps students follow for the Pythagorean theorem and lays the groundwork for the steps they will follow for the distance formula.

Have students work on **Problems 1 and 2** individually.

In **Problem 2,** students may want to compare the steps they wrote in the prior investigation's Share & Summarize to those written by Zach and Jin Lee. In any case, they should verify that they followed steps like those in Jin Lee's example when they calculated the distance in Problem 1.

Investigation  The Distance Formula

You can use the Pythagorean Theorem to find lengths of segments on a coordinate grid, whether that grid is on a map, an archaeological site, or a construction site. You will now learn about a special formula that is related to the Pythagorean Theorem: the *distance formula.*

1 Students learn that the Pythagorean theorem is related to the distance formula.

2
- Have students work on Problems 1 and 2 individually.
- Review answers with the whole class.

Problem Set C

1. 5 ft; Estimates will vary.

1. In the Explore activity on page 268, you looked at a diagram of an archaeological site. You estimated the distance between the corner where the two walls meet and the toy. Now use the Pythagorean Theorem to find the distance. How close was your estimate?

2. Zach and Jin Lee calculated the distance in Problem 1 differently.

Zach's Steps		Jin Lee's Steps	
Step 1	How far left or right do I go? Find this length.	*Step 1*	How far left or right do I go? Find this length.
Step 2	How far up or down do I go? Find this length.	*Step 2*	How far up or down do I go? Find this length.
Step 3	Add the two lengths.	*Step 3*	Square both lengths.
Step 4	Square the sum from Step 3.	*Step 4*	Add the two squared lengths from Step 3.
Step 5	Find the square root of the answer from Step 4.	*Step 5*	Find the square root of the sum from Step 4.

2a. Jin Lee's steps are correct. For Zach's Steps 3 and 4, he got the order backward: lengths must be squared, then added.

2b. Answers will vary.

a. Which student wrote the correct set of steps? Identify the mistakes the other student made.

b. How does your method for finding the distance (Problem 1) compare with the correct series of steps in the table? Do you have all the same steps? Are your steps in the same order?

LESSON 4.4 Finding Distances 273

Develop

Discuss **Problem 3** as a whole class. This leads into the example using the distance formula.

On the **Spot Assessment**

Watch for students having difficulty relating the symbols in **Problem 3** to the written steps in Problem 2. Have these students write the calculations they used to solve Problem 1 next to the relevant steps from Problem 2. Then have them substitute (x_1, y_1) and (x_2, y_2) for the coordinates and rewrite the steps using symbols. Then they can match the symbols in the problem to the ones they have written to identify the steps.

Introduce the distance formula to students. Then discuss the Example.

3

Example

Show them how to use this formula to find the length of a line segment by walking them through the Example. If students question how you know which point is (x_1, y_1) and which is (x_2, y_2), you may want to tell students that they will explore that situation in Problem 3 of the next problem set. Otherwise, you can rework the problem interchanging the points to show that the answer is the same whether a point is (x_1, y_1) or (x_2, y_2). Have students try to explain why they are the same.

3. The steps for finding the distance between two points can be written in symbols as well as with words. Let's use (x_1, y_1) to represent one point and (x_2, y_2) to represent the other.

Refer to the correct set of steps from Problem 2. Parts a–e each show one of the steps from that set in symbols. Tell which step the symbols represent.

a. $y_2 - y_1$ Jin Lee's Step 2

b. $(x_2 - x_1)^2$ and $(y_2 - y_1)^2$ Jin Lee's Step 3

c. $x_2 - x_1$ Jin Lee's Step 1

d. $\sqrt{(x_2 - x_1)^2 + (y_2 - y_1)^2}$ Jin Lee's Step 5

e. $(x_2 - x_1)^2 + (y_2 - y_1)^2$ Jin Lee's Step 4

1 Discuss Problem 3 with the entire class.

VOCABULARY
distance formula

The **distance formula** gives the symbolic rule for calculating the distance between any two points in the coordinate plane.

2 Introduce the distance formula.

Distance Formula

If (x_1, y_1) and (x_2, y_2) represent the points, then

$$\text{distance} = \sqrt{(x_2 - x_1)^2 + (y_2 - y_1)^2}$$

To find the distance between two given points, first decide which point will be (x_1, y_1) and which will be (x_2, y_2).

EXAMPLE

Find the distance between $(1, {}^-3)$ and $({}^-4, 5)$.

Let $(1, {}^-3)$ be (x_1, y_1), and let $({}^-4, 5)$ be (x_2, y_2). Substitute the coordinates into the distance formula.

$$\begin{aligned}\text{distance} &= \sqrt{(x_2 - x_1)^2 + (y_2 - y_1)^2} \\ &= \sqrt{({}^-4 - 1)^2 + (5 - {}^-3)^2} \\ &= \sqrt{({}^-5)^2 + 8^2} \\ &= \sqrt{25 + 64} \\ &= \sqrt{89} \\ &\approx 9.43 \text{ units}\end{aligned}$$

3
- Discuss the Example.
- Point out that $\approx$ means "approximately equal to."

Just the facts

The variables x_1, y_1, x_2, and y_2 are called *subscripted* variables. They are like any other variables, just with lowered numbers called *subscripts*.

Notice that the symbol $\approx$ is used in the last line above. This means that the distance between the points is *approximately equal* to 9.43 units.

Problem Set D Suggested Grouping: Pairs or Individuals

Students identify parts of the distance formula and use it to find distances.

Problems 1 and 2 ask students to apply meaning to different parts of the distance formula. For example, students relate the difference between the two x-coordinates to finding the length of the horizontal side of a right triangle drawn between two points.

In **Problem 3,** students explore interchanging the coordinates of two points as the (x_1, y_1) and (x_2, y_2) values in the distance formula.

In **Problems 4–7,** students can use either the Pythagorean theorem or the distance formula to find distance.

On the Spot Assessment

In **Problems 4–7,** watch for students who substitute the coordinates of one point as the value $(x_2 - x_1)$ in the distance formula. Remind them to use the x-coordinates from each point in the first expression of the formula and the y-coordinates in the second expression.

Share & Summarize

Help students see that the distance formula and the Pythagorean theorem involve most of the same steps. Some students may point out that when using the Pythagorean theorem, you are given the length of the sides, whereas in the distance formula, you have to subtract to find the lengths.

Troubleshooting If students are having trouble at this point, they may still be confused about how and when to use the Pythagorean theorem. If this is the case, help them describe steps for using the Pythagorean theorem in their own words. Once they are more comfortable with this, have them try some additional problems such as the ones that follow.

Find the length of a line segment that goes from

1. $(8, ^-2)$ to $(4, 3)$ *about 6.40*
2. $(^-3, ^-6)$ to $(^-5, 0)$ *about 6.32*
2. $(0, 7)$ to $(4, 2)$ *about 6.40*
3. $(2, ^-1)$ to $(^-4, ^-4)$ *about 6.71*

On Your Own Exercises

Practice & Apply: 7–11
Connect & Extend: 14–15
Mixed Review: 16–29

Just the facts

Although Pythagoras, who lived in the sixth century B.C., is commonly known for the theorem, the Pythagorean relationship was used for hundreds of years before Pythagoras lived—in Babylonia, Egypt, and India.

1. the coordinates of two points

2a. Possible answers: the number of horizontal units the segment spans; the length of one leg of the triangle

2b. Possible answers: the number of vertical units the segment spans; the length of the other leg of the triangle

3. See Additional Answers.

Problem Set D

1. What information do you need to use the distance formula?
2. Each part of the distance formula has a connection to applying the Pythagorean Theorem to a right triangle.
   - **a.** When you subtract the second x-coordinate from the first x-coordinate, what does that difference correspond to in a right triangle?
   - **b.** When you subtract the second y-coordinate from the first y-coordinate, what does that difference correspond to in a right triangle?
3. Zoe and Luis were trying to find the distance between the two points on this grid.
   - Zoe said, "I'm going to let (3, 1) be (x_2, y_2) and (6, ⁻4) be (x_1, y_1). When I find $x_2 - x_1$, I get 3 − 6, or ⁻3."
   - Luis said, "That's not right. You need to let (6, ⁻4) be (x_2, y_2) and (3, 1) be (x_1, y_1). When you find $x_2 - x_1$, you get 6 − 3, or 3."

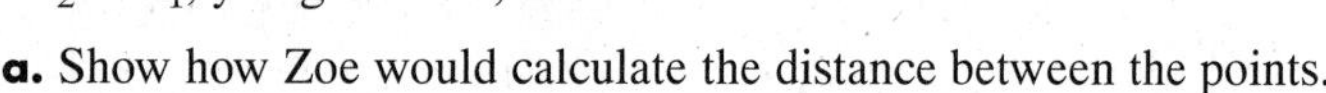

   - **a.** Show how Zoe would calculate the distance between the points.
   - **b.** Show how Luis would calculate the distance between the points.
   - **c.** Who is correct? Explain your answer.

Use the distance formula or the Pythagorean Theorem to find the distance between the given points.

4. (⁻3, ⁻5) and (7, ⁻1) $\sqrt{116} \approx 10.77$
5. (6, 4) and (2, ⁻3) $\sqrt{65} \approx 8.06$
6. (⁻1, 5) and (⁻10, ⁻4) $\sqrt{162} \approx 12.73$
7. (⁻3, 1) and (5, ⁻1) $\sqrt{68} \approx 8.25$

Share & Summarize

Explain how the distance formula and the Pythagorean Theorem are related. Use drawings or examples if they help you explain.

In the distance formula, you subtract x-coordinates and y-coordinates to find the horizontal and vertical distances between two points. This gives the same information as knowing the lengths of the legs in a right triangle. The remaining steps are the same in both methods.

1 Students work individually or in small groups to identify parts of the distance formula.

2 Students investigate interchanging coordinates of two points as the (x, y_1) and (x_2, y_2) values in the distance formula.

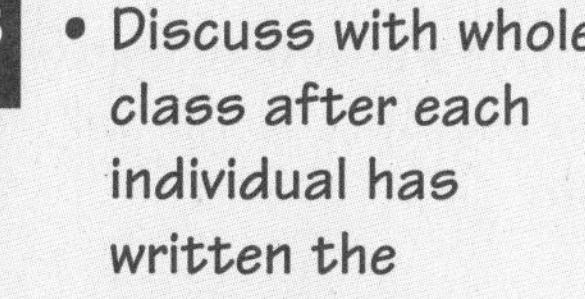

3
- Discuss with whole class after each individual has written the explanation.
- Encourage volunteers to demonstrate their answers using drawings and examples.

Additional Answers Problem Set D

3a. $\text{distance} = \sqrt{(x_2 - x_1)^2 + (y_2 - y_1)^2}$
$= \sqrt{(3-6)^2 + [1 - (^-4)^2]}$
$= \sqrt{(^-3)^2 + 5^2}$
$= \sqrt{9 + 25}$
$= \sqrt{36}$
$= 6$

3b. $\text{distance} = \sqrt{(x_2 - x_1)^2 + (y_2 - y_1)^2}$
$= \sqrt{(6-3)^2 + (^-4 - 1)^2}$
$= \sqrt{3^2 + (^-5)^2}$
$= \sqrt{9 + 25}$
$= \sqrt{36}$
$= 6$

3c. Both are correct. The order of the points does not affect the distance between them.

On Your Own Exercises

Investigation 1
Practice & Apply: 1–6
Connect & Extend: 12–13

Investigation 2
Practice & Apply: 7–11
Connect & Extend: 14–15

Assign Anytime
Mixed Review: 16–29

Exercise 2:
Students will not use the Pythagorean theorem to find the length of this line.

Exercises 3–6:
Make sure students notice that all the line segments span 4 units horizontally. They can compare the number of vertical units spanned by each line to make sure their answers are reasonable. For example, since line 5 spans more vertical units than line 4, its length will be longer.

On Your Own Exercises

Practice & Apply

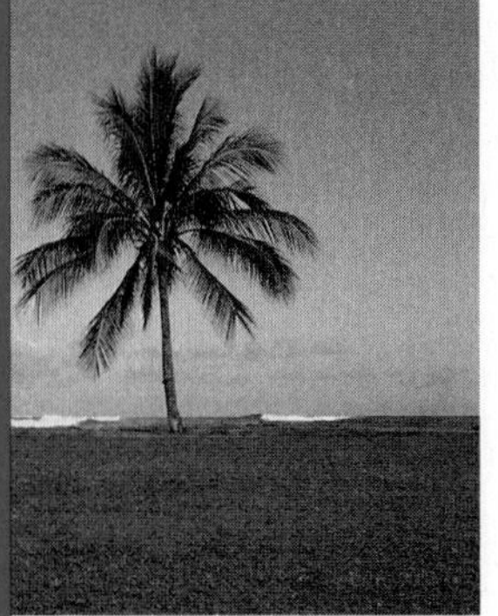

1. Four pirates are hunting for buried treasure on an island. They all start at the palm tree, which is at (2, 6) on their maps. All they know from their clues is that they must walk 10 paces either east or west, make a 90° turn, and walk another 12 paces. So each pirate walks 10 paces, two heading east and two heading west. Then one pirate from each pair heads north another 12 paces, while the other heads south for 12 paces.

a. Where did each pirate end? Give the coordinates of each. See below.

b. How far is each pirate from the palm tree, as the crow flies? ("As the crow flies" means "in a straight line from where you started.") Explain how you found your answers. See below.

For Exercises 2–6, use the Pythagorean Theorem to find the length of the segment.

2. 4
3. 5
4. $\sqrt{17}$, or about 4.12
5. $\sqrt{41}$, or about 6.40
6. $\sqrt{20}$, or about 4.47

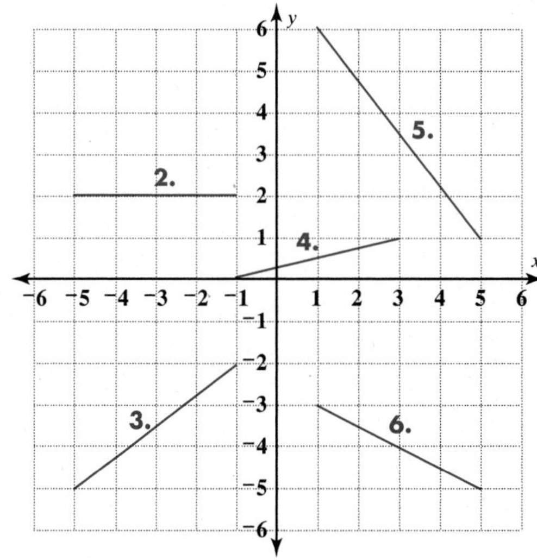

In your own words

You have been asked to write about something you have learned for the parents' *Math Newsletter.* Describe to parents how using the distance formula is just like using the Pythagorean Theorem to find the length of a segment.

Use the distance formula to find the length of each segment.

7. (4, 2) to (−5, −6) $\sqrt{145}$, or about 12.04

8. (0, −3) to (6, 2) $\sqrt{61}$, or about 7.81

9. (−9, 2) to (−10, 11) $\sqrt{82}$, or about 9.06

10. (6, 1) to (9, 5) 5

1a. (−8, 18), (−8, −6), (12, 18), (12, −6)
1b. All are $\sqrt{244}$, or about 15.6, paces away; Explanations will vary.

11. u ($\sqrt{17} \approx 4.12$), o (5), f ($\sqrt{26} \approx 5.10$)

11. Use the distance formula to order the segments below from shortest to longest. Give the length of each segment.

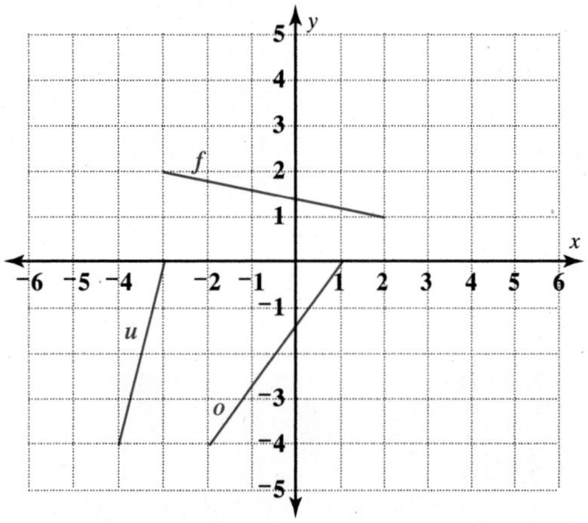

Connect & Extend

12. Life Science The grid shows the arrangement and length of mammal bones found embedded in a layer of the La Brea Tar Pits in California. (Assume the bones are lying flat in the tar pit, and are not tilted down into the pit.)

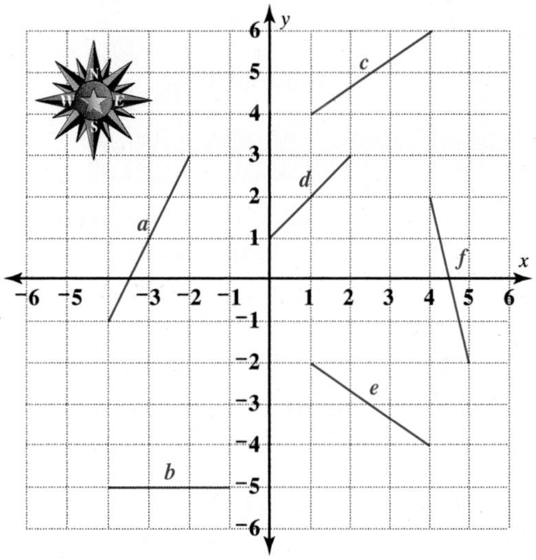

a. Which bone is the shortest? How long is it, if each unit on the grid represents 6 inches? bone *d;* about 17.0 in.

b. Which bone is the longest? How long is it? bone *a;* about 26.8 in.

Just the facts

Thousands of plant and animal fossils have been unearthed at the La Brea Tar Pits, in the heart of Los Angeles. The fossils date from the last Ice Age, between 10,000 and 40,000 years ago.

Exercise 12:
Students can use several methods to compare the lengths of the bones. Some students may count and compare the horizontal and vertical units spanned by the line segments. Other students may use the Pythagorean theorem.

Assign and Assess

Exercise 13:
In this exercise, **13a and b** are based on the premise that if two line segments span the same number of horizontal and vertical units, they will be the same length. **13c** looks at the converse: if two line segments are the same length, do they span the same number of vertical and horizontal units? You may wish to have students use Master 25, 10 by 10 Grids, to help them think about this exercise.

Exercises 22–23:
Watch for students that answer 4c for Question 22 and 12 for Exercise 23. Remind them that when they multiply a variable by itself two or more times, they should use exponents. When students add four variables that are the same, they count how many variables and write it as 4c. The same holds true for **Exercise 23.** Since the number 3 is multiplied by itself, they can write the answer using exponents with the exponent showing how many 3s there are in all.

Exercise 28b:
If students are troubled by this question, review the definition of *square feet* and *square yards.*

Exercise 28e:
Watch for students who find the size of the new corn plot but neglect to find the size of the total garden before computing the percentage.

13a. Yes; the distances between their endpoints are the same.

13b. Yes; they are identical segments. (Point *D* is the same point as Point *B*.)

13c. Possible answer: down 2 and right 5, right 5 and down 2

13. Use graph paper to help you think about this exercise. Draw a Point *A* somewhere in the middle of the graph paper. Draw a new point labeled *B* by moving from Point *A*, left 5 units and up 2 units.

a. From Point *A*, move left 2 units and up 5 units, and mark Point *C*. Is Segment *AC* the same length as Segment *AB*? Why or why not?

b. From Point *A*, move up 2 units and left 5 units, and mark Point *D*. Is Segment *AD* the same length as Segment *AB*? Why or why not?

c. Describe two ways you could move from Point *B* back to Point *A*.

14. Each grid unit on the map represents 15 miles. Suppose you are anchored at the point shown on White Sands Island.
See Additional Answers.

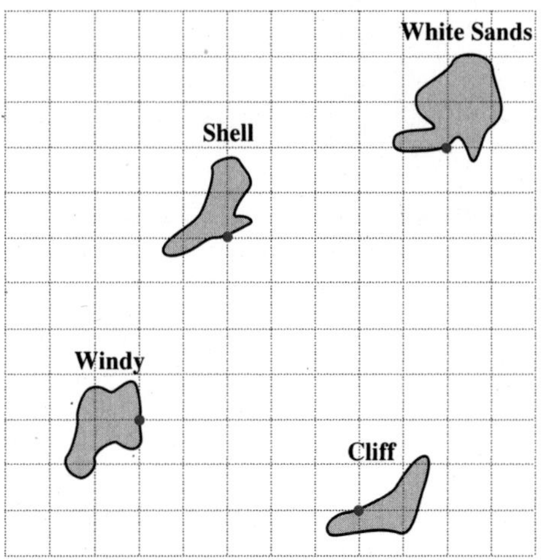

a. If you can sail 100 miles per day, to which other islands could you travel in a day? You must travel to the harbors marked by the dots.

b. Is there a pair of islands to which you could travel in the same day? If so, which are they? (For example, starting from White Sands to Shell to Windy?) If not, why not?

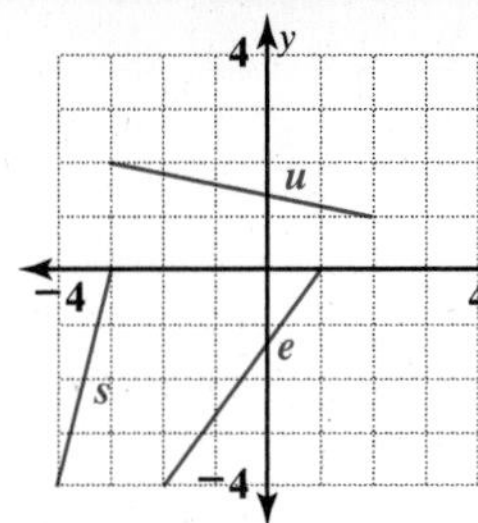

15. Make up a word problem to go with the graph at left. Design your problem so that you must use the distance formula to solve it. Word problems will vary.

Mixed Review

Find the value of the variable in each equation.

16. $6b = 15$ 2.5 **17.** $2k - 5 = 1.4$ 3.2 **18.** $a = 25a$ 0

19. $3.5m = 7$ 2 **20.** $6 - 22p = 6$ 0 **21.** $3n \div 7 = 3$ 7

Rewrite each expression in exponential notation.

22. $c \cdot c \cdot c \cdot c$ c^4 **23.** $4 \cdot 4 \cdot 4$ 4^3

Additional Answers

14a. Shell Island

14b. No; the closest distances are White Sands to Shell (about 81 mi), Shell to Windy (about 67 mi), and Windy to Cliff (about 81 mi).

278 CHAPTER 4 Working with Signed Numbers

Rewrite each number in standard notation.

24. 6×10^2 600

25. 9×10^5 900,000

Rewrite each number in scientific notation.

26. 654,000 6.54×10^5

27. 9,500,000,000 9.5×10^9

28. Shayla has made a sketch of the garden she would like to plant in the spring. Each grid square has an area of 1 square foot.

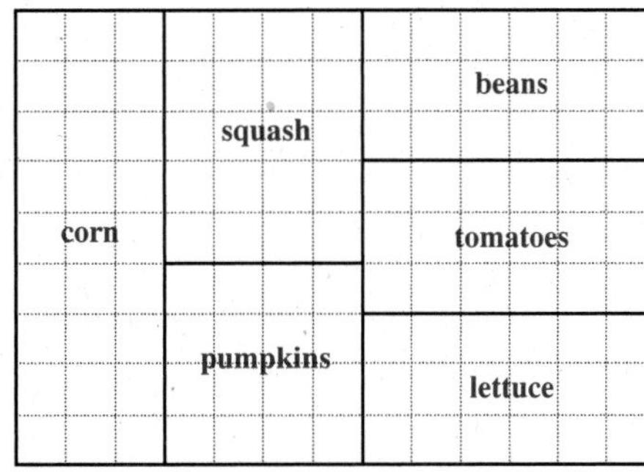

a. How many more square feet will Shayla plant in corn than in pumpkins? 11

b. How many more square yards will Shayla plant in corn than in pumpkins? (Be careful!) $1\frac{2}{9}$

c. What fraction of the total garden area will Shayla plant in squash? $\frac{20}{117}$

d. What percentage of the total garden area will Shayla plant in lettuce? about 15.4%

e. Suppose Shayla adds more space to her garden in order to triple the size of the corn plot. What percentage of the total garden area will be planted in corn? about 47.4%

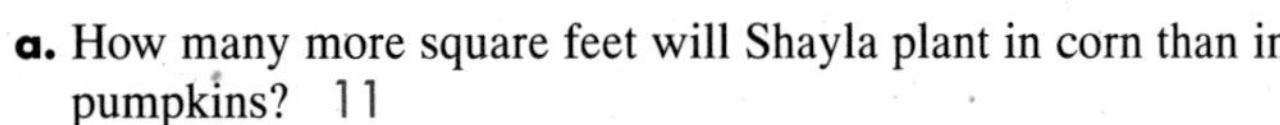

29. Match each point on the graph to the coordinates given.

a. (⁻2, 0) *E*

b. (1, ⁻3) *C*

c. (⁻2, 3) *F*

d. (⁻2, ⁻4) *D*

e. (2, 1) *A*

f. (3, 4) *B*

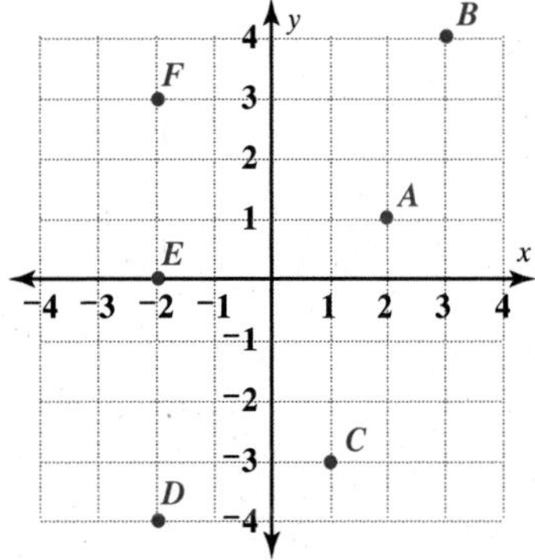

Quick Check

Informal Assessment

Students should be able to

- ✔ understand a variety of ways to compare lengths of line segments on a graph
- ✔ apply either the Pythagorean theorem or distance formula when finding lengths of line segments on a graph
- ✔ describe how the Pythagorean theorem and distance formula are related

Quick Quiz

1. Two line segments both span 4 vertical units. How can you tell which one is longer? *The line segment that spans the greatest number of horizontal units is longer.*
2. Find the length of a line segment with endpoints (4, ⁻3) and (⁻2, ⁻1). *about 6.32 units*
3. Use the distance formula to find the length of a segment with endpoints (3, 0) and (0, 5). *about 5.83 units*
4. How is using the Pythagorean theorem like using the distance formula in Exercise 3? *The distance formula is derived from the Pythagorean theorem.*

Teacher Notes

4.5

Negative Numbers as Exponents

Objectives

- To relate negative exponents to both multiplication by fractions and repeated division
- To evaluate simple expressions with negative exponents
- To apply laws of exponents to expressions with negative exponents
- To write numbers in scientific notation with negative exponents

Overview (pacing: about 3 class periods)

This lesson introduces the use of negative numbers as exponents. Students use shrinking machines to think about how negative exponents behave and learn to relate negative exponent notation to the model. They then revisit the laws of exponents and scientific notation, using negative exponents.

Advance Preparation

No advanced preparation is required to teach this lesson.

Lesson Planner

	Summary	Materials	On Your Own Exercises	Assessment Opportunities
Investigation 1 page T280	Students revisit the stretching and shrinking machine model from Chapter 3 in grade 7 and from chapters 2–4 in grade 6 to apply negative numbers as exponents in repeater machines. They look for patterns to explore the notation of negative exponents.		Practice & Apply: 1–13 Connect & Extend: 57–62 Mixed Review: 74–85	Share & Summarize, pages T284, 284 On the Spot Assessment, pages T281, T283 Troubleshooting, page T284
Investigation 2 page T284	This brief investigation provides practice evaluating a variety of expressions that use exponents and negative numbers.		Practice & Apply: 14–24 Connect & Extend: 63–71 Mixed Review: 74–85	Share & Summarize, pages T285, 285 On the Spot Assessment, page T285 Troubleshooting, page T285
Investigation 3 page T286	Students revisit familiar content from Chapter 3 on laws of exponents and scientific notation, now with negative exponents in the mix.		Practice & Apply: 25–56 Connect & Extend: 72–73 Mixed Review: 74–85	Share & Summarize, pages T287, 287 On the Spot Assessment, page T286 Troubleshooting, page T287 Informal Assessment, page 291 Quick Quiz, page 292

Introduce

This lesson revisits the stretching and shrinking machine model from Chapter 3 in grade 7 and from Chapters 2–4 in grade 6, to apply negative numbers as exponents in repeater machines. You may want to briefly review with students what a stretching machine and a shrinking machine each do.

Think & Discuss

This Think & Discuss helps students recall how stretching and shrinking machines work and revisits some of the laws of exponents.

As you discuss the hookup, focus on students' solving strategies. Collect the different ways that students thought about the problem and record them on the board. To help students understand which ways are equivalent, you might ask questions such as these:

> How is your way like this other way I wrote down?
>
> Why do both/all of these different ways work?
>
> Why isn't there just one way to do it?

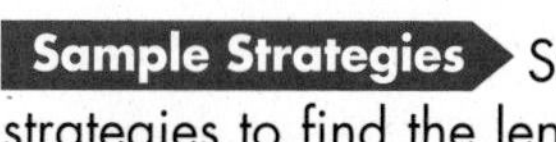

Sample Strategies Students may use one of these strategies to find the length of the gum.

- Most students will think in terms of first stretching the 1-inch stick by 3^5 and then shrinking it by 3^3. They may multiply 1 by 3, then multiply again by 3, and so on. Then they divide the final product by 3, then divide again by 3, and then divide again by 3.
- Some students may recall the laws of exponents right away and may combine the machines into one step that stretches the 1-inch stick by 3^2.

About the Mathematics

Because the stretching and shrinking machine model uses lengths of concrete objects such as gum or sticks, it does not make sense to have a negative length. Thus, the model excludes raising negative numbers to a power. These kinds of exercises will be addressed later in the lesson, separate from the model.

Investigation 1

Students review hookups of stretching and shrinking machines to remember how shrinking can undo stretching. The context of the machines provides a visual model for students to later make sense of methods for simplifying expressions with negative exponents. The lesson then uses patterns to introduce the notation of negative exponents.

4.5 Negative Numbers as Exponents

You have seen that negative numbers can be used to show amounts that are less than 0, such as low temperatures, debts, and elevations below sea level. Negative numbers can also be used as exponents.

In Chapter 3, you learned that positive exponents mean repeated multiplication. For example, 3^4 means $3 \cdot 3 \cdot 3 \cdot 3$. But what does 3^{-4} mean?

In this lesson, you will see that you can extend what you know about positive exponents to help you understand and work with expressions involving negative exponents.

1 Introduce idea that negative numbers can be used as exponents.

Think & Discuss

In Chapter 3, you used stretching and shrinking machines as a way to think about exponents.

Take a look at this hookup.

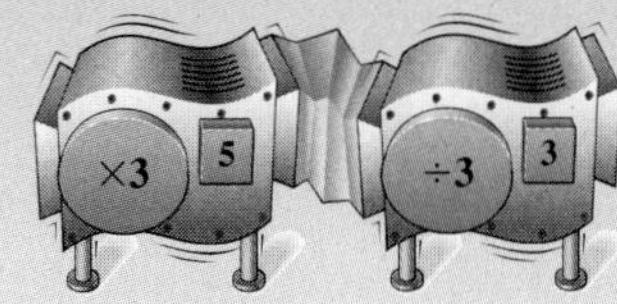

If you put a 1-inch stick of bubble gum through this hookup, how long will it be when it exits? Describe at least two ways you could figure this out.

9 in.; Possible strategies: Multiply the length by 3 five times, then divide by 3 three times. Or, stretching 5 times and shrinking 3 times is a net stretch of 2 times, so multiply by 3 twice. Or, one of the quotient laws of exponents says $3^5 \div 3^3 = 3^2$, so putting the gum through this hookup is equivalent to putting it through a $\times 3^2$ machine.

2 Review what a stretching machine and a shrinking machine can do.

3 Discuss strategies students may use to find the length of the gum.

Investigation 1 Shrinking with Negative Exponents

You will soon use shrinking machines to help you think about negative exponents. First, though, you will review hookups of machines with positive exponents.

Develop

Problem Set A **Suggested Grouping: Pairs or Individuals**

Students review how stretching and shrinking machines work as they simplify expressions through the context of the machines.

In **Problem 1,** students look at stretching machines. Some students may recall that they can add the exponents to find the value of a single machine if the bases are the same.

In **Problems 2 and 3,** students revisit fractions raised to a power. Some students may look at the exponents to find the number of times the fraction and its reciprocal are multiplied. Since a fraction and its reciprocal can be combined to make a repeater value of 1, students may match as many pairs as possible and then evaluate what remains.

On the **Spot Assessment**

In **Problem 3,** watch for students who think that 4^0 is zero. Remind students that they can think of the 0 exponent as meaning "don't apply the machine at all" to help them remember why n^0 is 1.

Problem Set Wrap-Up You might want to have students explain how they found each answer. This can help all students review the earlier concepts and ensure that they understand and can use the repeater model.

Discuss Jack's employment at the resizing factory and his test cases with base 3 machines.

Think & Discuss

Students review concepts from the earlier chapter. They should easily explain why each output in the pattern is $\frac{1}{3}$ less than the output for the previous machine.

Tell students that some machines have negative exponents and that they can continue the pattern to find the output for the $\times 3^{-1}$ machine, the $\times 3^{-2}$ machine, and the $\times 3^{-3}$ machine. They will do this in Problem Set B.

Problem Set A

If possible, find a single repeater machine that will do the same work as the given hookup.

1. 

2. 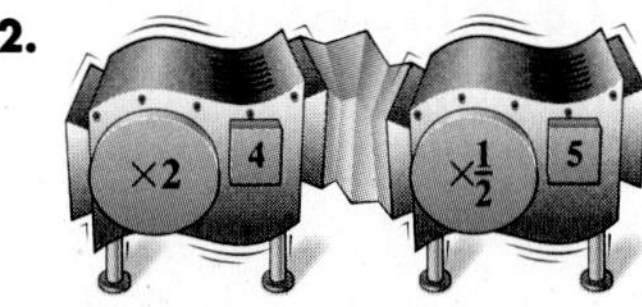

3. 

1. $\times 6^5$
2. $\times \frac{1}{2}$
3. $\times \left(\frac{1}{4}\right)^2$

Students can work individually or in pairs.

Jack is a new employee at the resizing factory. He is assigned to all the machines with base 3. A clown troupe has asked Jack to stretch some ribbons for their balloons. To get familiar with the machines, Jack sends 1-centimeter pieces of ribbon through them and records the lengths of the outputs.

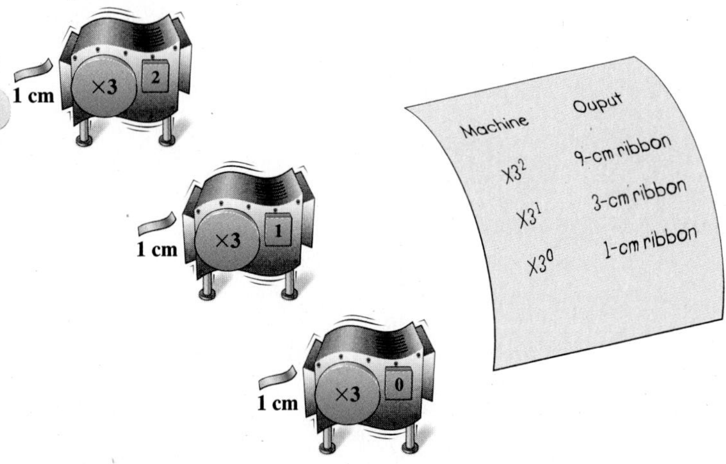

Think & Discuss

Jack noticed a pattern in the outputs: Each time the number of repeats is reduced by 1, the resulting length is $\frac{1}{3}$ the previous length. Why?

He is reducing the amount of stretch by a factor of 3.

Discuss why this statement is true.

Some of Jack's base 3 machines have negative exponents. When he puts 1-cm ribbons through a $\times 3^{-1}$ machine, a $\times 3^{-2}$ machine, and a $\times 3^{-3}$ machine, the pattern in the output length continues.

LESSON 4.5 Negative Numbers as Exponents 281

Problem Set B Suggested Grouping: Whole Class and Individuals

This problem set focuses on familiarizing students with negative-exponent notation and helping them relate it to the familiar machine model.

Discuss **Problems 1–3** as a whole class. Then have students work **Problems 4–7** individually, immediately followed by a whole-class review of the answers.

In **Problem 2,** be sure students understand that they can substitute any of these for machines for each other. If students have difficulty seeing that the machines do the same thing, you may want to have them use each machine to find outputs using the same input. Then have them compare the outputs.

Problem Set B

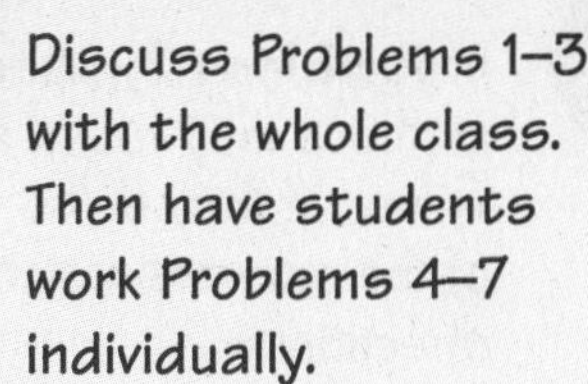

Discuss Problems 1–3 with the whole class. Then have students work Problems 4–7 individually.

1. Continue Jack's pattern in the chart below.

What Went In	Machine	What Came Out
1-cm ribbon	×3 [2]	9-cm ribbon
1-cm ribbon	×3 [1]	3-cm ribbon
1-cm ribbon	×3 [0]	1-cm ribbon
1-cm ribbon	×3 [−1]	$\frac{1}{3}$-cm ribbon
1-cm ribbon	×3 [−2]	$\frac{1}{9}$-cm ribbon
1-cm ribbon	×3 [−3]	$\frac{1}{27}$-cm ribbon

2. After conducting several experiments, Jack concluded that these three machines do the same thing:

a. Suppose you put an 18-inch length of rope into a $\times 3^{-1}$ machine. Describe two ways you could figure out how long the resulting piece would be. multiply by $\frac{1}{3}$ or divide by 3

b. Describe two other repeater machines—one that uses multiplication and one that uses division—that do the same thing as a $\times 3^{-2}$ machine. $\times\left(\frac{1}{3}\right)^2$ and $\div 3^2$

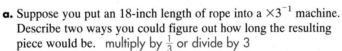

c. Describe two other repeater machines—one that uses multiplication and one that uses division—that do the same thing as a $\times 3^{-3}$ machine. $\times\left(\frac{1}{3}\right)^3$ and $\div 3^3$

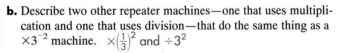

In **Problem 3,** students may want to use one of the methods they found in Problem 2 to calculate the output values. If they do so, have them verify that the pattern of the answers matches the pattern described in the directions.

Problems 4–7 give students practice applying the negative exponent notation. They may use either multiplication of fractions or repeated division to find the output.

On the **Spot Assessment**

Watch for students who are confused by the negative exponent notation in **Problems 4–7.** For instance, students may think that a 2^{-3} machine means to subtract 8 from the 72-inch pole rather than to divide the length by 8, or they may think it means a negative number, $^{-}8$. Have these students rewrite each negative exponent machine as a division machine to do the problems.

Problem Set Wrap-Up Be sure students can explain the patterns in Problems 1 and 3. These problems provide them with a reference point for seeing how negative exponents work.

3. Jack repeated the pattern shown in Problem 1 with two other bases.

a. With base 2, Jack found that each time the exponent was reduced by 1, the output length was half the previous output length. Complete the chart to show what happened to 1-cm ribbons.

b. A similar pattern appeared when Jack put 1-cm ribbons through base 4 machines. Complete the chart.

Machine	What Came Out
×2 2	4-cm ribbon
×2 1	2-cm ribbon
×2 0	1-cm ribbon
×2 −1	$\frac{1}{2}$-cm ribbon
×2 −2	$\frac{1}{4}$-cm ribbon
×2 −3	$\frac{1}{8}$-cm ribbon

Machine	What Came Out
×4 2	16-cm ribbon
×4 1	4-cm ribbon
×4 0	1-cm ribbon
×4 −1	$\frac{1}{4}$-cm ribbon
×4 −2	$\frac{1}{16}$-cm ribbon
×4 −3	$\frac{1}{64}$-cm ribbon

Machines with other bases also follow the pattern. If you put a 72-inch pole through each machine, how long would each output be?

4. 

36 in.

5. 

8 in.

6. 

9 in.

7. 

9 in.

1 Use any method found in Problem 2 to calculate the output values for Problem 3.

LESSON 4.5 Negative Numbers as Exponents 283

Share & Summarize

After discussing the generalization, students should understand that:

1. A negative exponent in a repeater machine does the same thing as a shrinking machine. A shrinking machine can involve dividing by a number greater than 1 or multiplying by a fraction between 0 and 1.
2. The base is the number being multiplied and the exponent is the number of times the number is multiplied. Students may state this fact in terms of the shrinking machine. Their answer might be that the "shrink factor" (the number in the circle on the machine) tells the factor by which you shrink and the repeater number (in the box, as the exponent) tells how many times to shrink.

You may wish to expand the discussion by having either pairs of students or the whole class generate a list of equivalent representations for $\times 2^{-4}$ such as $\times\frac{1}{16}$, $\div 2^4$, or $\left(\frac{1}{2}\right)^4$. Have students describe in their own words why these representations are equivalent.

Troubleshooting It is important that students understand how to put any length through a shrinking machine with a negative repeater number. If students are still struggling with this, give them some additional practice rewriting each machine as a series of repeated division steps or repeated multiplication of fractions. Students can revisit question 4 in Problem Set B and write an expression for each machine using either division of integers or multiplication of fractions.

On Your Own Exercises

Practice & Apply: 1–13
Connect & Extend: 57–62
Mixed Review: 74–85

Investigation 2

This investigation is a brief one that provides practice evaluating a variety of expressions that use exponents and negative numbers.

Example

Walk students through the Example on how to evaluate expressions with negative exponents. Students may have little difficulty evaluating the first expression (4^{-3}) if they think about the shrinking machines used in the first investigation. However, this is their first exposure to a hookup that has one machine with a negative exponent. After discussing why the machine works, you may want to ask:

> What single machine will do the same thing as the hookup of these machines? *a* $\times\frac{1}{2}$ *or a* $\times 2^{-1}$ *machine*

Share & Summarize

In general, when you put something in a multiplication machine with a negative exponent, like $\times 2^{-4}$, how can you find the output length? See ①.

1 Discuss the generalization.

Investigation 2 Evaluating Expressions with Negative Exponents

① Possible answers: Find the base to the exponent as if the exponent were positive, and divide the input length by the result. *Or*, change the base to a fraction by putting 1 over the base, and do the problem with the new base and the absolute value of the exponent.

Thinking about shrinking machines can help you evaluate expressions with negative exponents.

2 Discuss the Example.

EXAMPLE

Evaluate 4^{-3}.

Think about a $\times 4^{-3}$ machine. Putting something through a $\times 4^{-3}$ machine is equivalent to putting it through a $\times\left(\frac{1}{4}\right)^3$ machine, so $4^{-3} = \left(\frac{1}{4}\right)^3$, or $\frac{1}{64}$.

Evaluate $2^{-3} \times 2^2$.

Think about this hookup.

The $\times 2^{-3}$ machine halves the length of an input three times.

The $\times 2^2$ machine doubles the length twice.

The output is half the length of the original input. The hookup is the same as a $\times\frac{1}{2}$ or a $\times 2^{-1}$ machine. So $2^{-3} \times 2^2 = \frac{1}{2}$, or 2^{-1}.

Problem Set C Suggested Grouping: Pairs or Individuals

Students practice evaluating expressions with negative exponents.

Problems 1–12 are straightforward practice. In Problem 12, students may find changing 4^2 to a base of 2 simplifies their work.

Problems 13–15 help students develop a greater number sense about negative exponents.

On the Spot Assessment

In **Problem 13,** watch for students who think that 5^{-2} is greater than 5^{-1} because 2 is greater than 1. Have these students write each of these terms using division. Then have them calculate each term to see what they get.

You may also want to encourage students to look at the patterns they found in the previous investigation. Have them try the patterns using a fraction as the base. They can use these patterns to find that the smaller exponent will be a smaller number when the base is a positive number greater than 1.

In **Problem 14,** students are asked to come up with two repeater hookups that might give 5^0. The exponents for this pair of machines should be opposites, such as 5^3 and 5^{-3}.

You may wish to quickly review the notation involving exponents and parentheses before having students work on Problem Set D. Remind students that the way parentheses are placed can affect the value of the expression. You may want to have them evaluate two expressions with positive exponents, $^-4^2$ and $(^-4)^2$, to refresh their memory.

$$^-4^2 = {}^-(4 \cdot 4) = {}^-16$$

$$(^-4)^2 = {}^-4 \cdot {}^-4 = 16$$

Problem Set D Suggested Grouping: Pairs or Individuals

Students evaluate expressions with parentheses and negative exponents.

In **Problems 1 and 2,** students look at how parentheses affect the value of an expression with negative numbers and explain how to evaluate each example. These problems may take time and further explanation since they often cause confusion for students.

About the Mathematics

Negative numbers raised to powers are often initially confusing to students. In lesson 2, students learned that $^-3^2$ meant the opposite of 3^2. This can be written as $^-(3^2)$ or $^-9$. They learned that $(^-3)^2$ meant $^-3 \times {}^-3$, or 9. The same thing holds true with negative numbers raised to negative exponents. Help students remember that, assuming $b > 0$, $^-a^{-b}$ is the opposite of a^{-b}, or $^-(a^{-b})$, while $(^-a)^{-b}$ means $1/[(^-a) \times (^-a) \times (^-a) \ldots]$ b times.

In **Problems 5-10,** students practice evaluating expressions.

Problem Set Wrap-Up You might want to reiterate that even though all the answers to **Problems 5–10** are negative numbers, it does not mean that all negative numbers raised to a power will have a negative answer. Nor does it mean that all numbers raised to negative powers are negative. If students are still uncertain of your explanation, have them evaluate these expressions:

1. $(^-6)^{-2}$ $\frac{1}{36}$
2. $(^-5)^0$ 1
3. $(^-2)^4$ 16
4. $(^-3)^{-4}$ $\frac{1}{81}$

Share & Summarize

List the class's responses to **Questions 1–3** and compare them. Help students see that there are many correct responses. You may want to ask students what all the correct values have in common to help them generalize their work.

Troubleshooting If students are still struggling with how to evaluate expressions with negative exponents correctly, give them some additional practice rewriting problems as a series of repeated division steps or repeated multiplication of fractions. Students can revisit Problems 1 and 4 in Problem Set C and write an expression for each machine using division or using multiplication of fractions.

On Your Own Exercises

Practice & Apply: 14–24
Connect & Extend: 63–71
Mixed Review: 74–85

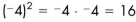

Now you will practice evaluating expressions with negative exponents. Pay attention to how you solve the problems, and be ready to share your approach with others in your class.

1 • Students can work individually or in pairs to evaluate expressions.

• Discuss Problems 13–15 with entire class.

Problem Set C

Evaluate each expression.

1. 3^{-4} $\frac{1}{81}$ **2.** 2^{-1} $\frac{1}{2}$ **3.** $3^{-3} \cdot 3^{5}$ 9

4. $7^{5} \cdot 7^{-7}$ $\frac{1}{49}$ **5.** $3^{9} \cdot 3^{-6}$ 27 **6.** $^{-}49 \cdot 7^{-2}$ $^{-}1$

7. $256 \cdot 4^{-3}$ 4 **8.** $32 \cdot 1^{-5}$ 32 **9.** $^{-}60 \cdot 6^{-1}$ $^{-}10$

10. $2^{-2} \cdot 3^{-1}$ $\frac{1}{12}$ **11.** $2^{-1} \cdot 3^{-1} \cdot 5^{-2}$ $\frac{1}{150}$ **12.** $2^{-2} \cdot 4^{2} \cdot 2^{-1}$ 2

13. Which is greater, 5^{-1} or 5^{-2}? Why?

14. Describe a hookup of two repeater machines, one with a negative exponent, that does the same work as a $\times 5^{0}$ machine.

15. Is it possible to shrink something to a length of 0 by using shrinking machines? Why or why not? See Additional Answers.

13. 5^{-1} is greater because $\frac{1}{5} > \frac{1}{25}$.

14. Answers will vary. The exponents must be opposites, as in $\times 5^{2} \times 5^{-2}$.

Problem Set D

2 Have students work in pairs or individually.

You sometimes need to take extra care to be sure you understand a mathematical expression. For example, in expressions such as $^{-}3^{-2}$ and $(^{-}3)^{-2}$, the two negative symbols give two different kinds of information.

1. Why is $^{-}3^{-2} = -\frac{1}{9}$? $^{-}3^{-2} = -(3^{-2}) = -\frac{1}{9}$

2. Why is $(^{-}3)^{-2} = \frac{1}{9}$? $(^{-}3)^{-2} = \frac{1}{(^{-}3)^{2}} = \frac{1}{9}$

3. What does $^{-}4^{-2}$ equal? $-\frac{1}{16}$

4. Write an expression that has a negative exponent and equals $-\frac{1}{27}$.

4. Possible answer: $^{-}3^{-3}$

Evaluate each expression.

5. $^{-}5^{-2}$ $-\frac{1}{25}$ **6.** $(^{-}3)^{3}$ $^{-}27$ **7.** $^{-}1^{-5}$ $^{-}1$

8. $(^{-}1)^{-5}$ $^{-}1$ **9.** $(^{-}5)^{-3}$ $-\frac{1}{125}$ **10.** $^{-}2^{4}$ $^{-}16$

Share & Summarize

3 List and compare students' responses to Questions 1–3.

1. Give two values of n for which $(^{-}2)^{n}$ is positive.

2. Give two values of n for which $(^{-}2)^{n}$ is negative.

3. Give two values of n for which $(^{-}2)^{n}$ is not an integer.

4. Write an expression with a negative exponent that equals $-\frac{1}{64}$.

Share & Summarize Answers

1. Any even values will work.

2. Any odd values will work.

3. Any negative values will work.

4. Possible answers: $^{-}8^{-2}$ *or* $(^{-}4)^{-3}$

Additional Answers
Problem Set C

15. Technically, no. You can get smaller and smaller lengths by repeatedly sending the input through standard shrinking machines, machines that multiply the length by fractions, or machines with negative exponents, but the length will never be 0. The result of $1 \div 10 \div 10 \div 10 \div 10 \div 10 \div 10 \div \cdots$, for instance, gets smaller each time you divide by 10, but it never reaches 0. In reality, with real materials such as gum you would eventually get such a small piece you would no longer call it a stick of gum.

Investigation 3

Students revisit familiar content from Chapter 3 on laws of exponents and scientific notation, now with negative exponents in the mix.

1 You may want to review the laws of exponents at the top of page 286 with your students. Some students may want to clarify how each law works by substituting numbers for the variables.

2 

Problem Set E **Suggested Grouping: Pairs or Individuals**

The questions in this problem set focus on reviewing the laws of exponents. For the first problems, students rewrite expressions with a single base and use a calculator to check their answers.

Problems 1–6 review the product laws of exponents that state $a^b \times a^c = a^{b+c}$ and $a^c \times b^c = (a \times b)^c$.

Problems 7–9 and 11 review quotient laws of exponents.

Problems 10 and 12 review power of a power law of exponents.

> On the **Spot Assessment**
>
> Watch for students who do not understand how to apply the laws of exponents to **Problems 1–12.** Instead, they may methodically try to calculate each problem to come up with a numerical answer. Encourage them to think about using a stretching or shrinking machine to find the value. Have them practice writing verbal descriptions for what each machine would do and use those descriptions to think about what will happen to the input length.
>
> For example, in **Problem 1,** students might write that the first machine shrinks the input by dividing it by 50 for six times. The second machine stretches the input by multiplying it by 50 for twelve times. The input length gets divided by 50 six times and then multiplied by 50 twelve times, so six of the times you multiply undoes the six times you divided. So in the end, it's as if you multiplied by 50 six times.

Problems 16 and 17 involve creating and evaluating complex fractions. For example, $\left(\frac{2}{3}\right)^{-1}$ can be written as $\frac{1}{\frac{2}{3}}$. If students are stuck, you may want to help them realize that this is really a division problem that they can do by finding $1 \div \frac{2}{3}$.

3 In **Problems 19–21,** students use the laws of exponents and the distributive property to simplify expressions.

Problem Set Wrap-Up You may want students to explain how they simplified the expressions in Problems 19–21. Some students may benefit from an explanation of why there is not a variable in the answer to Problem 21.

Investigation 3 Laws of Exponents and Scientific Notation

In Chapter 3, you learned about the laws of exponents, which describe how to simplify expressions with exponents.

Product Laws	Quotient Laws	Power of a Power Law
$a^b \times a^c = a^{b+c}$	$a^b \div a^c = a^{b-c}$	$(a^b)^c = a^{b \times c}$
$a^c \times b^c = (a \times b)^c$	$a^c \div b^c = (a \div b)^c$	

Now you will apply these laws to expressions with negative exponents.

Problem Set E

The product laws work for negative exponents as well as for positive exponents. In Problems 1–6, use the product laws to rewrite each expression using a single base. Use a calculator to check your answers.

1. $50^{-6} \cdot 50^{12}$ 50^6

2. $2^5 \cdot 2^{-6} \cdot 2^3$ 2^2

3. $0.5^{-10} \cdot 0.5^{-10}$ 0.5^{-20}

4. $3^{-1} \cdot 9$ 3^1, or 3

5. $^-3^{-3} \cdot 2^{-3} \cdot 4^{-3}$ $^-24^{-3}$

6. $10^{-23} \cdot 10^{23}$ 10^0, or 1

The quotient laws and the power of a power law also work for negative exponents. In Problems 7–12, use the appropriate law to rewrite each expression using a single base. Use a calculator to check your answers.

7. $7^3 \div 7^5$ 7^{-2}

8. $12^{-4} \div 4^{-4}$ 3^{-4}

9. $10^{-5} \div 10^3$ 10^{-8}

10. $(3^{-3})^2$ 3^{-6}

11. $2.3^2 \div 2.3^{-6}$ 2.3^8

12. $(2^{-5})^{-5}$ 2^{25}

Rewrite each expression using a single base or exponent.

13. $m^{23} \cdot m^{-17}$ m^6

14. $7^{-x} \cdot 7^x$ 7^0, or 1

15. $a^{-3} \div b^{-3}$ $\left(\frac{a}{b}\right)^{-3}$

Rewrite each expression using only positive exponents.

16. $\left(\frac{2}{3}\right)^{-1}$ $\left(\frac{3}{2}\right)^1$, or $\frac{3}{2}$

17. $\left(\frac{1}{2}\right)^{-3}$ 2^3

18. 10^{-7} $\left(\frac{1}{10}\right)^7$, or $\frac{1}{10^7}$

Simplify each expression as much as you can.

19. $^-3n \times {}^-3n$ $9n^2$

20. $5n \div 2n^{-2}$ $\frac{5}{2}n^3$

21. $4y^2 \times 3y^{-2}$ 12

1 Review laws of exponents.

2 Students work problems individually or in pairs.

3 Review the distributive property.

Develop

You may want to begin with a brief reminder of how to write numbers in scientific notation. Remind students that one factor is a number greater than 1 and less than 10 and the other factor is a power of 10. Then give students one or two examples of large numbers, such as 540,000 and 20,000,000, to write in scientific notation. $540{,}000 = 5.4 \times 10^5$ and $20{,}000{,}000 = 2 \times 10^7$

Problem Set F **Suggested Grouping: Whole Class**
Students write numbers less than zero in scientific notation. They write a number in standard form and in scientific notation.

Problems 1–3 resemble questions from Chapter 3 about scientific notation. Students practice applying negative exponents to small numbers written in scientific notation.

In **Problems 1–4,** ask students to describe in words what each of the machines does, before they actually calculate the answer.

2

Sample Strategies Students may use one of these strategies to find the length of the straw in **Problems 1–4.**

- Multiply 5.3 by $\frac{1}{10^n}$, with *n* being the absolute value of the exponent on the shrinking machine.
- Divide 5.2 by 10, *n* times, *n* being the absolute value of the exponent on the shrinking machine.

You may want to give students a few minutes individually or in pairs to work on **Problems 7–11** before you go over them with the whole class.

On the **Spot Assessment**

Watch for students who multiply rather than divide to find the number of days in one second in **Problem 11.** These students will find $1 \times 86{,}400 = 86{,}400$. Encourage them to think about the context of the problem to check the reasonableness of their answer. They might ask themselves whether there will be more or less than one day in one second.

Problem Set Wrap-Up Discuss students' work on **Problems 7–11.** Before you end the discussion, revisit **Problem 6.** Be sure that students understand that since 5.3 is the same for all numbers in scientific notation, they can order the numbers by looking at the power of 10. They should understand that the greater the power of 10, the greater the number.

Share & Summarize

Students can work with a partner to discuss each question and come up with a shared response before you discuss these questions with the whole class. Encourage students to justify their responses.

Troubleshooting If students are struggling with using negative exponents in scientific notation, have them create a chart as shown below and use it to record different numbers. Have them focus on patterns they see in the results and work with them to generate their own descriptions of the relationship between the 10^{-n} term and how the decimal point moves.

Number	What does it equal?	Exponent	How does decimal point move?
3.4×10^{-4}	.00034	−4	4 places left

On Your Own Exercises

Practice & Apply: 25–56
Connect & Extend: 72–73
Mixed Review: 74–85

Remember

In scientific notation, a number is expressed as the product of a number greater than or equal to 1 but less than 10, and a power of 10. For example, 5,400 is written 5.4×10^3.

In Chapter 3, you used scientific notation to represent very large numbers. You can also use scientific notation to represent very small numbers. For small numbers, scientific notation involves negative powers of 10.

Problem Set F

1 Discuss problems with entire class.

A 5.3-cm drinking straw is sent through each machine. Give the length of the straw that emerges from each machine. Write your answers as decimals.

2 Discuss strategies students can use to solve Problems 1–4.

1. **2.** **1–6.** See below.

3. **4.**

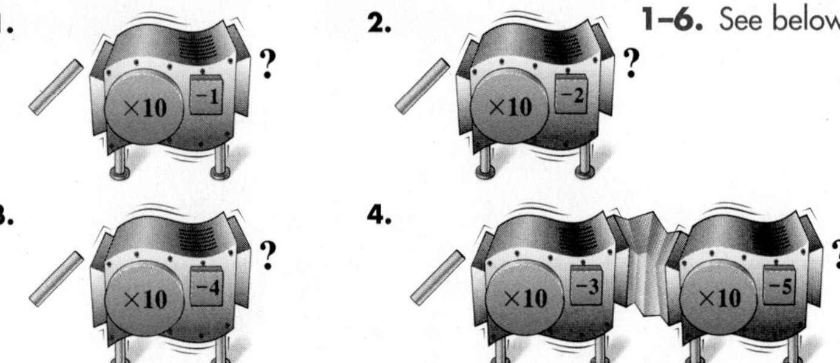

5. Write your answers for Problems 1–4 in scientific notation.

6. List your answers for Problem 5 from greatest to least.

Find each missing value.

7. $3 \times 10^? = 0.03$ $^-2$

8. $4.5 \times 10^? = 0.00045$ $^-4$

9. $? \times 10^{-3} = 0.0065$ 6.5

10. $1 \times ? = 0.00000001$ 10^{-8}

11. There are 86,400 seconds in a day. How many days long is a second? Express your answer in scientific notation. about 1.157×10^{-5}

Share & Summarize Answers

1. It is greater than 0 because both factors are greater than 0.

2. 1×10^{-7} because it has a smaller power of 10.

Share & Summarize

3 Students work in pairs to answer each question before sharing answers with entire class.

1. Without calculating the product, how can you tell whether $2^{-4} \times 2^3$ is greater than 0 or less than 0?

2. Which is smaller, 1×10^{-6} or 1×10^{-7}? How do you know?

Problem Set F Answers

1. 0.53 cm **2.** 0.053 cm

3. 0.00053 cm **4.** 0.000000053 cm

5. 5.3×10^{-1}, 5.3×10^{-2}, 5.3×10^{-4}, 5.3×10^{-8}

6. 5.3×10^{-1}, 5.3×10^{-2}, 5.3×10^{-4}, 5.3×10^{-8}

LESSON 4.5 Negative Numbers as Exponents 287

On Your Own Exercises

Investigation 1
Practice & Apply: 1–13
Connect & Extend: 57–62

Investigation 2
Practice & Apply: 14–24
Connect & Extend: 63–71

Investigation 3
Practice & Apply: 25–56
Connect & Extend: 72–73

Assign Anytime
Mixed Review: 74–85

Exercises 1–7:
If students are having difficulty solving these exercises, review the machine model from Chapter 3.

Exercises 8–13:
This set of exercises focuses on the use of negative exponents and gives students practice linking it to the machine model.

On Your Own Exercises

Practice & Apply

1. 18 in.
2. 12 in.
3. 16 in.
4. $\div 2^5$, or $\times 2^{-5}$
5. $\div 3^2$, or $\times 3^{-2}$
8. $\times 4^{-3}$
9. $\times 6^{-2}$
10. $\times 5^{-1}$
11. $\times 3^2$
12. $\times 4^{-3}$
13. $\times 10^{-2}$

Find the length of the output if an 144-inch input is sent through each machine.

1.

2.

3.

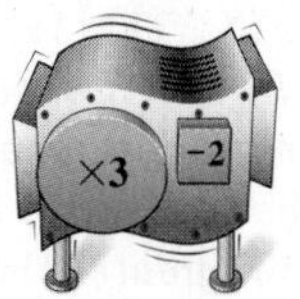

If possible, find a single repeater machine that will do the same work as the given hookup.

4.

5.

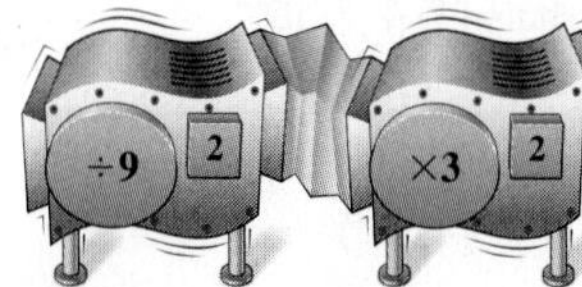

6.

$\times 2^4$

7.

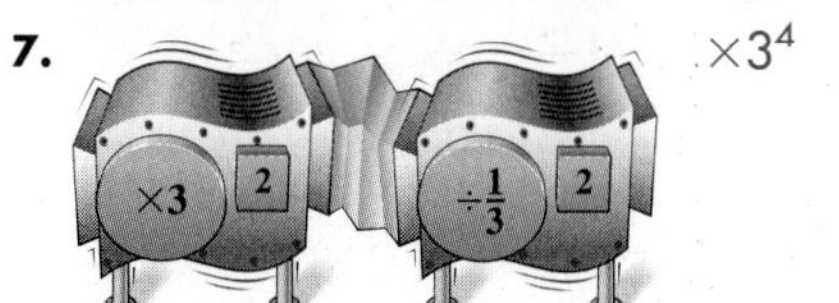

$\times 3^4$

Describe a machine with a negative exponent that does the same work as the given machine.

8. ÷4, 3

9.

10.

11.

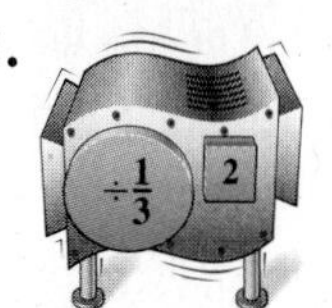

12.

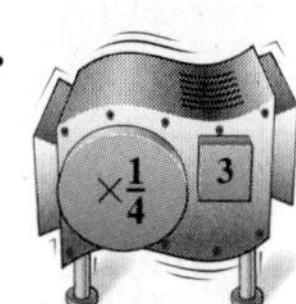

13.

14. Without calculating, figure out whether 4^{-3} or 4^{-4} is greater. Explain how you decided. 4^{-3} because $\frac{1}{4^3}$ is greater than $\frac{1}{4^4}$.

288 CHAPTER 4 Working with Signed Numbers

Evaluate each expression.

15. $^-343 \cdot 7^{-2}$ $^-7$ **16.** $^-1{,}375 \cdot 5^{-3}$ $^-11$ **17.** $128 \cdot 2^{-5}$ 4

18. $^-72 \cdot 9^{-1}$ $^-8$ **19.** $48 \cdot 6^{-1}$ 8 **20.** $243 \cdot 3^{-4}$ 3

21. $^-9 \cdot 1^{-3}$ $^-9$ **22.** $4{,}096 \cdot 8^{-2}$ 64 **23.** $^-11 \cdot 11^{-1}$ $^-1$

24. How could you rewrite Problem 22 as a division problem? As a multiplication problem using a positive exponent?

Decide whether each statement is true. If the statement is false, explain why.

25. $2^{-2} \cdot 2^{-1} = 2^{-3}$ true **26.** $5^{-3} \cdot 5^{-1} \cdot 5^2 = 5^{-2}$ true

27. $3^{-1} \cdot 4^{-3} = 12^{-4}$ **28.** $3^{-2} \cdot 3^{-3} = 9^{-5}$

29. $x^{-5} \div x^7 = x^{-12}$ true **30.** $k^{-2} \div k^{-5} = k^3$ true

31. $w^{-2} \div w^{-5} = w^{-7}$ **32.** $b^{-8} \div g^{-4} = bg^{-2}$

Without evaluating, tell whether each expression is greater or less than 1.

33. $3^{-4} \times 3^5$ **34.** $2^{-1} \times 2^{-3}$ **35.** $1^{-3} \div 2^{-3}$ **36.** $10^{-5} \div 10^3$

Evaluate each expression.

37. $^-4^{-2}$ $-\frac{1}{16}$ **38.** $(^-5)^{-1}$ $-\frac{1}{5}$ **39.** $^-2^3$ $^-8$ **40.** $(^-10)^4$ 10,000

Rewrite each expression using a single base and a single exponent.

41. $\frac{1}{2^{-2}} \times 4^{-2}$ 2^{-2} **42.** $100^{-20} \div {}^-25^{-20}$ $^-4^{-20}$

43. $^-3^{100} \times -\frac{5}{6^{100}} \times 10^{100}$ 5^{101} **44.** $\left(\frac{1}{3}\right)^{-a} \times \left(\frac{1}{5}\right)^{-a}$ $\left(\frac{1}{15}\right)^{-a}$, or 15^a

45. $^-1{,}000^0 \div 3^0$ 1^1 **46.** $15^{-5} \times \left(\frac{1}{5}\right)^{-5}$ 3^{-5}

Find the value of n in each equation.

47. $7.24 \cdot 10^n = 0.00724$ $^-3$ **48.** $5 \cdot 10^n = 0.5$ $^-1$

49. $n \cdot 10^{-4} = 0.000104$ 1.04 **50.** $9.2 \cdot n = 0.0092$ 10^{-3}

51. A mile is 1.609×10^5 centimeters. How many miles is a centimeter? Express your answer in scientific notation. about 6.215×10^{-6}

52. There are 7.8125×10^{-3} gallons in an ounce. How many ounces are in a gallon? Express your answer in scientific notation. 1.28×10^2

Challenge Simplify each expression.

53. $^-6a^{-2} \div 4a^{-4}$ $-\frac{6}{4}a^2$ or $-\frac{3}{2}a^2$ **54.** $-\frac{1}{2}x^{-3} \times x^4$ $-\frac{1}{2}x$

55. $z^2 \times 2z^{-3} \div {}^-6z^{-2}$ $-\frac{z}{3}$ **56.** $9b^4 \times 9b^{-8}$ $81b^{-4}$

24. $4{,}096 \div 8^2$; $4{,}096 \times \frac{1}{8^2}$

27. False; you can't add exponents of numbers with different bases.

28. False; when you multiply expressions with the same base, you do not multiply the bases: $3^{-2} \cdot 3^{-3} = 3^{-5}$.

31. False; when dividing, you subtract rather than add exponents: $w^{-2} \div w^{-5} = w^3$.

32. False; there are two different bases with different exponents, so you can't use either quotient law.

33. greater than 1

34. less than 1

35. greater than 1

36. less than 1

Exercises 53–56: Watch out for students who apply the exponent to the coefficient.

60. 16 m
61. 1,000 m

57. Challenge Describe a machine that has a negative exponent and that does the same work as the machine shown at right. $\times\left(\frac{1}{4}\right)^{-3}$

Find the length of the output if a meterstick is sent through each hookup.

58. 3 m

59. 16 m

60.

61.

62. A 1-inch stick of gum went into each machine. Complete the chart.

Machine	What Came Out	Machine	What Came Out
$\times\frac{1}{2}$ 2	$\frac{1}{4}$-in. stick	$\times\frac{1}{2}$ −1	2-in. stick
$\times\frac{1}{2}$ 1	$\frac{1}{2}$-in. stick	$\times\frac{1}{2}$ −2	4-in. stick
$\times\frac{1}{2}$ 0	1-in. stick	$\times\frac{1}{2}$ −3	8-in. stick

63. Challenge A strand of wire is sent through this hookup. It emerges 2 inches long. What was the starting length? 5,760 in.

290 CHAPTER 4 Working with Signed Numbers

In your own words

Write a letter to someone in your family who does not know what negative exponents are. In your letter, describe why 3^{-1} is equal to $\frac{1}{3}$.

Without calculating, figure out whether each expression is positive or negative and explain how you decided. See Additional Answers.

64. $(^-4)^{-1}$ **65.** $(^-4)^{-2}$ **66.** $(^-4)^{-3}$ **67.** $(^-4)^{-4}$

68. $(^-2)^{-3}$ **69.** $(^-2)^{-2}$ **70.** $(^-5)^{-1}$ **71.** $(^-10)^{-6}$

72. Prove It! It is true that $\left(\frac{1}{2}\right)^{-1} = (2^{-1})^{-1} = 2^1 = 2$. In Parts a–c, you will explain each step in this calculation.

a. Why does $\left(\frac{1}{2}\right)^{-1} = (2^{-1})^{-1}$? because $\frac{1}{2} = 2^{-1}$

b. Why does $(2^{-1})^{-1} = 2^1$? See margin.

c. Why does $2^1 = 2$? because any number to the first power equals that number

72b. because of the power of a power law, $(2^{-1})^{-1} = 2^{-1 \cdot -1} = 2^1$

73. Physics Protons, neutrons, and electrons are *stable* particles—they can exist for a very long time. But many other particles exist for only very short periods of time. A *muon,* for example, has an average life of 0.000002197 second.

a. Write this length of time in scientific notation. 2.197×10^{-6} s

b. A particular muon existed for half the average life of this type of particle. How long did it exist? about 1.099×10^{-6} s

c. Another muon existed for three times the average life of this type of particle. How long did it exist? 6.591×10^{-6} s

Mixed Review

Evaluate.

74. $11 \cdot 33$ 363 **75.** $11 \cdot 44$ 484

76. $11 \cdot 55$ 605 **77.** $3.5 + 0.251$ 3.751

78. $3.54 + 0.754$ 4.294 **79.** $3.5 - 1.6$ 1.9

80. See below.

80. Draw a flowchart to represent the expression $\frac{4x + 8}{2}$. Then use backtracking to find the solution to the equation $\frac{4x + 8}{2} = 10$.

Complete each table, and write another expression that gives the same values.

81. $\frac{n}{2} - \frac{1}{2}$ or $\frac{1}{2}n - \frac{1}{2}$

81.

n	1	2	3	4	5	100
$\frac{n-1}{2}$	0	$\frac{1}{2}$	1	$1\frac{1}{2}$	2	$49\frac{1}{2}$

82. $\frac{1}{2}q + 4$ or $\frac{q}{2} + 4$

82.

q	0	1	2	3	4	100
$\frac{q+8}{2}$	4	4.5	5	5.5	6	54

80.

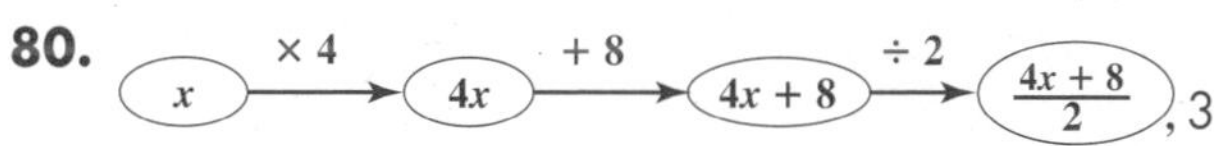

, 3

Quick Check

Informal Assessment

Students should be able to

- ✔ relate negative exponents to both multiplication by fractions and repeated division
- ✔ evaluate simple expressions with negative exponents
- ✔ apply the law of exponents to expressions with negative exponents
- ✔ write numbers in scientific notation with negative exponents

Additional Answers

64. Negative; $\frac{1}{-4}$ is negative.

65. Positive; $(^-4)^2$ is positive, so $\frac{1}{(^-4)^2}$ is positive.

66. Negative; $(^-4)^3$ is negative, so $\frac{1}{(^-4)^3}$ is negative.

67. Positive; $(^-4)^4$ is positive, so $\frac{1}{(^-4)^4}$ is positive.

68. Negative; $(^-2)^3$ is negative, so $\frac{1}{(^-2)^3}$ is negative.

69. Positive; $(^-2)^{-2}$ is positive, so $\frac{1}{(^-2)^2}$ is positive.

70. Negative; $\frac{1}{-5}$ is negative.

71. Positive; $(^-10)^6$ is positive, so $\frac{1}{(^-10)^6}$ is positive.

LESSON 4.5 Negative Numbers as Exponents 291

Assign and Assess

Quick Quiz

1. $5.4 \div (10 \times 10 \times 10)$
   a. Rewrite this expression as a multiplication expression. $5.4 \times \frac{1}{10} \times \frac{1}{10} \times \frac{1}{10}$
   b. Rewrite this expression using negative exponents. 5.4×10^{-3}
   c. Write the answer in scientific notation. 5.4×10^{-3}
2. Fill in the missing values.
   a. $3.9 \times 10^{?} = 0.00039$ -4
   b. $? \times 10^{-2} = 0.01$ 1
   c. $5.61 \times 10^{-1} = ?$ 0.561
3. Without actually calculating it, will $2^{-3} \times 2^{-2} \times 2^{7}$ be greater or less than zero? How do you know? *Greater than zero because all the factors are greater than zero.*
4. Find the value of ? in each equation.
   a. $3^{-2} \cdot 3^{7} = ?$ 243
   b. $\frac{1}{4} \cdot 4^{-2} = ?$ $\frac{1}{64}$
   c. $6^{-2} \cdot ? \cdot 6^{-1} = \frac{1}{6}$ 36
   d. $2 \cdot 2^{?} = \frac{1}{8}$ -4

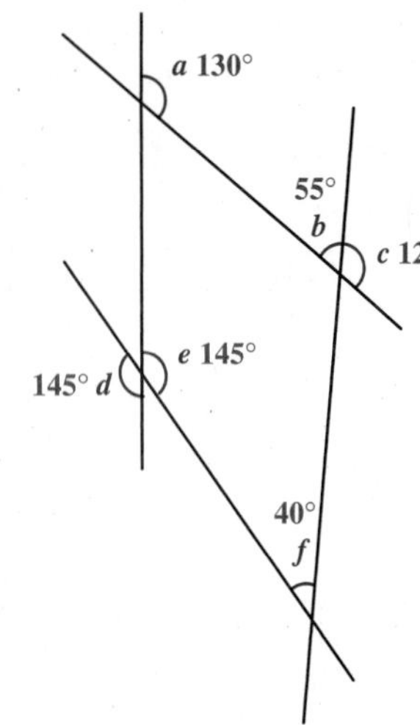

83. Use a protractor to measure the angles on the figure at left. Give your answers to the nearest 5°.

84. In 1997 you could have received about 36.313 Indian rupees for 1 U.S. dollar.

a. How many dollars could you have received in exchange for 100 Indian rupees? about 2.75

b. How many Indian rupees could you have received in exchange for 100 U.S. dollars? about 3,631

85. The table shows how long a person born in the given year was expected to live, on average. For example, a boy born in 1950 was expected to live 65.6 years.

Years of Life Expected at Birth

Year	Life Expectancy (years) Males	Females
1900	46.3	48.3
1910	48.4	51.8
1920	53.6	54.6
1930	58.1	61.6
1940	60.8	65.2
1950	65.6	71.1
1960	66.6	73.1
1970	67.1	74.7
1980	70.0	77.5
1990	71.8	78.8

Source: Reprinted with permission from *The World Almanac and Book of Facts 1999*. Copyright © 1998 Primedia Reference Inc.

a. By how many years did the life expectancy of a baby girl rise from 1900 to 1990? By how many years did the life expectancy of a baby boy rise in that time? 30.5, 25.5

b. By what percentage did the life expectancy of a baby girl rise from 1900 to 1990? By what percentage did the life expectancy of a baby boy rise in that time? 63.1%, 55.1%

c. What might have contributed to the dramatic rise in life expectancy between 1900 and 1990?

d. Estimate the life expectancies of a baby boy and a baby girl in the year 2000. Estimates will vary. The 1997 projected values were 73.6 years and 79.2 years.

85c. Answers will vary. Students might mention better medical care and hygiene.

VOCABULARY
distance formula
quadrant

Chapter Summary

You began this chapter learning about operations with signed numbers. Using the number-line model, you thought about addition and subtraction as facing a particular direction on a number line and moving forward or backward. You discovered some rules for these calculations, and then used them to develop rules for multiplication and division.

You extended your knowledge of positive and negative numbers by plotting points in all four quadrants. Next you looked at ways to calculate lengths of line segments on a graph, using two related formulas: the Pythagorean Theorem and the distance formula.

Finally, you learned what negative numbers mean as exponents. You learned that the laws of exponents apply when the exponents are negative. You also practiced writing very small numbers in scientific notation.

Strategies and Applications

The questions in this section will help you review and apply the important ideas and strategies developed in this chapter.

Adding and subtracting with signed numbers

Using the "walk the number line" model or any other strategy you know, describe how to compute each sum or difference.

1. $2 - {}^{-}9$ **2.** ${}^{-}9 + 3$

3. Write a word problem that can be solved in two ways, one involving subtraction with signed numbers and one involving addition with signed numbers. Then write an equation to represent each solution method. Answers will vary.

Multiplying and dividing with signed numbers

Describe how to compute each product or quotient.

4. ${}^{-}3.5 \times 4$ **5.** ${}^{-}9 \div {}^{-}4.5$

Without computing, determine whether each expression is greater than 0, less than 0, or equal to 0. Explain how you know.

6. $({}^{-}33)^5 \times ({}^{-}27)^2$ **7.** $\frac{{}^{-}5^{58} \times ({}^{-}12)^{23}}{{}^{-}5^3}$

1. Possible answer: To walk the number line, start at 2, point to the left, and move backward 9 units.
2. Possible answer: To walk the number line, start at ${}^{-}9$, point to the right, and move forward 3 units.
4. Strategies will vary; the product is ${}^{-}14$.
5. Strategies will vary; the quotient is 2.
6. See Additional Answers.
7. less than 0; The numerator is greater than 0 because the first factor is negative (no parentheses) and the second factor is negative (odd exponent), and negative × negative = positive; denominator is less than 0; positive ÷ negative = negative.

Chapter Summary This summary helps students recall the major topics of the chapter.

Vocabulary Students should be able to explain each of the terms listed in the vocabulary section.

Strategies and Applications The questions in this section help students review and apply the important mathematical ideas and problem-solving strategies developed in the chapter.

The questions are organized by mathematical highlight. The highlights correspond to those in "The Big Picture" chart on page T215a.

Exercises 1 and 2: Many students compute each answer mentally. Those students having less confidence may use the model to check their answers. Others may rely on the model altogether. Encourage students to use any method with which they feel comfortable.

Additional Answers

6. less than 0; The exponent on the first factor is odd, so the first factor is negative; the exponent on the second factor is even, so the second factor is positive; negative × positive = negative.

Exercise 11:
You may wish to discuss the vertical scale on the graph with your students. Watch for students who say the interval on the vertical scale is 100. Help them understand that the lines not labeled on the scale are halfway between the labeled lines, so the actual interval is 50. Then discuss the labels on the horizontal scale as students determine the time interval between lines.

Solve each equation.

8. $^{-}3x + 2 = {}^{-}4$ 2

9. $2a + 20 = 6$ $^{-}7$

10. The product of two integers is 10. What could the integers be? Name all the possibilities. 1 and 10, $^{-}1$ and $^{-}10$, 2 and 5, $^{-}2$ and $^{-}5$

Working with points in all four quadrants

11. The graph shows how a hiker's elevation changed during a hike.

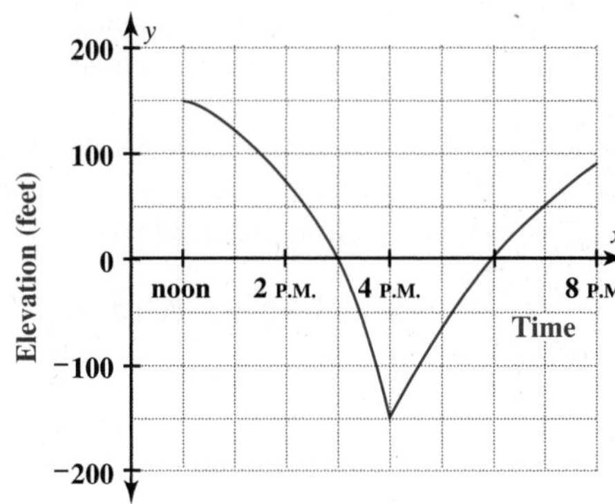

a. What was the lowest elevation the hiker reached, and when did she reach it? $^{-}150$ ft, 4 P.M.

b. What was the highest elevation the hiker reached, and when did she reach it? 150 ft, 12 P.M.

c. At what time or times was she at sea level (elevation 0)? 3 P.M. and 6 P.M.

d. At what elevation did she begin her hike? 150 ft

e. Between what times was the hiker above sea level? 12 P.M. to 3 P.M., and 6 P.M. to 8 P.M.

f. Between what times was she below sea level? 3 PM to 6 P.M.

12a.

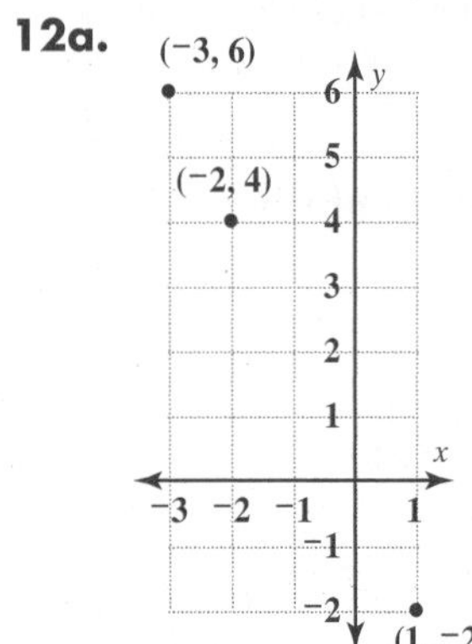

12. Think about all points (x, y) where $y = {}^{-}2x$—that is, where the y-coordinate is equal to the product of $^{-}2$ and the x-coordinate. Examples are $(1, {}^{-}2)$, $({}^{-}2, 4)$, and $({}^{-}3, 6)$.

a. Plot and label the three points listed above.

b. Plot and label four more points in which $y = {}^{-}2x$. Points will vary.

c. Imagine plotting all points for which $y = {}^{-}2x$. In what quadrants or on what axes would these points lie? Explain how you know. See Additional Answers.

Additional Answers

12c. Quadrants II and IV; If x is positive, y is equal to the product of $^{-}2$ and a positive number, so it will be negative and these points will be in Quadrant IV. If x is negative, y is equal to the product of $^{-}2$ and a negative number, so it will be positive and these points will be in Quadrant II.

294 CHAPTER 4 Working with Signed Numbers

Calculating lengths using the Pythagorean Theorem and the distance formula

13. Before moving into her new house, Susan is trying out furniture arrangements on graph paper. She wants to make sure there is enough room to walk around the furniture. She decides she needs at least 3 feet between pieces of furniture—except for the coffee table, which can be directly in front of the couch. Each square on her grid represents 1 square foot.

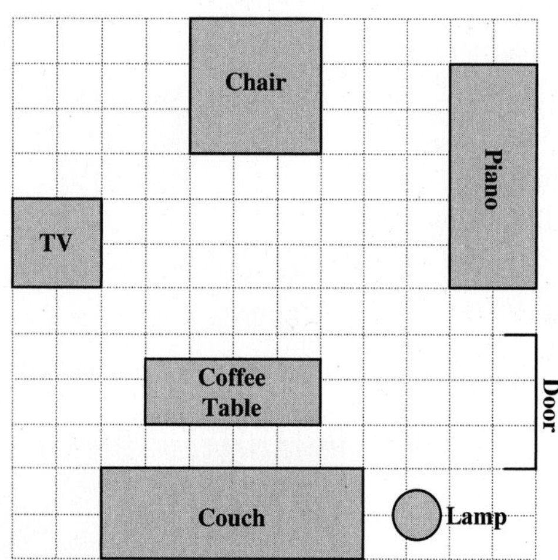

a. How many feet are there between the closest corners of the TV and the chair? $\sqrt{5}$ ft ≈ 2.24 ft

b. How many feet are there between the closest corners of the coffee table and the piano? $\sqrt{11.25}$ ft ≈ 3.35 ft

c. Are any pieces of furniture too close together?

14. Use the Pythagorean Theorem to find the missing side length. about 11.8

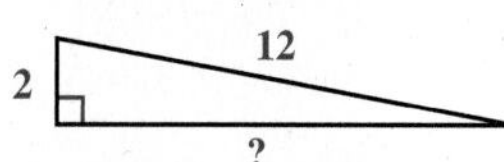

15. The distance formula is $\sqrt{(x_2 - x_1)^2 + (y_2 - y_1)^2}$.

a. When you calculate $(x_2 - x_1)$, what does the resulting number represent? The horizontal distance between the two points.

b. When you calculate $(y_2 - y_1)$, what does the resulting number represent? The vertical distance between the two points.

c. How is using the distance formula like using the Pythagorean Theorem?

13c. The TV is too close to the chair and to the coffee table.

15c. Possible answer: Since the two differences in the distance formula represent the horizontal and vertical distances, it's like a right triangle with the segment as the hypotenuse and the horizontal and vertical distances as the legs. For the formula and the theorem, the two distances are squared and added, and then the square root is taken.

Exercise 13:
You may wish to point out the distance formula is given in Exercise 15.

Review and Self-Assessment **295**

Evaluating expressions involving negative exponents

16. See Additional Answers.

17. As the exponent is reduced by 1, the value is divided by 2: $1 \div 2 = \frac{1}{2}$.

18. Since the bases are the same, you can add the exponents: $4 + {}^{-}6$ is ${}^{-}2$, and 3^{-2} is a fraction less than 1.

19b. $5 \cdot 10^{-1} \cdot 10^{-1} \cdot 10^{-1}$

16. What are two ways to figure out $\left(\frac{1}{2}\right)^{-1} \times \left(\frac{1}{2}\right)^{-1}$?

17. Use the facts that $2^2 = 4$, $2^1 = 2$, and $2^0 = 1$ to explain why $2^{-1} = \frac{1}{2}$.

18. How can you use the laws of exponents to tell whether $3^4 \times 3^{-6}$ is greater than 1 or less than 1?

19. Imagine putting a 5-foot fishing rod into this hookup of shrinking machines.

a. Write this problem as a multiplication problem. $5 \cdot \frac{1}{10} \cdot \frac{1}{10} \cdot \frac{1}{10}$

b. Write this problem using negative exponents.

c. What is the length of the exiting fishing rod? 0.005 ft

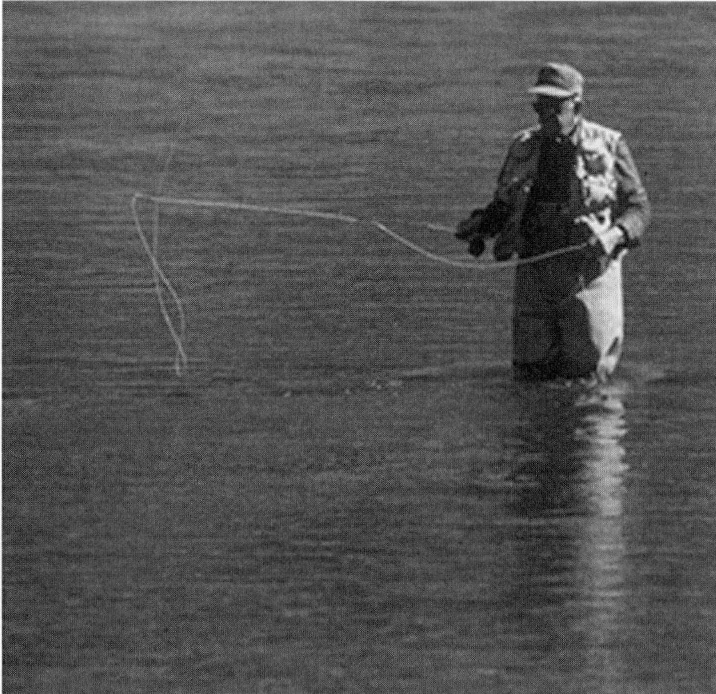

Additional Answers

16. Possible answers: $\left(\frac{1}{2}\right)^{-1} = \frac{1}{\frac{1}{2}} = 2$, and $2 \cdot 2 = 4$;

or $\left(\frac{1}{2}\right)^{-1} \cdot \left(\frac{1}{2}\right)^{-1} = \left(\frac{1}{2}\right)^{-1+-1} = \left(\frac{1}{2}\right)^{-2} = \left(\frac{1}{4}\right)^{-1} = \frac{1}{\frac{1}{4}} = 4$;

or $\left(\frac{1}{2}\right)^{-1} \cdot \left(\frac{1}{2}\right)^{-1} = \left(\frac{1}{2} \cdot \frac{1}{2}\right)^{-1} = \left(\frac{1}{4}\right)^{-1} = \frac{1}{\frac{1}{4}} = 4$

Demonstrating Skills

Compute each sum, difference, product, or quotient.

20. $3 \times {}^-3$ $^-9$

21. $^-2.3 - 7.9$ $^-10.2$

22. $5.2 \div {}^-2.6$ $^-2$

23. $3.4 + {}^-5$ $^-1.6$

24. $^-3.2 - {}^-0.9$ $^-2.3$

25. $^-3 \div {}^-12$ 0.25

26. $^-7 \times {}^-8.3$ 58.1

27. $({}^-2)^4 \times {}^-5$ $^-80$

28. $2 \times {}^-3^2$ $^-18$

29. $^-0.2 + 9.1$ 8.9

Without computing each sum, difference, product, or quotient, tell whether it will be less than 0, equal to 0, or greater than 0.

30. $9 - {}^-3$ greater than 0

31. $^-64 + 43$ less than 0

32. $4 \times {}^-6$ less than 0

33. $^-4 + {}^-3$ less than 0

34. $^-6.2 - {}^-8.3$ greater than 0

35. $^-98 \div {}^-3$ greater than 0

36.

36. Plot and label each point on a four-quadrant graph.

$T({}^-4, 3)$ $U(2, 5)$ $V({}^-2, {}^-6)$ $W(6, {}^-5)$

$X({}^-6, 0)$ $Y(0, {}^-2)$ $Z(0, 0)$

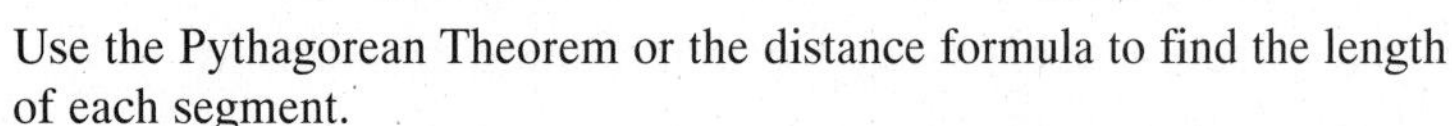

Use the Pythagorean Theorem or the distance formula to find the length of each segment.

37. $(4, 3)$ to $({}^-1, 1)$ $\sqrt{29} \approx 5.39$

38. $(5, {}^-2)$ to $({}^-3, 0)$ $\sqrt{68} \approx 8.25$

Find each missing value.

39. $8.3 \times 10^? = 0.0083$ $^-3$

40. $3.7 \times ? = 0.00037$ 10^{-4}

Simplify each expression as much as possible.

41. $256 \cdot 2^{-5}$ 8

42. $3y^2 \cdot y^{-3}$ $3y^{-1}$, or $\frac{3}{y}$

43. $4^{-1} \cdot 4^{-3}$ $\frac{1}{256}$

44. $^-1^{-3}$ $^-1$

45. $({}^-5)^{-2}$ $\frac{1}{25}$

46. $^-4^3$ $^-64$

Exercises 37 and 38: Remind students that the distance formula is provided in Exercise 15 on the preceding page for students having difficulty remembering the formula.

Exercises 41–45: This set of exercises provides practice in simplifying exercises that contain negative exponents.

CHAPTER 5

Looking at Linear Relationships

Chapter Overview

In this chapter, students will begin learning about rates and how to represent them in words, tables, symbolic rules, and graphs. Then they relate speed (a special rate) to the slope, both positive and negative, of a graph of distance over time.

Students learn how to use change to see if a pattern is linear or not. After graphing the relationships in the patterns, they learn how to determine the symbolic rule from the graph and how to predict the graph from the symbolic rule.

After being introduced to $y = ax + b$, the standard form for the symbolic rule for linear relationships, students are introduced to techniques for determining a and b in the rule. Inequalities are also informally introduced.

Chapter 5 Highlights	Links to the Past	Links to the Future
Understanding and representing rates and proportional relationships (5.1)	**Course 1:** Working with equivalent fractions	**Chapter 7:** Finding scale factors and missing side lengths for similar figures **Chapter 8:** Solving problems involving proportional relationships
Recognizing linear relationships from tables and graphs (5.2)	**Course 1:** Looking at situations with straight-line graphs	**Course 3:** Using linear relationships to model linear trends in data
Understanding slope and y-intercept in graphs (5.2)	**Chapter 2:** Exploring how the starting amount and the amount of change for a cube pattern relate to the equation for a problem	**Course 3:** Exploring the difference between steepness and slope
Understanding the connection between a linear equation and its graph (5.3)	**Chapter 3:** Understanding how the constant change in a linear relationship is represented in its equation and graph	**Course 3:** Finding the equation for a line given two points or a point and a slope
Using the method of constant differences to recognize and write equations for linear relationships (5.4)	**Course 1:** Describing patterns in data given in tables	**Course 3:** Using constant second differences to recognize and write equations for quadratic relationships

Lesson Objectives	Pacing	Materials	NCTM Standards
5.1 Understanding and Describing Rates page 299b • To develop strategies for describing rates • To recognize rates presented in symbolic and graphic forms • To develop strategies for comparing proportional and non-proportional relationships • To represent proportional and non-proportional relationships in words, tables, symbols, and graphs • To get hands-on experience with collecting data • To determine the nature of the relationship between two variables	4 class periods	• Master 10	2, 4, 5, 6, 9
5.2 Speed and the Slope Connection page 320a • To relate speed to the slope of a graph of distance over time • To develop an understanding of negative slope and a negative constant term • To gain skill in recognizing proportional and non-proportional relationships between distance and time • To recognize linear relationships from different forms: symbolic rules, graphs, patterns, and tables • To easily convert one form of representation into another	4 class periods	• Master 10 • Stopwatches • Yardstick	2, 4, 5, 6, 9
5.3 Recognizing Linear Shapes page 343b • To recognize linear relationships in a variety of representations: symbolic rules, graphs, visual patterns, and tables • To translate from one representation to another • To recognize the symbolic representation of a linear relationship in more than one form. • To explain the connection between the constant difference, the slope of the graph, and the symbolic representation of the relationship (the a in $y = ax + b$) • To determine b in the rule $y = ax + b$ from a graph (the y-intercept, the intersection with the vertical axis)	3 class periods	• Master 10	2, 3, 6
5.4 Tricks of the Trade page 361b • To learn that in a table showing the relationship between two variables, if the change in both variables is constant, then the two are linearly related; that if the change in *one* quantity is constant but the change in the other is *not* constant, then the quantities are not linearly related • To solidify understanding of the connection between the constant difference, the slope of the graph, and the symbolic representation of the relationship • To apply the concepts of a negative slope and a negative constant term • To learn how to determine b in the rule $y = ax + b$ from a graph (the y-intercept, the intersection with the vertical axis), and by checking the output of the rule when the input is 0	3 class periods	• Master 10	2, 6, 10

NCTM Curriculum and Evaluation Standards

1. Number and Operation
2. Patterns, Functions, and Algebra
3. Geometry and Spatial Sense
4. Measurement
5. Data Analysis, Statistics, and Probability
6. Problem Solving
7. Reasoning and Proof
8. Communication
9. Connections
10. Representation

Assessment Opportunities

Standard Assessment

Impact Mathematics offers three types of formal assessment. The Chapter 5 Review & Self-Assessment in the Student Edition serves as a self-assessment tool for students. In the Teacher's Guide, a Quick Quiz at the end of each lesson allows you to check students understanding before moving to the next lesson. The Assessment Resources include blackline masters for chapter and semester tests.

- **Student Edition** Chapter 5 Review & Self-Assessment, pages 378–381
- **Teacher's Guide** Quick Quizzes, pages 320, 343, 361, 377
- **Assessment Resources** Chapter 5 Test, Form A, pages 73–80; Chapter 5 Test, Form B, pages 81–89

Ongoing Assessment

Impact Mathematics provides numerous opportunities for informal assessment of your students as they work through the investigations. Share & Summarize questions help you determine whether students understand the important ideas of an investigation. If students are struggling, Troubleshooting tips provide suggestions for helping them. On the Spot Assessment notes appear throughout the teaching notes. They give you suggestions for preventing or remedying common student errors. Assessment Forms in the Assessment Resources provide convenient ways to record student progress.

- **Student Edition** Share & Summarize, pages 305, 308, 311, 325, 328, 329, 333, 347, 350, 353, 364, 368, 370
- **Teacher's Guide** On the Spot Assessment, pages T301, T306, T322, T325, T326, T327, T330, T344, T346, T352, T363, T365, T369
  Troubleshooting, pages T305, T308, T311, T325, T328, T329, T333, T347, T350, T353, T364, T368, T370
- **Assessment Resources** Chapter 5 Assessment Checklists, pages 111–112

Alternative Assessment, Portfolios, and Journal Ideas

The alternative assessment items in *Impact Mathematics* are perfect for inclusion in student portfolios and journals. The In Your Own Words feature in the Student Edition gives students a chance to write about mathematical ideas. The Performance Assessment items in the Assessment Resources provide rich, open-ended problems, ideal for take-home or group assessment.

- **Student Edition** In Your Own Words, pages 319, 341
- **Assessment Resources** Chapter 5 Performance Assessment, pages 90–93

Assessment Resources

The Assessment Resources provide a chapter test in two equivalent forms, along with additional performance items. The performance items can be used in a variety of ways. They are ideal for take-home assessment or in-class group assessment.

- Chapter 5 Test, Form A, pages 73–80
- Chapter 5 Test, Form B, pages 81–89
- Chapter 5 Performance Assessment, pages 90–93
- Chapter 5 Assessment Solutions, pages 94–102

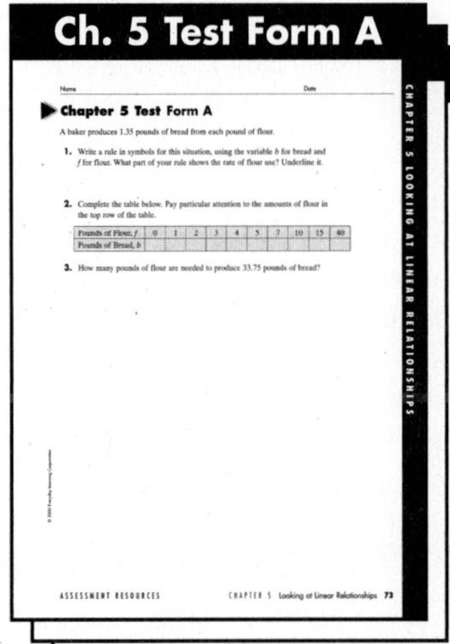

Ch. 5 Test Form A

Name Date

Chapter 5 Test Form A

A baker produces 1.35 pounds of bread from each pound of flour.

1. Write a rule in symbols for this situation, using the variable b for bread and f for flour. What part of your rule shows the rate of flour use? Underline it.

2. Complete the table below. Pay particular attention to the amounts of flour in the top row of the table.

Pounds of Flour, f	0	1	2	3	4	5	7	10	15	40
Pounds of Bread, b										

3. How many pounds of flour are needed to produce 33.75 pounds of bread?

CHAPTER 5 LOOKING AT LINEAR RELATIONSHIPS

ASSESSMENT RESOURCES CHAPTER 5 Looking at Linear Relationships 73

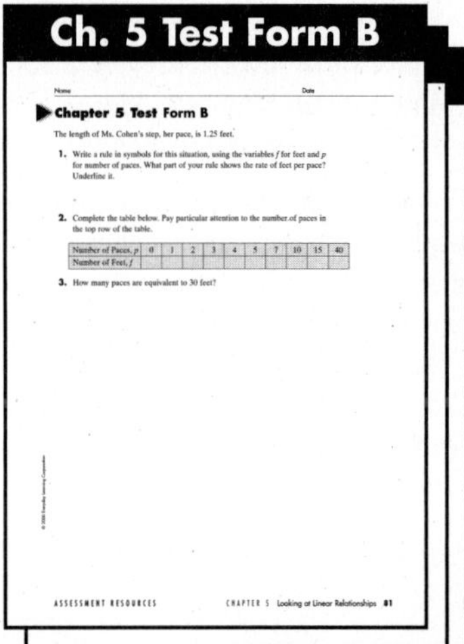

Ch. 5 Test Form B

Name Date

Chapter 5 Test Form B

The length of Ms. Cohen's step, her pace, is 1.25 feet.

1. Write a rule in symbols for this situation, using the variables f for feet and p for number of paces. What part of your rule shows the rate of feet per pace? Underline it.

2. Complete the table below. Pay particular attention to the number of paces in the top row of the table.

Number of Paces, p	0	1	2	3	4	5	7	10	15	40
Number of Feet, f										

3. How many paces are equivalent to 30 feet?

ASSESSMENT RESOURCES CHAPTER 5 Looking at Linear Relationships 81

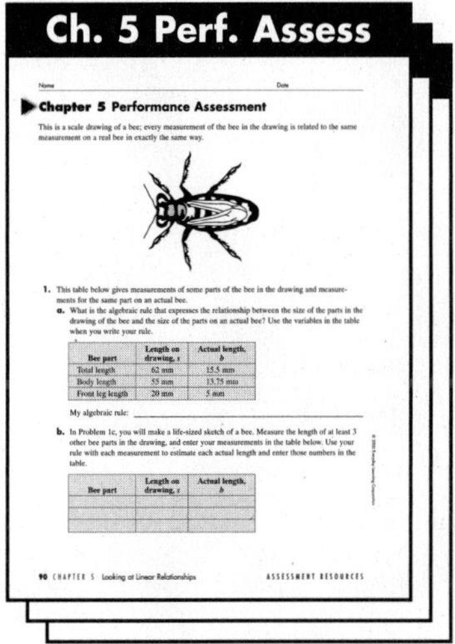

Ch. 5 Perf. Assess

Name Date

Chapter 5 Performance Assessment

This is a scale drawing of a bee; every measurement of the bee in the drawing is related to the same measurement on a real bee in exactly the same way.

1. This table below gives measurements of some parts of the bee in the drawing and measurements for the same part on an actual bee.
   a. What is the algebraic rule that expresses the relationship between the size of the parts in the drawing of the bee and the size of the parts on an actual bee? Use the variables in the table when you write your rule.

Bee part	Length on drawing, s	Actual length, b
Total length	62 mm	15.5 mm
Body length	55 mm	13.75 mm
Front leg length	20 mm	5 mm

   My algebraic rule: ______

   b. In Problem 1c, you will make a life-sized sketch of a bee. Measure the length of at least 3 other bee parts in the drawing, and enter your measurements in the table below. Use your rule with each measurement to estimate each actual length and enter those numbers in the table.

Bee part	Length on drawing, s	Actual length, b

90 CHAPTER 5 Looking at Linear Relationships ASSESSMENT RESOURCES

Additional Resources

Print

Moving Straight Ahead: Linear Relationships by Glenda Lappan, James T. Fey, William Fitzgerald, Susan N. Friel, Elizabeth Difanis, Dale Seymour Publications, 1997

Explore rates and linear relationships, including scope and y-intercept. Develop mathematical connections to other school subjects as well as to the world with which students are familiar.

The Ideas of Algebra, K-12, NCTM Yearbook, 1988

This book can help you improve classroom presentation of algebra. Topics include equations, expressions, word problems, and the use of technology in the algebra classroom

Software

Solving Equations Using Transformations, Edunetics Corporation

Find positive and negative slope; use transformations to solve equations.

Understanding Graphing™ Grades 7-10, Neufeld Learning Systems, Inc. 1999

Topics include Reading and Sketching Graphs, Points on a Grid, Linear Relations, Slope of a Line.

Measurement in Motion, Learning in Motion

Macintosh version 1.3, CD-ROM, 1995

Investigate relationships between lengths, angles, and time; and analyze or display data in numeric tables, line graphs, or bar graphs, and so on.

Video

Seeing is Believing: Special Effects, WQED Pittsburgh, PA

The firstvideo in the LIFE BY THE NUMBERS series illustrates how mathematics can help present visions to the world and define space. Students work with proportion and scale, the tangent function, slope, and patterns and fractals.

Rates and Ratios: Comparisons, Sunburst Communications, Inc.

Four videotapes on proportional reasoning encourages math explorations and experimentation. Teacher helps include curriculum links and correlation suggestions, as well as extensive teacher notes. Students are introduced to problems embedded in real-world situations.

Web sites

Visit the Everyday Learning Web site at **http://www.everydaylearning.com**

Middle School Student Center

http://forum.swarthmore.edu/students/middle/index.html

Choose from games, Internet activities, math software, Web sites built for and by kids and a Problem of the Week.

The Absurd Math: Pre-Algebra from Another Dimension

http://www.absurdmath.inter.net/abmath/index.html

Students apply pre-algebra knowledge of mathematics and explore formulas, integers, logical reasoning, patterns and puzzles, and problem solving.

Introduction
After a student reads aloud the first paragraph under "At Any Rate," ask the class whether they can think of other examples of rates involving speed. Then ask whether they can think of any examples of rates that do not involve speed, such as price per pound, and so on.

Direct students' attention to the photos on both pages. Ask them what all the pictures have in common. Some students may identify travel; others may identify trains. Then have the students compare differences. Most will talk about differences in speed and differences in appearance.

Then ask a student to read aloud the second paragraph and compare the actual speeds of the three trains. Some students may volunteer to do further research on trains and their speeds over the years. Other volunteers may want to do research on today's means of transportation: comparing speeds of people walking, horse and buggy, cars, planes, and rockets. Have each volunteer make a time-line chart to show the differences in speeds to the entire class.

CHAPTER 5

Looking at Linear Relationships

When you graph a relationship, sometimes all the points lie on a straight line. These types of relationships are called *linear*. In this chapter, you will learn to recognize linear relationships from tables, graphs, and algebraic rules.

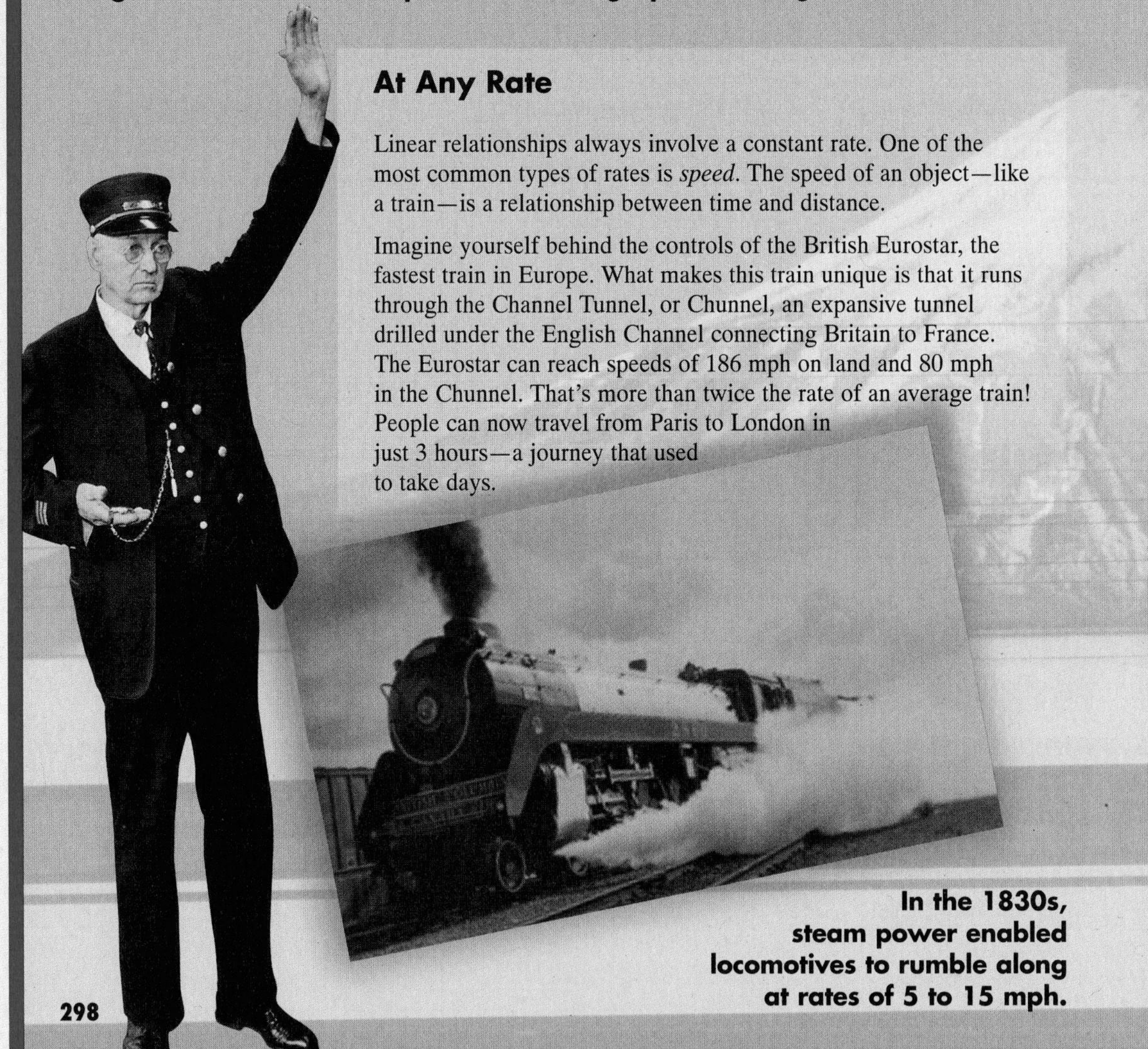

At Any Rate

Linear relationships always involve a constant rate. One of the most common types of rates is *speed*. The speed of an object—like a train—is a relationship between time and distance.

Imagine yourself behind the controls of the British Eurostar, the fastest train in Europe. What makes this train unique is that it runs through the Channel Tunnel, or Chunnel, an expansive tunnel drilled under the English Channel connecting Britain to France. The Eurostar can reach speeds of 186 mph on land and 80 mph in the Chunnel. That's more than twice the rate of an average train! People can now travel from Paris to London in just 3 hours—a journey that used to take days.

In the 1830s, steam power enabled locomotives to rumble along at rates of 5 to 15 mph.

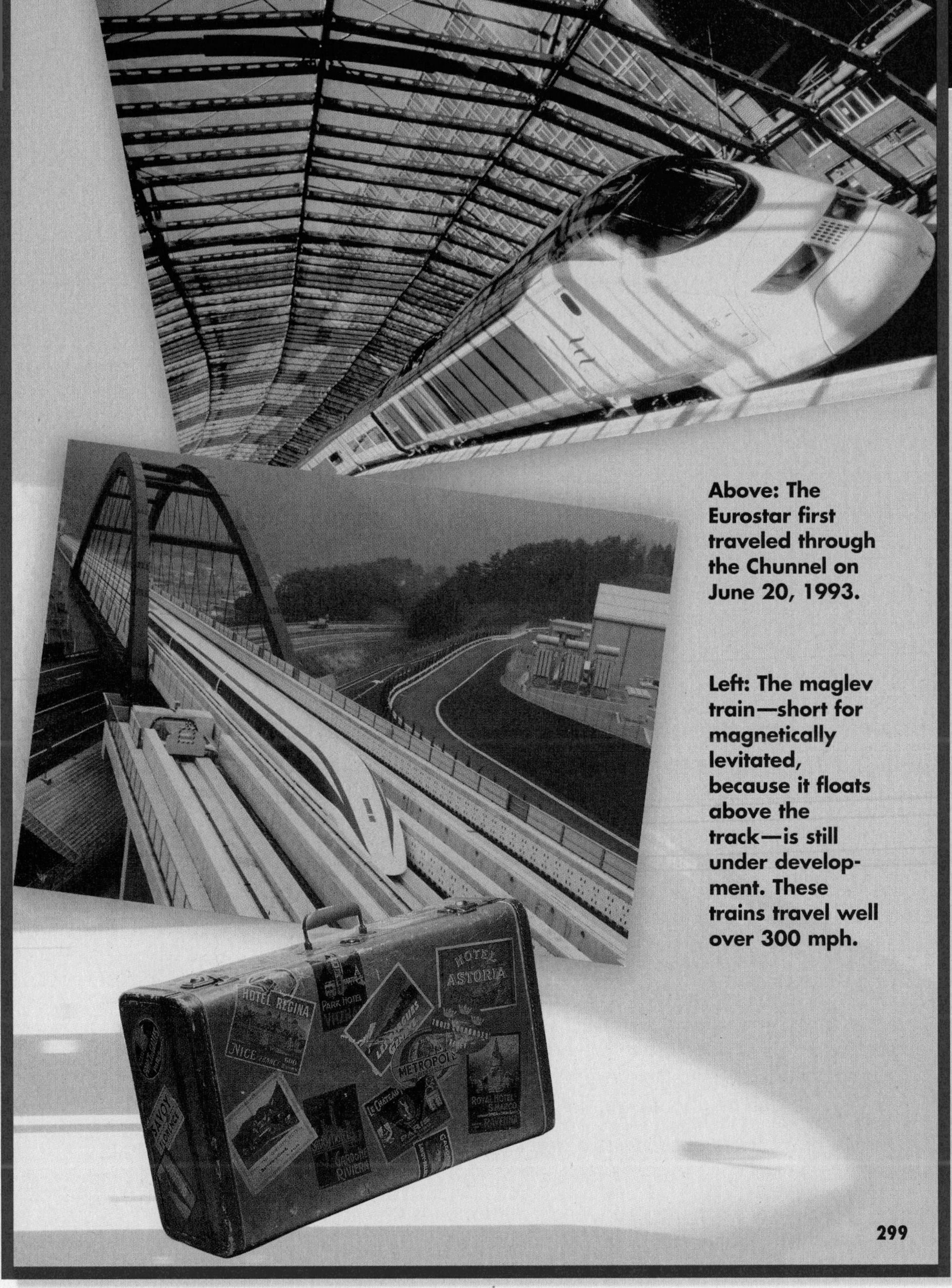

Above: The Eurostar first traveled through the Chunnel on June 20, 1993.

Left: The maglev train—short for magnetically levitated, because it floats above the track—is still under development. These trains travel well over 300 mph.

Ch. 5 Family Letter

CHAPTER 5 LOOKING AT LINEAR RELATIONSHIPS

family*letter*

Dear Family,

Chapter 5 in *Impact Mathematics* introduces linear relationships—where a change in one variable results in a fixed change in another variable. For example, a car traveling 30 miles per hour covers 30 miles in one hour, 60 miles in 2 hours, 90 miles in 3 hours, and so on. You can multiply a fixed amount, 30 miles, by any number of hours to find the total distance the car has traveled during that time.

In class we will describe situations, make tables of data about the situations, graph the data, and write linear equations that describe the relationships. Here is an example of one kind of problem we will be working with.

Three telephone companies have long-distance rates:

Easy Access Company	\$1.00 for the first minute; 25 cents per minute thereafter
Call Home	20 cents per minute
Metro Communication	\$3.00 for the first minute; 15 cents per minute thereafter

- Write an equation for each company's rate of charge. Use c for total cost and m for length of a call in minutes.
- For each company, calculate the amount due for calls lasting 5 minutes, lasting 15 minutes, and for two other lengths of time. Show your results in a table.
- On one set of axes, draw a graph for each card's rate of charge with minutes on the horizontal axis and dollars on the vertical axis.
- Is any company always a better buy? If so, which one? If not, tell when you would use each company to get the best buy.

We will also learn to predict which equations will produce a straight line on a graph before drawing them—just by looking at tables or algebraic rules. Then, from a graph or table, your son or daughter will be able to determine the slope and y-intercept.

During the next few weeks, your son or daughter may show interest in linear relationships or in different ways linear equations appear in the world outside of school. Together, you might enjoy using linear equations to calculate payments for jobs using different hourly rates.

TEACHING RESOURCES   CHAPTER 5 Looking at Linear Relationships 43

Mathematical Background

Chapter 5 introduces or extends many interrelated mathematical ideas such as

- rates and proportionality (with extra emphasis on speed as a special rate)
- nonproportional linear relationships
- positive and negative slope
- linearity of a relationship and methods for checking for linearity (looking at differences to see whether the change is constant or nonconstant and looking at a graph to see whether it is a straight line)
- connections between linear relationships and arithmetic sequences

The students investigate these ideas in the context of

- graphs
- symbolic (algebraic) expressions, primarily in the form $y = ax + b$, including how to determine a and b by analyzing a table or inspecting a graph
- tables
- visual patterns

They also learn to translate among these representations.

Presented as a list, this seems like a lot to learn, but the ideas are closely related and, if they are learned together as different facets of one idea, the task becomes quite reasonable.

The idea that runs throughout the chapter is looking at tables, graphs, or equations that show how two variable quantities are related to each other and then analyzing how a *change* in one of them is related to a *change* in the other. The focus is on how the variables *change* from one moment to the next, more than on what the variables *are* at any particular time.

Example 1

Alex is cutting rectangular lengths from a roll of adding-machine paper that is about 3 inches wide and comparing the *area* of these strips to their *lengths*. For any given length, he can compute the area: $A = 3l$. Can he also answer the following question?

> *Suppose Alex has a strip of some given length. If he makes a strip that is 1 inch longer, how much greater will its area be?*

This question *can* be answered. A 1-inch increase in the strip's length corresponds to a 3-square-inch increase in its area, no matter what length strip Alex started with.

Example 2

Tatiana is cutting squares of various sizes from a large sheet of wrapping paper and comparing the *area* of these squares to the *lengths* of their sides. For any given side length, she can compute the area: $A = l^2$. Can she also answer the following question?

> *Suppose Tatiana has a square of some given size. If she makes a square whose side is 1 inch longer, how much greater will its area be?*

• ***Teaching notes continued on page A392.***

5.1 Understanding and Describing Rates

Objectives

- To develop strategies for describing rates
- To recognize rates presented in symbolic and graphic forms
- To compare proportional and nonproportional relationships
- To represent proportional and nonproportional relationships in words, tables, symbols, and graphs
- To get experience with collecting data
- To determine the nature of the relationship between two variables

Overview (pacing: about 4 class periods)

This lesson focuses on describing rates. Students learn to represent these two types of relationships in words, tables, symbolic rules, and graphs. They also learn about two types of linear relationships: those where the two variables are proportional and those where the two variables are not proportional. Students use graphs and symbolic rules to distinguish these two types of linear relationships: graphically by finding the starting point of the graph and symbolically by finding the constant term in a rule.

Advance Preparation

You may want to use an overhead transparency of Master 10, Quarter-Inch Graph Paper, as you discuss the problems. Students will need several copies of Master 10 or sheets of graph paper to complete the problem sets and homework problems. You will need a heavy box and three cans to demonstrate the lab investigation. Student groups will need a book, two different-sized sets of cans or other cylindrical tubes with all cylinders in each set having the same diameter, lined paper, and graph paper to continue the lab investigation.

Lesson Planner

	Summary	Materials	On Your Own Exercises	Assessment Opportunities
Investigation 1 page T301	Students gain experience in describing rates using words, tables, symbolic rules and graphs.	• Master 10 (Teaching Resources, page 15)	Practice & Apply: 1–2 Connect & Extend: 7–9 Mixed Review: 13–36	Share & Summarize, pages T305, 305 On the Spot Assessment, page T301 Troubleshooting, page T305
Investigation 2 page T305	Students compare different ways of describing rates.	• Master 10	Practice & Apply: 3–5 Connect & Extend: 10 Mixed Review: 13–36	Share & Summarize, pages T308, 308 On the Spot Assessment, page T306 Troubleshooting, page T308
Investigation 3 page T309	Students are introduced to proportional and non-proportional relationships.	• Master 10	Practice & Apply: 6 Connect & Extend: 11–12 Mixed Review: 13–36	Share & Summarize, pages T311, 311 Troubleshooting, page T311 Informal Assessment, page 320 Quick Quiz, page 320
Lab Investigation page T312	Students collect their own data and describe the relationship between the variables.	• Master 10 • 1 box, 3 cans • For each group: 2 sets of cylindrical pens, 1 book, 1 piece of lined paper, graph paper		

Introduce

Most students have heard and used the term *rate* informally. However, they will vary widely in their understanding of what a rate is, and many will have only an informal sense of its meaning. This lesson helps students refine their notion of a rate by adding a mathematical meaning to the term. Students learn to represent simple rate relationships symbolically and graphically. You might introduce this lesson by inviting students to give examples of rates that they've heard of, looking for applications in and out of mathematics.

Think & Discuss

Have students read the four statements involving rates on page 300. You might ask students what each of these rates (pulse, exchange, pay, unit cost) means or in what sense each is a rate. Introduce the language of *per* and *for each*.

Students may work with a partner or group to think about three more rates. Give them about 5 minutes to write three statements involving rates. Then have a whole-class discussion to draw out their ideas. Ask students to describe the rates using the expression *for each*. Students may mention these rates:

pay rate—number of dollars earned for each hour worked

car efficiency rate—number of miles driven for each gallon of gas used

reading rate—number of pages read for each hour of reading

growth rate (of hair, for example)—number of inches of growth for each year

musical tempo—the number of beats for each measure of music

You may want to ask students whether they think the rates they listed fluctuate rapidly or remain relatively stable over time. Students should see a wide variety of rates that are in everyday use, and should understand the sense of *per* or *for each* that they all have in common.

5.1 Understanding and Describing Rates

In the statement "David types 30 words per minute," the rate *30 words per minute* describes the relationship between the number of words David types and time in minutes. The speed of light, 186,000 miles per second, is a rate that describes the relationship between the distance light travels and time in seconds. In general, a **rate** describes how two unlike quantities are related or how they can be compared.

VOCABULARY
rate

Here are some other statements involving rates:

Franklin's resting pulse rate is 65 beats per minute.

On February 19, 1999, the exchange rate from U.S. to British currency was 0.6115 pound per dollar.

When she babysits, Yoshi earns $3.50 per hour.

At the Better Batter donut shop, donuts cost $3.79 per dozen.

Just the facts

One type of spider spins an entire web in just 20 minutes. It weaves at the rate of 1,000 operations per minute.

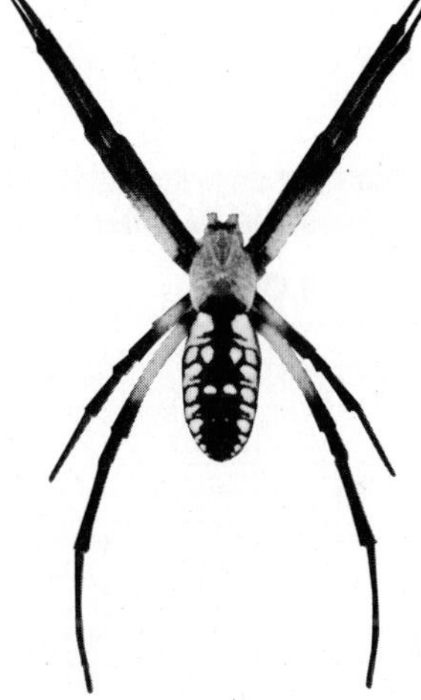

Think & Discuss

Each rate above involves the Latin word *per,* which means "for each." Try using the phrase "for each" to explain the meaning of each rate. For example, the exchange rate is the number of pounds you receive for each dollar you exchange. See ① in Additional Answers.

Work with a partner to write three more statements involving rates. Explain what your rates mean using the phrase "for each." Answers will vary.

You can use rates to write algebraic rules relating variables. For example, the equation $d = 186{,}000t$ uses the speed of light to describe the distance d in miles that light travels during a particular number of seconds t.

In this lesson, you will explore lots of situations involving rates, and you will look at tables, graphs, and algebraic rules for these situations.

Additional Answers
Think & Discuss

① 65 beats per minute describes the number of times Franklin's heart beats for each minute that passes. 0.6115 pound per dollar tells the number of pounds you get for each dollar exchanged. $3.50 per hour describes the number of dollars Yoshi earns for each hour she works. $3.79 per dozen tells the price for each dozen donuts.

Investigation 1

In this investigation, students use rules, tables, and graphs to explore rates. They first see how rates and rules can be used in a cooking situation. Then they draw a graph to show the linear relationship. They also look at situations where it is not reasonable to connect the points on a graph. Students will need graph paper or Master 10, Quarter-Inch Graph Paper, for Problem Sets A and B in this investigation.

Problem Set A Suggested Grouping: Pairs or Small Groups

In this problem set, students encounter rates used in the kitchen. In the first three problems, students look at rates and rules. In the last three problems, they explore graphing rates.

On the Spot Assessment

In **Problem 2,** watch for students who write $t = 5m$ as the rule for the statement "1 teaspoonful is 5 mL." You may want to ask these students which is bigger: the number of teaspoons in a certain amount (t) or the number of milliliters in the same amount (m).

The table in **Problem 3** gives students a way to use substitution to check whether their rule is correct.

Access for All Learners

Extra Help Students who have difficulty seeing the relationship between the number of teaspoons and the number of milliliters may find it helpful to draw a number line and shade the part representing each teaspoon a different color. For example, they can shade 0–5 red, 5–10 blue, and so on and count the number of colors to find the number of teaspoons. They can find the number of milliliters by looking at the number line.

Teaching Resources

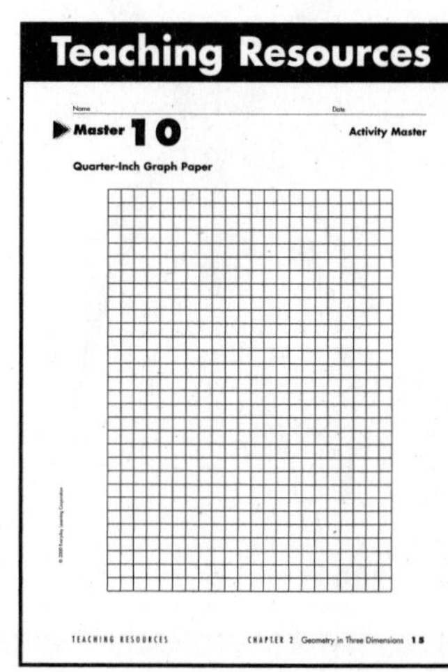

Master 10
Activity Master
Quarter-Inch Graph Paper

Investigation  Understanding Rates

You have probably used rates often, right in your own kitchen. Working with cooking measures will help you understand different ways of thinking about and describing rates.

MATERIALS
graph paper

Problem Set A

Here is a rate expressed in words:

A teaspoon contains 5 milliliters.

This rate could also be stated this way:

There are 5 milliliters per teaspoon.

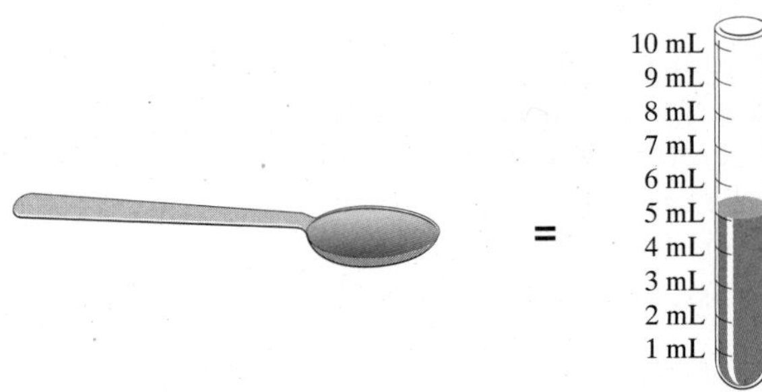

1. Suppose you double the number of teaspoons of some ingredient in a recipe. Does that double the number of milliliters? If you triple the number of teaspoons, do you triple the number of milliliters? yes, yes
2. Using m for the number of milliliters, write a rule that tells how many milliliters are in t teaspoons. $m = 5t$
3. A table of values can help you check that you have written a rule correctly. Copy this table. Without using your rule, complete the table to show the number of milliliters in t teaspoons. Use the table to check that your rule for t and m is correct.

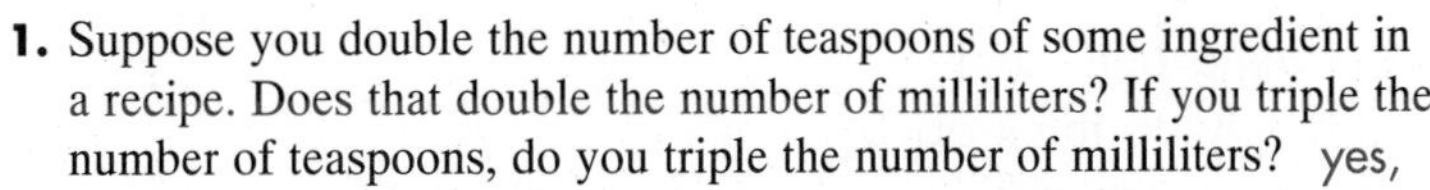

Teaspoons, t	0	1	2	3	4	5	10
Milliliters, m	0	5	10	15	20	25	50

1 Have students work in pairs or small groups.

2 Students explore using substitution to check whether their rule is correct.

1 **Problem Set Wrap-Up** Discuss **Problems 5 and 6** with the class. These problems raise the issues of when it makes sense to connect the points on a graph and when the graph can be extended. Students look at the domain and restrictions on the values of the variable, although they use a different vocabulary. They think about whether the values can be fractions as well as whole numbers. Students should realize that because they can have fractions of teaspoons, they can connect the points. Because the graph shows only Quadrant I, you may want to ask students whether the graph could be extended below (0, 0). Students should recognize that this extension makes no sense since there is no definition of a negative teaspoon. They should also see that they can extend the points for *all* values of t greater than or equal to 0 and that the points seem to lie on a line. You can move on to the next problem set even if not all students have mastered this idea. These issues will be raised again.

2 **Think & Discuss**

Discuss the cartoon and the rule relating pints and quarts. Some students may find it helpful to think about whether you need more pints or more quarts to fill a given container, such as the one below.

You may want to draw the measuring cup on the chalkboard and then ask students these questions:

How many pints of liquid are in the measuring cup? 3

How many quarts of liquid are in the measuring cup? $1\frac{1}{2}$

Which number is larger—the number of pints or the number of quarts? *number of pints, 3 is greater than $1\frac{1}{2}$*

Relate their answers to the rule. Remind students that they can make a table to check their rules.

4. On axes like those below, plot the data from your table.

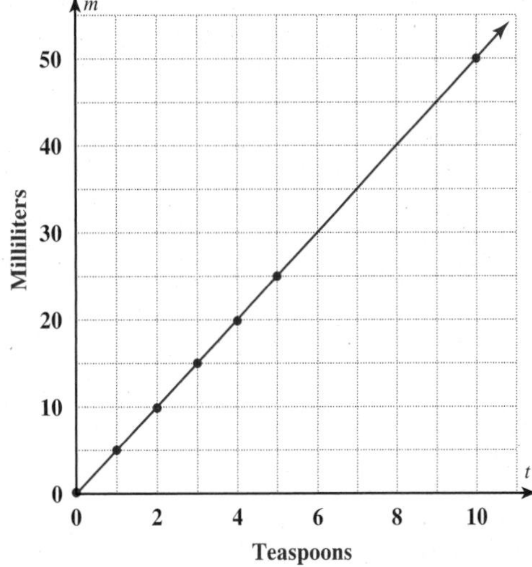

5. Does it make sense to connect the points on your graph with a line? Explain. If it does make sense, do it. See Additional Answers.

6. Does it make sense to extend your graph beyond the points? Explain. If it does make sense, do it.
Yes; it is possible to have more than 10 teaspoons of something.

Just the facts

A woodpecker has a tough head. It can pound its beak against wood at a rate of 20 times per second!

Think & Discuss

Darnell and Maya wrote rules relating pints and quarts.

Whose rule is correct? Explain your answer. Check your answer with values from your table. See ①.

① Maya's rule is correct. Darnell is multiplying the number of pints by 2, which gives, for example, 2 pints is 4 quarts, which is not true. Maya's rule multiplies the number of quarts by 2 to get the number of pints, which is correct.

1 Discuss when it makes sense to connect the points and when the graph can be extended.

2 Discuss the cartoon and decide with students which rule is correct.

Additional Answers
Problem Set A

5. Yes; you can have fractions of teaspoons. The points between the plotted points represent actual quantities, and the relationship is true for those quantities. For example, 2.5 tsp = 12.5 mL.

Develop

Have students look at their graph from Problem Set A. Tell students that the graph shows a *linear relationship.* Then explain what constitutes a linear relationship and discuss how the graph meets this criteria.

Point out the line students drew to connect the points on the graph. If necessary, have students reiterate why they could draw the line to show the relationship. Tell them that this is not true for all situations.

Direct students' attention to the graph showing the relationship between the number of wheels and the number of skateboards on page 303. Discuss why it is not sensible to connect the points on this graph.

VOCABULARY
linear relationship

The relationship between teaspoons and milliliters is called a **linear relationship** because the points on its graph lie on a straight line. In a linear relationship, as one variable changes by 1 unit, the other variable changes by a set amount. The amount of change per unit is the *rate.* In the rule $m = 5t$, the 5 shows that m changes 5 units per 1-unit change in t.

Because you can have 1.5 teaspoons, 2.25 teaspoons, and so on, it is sensible to connect the points you plotted in Problem 4 using a straight line. It is also sensible to extend the line beyond the points from the table since you can have 11, 16, 27, or even 148 teaspoons of an ingredient.

There are situations for which it is not sensible to connect the points on a graph. For example, this graph shows the relationship between the number of skateboards and the number of wheels they have.

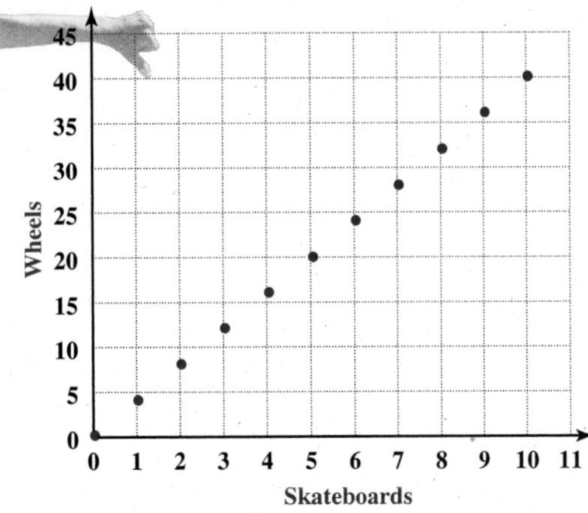

Connecting the points doesn't make as much sense in this case, because the points in between would represent partial skateboards. For example, you wouldn't connect the points for 5 skateboards and 6 skateboards, because you couldn't have 5.5 skateboards or 5.976 skateboards.

Even when it doesn't make sense to connect the points on a graph, sometimes you may want to do so anyway to help you see a relationship. In this case, it's best to use a dashed line. You will learn more about this later.

1
- Have students look at their graph from Problem Set A.
- Discuss the meaning of *linear relationship.*

2
Discuss why it is not reasonable to connect the points on this graph.

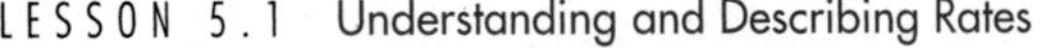

Develop

1 **Problem Set B** **Suggested Grouping: Pairs**
The questions in this problem set are similar to those in Problem Set A. It is important for students to realize that they can use a variety of representations to obtain information about the relationship between *c* and *p*.

Students will need to use graph paper or Master 10, Quarter-Inch Graph Paper, to complete **Problem 3.**

Problem 4 again opens up the domain of the relationship to nonintegers.

In **Problem 5,** students use a graph to find the value of *p*, given $c = 7$.

2 **Problem 7** asks students to compare working with the graph and working with the rule. It is important to mention here that the graph may not give exact information regarding the value of the points. You may want to ask students to compare graph-based answers with rule-based ones.

Access for All Learners

For Early Finishers Have students write and answer problems that can be solved using either the rule or the graph. You may wish to have students present their problems to the class or to use the problems to provide additional practice for students having difficulty solving **Problems 5 and 6.**

MATERIALS
graph paper

Problem Set B

Some recipes give quantities in *weight.* However, in the United States, most recipes specify quantities by *volume,* using such measures as teaspoons, tablespoons, and cups. If you know how much a cup of a particular ingredient weighs, you can write a rate statement to calculate the number of cups for a given weight. For example, it is a fact that 1 cup of sugar contains about a half pound of sugar.

1. Rewrite the fact above using the word *per.*

2. Write an algebraic rule relating the number of cups of sugar c and weight in pounds p. Check that your rule is correct by completing the table. $p = \frac{1}{2}c$ or $2p = c$

Cups, c	0	1	2	3	4	5	10
Pounds, p	0	0.5	1	1.5	2	2.5	5

3. Use the data in your table to help you draw a graph to show the relationship between the number of cups of sugar and the number of pounds. Use a set of axes like the one shown.

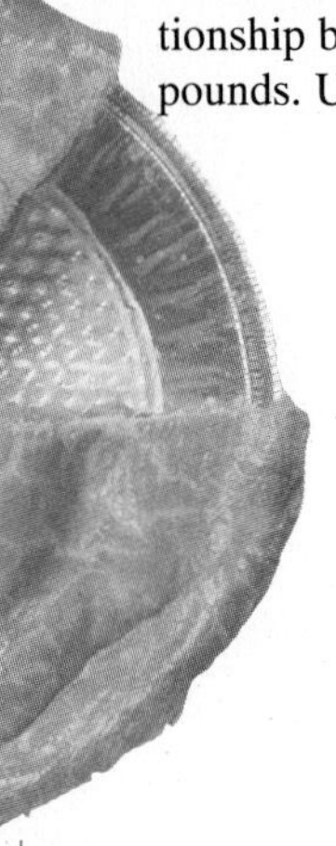

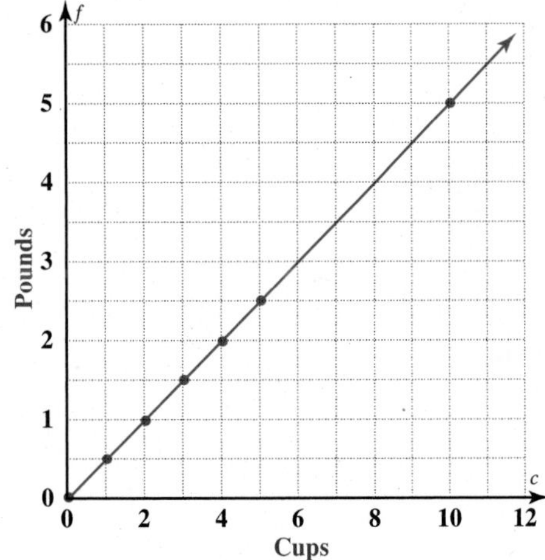

4. Does it make sense to connect the points on your graph? Does it make sense to extend the graph beyond the points? If so, do these things. Explain your reasoning.

5. From your graph, find the value of p when c is 7. Is that value what you would expect from your rule?

6. From the graph, find how many cups of sugar you would need if a recipe calls for 1.4 pounds. Is your answer what you would expect from your rule? about 2.8 c, yes

7. Do you find it easier to work from the graph or the rule? Explain.

1. There is 1 cup of sugar per $\frac{1}{2}$ pound (or $\frac{1}{2}$ pound of sugar per cup).

4. Yes; connect the points to show the number of pounds for fractional numbers of cups, and extend the graph to show the number of pounds for more than 10 cups.

5. When c is 7, p is 3.5, which is what I would expect from my rule, $p = \frac{1}{2}c$.

7. Answers will vary.

1 As students work in pairs, encourage them to explore the ways in which they can represent rates.

2 Students compare working with the graph and working with the rule.

Share & Summarize

These questions provide students with hands-on experience in finding a pulse rate, describing it, and using it in relating the number of pulses to the number of minutes. Be sure students can explain how they found their rates and what their equations mean.

Troubleshooting If students still have trouble writing a correct equation for **Question 2,** you might ask them what is bigger: the number of pulses or the number of minutes. In this way they can check their formula.

On Your Own Exercises

Practice & Apply: 1–2
Connect & Extend: 7–9
Mixed Review: 13–36

Investigation 2

This investigation starts by giving three representations—words, symbols, and graphs—to describe a rate. The problem sets provide students with describing proportional (Problem Sets C and D) and then nonproportional types of relationships (Problem Set E). Students do not use the term *proportional.* All three representations are used to describe two types of relationships within a context of a pay rate.

Think & Discuss

Ask students to read the cartoon. Ask them whether these three students are describing the same or different relationships, and to explain their thinking.

Make sure students understand that each representation describes the same relationship. However, sometimes it is more convenient to talk about the relationship in words, at other times symbols are helpful, and at still other times graphs are a better way to show the relationship. You may want to ask whether any of these give more information than the others. The goal is to be able to move easily among the various ways of expressing the relationship.

1. Pulse rates will vary. This is a rate because we're comparing the number of pulses to the amount of time; for example, "80 pulses per minute."

Share & Summarize

1. You may have noticed that on many visits to the doctor, someone measures your pulse to determine how fast your heart is beating. Measure your pulse yourself by putting your fingers to the side of your neck and counting the number of pulses you feel. Record the number of pulses in 1 minute. Explain what makes the number of pulses per minute a *rate.*

2. Use your pulse rate to write an equation relating the number of pulses p to any number of minutes timed t. Explain what your equation means.
Equations should look like $p = rt$, where r is the rate from Question 1. An equation with a rate of 80 means the heart is beating 80 times per minute.

1 Discuss answers.

Investigation 2 Describing Rates

Rate relationships can be described in many ways.

The same; all three describe the same rate of typing, which is 30 words per minute. The descriptions look different because the same rate is represented in different ways.

Think & Discuss

Are these three students describing the same or different relationships? Why do you think so?

2 After students have read the cartoon, have them explain whether or not the three students in the cartoon are thinking of the same rate.

Develop

Problem Set C **Suggested Grouping: Individuals**
In this problem set, students learn how a rate can be represented in a symbolic rule. They use words and rules to represent the total pay for two boys. Students should begin to realize that the rate of pay is the number that multiplies the number of hours, *h*.

Students should understand that if they double the number of hours, the pay should also be doubled, as asked in **Problems 1 and 7.** Questions like this call attention to strict proportionality and are repeated throughout the lesson.

> On the **Spot Assessment**
>
> Watch for students who mistake rate of pay with total pay. Show with examples that rate is the number that multiplies the number of hours.

Sample Strategies Students may use one of these methods to solve **Problem 6:**

- Some students may use mental math and think 10 times what number equals 300.
- Other students may backtrack, possibly using a flowchart or following the steps to solve an equation.
- Still other students may continue the table until the pay is $300.

In **Problem 8,** students should understand that the number multiplied by *h* to find Alec's total pay is different from the number used to calculate Mario's pay.

Problem Set Wrap-Up You may ask students to share their answers to **Problems 4, 10, and 12.** Students should recognize that the rates in the rules are different.

Problem Set C

Mario works in a market. His rate of pay is $10 per hour.

1. If Mario works twice as many hours one week than he does another week, will he earn twice as much? If he works three times as many hours, will he earn three times as much? yes, yes

2. Copy and complete the table to show what pay Mario should receive for different numbers of hours worked.

Hours, *h*	0	1	2	3	4	5	10	15
Pay (dollars), *p*	0	10	20	30	40	50	100	150

3. Write a rule in words that relates Mario's pay in dollars to the number of hours worked. Begin your rule, "The number of dollars earned is equal to. . . ." Then rewrite the rule using the symbols p for pay and h for hours.

4. What part of your rule shows Mario's rate of pay? the 10

5. Mario usually works a 35-hour week. How much does he earn in a typical week? $350

6. One week Mario earned $300. How many hours did he work that week? 30

Alec works in a local takeout restaurant. His rate of pay is $7 per hour.

7. If Alec works twice as many hours one week than he does another week, will he earn twice as much? If he works three times as many hours, will he earn three times as much? yes, yes

8. Complete the table to show what Alec would be paid for different numbers of hours worked.

Hours, *h*	0	1	2	3	4	5	10	15
Pay (dollars), *p*	0	7	14	21	28	35	70	105

9. Write a rule for Alec's pay in words and in symbols.

10. What part of your rule shows Alec's rate of pay? the 7

11. One week Alec worked 30 hours. How much did he earn that week?

12. Compare your symbolic rules for Mario and Alec. How are they the same? How are they different?
Mario: $p = 10h$; Alec: $p = 7h$; Both rules have p equal to a number multiplied by h, but the numbers are different to match the rates.

3. The number of dollars earned is equal to 10 times the number of hours worked; $p = 10h$.

9. The number of dollars earned is equal to 7 times the number of hours worked; $p = 7h$.

11. $210

1 After working on the problems individually, students begin to realize that the rate of pay is the number that multiplies the number of hours.

2 You may want to have students share their problem-solving strategies.

3 Discuss the rules and rates of pay for Mario and Alec.

Develop

Problem Set D **Suggested Grouping: Individuals**
In this problem set, students learn informally to associate the value of the rate with the steepness of the line. At this stage, the relationships are confined to non-negative values. Students will use graphs produced in this problem set again in On Your Own Exercise 4d where they will graph another rate of pay and then compare the three graphs. Make sure that students save these graphs to use later.

In **Problem 1,** students will need graph paper or a copy of Master 10, Quarter-Inch Graph Paper to complete the problem.

In **Problem 2,** students look at the domain and determine whether there are any restrictions on the value of *p*.

In **Problem 5,** students visualize how the graph of pay rate of $15 per hour would look and compare that graph to the two graphs they have drawn. If students have difficulty visualizing the graph, have them draw the graph on the grid and then compare the three graphs.

Problem Set Wrap-Up Invite students to present their answers to **Problem 4.** Encourage them to use their own words in describing the steepness. For example, they might use a skiing analogy: which lines would be faster to ski down?

MATERIALS
graph paper

Problem Set D

In addition to symbols, tables, and words, graphs are useful for comparing rates of pay.

1 Have students work the problems individually.

1. Draw a graph of the data for Mario's pay. Use a set of axes like the one below.

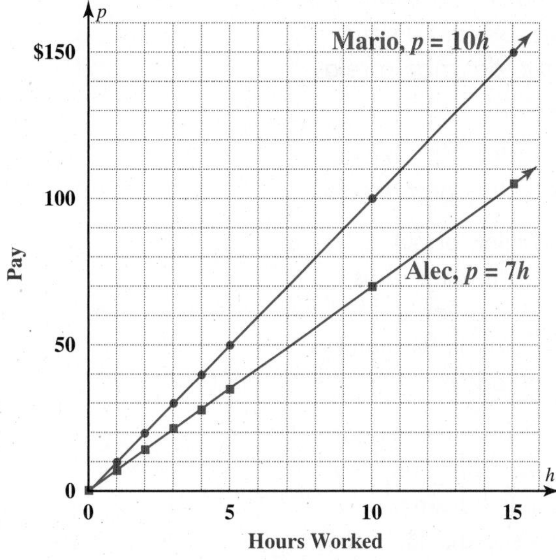

2. Does it make sense to connect the points on your graph? Does it make sense to extend the graph beyond the points? If so, do these things. Explain your reasoning.

2. Yes; connect the points to show what he earns for fractions of hours, and extend the graph to show what he earns for longer times worked.

3. On the same grid, draw a graph to show how much Alec earns. Label your graphs so you know which is for Mario and which is for Alec. Write each symbolic rule from Problem Set C next to the appropriate graph. See the graph.

2 Have students save graphs to use in On Your Own Exercise 4d.

4. Compare the graphs for Mario and Alec. In what ways are they the same? In what ways are they different? Which is steeper?

4. The graphs both start at 0 and are straight lines. Mario's graph is above Alec's. Mario's is steeper.

3 Students compare steepness of graphs.

5. Joelle earns $15 per hour. If you added a line to your graph to show Joelle's pay, how would it compare to Mario's and Alec's graphs? The line would be steeper than and above both Mario's and Alec's lines.

Problem Set E **Suggested Grouping: Individuals**
Problem Set E is different from Problem Set C and Problem Set D because it intends to help students distinguish rate situations that involve a constant amount from the situations that do not involve constant amount. Students use all three representations to describe a relationship between hourly rates and total pay.

Students will need graph paper, or Master 10, Quarter-Inch Graph Paper, to graph the data in this problem set.

In **Problem 4,** students are asked to think about what the different numbers and symbols in their rules represent. The fixed amount paid for being "on call" is the number added on, and the rate of pay is the number that multiplies the number of hours worked, *h*.

Problem Set Wrap-Up Ask several students to share their answers to **Problems 2 and 4.** In Problem 2, it is important for students to realize that if Tamsin works two times as many hours this week as she did last week, she will *not* earn two times as much money. In the next investigation, the term *proportional* is introduced and the link is made with fixed rates and the associated graphs.

Share & Summarize
Students should notice that the graphs showing Mario's and Alec's earnings pass through the origin and that Tamsin's graph does not. They should associate this characteristic with the symbolic representation of the rule: Tamsin's rule has a constant amount added on.

Troubleshooting In comparing Tamsin's graph with those for Alec and Mario, students may tend to focus only on the steepness of the line. If necessary, draw their attention to where the graph begins, that is, the point where it intersects the vertical axis.

Don't worry if the students did not make the connections between the rules and the graph for the two types of relationships. The next investigation will explore the differences between simple fixed rate and a rate plus a constant in greater detail.

On Your Own Exercises

Practice & Apply: 3–5
Connect & Extend: 10
Mixed Review: 13–36

MATERIALS
graph paper

Problem Set E

Tamsin lives in the country and works for an automobile association. Every second weekend, she is "on call." This means she must be available all weekend in case a car breaks down in her area. She is paid a fixed amount of $40 for the weekend, even if she doesn't have to work. If she is called, she earns an additional $10 per hour worked.

1. Complete the table to show what Tamsin would be paid for different numbers of hours worked during a single weekend.

Hours, h	0	1	2	3	4	5	10	15
Pay (dollars), p	40	50	60	70	80	90	140	190

2. If Tamsin works twice as many hours one week as she does another week, will she earn twice as much? Explain.
3. Write the rule for Tamsin's pay for a single weekend in words and in symbols.
4. What part of your rule shows the amount Tamsin earns for being on call? What part shows her hourly rate? the 40, the 10
5. Use the data in your table to draw a graph showing how much Tamsin earns for various numbers of hours worked. Use the same grid you used for Problem Set D or a similar one.

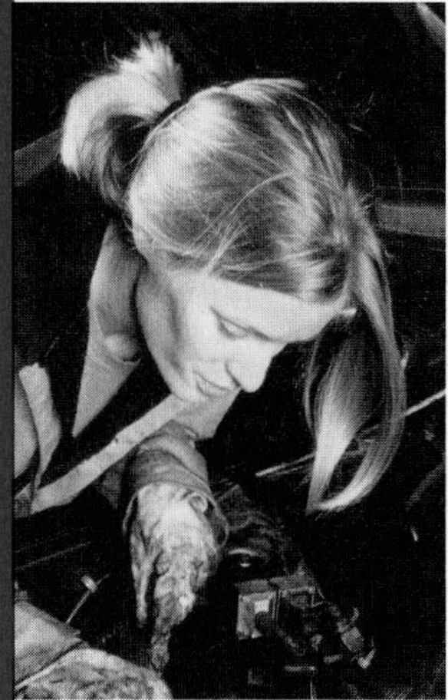

Problem Set E Answers

2. No; the constant amount of $40 is added to an hourly rate.
3. Tamsin's pay is $40, plus $10 multiplied by the number of hours worked; $p = 40 + 10h$.
5.

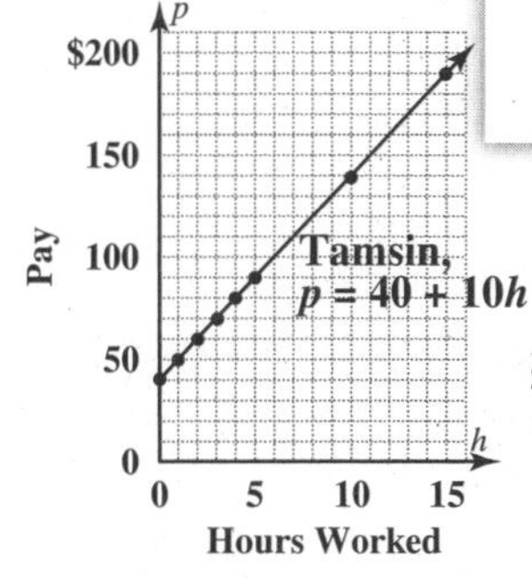

Share & Summarize

1. Look again at the graphs that show how much Alec, Mario, and Tamsin earn. How do the graphs show differences in pay? How is a higher rate shown in a graph?
2. How do the symbolic rules show the differences in the rates at which the three people are paid? How is a higher rate shown in a symbolic rule?

Share & Summarize Answers

1. Tamsin's graph starts at (0, 40) because she earns money even for working zero hours. The graphs have different degrees of steepness, which shows that the people are paid at different rates. A steeper graph indicates a higher rate.
2. The numbers multiplying the variables are the pay rates. A greater number indicates a higher rate.

1 Have students work the problems individually.

2 Students distinguish between the fixed amount and the rate of pay.

3 Students explore graphs that pass through the origin and those that do not.

Investigation 3

Investigation 3 further develops the notion of proportional versus non-proportional relationships. Although both problem sets deal with proportional relationships only, the Think & Discuss and homework problems deal with both types of relationships.

Use the Share & Summarize questions in Investigation 2 to launch this investigation. Explain to students that we sometimes use the word *proportional* to describe the kind of relationship between the two variables that exist in Mario's and Alec's situations: if they work double the number of hours, they get double the pay. If they work triple the hours, they get triple the pay, and so on. Relate this rule to the two graphs of the boys' wages. You may wish to make a transparency of the two graphs, or direct students' attention to the graphs on page 309 labeled *Alec's Graph* and *Mario's Graph*. Make it clear that the graph of a proportional relationship is a straight line that passes through (0, 0).

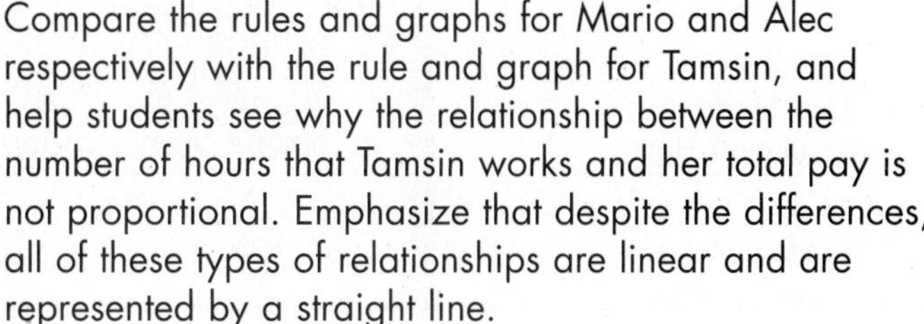

Compare the rules and graphs for Mario and Alec respectively with the rule and graph for Tamsin, and help students see why the relationship between the number of hours that Tamsin works and her total pay is not proportional. Emphasize that despite the differences, all of these types of relationships are linear and are represented by a straight line.

Investigation 3 Proportional Relationships

Alec and Mario, from Investigation 2, are paid at a simple hourly rate. If they work double the number of hours, they receive double the pay. If they work triple the hours, they receive triple the pay, and so on.

VOCABULARY
proportional

The word **proportional** is sometimes used to describe this kind of relationship between two variables. We can say that for Alec and Mario, the number of dollars earned is proportional to the number of hours worked. The graphs for Alec's pay and Mario's pay are shown below. They are each a straight line that begins at the point (0, 0).

1 Discuss the meaning of *proportional* and *not proportional*.

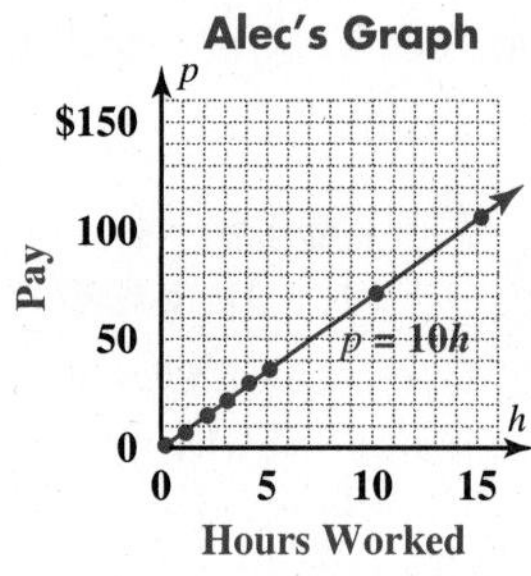

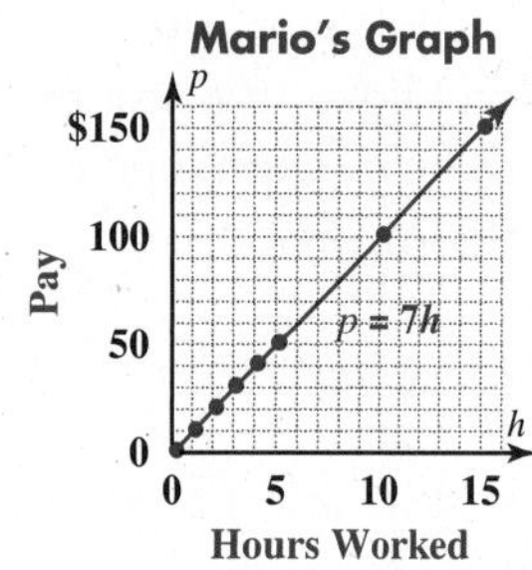

Tamsin is not paid at a simple hourly rate. She receives a fixed amount plus an hourly rate. For Tamsin, doubling the number of hours worked does not double the total pay received. The number of dollars earned is *not* proportional to the number of hours worked. The graph for Tamsin's pay is also a straight line, but it does not begin at the point (0, 0).

2 Examine graphs to determine which are proportional.

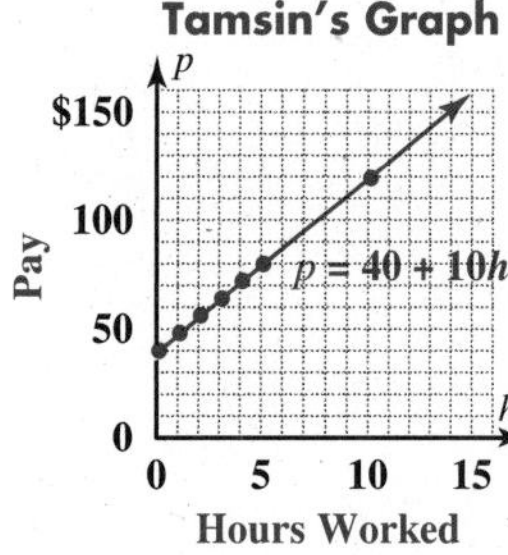

Although the relationships for Alec and Mario are proportional and the relationship for Tamsin is not, all three relationships are *linear relationships* because their graphs are straight lines.

3 Be sure students understand that all three graphs describe linear relationships.

LESSON 5.1 Understanding and Describing Rates 309

Think & Discuss

Ask students to explain why some of the relationships between the rate and time on the calling cards are proportional and others are not. Access, Budget, and Cheap cards have rates proportional to the number of minutes of long distance calls while Dollar, Easy, and Fantastic cards are not proportional since there is a standard fee regardless of usage.

At the end of the discussion mention that if a rate, y, is proportional to a total, x, then the total, x, is also proportional to the rate, y. You don't have to dwell on that concept, because students will have experience with these inverse relationships later in Lesson 2.

Problem Set F Suggested Grouping: Individuals or Pairs

This problem set provides practice describing a variety of rate situations with symbolic rules. All of these relationships are proportional.

Problem Set Wrap-Up You can wrap up this problem set by asking several students to state their symbolic rules and define whether the relationships are proportional.

After students finish Problem Set F, you may wish to give them an additional example that shows a non-proportional relationship.

3

Additional Example The first year of a dog's life is equivalent to about 16 years of human life. Each following year of the dog's life is equivalent to approximately 6 years of human life. So the rate for the first year is different than the rate for all other years. In order to calculate what human age corresponds to the dog's age, you can use a rate of 6 and add a constant amount of 10. (This is how much more than six the rate was in the first year.)

Problem Set G Suggested Grouping: Individuals or Pairs

This problem set provides an additional practice for representing proportional rates in table and graphs, while also reviewing percents.

Students will need graph paper or Master 10, Quarter-Inch Graph Paper, to draw the graph in this problem set.

In **Problems 1–4,** students look at how the number of correct answers and the percentage are related.

Access for All Learners

Extra for Experts For **Problem 2,** have students explain why the problem is restricted to Carol's answering 20 or fewer questions correctly. Students should realize that although the relationship is proportional, it doesn't make sense that Carol would answer more questions than were on the test.

Think & Discuss Answer

Access, Budget, and Cheap are proportional; Dollar, Easy, and Fantastic are not. Since the first three don't have a charge other than the rate, they are proportional. Talking twice as long will cost twice as much, and the graphs of charge versus time will go through (0, 0).

Think & Discuss

Many companies issue cards for charging telephone calls. For which cards below are the charges proportional to the number of minutes? For which are they not proportional? Explain. See Additional Answers.

1 Have students share their explanations.

Problem Set F

2 Have students work problems individually or in paris.

In Problems 1–4, the rule describes two variables that are proportional to each other. Rewrite each rule in symbols.

1. The circumference of a circle c is twice π times the radius r. $c = 2\pi r$
2. The perimeter of a square p is 4 multiplied by the length of a side L.
3. At a certain time of day, the length of a shadow s cast by an object is twice the length of the object L. $s = 2L$
4. Each length h in a copy is $\frac{1}{100}$ the length k in the original. $h = \frac{1}{100}k$
5. Compare the four rules you developed in Problems 1–4. In what ways are they similar? In what ways are they different?

2. $p = 4L$

5. Possible answer: Since none has a constant term, they are all proportional relationships. They differ in that they have different rates.

3 Extend students' thinking by using the Additional Example on page T310 that shows a nonproportional relationship.

MATERIALS

graph paper

Problem Set G

4 Have students work individually or in pairs.

Ms. Tsoleides gave her class a test with 40 questions.

1. Shaunda got 100% correct; Kate got only 50% correct. How many of the 40 questions did each answer correctly? 40, 20
2. Carol got fewer than 20 questions correct. If she could retake the test and double the number right, would that double her percentage? yes
3. Does halving the number of correct answers out of 40 halve the percentage? yes
4. Is the number of correct answers out of 40 proportional to the percentage? yes

In **Problem 5,** students graph the relationship. They should understand that it does not make sense to extend the graph beyond the point (40,100) because no one answered more than 40 questions.

In **Problem 6,** you might want to ask students to find the pattern in the percentages and explain that this pattern will help Mrs. Tsoleides read the graph and find the correct percentages. Students may see that each answer is worth 2.5 points, so all scores will end in 0.0, 2.5, 5.0, or 7.5. Although students may have inaccurate graphs and not have exact answers, you might want to reassure them that the teacher has ways to correctly score the tests.

Make sure that students can easily convert between scores and percents in **Problems 6 and 7.**

Problem Set Wrap-Up Discuss **Problems 2 and 5,** with the class. In answering **Problem 2,** students need to understand that if multiplying a score by a certain number multiplies the percent by the same number, it means that the relationship is proportional.

Share & Summarize

By this time students should be able to distinguish between proportional and nonproportional relationships in a graphical representation. These problems assess their understanding.

Troubleshooting If students are not able to solve the problems correctly, give them an additional example and ask them where the graph begins and whether or not the relationship is proportional.

Additional Examples

1. Mark started a new baseball card collection. At the beginning his father bought him 30 cards, and then he bought 5 additional cards every week. *Graph starts at (0, 30). Relationship is not proportional.*
2. Human hair grows 8–12 cm per year on average. Calculate the rate of growth per month. *Amount of growth starting at a particular time is strictly proportional to time. Hair length could be proportional (if a person starts with a hair of 0 length) or non-proportional (if the person starts with h cm of hair). In the proportional relationships, graphs start at (0, 0). In the nonproportional relationship, graphs start at (0, h).*

On Your Own Exercises

Practice & Apply: 6
Connect & Extend: 11–12
Mixed Review: 13–36

5. One evening Ms. Tsoleides had to convert her class's test results into percentages. She had left her calculator at school and decided to use a graph to help her.

a. She first calculated a few values and put them in a table. Copy and complete her table.

Number Correct (out of 40), n	0	10	20	30	40
Percentage Correct, p	0	25	50	75	100

5b. See Additional Answers.

b. Ms. Tsoleides then drew a graph on graph paper by plotting the points from her table and drawing a line through them. She made the horizontal axis the number of correct problems out of 40, with one grid unit on the axis equal to 2 questions correct. She put percentage points on the vertical axis, with one grid unit on the axis equal to 5 percentage points. She could then quickly read percentages from the graph for the various scores out of 40.

Draw Ms. Tsoleides' graph. Does it make sense to extend the line beyond the point (40, 100)? Explain your thinking.

1 Be sure students understand why the graph will not make sense if extended beyond the point (40, 100).

6. Note: Answers will vary, depending on the accuracy of the graphs.

6. Use your graph to convert each score out of 40 into a percentage.

a. 38 95%
b. 36 90%
c. 33 82.5%
d. 29 72.5%
e. 25 62.5%
f. 23 57.5%

2 Review how to convert between scores and percentages using a graph.

7. Neeraj, Zoe, and Simon scored 65%, 75%, and 85%, respectively, on the test. How many problems out of 40 did each get correct?
26, 30, 34

Share & Summarize

1. Without graphing, do you think the graphs of the relationships described in Problems 1–4 of Problem Set F would pass through the origin? Why do you think so?
2. A graph of a linear relationship goes through the point (0, 4). Is this a proportional relationship? Explain your reasoning.
3. Is $y = 5x + 7$ a proportional relationship? Explain your thinking.

Remember
The point (0, 0) is called the origin.

3
- Be sure students can distinguish between proportional and nonproportional graphs.
- Use Additional Examples to help struggling students.

Share & Summarize Answers

1. Yes; all the relationships are proportional.
2. No; the graph of a proportional relationship must pass through (0, 0).
3. No; it has a constant term added, so the graph would go through (0, 7), not (0, 0).

• Additional Answers on page A394.

Lab Investigation

Grouping: Small Groups

Materials and Preparation

You will need a box and three cans for the demonstrations to begin the investigation. Students will need two different-sized sets of cylindrical pens or other tubes, with all cylinders in each set having the same diameter. They will also need lined paper, a hard-cover book, and Master 10, Quarter-Inch Graph Paper, or graph paper. Other materials can be used to conduct the experiment, such as straws or wooden dowels instead of pens. Be aware that pencils are usually not smooth on the surface and may not roll properly. You may wish to use a paper pad in place of a book.

Introduce the Investigation by telling students that our knowledge about the nature of the relationships usually comes from collecting data. Let them know that they will be collecting measurements to determine whether or not the relationship between two variables is proportional.

Work with Your Class

Begin with a demonstration of a heavy box rolling over three aluminum drink cans. The box will move on the cans while the cans will be coming out from behind the box. This happens because the book moves relative to the cans, while the cans move relative to the table. You may want to point out the Just the Facts feature to provide students with an example of how this method was used in real life. Then discuss **Questions 1–3.**

Try It Out

Divide students into groups of 2–4 students and ask them to try a similar experiment using pens and books, or other materials of your choice. It is important that students use lined paper for their experiments so they can reliably measure the distance. Remind them to count carefully.

Lab Investigation ▶ Rolling Along

MATERIALS
- 2 cylindrical pens or pencils (without edges) with different diameters
- lined paper
- hardcover book
- graph paper

Just the facts

Historians believe that this method of rollers was used to move the very heavy stones used to build the Egyptian pyramids.

In this investigation, you will conduct an experiment and collect some data. You will use your data to try to understand the relationship between two variables.

Work with Your Class

Watch how a heavy box rolls on three drink cans. The rollers will keep coming out from behind the box!

1. Do the rollers go backward? no
2. Does the box go faster than the rollers? yes
3. Why do the rollers keep coming out the back? The box moves faster than the rollers, so it eventually rolls off them.

Try It Out

With your group, conduct an experiment that involves rolling one object on top of another. Use a cylindrical pen or pencil (one that is perfectly round), a book, and a sheet of lined paper (wide lines work best). Put the pen on the paper so that it lies along one of the lines. Put the book on top of the pen so the edge of the book also aligns with one of the lines.

4. Roll the book on the pen until the pen has moved 2 line spaces. How far has the book moved? 4 line spaces

1 After completing the demonstration, point out the Just the Facts feature before discussing the questions.

2 Have students work in small groups to conduct the experiment and gather data.

Develop

In **Questions 4–7,** students look at the relationship between the number of spaces the pen has moved and the number of spaces the book has moved, then organize their data in a table.

In **Question 6,** students are asked to come up with a rule that describes the relationship. It is important for students to express the rule in words as well as in symbols. The rule $b = 2p$ may look abstract to many students until they can read it as *the book goes twice as far as the pen.*

Students determine domain and restrictions on the values of the variables when they graph their data in **Question 7.**

Apply Your Results

Students use their rules to make a prediction in **Question 8.** If their prediction was reasonable, they may want to use the same strategy to answer **Question 9.**

Questions 10 and 11 introduce the inverse relationship between the distance moved by the book and the distance moved by the pen. Point this out to students. These questions emphasize the ability to work backward from the answer to the question. They also provide an informal introduction to the concept of inverse functions.

Try It Again

Students repeat the experiment using a different-sized pen. You may want them to predict how the rule will change. They may be surprised to find that the results are the same as in the previous experiment.

What Did You Learn?

Students' reports should discuss the factors that define the rule. It is important that students understand that the book is moving twice as far as the pen regardless of the size of the diameter of the pen or the size of the evenly spaced lines on the paper. They may recognize that this is because of the addition of the two equal speeds—the speed of the book and the speed of the pen.

Students may also mention that because the relationship is proportional, the graph will begin at (0, 0).

5. Continue to roll the book so you can complete the table. When you collect your data, count and measure accurately! Otherwise, you might not see the patterns that show the relationship between the variables.

Line Spaces Moved by Pen, p	0	2	4	6	8	10
Line Spaces Moved by Book, b	0	4	8	12	16	20

1 Students organize data in a table.

Analyze Your Data

2 Students analyze data.

6. With your group, describe in words how the distance the book moves is related to the distance the pen moves. Then write the relationship using the symbols p and b.

6. The book moves twice as far as the pen; $b = 2p$.

7. Draw a graph with the distance moved by the pen on the horizontal axis and the distance moved by the book on the vertical axis. Plot the values you found in Problem 5. If you think it makes sense to do so, join the points with a line, and extend the line.

7.

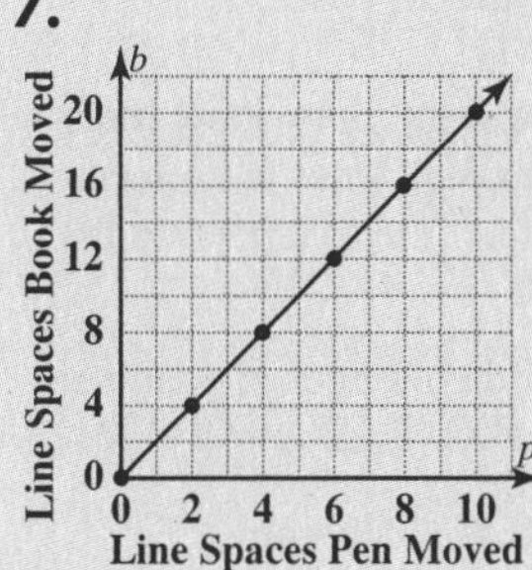

Apply Your Results

3 Students make a prediction.

8. Using your rule, predict how far the book will move when the pen moves 16 line spaces. Check by doing it. 32 line spaces

9. How many line spaces does the book move if the number of line spaces moved by the pen is 0.5? 1.5? 7.5? 1,350? 1; 3; 15; 2,700

10. If the book moves 9 line spaces, how far does the pen move? Test it with your equipment. 4.5 line spaces

4 Point out the inverse relationship between the distance moved by the book and the distance moved by the pen.

11. Describe in words how the distance the pen moves is related to the distance the book moves. Write this rule in symbols.

11. The pen moves half as far as the book; $p = 0.5b$.

Try It Again

You might wonder whether a different-sized pen or cylinder will give the same relationship between the distances moved by the pen and the book. Replace the pen with a different-sized pen or some other cylinder, and repeat the experiment.

5 Students repeat the experiment using a different-sized pen.

12. Complete a new table.

Line Spaces Moved by Pen, p	0	2	4	6	8	10
Line Spaces Moved by Book, b	0	4	8	12	16	20

13. Are your results the same? yes

14. Is this a proportional relationship? How can you tell?

14. Yes; the relation is linear and includes the point (0, 0).

What Did You Learn?

6 Students write about their work and its results.

15. Write a short report describing your experiments and the results. Reports will vary.

LESSON 5.1 Understanding and Describing Rates 313

On Your Own Exercises

Investigation 1
Practice & Apply: 1–2
Connect & Extend: 7–9

Investigation 2
Practice & Apply: 3–5
Connect & Extend: 10

Investigation 3
Practice & Apply: 6
Connect & Extend: 11–12

Assign Anytime
Mixed Review: 13–36

Exercises 1–2 and 7–10:
These exercises not only review the concepts taught in the first investigation, but, in many cases, they also provide practice converting between metric and English measures of weight and volume.

On Your Own Exercises

Practice & Apply

1a. There are 1,000 grams per kilogram.

1b. $g = 1{,}000k$

1d.

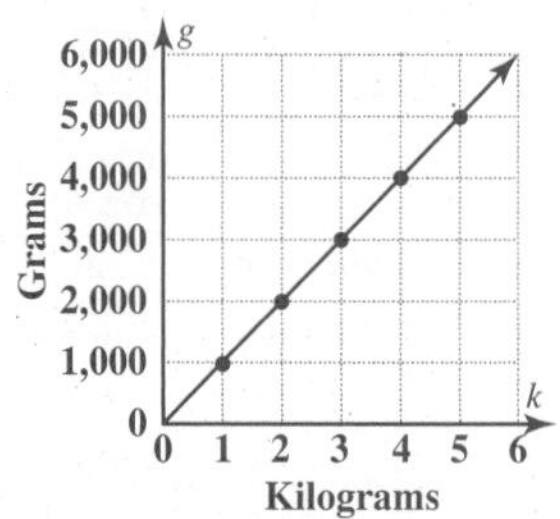

2a. There is 0.453 kilogram per pound.

2b. $k = 0.453p$

Remember

When you plot points from a table of data, connect the points and extend the line beyond the points, if it makes sense to do so.

2d.

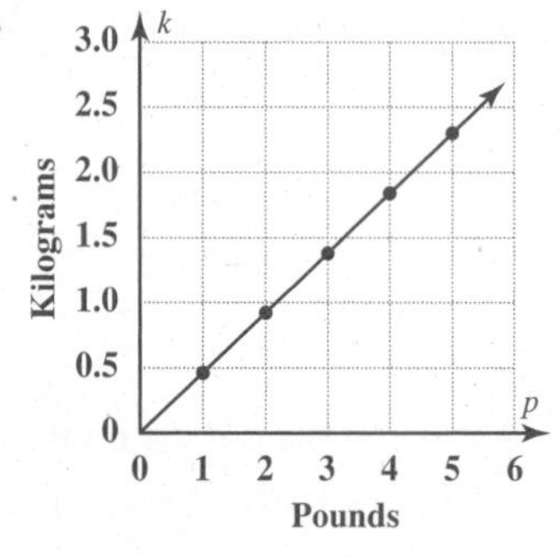

1. Measurement A kilogram is equivalent to 1,000 grams.

a. Describe this relationship in words using the word *per.*

b. Write a rule in symbols that relates the two measures. Use k to represent the number of kilograms and g the number of grams.

c. Copy and complete the table without using the rule. Then use your table to check that your rule correct.

Kilograms, k	1	2	3	4	5
Grams, g	1,000	2,000	3,000	4,000	5,000

d. Use the data in the table to help you draw a graph to show the relationship between the measures. If it makes sense to connect the points, do so. If it makes sense to extend the line beyond the points, do so.

e. Use your table, formula, or graph to find the number of grams in 1.5 kg, 3.2 kg, 0.7 kg, and 0.034 kg. 1,500; 3,200; 700; 34

2. Measurement A pound is equivalent to 0.453 kilogram.

a. Describe the relationship in words using the word *per.*

b. Write a rule in symbols that relates the two measures. Use p for the number of pounds and k for the number of kilograms.

c. Complete the table without using your rule. Then use your table to check that your rule is correct.

Pounds, p	1	2	3	4	5
Kilograms, k	0.453	0.906	1.359	1.812	2.265

d. Use the data in the table to help you draw a graph to show the relationship between the measures.

e. Use your table, formula, or graph to find the number of kilograms in 7 lb, 40 lb, 100 lb, and 0.5 lb. 3.171; 18.12; 45.3; 0.2265

314 CHAPTER 5 Looking at Linear Relationships

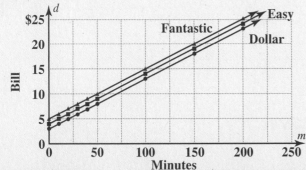

Exercise 3:
Students get their data from calling cards to determine rates.

Exercise 3f:
Be sure students understand that the 85 minutes occurred in the same month.

3. These three phone cards have different charge plans for their customers.

3a. Dollar: $d = 3 + \underline{0.10}m$; Easy: $d = 4 + \underline{0.10}m$; Fantastic: $d = 5 + \underline{0.10}m$

a. Write the rule for each card's charge plan for 1 month, using *d* for charge in dollars and *m* for call length in minutes. Underline the part of each rule that shows the rate of charge.

b. Copy the table. For each card, fill in the table to show the monthly bill for different numbers of minutes of calls.

Minutes, *m*	0	10	20	30	40	50	100	150	200
Dollar Bill (in dollars)	3	4	5	6	7	8	13	18	23
Easy Bill (in dollars)	4	5	6	7	8	9	14	19	24
Fantastic Bill (in dollars)	5	6	7	8	9	10	15	20	25

3c. See Additional Answers.

3d. It makes sense to connect the points because a person can talk any number of minutes. It makes sense to extend the graphs because a person can talk more than 200 min in a month.

3e. The graphs have the same steepness, but they start at different points.

3f. $11.50

c. On one set of axes, draw a graph for each card's charge plan. Put minutes on the horizontal axis and dollars on the vertical axis. Label the graphs to identify which card goes with which graph.

d. Does it make sense to connect the points? Does it make sense to extend the graphs beyond the points? If so, do it.

e. How are the graphs similar? How are they different?

f. How much would you pay for 85 minutes with the Dollar card?

g. For $12, how many minutes of calls could you make with the Dollar card? With the Easy card? With the Fantastic card? If your answers are more than 59 minutes, convert them to hours and minutes.
Dollar: 1 h 30 min;
Easy: 1 h 20 min;
Fantastic: 1 h 10 min

Additional Answers

3c.

d
$25
20
15
10
5
0
Bill
Fantastic
Easy
Dollar
0 50 100 150 200 250
m
Minutes

Assign and Assess

Exercise 4b and 4d: Have students refer to and use their graphs from Problem Set D in order to answer these problems.

Exercise 5e: Students work backward to find the number of minutes given the total number of revolutions.

4. In Problem Sets C and D, you solved problems about Alec's and Mario's rates of pay. Suppose that Alec receives a raise to $8 per hour.

a. Write a rule in symbols relating the number of dollars p that Alec earns to the number of hours h that he works. $p = 8h$

b. What would the graph that shows his new pay rate look like? How would it compare to the two graphs you have already drawn (for Mario's pay and Alec's pay at the old rate)?

4b. It would be a straight line between the two lines already drawn.

c. Make a table to show what Alec would now earn for 0, 1, 2, 3, 4, 5, and 10 hours of work. See below.

d. On your grid from Problem Set D, draw a graph to show how much Alec is paid at the new rate. Does the graph look as you predicted in Part b? If not, try to figure out where your thinking went wrong. See Additional Answers.

5. Before compact discs became popular, people listened to music and other sound recordings on record players. A record player that runs at 45 rpm turns a record 45 times per minute. The unit rpm is an abbreviation for *revolutions per minute.*

a. Complete the table to show the number of times a record turns in a given number of minutes.

Minutes, t	1	2	3	4	5	6
Revolutions, r	45	90	135	180	225	270

b. Write in words a rule that gives the number of times a record turns in a given number of minutes. Then write the same rule in symbols. Underline the part of your rule that shows the constant rate of turning.

5b. The number of revolutions is equal to 45 times the number of minutes; $r = \underline{45}t$.

c. Using your rule, predict the number of revolutions in 12 seconds (0.2 minute). $r = 45 \times 0.2 = 9$

d. Draw a graph to show how the number of revolutions is related to time. Put time on the horizontal axis.

5d.

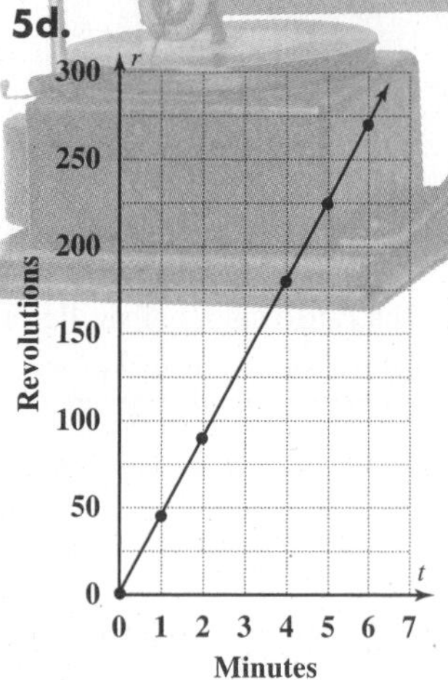

e. Use your graph to estimate how long it would take for a record to revolve 100 times and 300 times.

5e. about 2.2 min, about 6.7 min

4c.

Hours, h	0	1	2	3	4	5	10
Pay (dollars), p	0	8	16	24	32	40	80

316 CHAPTER 5 Looking at Linear Relationships

• ***Additional Answers on page A394.***

6. A painter needs about 1 fluid ounce of paint for each square foot of wall she paints.

   a. Write a rule in symbols for this situation, using p for fluid ounces of paint and f for square feet. Underline the part of your rule that shows the constant rate of paint use. $p = \underline{1}f$

   b. Complete the table.

Paint (fluid oz), p	0	10	20	30	40	50	80	100	140	170	220
Area (sq ft), f	0	10	20	30	40	50	80	100	140	170	220

6e.

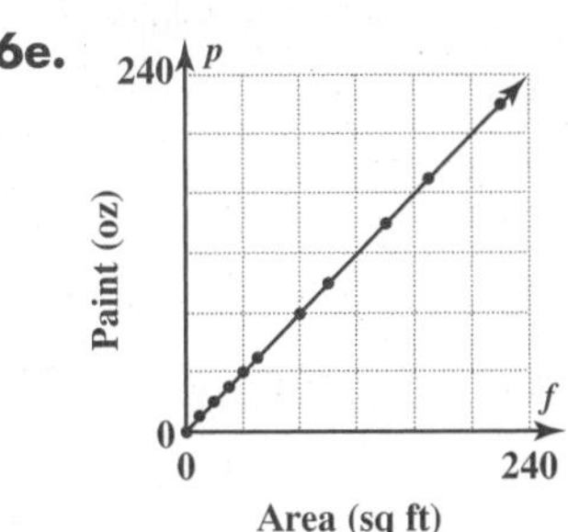

6f. 128 sq ft, 256 sq ft, 384 sq ft

   c. How many fluid ounces of paint are needed to paint a wall with area 120 sq ft? 120

   d. How many gallons of paint are needed to cover 450 sq ft? There are 128 fluid ounces in 1 gallon. 3.52

   e. Draw a graph to show how the amount of paint depends on the area to be painted. Put area on the horizontal axis.

   f. Use your graph to estimate the area covered with 1 gallon of paint, 2 gallons of paint, and 3 gallons of paint.

   g. If a painter uses twice as much paint, can she cover twice as much area? If she uses three times as much paint, can she cover three times as much area? Is the relationship between area and amount of paint proportional? yes, yes, yes

7. **Measurement** 24 ounces is equivalent to 680 grams.

   a. Describe the relationship in words using the word *per.*

   There are 680 g per 24 oz, or 28.33 g per oz.

   b. Complete the table.

Ounces, z	0	1	2	3	4	5	6
Grams, g	0	28.33	56.66	84.99	113.32	141.65	169.98

The metric system was first proposed in 1670 and is now used in most countries around the world.

   c. Write a rule in symbols that relates the two measures. Use your table to check that your rule is correct. $g = 28.33z$

   d. Use the data in the table to help you draw a graph to show the relationship between the measures. If you think it makes sense to do so, join the points with a line, and extend the line.

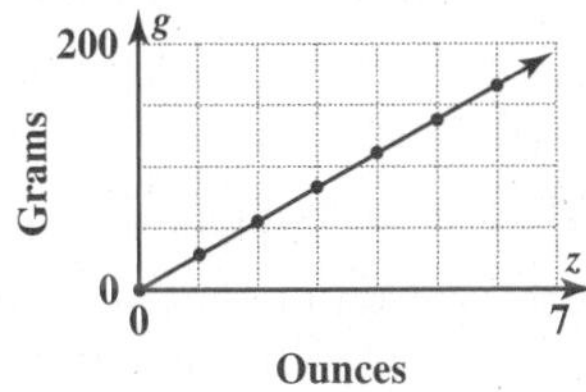

Exercise 6:
Watch for students who have trouble recognizing the rate in $p = f$. Some may say there is no rate; others may say the rate is f. Remind them that when there is no number in front of a variable that the variable is multiplied by 1; therefore, the rate is 1.

Exercise 6d:
Tell students to round their answers to the nearest hundredth.

LESSON 5.1 Understanding and Describing Rates 317

Assign and Assess

Exercises 10d and 10e:
In order to make the conversions, students may need to be reminded that 1,000 mL = 1 L and that 16 c = 1 gal.

8. 453, 906, 271.8, 45.3

1 fl oz = 29.573 mL
1 oz = 28.350 g
1 gal = 3.785 L

Just the facts

The very first movie theaters were built in the late 1890s. By the 1920s and 1930s, grand "picture palaces" were springing up everywhere. And the first drive-in movie opened in 1933.

Measurement A kilogram (kg) is equivalent to 1,000 grams (g). A pound (lb) is equivalent to 0.453 kilogram (kg).

8. Find the number of grams in 1 lb, 2 lb, 0.6 lb, and 0.1 lb.

9. Find the number of pounds in 3 kg, 17 kg, 0.5 kg, 900 g, 300 g, and 56 g. 6.62, 37.53, 1.10, 1.99, 0.66, 0.12

10. Challenge Darnell bought a gallon of spring water. The label indicated that a serving size is 1 cup, or 236 mL. Use the conversions at left to answer the questions.

a. What is the volume of the serving size (1 cup) in fluid ounces? 8

b. The mass of 1 mL of water is 1 g. What is the mass of 1 cup of water in grams? 236

c. What is the weight of 1 cup of water in ounces? 8.32

d. What is the volume of 1 cup of water in liters? 0.236

e. What is the volume of 1 cup of water in gallons? 0.0625

f. There are 16 ounces in a pound. What is the weight of 1 cup of water in pounds? 0.52

g. How many cups are in 1 gallon? 16

11. Challenge An architect is designing a building with two movie theaters. The Green Theater will be rectangular in shape, with each row holding 16 seats. The Blue Theater will be wider at the back: the first row will have 8 seats, the second row will have 16 seats, and all other rows will have 20 seats. The architect will decide how many rows to put in each theater on the basis of the number of people it is meant to hold. **11a–11d.** See Additional Answers.

a. Make a table showing how the number of seats for each theater relates to the number of rows. Assume each theater will have at least 3 rows.

b. On one set of axes, draw graphs to show how the number of seats in each theater depends on the number of rows.

c. Does it make sense to connect the points on the graphs? Explain.

d. For each theater, write a rule in symbols that tells how the number of seats depends on the number of rows.

e. How many rows should be in each theater to give the theaters an equal number of seats? 4

f. Which theater will have more seats if both have 11 rows? Blue

g. Is the number of seats in each theater proportional to the number of rows? Why do you think so? See Additional Answers.

Additional Answers

11a. Possible table:

Rows, r	3	4	5	6	7	10	20
Seats in Green Theater, g	48	64	80	96	112	160	320
Seats in Blue Theater, b	44	64	84	104	124	184	384

11b–d, g. See Additional Answers on page A394.

In your own words

How can you find the rate of a linear relationship using a graph? Using a symbolic rule? Using a table? Which representation do you prefer for this task? Why?

12b, 12c. See Additional Answers.

12g. Emma: 11:40; Susan: 1:30

12. Emma started to read a book at 10:20 in the morning. She usually reads a page in 2 minutes. Half an hour later, her friend Susan started to read. She reads 15 pages per hour.

a. How many pages did Emma read before Susan started to read? 15

b. Create a table showing how many pages Emma and Susan read by 10:50, 11:00, 11:10, 11:20, 11:30, 11:40, 11:50, and 12:00.

c. Based on your table, draw graphs on the same axes showing how many pages Emma and Susan read between 10:50 A.M. and noon. Does it make sense to connect the points on the graphs? Does it make sense to continue the lines beyond the 12 o'clock mark? Explain your answers.

d. Write a rule in symbols for the number of pages Emma read since 10:50. Write a rule in symbols for the number of pages Susan read since 10:50. Use *m* for number of minutes passed after 10:50. Underline the parts of the rules that show the constant rates of reading. Emma: $E = 15 + \underline{0.5}m$; Susan: $S = \underline{0.25}m$

e. Is the relationship for Emma proportional? Is the relationship for Susan proportional? no, yes

f. How many pages would each girl read in 5 min? In 16 min? In 48 min? Emma: 2.5, 8, 24; Susan: 1.25, 4, 12

g. At what time will Emma finish 40 pages of her book? At what time will Susan finish 40 pages of her book?

h. At what time will the number of pages Emma has read be three times the number of pages Susan has read? 11:50

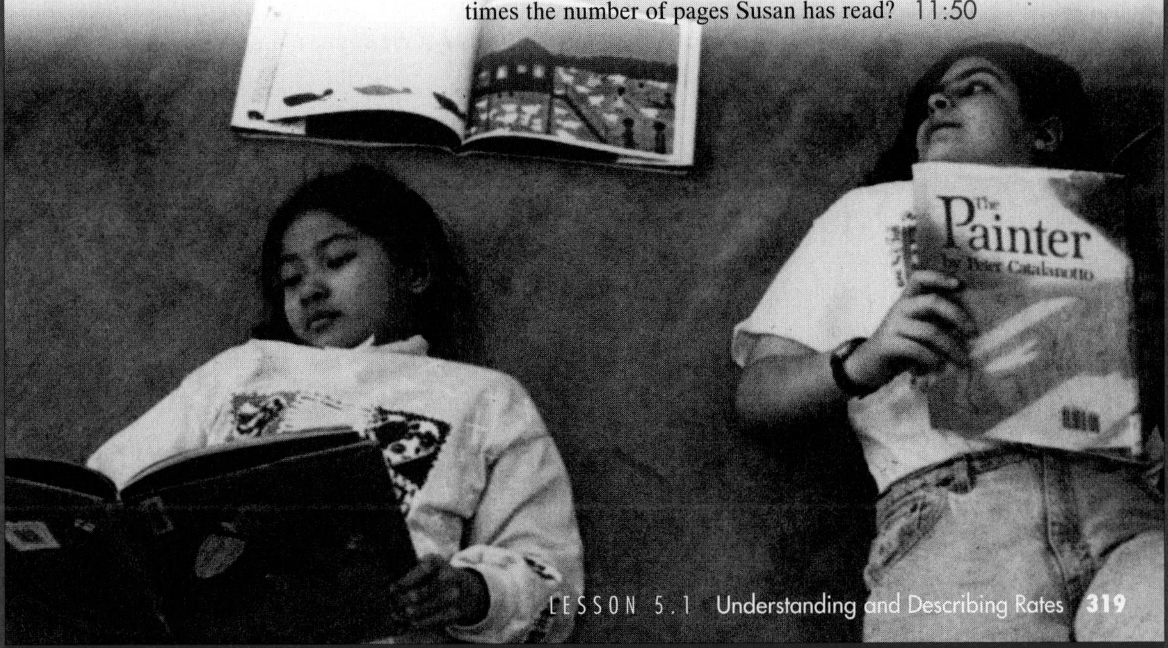

LESSON 5.1 Understanding and Describing Rates 319

Exercise 12: Watch for students who are having trouble writing the rule. Although the table shows the change every 10 minutes, the rule has to show the change every minute.

Additional Answers

12b. Possible table:

Time	10:50	11:00	11:10	11:20	11:30	11:40	11:50	12:00
Pages Emma Read, *E*	15	20	25	30	35	40	45	50
Pages Susan Read, *S*	0	2.5	5	7.5	10	12.5	15	17.5

12c. See Additional Answers on page A395.

Assign and Assess

Quick Check

Informal Assessment
Students should be able to

✔ develop strategies for describing rates

✔ recognize rates presented in symbolic and graphic forms

✔ compare proportional and nonproportional relationships

✔ represent proportional and nonproportional relationships in words, tables, symbols, and graphs

✔ get hands-on experience with collecting data

✔ determine the nature of the relationship between two variables

Quick Quiz

1. For the following relationships, determine the rate.
   a. $y = 53x$ 53
   b. $y = 15 + 0.1x$ 0.1
2. State an equation that describes a proportional relationship.
   Answers will vary. Possible answer: $y = 2x$

Mixed Review

13. $0.2, 0.4 = \frac{2}{5}, \frac{3}{5}, \frac{5}{3}$
14. 0.025, 0.18, 0.25, 0.7, 0.75

Order each group of numbers from least to greatest.

13. $\frac{2}{5}$, 0.2, $\frac{3}{5}$, 0.4, $\frac{5}{3}$

14. 0.75, 0.18, 0.25, 0.025, 0.7

Fill in the blanks to make each a true statement.

15. $\frac{1}{8} + \frac{1}{3} + \underline{\frac{13}{24}} = 1$

16. $\frac{2}{7} + \frac{3}{10} + \underline{\frac{29}{70}} = 1$

17. Geometry Find the area and perimeter of the circle.

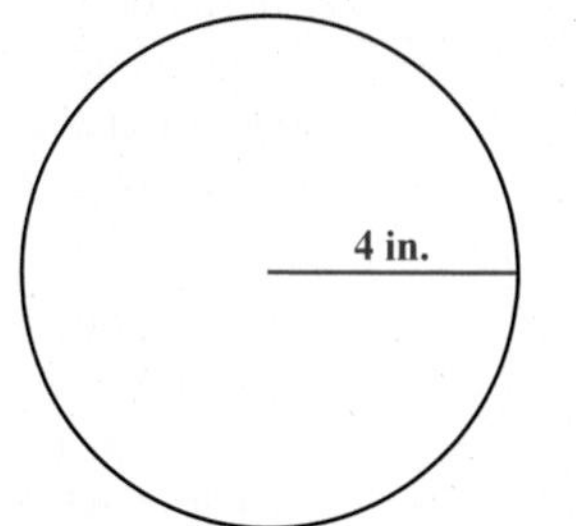

area = 16π sq in., or 50.27 sq in.; perimeter = 8π in., or 25.13 in.

18. Find 33% of 140. 46.2

19. Find 14% of 31. 4.34

20. What percent of 250 is 15? 6%

21. What percent of 12 is 0.12? 1%

Use the distributive property to rewrite each expression with parentheses.

22. $18 - 4f$ $2(9 - 2f)$

23. $13 - 26m$ $13(1 - 2m)$

Find each product. Express your answers in scientific notation.

24. 5.5×10^{28}
25. 4.8×10^{16}

24. $(5 \times 10^{14}) \times (11 \times 10^{13})$

25. $(8 \times 10^{9}) \times (6 \times 10^{6})$

Find the distance between the endpoints of the segment drawn on each number line.

26. −3 0 3 6

27. −3.5 0 1 4.5

Rewrite each expression as addition, and calculate the sum.

28. $4 + 3 = 7$
29. $10 + 4 = 14$
30. $13 + 10 = 23$
31. $^-7 + 8 = 1$

28. $4 - {}^-3$ **29.** $10 - {}^-4$ **30.** $13 - {}^-10$ **31.** $^-7 - {}^-8$

Rewrite each expression in the form c^m.

32. $5^3 \times 5^2$ 5^5 **33.** $2^7 \times 2^2$ 2^9 **34.** $7^2 \times 7^7$ 7^9 **35.** $a^2 \times a^3$ a^5

36. Number Sense Could the number 3,028,046,908 be some power of 4? Explain how you know. No; all powers of 4 have a final digit of either 4 or 6.

• *Quick Quiz continued on page A395.*

320 CHAPTER 5 Looking at Linear Relationships

5.2 Speed and the Slope Connection

Objectives

- To relate speed to the slope of a graph of distance over time
- To develop an understanding of negative slope and a negative constant term
- To gain skill in recognizing proportional and non-proportional relationships between distance and time
- To recognize linear relationships from symbolic rules, graphs, patterns, and tables and to convert one form into another.

Overview (pacing: about 4 class periods)

This lesson focuses on one particularly common and important rate, *speed,* and develops students' understanding of proportional and nonproportional linear relationships in the context of speed. They learn to relate speed to the slope of the line by investigating the relationship between distance and time. They learn about negative slope by looking at situations in which distance decreases over time.

In this program, the axes in a coordinate grid are referred to as the *horizontal axis* and the *vertical axis.* These terms are preferred because they are more descriptive. At the end of this lesson, the terms *x*-axis and *y*-axis are introduced when students study *y*-intercepts.

Advance Preparation

You will need stopwatches or watches with second hands for students and a yardstick or other measuring device for the Explore on page 321. Students will also need several copies of Master 10, Quarter-Inch Graph Paper, or graph paper throughout the lesson.

Lesson Planner

	Summary	Materials	On Your Own Exercises	Assessment Opportunities
Investigation 1 page T322	Students learn about speed as a special rate and make a connection between speed and the slope of the graph relating distance and time.	• Master 10 (Teaching Resources, page 15) • Stopwatches • Yardstick	Practice & Apply: 1–3 Connect & Extend: 13, 15, 18–21, 23 Mixed Review: 34–58	Share & Summarize, pages T325, 325 On the Spot Assessment, pages T322, T325 Troubleshooting, page T325
Investigation 2 page T326	A negative slope is introduced to students through distance decreasing with time. Students learn to interpret graphs.	• Master 10	Practice & Apply: 4–5 Connect & Extend: 14, 16, 17, 22, 24–31 Mixed Review: 34–58	Share & Summarize, pages T328, 328 On the Spot Assessment, pages T326, T327 Troubleshooting, page T328
Investigation 3 page T328	Students learn to extract the essential information about the movement of the objects such as speed, direction, and relative location from the graphs. The distinction between the speed and velocity is introduced.	• Master 10	Practice & Apply: 6 Connect & Extend: 32 Mixed Review: 34–58	Share & Summarize, pages T329, 329 Troubleshooting, page T329
Investigation 4 page T330	Students practice distinguishing between proportional and non-proportional relationships. The negative constant term is introduced with the discussion of the direction of a distance.	• Master 10	Practice & Apply: 7–12 Connect & Extend: 33 Mixed Review: 34–58	Share & Summarize, pages T333, 333 On the Spot Assessment, page T330 Troubleshooting, page T333 Informal Assessment, page 343 Quick Quiz, page 343

Introduce

This lesson helps students develop a stronger understanding of speed as a rate of change of distance over time. Students explore problems involving increasing or decreasing distances from a fixed point and think about how slope relates to the situation.

1 Many students are familiar with at least one rate of speed. Ask them to use their familiarity to explain why speed is a rate and to give some examples of how speed can be measured.

The first Explore activity gives you an opportunity to see what students know about the concept of speed—how rate, time and distance interact—and to gauge whether they have a good sense of different rates.

Explore

The purpose of this activity is to help students develop an understanding of the relationship between time and walking speed. Some students have very little sense of speed, so this activity provides a valuable common experience for the class to discuss. It also gives students a concrete experience that they can draw upon as they investigate the notion of speed in this lesson. For this activity, students will need a stopwatch or a watch with a second hand and a way to measure the length of the room.

Begin the lesson by asking students to guess their normal walking speed and to record their guesses. Ask several students to share their guesses and record their responses on the chalkboard. It is fine if the answers are in different units of measurement. You can use them later to discuss how the same speed may be expressed in different ways.

Have one or two students measure the length in feet of the room with a yardstick or measuring tape. Put this measure on the board. Then choose several students to walk, one at a time, from the back wall of the classroom to the front wall.

You might say to the first student

> Think hard before you start walking. Your job is to try to cover this distance, walking at a steady pace, in exactly 15 seconds. We'll time you to see how long it *really* takes. Ready? Go.

Ask the rest of the class to measure the time with their stopwatches. Be sure that the walkers understand that no speeding or slowing down should occur once they have started. Ask students to calculate the speed of the walker in feet per second and record it on the chalkboard.

Now, ask a second student to walk at a steady pace and cover the same distance in exactly 10 seconds. Again, the rest of the class records the time. Ask other students to complete their walk in longer or shorter amounts of time. The amount of time you set for the walkers will depend on the size of your classroom. Try to include different speeds ranging from a very slow walk to a very fast walk or run. Write all these speeds on the chalkboard. Have students compare the actual speeds with their estimated speeds.

Then discuss the last three questions in this section.

5.2 Speed and the Slope Connection

Speed is a very common rate. It tells how the distance something travels depends on the time traveled. Speed can be measured in many ways. Here are a few common units of speed.

- miles per hour (mph)
- kilometers per hour (km/h or kph)
- feet per second (ft/s)
- meters per second (m/s)
- millimeters per second (mm/s)

1 Discuss common units of speed.

MATERIALS
- stopwatch
- yardstick

Explore

Guess an average student's normal walking speed and record your guess. Then, one person in the class should walk at a "normal" speed from the back of the classroom to the front while another person accurately times him or her. Record that time and the distance the student walked, in feet.

Now here is a challenge: Several students should try to cross the classroom at a steady pace taking the amounts of time specified by the teacher—some greater and some less than it takes to cross at a "normal" speed.

You or a classmate should time how long it actually takes each student to cross the room. Then everyone in the class can compute the students' true speeds. To find the speeds, divide the distance walked by the time it took.

After you have an idea about how fast or slow the various speeds are, answer these questions:

- If a person travels 1.5 feet per second, is this a fast walk, a slow walk, or a run? slow walk
- If a second person moves with a speed of 9 feet per second, is this a fast walk, a slow walk, or a run? run
- How much faster is the second person in comparison with the first? 6 times faster

2
- Have students guess their walking speed.
- Have volunteers walk across the room at a steady pace.

3 Discuss questions.

Develop

Investigation 1

Ask students whether they ever have to change their walking rate when walking with someone else. You may want to discuss how the rates may vary.

Problem Set A **Suggested Grouping: Pairs**
Students represent various speeds with symbolic rules and graphs as they did with rates in Lesson 1.

Students will need graph paper or copies of Master 10, Quarter-Inch Graph Paper, to complete the problem set.

On the **Spot Assessment**

Watch for students who say that the relationship in **Problem 3** is proportional because one solution could be graphed at (0, 0). Remind them that this is only one characteristic of a proportional relationship. Students must also know that the relationship is linear.

Remind students to use values from their table to test that the rule they wrote in **Problem 4** is correct.

Investigation 1 Walking and Jogging

1 Discuss how rates of walking may vary.

Some people walk quickly, taking several steps in a few seconds. Others walk more slowly, taking more than a second for each step. Some people naturally take longer strides than others. When you're walking with a friend, one or both of you probably changes something about the way you walk so you can stay side by side.

MATERIALS
graph paper

Problem Set A

2 Have pairs complete the problems.

Zach's stride is 0.5 meter long. Imagine that he's walking across a room, taking one step each second.

1. At what speed is Zach walking? 0.5 m/s
2. Copy and complete the table to show Zach's distance from the left wall at each time.

Time (seconds), *t*	0	1	2	3	4	5	6
Distance from Left Wall (meters), *d*	0	0.5	1	1.5	2	2.5	3

3. At this constant speed, is the distance traveled proportional to the time? How do you know?

3. Yes; if you multiply the time by any number, the distance is multiplied by the same amount.

4. Write a rule that shows how to compute d if you know t. $d = 0.5t$

3 Remind students to use values from the table to test that the rule they wrote is correct.

5. What would Zach's speed be if he lengthened his stride to 1 meter but still took 1 second for each step? Make a table of values, and write a rule for this speed. 1 m/s; $d = t$; Possible table:

Time (s), *t*	0	1	2	3	4	5	6
Distance from Left Wall (m), *d*	0	1	2	3	4	5	6

Develop

Students should draw three graphs on the same axes as suggested in **Problem 7** and, prior to a whole-class discussion of the Think & Discuss, talk with their partners about what their graphs show.

Think & Discuss

The questions in the Think & Discuss call for an understanding of speed as a rate. The steepness of the distance-time graphs indicates the relative speed of each person. Later students will be able to determine speed by looking at the graph.

Draw a parallel with the questions about rate from Lesson 1, such as

> How do the graphs show differences in speed?
>
> How is faster speed shown on the graph?

Problem Set B **Suggested Grouping: Individuals**

Problem Set B problems are similar to those of Problem Set A. Students should be able to complete this problem set independently. Students will need graph paper or copies of Master 10, Quarter-Inch Graph Paper, to complete this problem set.

7.

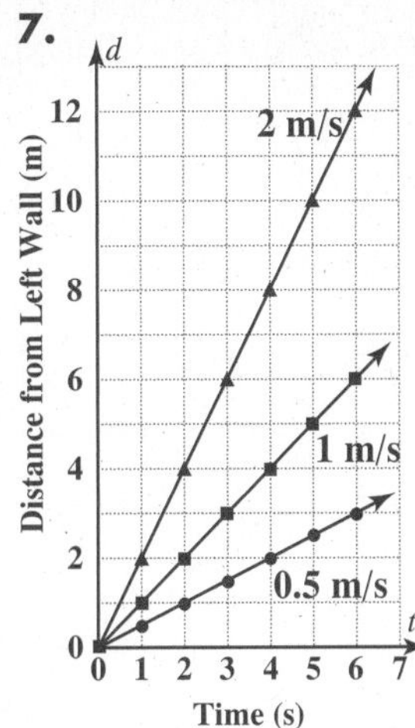

6. Imagine that Maya is also crossing the room, but she is taking two steps each second and her steps are 1 meter long. What is her speed? Make a table of values, and write a rule for her speed. See below.

7. For all three tables, plot each set of points in the table and then draw a line through them. Put all three graphs on one grid, with time on the horizontal axis. Label each graph with its speed.

Think & Discuss

Compare the three graphs you drew in Problem 7.

- In what ways are they the same? In what ways are they different? See ①.
- What does the steepness in these distance-time graphs show? The steeper the graph, the faster the walking speed.

1 These questions depend on students' understanding of speed as a rate.

MATERIALS
graph paper

Problem Set B

Many joggers try to jog at a steady pace throughout most of their runs. This is particularly important for long-distance running.

- Terry tries to jog at a steady pace of 4 meters per second.
- Maria tries to jog at a steady pace of 3 meters per second.
- Bronwyn doesn't know how fast she jogs, but she tries to keep a steady pace.

1. Make tables for Terry and Maria to show the distances they travel (d meters) in various times (t seconds). See Additional Answers.

2. Write rules that show how distance d changes with time t for Terry and for Maria. Terry: $d = 4t$; Maria: $d = 3t$

2 Have students work individually to complete problems.

Just the facts

The maximum speed a human being has ever run is about 27 miles per hour. The fastest animal on Earth, the cheetah, has been clocked at about 60 miles per hour.

Think & Discuss Answer

① They are all straight lines that go through (0, 0), so they are all proportional, but they have different degrees of steepness.

Additional Answers
Problem Set A

6. 2 m/s; $d = 2t$; Possible table:

Time (s), t	0	1	2	3	4	5	6
Distance from Left Wall (m), d	0	2	4	6	8	10	12

Problem Set B

1. Possible table:

Time (s), t	0	5	10	15	20
Terry's Distance (m), d	0	20	40	60	80
Maria's Distance (m), d	0	15	30	45	60

LESSON 5.2 Speed and the Slope Connection **323**

Develop

1 Students will need to save their graphs from **Problem 4** to use later in this investigation.

2 **Problem Set Wrap-Up** Have students share the rules they wrote for **Problems 2 and 3.** You may want to point out the general rule, $d = rt$, in the Just the Facts feature in the margin on page 324. Some students may find that knowing the general rule helps them write and check the rules they write.

Ask students what the steepness of the lines on their distance graphs indicate. Most students will realize that it indicates relative speed: a steeper line shows a faster speed. Then relate the steepness to how much the distance changes over a given amount of time. Tell students that another way to describe steepness is *slope.*

3 Discuss the definition of *slope.* You might want to prepare an overhead or direct students' attention to the graph showing rise and run, the changes in x- and y-values, on page 324. It is essential that they be familiar with the term *slope* before moving on.

The general rule connecting distance, rate, and time is $d = rt$, where d is the distance, r is the rate or speed, and t is the time.

3. 3.5 m/s, $d = 3.5t$
4. See Additional Answers.
5. The graph of the fastest jogger is the steepest, and the graph of the slowest jogger is the least steep.

3. A timekeeper measured times and distances traveled for Bronwyn and put the results in a table.

Time (seconds), t	0	5	10	15	20
Distance (meters), d	0	17.5	35	52.5	70

How fast does Bronwyn jog? Write a rule that relates Bronwyn's distance to time.

4. On one grid, draw graphs for Terry, Maria, and Bronwyn. Put time on the horizontal axis. Label each graph with the name of the person and the speed.

5. Explain how you can tell from looking at the graph who jogs most quickly and who jogs most slowly.

All the points on each graph you drew are on a line through the point (0, 0). The steepest line is the one for which distance changes the most in a given amount of time—that is, when the speed is the fastest. The line that is the least steep is the one for which distance changes the least in a given amount of time—that is, when the speed is the slowest.

1 Have students save graphs for Problem 4 to use in Think & Discuss on page 325.

2 Point out the general rule connecting distance, rate, and time in the Just the Facts feature.

VOCABULARY
slope

Slope describes the steepness of a line. In this case, the slope tells how much the distance changes per unit of time. More generally, the **slope** of a line tells how much the y variable changes per unit change in the x variable.

3 Discuss the definition of *slope.*

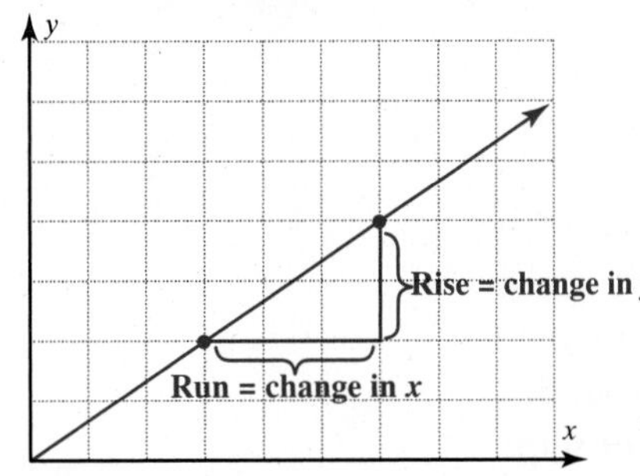

Sometimes slope is described as *rise* divided by *run.* This makes sense because y changes in the vertical direction, or "rises," and x changes in the horizontal direction, or "runs."

• ***Additional Answers on page A395.***

Develop

Example

Walk students through the Example showing how to find the slope of a line. Some students may need verification that the slope for a given line remains the same regardless of the two points chosen. You may wish to let students choose two other points to show that this is true.

Remind students that the terms *rise* and *run* describe the movement along the axes. Be sure that students understand that the term *run* has nothing to do with the fact that distance is being graphed.

> **Tips from Teachers**
>
> I like to help students remember the terms *rise* and *run* by associating the terms with the actions they take on the axes. When something rises, it comes up, so the term *rise* describes movement on the vertical axis. Likewise when animals run, they move forward, so this term describes movement on the horizontal axis.

Think & Discuss

Students refer to their graphs from Problem Set B. Give them time to think about and solve these problems before discussing them. Have students' describe how they found the slope and what points they used to make their calculations. Students who have a solid understanding at this point will see the relation of slope to speed. They may use this reasoning to explain the relationship: If Maria's graph has a slope of 3, this means that her distance changes 3 meters every second. That is her speed.

> **On the Spot Assessment**
>
> Watch for students who cannot attach a unit of measure to the slope. To help these students, ask them what the units of measurement are for the horizontal axis and for the vertical axis. They may need to write their ratios with the units of measure to better see how slope and speed relate in the graph.

Share & Summarize

These questions take students' understanding of the relation of slope to speed to another level. Students determine slope from speed without looking at a graph.

Troubleshooting If students cannot relate slope to speed by this point, you may use the Additional Examples below to illustrate these connections. Ask what the slope would be for the graphs that represent the distance moved in one unit of time for each of these vehicles.

Additional Examples

1. The bicyclist can move at a speed of 45 km/h. 45
2. The car moves at a speed of 60 mi/h. 60
3. The ship goes at a speed of 22 mi/h. 22
4. The satellite moves at a speed of 17,500 mi/h. 17,500
5. The wind blows at a speed of 5 m/sec. 5
6. The airplane flies at a speed of 560 mi/h. 560

On Your Own Exercises

Practice & Apply: 1–3
Connect & Extend: 13, 15, 18–21, 23
Mixed Review: 34–58

EXAMPLE

This graph shows how Terry's distance changed over time. To find the slope, choose two points, such as (10, 40) and (20, 80). From the left point to the right point, the y value changes from 40 to 80. The *rise* between these points is $80 - 40$, or 40. The x value changes from 10 to 20, so the *run* between these points is $20 - 10$, or 10. The slope—the rise divided by the run—is $\frac{40}{10}$, or 4.

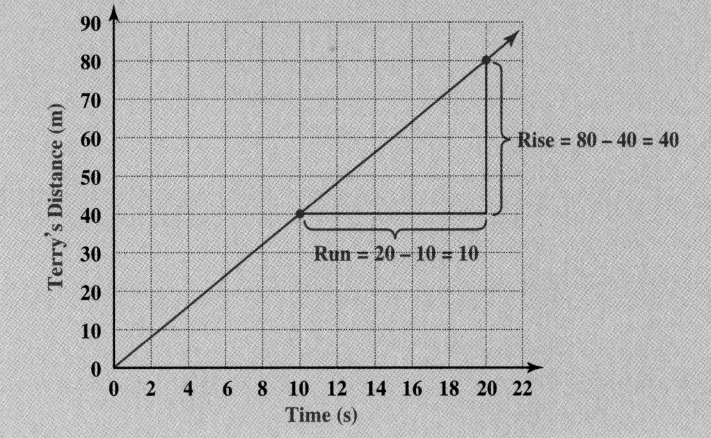

1 • Discuss the Example.

• Remind students that *run* describes movement on the graph, not the subject being graphed.

Think & Discuss Answer

3, 3.5; The slope is the same as the speed. A slope of 4 means distance changes 4 m for each 1-s increase in time; a slope of 3 means distance changes 3 m in 1 s; and a slope of 3.5 means distance changes 3.5 m in 1 s.

Think & Discuss

Look at your graphs for Maria and Bronwyn. What are the slopes of Maria's and Bronwyn's lines? What does the slope mean in Terry's, Maria's, and Bronwyn's graphs?

2 Students determine slope by looking at the graphs from Problem 4 in Problem Set B.

Share & Summarize

1. John walks at a speed of 5 feet per second. If you graphed the distance he walks over time, with time in seconds on the horizontal axis and distance in feet on the vertical axis, what would the slope of the line be? 5

2. Natasha walks at a speed of 7 feet per second. Suppose you graphed the distance she walks over time on the same grid as John's line. How would the steepness of her line compare to the steepness of John's line? Explain.
Natasha's line would be steeper because her speed is greater.

3 Students determine slope from the speed without looking at a graph.

Investigation 2

This investigation introduces situations in which distance decreases with time. The graphs for these situations consequently have negative slope.

Think & Discuss

Present the example of distance decreasing with time from the student book. Then ask students to think of other situations when the distance decreases instead of increases with time. Some situations students suggest might include an approaching car; one person running after another and getting close; something falling to the ground.

Problem Set C Suggested Grouping: Pairs

In this problem set, students work out a situation in which the distance between the person and the wall is decreasing over time. They make a table, draw a graph, and write a symbolic rule to describe the distance. Be sure students have graph paper or copies of Master 10, Quarter-Inch Graph Paper, before beginning Problem Set C.

In **Problem 2,** make sure students understand that the distance is decreasing as time passes.

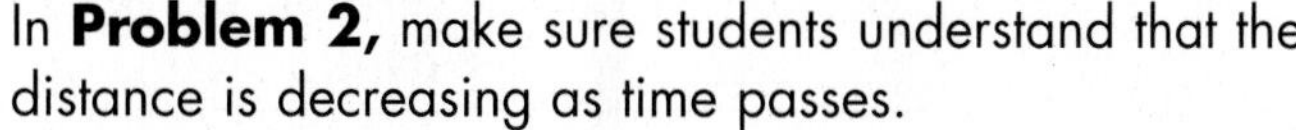

In **Problem 4,** students find a negative slope for the first time in problem sets. You may want to emphasize that when calculating slope, the *x*-coordinates must be subtracted in the same order as the *y*-coordinates.

On the Spot Assessment

Watch for students who add $1.5t$ instead of subtracting it in **Problem 7.** Have these students substitute values from their table in their rules to see that it doesn't make sense that the distance becomes greater as the person nears the wall. In the following class discussion, make sure that all students understand where the negative sign comes from.

Problem Set Wrap-Up Discuss **Problems 4 and 7.** Students should realize that even though a slope can be positive or negative, the calculation is the same. They should also see how the negative slope, $^{-}1.5$, is shown in the symbolic rule.

Investigation  Decreasing Distance with Time

An airplane flies from New York to Los Angeles. There are two distances that are changing: the distance between the airplane and the New York airport, and the distance between the airplane and the Los Angeles airport.

1 Situations in which distance decreases with time are introduced.

Think & Discuss

Which of the two distances described above is decreasing over time? See ①.

Think of other situations in which distance decreases over time.
Possible answer: driving to school, walking toward a friend, dropping a book onto a table (distance between book and table decreases)

① distance between the airplane and the L.A. airport

2 Discuss other situations in which distance decreases with time.

MATERIALS
graph paper

Problem Set C

In Problem Set A, Zach and Maya were walking from the left wall of a room to the right wall. You figured out how far each person was from the left wall at different points in time. Suppose instead you want to know how far the person is from the *right* wall at each point in time.

1. When is the person closest to the right wall: at the beginning of the walk or at the end of the walk? the end

2. Suppose Maya walks at 1.5 meters per second across a room that is 10 meters wide. Copy and complete this table.

Time (seconds), t	0	1	2	3	4
Distance from Right Wall (meters), d	10	8.5	7	5.5	4

3. Use the data in Problem 2 to draw a graph that shows the relationship between Maya's distance from the right wall and time.

4. What is the slope of the line you drew? $^{-}1.5$

5. Use your graph to estimate when Maya would reach the right wall.

6. Explain how you can find the distance from the right wall if you know the time.

7. Write a symbolic rule that relates d to t. $d = 10 - 1.5t$

3. See Additional Answers.
5. just before 7 s
6. The distance walked can be found by multiplying the time by Maya's speed, 1.5 m/s. Since the wall is 10 m away to begin, and the distance decreases over time by the distance walked, subtract the distance walked from 10.

3 Students find a negative slope for the first time in problem sets.

4 Be sure that students understand that even though a slope can be positive or negative, the calculation is the same.

• Additional Answers on page A396.

Develop

1 Think & Discuss

This section presents two correct rules for the same situation. Both rules have a negative sign before $2t$ which shows that the distance is decreasing. Remind students that subtracting $2t$ has the same result as adding $^{-}2t$. If they think of the rule $20 - 2t$ as $20 + {}^{-}2t$, they can apply the commutative property of addition to verify that both $d = 20 - 2t$ and $d = {}^{-}2t + 20$ are correct rules.

2 Problem Set D Suggested Grouping: Individuals

In this problem set, students estimate the speed, distance, and time from a graph and further develop their understanding of slope.

In **Problems 1–3 and 5,** students interpret the graphs.

In **Problems 4 and 6,** students use data from the graph to make calculations.

On the Spot Assessment

Watch for students who calculate incorrect speeds in **Problem 4** and incorrect slopes in **Problem 6.** Check that they have made reasonable estimates of the values in the graphs, made the proper calculations, and rounded correctly.

① Yes; order doesn't affect sums, so $^{-}2t + 20 = 20 + {}^{-}2t$. Adding the opposite of $2t$ is the same as subtracting, so $^{-}2t + 20 = 20 - 2t$.

Think & Discuss

Deborah and David solved a problem on a quiz. Deborah wrote this rule: $d = {}^{-}2t + 20$. David wrote this rule: $d = 20 - 2t$. Can they both be right? Explain your thinking. See ①.

Create a problem that can be described by one or both of these rules.
Possible answer: A turtle is moving at a speed of 2 ft/min toward a creek 20 ft away. How far is the turtle from the creek after t seconds?

1 Remind students that subtracting $2t$ gives the same result as adding $^{-}2t$.

Problem Set D

2 Have students work the problems independently.

Bobby and Kristen started walking away from a fence at the same time. Bobby walked at a brisk pace, and Kristen walked at a slow pace. They each measured the distance they had walked in 10 seconds. From this, they estimated how far from the fence they would have been at various times if they had continued walking. They drew distance-time graphs from their data.

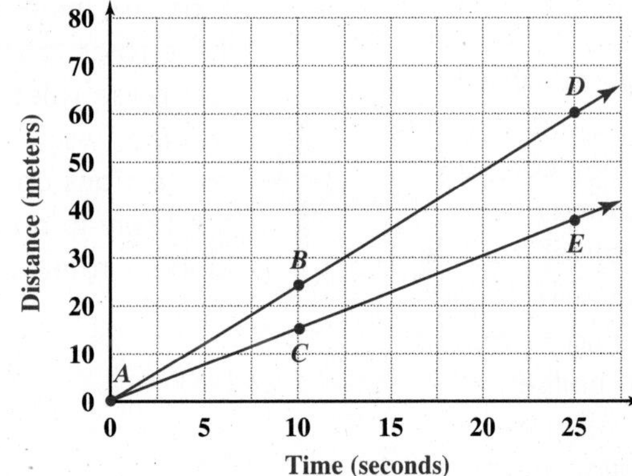

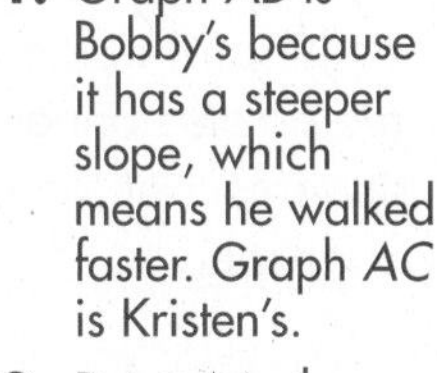

1. Graph AB is Bobby's because it has a steeper slope, which means he walked faster. Graph AC is Kristen's.
2. Point A is the starting point at the fence. Points B and C represent Bobby's and Kristen's distance after 10 s.
3. They tell how far Bobby and Kristen would have traveled after 25 s and show that Bobby would have traveled farther.
4. Bobby: 2.4 m/s; Kristen: 1.5 m/s
6. Bobby: 2.4; Kristen: 1.5; The slopes are the speeds.

1. Which graph represents Bobby's walk, and which represents Kristen's? Explain how you know.
2. What events in the story above match points A, B, and C?
3. What do points D and E tell you about the positions of Bobby and Kristen?
4. Use the graphs to estimate each person's walking speed in meters per second. Give your answers to the nearest tenth.
5. Which line has the greater slope, Bobby's or Kristen's? Explain why. Bobby's; his speed is greater.
6. What are the slopes of the two lines? How are they related to Bobby's and Kristen's speeds?

LESSON 5.2 Speed and the Slope Connection 327

Share & Summarize

After students think about these questions for a few minutes, discuss the questions as a class. Students should notice that the graph in Problem Set C decreases while the graphs in Problem Set D grow over time. They may note that the increasing graph goes through the origin while the decreasing graphs do not.

They should also notice that the rates for the increasing graphs are positive, while the rate for a decreasing graph is negative. They should see that the signs for these rates are shown in the rule and that the rule for the decreasing graph has a constant number.

Finally students should note that the signs of the rates in the rule indicate the direction of the graph.

Troubleshooting Students may be confused about how to interpret the difference between slope and speed on graphs with a negative slope. When they compare the rates and they see opposite signs, you may hear questions such as, " Is the slope also negative?" or, "Is the speed also negative?" To help students understand the negative slope, make clear what is being measured. Speed is positive and, in these examples, neither increases nor decreases. Time increases. Distance decreases. It is the *difference between distances* in consecutive times, or the *change in distance per unit time,* that is shown by the slope, and that change is negative. This idea of *differences* will be explored in depth in Lesson 4 of this chapter.

The distinction between always positive speed and either positive or negative velocity (which corresponds directly to the positive or negative slope) will be made in the next investigation.

On Your Own Exercises

Practice & Apply: 4–5
Connect & Extend: 14, 16, 17, 22, 24–31
Mixed Review: 34–58

Investigation 3

In this investigation, students learn to extract the essential information about the movement of different objects from the graph. Students build on their experience in the prior investigations as they encounter positive slopes which characterize the graphs of people or objects moving away from the point of reference, and negative slopes which characterize the people or objects approaching the point of reference.

Ask students to name some of the rates they have studied in this chapter. They may mention speed, wage, measurement conversions, and pulse, among others. Then ask them how long they would expect each of these rates to stay the same. Students should note that pulse rates change frequently, speed rates often change, wages change occasionally, and measurement conversions can be considered *fixed rates* because they are likely to never change. Tell students that the changes in these rates can be shown by a graph.

1. In C the line goes down from left to right, and in D the lines go up.
2. The rule in C has a negative sign in front of the rate; the rules in D have positive signs. The rule in C has a constant term; the rules in D do not. They all represent straight lines.

Share & Summarize

1. How are the graphs in Problem Set D different from the graphs in Problem Set C?
2. How is the rule in Problem Set C different from the rules in Problem Set D? How are they the same?
3. Explain how the differences in the rules relate to the differences in the graphs. The negative sign means the line is going down (the slope is negative), and the constant term means the line doesn't start at (0, 0).

1 Discuss with students the differences in the rules and the graphs for Problem Sets C and D.

Investigation 3 Describing Graphs

2 Review meaning of fixed rates.

Some rates vary. For example, if you count your pulse for one minute, and then count it for another minute, you will probably get different results. It is normal for pulse rates to fluctuate, or change.

You would expect other rates to be fixed, or stay the same, at least for a while. For example, if your employer said your pay rate was $7 per hour, you would expect to earn that for each hour you work.

In this investigation, you will inspect the graphs below to find essential information about the movement of a group of cars along a particular highway: their directions, their speeds, and their relative locations.

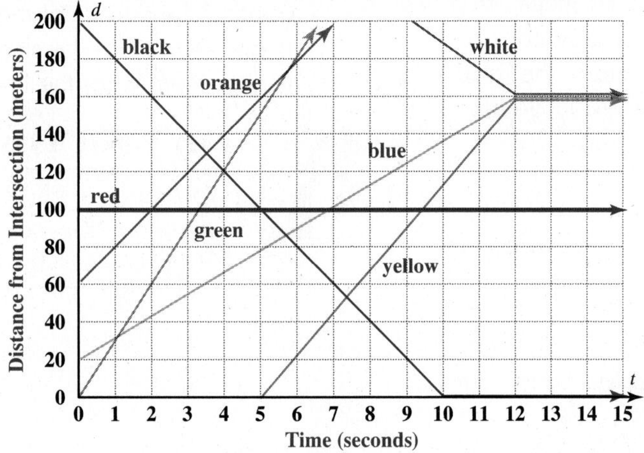

Problem Set E Grouping: Small Groups

Problem Set E asks students to create a story on the basis of the information they can extract from the graph. Divide students into groups of 3–5. Tell them to take 5–10 minutes to talk about what they can see in the graph. Then ask them to answer the questions in their groups.

Assign one specific car to each group in the class and have students imagine that their car is driving along the section of the road shown in the graph. Ask them to prepare a group report giving details of their car trip for these 15 seconds shown on the graph. Tell them that each group will have 2 minutes to present their reports. You might model a partial report for them, like this:

> We left the telephone booth and jumped into our green Ferrari and raced off towards home at 36 meters per second (129.6 km/h).
>
> That blue car 20 meters ahead of us is going pretty slowly!
>
> Time = 1 (intoned by the car microcomputer)
>
> As we passed the blue car (about 30 meters from the phone box) we could see an orange car up ahead, a red car parked by the side of the road, and 150 meters ahead there was this large black truck coming towards us.
>
> Time = 2
>
> Did you see that orange car nearly sideswipe the parked car as it passed?
>
> Time = 3 and a bit
>
> Hey, look! The red car belongs to Mr. Smith, our math teacher. He's got a flat tire . . .
>
> (Continues)

If there is not enough time for groups to finish their work by the end of the day, ask them to take the ideas from their group discussions and complete individual reports at home. Collect their written reports on the next day.

In **Problem 4,** there is more than one way to interpret the data. Some students may assume two cars that are the same distance from the intersection are side-by-side. Other students may assume that the two cars are on a straight line with the intersection forming the midpoint of the line. For example, after 6 seconds, both the orange car and the green car are 180 m from the intersection. They could either be next to one another or 360 m apart.

Problem Set Wrap-Up Have groups present their reports to the class. Discuss how they made the observations noted in the reports.

3 The text after Problem Set E explains that the concept of velocity directly corresponds to positive and negative slopes. That is, velocity can accept both positive and negative values depending on the direction the object is moving. In contrast, speed can only accept positive values and is the absolute value of velocity. The distinction between these two concepts deserves a good discussion because it previews the concepts of a vector and of an absolute value.

Share & Summarize

These questions ask students to explain how they came up with the answers for Problem Set E. Students have to realize that features of the graphs such as the value of the slope and the sign of the slope give us information about the speed and direction of the car. **Problem 3** calls for an interpretation of a horizontal line as a change in time with no change in space.

Troubleshooting If students are not sure how to figure out that the car is not moving, ask them what the speed is and then what the slope of the graph for such a car is. Ask them what the line with slope 0 would look like.

On Your Own Exercises

Practice & Apply: 6
Connect & Extend: 32
Mixed Review: 34–58

Problem Set E

Suppose seven cars are all near an intersection. The graphs on page 328 show the distances between the cars and the intersection as time passes.

In your group, study the graphs carefully. Then discuss the following questions. Record your group's decisions, and be prepared to talk about them in class.

1. In what direction is each car moving in relation to the intersection?
2. Compare the cars' speeds.
3. Do any of the cars stop during their trips? If so, which cars?
4. Prepare a group report for one of the cars. Imagine you are in that car, and give the highlights of your trip for these 15 seconds. Include such observations as where and when you started the trip and what you saw going on around you—in front of the car, to the sides, and through the rearview mirror. See teaching notes.

1. See Additional Answers.
2. Answers will vary. From slowest to fastest (during the time when the blue, yellow, white, and black cars are moving), the cars are: red, blue, white, orange and black (tie), yellow, and green.
3. yes; yellow, blue, white, and black

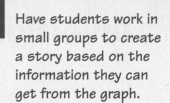

1 Have students work in small groups to create a story based on the information they can get from the graph.

2 Have students present their reports to the class.

People often use one of two words when they describe how fast something is moving: *speed* or *velocity.* In fact, these two words mean mathematically different things.

3 Discuss meaning of speed and velocity.

VOCABULARY
speed
velocity

Speed is always positive. It shows how fast an object is moving, but it does not reveal anything about the object's direction.

Velocity can be either positive or negative (as slope can). The sign of the velocity shows whether an object is moving from or toward a designated point. The absolute value of the velocity is the same as the speed. While the black car is moving, for example, it has a positive speed of 20 meters per second. However, its distance to the intersection is decreasing, so its velocity is $^{-}20$ meters per second.

Share  Summarize

1. How can you determine from the graph whether a car is moving toward or away from the intersection?
2. How can you determine the speed of a car from the graph?
3. How can you determine from the graph whether a car is moving?

1. By the slope; if the graph moves down from left to right (negative slope), the car is moving toward the intersection.
2. by the absolute value of the slope
3. When a car isn't moving, the graph of the distance in relation to time is a horizontal line.

4
- Discuss questions and answers with entire class.
- Emphasize that features of the graphs give us information about the speed and direction of the car.

Additional Answers
Problem Set E

1. The orange, green, yellow, and blue cars are moving away from the intersection, but the yellow and blue cars stop moving at 12 s. The black and white cars are moving toward the intersection, although they also stop moving at 10 s and 12 s, respectively. The red car isn't moving at all.

Investigation 4

Investigation 4 brings up the comparison between proportional and nonproportional relationships in the context of speed. It also introduces a negative constant term in a linear relationship, using an example of five brothers starting a race at staggered starting points.

Problem Set F **Suggested Grouping: Individuals or Pairs**

This problem set compares proportional and non-proportional relationships between distance and time. Although Lesson 1 addressed the same idea, this context will be relatively new for students. Students will need graph paper or copies of Master 10, Quarter-Inch Graph Paper, to complete Problem Set F.

Encourage students to find the similarities as well as the differences for the graphs in **Problem 2.** Some similarities that students might mention are that both graphs are linear and have positive slopes. They both contain the point (4, 12). Some differences are the endpoint on the y-axis and the slope of the line.

On the Spot Assessment

Watch for students who start the graph for Joanna in Problem 2 at (4, 0) instead of (0, 4). Remind them which variable is represented by the horizontal coordinate (time) and which is represented by the vertical coordinate (distance).

Problem Set Wrap-Up You may want to check the answers for **Problem 4** before moving on. Look for correct rules: $d = 3t$ for the older sister and $d = 2t + 4$ for the younger sister. Students should note that the proportional relationship does not have a constant, while the nonproportional relationship does. Also make sure students understand that the graph of the proportional relationship starts at the origin and the graph of the non-proportional relationship starts at point (0, 4).

Investigation  Changing the Starting Point

You will now explore a situation in which runners start a race at different points. You'll see how rules and graphs show these differences.

MATERIALS
graph paper

Problem Set F

Kate ran a race with her younger sister, Joanna. Kate let Joanna start 4 meters ahead of the starting line. Kate ran at a steady rate of 3 meters per second while Joanna ran at a steady rate of 2 meters per second.

Remember
When you compare two things, look at both similarities and differences.

1. Make a table to show how many meters each sister was from the starting line at various times.
2. On the same grid, draw a graph for each sister showing the relationship between distance from the starting line and time. Compare the graphs.
3. Is Kate's distance from the starting line proportional to time? Is Joanna's distance proportional to time? yes, no
4. For each sister, write a rule in symbols to relate distance d and time t. How are the numbers in the rules reflected in the graphs?
Kate: $d = 3t$; Joanna: $d = 4 + 2t$; The number multiplied by t gives the slope of the graph. The 4 in Joanna's rule shows that her graph starts at (0, 4) instead of (0, 0).

1. Possible table:

Time (s)	0	1	2	3	4	5
Kate's Distance from Start (m)	0	3	6	9	12	15
Joanna's Distance from Start (m)	4	6	8	10	12	14

2. Kate's graph is steeper and starts at (0, 0).

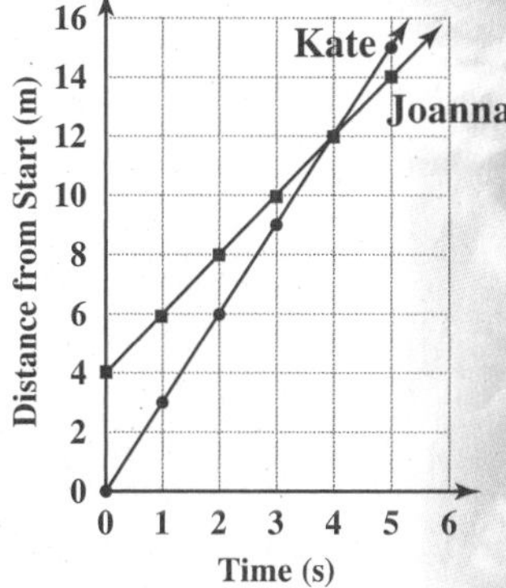

1 Individuals or pairs of students work problems that compare proportional and nonproportional relationships between time and distance.

2 Be sure students can relate their rules to their graphs.

Develop

Think & Discuss

This discussion introduces the idea of the sign associated with distance to indicate the direction from a given starting point. Students will encounter this idea in the Problem Set G. This builds on the content of Chapter 4 in which students dealt with positive and negative numbers in different contexts, such as elevations above and below sea level.

Ask students to come up with more examples of the same kind. Students might think of going opposite directions from one point, or suggest an elevator coming down from the ground level to basement levels 1, 2, and so on. Help them notice the connection between the *direction* of a distance as it relates to a given point, such as sea level, and the *sign* (positive or negative) attached to it. For example, a distance below or behind a given point may be shown as a negative number.

Problem Set G **Suggested Grouping: Pairs**

In this problem set, students use rules to find rate information. Then they interpret information from graphs and match the graphs to symbolic rules. Suggest that students work in pairs and take turns asking each other questions from the problem set.

In **Problems 1 and 2,** students are asked to interpret the meaning behind the terms in a rule. Students should realize that Adam and David began at the starting line because their respective rules do not contain any constants. They should realize that Eric started behind the starting line because the constant in this rule is a negative number—subtracting 5 has the same result as adding $^{-}5$.

In **Problem 2,** students use coefficients to determine speed and constants to determine starting place.

① Possible answer: locations of numbers on a number line, where negative means to the left of 0; distance from the top of mercury in a thermometer to the 0° mark, where negative means below the 0° mark

Think & Discuss

In Chapter 4, you learned about elevations below sea level. For example, suppose Colleen ended a hike at an elevation of $^-150$ feet. The number $^-150$ shows two things. First, the 150 tells Colleen's distance from sea level. What does the negative sign show? that this distance is *below* sea level

Describe some other situations in which you might use a negative sign along with a distance. Explain the meaning of the negative sign in each situation. See ①.

1 Have students suggest other situations where a negative sign may be used along with a distance.

Problem Set G

2 Have students work in pairs and take turns asking each other questions from the problem set.

Five brothers ran a race. The twins began at the starting line. Their older brother began behind the starting line, and their two younger brothers began at different distances ahead of the starting line. Each boy ran at a fairly uniform speed. Here are rules for the relationship between distance (d meters) from the starting line and time (t seconds) for each boy.

Adam: $d = 6t$

Brett: $d = 4t + 7$

Caleb: $d = 5t + 4$

David: $d = 5t$

Eric: $d = 7t - 5$

3 Students interpret the meaning behind the terms in a rule.

1. Which brothers are the twins? How do you know? Which brother is the oldest? How do you know?

   1. Adam and David are the twins because they both began at the starting line. Eric is the oldest because he began behind the starting line.

2. For each brother, describe how far from the starting line he began the race and how fast he ran. Adam: at the starting line, 6 m/s; Brett: 7 m in front, 4 m/s; Caleb: 4 m in front, 5 m/s; David: at the starting line, 5 m/s; Eric: 5 m behind, 7 m/s

LESSON 5.2 Speed and the Slope Connection 331

Develop

The graph in **Problem 3** shows negative values of d to represent a runner starting behind the starting line. Encourage students to verbalize how this information helps them know which graph represents Eric.

Access
for All **Learners**

Extra Help When solving **Problems 5–8,** some students may confuse the five graphs on the grid. These students may benefit by placing a piece of tracing paper over the grid and writing the brothers' names beside their respective graphs.

Problems 5–7 may be challenging for students. In **Problem 5,** students need to focus on the vertical line going through $t = 2$ and through $t = 3$ and order the points of intersection from the bottom up on each line. This orders the runners from last to first.

In **Problem 6,** help students realize that since Caleb and David run at the same rate, the lines representing them on the graph are parallel. Therefore the vertical distance between the lines is constant.

In **Problem 7,** students should draw or imagine a horizontal line going through $d = 30$ and find the intersecting line that has the smallest value for t.

Problem Set Wrap-Up Discuss how to represent the negative values of distance on a graph. Then discuss students' answers to **Problems 5–7.**

3. Adam: iii; Brett: i; Caleb: ii; David: iv; Eric: v

3. Which graph below represents which brother?

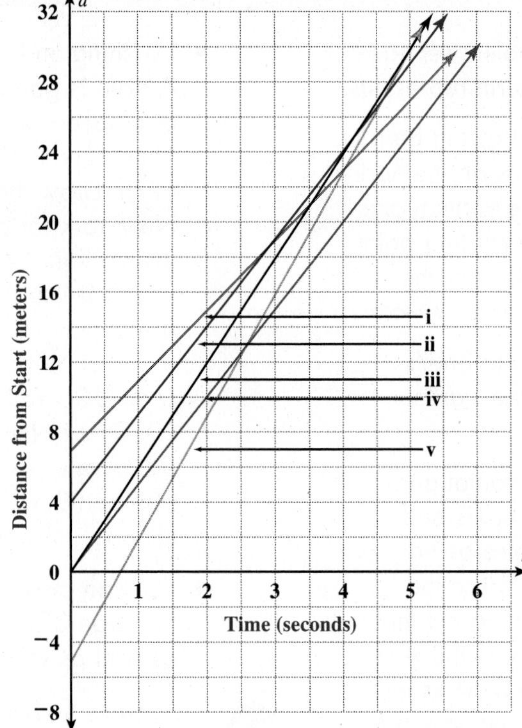

4. What events match the intersection points of the graphs? See below.

5. Use the graphs to help you find the order of the brothers at the given times.

a. 2 seconds after the race began

b. 3 seconds after the race began

6. Which two brothers stay the same distance apart throughout the race? How do you know?

7. If the finish line was 30 meters from the starting line, who won?

8. Which brothers' rules are proportional, and which are not?

5a. Brett (in the lead), Caleb, Adam, David, Eric

5b. Caleb and Brett (tied for the lead), Adam, Eric, David

6–8. See below.

4. These are times when two brothers are side by side. Except for the intersection of the twins' lines at the origin, these are also times when one boy passes another.

6. Caleb and David; they travel at the same speed, and their graphs (ii and iv) are the same distance apart at all points.

7. It was a tie between Adam and Eric.

8. Adam's and David's are proportional; the others aren't.

1 Encourage students to verbalize how they know which graph represents Eric.

2 Have students discuss Problems 5–7 as a class after they complete them.

Develop

1 Tell students that the rules in the prior problem set have the form $d = rt + p$. Discuss what each term represents.

Have students think about how they might graph Brett's rule, $d = 4t + 7$, if they graph the t values on the horizontal axis, or x-axis, and d values on the vertical axis, or y-axis. Help students see that since the starting point of the race is at 0 seconds, the starting point of the runner will be plotted on that line, the vertical or y-axis.

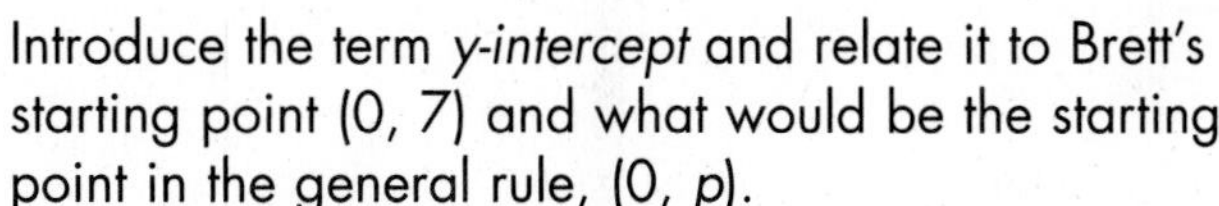

2 Introduce the term *y-intercept* and relate it to Brett's starting point (0, 7) and what would be the starting point in the general rule, (0, p).

Be sure that students understand that horizontal and vertical axes are often referred to as the x-axis and y-axis, respectively, even when the variables being graphed are not x and y. You may want to use the graph on page 333 as an example, pointing out that the axis labeled t, for Time, is also known as the x-axis and the axis labeled d, for Distance from Start, is also known as the y-axis. This terminology is used in some homework problems.

3 **Share & Summarize**

By this time students should be able to recognize the roles of the rate and constant term in the symbolic rules and graphs of linear relationships. They should be able to interpret the positive or negative sign for both the rate and the constant term.

Troubleshooting If students are having difficulty interpreting the terms in a rate, give them some additional examples. Ask them what the value and the sign of the rate and the constant term tell us about the speed of the person and his or her position at the beginning of the movement.

Additional Examples

- This first set of problems uses the same graph used with the Share & Summarize questions.
  In Problem Set G, who began at the starting line? Which part of the graph shows this? Which part of the rule shows this? Adam and David; the y-intercept; the constant or the number added

  Suppose Brittany joined the race. Her rule is $d = 8 + 5t$. What does the rule reveal about her speed and starting position? She began 8 meters in front of the starting line and is running at a speed of 5 meters/second.

  In what direction is Brittany running? toward the finish line

- Washington D.C. and New York are 300 miles apart. A train is going from Washington, DC to New York at a speed of 40 mi/h. Another train is moving from New York to Washington, D.C. at a speed of 65 mi/h. Draw the graphs showing the distance from New York for both trains and interpret them. Possible graph description: A first quadrant graph with a x-axis labeled time (h) and vertical axis labeled distance (mi). The x-axis scale is from 0 to 8 marked at the increments of 1. The y-axis is from 0 to 300 marked at the increments of 50. Name (0, 0) as New York and (0, 300) as Washington, D.C. Draw two lines, the first going through the points (0, 0) and (4, 260), and the second going through the points (0, 300) and (6, 60).

- You can also use the graph for Problem Set E shown on page 328 to discuss positive and negative slopes as well as various constant terms.

On Your Own Exercises

Practice & Apply: 7–12
Connect & Extend: 33
Mixed Review: 34–58

The rules in Problem Set G have the form $d = rt + p$, with numbers in place of r and p. The value of r is the velocity—it gives the rate at which distance changes as time passes. The value of p tells the starting point. For example, Brett's rule is $d = 4t + 7$. His velocity is 4 meters per second, and he began 7 meters ahead of the starting line.

1 Discuss with students the meaning of each term in $d = rt + p$.

VOCABULARY
y-intercept

If you graph $d = rt + p$, with t on the horizontal axis, or x-axis, and d on the vertical axis, or y-axis, the coordinates of the starting point on the graph are $(0, p)$. When $t = 0$, $d = p$. Therefore, p is the value of d at which the graph intersects the y-axis. That is why p is also called the ***y*-intercept.** For Brett's rule, the y-intercept is 7.

2 Introduce the term *y-intercept* and its meaning.

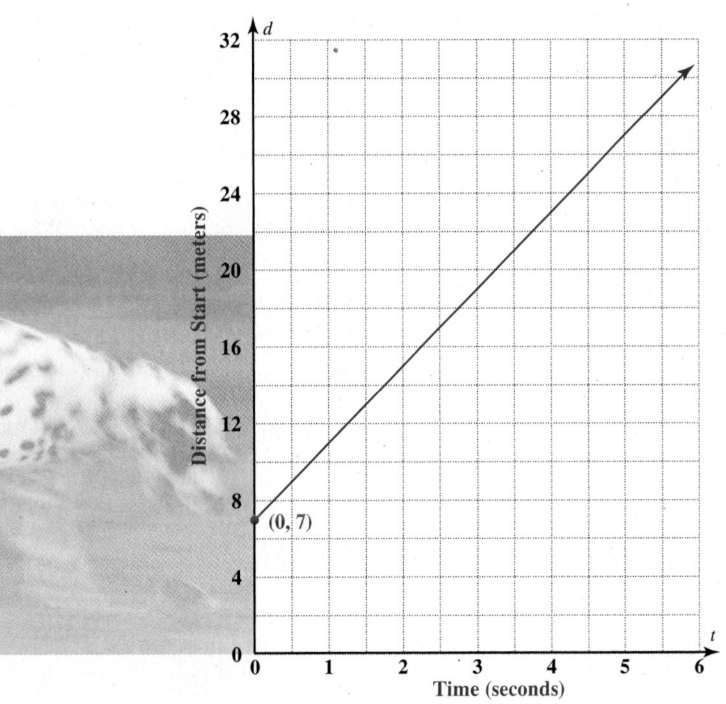

Share & Summarize

1. In Problem Set G, who began behind the starting line? Which part of the graph shows this? Which part of the rule shows this?
2. The brothers' dog, King, ran the race with them. His rule was $d = {}^{-}15 - 2t$. What does the rule reveal about King's speed and starting position?
3. In what direction is King running? away from the finish line

1. Eric; his graph starts below the x-axis, and his rule has a negative constant term.
2. His speed was 2 m/s, and he began 15 m behind the starting line.

3 Students should be able to interpret the positive or negative sign for both the rate and the constant term.

On Your Own Exercises

On Your Own Exercises

Investigation 1
Practice & Apply: 1–3
Connect & Extend: 13, 15, 18–21, 23

Investigation 2
Practice & Apply: 4–5
Connect & Extend: 14, 16, 17, 22, 24–31

Investigation 3
Practice & Apply: 6
Connect & Extend: 32

Investigation 4
Practice & Apply: 7–12
Connect & Extend: 33

Assign Anytime
Mixed Review: 34–58

Exercise 1d:
Students use dimensional analysis as they convert their answers from ft/s to mi/h. Watch for students who give their answers in feet. Remind them to divide the number of feet by 5,280.

Practice & Apply

1. Sports Suppose you are riding a bicycle at a steady rate of 16 feet per second.

a. Imagine that you rode at this pace for various lengths of time. Copy and complete the table.

Time (s)	0	10	20	30	35	40	50	55	60	70
Distance (ft)	0	160	320	480	560	640	800	880	960	1,120

1b. $d = 16t$; $900 = 16t$ so $t = 56.25$ and time = 56.25 s

Remember
1 mile = 5,280 feet

1d. 57,600 ft or 10.9 mi in an hour; 10.9 mph

1h. The ft/s slope is greater than the mph slope. Since the units aren't the same for the variables, it makes sense that the graphs could have different slopes.

b. Write a rule relating the number of feet you travel d to the time in seconds t. Use your rule to find how long it would take you to travel 900 feet.

c. From your table, find how many feet you ride in 1 minute. About how many miles is this? 960 ft, about 0.18 mi

d. Use the distance you travel in 1 minute to find how far you could ride in 1 hour if you kept up your pace. What is your traveling speed in miles per hour?

e. Write a second rule that relates the number of miles you travel d to the time in hours t. $d = 10.9t$

f. Draw a graph for the distance in feet traveled in relation to time in seconds. Draw another graph for the distance in miles traveled in relation to time in hours.

g. What is the slope of each line you graphed? ft/s: 16; mph: 10.9

h. Compare the two slopes. How can they be different if the speeds are the same?

1f.

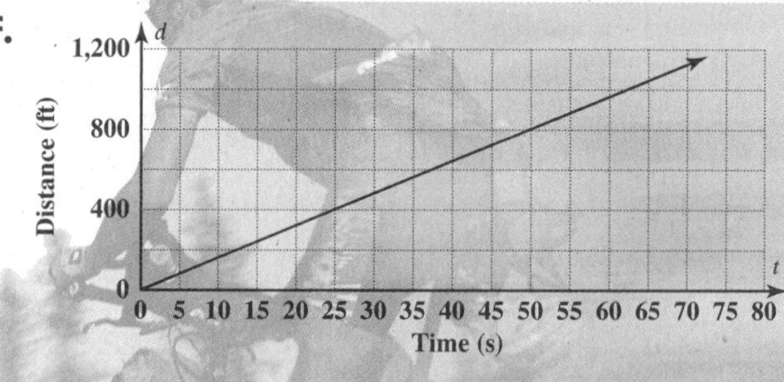

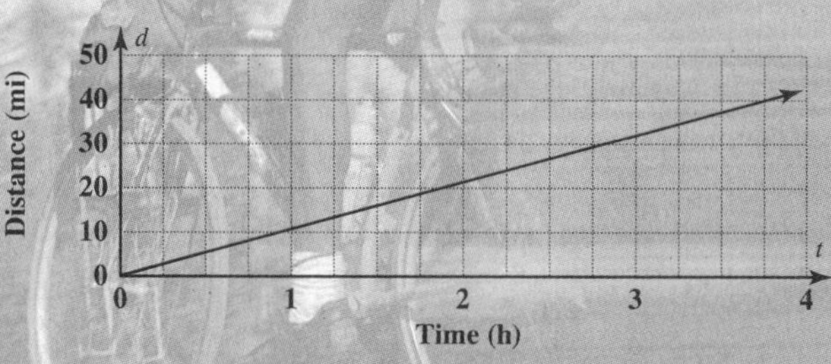

334 CHAPTER 5 Looking at Linear Relationships

2. A 90-minute cassette tape plays for 45 minutes per side. The tape is about 26 meters long and moves at a steady rate.

a. Complete the table to show how many meters of tape play in given numbers of minutes.

Time (min), t	0	1	10	20	30	40	45
Length Played (m), L	0	0.58	5.8	11.6	17.3	23.1	26

b. Write a rule relating length of tape played to time. $L = 0.58t$

c. What is the speed of the tape through the recorder in meters per minute? If you graphed the length of tape played in relation to time, what would the slope of the line be? 0.58 m/min, 0.58

d. Find the length of a 60-minute cassette tape, which has 30 minutes per side. Assume that tapes of different lengths run at the same speed.

2d. 30 min requires 17.3 m of tape, so a 60-min tape is approximately 34.7 m long.

Exercise 2b:
If students write the rule as $t = 0.58L$, have them substitute the data from the table into their rule to see that their rule will not work.

3. **Sports** A marathon is a race of 26.2 miles. Nadia and Mark are running a marathon. Nadia's speed is 5.2 miles per hour, and Mark's is 3.8 miles per hour. Assume their speeds are steady throughout the race.

a. Complete the table for Nadia and Mark. Distances are in miles.

Time (hours), t	0	1	2	3	4
Nadia's Distance from Start, N	0	5.2	10.4	15.6	20.8
Mark's Distance from Start, M	0	3.8	7.6	11.4	15.2
Distance between Nadia and Mark, d	0	1.4	2.8	4.2	5.6

b. On a single grid, draw graphs that show these three relationships:

- time and Nadia's distance from start
- time and Mark's distance from start
- time and the distance between Nadia and Mark

3b–3d. See Additional Answers.

c. What is the slope of each line? Which line is the steepest? Which line is the least steep? Why?

d. Write a rule for each of these three relationships.

e. Think about the distance between Nadia and Mark. How is the rate this distance changes related to Nadia's speed and Mark's speed? The rate is the difference between Nadia's speed and Mark's speed.

Just the facts

The word *marathon* comes from the name of a famous plain in Greece. In 490 B.C., a runner was sent from this plain to Athens, about 25 miles away, to report the Athenians' victory in a battle against the Persians.

Additional Answers

3b. See Additional Answers on page A396.

3c. Nadia: 5.2; Mark: 3.8; between: 1.4; Nadia's line is the steepest because it has the greatest slope. The line representing the distance between the runners is the least steep because it has the least slope.

3d. $N = 5.2t$, $M = 3.8t$, $d = 1.4t$

Exercise 4e: Students will need to refer to Problem Set B to answer this question.

4b.

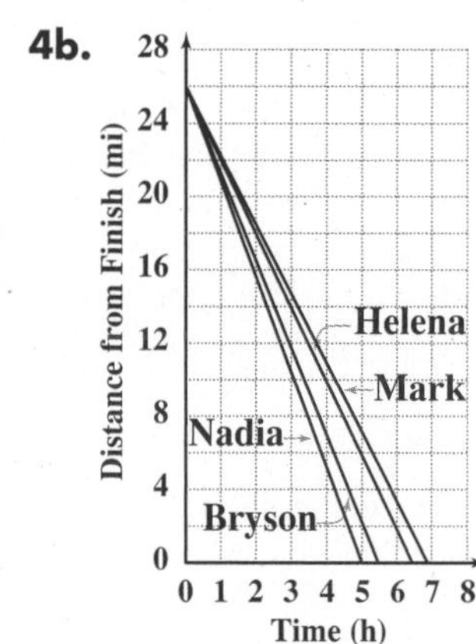

4c. All show distance decreasing with time, so their slopes are negative and the lines slant down from left to right. They all have different slopes (steepness): Nadia: $^-5.2$; Helena: $^-4.1$; Bryson: $^-4.85$; Mark: $^-3.8$. (Note: Slopes may be estimates.)

4d. Nadia: about 5.0 h; Helena: about 6.4 h; Bryson: about 5.4 h; Mark: about 6.9 h

4. Sports Nadia, Helena, Bryson, and Mark start their marathon run, which is 26.2 miles long. Nadia's speed is 5.2 miles per hour, Helena's is 4.1 miles per hour, Bryson's is 4.85 miles per hour, and Mark's is 3.8 miles per hour. Assume their speeds are steady throughout the run.

a. Complete the table. Distances are in miles.

Time (hours), t	0	1	2	3	4
Nadia's Distance from Finish, N	26.2	21	15.8	10.6	5.4
Helena's Distance from Finish, H	26.2	22.1	18	13.9	9.8
Bryson's Distance from Finish, B	26.2	21.35	16.5	11.65	6.8
Mark's Distance from Finish, M	26.2	22.4	18.6	14.8	11

b. On a single grid, draw graphs that show the relationships between time and distance from the finish for all four runners.

c. Compare the four graphs. In what ways are they similar, and in what ways are they different? What is the slope of each graph?

d. How much time will it take for each of the four runners to finish the marathon? You may want to extend your graph or table.

e. For each runner, write a rule in symbols that relates that runner's distance from finish (N, H, B, or M) to t. Compare your rules to those in Problem Set B. How are they different? How are they similar? See Additional Answers.

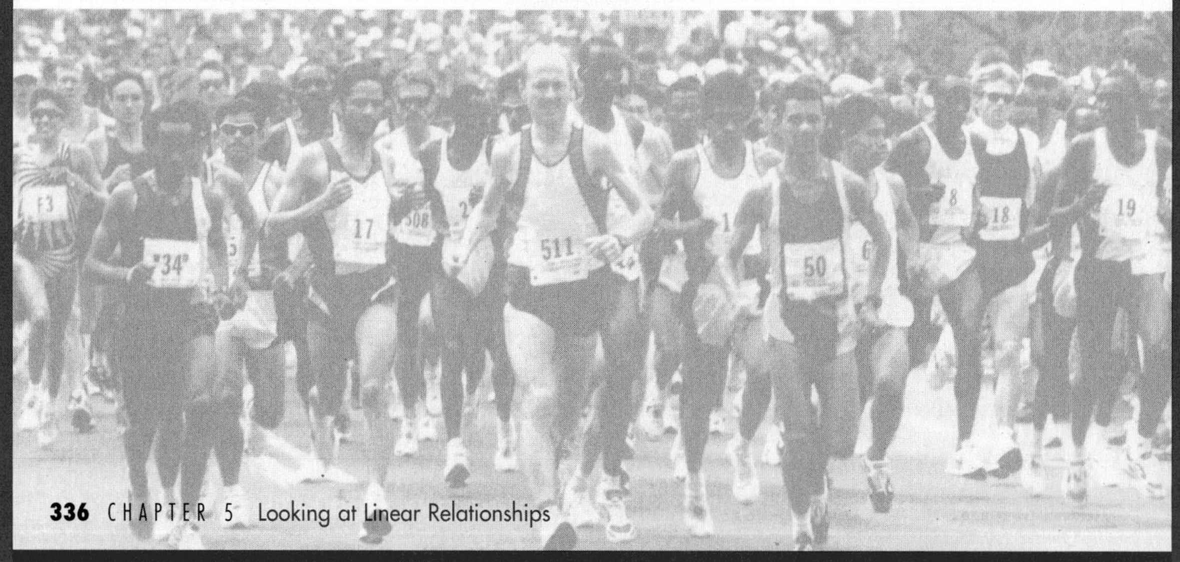

Additional Answers

4e. $N = 26.2 - 5.2t$, $H = 26.2 - 4.1t$, $B = 26.2 - 4.85t$, $M = 26.2 - 3.8t$; These rules are similar in two ways: they all have a constant term, and the rates are negative.

5. Geography Soon after Jenni's trans-Australia flight left Adelaide for Darwin, the pilot announced they were 200 kilometers from Adelaide and cruising at a speed of 840 kilometers per hour. The plane was flying north from Adelaide, toward the South Australia border. To pass the time, Jenni decided to calculate her distance from Adelaide at various times after the pilot's message.

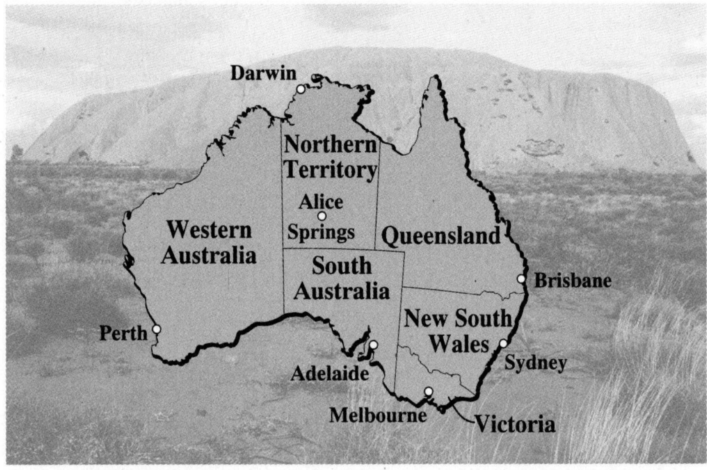

a. Complete the table to show the distance (in kilometers) from Adelaide at various times (in minutes) after the pilot spoke.

Time after Pilot's Message (min), t	0	1	15	30	60	90	120
Distance from Adelaide (km), d	200	214	410	620	1,040	1,460	1,880

5b.

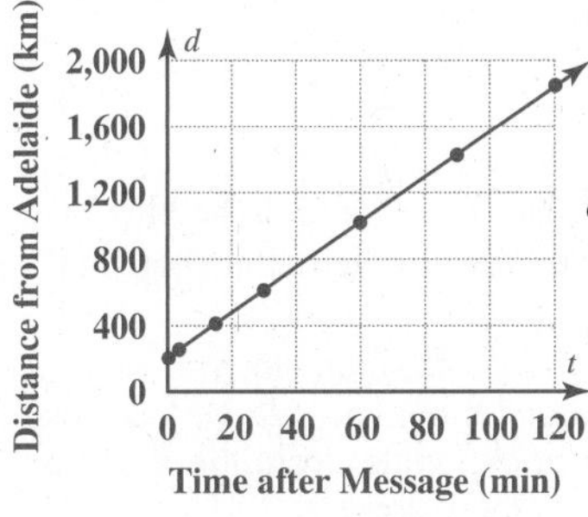

b. Draw a graph of the data.

c. The South Australia border is 1,100 km from Adelaide. Use your graph to determine about how long after the pilot's message the plane crossed the border. about 64 min

d. Alice Springs is 1,400 km from Adelaide. How long after the message would Jenni expect to pass over it? about 86 min

e. Explain in words how to find the distance from Adelaide if you know the time after the pilot's message. Write the rule in symbols. Explain how each number in your rule is shown in the graph. Multiply by 14 and add 200; $d = 14t + 200$; 200 is the intercept on the d-axis, and 14 is the slope.

Exercise 5a:
Some students may forget to add 200 when calculating distance. Remind them to find $14t$ and then add 200 to find the total distance.

LESSON 5.2 Speed and the Slope Connection 337

Exercise 6:
Be sure students understand that a line on this graph reflects distance traveled on the vertical axis and time traveled on the horizontal axis.

6. One Sunday, Martin, Julie, Sook Leng, Edan, and Amy visited a park at different times. They rented bikes of different colors and rode them along the park's bike route. The bike route goes from the rental shop to a cafe. It also goes in the opposite direction, from the rental shop to a lake.

The graphs show the friends' locations from noon until 2 P.M.

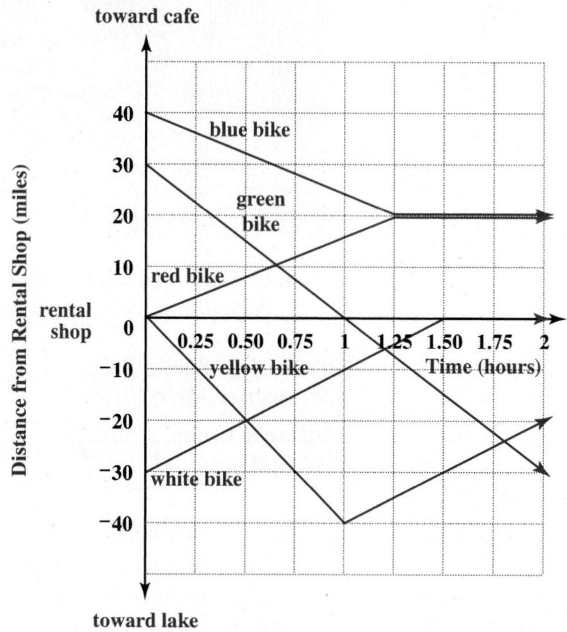

a. Describe the route taken by each bike. For example, the blue bike moves from the direction of the cafe toward the rental shop, and then stops.
red: from the rental shop toward the cafe, then stops; green: from the direction of the cafe toward the lake; yellow: from the rental shop toward the lake and back; white: from the direction of the lake toward the rental shop, then stops

6b. blue: 16 mph, 0 mph; red: 16 mph, 0 mph; green: 30 mph; yellow: 40 mph, 20 mph; white: 20 mph, 0 mph

6d. Martin: yellow; Sook Leng: green; Edan: white

6e. blue: $^-16$, 0; red: 16, 0; green: $^-30$; yellow: $^-40$, 20; white: 20, 0

6f. No; the speeds are always positive, but the slopes can be positive or negative. The slopes are positive if the bikes are moving toward the cafe, negative if they are moving toward the lake.

Connect & Extend

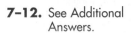

7–12. See Additional Answers.

14. $^-4.6$

15. 3

17. $^-0.21$

18. $\frac{1}{4}$

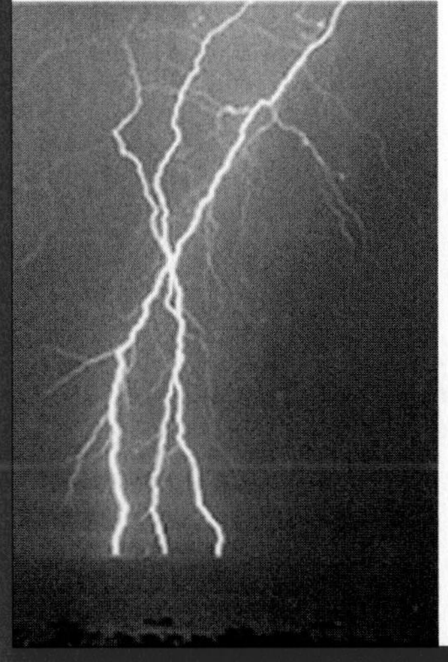

b. Determine the speed of each bike. If a bike's speed changes, list all of its speeds.

c. Amy and Julie met about 20 miles from the rental shop and talked for an hour. Julie had come directly from the rental shop, and Amy had already visited the cafe and was returning her bike. What were the colors of their bikes? Julie: red; Amy: blue

d. From noon to 1 P.M. Martin had the highest speed, Sook Leng had the second highest, and Edan had the lowest. What color bikes were Martin, Sook Leng, and Edan riding?

e. Determine the slope of the line for each bike. If the slope changes, list all of them.

f. Are the bikes' speeds and the slopes of their lines always equal to each other? Why or why not?

For each equation, give the coordinates of the graph's intersection with the y-axis (in other words, give the y-intercept).

7. $y = 3x - 5$ **8.** $y = {}^-7x + 14$ **9.** $y = 1.5x + 2.4$

10. $y = 27 - 9x$ **11.** $y = {}^-35 + 3.1x$ **12.** $y = -\frac{3}{5} + \frac{3}{5}x$

Determine the slope of each line.

13. $y = 7x - 12$ 7 **14.** $y = 31 - 4.6x$ **15.** $y = 8 + 3x$

16. $y = {}^-x - 1$ $^-1$ **17.** $y = {}^-0.21x + 98$ **18.** $y = \frac{1}{4}x - \frac{7}{2}$

19. Physical Science When you see lightning and then hear the clap of thunder, you are hearing what you have just seen. The thunder takes longer to reach you because sound travels much more slowly than light. Sound takes about 5 seconds to travel 1 mile, but light travels that distance almost instantly.

a. Complete the table to show the relationship between d, the distance in miles from a thunderstorm, and t, the time in seconds between seeing the lightning and hearing the thunder.

Seconds between Lightning and Thunder, t	0	5	10	15	20	25
Distance from Storm (mi), d	0	1	2	3	4	5

b. If thunder and lightning happen at the same time, where is the storm? very close to the observer

c. How could you calculate how far away a storm is? Write a rule that relates distance d from a storm to the time t between seeing it and hearing it. $d = t \div 5$

Exercise 19 Extension: You may wish to suggest to students that they try out this rule the next time a thunderstorm is in the area.

Additional Answers

7. (0, $^-5$) **8.** (0, 14) **9.** (0, 2.4)

10. (0, 27) **11.** (0, $^-35$) **12.** (0, $-\frac{3}{5}$)

Exercises 26–31: Caution students that the speed must be expressed in *feet per minute* so they can order the speeds in Exercise 31. Tell students to save their answers and their work for Exercises 28 and 30 to use when working Exercise 32.

Graph a line with the indicated slope.

20. 1

21. 12

22. $^-3$

23. 0.37

24. $^-270$

20–24. Possible graphs:

25. Astronomy The spacecraft *Pioneer 10* was launched on March 3, 1972. Designed to last at least 21 months, it outlived and outperformed the fondest dreams of its creators. In April 1983, *Pioneer 10* sent radio signals to Earth from Pluto, 4.58×10^9 km away.

a. Radio signals travel at the speed of light (about 3.00×10^5 km/s). How long did it take signals to reach Earth from Pluto?

b. Challenge What was *Pioneer 10*'s average speed, in kilometers per hour (kph), between March 3, 1972, and April 25, 1983?

In Exercises 26–30, do Parts a, b, and c for the given speed.

a. Express the speed in feet per minute.

b. Graph the distance moved over time, with time in minutes on the horizontal axis and distance in feet on the vertical axis.

c. Determine the slope of the graph.

25–30. See Additional Answers.

31. 3 m/min, 45 ft/s, 15 m/s, 60 kph, 75 mph

26. 3 meters per minute (1 foot is approximately 0.3 meter.)

27. 15 meters per second

28. 60 kilometers per hour

29. 45 feet per second

30. 75 miles per hour

31. Write the speeds given in Exercises 26–30 from slowest to fastest.

32. Redraw the two graphs for Exercises 28 and 30 on a single grid.

a. What do you notice about the slopes of the two graphs? (Hint: Look at the angle each line makes with the horizontal axis.)

b. Explain your result in Part a.
When both speeds are expressed in ft/min, the second slope is about twice the first (6,600 versus 3,300).

Remember
1 mile = 5,280 feet

32a. The slope for 75 mph is about twice the slope for 60 kph.

Additional Answers

25a. about 15,267 s, or 4.24 h

25b. about 4.69×10^4 km/h
(11 years 53 days is about 97,600 h; 4.58×10^9 km $\div$ 97,600 h gives the average speed.)

26–30. See Additional Answers on page A396.

340 CHAPTER 5 Looking at Linear Relationships

33. A lion surveying his surroundings from a tall tree saw a horse half a kilometer to the south. He also spotted a giraffe 1 kilometer to the west. The lion jumped from the tree to chase one of these animals, and both the horse and the giraffe ran away from the lion with the maximum speed.

A lion can run 200 meters in 9 seconds, a horse can run 200 meters in 10 seconds, and a giraffe can run 200 meters in 14 seconds. The lion went after the animal that would take him less time to catch. After you solve this problem, you will know which animal he pursued.

a. Complete the table. For the distance between the lion and each of the other animals, assume the lion is running toward the animal. Distances are in meters.

Time (seconds)	0	50	100	150	200
Lion's Distance from Tree	0	1,111	2,222	3,333	4,444
Horse's Distance from Tree	500	1,500	2,500	3,500	4,500
Giraffe's Distance from Tree	1,000	1,714	2,429	3,143	3,857
Distance between Lion and Horse	500	389	278	167	56
Distance between Lion and Giraffe	1,000	603	206	$^-190$	$^-587$

33b–33h. See Additional Answers.

b. On a single set of axes, with time on the horizontal axis and distance on the vertical, draw these three graphs:

- the lion's distance from the tree
- the horse's distance from the tree
- the giraffe's distance from the tree

c. On another set of axes, draw these two graphs:

- the distance between the lion and the horse
- the distance between the lion and the giraffe

d. How are the five graphs similar, and how are they different?

e. What events match the points of intersection of the graphs for Part b?

f. Use the graphs to help you find how much time it would take the lion to catch the horse and how much time it would take the lion to catch the giraffe.

g. What are the slopes of the five lines? How are they different and why?

h. Write a rule in symbols for each line you graphed.

In your own words

Explain how the speed in a distance-time situation is related to the slope of the graph for the situation.

Exercise 33 Extension: Ask students to write a short report stating which animal the lion pursued and why the lion would have chosen this animal to pursue.

Additional Answers

33b–d. See Additional Answers on page A397.

33e. The points of intersection indicate when the lion would catch the horse and the giraffe.

33f. about 230 s, about 130 s

33g. lion: 22.2; horse: 20; giraffe: 14.3; lion-horse distance: $^-2.2$; lion-giraffe distance: $^-7.9$; Slopes for lion, horse, and giraffe are positive because distance increases with time; slopes for lion-horse and lion-giraffe distances are negative because distance decreases with time.

33h. lion: $d = 22.2t$; horse: $d = 20t + 500$; giraffe: $d = 14.3t + 1{,}000$;
lion-horse distance: $d = 500 - 2.2t$; lion-giraffe distance: $d = 1{,}000 - 7.9t$

Exercise 36: This review helps students prepare for the first example in Lesson 5.3.

Mixed Review

Fill in the blanks to make each a true statement.

34. $\frac{3}{12} + \frac{4}{12} + \underline{\frac{5}{12}} = 1$

35. $\frac{6}{8} + \frac{7}{8} + \underline{\frac{3}{8}} = 2$

36. Geometry Find the area and perimeter of the figure. 36 cm^2, 24 cm

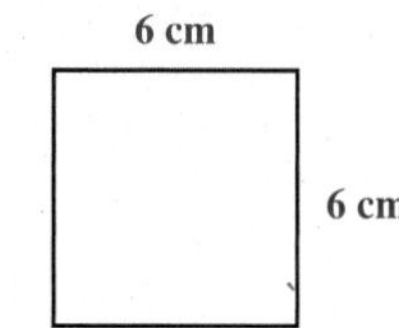

37. Geometry A rectangular prism has a base 5 inches long and 2 inches wide. The prism is 6 inches tall.

a. What are the prism's volume and surface area? 60 $in.^3$, 104 $in.^2$

b. Another block prism is four times the height of the original prism. What are its volume and surface area? 240 $in.^3$, 356 $in.^2$

c. If a cylinder has the same volume as the original prism and the area of its base is 10 square inches, what is the cylinder's height?

37c. 6 in.

38. Write this expression in two other ways: $x \div 7$. $\frac{x}{7}$, $\frac{1}{7}x$

39. Use the expression given to complete the table. Then write another expression that gives the same values. Check your expression with the values in the table. $2m - 2$

m	1	2	3	4	5	100
$2(m - 1)$	0	2	4	6	8	198

Find each product.

40. $4 \times \frac{1}{10^2}$ 0.04

41. $61 \times \frac{1}{10^2}$ 0.61

42. $842 \times \frac{1}{10^3}$ 0.842

Rewrite each expression as addition, and calculate the sum.

43. $^-6 - {^-12}$

44. $7 - {^-4}$

45. $0 - {^-4}$

43. $^-6 + 12 = 6$
44. $7 + 4 = 11$
45. $0 + 4 = 4$

Write each number in standard notation.

46. 6×10^2 600

47. 8.6×10^3 8,600

48. 1.39×10^4 13,900

342 CHAPTER 5 Looking at Linear Relationships

49. 1 and 12, $^-1$ and $^-12$, 2 and 6, $^-2$ and $^-6$, 3 and 4, $^-3$ and $^-4$

51. No; the first procedure models 6^3, which is 216, while the second models 3^6, which is 729.

49. The product of two integers is 12. What could the integers be? List all possibilities.

50. Algebra Solve for y: $^-2y + 5 = 11$. $^-3$

51. Suppose you put a 1-inch stick of gum through a ×6 stretching machine, three times. Do you get the same result by putting a 1-inch stick of gum through a ×3 machine, six times? Explain how you know.

Use exponents to write the prime factorization of each number. For example, $200 = 2^3 \times 5^2$.

52. 25 5^2 **53.** 72 $2^3 \times 3^2$ **54.** 90 $2 \times 3^2 \times 5$

55. Find 13% of 2,375. 308.75 **56.** Find 178% of 312. 555.36

57. What percent of 200 is 35? 17.5%

58. The table lists the average daily temperatures for one week in Algeville.

Monday	Tuesday	Wednesday	Thursday	Friday	Saturday	Sunday
64°F	68°F	73°F	60°F	64°F	63°F	60°F

Use positive or negative numbers to express the change in temperature from

a. Monday to Tuesday 4°F **b.** Tuesday to Wednesday 5°F

c. Wednesday to Thursday $^-13$°F **d.** Thursday to Friday 4°F

e. Friday to Saturday $^-1$°F **f.** Saturday to Sunday $^-3$°F

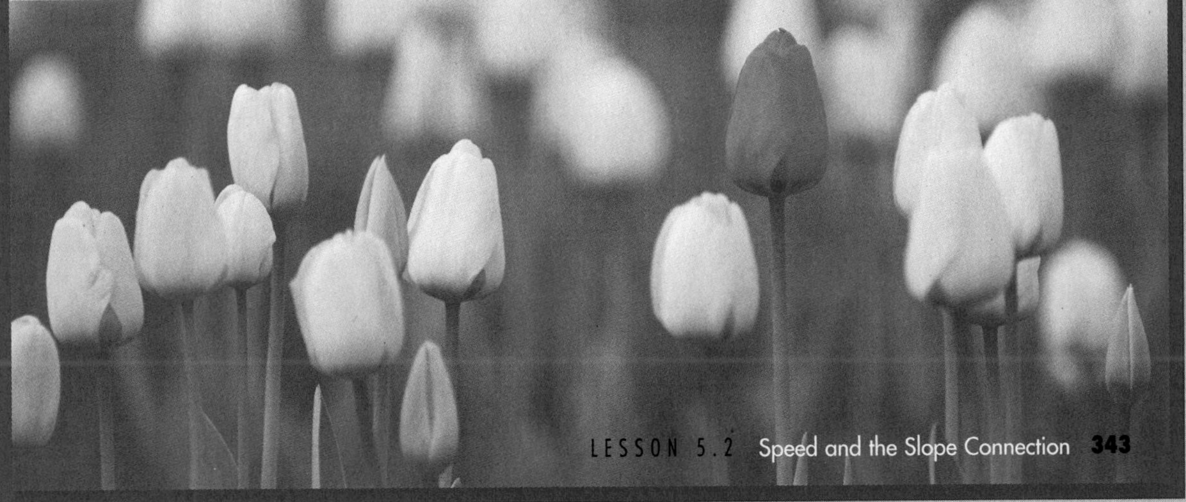

Quick Check

Informal Assessment

Students should be able to

- ✔ relate speed to the slope of a graph of distance over time
- ✔ develop an understanding of negative slope and a negative constant term
- ✔ gain skill in recognizing proportional and non-proportional relationships between distance and time
- ✔ recognize linear relationships from different forms: symbolic rules, graphs, patterns, and tables
- ✔ easily convert one form of representation into another

• ***Quick Quiz begins on page A397.***

Teacher Notes

5.3

Recognizing Linear Relationships

Objectives

- To recognize linear relationships in a variety of representations
- To translate from one representation to another
- To recognize the symbolic representation of a linear relationship in more than one form
- To explain the connection between the constant difference, the slope of the graph, and the symbolic representation of the relationship (the a in $y = ax + b$)
- To determine b in the rule $y = ax + b$ from a graph (the y-intercept, the intersection with the vertical axis)

Overview (pacing: about 3 class periods)

Students learn to recognize linear relationships represented as symbolic rules, graphs, visual patterns, and tables. They start by extending patterns and describing them symbolically. They learn how to use *change*—the difference between one stage and the next in the patterns—to determine whether the pattern is linear or not, and they learn how the rate of growth is reflected in the symbolic rule. Students graph the relationships in the patterns and learn to make links between the rules and the graphs; they learn how to determine the symbolic rule from the graph and how to predict the graph from the symbolic rule.

In this lesson, the symbolic rule for linear relationships is generally given in a standard form, $y = ax + b$, but students also encounter it in other forms and learn to rewrite it in the standard form. Inequalities are also informally introduced.

Advance Preparation

You may want to use an overhead transparency of Master 10, Quarter-Inch Graph Paper, as you discuss the problems. Students will need several copies of Master 10 or sheets of graph paper to complete the problem sets and homework problems.

	Summary	Materials	On Your Own Exercises	Assessment Opportunities
Investigation 1 page T345	Students investigate patterns and write rules to describe them.		Practice & Apply: 1–2 Connect & Extend: 11–13 Mixed Review: 18–34	Share & Summarize, pages T347, 347 On the Spot Assessment, pages T344, T346 Troubleshooting, page T347
Investigation 2 page T348	Students describe patterns with graphs and practice to match graphs to their rules	• Master 10 (Teaching Resources, page 15)	Practice & Apply: 3–8 Connect & Extend: 14–16 Mixed Review: 18–34	Share & Summarize, pages T350, 350 Troubleshooting, page T350
Investigation 3 page T351	Students learn to recognize multiple forms of symbolic representations of linear relationships.	• Master 10	Practice & Apply: 9–10 Connect & Extend: 17 Mixed Review: 18–34	Share & Summarize, pages T353, 353 On the Spot Assessment, page T352 Troubleshooting, page T353 Informal Assessment, page 361 Quick Quiz, page 361

Introduce

In this lesson students learn to recognize linear relationships in various contexts and from various types of information. The lesson reviews the content of observing and describing patterns from Chapter 8 of Course 1: Expressions and Equations. It also builds on ideas presented in Chapter 2, Solid Geometry, of this course.

You might begin this lesson by reminding students of the various patterns they encountered last year in Course 1 such as matchstick patterns, dot patterns, and square patterns, as well as other patterns they've seen. They may recall 3-dimensional cube patterns from Chapter 2 this year or hexagon and tile patterns from last year. You might provide examples of patterns or ask other students to do this for those students who did not study this curriculum in Course 1.

Explore

Ask students to look at the two patterns in the Explore section and find the rules for different sizes of these patterns. The patterns for perimeter present a linear relationship, and the patterns for area present a quadratic relationship. This activity prepares students to be attentive to the features that characterize linear relationships in comparison to other relationships. Students may remember the formulas for area and perimeter, count individual tiles, or use other methods to find these rules.

On the Spot Assessment

Watch for students who forget to subtract 2 from both dimensions when using the formula for area for the nonborder tiles. Remind them that they are looking for the area of an interior section that is not as large as the entire tiled area.

5.3 Recognizing Linear Relationships

You have learned about linear relationships between variables such as pay earned and time worked. In this lesson, you will look at both linear and nonlinear relationships—but it won't always be obvious which is which!

Just the facts

Tiles are typically made from clay that has been hardened by being *fired*, or baked at very high temperatures, in a special oven called a *kiln*. A glaze might then be applied to the tiles.

Explore

Pat and Tillie are patio tilers who specialize in two-color rectangular patios. All their patios are constructed from tiles measuring 1 foot by 1 foot. The border is one color, and the center is another color. The patio shown here is 9 feet by 6 feet.

Their Totally Square line of patios contains a variety of square patio designs. Below is a Totally Square patio measuring 6 feet by 6 feet.

Find a rule that tells how many border tiles will be used on a Totally Square patio of a specified size. Then find a rule that tells how many nonborder tiles there will be. Tell what each variable in your rules represents. See ①.

① $b = 2s + 2(s - 2)$, or $b = 4s - 4$; $c = (s - 2)^2$, where s is the side length of the patio, b is the number of border tiles, and c is the number of center (nonborder) tiles

Pat and Tillie call their patio designs that aren't square their ColorQuad line. Find a rule that expresses the number of border tiles in a ColorQuad patio with width w and length l. Then write a rule that expresses the number of nonborder tiles in a ColorQuad patio. $b = 2w + 2l - 4$, $c = (w - 2)(l - 2)$

1 Students write rules for finding the number of border tiles and nonborder tiles for both designs.

Investigation 1

The problems in this investigation require that students extend and/or describe the pattern symbolically. Students will refer back to these tables and rules in subsequent investigations. You may want to suggest that they save their work and bring it to class with them each day.

Problem Set A Suggested Grouping: Pairs

In this problem set, students find relationships and rules for numbers in hexagon patterns and for square numbers.

In **Problem 1,** students have to find what numbers fit into the shaded and white hexagons above 10, and which numbers fit into the hexagons around number 59. Students also must find what numbers belong in four of the squares. If students are confused by all the different numbers in the pattern, draw their attention to the numbers in the squares. These numbers are orderly enough to be a kind of index to the pattern of numbered hexagons.

Sample Strategies Students may use one of these strategies to solve **Problem 1a.**

- They may notice that each number in the shaded hexagons is 3 more than the previous one. This, however, can be a risky strategy since two numbers do not form a pattern.
- Some may notice the multiples of 3 in the lower row of white hexagons, and some may see that 0, 1, and 2 lie on an oblique line; 3, 4, and 5 lie on the parallel oblique line to the right; and then 6, 7, and 8 lie on the next line to the right, and so on.

Any of these patterns can allow them to calculate all missing numbers.

For **Problem 1b,** students may come up with a rule that will help them connect the stage number with a matching number in the hexagon. Other students will work the problem by matching the numbers in the hexagons to certain stages.

Problem 2 is similar to problems students solved in Chapter 2.

Investigation 1 Exploring and Describing Patterns

In the next set of problems, you will review and extend your ability to find patterns and to write rules in symbols.

1 Have students save answers to use in later investigations.

2 Student pairs find relationships and rules for numbers in hexagon patterns and square numbers.

Problem Set A

1. This hexagon pattern can continue in either direction.

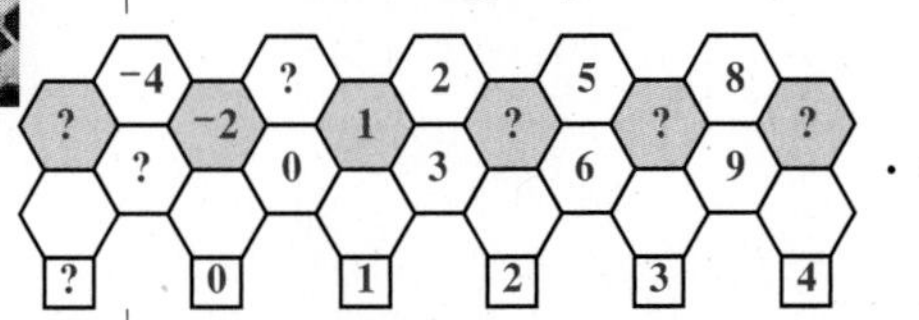

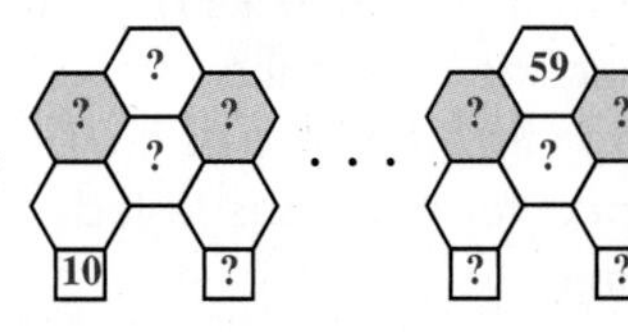

a. Find the missing numbers in the hexagon pattern. Then copy and complete the table. Discuss with your partner how you found the numbers.

Number in Square, *s*	0	1	2	3	4	10	11	20	21
Number in Shaded Hexagon, *h*	$^-2$	1	4	7	10	28	31	58	61

b. Write a rule in symbols for computing h if you know s.

$h = 3s - 2$

2. This sequence of squares is made from small tiles.

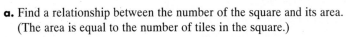

Square 1 Square 2 Square 3 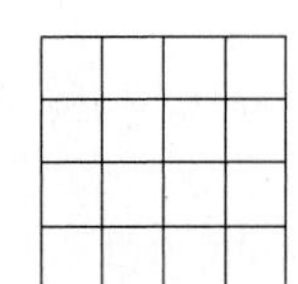 Square 4

a. Find a relationship between the number of the square and its area. (The area is equal to the number of tiles in the square.)

2a. $A = n^2$, where A is the area and n is the square number

b. Complete the table to show the area of each square.

Square Number	1	2	3	4
Area of Square	1	4	9	16

LESSON 5.3 Recognizing Linear Relationships 345

Problem Set B **Suggested Grouping: Pairs**
Problem Sets B and C help develop students' ability to translate from the features of a visual geometric pattern to the numbers that describe these features. They ask
2 students not merely to follow the pattern but to come up with the rule that describes the pattern. Students must justify their rule, or generalization, first by checking special cases and then by relating the rule to the structure of the pattern, convincing themselves and their partner not only that the rule works for the cases tested, but also that the rule is always true.

On the Spot Assessment

Watch for students who multiply the stage number and a rate but neglect to add the constant term. For example in **Problem 3,** students may forget to add 3 to $2n$ when writing the rule. It can help to ask these students to identify the part in the shapes that remains constant in all stages and also the part that changes.

Problem Set Wrap-Up If students have difficulties coming up with the rules for patterns, you may draw these patterns on the board and use different colors for the constant and the changing parts of each pattern so students can better visualize them. If you do it with several patterns, this will give a firm base for students' understanding of where the rule comes from. You may then move on, because the next investigations will continue to work with patterns.

Problem Set C **Suggested Grouping: Pairs**
This problem set practices translating the structure of the pattern into the rule that describes this pattern.

Problem Set B

This pattern of Z-shapes is made from small squares.

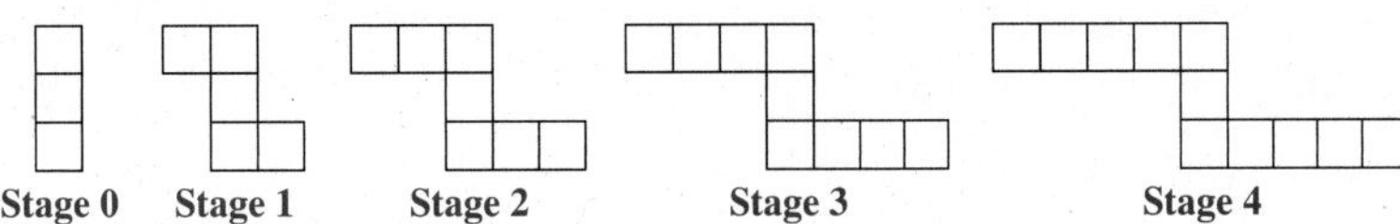

1. Complete the table.

Stage Number, n	0	1	2	3	4	5	9	10
Squares, s	3	5	7	9	11	13	21	23

2. Zach found it took 21 squares to make Stage 9. How many will it take for Stage 10? Add two columns to your table for Stages 9 and 10. See the table.
3. Explain how the number of squares in a stage is related to the stage number. Be sure your explanation will work for all stages. Write a symbolic rule for finding s if you know n.
4. Use your rule to predict how many squares are needed for Stages 11 and 12. Draw the stages to test your rule. See below.
5. Explain how the two numbers in your rule relate to the pattern of Z-shapes.

3. The number of squares is equal to 2 multiplied by the stage number, plus 3; $s = 2n + 3$.

5. The 2 is how many squares are added at each stage; the 3 represents the 3 squares in the center column.

1 Students work in pairs to determine problems.

2 Students find the rule that describes the pattern.

Problem Set C

Now you will investigate this pattern of T-shapes.

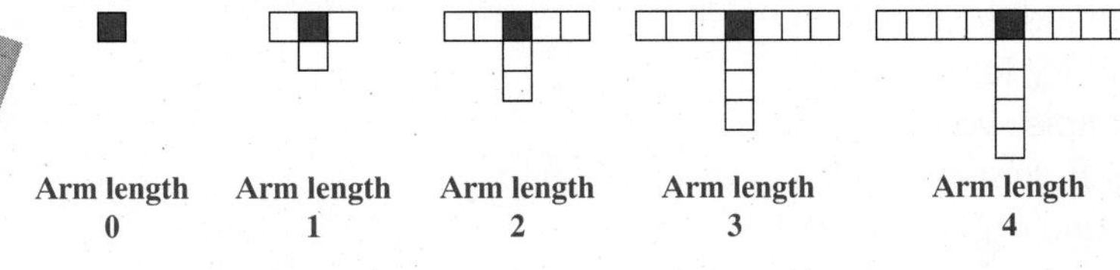

1. Complete the table.

Arm Length, L	0	1	2	3	4	5	100	1,000
Squares, s	1	4	7	10	13	16	301	3,001

3 Have pairs of students work each problem.

Problem Set B Answer

4. Stage 11: 25 squares; Stage 12: 27 squares

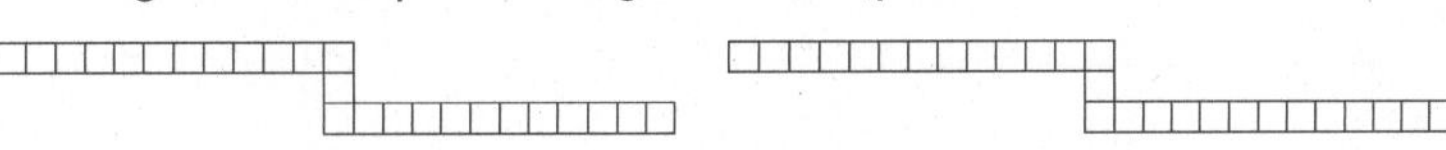

In **Problem 3,** the term *rule* is used with the term *formula* as students are asked to write the formula in words and in symbols.

In **Problem 6,** students work backward from the total number of squares to find the arm length in the T-shape. This prepares them to solve the last two problems.

Problem 8 prepares students for the discussion of discrete sets of numbers. Simon cannot make a shape with 200 squares because there is no stage that uses this number of squares.

Problem Set Wrap-Up Discuss **Problems 5–8** as a whole class. Students can tell how the numbers in the formula relate and share their strategies for solving the last three problems.

Share & Summarize

The purpose of these questions is to make students aware that the amount of growth from stage to stage in these patterns remains constant and that this amount of growth relates to the rate in the rule.

Troubleshooting If students have difficulties relating the amount of growth to the rate, remind them of some examples from Lessons 1 and 2, and try to make connections between these. For example, you may use the table in Lesson 5.1, Problem Set E, that shows the amount Tamsin gets paid. Draw an analogy between the number of hours Tamsin worked (0, 1, 2, 3, . . .) and the stage number in the pattern. Similarly, draw an analogy between the number of dollars she was paid and the number of tiles or squares in the pattern. Ask students the ways they figured out the rate of Tamsin's pay, and tell them to use the same strategy for figuring out the rule for the patterns. You may then move on, as students will practice this skill in later investigations.

On Your Own Exercises

Practice & Apply: 1–2
Connect & Extend: 11–13
Mixed Review: 18–34

2. Each arm has 100 squares, so three arms have 300 squares, plus 1 in the center is 301. Each arm has 1,000 squares, so three arms have 3,000, plus 1 is 3,001.
3. Multiply the arm length by 3 and add 1; $s = 3L + 1$.
4. Possible answer: arm length 6: 19; arm length 10: 31
5. The 3 is the number of squares added each time; the 1 is the purple square in the center.
6. $160 = 3L + 1$, so $3L = 159$ and $L = 53$. The arm length is 53.
7. Yes; $33 \times 3 + 1 = 100$, so the arm length would be 33.
8. No; there is no whole number L so that $3L + 1 = 200$.

2. How did you decide how many squares were needed to make a T-shape with arm length 100? With arm length 1,000?
3. Write a general formula (or rule) in words, and then in symbols, to relate the total number of squares to the arm length.
4. Use your formula to predict the number of squares for other arm lengths. Draw the shapes to check that your formula works.
5. Explain how the two numbers in your formula relate to the T-shapes.
6. Simon made a T-shape with 160 squares. Write and solve an equation to find its arm length.
7. Could Simon make a T-shape with 100 squares? Explain your reasoning.
8. Could Simon make a T-shape with 200 squares? Explain your reasoning.

Share & Summarize

Look at the tables you made for the Z-shapes and the T-shapes. The numbers in the second row show how each pattern grows.

1. How much does each pattern grow from stage to stage?
2. For each table, compare the amount of growth with the rule you wrote. How is the growth reflected in the rule?
3. How does this growth relate to the rate of change?

Share & Summarize Answers

1. Z-shapes grow by 2; T-shapes grow by 3.
2. The amount of growth is the number that is multiplied by the variable.
3. The amount of growth is the rate of change.

1 Students work backward to solve the problem.

2 Discuss Problems 5–8 as a whole class.

3 Be sure students understand that the amount of growth remains constant and relates to the rate in the rule.

Investigation 2

Students revisit patterns from Investigation 1 and draw graphs of the pairs of values generated by the patterns. They should draw on the ideas about graphs developed in Lessons 1–3, and make a link between their graphs and the rules they generated in Investigation 1. Students will need graph paper or copies of Master 10, Quarter-Inch Graph Paper, to complete problems in Investigation 2.

Think & Discuss

Ask students to draw a graph for the T-shape pattern. Students should be able to relate the rate in the rule to the slope of the graph and relate the constant term to the *y*-intercept of the graph.

Students already encountered the question about connecting the dots in the graph many times in Lessons 1–3. This time there are no stages between stages 1 and 2 or 2 and 3, so there is no sense in connecting the points in this graph. These points are said to be discrete.

About the Mathematics

Some mathematicians feel entirely comfortable sketching a solid line here to express the relationship of discrete points, as long as it is well understood that the picture does not represent all aspects of the relationship. A solid line can be a sketch—an approximation of sorts—rather than an explicit statement that all the points on it are really part of the table. What is important for your students is that they attend seriously to the *domain* of a relationship—what numbers can and cannot be inputs. It is then up to you and your students how explicit you want to make that understanding as you draw your graphs. However, the text frequently refers to drawing dashed lines to show this relationship.

Investigation  Graphs and Rules from Patterns

In the last investigation, you wrote rules to describe visual patterns. As you know, graphs can help you find rules for patterns.

Think & Discuss

Look again at the T-shapes you studied in Problem Set C.

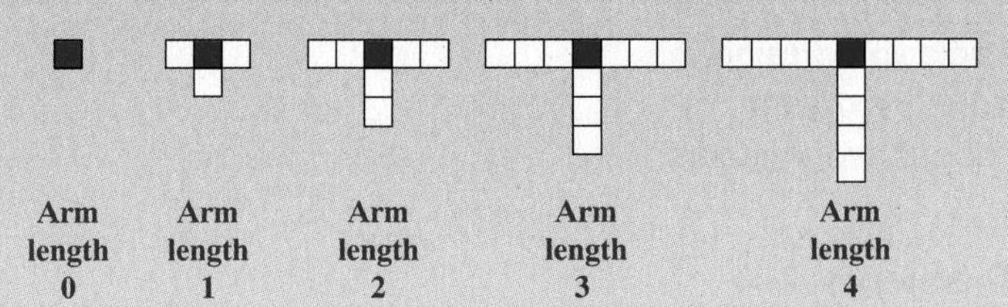

① The graph is a series of points that would lie on a line if they were connected.

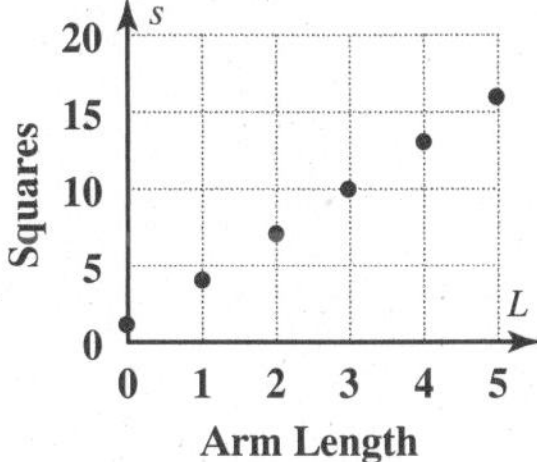

- Draw a graph of the table data shown below. Put the arm length on the horizontal axis. What is the shape of the graph? See ①.

Arm Length, L	0	1	2	3	4	5
Squares, s	1	4	7	10	13	16

- What is the rule for this pattern? $s = 3L + 1$
- Where do the two numbers in the rule appear in your graph? The slope of the graph is 3, and the graph crosses the s-axis at 1.
- Does it make sense to connect the points in this graph? Why or why not? No; you can't have a fraction of an arm length.

1 Ask students to draw a graph for the T-shape pattern.

2 Students relate rate of the rule to slope and constant term to y-intercept.

As you've seen before, when you graph data for some situations, it can be helpful to sketch a line through the points even though you know not all of the points on the line make sense for the situation. The line can help you find other points that do make sense. It can also help you show the relationship between the variables.

If all the points on a line don't really make sense, draw a dashed line instead of a solid one. This will show that the line isn't really part of the graph.

Develop

Problem Set D **Suggested Grouping: Pairs**
Students graph pairs of values generated from the pattern discussed in Problem Set B. From the graphs, they derive rules for the patterns. They will need graph paper or copies of Master 10, Quarter-Inch Graph Paper, to solve these problems.

For **Problems 4 and 5,** you may want to remind students that their predictions may not exactly match the values in the table or the value they calculated using the rule. Unless the scale to graph the data is extremely large, predictions should fall within about two numbers of the value in the table.

Problem Set Wrap-Up Discuss **Problems 2–4** together. Remind students that, though it does not make sense to connect the points because the values between the points do not exist, a dashed line helps one see the relationship and predict values for points not found in the table.

Then discuss **Problems 6–8** to revisit the concepts of slope and *y*-intercept on this graph and relate them to the structure of the pattern. The shape at Stage 0 has 3 squares; the *y*-intercept is 3. The slope of the line reflects the number of squares added on from stage to stage.

Problem Set E **Suggested Grouping: Individuals or Pairs**
Students revisit the hexagon pattern they worked with in Problem Set A. In this problem set, the information about the pattern is given not in table form but as a set of coordinate pairs. Students practice the sequence **coordinates** → **graph** → **rule.** They check their rules with examples.

MATERIALS

graph paper

1. No; you can't have a fraction of a stage number or of a square.

2.

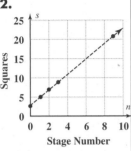

6. It crosses the s-axis at 3, which is the number of squares for Stage 0.

7. The slope is 2, which is the number of squares added at each stage.

8. The graph crosses the s-axis at 3; 2 is the slope of the line.

Problem Set D

Look again at the Z-shape pattern from Problem Set B.

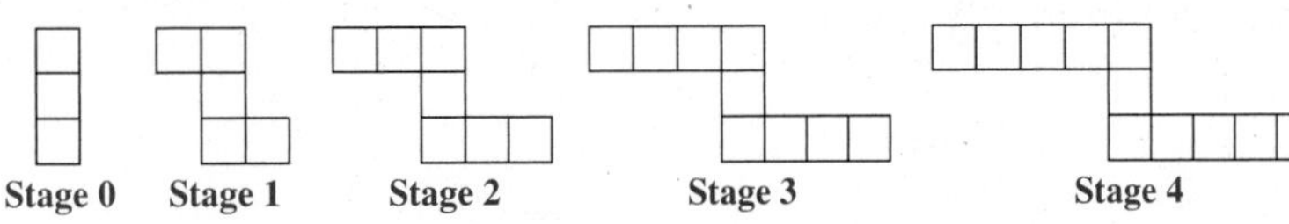

Stage Number, n	0	1	2	3	9
Squares, s	3	5	7	9	21

1. Would it make sense to connect points on a graph of these data? Explain.
2. Draw a graph of the table data. Try to draw a line through the points. Use a dashed line or a solid line, whichever makes more sense.
3. What kind of pattern do the points make? linear
4. Use your graph to predict the value of s if n is 8. Check with your table and your rule from Problem Set B to see if you are correct. 19
5. Use your graph to predict the value of n if s is 17. Check with your table and your rule to see if you are correct. 7
6. Does a point fall on the s-axis? What part of the pattern of Z-shapes does this show?
7. How does the slope of your line relate to the pattern of Z-shapes?
8. The rule for this pattern is $s = 2n + 3$. Explain where each number in the rule appears in your graph.

Problem Set E

You investigated this pattern in Problem Set A.

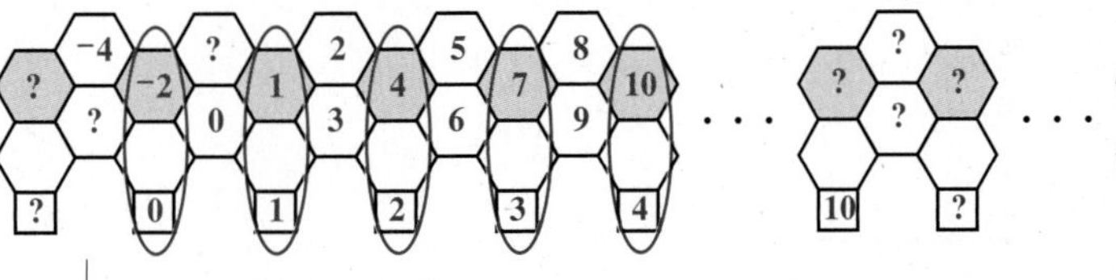

1. Five pairs of numbers have been circled: $(0, {}^-2)$, $(1, 1)$, $(2, 4)$, $(3, 7)$, and $(4, 10)$. What is the next pair of numbers in this sequence? (Note: This part of the pattern is not visible.) (5, 13)

1 Students revisit the Z-shape pattern first seen in Problem Set B.

2 Students' predictions may not match exactly the value they calculated using the rule.

3 Review concepts of slope and y-intercept and relate it to the structure of the pattern.

4 As students work individually or in pairs, they revisit the hexagon pattern first seen in Problem Set A.

LESSON 5.3 Recognizing Linear Relationships 349

Develop

Students plot points and interpret data from a graph in **Problems 2–4.**

Access for All Learners

For Early Finishers Have students copy the hexagon structure in the Problem Set and create their own numerical patterns. You could use some of these patterns to provide additional practice for struggling students.

Share & Summarize

Problem 1 assesses students' grasp of one of the major points developed in this investigation—the distinction between continuous and discrete graphs. **Problem 2** assesses students' understanding of the second major emphasis of this investigation—the relations between the numbers in a rule and the features of its graph.

Troubleshooting If students have trouble relating slope and *y*-intercept to numbers in the rule, review some of the graphs in this investigation again, and call students' attention to the *y*-intercept. Using examples, show them that this number is the constant term in the rule. Similarly, on all of these graphs, draw right triangles with a horizontal change of one unit, and draw students' attention to the fact that the vertical change in these triangles shows the rate in the rule.

On Your Own Exercises

Practice & Apply: 3–8
Connect & Extend: 14–16
Mixed Review: 18–34

2. Plot the points from Problem 1 on a copy of the grid shown below. If the points lie on a straight line, draw the line using a dashed or a solid line, whichever makes more sense.

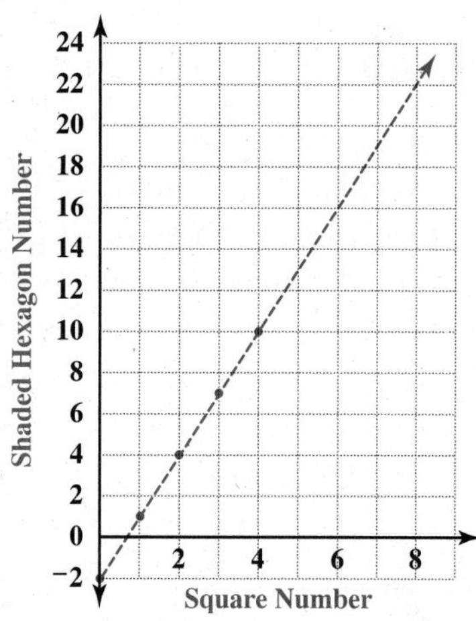

1 Students plot points and interpret data.

3. If you continue the sequence and graph the points, what would the coordinates of the ninth point on the graph be? Continue the pattern of hexagons, and check that your prediction is correct. (8, 22)

4. Use your graph to help you write a rule to link the two numbers in each pair. Choose letters to represent each variable. Check your rule with the pairs of values you already have.

5. Fill in the missing numbers in this part of the pattern. Use your rule to check your work.

149
148 ? ? ? 151
150
?
50

4. If the first number is f and the second number is s, then $s = 3f - 2$.

Share & Summarize Answer

1. Possible answer: It makes sense to connect points when one variable is the side length of a square and the other is the square's area, because length and area can be any positive number. It doesn't make sense when one variable is number of people and the other is total number of eyes, because you can't have a partial person.

Share & Summarize

1. Describe a situation in which it makes sense to connect the points on a graph. Then describe a situation in which it does not make sense to connect the points on a graph. Explain your thinking.

2. What is the slope of the line described by the rule $y = {}^{-}0.5x + 8$? What is the y-intercept of the line? $^{-}0.5$, 8

2 Students make a distinction between continuous and discrete graphs.

3 Students relate the numbers in a rule and the features of its graph.

Investigation 3

Investigation 3 provides students with experience in linking symbolic and graphical representations of linear relationships. The symbolic rule will be given in more than one form. Students will learn to rewrite the relationship in standard form. Having decided it is a linear relationship, students need only find two points (two points determine a line; a third might be useful to pick up errors) to produce the graph. Inequalities are introduced informally.

In the beginning of the investigation, students can read a table that summarizes the relations between the structure of the pattern, the numbers in the corresponding rule, and the features of the corresponding graph. Remind them that these connections are appropriate only for linear relationships and are not appropriate for any other kind of relationships (quadratic, cubic, exponential, etc.). Any relationship that can be expressed in the form $y = ax + b$ is linear; all linear relationships can be expressed in that form, but they can also be expressed in other forms. Students will encounter these other forms in today's investigation.

Students might use a graphing calculator or one of the computer graphing packages for some of these activities. Be sure students have a supply of graph paper or copies of Master 10, Quarter-Inch Graph Paper, to complete problems in this Investigation.

Think & Discuss

Ask students to read the cartoon and decide which of the children has a correct rule for the graph. Ask several students in your class to provide these explanations for the whole class. Discuss their reasoning with the rest of the class.

Investigation 3 From Rules to Graphs

In Investigation 2, you probably found that whenever a rule looked like

$$y = ax + b \qquad \text{(with numbers instead of } a \text{ and } b\text{)}$$

the graph of the points formed part of a straight line. In fact, whenever a rule looks like this, you can be sure that all the points in its graph will be on a straight line. This is why these relationships are called *linear.*

The table summarizes the relationships among the numbers in the rule $y = ax + b$, the features of the pattern described by this rule, and the features of the graph of this rule.

1 • Discuss the table and its meaning.

• Relate the table to the equation for linear relationships: $y = ax + b$.

In Patterns	On Graphs
As the quantity x changes by 1 unit, the quantity y changes by a units.	The number a is the slope of the line. It shows the rate at which y changes as x changes.
b is the constant, or fixed, part of the pattern.	b is the constant. It shows where the line crosses the y-axis. b is called the y-intercept.

You can tell a lot about how a graph will look just by inspecting its rule.

Simon's ($y = x + 2$); Possible explanation: Jin Lee: Point out that if x is 0, y would be $^-2$ in her equation; Zoe: Point out that the slope must be 1, not 2.

Think & Discuss

Whose equation is correct? How could you explain to the other two students why they are incorrect?

2 Have students decide which rule is correct and explain why.

Problem Set F **Grouping: Pairs**

This problem set provides practice matching rules with their graphs through a two-person game. Allow about 15 minutes for this problem set. Students will need graph paper or copies of Master 10, Quarter-Inch Graph Paper, to complete the problem set.

The rules in **Problem 1** are specially designed so that pairs of them are similar in all but one feature. For example, $c = 2d + 3$ and $c = d + 3$ differ only by the value of the slope. The equations $c = 2d + 3$ and $c = -2d + 3$ differ only by the sign of the slope. And $c = d + 3$ and $c = d + 4$ differ by the *y*-intercept. This should help students to pay closer attention to the individual features of the rules and how they relate to the features of the graphs. Students don't have to graph all nine rules if they seem to be clear about the connections after graphing only a few equations.

Problem 3 introduces the rules in a nonstandard form, which may be a challenge for some students. Although students have had no formal experience with strategies for transforming a rule into a standard form in order to graph it, the rules are made simple enough so students can intuitively find ways to calculate *y* for each *x*. Students are not expected to master graphing linear relationships in a nonstandard form. The purpose of this exercise is to make them aware that other forms of rules can produce lines.

On the **Spot Assessment**

Watch for students who have no strategy for determining how to draw the graphs and match them to the equations in **Problem 3.** You might suggest that students make a table of *x* and *y* values in order to make the graphs and then have their partners independently make their own tables in order to check the match between the graph and the rule.

Discuss the text after this problem set that defines a standard form of a linear relationship and provides examples of rules in standard and nonstandard forms.

MATERIALS
graph paper

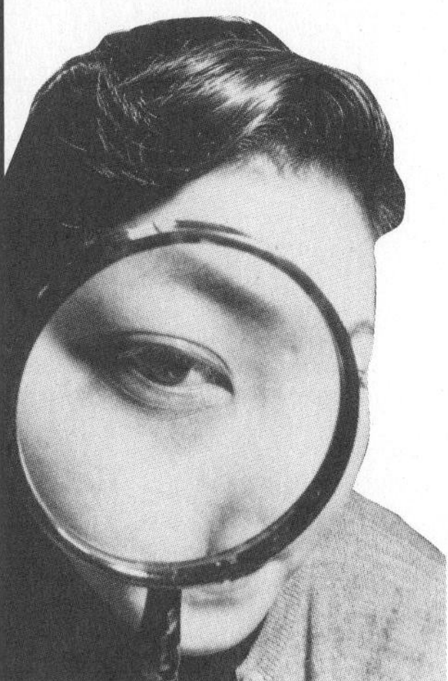

1, 3. See Additional Answers.

Problem Set F

You and a partner are going to play a detective game. One of you will draw a graph for one of the rules below. The other will be the detective, looking for clues in the graph to decide which rule was used.

$c = 2d + 3$	$c = 2d - 1$	$c = d + 4$
$c = d + 3$	$c = 10 - d$	$c = 10 - 2d$
$c = {}^{-}2d + 3$	$c = 10 + d$	$c = 10 + 2d$

1. Take turns drawing and being the detective until each of you has drawn four graphs. Use d for the horizontal axis and c for the vertical axis.

2. Explain in a few sentences how you matched each graph with an equation. See below.

Here is another set of equations that can be graphed. These equations aren't quite like the others, so you may need to look harder for clues.

$x = 7 + y$	$2x = 2(6 + y)$	$3x = 3y - 9$
$x = 7 - y$	$2x = 2(6 - y)$	$3x = 3y + 9$

3. Take turns drawing and being the detective until you and your partner have each drawn two graphs. Use x for the horizontal axis and y for the vertical axis.

4. Explain how you matched each graph with an equation. See below.

Most of the equations you have encountered in this chapter that describe linear relationships were in the form $y = ax + b$ (for example, $y = 2x + 7$). Linear relationships can also be described by other forms of equations.

As you have just seen, a graph is a good way to figure out whether a relationship written in a form other than $y = ax + b$ is linear. A graph will also help you to find the answers to the next problem set.

2. Possible answer: I looked at where the line intersected the vertical axis, which gave me the constant term for the rule. If the graph went down from left to right, the slope was negative, so I could narrow my choices further. Then if I needed to, I looked closer to see if the slope was 1 or 2 (or $^{-}1$ or $^{-}2$).

4. Possible answer: The slopes and intercepts were harder to see in these rules, so I rewrote them first. Then I used the same strategy as before.

1 Have students match rules with graphs while playing a detective game.

2 Rules are introduced in a nonstandard form.

• ***Additional Answers on page A398.***

Develop

Problem Set G Suggested Grouping: Whole class

In this problem set, students encounter a relationship written in a nonstandard form and preview inequalities.

In **Problem 1,** students essentially graph the rule $s + r = 15$ taking into account the constraints $s < 11$ and $r < 11$.

Problems 2 and 3 informally introduce inequalities. For **Problem 2,** you might write all three constraints on the chalkboard. Ask students to write all pairs of numbers (s, r) they can come up with that satisfy these constraints and then plot them on their grids. Then ask students how these points relate to the constraints on the board. Finally ask students to graph the constraints. This may be an unfamiliar way to graph data for some students. You may want to have a completed graph against which students can check their answers.

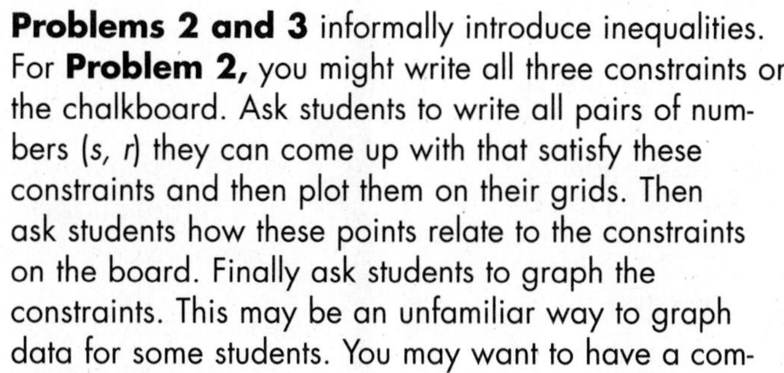

For **Problem 3,** ask students which of the following rules describe the scores for fit people. Then have them explain their answers. Depending on your class, you may want to have students notice that the correct rule $s + r \geq 15$ does not consider the constraints on s and r since it includes points such as (100, 100).

Share & Summarize

These questions summarize the important point of this investigation—multiple forms for linear relationships.

In **Question 1,** students should notice that all four rules represent the same graph.

They may explain this situation differently in **Question 2.** For example, they can say that each rule produces the same *d* for each *c*. Or they can say that these rules are different forms of the same rule. Or they can say that you can get one rule from another by some manipulations.

Question 3 asks students to provide an additional form of the same rule.

Troubleshooting Don't worry too much if some students remain puzzled that different formulas can describe the same relationship and be represented by the same graph. They will return to this idea later in the year.

On Your Own Exercises

Practice & Apply: 9–10
Connect & Extend: 17
Mixed Review: 18–34

MATERIALS
graph paper

Problem Set G

A fitness test has two parts: skipping, and running in place. For each part of the test, you can earn a whole-number score from 0 to 10. Your total score is given by the rule

$$\text{total score} = s + r$$

where s is the skipping score and r is the running score.

1. To be classified as "fit," you need a total score of at least 15. Use a grid like this one to represent all the ways a person doing this test could earn *just enough* points to be judged "fit." See the dots and the dashed line.

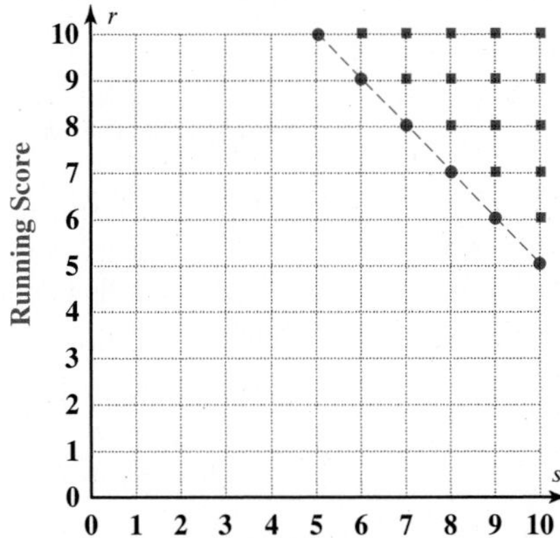

2. Use the same grid to represent *all* the ways a person could be judged fit. Use a different color from Problem 1.

3. Which of the following describe the possible scores for fit people? Explain your reasoning.

$s + r = 15$ $\quad$ $s + r \leq 15$ $\quad$ $s + r \geq 15$

2. See the squares on the graph.

3. $s + r \geq 15$, because $s + r$ must be at least 15 in order for a person to be judged fit.

Remember

If some of the points on a line don't make sense, draw a dashed line instead of a solid one.

Share & Summarize

Consider these four equations.

$10 - 2d = 2c \quad 2c = 2(5 - d) \quad 2(c + d) = 10 \quad d = 5 - c$

1. Draw graphs of the equations, and discuss what you notice. Put c on the horizontal axis.
2. Explain *why* what you noticed is happening.
3. Find some other equations that fit the pattern.

Share & Summarize Answer

1. All four graphs coincide.

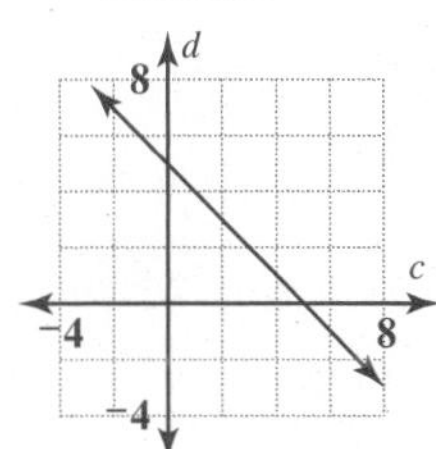

2. Possible explanation: For each c, all four equations produce the same d.
3. Possible answer: $10 = 2c + 2d$, $5 = c + d$, $c = 5 - d$

1 Discuss problems with the entire class.

2 Students are introduced informally to inequalities.

3 Students explore multiple forms for linear relationships.

On Your Own Exercises

Investigation 1
Practice & Apply: 1–2
Connect & Extend: 11–13

Investigation 2
Practice & Apply: 3–8
Connect & Extend: 14–16

Investigation 3
Practice & Apply: 9–10
Connect & Extend: 17

Assign Anytime
Mixed Review: 18–34

Exercise 2:
Some students may have difficulty identifying the pattern. If they need a hint, tell them that no matter what the length, the end tiles are the same. Any change affects only the sets of four tiles in the middle.

On Your Own Exercises

Practice & Apply

1. Shaunda made this pattern from toothpicks.

Stage 0 | Stage 1 | Stage 2 | Stage 3

a. How many toothpicks are needed for Stage 4? For Stage 5? 21 26

b. Shaunda used 56 toothpicks to make Stage 11. How many would it take to make Stage 12? 61

c. Copy and complete the table.

Stage, n	0	1	2	3	4	5	11	12
Toothpicks, t	1	6	11	16	21	26	56	61

1d. Multiply the stage number by 5 and add 1; $t = 5n + 1$.

d. Describe a general rule that shows how you can find the number of toothpicks from the stage number. Write the rule in symbols, and check that your rule works on all pairs of numbers in the table.

e. Use your rule to predict the number of toothpicks needed for some other stages. Test your prediction by building or drawing the stages. Possible answer: Stage 6, 31; Stage 7, 36

1f. Stage 0 starts with 1 toothpick, and each stage adds 5 toothpicks. So for n stages, $5n$ toothpicks are added to the original 1.

f. Use the way the pattern grows from stage to stage to explain why your rule always works.

2. The patio tilers, Pat and Tillie, designed a tile pattern that can be adapted for floors of various sizes. The strip of tiles can be any length, as long as it begins and ends with a column of white tiles.

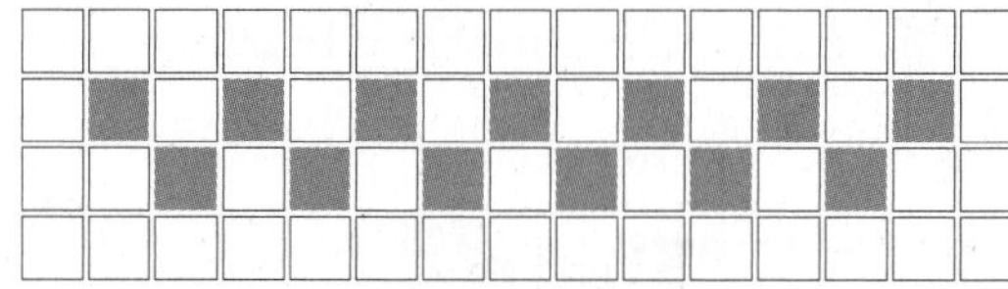

Write a rule for the pattern, giving the relation between the number of white tiles and the number of purple tiles for various lengths of the strip. $w = 3p + 8$

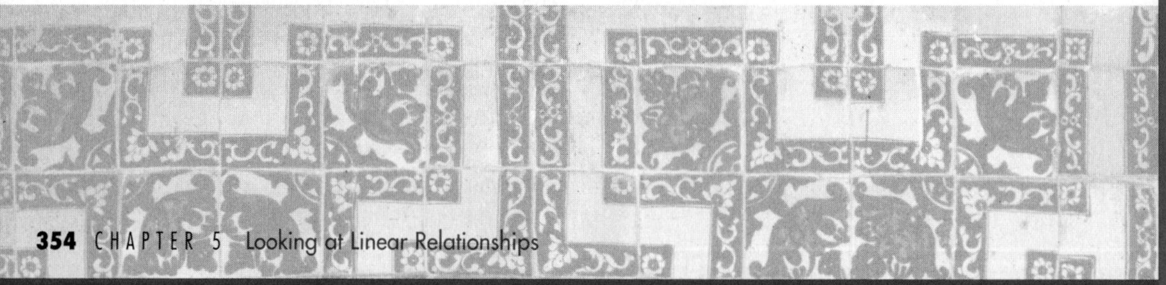

354 CHAPTER 5 Looking at Linear Relationships

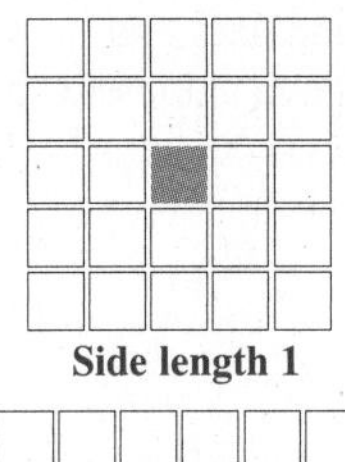

Side length 1

Side length 2

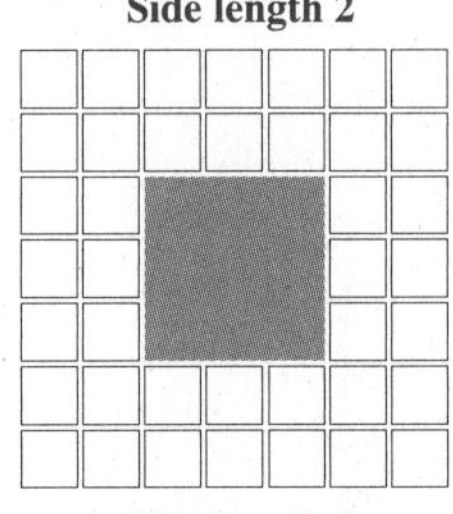

Side length 3

3. Jin Lee and Kate made a sequence of tile designs from square white tiles surrounding one square purple tile. The purple tiles come in many sizes. Three of the designs are shown at left.

a. Copy and complete the table.

Side Length of Purple Tile, s	1	2	3	4	5	10	100
White Tiles in Border, b	24	32	40	48	56	96	816

b. Find a rule to link the number of white tiles in the border to the side length of the purple tile. Describe the rule in words and symbols.

c. Draw a graph using the first five pairs of numbers in your table. (When graphing an ordered pair, refer to the horizontal axis for the first number and to the verical axis for the second number.)

d. Do the points lie on a line? Is this what you expected? Tell why or why not.

3b–3d. See Additional Answers.

Exercises 3–4:
Watch for students who try to graph on a grid with 4 quadrants. While the end result may not be incorrect, it is more common to make a graph with only one quadrant when there are no negative numbers.

4. Rick and Cheri, who are also patio tilers, created a different type of patio.

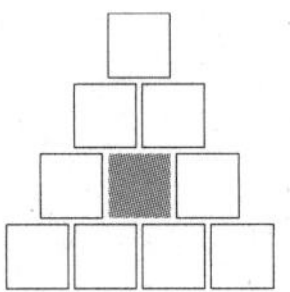

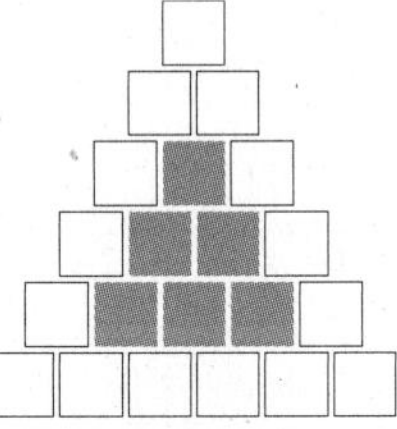

a. Complete the table.

Rows, r	4	6	8
White Tiles, w	9	15	21
Purple Tiles, p	1	6	15

4b.

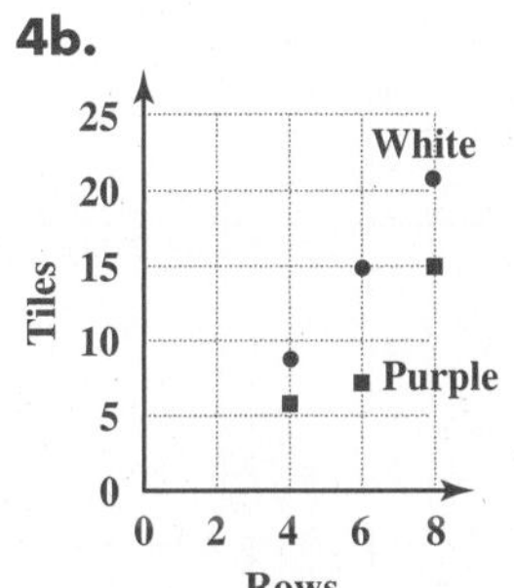

b. Make a graph that shows how the number of rows relates to the number of white tiles. Make another graph that shows how the number of rows relates to the number of purple tiles. Put the number of rows on the horizontal axis.

c. Which graph is linear, the graph for the white tiles or the graph for the purple tiles? white

d. Write a rule for the linear graph, and check it with the numbers in the table. $w = 3r - 3$

Additional Answers

3b. Possible answer: The number of white tiles is 2 side lengths taken 4 times, added to 4 tiles at each of the 4 corners; $b = 4(2s) + 4(4) = 8s + 16$.

3c. See Additional Answers on page A399.

3d. Yes; this is expected because the numbers increase by 8 each time.

LESSON 5.3 Recognizing Linear Relationships **355**

For each equation, draw a graph with x on the horizontal axis and y on the vertical axis. Draw four-quadrant graphs (include negative values for both x and y).

5–8. See Additional Answers.

5. $0.4y = 3x - 7$

6. $y = 5(x + 5)$

7. $y - 3x = 6$

8. $2.5(y + x) = 9$

9. Match each equation with one of the graphs below.

a. $y = 2x$ iv

b. $y = 0.5x$ i

c. $3y + 1.5x = 11$ iii

d. $x = 0.3(y - 4)$ ii

i.

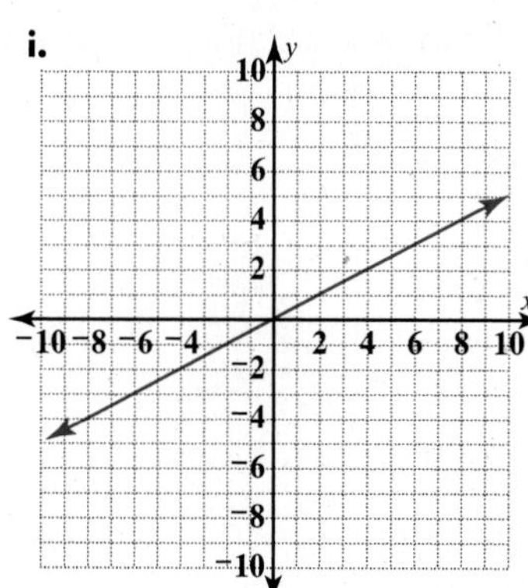

ii.

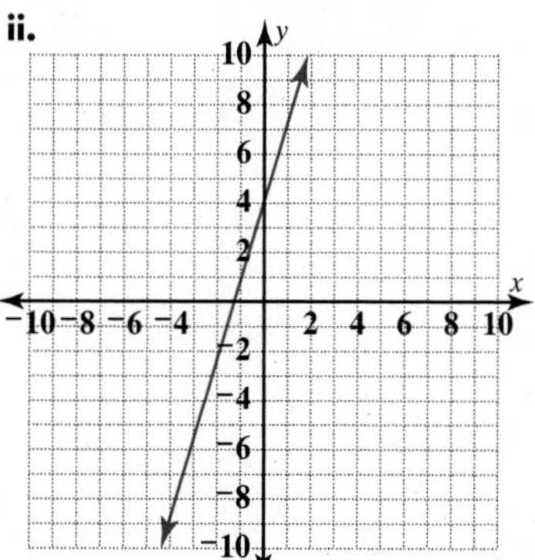

iii.

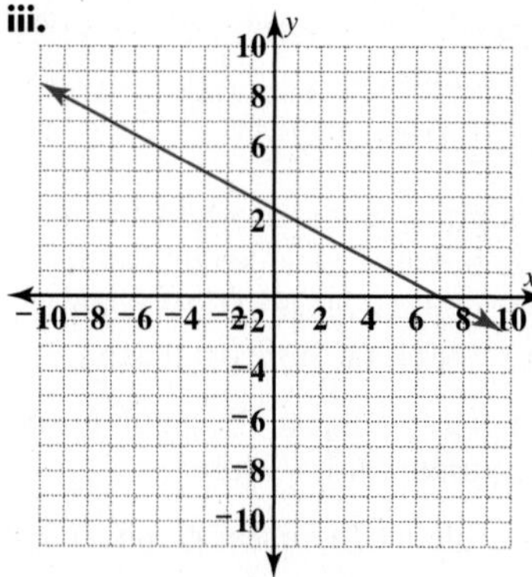

iv.

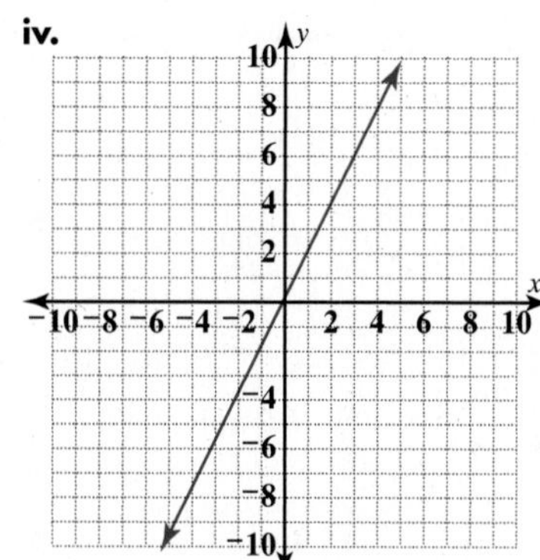

• ***Additional Answers on page A399.***

356 CHAPTER 5 Looking at Linear Relationships

10. When Zoe's family checked into a campground, the manager gave them a 20-meter piece of rope. He said they could mark out any campsite they liked, as long as its border was no longer than the rope.

a. Zoe suggested they use all the rope to make a rectangular shape. She choose some values for the side of the rectangle they wanted to place facing the river. Then she calculated the other side of the rectangle. Copy and complete her table.

Length of River Side (meters), a	0	1	2.5	3	4.2	5.5	9.9	10
Length of Other Side (meters), b	10	9	7.5	7	5.8	4.5	0.1	0

b. Draw a graph to show all possible side lengths for a rectangle with a 20-meter perimeter. Put the length of the river side on the horizontal axis.

c. Does it make sense to connect the points? Why or why not?

d. Use your graph to write a rule relating a and b.

e. The length of rope was the *maximum* border Zoe's family could use. They could also have used less rope. List the dimensions of five other rectangles that would be acceptable but that use less rope. Plot points on your graph to represent these rectangles.

f. What do you notice about the location of the points you chose, in relation to the line? On your grid, shade the region that includes these points.

g. Which equation or inequality below describes the shaded region of your graph? Explain in words what it means.

$2(a + b) = 20 \qquad 2(a + b) \le 20 \qquad 2(a + b) \ge 20$

h. Choose some points in the shaded region, other than the points in Part e. Test these points in the equation or inequality you chose for Part g. What do you notice?
Possible answers: (2, 6); (1, 4); (3, 3); all make the inequality true.

10b. See Additional Answers.

10c. Yes; sides can have fractional lengths, not just whole-number lengths.

10d. Possible rule: $b = 10 - a$

10e. See Additional Answers.

10f. The points are all on the same side of the line; see graph in answer to Part e.

10g. $2(a + b) \le 20$; The lengths of all four sides add to 20 or less than 20.

Exercise 10a:
Be sure students understand they are to use the entire rope, or 20 meters, to mark the entire border.

Exercise 10e:
Students consider a shorter portion of the 20-meter rope for this exercise. They plot points showing an inequality.

Exercise 10f:
You might want to suggest that students check a part outside the shaded area they are testing. This may make them feel more confident about their answers, but it does not ensure that their answer is correct.

• ***Additional Answers on page A399.***

Exercise 11: Some students may not see the restriction on w in this exercise.

Exercises 13a and 13c: You may wish to have a discussion allowing students to share their patterns from 13a and their answers for 13c.

Exercise 14: Students must use Problem 2 of Problem Set A when working this problem.

Connect & Extend

12a. Possible pattern:

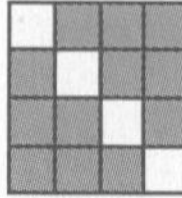

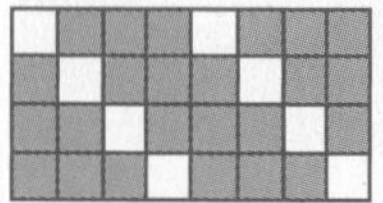

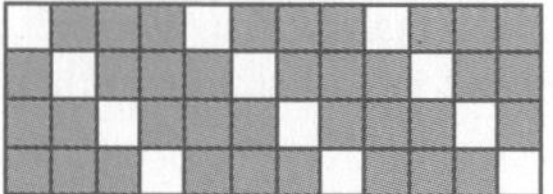

13a. Possible pattern:

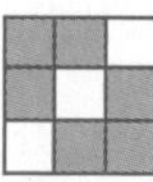

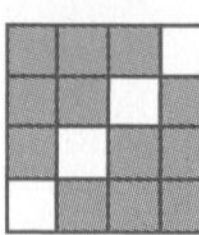

13c. Possible answer: If you graph the table values, the points don't lie on a straight line.

13d. Possible answer: $g = y^2 - y$

14a.

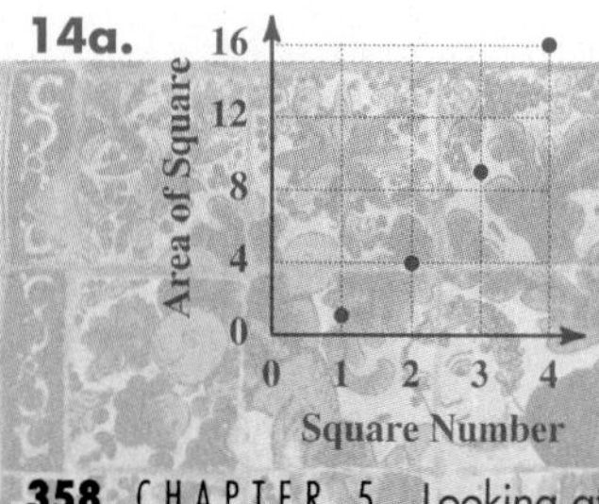

11. This tiling pattern can be any length as long as the pattern is complete (the first two columns and last two columns must look as shown here). Write a rule for the pattern, giving the relation between the number of white tiles and the number of purple tiles for various strip lengths. $p = w + 5$; w must be 2, 5, 8, 11, ...

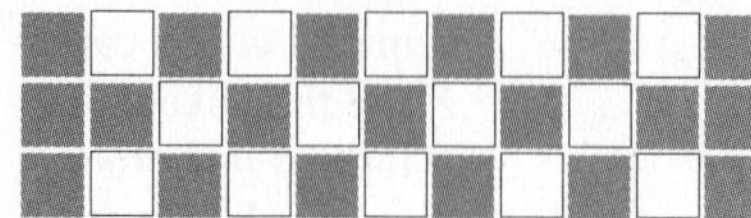

12. Invent a tiling pattern that shows a *linear* relationship between the number of purple tiles and the number of white tiles.

a. Draw a few examples of your pattern.

b. Create a table that shows the number of purple tiles and the number of white tiles for your examples. See Additional Answers.

c. Write a symbolic rule for that relationship. Possible answer: $p = 3w$

13. Challenge Invent a tiling pattern with green tiles and yellow tiles in which the relationship between the numbers of green tiles and yellow tiles is *nonlinear.*

a. Illustrate your pattern with a few examples.

b. Make a table for your pattern. See Additional Answers.

c. Write a clear explanation of how you know the relationship is nonlinear.

d. If possible, write a rule describing the relationship between the number of yellow tiles and the number of green tiles in your pattern.

14. Look back at your table for Problem 2 of Problem Set A. The pattern in that table is different from most of the patterns you worked with in this investigation.

a. Draw a graph for the pairs of numbers in that table.

b. How is this graph different from the graphs you drew in Problem Sets D through F? The points don't lie on a straight line.

Additional Answers

12b. Possible answer:

White Tiles, w	4	8	12
Purple Tiles, p	12	24	36

13b. Possible answer:

Yellow Tiles, y	1	2	3	4
Green Tiles, g	0	2	6	12

358 CHAPTER 5 Looking at Linear Relationships

15a, 15c, 15d. See Additional Answers.

15e. The line crosses the w-axis at 6 and has a slope of 2.

15f. The 2 is multiplied by p because there are 2 rows of white tiles, 1 on each side of and equal in length to the row of purple tiles. The 6 shows that there are 3 + 3 white tiles on the ends of these 3 rows.

16a. i: yes; ii: yes; iii: no; iv: yes; v: no

16c.

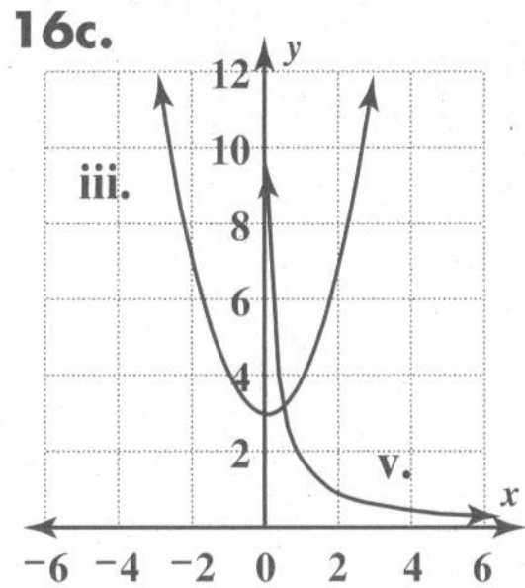

15. Pat and Tillie often tile walkways by surrounding a single strip of purple tiles with white tiles. Here is one walkway they made.

a. Draw this pattern for 1, 2, and 3 purple tiles.

b. Write a rule that relates the number of white tiles w to the number of purple tiles p. $w = 2p + 6$

c. Use your rule to make a table of values for the tiles needed for walkways of different lengths.

d. Draw a graph from your table. Put the number of purple tiles on the horizontal axis. Connect the points using a dashed line or a solid line, whichever makes more sense.

e. How are the two numbers in your rule shown in your graph?

f. How do these two numbers relate to the pattern of tiles in the walkway?

16. If you mark two points, only one straight line can be drawn through them. This means that when you have the rule for a linear relationship, you need to plot only two points to draw the line. Of course, even if you use this handy "two point" rule, it's not a bad idea to check a couple of more points to make sure you haven't made a mistake.

16b.

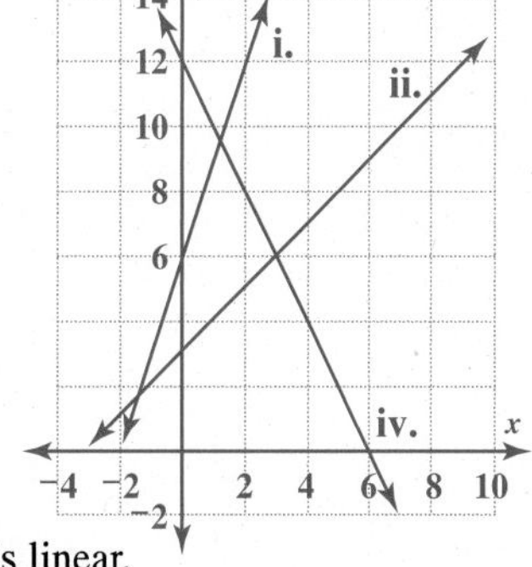

Here are five rules.

i. $y = 3x + 6$

ii. $y = x + 3$

iii. $y = x^2 + 3$

iv. $y = 12 - 2x$

v. $y = \frac{2}{x}$

a. Decide whether each of the rules is linear.

b. For each relationship you think is linear, find two points that will be on the graph, and use them to draw the graph. Then find a third point and check that it is on your line. See above.

c. For each relationship you think is *not* linear, find several points and use them to draw the graph.

Exercise 16: Students practice using the two-point rule to graph linear equations.

Additional Answers

15a.

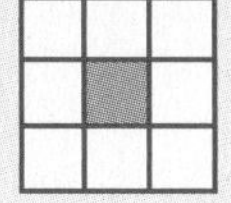

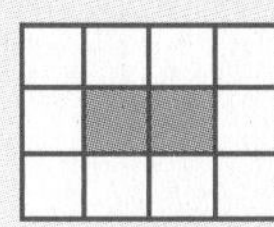

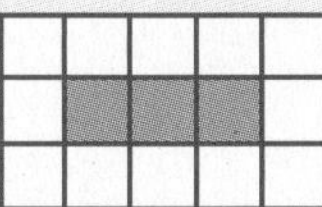

15c. Possible table:

Purple Tiles, p	2	4	6	8	10
White Tiles, w	10	14	18	22	26

15d. See Additional Answers on page A400.

Assign and Assess

Exercise 17b: Watch for students who answer 30 cm. Remind them that 30 cm must be divided by 2 if each twin receives an equal part.

Exercise 24a: Some students may have difficulty completing the table. Point out that they must add the people that have already been informed in the previous round to the number that were called in this round.

Exercise 24c: You may wish to ask students to extend the table to find the answer.

Exercise 24d: Watch for students who divide 256 by 3 and come up with an answer of $83\frac{1}{2}$. Explain that one cannot make a fraction of a call so the answer must be incorrect. Ask students how many calls Neeraj makes for each round. Then point out that he makes 3 calls each round as does everyone else who has been informed. Ask them what they must do to find out the total number of calls.

17. The three Pauli children all love licorice. Their mother often buys them a 30-centimeter strand of licorice. After the twins, Carmelo and Biagio, have had some, the rest goes to Maria, the youngest child. The twins have the same amount each.

a. What is the least amount the twins could have? How much would Maria then get? 0 cm, 30 cm

b. What is the greatest amount each twin could have? How much would Maria then get? 15 cm each, 0 cm

c. Choose some values for the length each twin has, and then calculate how long Maria's piece will be. See below.

d. Write a rule in symbols for finding the length of Maria's piece if you know the length of each twin's piece. $M = 30 - 2T$

e. Use your rule to find how long Maria's piece will be if Carmelo and Biagio have 5.5 cm each. 19 cm

f. Draw a graph of your data. Don't forget to label the axes. If it makes sense to draw a line through your points, do so.

g. Use your graph to predict the length of the twins' pieces if Maria's piece is 9 cm long. Check your prediction with your rule. 10.5 cm

17f.

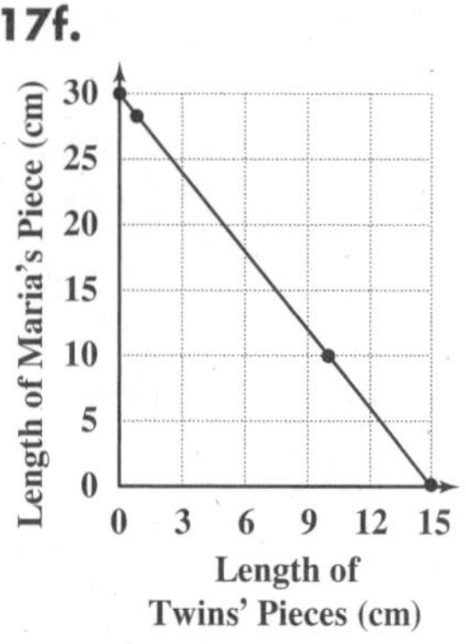

Mixed Review

Simplify.

18. $\frac{1}{25} + \frac{4}{25}$ $\frac{5}{25}$, or $\frac{1}{5}$

19. $\frac{1}{10} + \frac{6}{10}$ $\frac{7}{10}$

20. $\frac{2}{5} + \frac{1}{5} + 3$ $3\frac{3}{5}$, or $\frac{18}{5}$

21. Use the expression given to complete the table. Then write another expression that gives the same values. Check with the values in the table. $\frac{n}{2} + \frac{1}{2}$, or $\frac{1}{2}n + \frac{1}{2}$

n	0	1	2	3	4	100
$\frac{n+1}{2}$	$\frac{1}{2}$	1	$1\frac{1}{2}$	2	$2\frac{1}{2}$	$50\frac{1}{2}$

Expand each expression.

22. $3(n + 7)$ $3n + 21$

23. $8(k + 11)$ $8k + 88$

17c. Possible answer:

Length of Twins' Pieces (cm), *T*	0	1	10	15
Length of Maria's Piece (cm), *M*	30	28	10	0

24. Neeraj belongs to a regional drama club. There are a lot of students in the club, making it difficult for one person to contact everyone when necessary.

If the club director has to cancel a meeting, she calls Neeraj. He is in charge of starting a chain of phone calls to inform people of the cancellation. Neeraj is assigned to first call three people: Tom, Shaunda, and Cori. Then Neeraj, Tom, Shaunda, and Cori each call three people. This pattern continues until everyone has been informed.

a. Complete the table.

Round	0	1	2	3
Number of People Informed	1 (just Neeraj)	4	16	64

b. After which round will at least 50 people know about the cancellation? 3

c. If 256 people need to be informed, how many rounds of calls must be made? 4

d. How many calls will Neeraj have made by the time 256 people have been informed? 12 (3 calls for each round)

Supply the missing exponent.

25. $24 \times 10^? = 24{,}000$ 3

26. $2.8 \times 10^? = 28{,}000$ 4

Rewrite each expression as addition, and calculate the sum.

27. $12 - {}^-4$ **28.** ${}^-8 - {}^-8$ **29.** ${}^-3 - {}^-2$

27. $12 + 4 = 16$
28. ${}^-8 + 8 = 0$
29. ${}^-3 + 2 = {}^-1$

Find the distance between the endpoints of the segment.

30. 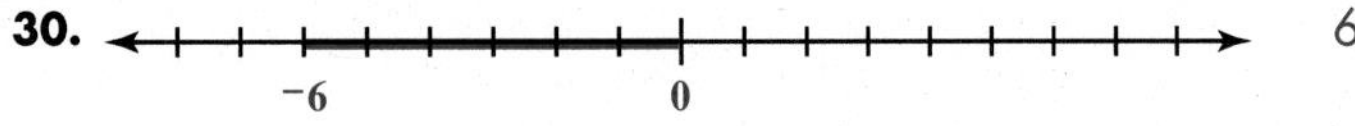 6

31. −4.5 to 0 4.5

Rewrite in the form c^m.

32. $6^9 \times 6$ 6^{10} **33.** $3^5 \times 3^5$ 3^{10} **34.** $10^{11} \times 10^5$ 10^{16}

Quick Check

Informal Assessment
Students should be able to

- ✔ recognize linear relationships in a variety of representations: symbolic rules, graphs, visual patterns, and tables
- ✔ translate from one representation to another
- ✔ recognize the symbolic representation of a linear relationship in more than one form
- ✔ explain the connection between the constant difference, the slope of the graph, and the symbolic representation of the relationship (the a in $y = ax + b$)
- ✔ determine b in the rule $y = ax + b$ from a graph (the y-intercept, the intersection with the vertical axis)

• *Quick Quiz begins on page A400.*

Teacher Notes

5.4 Tricks of the Trade

Objectives

- To learn that in a table showing the relationship between two variables, if the change in both variables is constant, then the two are linearly related, and that if the change in *one* quantity is constant but the change in the other is *not* constant, then the quantities are not linearly related
- To solidify understanding of the connection between the constant difference, the slope of the graph, and the symbolic representation of the relationship
- To apply the concepts of a negative slope and a negative constant term
- To learn how to determine b in the rule $y = ax + b$ from a graph (the y-intercept, the intersection with the vertical axis), and by checking the output of the rule when the input is 0.

Overview (pacing: about 3 class periods)

In earlier lessons, students worked with linear and some nonlinear relations, largely in context. They learned, for example, that a constant speed implies a constant change in distance over time: every second the distance changes by the same amount. This lesson steps out of these contexts to focus explicitly on the mathematical ideas associated with constant change. Students examine tables to see whether the change (difference) from one value to the next is constant, and to recognize that if it is, the relation is linear and the graph will be a line. They also learn that when the input numbers in the table differ by 1, the constant difference is the slope of the line. They are introduced to techniques for determining a and b in $y = ax + b$ by trying various inputs (x) and examining the change in the output (y).

Advanced Preparation

In preparation for this lesson, you may want to briefly introduce the phrase "tricks of the trade" and ask students to find examples from friends or family members to share in a class discussion. Students will also need copies of Master 10, Quarter-Inch Graph Paper, or sheets of graph paper.

	Summary	Materials	On Your Own Exercises	Assessment Opportunities
Investigation 1 page T362	Students try to develop an effective strategy to discover the symbolic rule from the data.	• Master 10 (Teaching Resources, page 15)	Practice & Apply: 1–5 Connect & Extend: 13 Mixed Review: 18–33	Share & Summarize, pages T364, 364 On the Spot Assessment, page T363 Troubleshooting, page T364
Investigation 2 page T365	Students learn and practice the method of constant differences to decide whether a relationship is linear.	• Master 10	Practice & Apply: 6–10 Connect & Extend: 14–16 Mixed Review: 18–33	Share & Summarize, pages T368, 368 On the Spot Assessment, page T365 Troubleshooting, page T368
Investigation 3 page T368	Students analyze linear graphs in four quadrants and relations between symbols and graphs.		Practice & Apply: 11–12 Connect & Extend: 17 Mixed Review: 18–33	Share & Summarize, pages T370, 370 On the Spot Assessment, page T369 Troubleshooting, page T370 Informal Assessment, page 376 Quick Quiz, page 377

The major purpose of this lesson is to develop the idea and the appropriate skills of examining differences—rate of change—in order to determine whether the change is constant and linear.

1 Think & Discuss

Begin this lesson by being sure students know what is meant by "tricks of the trade." Have them think of some activities that they know how to do really well. Then ask them to describe any tricks that may help them to perform that activity with less effort and more efficiency.

If you asked students to prepare for this discussion beforehand by talking with friends and relatives, they may contribute a variety of "tricks of the trade" to the discussion. Students who have just been introduced to the phrase might look for other mathematical tricks of the trade they know and use, such as calculator shortcuts.

Investigation 1

The problems in this investigation require that students describe a pattern symbolically. You will need to have copies of Master 10, Quarter-Inch Graph Paper, or graph paper available for students as they complete the problems in this investigation.

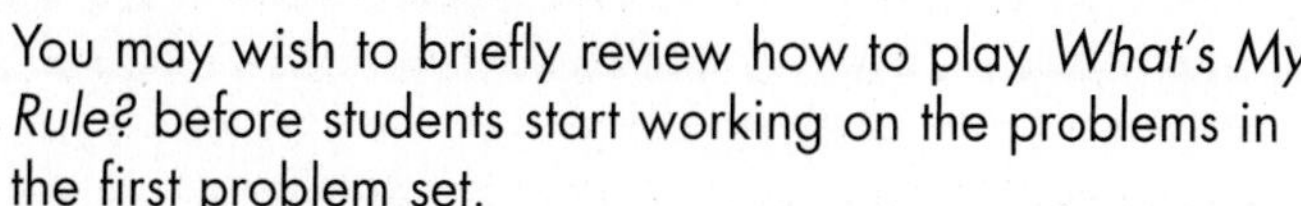

2 You may wish to briefly review how to play *What's My Rule?* before students start working on the problems in the first problem set.

3 Problem Set A Grouping: Pairs

Students use input and output pairs from given *What's My Rule?* games to find relationships. They do not actually play the games themselves.

5.4 Tricks of the Trade

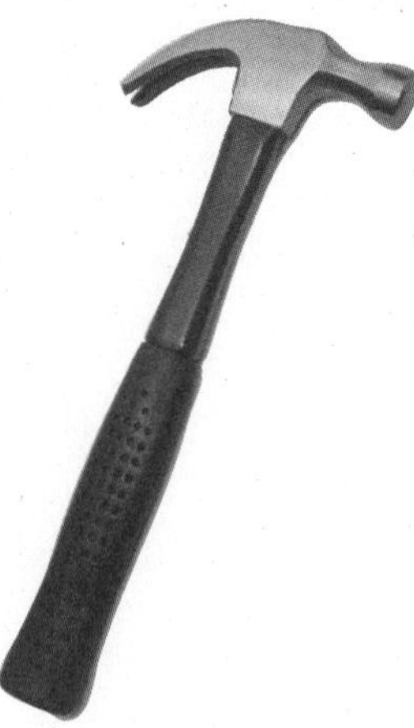

People who are skilled at something—like cooking or carpentry—learn or develop "tricks of the trade" that make their work more successful. For example, putting a little cooking oil in boiling water helps stop spaghetti from sticking. Many tricks of the trade seem like magic at first, but once you know them, you might wonder why you hadn't thought of them before!

1
- Have students discuss the meaning of "tricks of the trade."
- Encourage students to share "tricks of the trade" for an activity they can do well.

Think & Discuss

Think of something you know how to do well, such as a sport, job, hobby, or household task. Can you think of a few tricks of the trade you might share with someone just learning?

In this lesson you will learn a trick of the mathematician's trade for helping to find rules for linear relationships.

Investigation 1 Finding Secret Rules

2 Review how to play *What's My Rule?* with the entire class.

You can use some of the things you have learned about relationships to help you discover the secret rules in games of *What's My Rule?*

MATERIALS
graph paper

Problem Set A

3 Partners use input and output values to find relationships.

Several students are playing *What's My Rule?*

1. In this game, Shaunda is the Rule Keeper and Luis is the Guesser.

Develop

In **Problems 1 and 2,** students use data from the cartoons to make graphs and write symbolic rules for the number pairs. Be sure that they understand the importance of telling what each variable in their rule stands for.

> **On the Spot Assessment**
>
> In **Problem 2,** watch for students who sometimes graph an input value as the *x*-coordinate and sometimes as a *y*-coordinate in the same graph. They may need to list the input/output values in a T-chart, table, or other list to organize their data before plotting the points.

Students will probably need to graph the points in **Problems 3 and 4** to determine whether the relationship is linear, even though this is not specified in their textbooks.

Problem Set Wrap-Up Discuss **Problem 5** as a class. Have students share any illustrations they made. This trick allows students to use what they have learned about slope and about what the terms in a rule signify.

Remember

One Rule Keeper and any number of Guessers can play *What's My Rule?* The Rule Keeper makes up a secret rule that takes inputs and produces outputs. Guessers give inputs to the Rule Keeper, who gives outputs until someone guesses the rule.

1b. Possible rule: $b = 2a + 3$, where a is the input and b is the output

3. The points do not lie on a line, so it isn't linear. The rule could be $y = x^2$.

4. The points lie on a line, so it could be linear. The rule could be $y = 10 - x$.

a. On a graph, plot the pairs of inputs and outputs. Decide whether the relationship could be linear. See Additional Answers.

b. Find a symbolic rule that fits the number pairs. Choose letters for the inputs and outputs, and be careful to make it clear which is which.

2. In this game, Darnell is the Rule Keeper and Kate is the Guesser.

a. On a graph, plot the pairs of inputs and outputs. Decide whether the relationship could be linear. See Additional Answers.

b. Find a symbolic rule that fits the numbers. Choose letters for the inputs and outputs, and make it clear which is which. See below.

For each set of input/output pairs, tell whether the relationship could be linear. Then find a rule that fits the pairs.

3. (4, 16), (1, 1), $(\frac{1}{2}, \frac{1}{4})$, (3, 9)

4. (10, 0), (2, 8), (4.5, 5.5), (5, 5)

2b. Possible rule: $q = 3p - 4$, where p is the input and q is the output

5. Jin Lee is the class *What's My Rule?* champion. Her secret is to plot points to see whether they lie along a line. If the rule describes a linear relationship, she can look at the graph and guess a rule that fits the points.

Explain how Jin Lee might derive a rule from the graph. Use illustrations, if you like.
See Additional Answers.

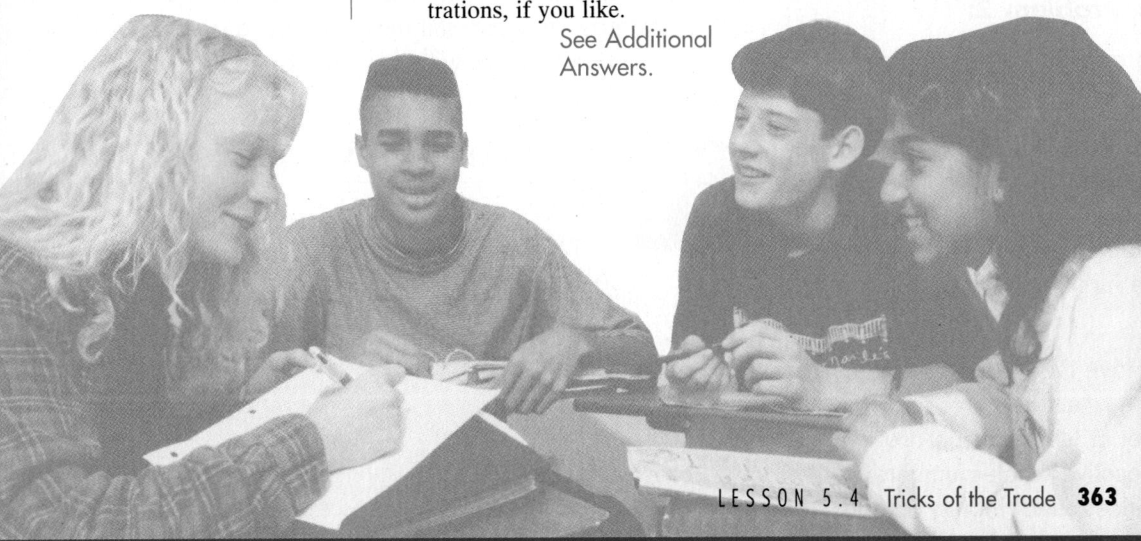

1 Students use data from cartoons to make graphs.

2 Have students graph the points if necessary.

3 Discuss Problem 5 with the entire class.

Additional Answers Problem Set A

1a. The points lie on a line, so it could be linear.

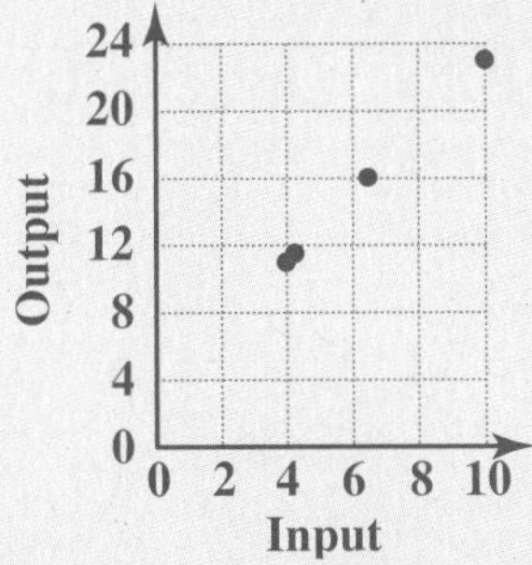

5. See Additional Answers on page A401.

2a. The points lie on a line, so it could be linear.

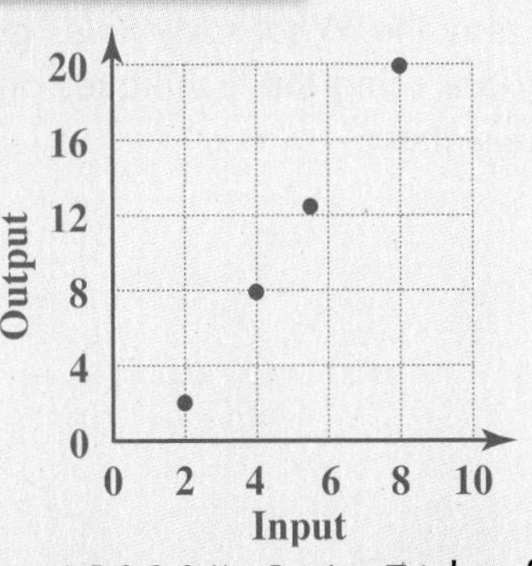

Develop

Problem Set B Grouping: Pairs

Problem Set B asks students to figure out the strategy of looking for constant differences that Jin Lee uses for finding out the rule. The strategy relies on her choice of *consecutive* numbers as input numbers. This is important because by choosing consecutive whole numbers, the difference in the outputs (if it is constant) is the slope of the graph, or a in the rule $y = ax + b$.

Students find the value of the constant term b in the rule $y = ax + b$ by finding the output when the input is 0. This can be done in *What's My Rule?* games just by giving the input of 0. In the case of the tables, some of which do not contain 0 as input, students must extend the table backward. Students continue to explore this concept in Problem Set C in the next investigation.

Some of the students may try to guess the rule without graphing the points by simply calculating the differences between input and output numbers. This works quite well as long as the input numbers differ by 1, which is the case here. However this method is incomplete if the input numbers differ by more or less than 1, even if they are equally spaced. Encourage students to check their guess with a graph.

Sample Strategies Students may use one of these strategies to write the rule in **Problem 2:**

- Some students may use graphs to help them find the rule.
- Other students may discover quickly that since the input numbers are consecutive, they can use the difference in output numbers to determine the slope if the differences are, in fact, constant. They can use the output value when the input value is 0 as the constant.

Problem Set Wrap-Up Have the students explain their strategies for finding the rule. Their wording may vary, but if their ideas do not at least paraphrase the key techniques—using consecutive whole numbers, attending to constant differences, and finding output value when input is 0—you might refer back to a problem, or play the *What's My Rule?* game to see whether they are using the techniques and merely forgetting to list them.

Share & Summarize

The final question asks students how they can use a graph to figure out other pairs that are not in the table. You may want to ask students this valuable additional question:

> What kinds of input/output pairs can you not expect to figure out from a graph? *Any that would require too large a graph, too much precision in reading the graph, etc. For these, the rule allows one to calculate new entries more easily.*

A class discussion of these questions, possibly livened up with a game of *What's My Rule?* can help students articulate the strategies sought in the Wrap-Up.

Troubleshooting Though graphs are in some ways more flexible than Jin Lee's strategy—they'll work even if the tables are drawn from data that is messy, with no discernible pattern in the input numbers—it is important that students understand the new technique. If students continue to have difficulties determining the rule from the table without using a graph, remind them to look for consecutive whole number inputs and then ask how they can determine the slope from their respective outputs.

Students are not yet expected to be masters of the new strategy. You can still move on, because students will continue to work with this strategy in the following investigations.

On Your Own Exercises

Practice & Apply: 1–5
Connect & Extend: 13
Mixed Review: 18–33

MATERIALS
graph paper

Problem Set B

Jin Lee developed a quick strategy for finding rules in the game. She found that if she chooses consecutive integers as inputs, she can tell whether the relationship could be linear *just by looking at how the outputs change.* Look at the numbers she collected for four games she played.

Game 1

Input	1	2	3	4	5
Output	4	7	10	13	16

Game 2

Input	0	1	2	3	4
Output	1	6	11	16	21

Game 3

Input	0	1	2	3	4
Output	29	27	25	23	21

Game 4

Input	2	3	4	5	6
Output	10	15	21	28	36

1. Jin Lee concluded that Games 1, 2, and 3 could be linear, but that Game 4 couldn't be. Inspect her tables of input/output pairs. What pattern might have led Jin Lee to her decision?
2. For each game that Jin Lee thinks could be linear, write a symbolic rule that fits all the input/output pairs. Choose letters for the inputs and outputs, and be careful to say which is which.
3. Make a graph for each of the four games. Extend your graphs, and use them to estimate the output each game's rule would give for an input of $^{-}3$. Which estimates are you confident are most accurate? Explain. See Additional Answers.

1. If the output increases or decreases by equal amounts, the relationship could be linear.
2. Game 1. input m, output n: $n = 3m + 1$ Game 2. input d, output c: $c = 5d + 1$ Game 3. input v, output z: $z = 29 - 2v$

Share & Summarize

1. Using just a graph, you can tell whether a rule could describe a linear relationship. How?
2. Using just a table with consecutive integers for inputs, you can tell whether a rule could describe a linear relationship. How?
3. Suppose a table shows some input/output pairs in a linear relationship. How can you use a graph of the table values to find other input/output pairs?

Share & Summarize Answers

1. If the points lie on a line, the relationship could be linear.
2. If the differences between consecutive outputs are constant, the relationship could be linear.
3. Draw a line through the plotted points, and then find coordinates for other points on the line.

1 As students work in pairs, ask questions about the strategies they are developing to decide whether a rule is linear.

2 Discuss questions with entire class.

• *Additional Answers on page A401.*

Investigation 2

This investigation formally introduces the constant difference method that students discovered in the previous investigation. It continues with activities familiar from that investigation. If you care to introduce it further, you might review the ideas generated in the previous day's Problem Set Wrap-Up. You may wish to have several copies of Master 10, Quarter-Inch Graph Paper, ready when students complete the problem sets in this investigation.

Problem Set C **Suggested Grouping: Individuals**
This problem set provides additional practice in finding the rule for a linear relationship without graphing. It also asks students to distinguish between linear and nonlinear relationships and use a graph to check whether their decisions were correct. Finally, it focuses attention on the need to look at the input numbers because if the entries in the table are not consecutive, the differences between neighboring output numbers is meaningless.

Problems 2 and 4 show nonlinear relationships.

In **Problem 3,** the coefficient is a negative number.

On the Spot Assessment

Watch for students who do not notice that the input values in the tables in **Problems 4–6** are out of order. Students who look only at the output values may conclude that the rule in **Problem 4** is linear since the output numbers appear to increase by 10 as we move to the right. They may also conclude that the rules in **Problems 5 and 6** are nonlinear since the differences between adjacent output values in the tables vary. Plotting the input/output pairs shows that the rules in Problems 5 and 6 *are* linear and that the rule in Problem 4 is nonlinear.

Problem Set Wrap-Up Help students notice that the method of identifying constant differences to check for linearity works only if the input numbers are in order and are spaced evenly. In Problem Set C, the input numbers, when arranged in order, always differ by 1.

Investigation 2 The Method of Constant Differences

1. could be linear; $q = 10p + 3$

2. not linear

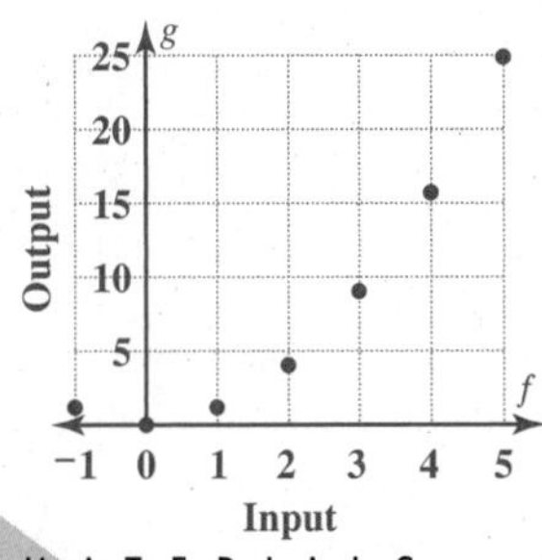

MATERIALS
graph paper

3. could be linear; $u = {}^{-}0.5t$

4. not linear

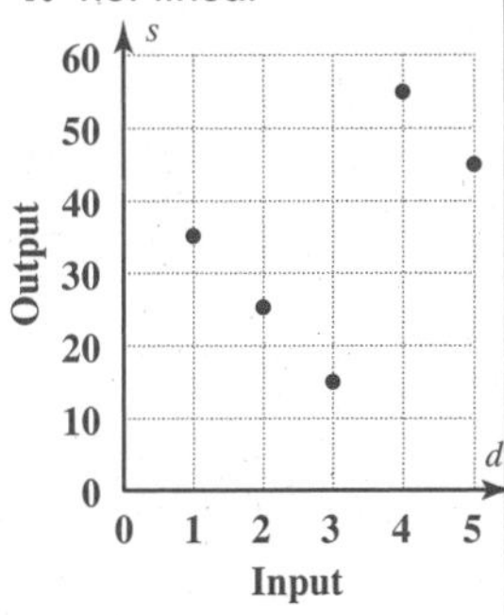

5. could be linear; $y = 9x - 2$

6. could be linear; $n = 3m$

7. 0; The output would be b.

Jin Lee's method is a mathematical "trick of the trade." She makes her table in a special way, using consecutive integers for inputs. Then she finds the *differences* of neighboring pairs of outputs to see if they make a recognizable pattern.

If the difference between two neighbors is the same no matter which pair Jin Lee chooses, they are *constant differences.* In that case, a plot of the input/output pairs will lie along a line, and the relationship could be linear. Jin Lee can then use the constant difference to quickly find a rule that describes the linear relationship and fits the input/output pairs.

Problem Set C

1

- Students work independently to distinguish whether a relationship is linear or nonlinear without graphing.
- Students determine a rule for a linear relationship without graphing.

Below are several tables you can use to try Jin Lee's trick. For each, if you think the relationship could be linear, find a rule and check it with the pairs in the table. If you think the relationship isn't linear, draw a graph to check. Pay attention to the order of the inputs!

1.

Input, *p*	⁻3	⁻2	⁻1	0	1	2	3
Output, *q*	⁻27	⁻17	⁻7	3	13	23	33

2.

Input, *f*	⁻1	0	1	2	3	4	5
Output, *g*	1	0	1	4	9	16	25

3.

Input, *t*	⁻2	⁻1	0	1	2	3	4	5
Output, *u*	1	0.5	0	⁻0.5	⁻1	⁻1.5	⁻2	⁻2.5

4.

Input, *d*	3	2	1	5	4
Output, *s*	15	25	35	45	55

5.

Input, *x*	0	2	1	5	4	3
Output, *y*	⁻2	16	7	43	34	25

6.

Input, *m*	4	1	3	2	5
Output, *n*	12	3	9	6	15

7. Imagine you are playing *What's My Rule?* and already know that the rule is linear. This means you can write the rule as $y = ax + b$, with numbers in place of a and b and with x as the input and y as the output. What input would you use so you could find the value of b? Why would you use that input? If you need ideas, look back at the tables you have seen and the rules you have written for them.

Develop

Problem Set D **Suggested Grouping: Individuals**
In this problem set, students explore why the constant-differences method works. The problems help them progress through the reasoning process as they find the explanation.

Problem Set Wrap-Up Discuss the problems as a class to allow students to help each other understand why the method works.

Problem Set E **Suggested Grouping: Individuals**
Students practice using the constant differences method to determine whether input/output values have linear relationships and if so, they write the rules for those relationships. They verify their response by graphing the data and finding the slope to confirm that their rules are correct.

Two of the tables in this problem set show nonlinear relations, but other strong patterns in their differences allow students to predict how the patterns continue. The tables were designed to connect with other ideas in the book—quadratic and exponential (or "roughly exponential") growth—while exercising the idea that linearity means constant change (constant differences).

The differences in the table in **Problem 1** are the same as the output numbers themselves, doubling every time. This pattern where the differences of the outputs mimic the outputs is characteristic of exponential growth. Students may relate this to ideas about exponents that they learned in Chapter 3. If no one does, you might suggest the idea.

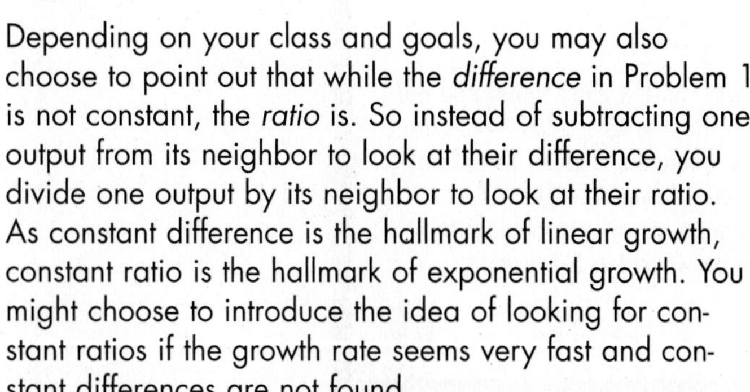

Depending on your class and goals, you may also choose to point out that while the *difference* in Problem 1 is not constant, the *ratio* is. So instead of subtracting one output from its neighbor to look at their difference, you divide one output by its neighbor to look at their ratio. As constant difference is the hallmark of linear growth, constant ratio is the hallmark of exponential growth. You might choose to introduce the idea of looking for constant ratios if the growth rate seems very fast and constant differences are not found.

In **Problem 2,** the input values are not evenly spaced.

Access for All Learners

Extra for Experts You might introduce students to the idea of checking the second differences if the first differences are not constant. For example, in the table in **Problem 3,** the differences are not constant and the relationship is not linear. Have students write out all the differences as a sequence and then compute *their* differences, or the "second differences." They will see that these second differences *are* constant. The values in this table illustrate a quadratic relationship. In any quadratic relationship, the first differences are not constant but bear a linear relationship with the input numbers, and so their differences must be constant. The concept of second differences is introduced to all students in Course 3.

In **Problems 4 and 6,** the differences are constant and therefore the relationships are linear.

In **Problem 5,** the input values are not consecutive.

Just the facts

In downhill skiing, ski slopes are rated by their difficulty. Beginner's slopes are indicated by green dots, intermediate slopes by blue squares, and advanced slopes by black diamonds.

1–3. See Additional Answers.

Problem Set D

You will now think some more about *why* Jin Lee's strategy for finding rules works.

1. The differences in the output values in this table are all 3.

x	1	2	3	4	5
y	4	7	10	13	16

Think of a situation—like those you have studied in this chapter—that might have this table. Describe what the difference of 3 means for your situation. Does it make sense that the relationship between these variables could be linear? Explain.

2. If you made a graph showing how y changes as x changes, what would its slope be? What does this slope mean for your situation in Problem 1?

3. Recall how we defined *slope*. Look back in your book if necessary. How does using consecutive integers for your inputs help you find the slope?

1
- Students work problems independently.
- Discuss answers as a whole class.

MATERIALS
graph paper

Problem Set E

Use the differences method to analyze the pattern in each table. Predict the missing outputs.

1.

Input, x	1	2	3	4	5	6	7	8
Output, y	1	2	4	8	16	32	64	128

2.

Input, s	1	3	4	8	11	12	13	14
Output, t	8	18	23	43	58	63	68	73

3.

Input, a	1	2	3	4	5	6	7	8
Output, b	1	2	4	7	11	16	22	29

4.

Input, g	1	2	3	4	5	6	7	8
Output, h	7.5	6	4.5	3	1.5	0	$^-1.5$	$^-3$

5.

Input, m	$^-3$	$^-1$	1	3	5	7	9	11
Output, n	2	$^-2$	$^-6$	$^-10$	$^-14$	$^-18$	$^-22$	$^-26$

6.

Input, p	0	1	2	3	4	5	6	7
Output, r	$^-10$	12	34	56	78	100	122	144

2 Students determine whether input/output tables have linear relationships.

3 Although the difference in Problem 1 is not constant, the ratio is. So the growth is exponential.

Additional Answers
Problem Set D

1. Possible answer: x is the number of squares created with y toothpicks, and 3 is the number of toothpicks needed to add another square. It makes sense, because there is a single rate of change, as with all the other linear relationships we've seen.

2. 3; Possible answer: This is the rate of growth, or how many toothpicks are added at each stage.

3. The slope tells how many units the output changes when the input changes by 1 unit. Since we're making the input change by 1 unit, the difference in the outputs, if they are always the same, must be the slope.

Develop

Problem Set Wrap-Up Discuss **Problems 7–9.** Have students give the rules they wrote in **Problem 7.** Then have students identify the slopes in these rules. You may want to have students display their graphs for **Problem 8** on an overhead to check their accuracy.

Example

Present the examples to the class. Be sure students understand why the constant in $y = 4x - 3$ is $^-3$ and why the coefficient in $y = x + 12$ is 1.

8–10. See Additional Answers.

7. In which tables do the differences tell you the relationships could be linear? Write rules for those relationships. See below.

8. Plot the data in each table. For the graphs that seem to be linear, draw a line through the points. Extend the linear graphs to show the value of the output when the input is 0, $^-1$, and $^-2$, and label those points with their coordinates.

9. Find the slope of each line you drew in Problem 8. Compare the slopes to the rules you wrote for Problem 7.

10. In Problem 7, did you choose all the relationships that could be linear? Did you write a correct rule for each of them? If not, figure out what went wrong, and write new rules for those relationships.

1 Have students share their rules with the class and then identify the slope for each rule.

Nearly all the rules you have encountered in this chapter can be written in this form:

$$y = ax + b$$

VOCABULARY
variable
coefficient
constant term

The outputs y and the inputs x are called **variables** because their values can vary. The other two numbers also have special names.

A number that is multiplied by the input, like a, is called a **coefficient.** In the equation $y = ax + b$, we say that "a is the coefficient of x."

A number that stands by itself, like b, is often referred to as the **constant term.**

EXAMPLE

$y = 2x + 6$	The 2 is a coefficient and the 6 is the constant term.
$y = 4x - 3$	The 4 is a coefficient, but what is the constant term? It helps to rewrite the rule in the form $y = ax + b$. Since subtracting a number is the same as adding its opposite, this rule can be rewritten as $y = 4x + {}^-3$. So, the constant term is $^-3$.
$y = x + 12$	You can see that the constant term is 12, but there's no number being multiplied by x. Is there a coefficient? You can rewrite this rule, too: $y = 1x + 12$. Here, a is 1, so 1 is the coefficient.

2
- Discuss the Example.
- Be sure students can identify the variable, coefficient, and constant in each equation.

7. Tables 2, 4, 5, and 6; 2: $t = 5s + 3$, 4: $h = 9 - 1.5g$, 5: $n = {}^-2m - 4$, 6: $r = 22p - 10$ (Note: Students may miss the pattern in Table 2 if they overlook the fact that the inputs do not change by a constant amount.)

Additional Answers

8. See Additional Answers on page A402.

9. 2: 5, 4: $^-1.5$; 5: $^-2$; 6: 22; They are equal to the coefficient of the input variable. (Note: Some students may not have identified Problem 2 as linear, and some may have used $^-4$ instead of $^-2$ in the rule for Problem 5.)

10. Possible answer: In Problem 2, the inputs are in order, but they are not evenly spaced. Because they skip values, you can't use the method of constant differences; the output numbers also skip. The rule should be $t = 5s + 3$. In Problem 5, my rule was $n = {}^-4m - 4$. I used the constant difference for the slope because I didn't notice that the inputs aren't consecutive. The rule should be $n = {}^-2m - 4$. (Note: If students got Problem 7 correct, their answers to both questions will be yes.)

Share & Summarize

This question reviews the main ideas of the entire chapter, leaving only a broadening of the ideas to Investigation 3.

Troubleshooting The most important ideas of the chapter are given here.

1. The method of constant differences can determine whether a relationship is linear.
2. The graph of a linear relationship is a straight line.
3. If the input numbers differ by 1, then the constant difference tells the coefficient a in $y = ax + b$ (the slope of the graphed line).
4. When the input number is 0, the output number tells the constant term b in $y = ax + b$ (the place where the graphed line intersects the vertical axis).

If students have difficulties applying these ideas, it might be good to have students give examples of each of them and show how, if at all, they used these in solving the problems. Then students can move on because they will have more practice applying these ideas in Investigation 3.

On Your Own Exercises

Practice & Apply: 6–10
Connect & Extend: 14–16
Mixed Review: 18–33

Investigation 3

With some non-standard problems, this investigation pulls together all of the ideas about the symbolic, graphical, and tabular representations of linear relationships covered in the chapter. Students will need copies of Master 10, Quarter-Inch Graph Paper, or sheets of graph paper so that they can complete the problem sets in Investigation 3.

Problem Set F Suggested Grouping: Pairs

This problem set asks students to think about several ways in which a and b affect the graph of $y = ax + b$ and to explain their answers. Ideally, students would grapple with each problem by themselves, then compare their answers with a partner, and hone their skills at explaining their reasoning.

This set reviews ideas about all four quadrants of a graph (Problems 3–9), slope (Problem 1), and intersections with the axes (Problems 2, 10, and 11).

In **Problem 3,** be sure students understand why $y = 3$ can be included in the table.

1. If the inputs are evenly spaced, the outputs must be evenly spaced (have a constant difference) for the relationship to be linear.
2. See Additional Answers.

Share & Summarize

1. Explain how to determine whether the input/output pairs in a table could be related in a linear way.
2. Using the new vocabulary terms on the previous page, explain how to write a symbolic rule for a table that you have determined could describe a linear relationship.

1 You may wish to have students give examples of how to use these ideas to solve problems.

Investigation  3 Understanding the Symbols

In this chapter, you have looked at relationships that describe real situations. Most of these relationships were *linear:* they could be graphed as a line and expressed in a rule that looks like $y = ax + b$.

Now you will extend what you know about the coefficient and the constant term, a and b, by investigating how they affect the quadrants the graph passes through.

MATERIALS
graph paper

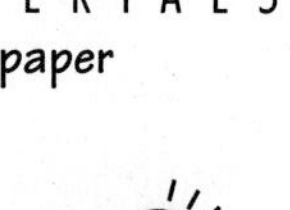

Remember
The four quadrants of a graph are numbered like this:

II second quadrant	I first quadrant
III third quadrant	IV fourth quadrant

Problem Set F   1. the slope   2. the y-intercept

2 Students work independently and then compare answers with a partner.

1. What does the coefficient a tell you about the graph of $y = ax + b$?
2. What does the constant term b describe about a graph of $y = ax + b$?
3. For each equation in the table below, $a = 0$ and $b \neq 0$.
   a. Complete the table. Choose two more equations for which $a = 0$ and $b \neq 0$, and add them to your table. Possible answers:

x	$^-2$	$^-1$	0	1	2	3
$y = 0x - 2$	$^-2$	$^-2$	$^-2$	$^-2$	$^-2$	$^-2$
$y = 3$	3	3	3	3	3	3
$y = 4$	4	4	4	4	4	4
$y = 1$	1	1	1	1	1	1

   b. On one set of axes, graph all four equations. See Additional Answers.
4. How many quadrants does each graph pass through? Do you think this will always be true for $y = ax + b$ when $a = 0$ and $b \neq 0$? Test several more rules of your own to check. two, yes

Additional Answers
Share & Summarize

2. If the inputs are 1 unit apart, such as consecutive integers, the difference in the outputs is the coefficient. The output for an input of 0 is the constant term. If you don't have 0 as an input, you can find the constant term by multiplying any input by the coefficient and subtracting the product from the output.

Problem Set F

3b. See Additional Answers on page A403.

Develop

In **Problem 5,** students should understand that when $b = 0$, the equation $y = ax + b$ can also be written $y = ax + 0$ or $y = ax$.

In **Problem 7,** some students may need to be reminded that the axes of a coordinate grid do not lie in any quadrant.

On the Spot Assessment

In **Problem 8,** watch for students who answer two quadrants because that is reflective of what has been graphed in this problem set. Ask them to graph the values for Game 1 or Game 2 in Problem Set B on page 364 which passes through three quadrants, and then reconsider their answer.

It is important for students to realize that knowing a few entries in a table may *not* provide enough information to determine a rule unless they already know, or can assume, more about the rule, such as it is linear. For example, looking only at the first four entries in the two tables at the bottom of page 369, one might expect it to continue as the table at the top of page 369 does.

5. For each equation in the table below, $a \neq 0$ and $b = 0$.

a. Complete the table. Choose two more equations for which $a \neq 0$ and $b = 0$, and add them to your table. Possible answers:

x	$^-2$	$^-1$	0	1	2	3
$y = x$	$^-2$	$^-1$	0	1	2	3
$y = {}^-2x$	4	2	0	$^-2$	$^-4$	$^-6$
$y = 3x$	$^-6$	$^-3$	0	3	6	9
$y = {}^-x$	2	1	0	$^-1$	$^-2$	$^-3$

b. On one set of axes, graph all four equations. See Additional Answers.

6. How many quadrants does each graph pass through? Do you think this will always be true for $y = ax + b$ when $b = 0$ and $a \neq 0$? Test some more rules to check. two, yes

7. How many quadrants do you think $y = ax + b$ will pass through if $a = 0$ and $b = 0$? Graph the equation $y = 0$. How many quadrants does the graph pass through? See Additional Answers.

8. Look back at the graphs in this chapter. How many quadrants can $y = ax + b$ pass through *at the most*? Explain your reasoning.

9. How many quadrants can $y = ax + b$ pass through *at the least*? Explain your reasoning.

10. Look at your graphs for this problem set for graphs that don't cross the horizontal axis. What do their rules have in common? Do you think all such rules will have graphs that don't cross the horizontal axis? $a = 0$, yes

11. Are there any graphs in your examples, or elsewhere in this chapter, that do not cross the vertical axis? Can you think of a rule in the form $y = ax + b$ with such a graph? no, no

8. three; To pass through four quadrants, it would have to curve.

9. None, or two if you don't count $y = 0$. If the line is $y = 0$, it lies on the x-axis and passes through no quadrants. If the line is horizontal, it passes through two quadrants (I and II, or III and IV). If it is not horizontal, the fewest it can pass through is two (I and III, or II and IV), if it goes through the origin.

The outputs in the two tables below start out the same way—both begin with 1, 2, 4, and 8—but they continue differently.

Input	1	2	3	4	5	6	7	8
Output	1	2	4	8	16			

Input	1	2	3	4	5	6	7	8
Output	1	2	4	8	15			

Even though these two tables match in four places, they do not match in the fifth place—and maybe will never match again! This shows that if someone gives you a sequence of numbers like 1, 2, 4, 8, . . ., you can't reliably say what number will come next without knowing more.

1 Be sure students understand that when $b = 0$, $y = ax + b$ can be written as $y = ax + 0$ or $y = ax$.

2 Remind students that axes of a coordinate grid do not lie in any quadrant.

3 Be sure students realize that knowing a few entries in a table may not provide enough information to determine a rule.

• ***Additional Answers on page A403.***

LESSON 5.4 Tricks of the Trade 369

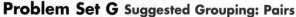

Develop

Problem Set G **Suggested Grouping: Pairs**
This problem set focuses on graphing linear relationships and writing rules in the form $y = ax + b$.

Problem 1 shows how a linear graph can be determined from only two points. The introduction to this problem reiterates the idea that a pattern cannot be extended by examining a table of data alone—something else must be known or assumed (for example, that the pattern is linear) if one is to extrapolate from data.

Problem 2 foreshadows ideas about manipulating one symbolic form to convert it into another equivalent one.

Problem Set Wrap-Up Have students share their answers and explanations for **Problem 1a.** Remind them that this is true because they were told that the relationship was linear. They should realize that they could not draw a graph when given two points if that relationship were not known. Then have students explain how they determined their answers to **Problem 2.**

Share & Summarize
This Share & Summarize extends the Share & Summarize of Investigation 2 to include graphs. Students pull together all of their ideas about how graphs and tables can be analyzed to determine a rule and are asked to articulate these ideas clearly.

Troubleshooting Because this lesson comes at the end of a chapter in which students have had a fair amount of practice, they should be familiar with most of the important ideas in this lesson. On the other hand, the idea of manipulating one symbolic form to convert it into another, introduced in Problem Set G, Problem 2, is quite new. If they have trouble with this, provide another example such as $3y = 6x + 3$ and $2y = 3x + 4$ for them. These can be rewritten as $y = 2x + 1$ and $y = \frac{3}{2}x + 2$ respectively. It is not essential that students master these new ideas now: they foreshadow skills that will be developed more fully later on. On Your Own Exercise 17 gives them further exercise with these ideas, and they will return to them in Chapter 6.

On Your Own Exercises

Practice & Apply: 11–12
Connect & Extend: 17
Mixed Review: 18–33

MATERIALS
graph paper

1a. two; Possible explanation: One point isn't enough because I can draw lots of lines through it. With two points, I can draw only one line. The second point gives me a direction and a steepness for the line.

1b.

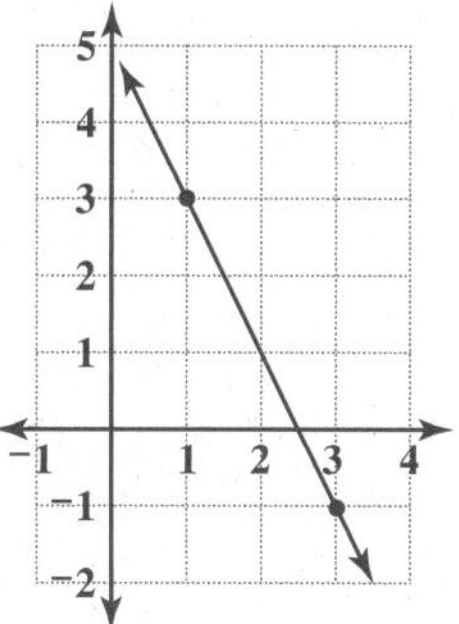

2a.

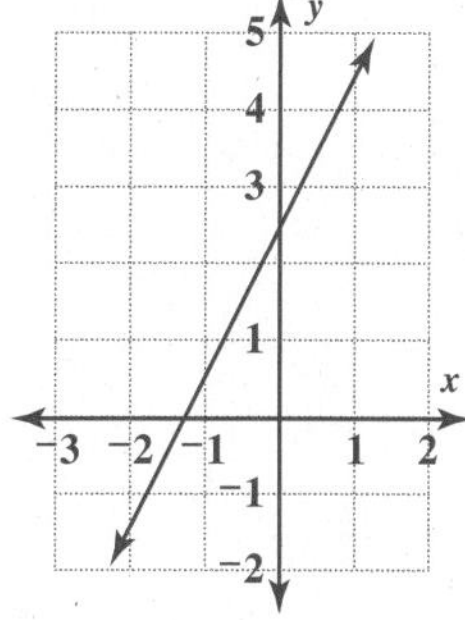

Problem Set G

In sequences like the one just mentioned, it helps to have information about what kind of relationship is being described. For example, if you know that a relationship is linear, you can quickly find the rule from just a few points.

1. This table describes a linear relationship.

Input	1	2	3	4	5
Output	3	1	$^-1$	$^-3$	$^-5$

a. Think about how many points you need to plot in order to draw the line for this relationship. What is the *fewest* number of points needed? Explain.

b. Draw the graph for the relationship using no more points than you need.

c. Use your graph to find a rule for this relationship. $y = {}^-2x + 5$

Not all linear rules are in the form $y = ax + b$. If you can rearrange a rule into this form, you know that its graph will be a line.

2. Consider the equation $2y = 4x + 5$.

a. Graph the equation to show that it is a linear rule.

b. Write a new rule, using the form $y = ax + b$, that has the same graph as $2y = 4x + 5$. $y = 2x + 2.5$

Share & Summarize

1. Explain how the graph of a linear relationship can help you to guess the rule.

2. Explain how the method of constant differences can help you to guess the rule for a relationship.

Share & Summarize Answers

1. In a graph of $y = ax + b$, the "rise" or "fall" of the line in one step to the right is a, the slope. If the line rises from left to right, a is positive; if it falls from left to right, a is negative. The place where the line intersects the y-axis is b.

2. If the difference between inputs is 1, the constant difference between outputs is a. You can then either use the value of y when x is 0 for b, or, once you know the constant difference, multiply it by any input and subtract the product from the output to get b.

1 Have students work in pairs.

2 Students draw a linear graph using only two points.

3 Students explain how a graph of a linear relationship as well as the method of constant differences can help them guess the rule.

Teacher Notes

On Your Own Exercises

In Exercises 1–5, do Parts a and b.

a. Plot the input/output pairs, and decide whether the rule could be linear.

b. If you think the rule could be linear, find a rule that fits the numbers and write it in symbols.

1–3. See Additional Answers.

4a. could be linear

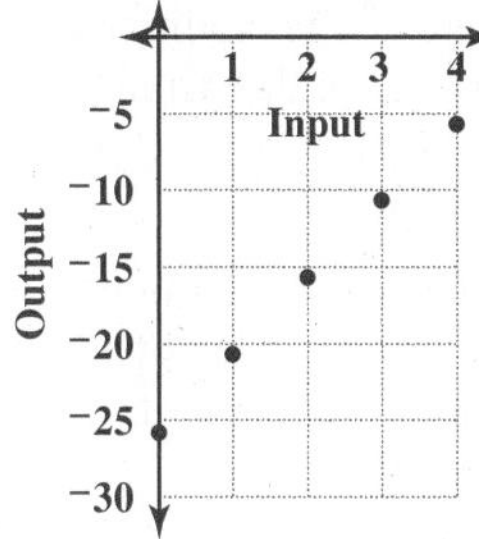

4b. $o = 5i - 26$

1.

Input	1	2	3	4	5
Output	3	20	37	54	71

2.

Input	1	2	3	4	5
Output	1,599	1,561	1,523	1,485	1,447

3.

Input	1	2	3	4	5
Output	12	8	4	$^-2$	$^-12$

4.

Input	0	1	2	3	4
Output	$^-26$	$^-21$	$^-16$	$^-11$	$^-6$

5.

Input	1	2	3	4	5
Output	17	1	$^-12$	$^-22$	$^-29$

Decide whether each relationship could be linear. If you think it could be, find a rule and write it in symbols, and then check your rule with each input/output pair.

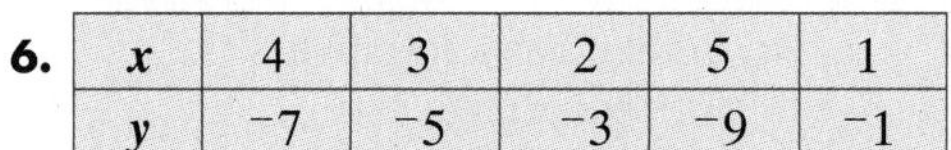

Remember
Watch whether the inputs are in order and consecutive!

5a. not linear

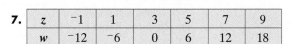

6.

x	4	3	2	5	1
y	$^-7$	$^-5$	$^-3$	$^-9$	$^-1$

could be linear; $y = 1 - 2x$

7.

z	$^-1$	1	3	5	7	9
w	$^-12$	$^-6$	0	6	12	18

8.

x	3	$^-1$	0	2	4	5	1
y	10	2	1	5	17	26	2

9.

m	4	7	5	3	6
n	31	19	26	35	22

not linear

10.

u	10	12	8	13	7
z	64	76	52	82	46

could be linear; $z = 6u + 4$

7. could be linear; $w = 3z - 9$

8. not linear

On Your Own Exercises

Investigation 1
Practice & Apply: 1–5
Connect & Extend: 13

Investigation 2
Practice & Apply: 6–10
Connect & Extend: 14–16

Investigation 3
Practice & Apply: 11–12
Connect & Extend: 17

Assign Anytime
Mixed Review: 18–33

Exercises 6–10:
The input values are not in consecutive order. Students will need to order them sequentially to find the rules without plotting the points. Students may also need to add values to the tables to have consecutive input values.

• *Additional Answers on page A403.*

Exercise 11:
You may wish to have students who are struggling, write the rule $b = rm + s$ using words before they begin the exercise.

Exercise 12c:
You may wish to remind students that they can find information on quadrants in the margin of the student book on page 368.

11a. All values of r and s must be positive, m can be positive or 0, and b must be equal to s or greater.

11b. $r = 0$; The graph passes through only Quadrant I.

11c. $s = 0$; The graph passes through only Quadrant I.

11d. The graph passes through only Quadrant I. Since we can't have a negative number of minutes, or be charged a negative number of dollars, all data pairs must be in Quadrant I.

11e. The graph passes through only Quadrant I, unless the service is entirely free of charge, in which case the graph lies on the horizontal axis and passes through no quadrants.

11. The telephone service PhoneHome charges a fee of r dollars per minute. Customers also pay a service charge of s dollars every month, regardless of how long they use the phone. If m is the number of minutes you use the phone, then your monthly bill b in dollars can be computed with the rule $b = rm + s$.

a. Think about the four variables in this situation. What kinds of values can each variable have? For example, can r be 5? Can it be $^-3$? Can s be 3.24? Can it be 0? Can m be 5?

b. PhoneHome offers a special calling plan, the Talker's Delight plan. This plan has a monthly rate of s dollars and no additional charge per minute, no matter how long you talk. In this arrangement, what is the value of r? How many quadrants does the graph of $b = rm + s$ pass through for this charge plan?

c. PhoneHome also offers the TaciTurn plan. There is no monthly fee, but you *are* charged by the minute. What is the value of s in this pricing plan? How many quadrants does the graph of $b = rm + s$ pass through?

d. Assuming any values of r and s, how many quadrants can the graph of $b = rm + s$ pass through *at the most,* if m is time in minutes and b is your monthly phone bill? Explain your reasoning.

e. How many quadrants must $b = rm + s$ pass through *at the least*? Explain your reasoning.

12. Four graphs are drawn on the axes.

Graph A
Graph B
Graph C
Graph D

a. Point a has a negative first coordinate and a positive second coordinate. On which graphs could Point a be located? Graphs A, B, or D

b. Point b has two negative coordinates. On which graphs could Point b be located? Graphs C or D

c. Which graphs contain points in both Quadrants II and IV?

d. Which graphs contain points on both the x-axis and the y-axis?

e. Which graph could contain points $(2, {}^-6)$ and $({}^-2, {}^-6)$?

12c. Graphs B and D
12d. Graphs B, C, and D
12e. Graph D

372 CHAPTER 5 Looking at Linear Relationships

Connect  Extend

13c. If you graph the pairs of values, they will lie on a line.

13d. The differences between consecutive inputs (toothpicks along side of square) and their outputs (toothpicks to make square) are both constant.

13e. $p = 4s$, where p is the number of toothpicks needed to make the square and s is the number of toothpicks along each side

13. This set of squares is made from toothpicks.

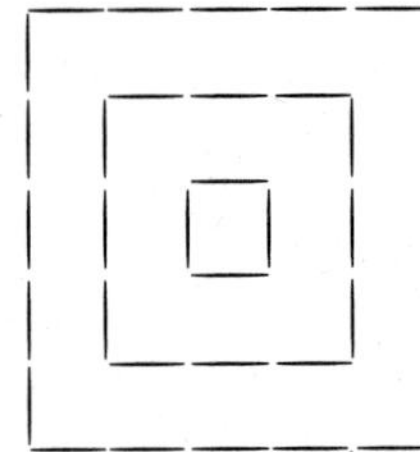

inner: 4; middle, 12; outer: 20

a. How many toothpicks are needed for each square shown?

b. Copy and complete the table.

Toothpicks along Side of Square	1	3	5	7	9	11	15	19
Toothpicks to Make Square	4	12	20	28	36	44	60	76

c. The relationship shown in the table is linear. How could you prove this with a graph?

d. How could you prove the relationship is linear by inspecting the table?

e. Write a rule to calculate the number of toothpicks needed to make a square for a given number of toothpicks along the side of the square.

14. This pattern of triangular shapes is made from squares.

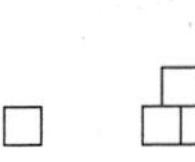 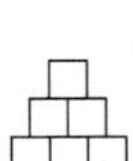 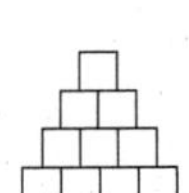 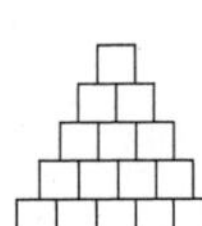 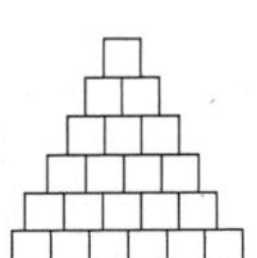

a. Complete the table. The *first* differences d are the differences between adjacent values of A. The differences between adjacent values of d are the *second* differences.

Base Length, b	1	2	3	4	5	6	7
Total Area, A	1	3	6	10	15	21	28
First Differences, d		2	3	4	5	6	7
Second Differences, s		1	1	1	1	1	

b. Is the relationship between b and A linear? How do you know? No; first differences vary.

c. Are the second differences constant? yes

Exercise 13 Extension: Encourage students to predict how many toothpicks it takes to make a square that has 50 toothpicks on each side. Then have them explain why they feel their answer is correct. After explaining, students should check their prediction using the rule they wrote in 13e.

Exercise 14 Extension: You may wish to discuss triangular numbers with your students. Inform them that the pattern can also be shown using circles or dots instead of squares. Encourage students to draw the pattern using dots.

Assign and Assess

Exercise 15b Extension:
After a review of square numbers taught in the last investigation, have students use dots to draw a geometric pattern that represents square numbers. Ask a volunteer to research Fibonacci numbers and make a special report to the class. Then encourage students to look for this sequence in nature patterns.

d. Here's another geometric pattern. Make a table of base length, area, and first and second differences. Do you find any constant differences? See Additional Answers.

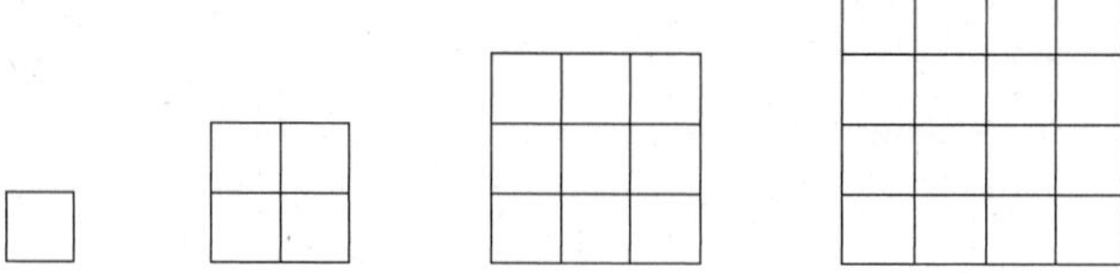

e. Write an equation for the area of the squares in Part d. $A = b^2$

f. The equation for the triangle numbers in Part a is $A = \frac{b^2 + b}{2}$. What do you think constant second differences might tell you about a relationship's equation?

14f. Possible answer: The equation includes a variable with an exponent of 2.

15. The last few lessons have been mostly about linear relationships, but there are several very important (and *common!*) sequences of output numbers that are not linear. Below are tables of some of these sequences. You'll see these patterns again and again as you continue to study mathematics.

a. Find the pattern and complete each table.

i.

Input	1	2	3	4	5	6	7	8	9	10	11
Output	1	4	9	16	25	36	49	64	81	100	121

ii.

Input	1	2	3	4	5	6	7	8	9	10	11
Output	1	3	6	10	15	21	28	36	45	55	66

iii.

Input	1	2	3	4	5	6	7	8	9	10	11
Output	1	2	3	5	8	13	21	34	55	89	144

iv.

Input	0	1	2	3	4	5	6	7	8	9	10
Output	1	2	4	8	16	32	64	128	256	512	1,024

15b. i: square numbers; ii: triangular numbers, iii: Fibonacci numbers; iv: powers of 2

15c. i: consecutive odd numbers; ii: counting numbers, iii: Fibonacci numbers; iv: powers of 2

b. These sequences are so important that each has its own special name. One sequence is related to triangular patterns, so it is called the *triangular numbers.* One is related to square patterns and is called the *square numbers.* The other two are called *powers of 2* and *Fibonacci numbers.* Try to match each name to its sequence.

c. The first differences of each sequence *also* have names. Try to name each set of first differences.

Additional Answers

14d. Second differences are constant.

Base Length, *b*	1		2		3		4		5		6		7
Total Area, *A*	1		4		9		16		25		36		49
First Differences		3		5		7		9		11		13	
Second Differences			2		2		2		2		2		

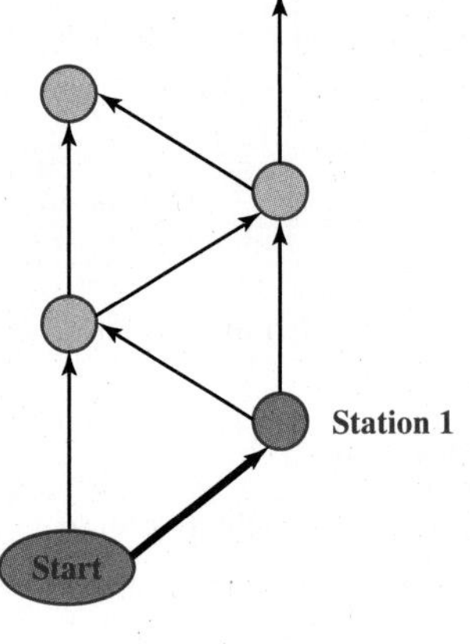

16. Firefighters, police, and other safety workers must have efficient routes from place to place within a city. They must also know about alternate routes. Finding the most efficient routes for snowplowing, street cleaning, meter reading, and patrolling requires an analysis of the city maps. Real city street plans are often messy, and counting the number of ways to travel efficiently from one place to another can be very complicated. An entire branch of mathematics is devoted to exactly such studies.

At left is an imaginary street plan with a pattern to explore. The arrows represent one-way streets, and the circles are stations where someone would stop (meters to read or hydrants to check, for example). You can see that there is only one path from Start to Station 1 along the one-way streets. It is indicated by a heavy arrow.

There are two paths from Start to Station 2, following the arrows.

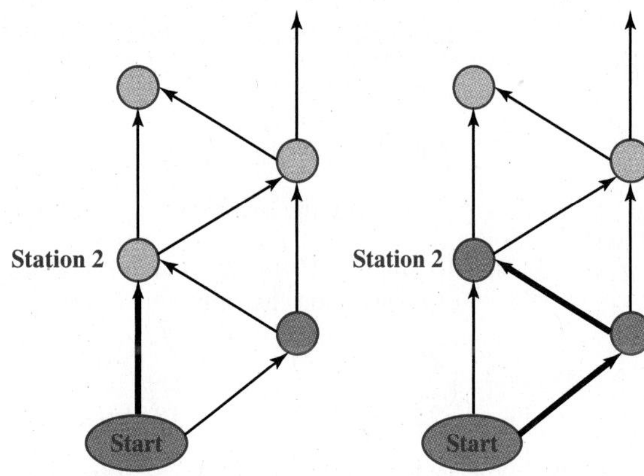

a. How many paths are there from Start to Station 3? 3

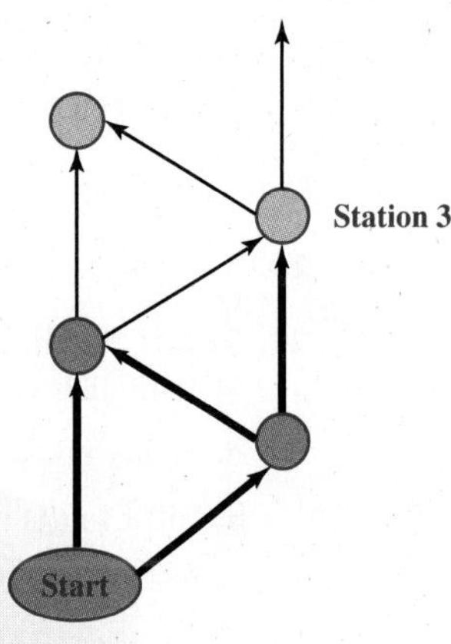

LESSON 5.4 Tricks of the Trade **375**

Assign and Assess

Exercises 18–19: You may wish to review order of operations before assigning these exercises.

Exercises 22–24: For each false expression, encourage students to verbalize why it is false before writing the correct equations.

Quick Check

Informal Assessment
Students should be able to

- ✔ learn that in a table showing the relationship between two variables, if the change in both variables is constant, then the two are linearly related; that if the change in *one* quantity is constant but the change in the other is *not* constant, then the quantities are not linearly related
- ✔ solidify understanding of the connection between the constant difference, the slope of the graph, and the symbolic representation of the relationship
- ✔ apply the concepts of a negative slope and a negative constant term

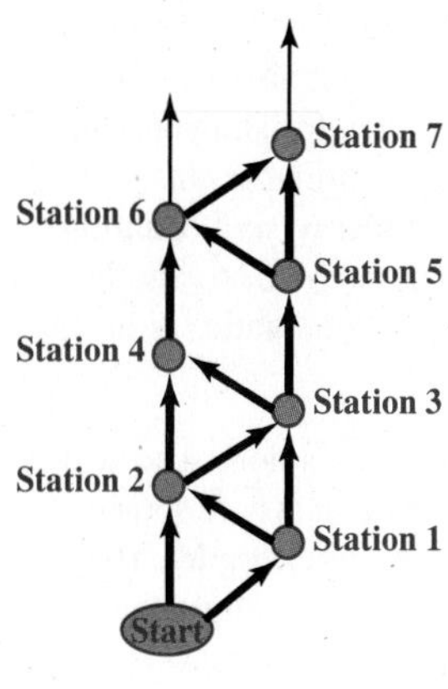

The drawing at left shows how the map continues.

b. Complete the table to show how many paths go from Start to each station.

Station Number	1	2	3	4	5	6	7
Ways to Get There	1	2	3	5	8	13	21

c. Does the relationship between the station number and the number of ways to get there appear to be linear? no

17. The equation $3y = 2x + 6$ is in the form $sy = tx + r$.

a. Find a rule in the form $y = ax + b$ that has the same graph.

b. Find a rule in the form $x = py + q$ that has the same graph.

c. Find another way to write a rule that has the same graph.

Mixed Review

Insert parentheses to make each equation correct.

18. $3 \times 3 + 12 = 45$ **19.** $4 + 3 \times 12 = 84$

20. Use a factor tree to show all of the prime factors of 32.

21. Write the expression $\frac{m}{3}$ in two other ways.

Decide whether each equation is true or false. If false, rewrite the expression on the right side of the equation to make it true.

22. $2(x + 3) = 2x + 3$ false, $2x + 6$

23. $2(x + 9) = 2x + 18$ true

24. $3(2x + 1) = 2x + 3$ false, $6x + 3$

25. Which of the following expressions are equal to each other?

a. $m + m + m + m + m$ **b.** $(5m)^5$ **c.** $5m$ **d.** m^5

e. $3 \times 3 \times 3 \times 3$ **f.** 4×3 **g.** 4^3 **h.** 3^4

Write each number in standard notation.

26. 6×10^4 **27.** 4.8×10^3 **28.** 16.2×10^6

29. Social Studies In the 1992 U.S. presidential election, about 104,400,000 votes were cast.

a. Write this number of votes using scientific notation. 1.044×10^8

b. Bill Clinton received about 43% of these votes. Approximately how many votes did he receive? about 44,892,000

17a. $y = \frac{2}{3}x + 2$
17b. $x = \frac{3}{2}y - 3$
17c. Possible answers: $3y = 2(x + 3)$ *or* $3y = x + 4 + x + 2$
18. $3 \times (3 + 12) = 45$
19. $(4 + 3) \times 12 = 84$
20. Possible answer:

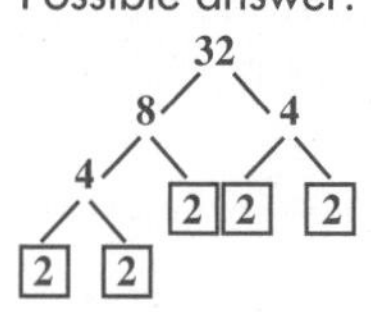

21. Possible answer: $m \div 3, \frac{1}{3}m$
25. a and c, e and h
26. 60,000
27. 4,800
28. 16,200,000

376 CHAPTER 5 Looking at Linear Relationships

30. 1 and $^-12$, $^-12$ and 1, 2 and $^-6$, $^-2$ and 6, 3 and $^-4$, $^-3$ and 4

30. The product of two integers is $^-12$. List all possibilities for the two integers.

31. Algebra Solve for y: $^-3y + 8 = 11$. $^-1$

32. Number Sense Could the number 603,926,481 be a power of 6? Explain how you know. No; all powers of 6 have a final digit of 6.

33. Preview Geoff and Lana collect baseball cards. They visited a card dealer's shop together.

a. Geoff bought 5 packs of cards plus 3 single cards. Write an expression to show how many cards he bought. Let p stand for the number of cards in each pack. $5p + 3$

b. Lana bought 11 single cards plus 4 packs of cards. Write an expression to show how many cards she bought. Each pack has the same number of cards as the packs Geoff bought. $4p + 11$

c. Geoff and Lana bought the *same number* of baseball cards. How could you show this using the two expressions you wrote? Do it.

d. Use your expressions to find how many cards are in a pack. Hint: The answer is greater than 5 but less than 10. 8

e. Substitute your answer to Part d into your answer for Part c. What do you notice?

f. What does your answer to Part e mean in terms of the situation? Geoff and Lana both bought 43 cards.

33c. Set them equal to each other: $5p + 3 = 4p + 11$.
33e. The sides are both equal to 43: $5(8) + 3 = 4(8) + 11$.

✔ learn how to determine b in the rule $y = ax + b$ from a graph (the y-intercept, the intersection with the vertical axis), and by checking the output of the rule when the input is 0

Quick Quiz

1. Ross left home and went to school traveling at a speed of 3 ft/s. His school is 1.2 miles from his home.

   a. Write a rule that relates Ross's distance in miles from school to the time from when he left home.
   1.2 mi = 6,336 ft; Ross's speed is 3 ft/s or 2.05 mi/h. The rule is: $d = 1.2 - 2.05t$ where distance is expressed in miles and time is expressed in hours. Other rules are possible if time is expressed in seconds or minutes, and distance is expressed in feet or miles. For example, the rule where time is expressed in minutes and distance in feet would be $d = 6{,}336 - 180t$.

• ***Quick Quiz continues on page A404.***

Chapter Summary
This summary helps students recall the major topics of the chapter.

Vocabulary
Students should be able to explain each of the terms listed in the vocabulary section.

Strategies and Applications
The questions in this section help students review and apply the important mathematical ideas and problem-solving strategies developed in the chapter.

The questions are organized by mathematical highlight. The highlights correspond to those in "The Big Picture" chart on page 297a.

Exercise 1:
Students review the concepts of rate and proportional relationships described by a symbolic rule and a graph.

VOCABULARY
coefficient
constant term
linear relationship
proportional
rate
slope
speed
variable
velocity
***y*-intercept**

Chapter Summary

In this chapter, you looked at linear relationships. The relationship between two variables is *linear* if all possible points, when graphed, are on a straight line. You began looking at linear relationships defined by a *rate,* which describes how two quantities change in relation to each other.

Most of the equations in this chapter are in the form $y = ax + b$. In this equation, y and x are the variables. The *coefficient* a represents the rate of change. When the line is graphed, a is the *slope* of the line. The *constant term* b doesn't change when x changes. The value of y when x is 0 is given by b, so b is also called the *y-intercept.* When b is 0, the relationship between y and x is *proportional.*

You may be able to guess whether a linear relationship will describe a situation just by looking at the equation. You can find an equation for a line from a graph or a table of values. From a graph, you can determine the slope a and the y-intercept b. From a table, you may be able to use the method of constant differences to find the slope. If you can't get the y-intercept directly from the table, you can use the slope and one data pair to calculate it.

Strategies and Applications

The questions in this section will help you review and apply the important ideas and strategies developed in this chapter.

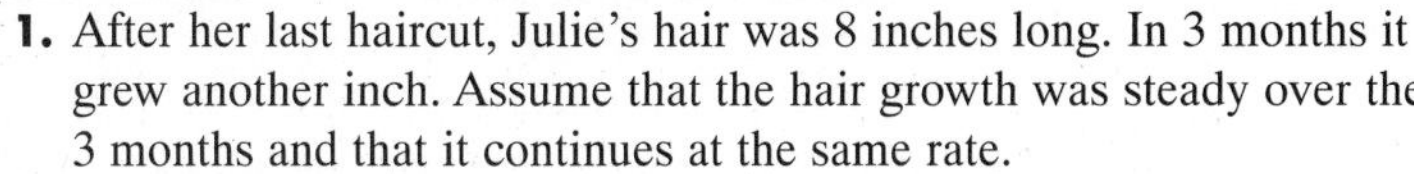

Understanding and representing rates and proportional relationships

1. After her last haircut, Julie's hair was 8 inches long. In 3 months it grew another inch. Assume that the hair growth was steady over the 3 months and that it continues at the same rate.

a. Write the rate that shows Julie's hair growth per month.

b. If you drew a graph showing the relationship between Julie's hair length and time, where would the graph start? at (0, 8)

c. Is Julie's hair length proportional to the time it is allowed to grow since the haircut? Explain. No; it starts at 8 in., not at 0 in.

d. Write the rule for this relationship. Be sure to define your variables.

1a. 0.3 in., or $\frac{1}{3}$ in., per month
1d. $h = \frac{1}{3}m + 8$, where h is hair length in inches and m is months since the haircut

378 CHAPTER 5 Looking at Linear Relationships

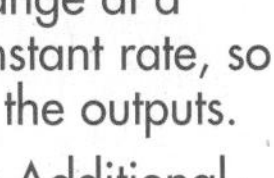

2b. Yes; as the inputs change at a constant rate, so do the outputs.

2c. See Additional Answers.

2d. Yes; the points lie on a line.

2e. Yes; the line goes through (0, 0).

3a. $d = 45t + 3$ (for distance d in miles and time t in hours) or $d = 0.75t + 3$ (for distance d in miles and time t in minutes)

Recognizing linear relationships from tables and graphs

2. The thickness of a book depends on several things, including the number of sheets of paper it has and how thick the paper is. For one type of paper, a stack of sheets 1 inch thick contains 225 sheets.

a. Complete the table for this relationship.

Number of Sheets	0	225	550	775	1,000	1,225
Thickness of Stack (in.)	0	1	2	3	4	5

b. From the table, do you think this is a linear relationship? Explain.

c. Plot the data points in your table. Put the number of sheets on the horizontal axis and the thickness of the stack on the vertical axis.

d. From your graph, do you think this is a linear relationship? Explain.

e. Is this relationship proportional? Explain.

Understanding slope and *y*-intercept in graphs

3. Wayne left home in his car and drove 3 miles to the gas station. At a speed of 45 mph, he continued in the same direction to work. The drive from the gas station to work took 25 minutes.

a. Write a rule that represents Wayne's distance from home at any time since he left the gas station until he arrived at work.

b. Graph this relationship.

c. What is the slope of the line? What does this number represent?

d. What are the coordinates of the point where the line intersects the vertical axis? What does this tell you about Wayne's distance from home?

e. Is the relationship between Wayne's distance from home and the time proportional? no

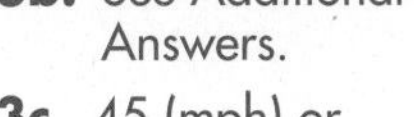

3b. See Additional Answers.

3c. 45 (mph) or 0.75 (mi/min), Wayne's speed

3d. (0, 3); Wayne is 3 mi from home when he leaves the gas station, at $t = 0$.

4a. i: up, intersects at 1; ii. down, intersects at 2; iii. up, intersects at $^-1$; iv. down, intersects at $^-2$

Understanding the connection between a linear equation and its graph

4. Consider these rules for lines.

i. $a = b + 1$ **ii.** $a = {}^-3b + 2$

iii. $a = 2b - 1$ **iv.** $a = {}^-b - 2$

a. Predict what the graph of each rule will look like before you draw it. Will the line go up or down as you look from left to right? Where will it intersect the vertical axis?

b. On one grid, draw the graph for each rule. Test your predictions on a new rule and its graph. See Additional Answers.

Exercise 3: Watch for students who do not include the 3 miles Wayne drove to the gas station when they write their equation. Remind them that those 3 miles are part of the total distance.

Exercises 4–5: These exercises review students' understanding of the associations between the features of a symbolic rule and the graph.

In 4b, encourage students to verbalize why their predictions did or did not match the rule and how they might use the rule to predict more accurately in the future.

• ***Additional Answers on page A403.***

Review and Self-Assessment **379**

Exercises 6–16: Students exhibit their understanding of what constitutes a linear relationship by looking at symbolic rules in the form $y = ax + b$ and by looking for constant differences in data displayed in tabular form and as number pairs.

5. $y = -2x - 3$; Possible answer: I found the slope (the coefficient) by looking at how many units y changes when x changes 1 unit. I found the y-intercept by looking at where the graph hit the y-axis (the constant term).

6a. The constant difference is 2, so it could be linear.

6b. $r = 2a + 1$

7a. There's no constant difference, so it is not linear.

7b.

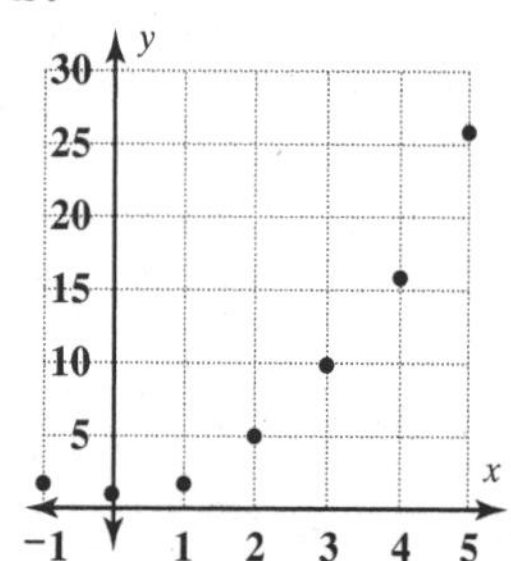

8a. The constant difference is 2, so it could be linear.

8b. $n = 2m - 2.5$

9a. You can't use constant differences because the inputs are not evenly spaced. Possible alternate method: Plot the points and try to draw a line through them. The relationship could be linear.

9b. $s = 5t + 3$

5. The graph shows a linear relationship. Write an equation for the line, and explain how you found your equation.

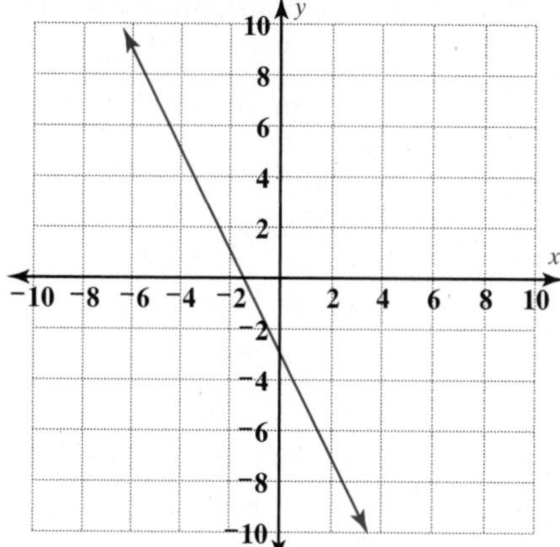

Using the method of constant differences to recognize and write equations for linear relationships

For each table in Questions 6–9, do Parts a and b.

a. Try to use the method of constant differences to decide whether the table could describe a linear relationship. If you can't use this method, explain why not, and find another way to decide whether the relationship could be linear.

b. For the relationships that could be linear, write an equation. For the relationships you think are not linear, plot the points to check.

6.

a	-2	-1	0	1	2	3	4
r	-3	-1	1	3	5	7	9

7.

x	-1	0	1	2	3	4	5
y	2	1	2	5	10	17	26

8.

m	0	1	2	3	4	5
n	-2.5	-0.5	1.5	3.5	5.5	7.5

9.

t	1	3	4	8	11	12
s	8	18	23	43	58	63

380 CHAPTER 5 Looking at Linear Relationships

Demonstrating Skills

Graph each linear relationship.

10–12.

10. $y = 3x + 19$ **11.** $y = {}^-1.7x + 7$ **12.** $y = {}^-5x - 1$

Decide whether you need two points or more than two points to graph each relationship.

13. $y = x^2 + 3$ more than 2 **14.** $y = 8 + 15x - 7$ 2

Decide whether each set of number pairs could describe a linear relationship.

15. (0, 20); (2, 0); (1, 10); (3, ⁻10); (⁻1, 30) yes

16. (⁻1, 21); (1, 25); (3, 29); (⁻3, 17); (0, 23) yes

Decide whether each linear relationship is proportional.

17. $f = 5g$ yes **18.** $p = {}^-15r + 1$ no **19.** $u = {}^-7 + 3v$ no

Graph a line with each of the given slopes. Graphs will vary.

20. 7 **21.** ⁻2.5 **22.** 0.26 **23.** ⁻348

Determine the slope and give the coordinates of the y-intercept for each relationship.

24. $y = 3x + 9$ **25.** $y = {}^-15x + 39$ **26.** $y = x - 17$

24. 3; (0, 9)
25. ⁻15; (0, 39)
26. 1; (0, ⁻17)
27. $g = 4b - 5$
28. $g = {}^-6b + 13$

Find a rule for each pattern.

27.

b	0	1	2	3	4	5	6
g	⁻5	⁻1	3	7	11	15	19

28.

b	0	1	2	3	4	5	6
g	13	7	1	⁻5	⁻11	⁻17	⁻23

Find a rule for each graph.

29. $y = 6 - 3x$
30. $y = 0.125x$

29.

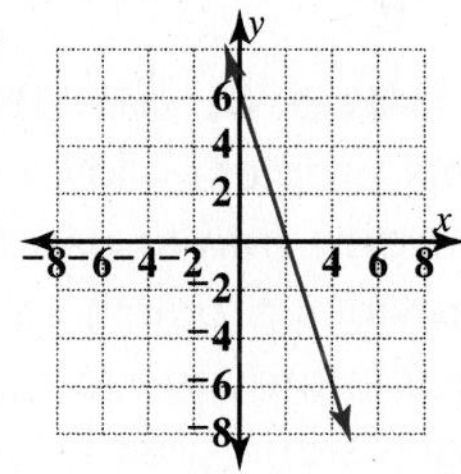

30.

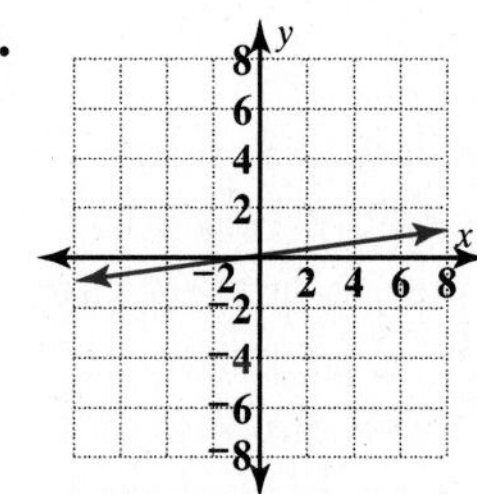

Exercises 17–19: These exercises test students' understanding of whether or not a given linear relationship is proportional.

Exercises 20–23: You may wish to permit students to draw multiple graphs on the same grid as long as they can explain why each graph is correct.

Exercises 27–28: Students figure out the symbolic rules for linear relationships from the data in the tables.

Exercises 29–30: These exercises test students' ability to figure out the symbolic rules from the graphs.

Review and Self-Assessment **381**

Chapter 2 Mathematical Background

Page 77a Notes, continued

The advent of the computer age has made recursively defined rules more useful; a computer takes no time at all to do the required 999 computations. Recursive rules are often easier to discover and easier to relate to the initial context so you can prove they are right. It is important that students begin thinking about these kinds of rules as well.

There is some danger in predicting from patterns. In principle, many rules yield the same results for a finite number of cases. If you have an input/output table, for example, that can be modeled by a linear rule, it can also be modeled by an infinite number of polynomials. However, identifying "friendly numbers," such as doubles, squares, and so on, and how quickly different functions grow, can be useful in making conjectures. Be sure students are aware that their rules may match the patterns given, but that there are other possibilities as well.

After working with visualizing and building three-dimensional solids, students go on to think about surface area and volume of these solids. After they learn the basics of these ideas, they explore this scientific application. Babies are in more danger of dehydration than adults because they have more surface area per unit volume. By talking about surface area and volume of people and other objects, students can begin drawing conclusions based on the data.

Students explore nets and the connection to surface area. Two of the questions students explore relate to making nets from just one shape, primarily just squares or just triangles. This could lead to an exploration of Platonic solids. A Platonic solid is a three-dimensional solid in which all faces are the same regular polygon and the same number of faces meet at each vertex. Within a given Platonic solid, all faces must be equilateral triangles, squares, or other regular polygons. More information about Platonic solids can be found on page A385. With some guidance, middle school students can create the proof that there are only five possible solids meeting these requirements.

Chapter 2, Lesson 2.1

Page T82 Notes, continued

On Your Own Exercises

Practice & Apply: 4–5
Connect & Extend: 13–16
Mixed Review: 19–38

Investigation 3

Building Block Patterns

In this investigation, students create new block patterns that grow numerically in a prescribed way. The Think & Discuss provides examples of this kind of reasoning.

Think & Discuss

Encourage students to start by analyzing Zoe's thinking. Does her strategy really work for any stage of the double staircase no matter how big? When they are comfortable with Zoe's process, ask students to find a way to reverse it—go from the square to the double staircase for any stage of the pattern.

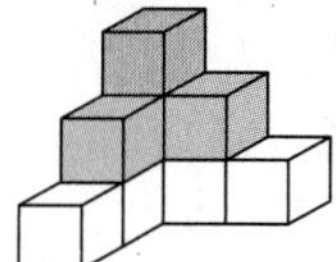

Page T83 Notes, continued

Share & Summarize

This problem allows students to invent their own block patterns and to use the knowledge they've gained in the previous problem sets. It also allows them to use a general expression to represent the number of blocks in each stage. Ask three or four students to present the first three stages of their patterns and challenge the class to find a rule to describe each pattern.

Troubleshooting The point of this chapter is visualization and ideas behind surface area and volume. If students are having trouble creating patterns to fit prescribed numerical growth, it is not essential to spend more time on it. Throughout the algebra strand, students will have opportunities to practice writing expressions to fit situations and describing situations that fit given expressions.

On Your Own Exercises

Practice & Apply: 6–8
Connect & Extend: 17–18
Mixed Review: 19–38

Chapter 2, Lesson 2.2

Page 90 Notes, continued
Quick Quiz, continued

2. Create a block pattern that has the following number of blocks in each stage:

stage	1	2	3	4
blocks	3	5	7	9

a. Draw top-count views for the first three stages in your pattern. Answers will vary.

b. Write an expression for the total number of blocks in stage s. $2s + 1$

Page T94 Notes, continued

3 **Problem Set Wrap-Up** Have students share their answers to **Problem 2** with the whole class, and then compile a master list. How many different structures did the class find?

Access for all Learners

Extra for Experts You may want to pose an extra-credit problem for students who are interested in exploring the different structures possible in Problem 2 on their own: Find all the possible structures that fit these three views and explain how you know you have all of them.

Page T97 Notes, continued

We have simplified the drawing technique that engineers use to make it more accessible to students. When students build their own structures in **Problem 7,** it may come up that the technique shown will not differentiate between these two structures:

2	2	2
2	1	2
2	2	2

2	2	2
2	0	2
2	2	2

For both, the views will be:

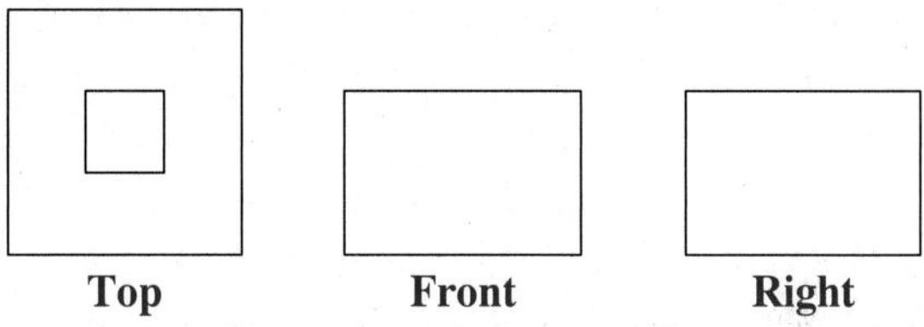

In fact, engineers can distinguish these two structures. They use dashed lines to show hidden levels. For the first structure, the views would really be:

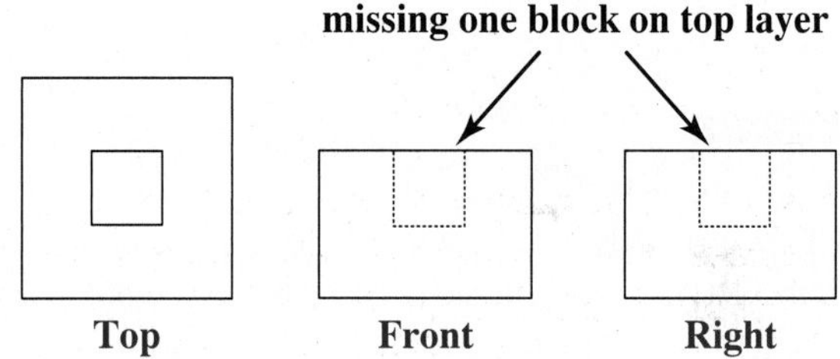

And for the second structure, they would be:

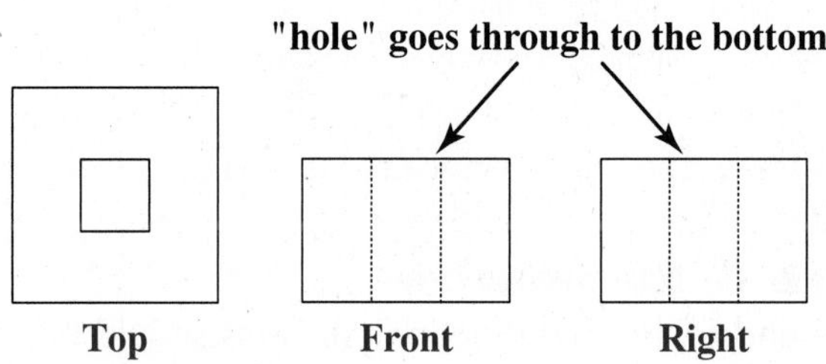

Here is another example where the dashed lines would be used.

3	2	3
3	3	3

3	1	3
3	3	3

For both these structures, the views will be:

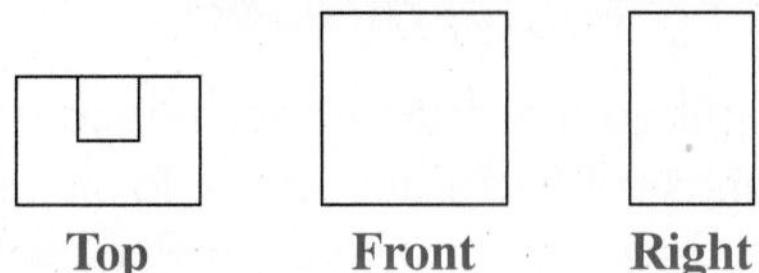

The dashed lines would show if there is one block "missing" (2 in the stack) or two blocks "missing" (one in the stack).

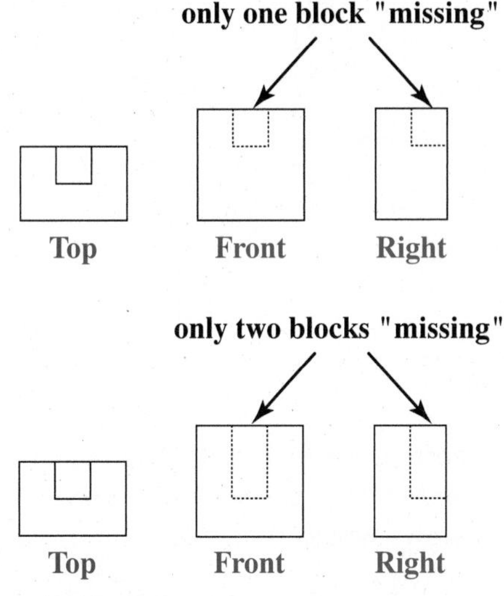

Access for all Learners

For Early Finishers If students finish early and are comfortable with the drawing technique, you may want to point out that the technique is not exactly what engineers do. Challenge them to find two structures with the same engineering views (you can give them a hint about building a "hole" in the middle of the structure). If they find two such structures, you might show on the student's three-view drawing, how an engineer would distinguish them.

Share & Summarize

By the end of this investigation, students should be comfortable with top-count views; they will use top-count views throughout the rest of the Lesson, so this is the most important piece. Students should be able to make a good attempt at the other views. Using only 6–10 blocks should keep the structures of a manageable size.

There is no right answer for **Question 2.** Most people find the regular views easier to create and to build from; however, the three unmodified engineering views are more useful because they describe a unique structure. The modified views drawn by students describe a unique structure only when there are no "holes" in the structure.

Troubleshooting If students are still having difficulty drawing the different views for structures, the first key is to be sure they are comfortable with top-count views. If they are, some of the strategies on page T97 will help them translate to the other kinds of views. You may also ask some of the students who are successfully creating the drawings to describe their strategies to the class, maybe working an example on the board as other students watch and ask questions. If students don't ask questions, you can ask "Why did you draw a line there? Why isn't there a line here?" and so on.

It is not essential that students are proficient at making and interpreting the three engineering views, but they should understand what is communicated in the views (rather than division between blocks, it is division between levels) and that the views give more information than regular views. From now on, we will be using the easier top-count views because we will continue to work with blocks.

On Your Own Exercises

Practice & Apply: 6–7
Connect & Extend: 26–28
Mixed Review: 33–56

Chapter 2, Lesson 2.3

Page T116 Notes, continued

From science classes, students may have learned that the body cools off in several ways. **Convection:** You heat the air around your body. The hot air is replaced by cooler air, which you heat, and so on. **Radiation:** Your body emits UV rays. **Breathing:** The air you exhale is as hot as your body temperature; the air you inhale is generally cooler. **Sweat:** Sweat is the only one that your body can control; the rest of them depend on your environment and how cool or warm it is compared with your body.

Ask students why they think sweat cools you off. (As the sweat on the skin dries, it cools you off.) The important part is that, except for breathing, all ways of cooling (and in particular the one your body controls) happens at the surface of your skin, so it depends directly on your surface area.

It is important to connect these ideas to things directly in students' experiences. Ask students this question: Which will take longer to melt? A big tub of ice cream or the same amount of ice cream dished up into lots of single bowls? The tub takes longer because it has much less exposed surface area. You might also point out that in cold weather, animals tend to sleep balled up, and that in warm weather, they stretch out. Why? They want to expose more surface area (to cool off better) when it is warm out, and they want to cover up the surface area (to cool off less) when it is cold out.

Chapter 2, Lesson 2.4

Page T134 Notes, continued

Regular Polygon	**Number of faces meeting at a vertex**			
	3	4	5	6
Equilateral triangles	tetrahedron 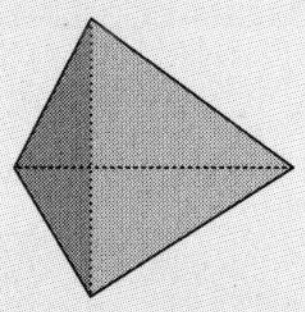	octahedron 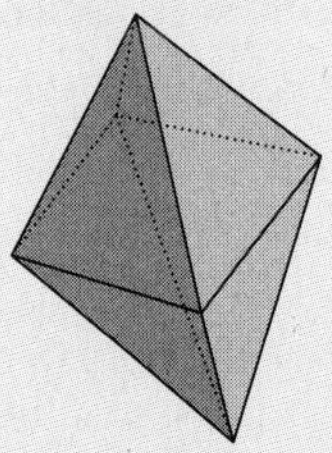	icosahedron 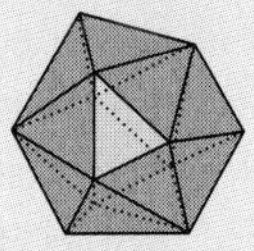	lies flat (won't fold)
Squares	cube 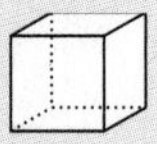	lies flat (won't fold)		
Regular pentagons	dodecahedron 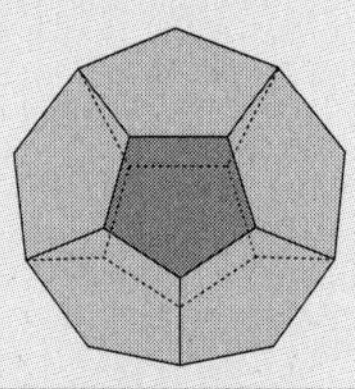	more than 360 degrees around the vertex (won't fold)		
Regular hexagons	lies flat (won't fold)			
Regular heptagons (and up)	more than 360 degrees around the vertex (won't fold)			

This exercise may also be the first encounter students have with a mathematical impossibility proof. That is, no matter how clever and patient you are, you simply can't make a Platonic solid out of hexagons. In high school geometry, students will likely encounter three other impossible problems of antiquity: doubling the cube, tri-secting the angle, and squaring the circle.

Page T135 Notes, continued

4 **Problem Set Wrap-Up** Ask one student from each group to report on what the group decided for **Problem 4.** An important point is that this is just a conjecture based on evidence and not a definite answer to the question. You may want to share with students the real answer: the can with minimal surface area is the one where the height is the same as the diameter. A nice way to think about this is that it is the most "cube-like" cylinder. There are mathematical proofs of this using techniques from advanced algebra and proofs using calculus. It is not important to work through the proofs. Instead let students know that the next step after finding data and making a conjecture, is to look for justification. You may want to inform students that they will be studying more of these kinds of problems if they continue on in mathematics in a calculus course. ■

Share & Summarize

Students will realize that the shape generally used for soft drink cans does not minimize the surface area for the volume. In thinking about why soda companies do not choose this "best" shape, (least surface area) you might consider issues like: How easy would it be to hold a can of the best shape? How easily could the companies display their logos? Is the shape they chose much worse, or just a little worse than the "best" shape, in terms of how much material it uses?

5 **Troubleshooting** If some students had trouble with the Share and Summarize question, you may ask other students to share and explain their answers. There is nothing in this investigation that is essential for students to master before moving on in the text, but it's nice for the closing activity to resonate somewhat with each student.

On Your Own Exercises

Practice & Apply: 9–12
Connect & Extend: 20
Mixed Review: 21–36

Page 135 Additional Answers, continued

Problem Set D Answers

1. See Problem 2 for possible answers.

2. Possible answer:

Radius (cm)	Height (cm)	Surface Area (cm^2)
11.27	1	869
5.041	5	318
3.565	10	304
2.911	15	328
1.594	50	517

3. Answers will vary. Cans with slightly less height than the standard can will have less surface area. Cans with much less height or with greater height will have more surface area.

Page 140 Additional Answers

36a. Note: Percentages do not add to 100% because of rounding.

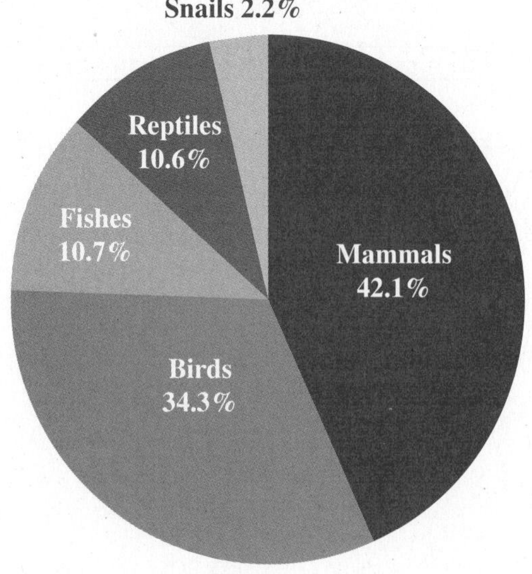

Chapter 3 Mathematical Background

Page 145a Notes, continued

Specifically, we have

$a^m = a \cdot a \cdot \ldots \cdot a$ (m times) and
$a^n = a \cdot a \cdot a \cdot \ldots \cdot a$ (n times).

Hence,

$$\begin{aligned} a^m \cdot a^n &= \underbrace{(a \cdot a \cdot \ldots \cdot a)}_{m\ a\text{'s}} \cdot \underbrace{(a \cdot a \cdot \ldots \cdot a)}_{n\ a\text{'s}} \\ &= \underbrace{a \cdot a \cdot \ldots \cdot a}_{(m+n)\ a\text{'s}} \\ &= a^{m+n} \end{aligned}$$

For $(a \cdot b)^m = a^m \cdot b^m$, we can construct a similar proof that requires some regrouping. The fact that $a \cdot (b \cdot c) = (a \cdot b) \cdot c$ (associative property of multiplication) is the key in this case.

$$\begin{aligned} (a \cdot b)^m &= \underbrace{(a \cdot b) \cdot (a \cdot b) \cdot \ldots \cdot (a \cdot b)}_{m\ (a \cdot b)\text{'s}} \\ &= \underbrace{(a \cdot a \cdot \ldots \cdot a) \cdot (b \cdot b \cdot \ldots \cdot b)}_{m\ a\text{'s and } m\ b\text{'s}} \\ &= a^m \cdot b^m \end{aligned}$$

Similarly,

$$\begin{aligned} (a^m)^n &= \underbrace{a^m \cdot \ldots \cdot a^m}_{n\ (a^m)\text{'s}} \\ &= \underbrace{(a \cdot a \cdot \ldots \cdot a) \cdot \ldots \cdot (a \cdot a \cdot \ldots \cdot a)}_{(n \cdot m)\ a\text{'s}} \\ &= a^{m \cdot n} \end{aligned}$$

After students are comfortable working with numbers written with exponents and with the laws of exponents, they spend some time thinking about exponential growth and exponential decay. Students will encounter these concepts again as they learn more about functions, graphing, and other topics in algebra. The early investigations here are designed to introduce several key points:

- Compared with linear and polynomial growth—students will not use these terms, but rather specific examples of them—exponential growth is very fast.
- If the number being raised to a power is greater than 0 but less than 1, the result actually shrinks exponentially, growing smaller and smaller but never reaching 0.

Ideas of scientific notation build on rules of exponents and what students already know about adding, subtracting, multiplying, and dividing.

Lesson 3.1

Page 148 Answers, continued

Problem Set A

5a.

×1 See teaching notes.	×2 essential	×3 essential	×4 ×2×2	×5 essential	×6 ×2×3
×7 essential	×8 ×2×2×2	×9 ×3×3	~~×10~~ ×2×5	×11 essential	×12 ×2×2×3
×13 essential	×14 ×2×7	×15 ×3×5	×16 ×2×2×2×2	×17 essential	×18 ×2×3×3
×19 essential	~~×20~~ ~~×4×5~~ ×2×2×5	×21 ×3×7	×22 ×2×11	×23 essential	×24 ×2×2×2×3
×25 ×5×5	×26 ×2×13	×27 ×3×3×3	×28 ×2×2×7	×29 essential	×30 ×2×3×5
×31 essential	×32 ×2×2×2×2×2	×33 ×3×11	×34 ×2×17	×35 ×5×7	×36 ×2×2×3×3

Lesson 3.2

Page 175 Answers, continued

On Your Own Exercises

73b. 288π in^3, or about 904.8 in^3

73c. 144π in^3, or about 452.4 in^3

81. Possible answer:

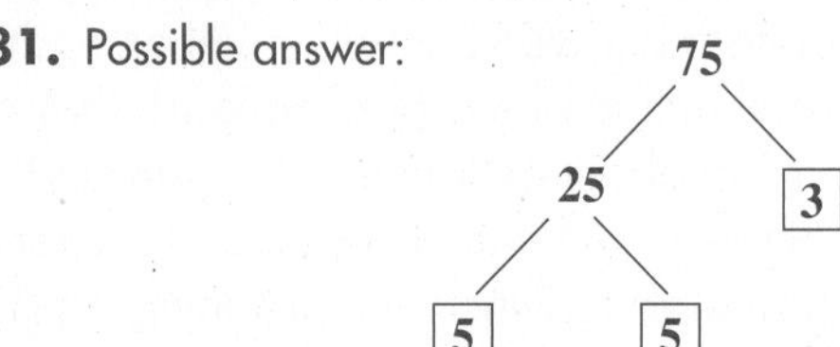

82. Possible answer:

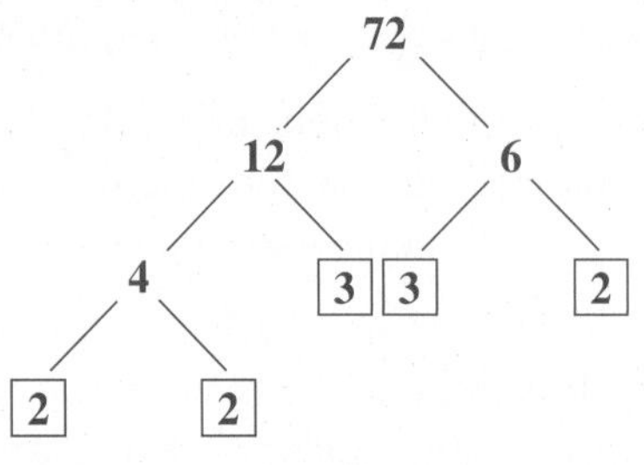

83. Possible answer:

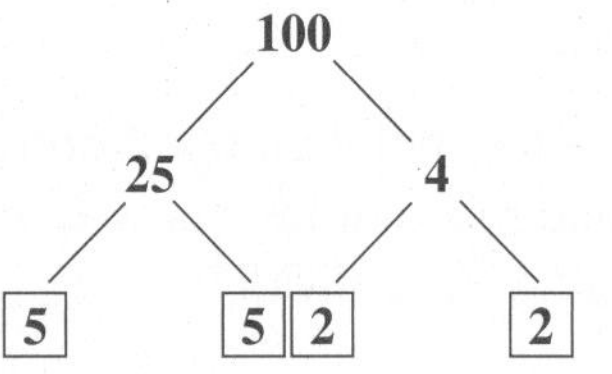

Lesson 3.3

Page T182 Notes, continued

Share & Summarize

> About how long will it take for each car to be worth about $5,000? *85%: 4 years; 88%: 5 years; 90%: 6-$\frac{1}{2}$ years; 92%: 8 years*
>
> About how many years will it take for each car to depreciate from about $8,000 to $4,000? *85%: 4 years; 88%: 5 years; 90%: 6 years; 92%: 8 years*

Students will need to extend their tables to answer the last two questions.

Access for All Learners

Extra for Experts For exponential decay, a nice activity involves investigating the half-life of radioactive substances. Each type of radioactive material has a typical decay rate—the time it takes to break down to a more stable, nonradioactive substance. Half-life is the length of time it takes half of a given amount of a radioactive substance to break down to more stable, nonradioactive substance. For instance, the half-life of radon is about 4 seconds, while the half-life of uranium 238 is 4.4×10^9 years. Have students investigate the half-lives of other radioactive substances, particularly carbon 14, which is used to determine the age of fossils and other ancient artifacts.

On Your Own Exercises

Practice & Apply: 5–6
Connect & Extend: 8–20
Mixed Review: 21–32

Lesson 3.4

Page T191 Notes, continued

If students have trouble with **Problem 2b,** you might want to suggest that they try some of the sample strategies described below.

Sample Strategies Students may use one of the following strategies:

- Students already know from **Problem 2a** that 1 million quarters laid end to end would be 1 million inches; so they can convert that measurement to miles and compare the distance with the length of the equator.
- Students may convert the length of the equator to inches and see whether it is more or less than a million since a million quarters laid end to end will reach a million inches.

The advantage of the second strategy is that you immediately know how many quarters it *would* take, whereas with the first strategy, you need to do an additional computation to answer the second question in Problem 2b. Similar dual strategies will work for each of the other problems as well.

After most students have finished Problem 2, ask for solutions and discuss rough estimates for checking the reasonableness of answers. If there were problems with conversion, ask for the number of inches a million quarters reach. Then ask:

> Without calculating exactly, can you tell *about* how many feet that is?

One estimate is that there are close to 10 inches in a foot; so the number of feet would be close to $\frac{1}{10}$ of 1 million or about 100,000.

Chapter 4 Mathematical Background

Page 217a Notes, continued

The rules for arithmetic with signed numbers often handle sign and magnitude separately. That's why we can make statements like "negative times positive is negative" or "negative plus negative is negative." These statements deal only with the sign. We can't make a similarly general statement for "negative plus positive," because the outcome depends on both sign and magnitude.

In the arithmetic expression $^-4 - {}^-5$, we see the "minus sign" used three times. Two of those times, it specifies the sign of a number. Once—in the middle—it specifies an *operation:* a piece of arithmetic to be done. It is not conventional to see such numbers such as $^{--}5$ or, worse yet, $^{----}5$ to represent the number $^+5$, but it *is* helpful for students to get the idea that each negative sign negates the value of the number that follows. It is for that reason that we cannot say that "$-x$" is a negative number, unless we already know that x is positive. If the value of x is $^-5$, then "$-x$" is truly $^{--}5$, or simply 5.

The Pythagorean Theorem has many applications. The idea is this: If a right triangle *ABC* has legs of length a and b, and a hypotenuse of length c, then $c^2 = a^2 + b^2$.

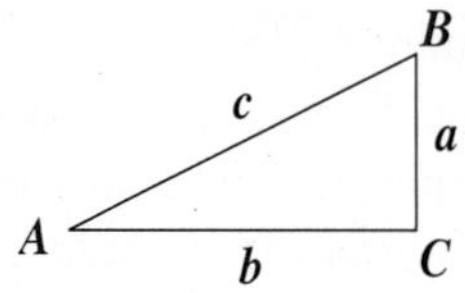

Another way of saying that is that the distance between points A and B is $\sqrt{a^2 + b^2}$.

The Pythagorean relationship also tells where the circumference points of circles are, in relationship to the center. Imagine all the points that are one specific distance, say 5, from the origin of a graph. They form a circle around the origin, with a radius of 5. Here's a picture.

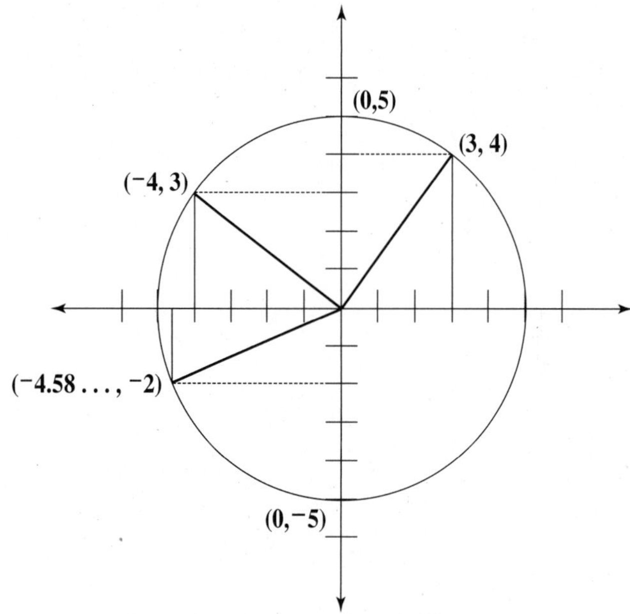

It appears that the point (3, 4) is on the circle. How could we know that it is exactly (3, 4), and not, say, (3.0000001, 4.0000237)?

The point (3, 4) is exactly 4 units from the *horizontal* axis, and exactly 3 units from the *vertical* axis. We see a right triangle. If its hypotenuse is 5, then the point (3, 4) would be 5 units from the origin, which would put it on the circle. $3^2 + 4^2 = 9 + 16 = 25 = 5^2$, so (3, 4) is on the circle. This is the Pythagorean relationship again:

$$c^2 = a^2 + b^2 \text{ where } c = 5,\ a = 3, \text{ and } b = 4 \text{ gives } 5^2 = 3^2 + 4^2$$

So are (0, 5), (0, $^-5$), ($^-4$, 3), and infinitely many other points like ($^-4.58257569. . .$, $^-2$), whose coordinates, when squared and added, produce 5^2.

The distance formula is derived from the Pythagorean Theorem. It will take on added meaning for your students when they take geometry and still more meaning in trigonometry.

Lesson 4.1

Page T220 Notes, continued

The Captain's Game

After reading through the description of the game with students, you might want to demonstrate sample moves of the game so that students understand how to play the game. In particular, you will probably want to make sure students understand that they stand *on* the line in the center of the plank; they do not stand in the spaces between the lines.

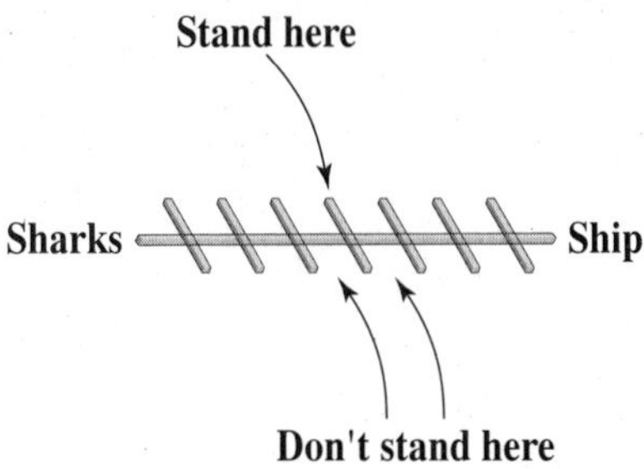

When they reach the line that marks the end of the plank, they should think of themselves as either being on the ship or in the shark-infested water.

Page T225 Notes, continued

In **Problem 10,** students are confronted with a much larger range of numbers than in previous problems. This will require them to either incorporate the new parameters into the "walking the number line" model or to use a different problem-solving strategy.

Sample Strategies Students may use one of these strategies to solve **Problem 10:**

- Some students may use the "walking the number line" model using a number line that includes the range of $^-150$ to 300. Many students will use a scale with intervals of 50.
- Other students may draw a vertical number line to mirror the vertical direction of the hike. They may count the spaces from 300 to $^-150$.
- Still others may use logical reasoning to find their answer. They may break apart the hike into two parts. First they consider that Colleen hiked 300 feet to sea level. Then they subtract 300 from 450 to the distance Colleen hiked below sea level. Since $450 - 300 = 150$, she ended her hike at an elevation of $^-150$ feet.

Problem Set Wrap-Up Have students discuss the strategies they used to solve **Problems 9 and 10.** These discussions can help students gain greater insight into the structure of the number line.

For Problem 9, you might want to highlight the strategy of drawing a vertical number line with the class. For some students, the vertical number line will make more sense than the horizontal number line. It also foreshadows thinking of a coordinate plane as the intersection of two number lines, an important concept introduced in Lesson 3.

For Problem 10, you may wish to have students who used number lines discuss the scale that they used. Students will be confronted with the decision of scale again in Lesson 3 when they use coordinate planes.

Page 228 Answers

Think & Discuss Answer

If the pointer faces the positive direction, the drawing looks like this and the equation is $^-3 + 5 = 2$:

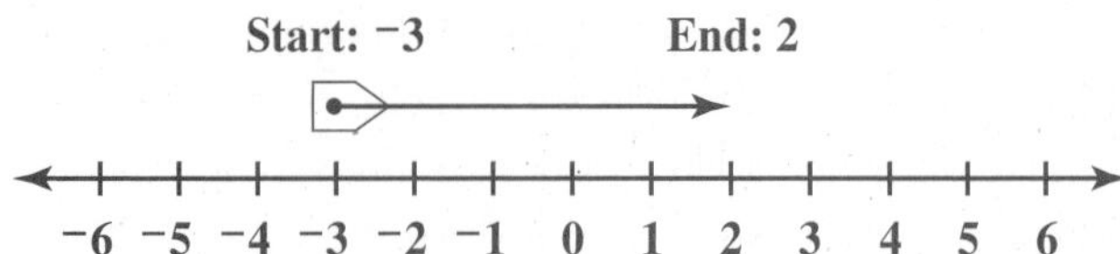

If the pointer faces the negative direction, the drawing looks like this and the equation is $^-3 - {^-5} = 2$:

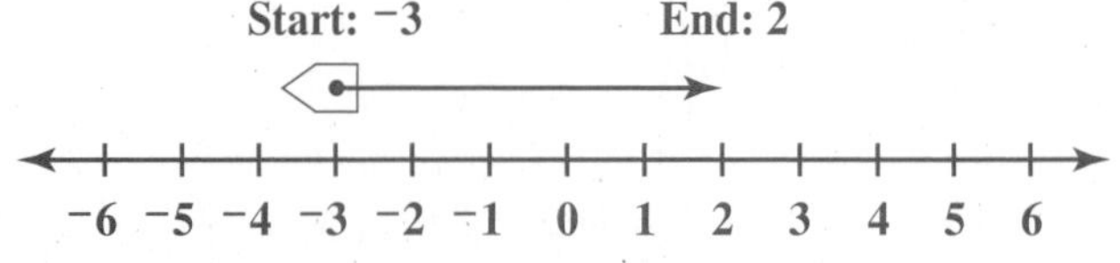

Page T232 Notes, continued

In **Problem 10,** students relate their finding to the data in Problems 4–6 to generalize to find a sum less than zero when given a positive addend and again when given a negative addend.

Problem Set Wrap-Up You might want to have students discuss their answers and the strategies they used to solve **Problems 8 and 10.** Students should share their thinking on Problem 8 and talk about how they used their work in Problems 4–7 to help arrive at the generalization. Continue the discussion by talking about how students derived their answers to Problem 10. You may want to have students randomly test numbers to show that their answer is reasonable.

Page T234 Notes, continued

- Some students might actually prove some of their results by showing that they are equivalent to previous results. Following is an example of such a proof you might get for **Problem 7** from a student using this strategy.

  Whenever you subtract a negative number from a positive number, you get a positive number. I know this because subtracting a negative is equivalent to adding a positive. So, subtracting a negative from a positive is equivalent to adding a positive to a positive. I showed in Problem 1 that the sum of two positives is positive, so that means that a positive minus a negative must also be positive.

On the Spot Assessment

Watch for students who use equations to prove their answers to Problems **2, 4, 5, and 8** and do not try enough test cases to find examples of all three results. Encourage students to try various combinations of numbers, including one near zero and one farther away on a number line.

Page 234 Answers, continued

Problem Set I Answers

4. sometimes positive, sometimes negative, and sometimes 0; Possible explanation: These three examples show the three possibilities: $^-2 + 3 = 1$, $^-5 + 2 = {}^-3$, $^-3 + 3 = 0$.
5. sometimes positive, sometimes negative, and sometimes 0; Possible explanation: These three examples show the three possibilities: $3 - 2 = 1$, $3 - 5 = {}^-2$, $3 - 3 = 0$.
6. always negative; Possible explanation: A negative minus a positive is the same as a negative plus a negative. The answer to Problem 3 shows that the result is always negative.
7. always positive; Possible explanation: A positive minus a negative is the same as a positive plus a positive. The answer to Problem 1 shows that the result is always positive.
8. sometimes positive, sometimes negative, and sometimes 0; Possible explanation: A negative minus a negative is the same as a negative plus a positive. The answer to Problem 4 shows that the result may be positive, negative, or 0.

Page 236 Answers, continued

18. $5 - 7 = {}^-2$

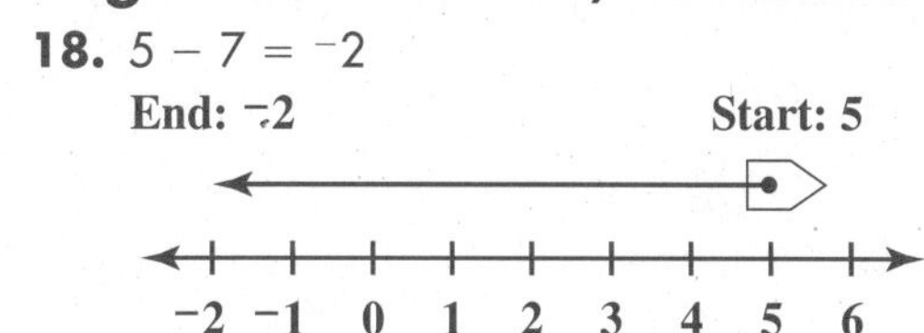

19. $^-3 + 11 = 8$

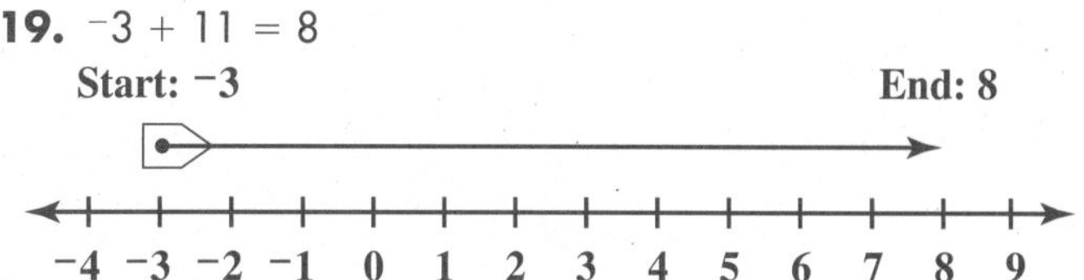

20. $2.2 - 1.4 = 0.8$

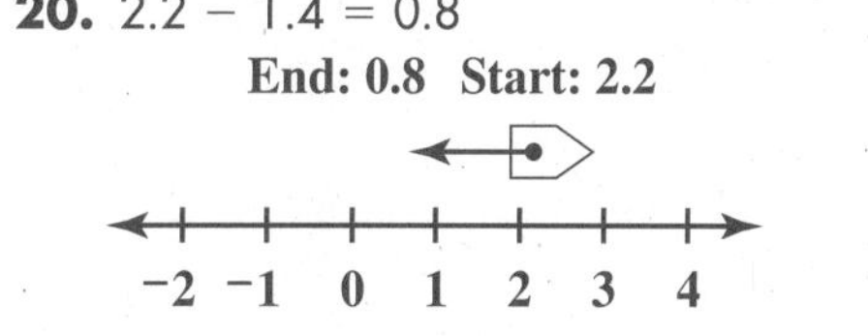

21. $^-5\frac{1}{3} + 2\frac{5}{6} = {}^-2\frac{1}{2}$

Start: $-5\frac{1}{3}$ End: $-2\frac{1}{2}$

−8 −7 −6 −5 −4 −3 −2 −1 0

Lesson 4.3

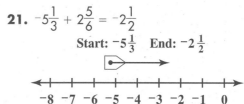

Page 265 Answers, continued

5c. The black points are on the line $y = x$ on both planes. In the first graph, the blue points, showing $y > x$, are above the line; the red points, showing $x > y$, are below the line. In the second graph, the red points, showing $y > x$, are above the line; the blue points, showing $x > y$, are below the line.

6a.

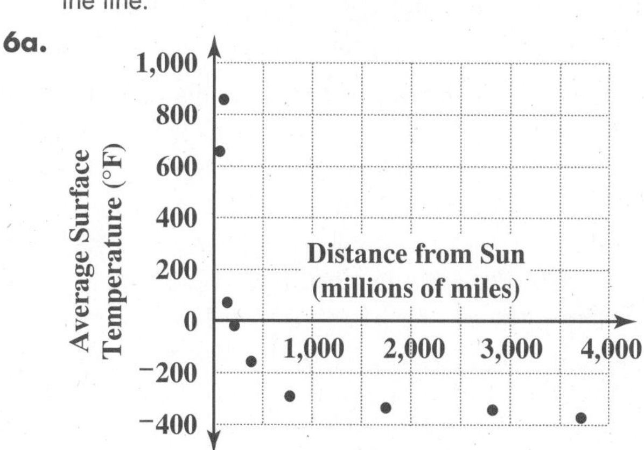

6b. It decreases.

6c. As planets get farther from the sun, less energy from the sun reaches them.

6d. Possible answer: Venus and Mercury don't fit the pattern; the temperature of Venus should be less than 662°F, or Mercury's should be greater than 860°F. Composition of the planet might affect its temperature, and the effect of distance might be more complicated than the pattern in Part b.

Page 266 Answers, continued

10b. They are the same, except that all points on the *x*-axis are green. Products and quotients follow the same rules for signs, except when the divisor is 0 you can't calculate the quotient.

14.

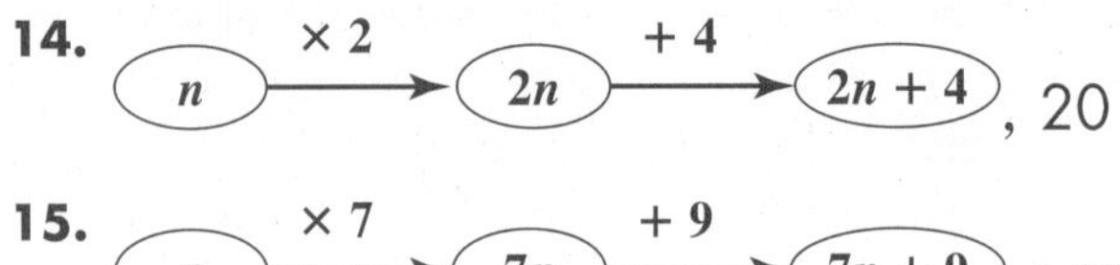

, 20

15. $n \xrightarrow{\times 7} 7n \xrightarrow{+9} 7n + 9$, 149

Page 267 Notes, continued

Quick Quiz

1. This graph represents the fluctuation in the amount of money in Lisa's bank account over a period of a year. The *x*-axis represents the number of months from Lisa's birthday. The *y*-axis represents the amount of money in her account.

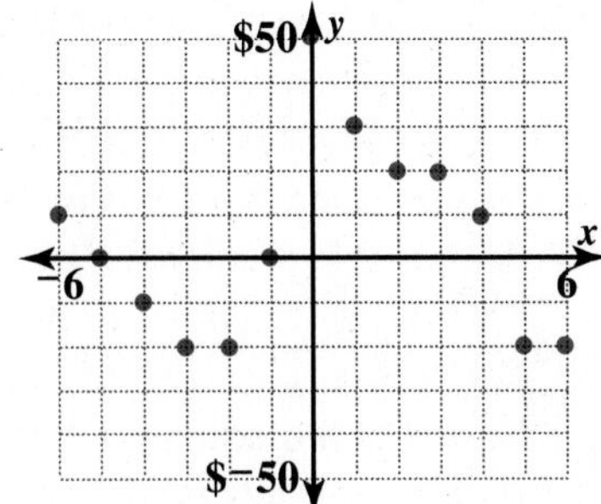

a. When did Lisa have positive amounts of money in her account? What part of the graph did you look at to answer the question? Why? *6 months before her birthday, on her birthday, and each month for 4 consecutive months after her birthday. Possible explanation: I looked at the part of the graph above the x-axis (Quadrants I and II, including the amount located at (0, y)) because that's where the dollar amounts are positive.*

b. What part of the graph would you look in to find out about when Lisa has a negative amount of money after her birthday? Why? *I'd look below the x-axis (Quadrants III and IV) because that's where the dollar amounts are negative.*

c. Where would you look to find out when Lisa had exactly $0 in the bank? *on the x-axis*

d. How much money did Lisa have in her account on her birthday? *$50*

2. Here is a picture of the coordinate plane you colored in to represent multiplication of signed numbers. A point (c, d) is red if $c \times d$ is positive, blue if $c \times d$ is negative, and black if $c \times d$ is equal to zero.

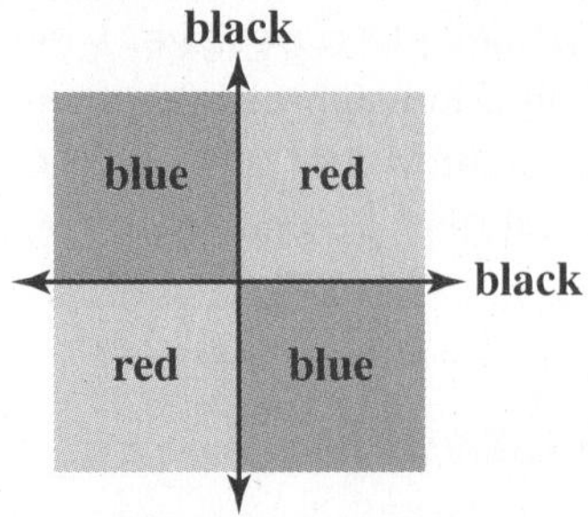

Use the graph to solve $^-4x < 0$. Then explain clearly all of your steps. *Possible answer: x must be a positive number. Since the product is less than zero, it is a negative number. Therefore it must be one of the blue quadrants. Since $y = {}^-4$, the quadrant must also be below the x-axis. Therefore the solution falls in Quadrant IV and x must be a positive number.*

Chapter 5 Mathematical Background

Page 299a Notes, continued

At first it might seem that Tatiana should be able to answer this question, just as Alex was able to answer the first one, but she cannot.

With the rectangles from the roll of adding-machine paper, Alex could tell how much the area increased without knowing what the starting area was. But with the squares, the problem is not so straightforward. An increase of 1 inch in side length does not correspond to a particular increase in area. Before Tatiana can say how much the square's area increased, she must know how big it was to begin with.

The first relationship (length and area of a fixed-width strip) is known as a linear relationship; the relationship between side-length and area of a square is not linear. One reason that this distinction is worthy of its own special name is the fact that in linear relationships one can predict the effects of a change without needing also to know where we were before the change took place.

Here's how this fact shows up in a table.

Length of strip	1	2	3	4	5	6	7
Area of strip	3	6	9	12	15	18	21

The difference between any two neighboring areas is always 3, no matter which pair of neighbors is chosen. We say the difference is *constant* because it does not change from pair to pair. Of course, this constancy depends on how the table was made. Another table, for example, might look like this:

Length of strip	1.1	1.3	2	10	11.2	. . .
Area of strip	3.3	3.9	6	30	33.6	. . .

There is no particular pattern in the outputs (areas), but there really is no reason to expect to find one since the inputs (lengths) are all arbitrarily chosen.

But in the case of the squares, even if the inputs are chosen in an orderly fashion, we do not see a constant change in the outputs.

Length of side	1	2	3	4	5	6	7
Area of square	1	4	9	16	25	36	49

The areas certainly change in a regular way. From 1 to 4, there is an increase (a difference) of 3, and from 4 to 9 an increase of 5, and from 9 to 16 an increase of 7. In fact, we could make a table of these differences like this:

Length of side	1	2	3	4	5	6	7
Area of square	1	4	9	16	25	36	49
Increase	3	5	7	9	11	13	

The differences form a strong pattern—they are predictable, but they are not constant. We cannot predict the change in area from one cell to the next without knowing first what the area was.

The name *linear* comes from the shape of the graph of a linear relationship. For example, if we graph the input/output pairs (1.1, 3.3), (1.3, 3.9), (2, 6), and so on, from the table of strip areas, they will all lie on a straight line, even though we've picked points from the arbitrarily constructed table. The same is not true of the graph of the input/output pairs from the table of the areas of squares.

A sequence of numbers in which the numbers increase at a fixed rate is called an *arithmetic sequence*. A table of a linear relationship can clearly be arbitrary, but if its input numbers form an arithmetic sequence—if they increase at fixed intervals—then the output numbers must increase at fixed intervals, too. The change in the output is proportional to the change in the input.

In the algebraic rule $y = ax + b$, where the input is represented by x and the output by y, the rate of change of y is represented by a. If x increases by 1, y increases by a; if x increases by 2, y increases by $2a$; and so on. In the graph of $y = ax + b$, a is called the slope of the line, with steeper lines representing greater rates of change. If there is nothing else to the relationship (if b is 0), then we say that y is proportional to x. That is the case in both tables of areas of strips of adding-machine paper. The ratio of length to area stays the same throughout the table: the two values are proportional.

That is not the case with the table of areas of squares, and is, in fact, not the case in *any* relationship that is not linear.

It is also not true with *all* linear relationships. Here is an example. For an increase of 1°C, there is an increase of 1.8°F, no matter what the starting temperature. The two ways of reporting temperature are linearly related. A table that shows evenly spaced values in °C will have evenly spaced corresponding values of °F. The change in the output is proportional to the change in the input. But the ratio of input to output is not constant (for example 0°C/32°F is not the same as 100°C/212°F), so the output and input themselves are not proportional. This is a nonproportional linear relationship.

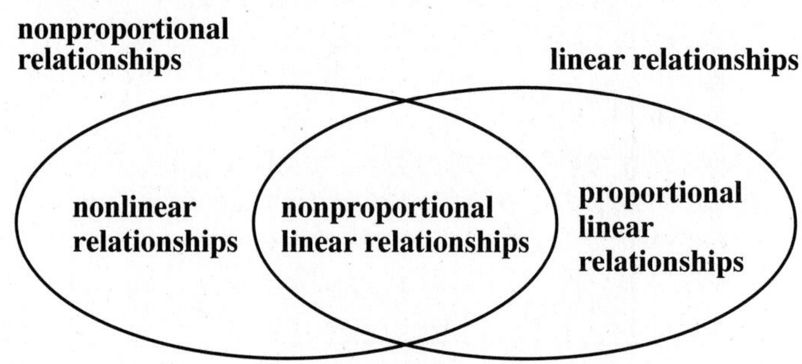

It is increasingly common in high school and even middle school curricula to see these ideas developed using the language and notation of functions. The language of relationships used in this chapter is more general than functions—that is, a function is one particular kind of relationship—but in fact, every relationship in this chapter is a function. Instead of introducing function notation $f(x) = ax + b$ at this time, *Impact Mathematics* has chosen to focus on the relationship between two variables—x and y—and use a notation that emphasizes the separateness of those two variables. Function notation and the functional way of thinking appears fully in Course 3.

In this chapter, and in many mathematics curricula, students are asked to extend sequences of numbers on the basis of patterns they find in the numbers. One of the subtleties of making predictions on the basis of data alone is that this simply cannot be done with any certainty at all. Only a mechanism—a rule, a physical principle, or the like—can tell one whether the pattern that presents itself so far actually continues. So, for example, the obvious pattern suggested by the sequence 1, 2, 3, 4, 5, 6, 7, 8, 9, 10, . . ., even despite the very long string of data is followed by 11 and 12 but is not followed by 13 if what the numbers represent on a clock is time.

The chapter gives a few examples of patterns that seem to suggest one pattern and then do not continue as expected. One begins 1, 2, 4 and then continues with 7 instead of 8. Another goes a step further 1, 2, 4, 8 and then continues with 15 instead of 16.

Lesson 5.1

Page 311 Answers, continued

5b. No; no one could have answered more than 40 questions.

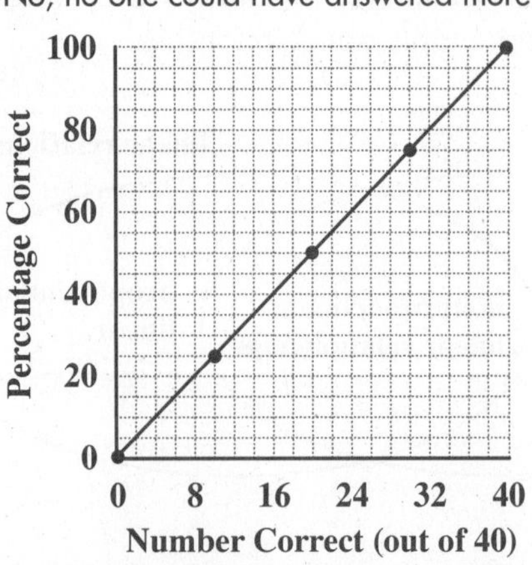

Page 316 Answers, continued

4d.

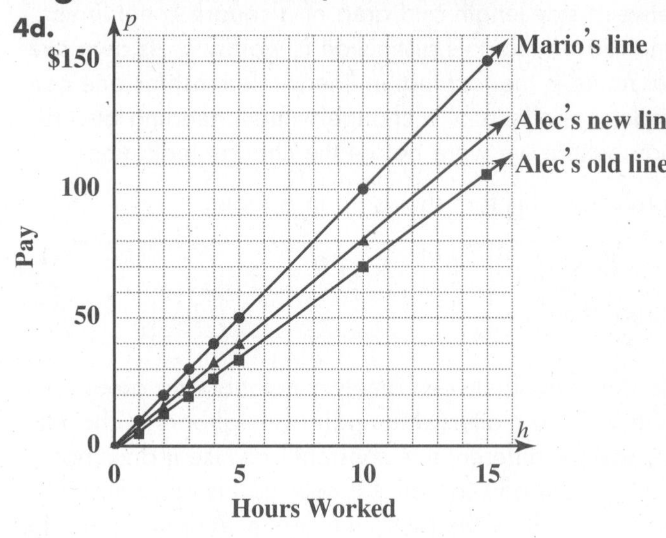

Page 318 Answers, continued

11b.

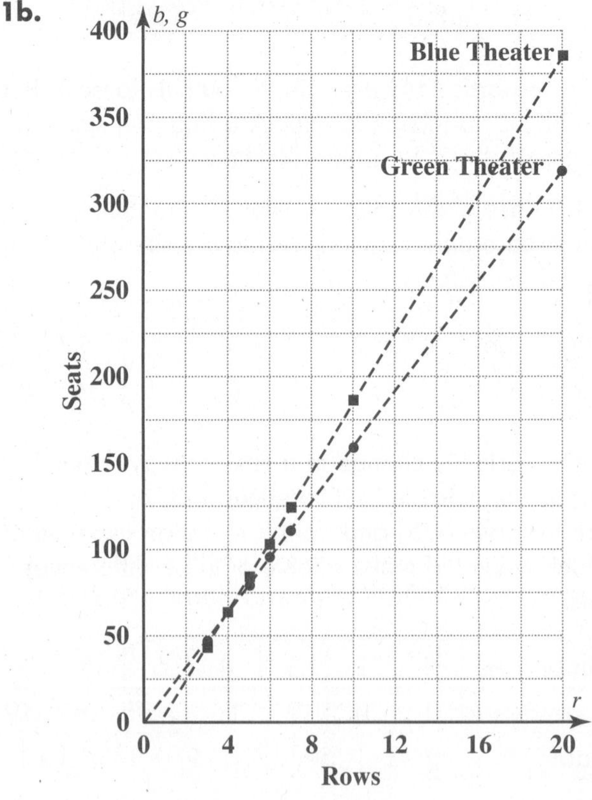

11c. No; there can be only whole numbers of rows in the theater. However, dashed lines might be drawn to help show the relationship between the variables.

11d. Green: $g = 16r$; Blue: $b = 24 + 20(r - 2)$

11g. Green: yes, Blue: no; The Green Theater's graph is a series of points that fall on a line that goes through (0, 0). The Blue Theater's graph is a series of points that fall on a line that does not go through (0, 0). (Note: Students may need to draw lines through the points to see these relationships.)

Page 319 Answers, continued

12c.

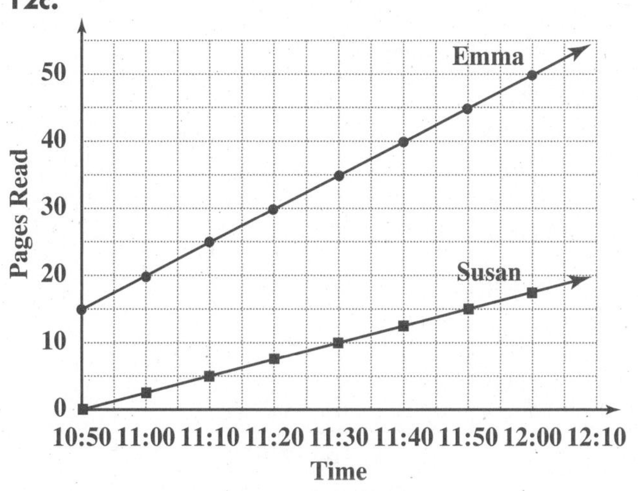

It makes sense to connect the points since each girl is reading at other times, like 10:52 and 11:23. It makes sense to continue the line beyond 12:00 if the girls are still reading.

Page 320 Quick Quiz, continued

3. State an equation that describes a nonproportional relationship. *Answers will vary. Possible answer:* $y = 2x + 3$

4. On the same axes draw two graphs: one for a proportional relationship and one for a nonproportional relationship. Label which graph is proportional and which is nonproportional. *Check students' graphs. The proportional relationship will be linear with a point at (0, 0). The nonproportional graph will have none or only one of these characteristics but not both.*

5. Caitlin works for a fresh-fish supplier. They offered a special price to restaurants for shrimp at $7 per pound. A local restaurant wanted a quote for the cost of enough shrimp for 40 shrimp cocktails. Each cocktail needs six shrimp.
   Clearly, Caitlin would not want to waste time counting all the shrimp. Work out an easy way to estimate the weight of shrimp the restaurant should order and the cost. What might Caitlin do to estimate the cost? *Caitlin can weigh 6 shrimp and multiply by 40 to get the total weight. To find the cost, she would multiply the total weight by $7. Or she can weigh 1 pound of shrimp to find how many shrimp per pound and then divide 240 by the number in the pound to find the number of pounds needed. To find the cost, she will multiply the total number of pounds needed by $7. She will try to be reasonably close but will over-estimate a little so there is enough shrimp to make all 40 shrimp cocktails.*

Lesson 5.2

Page 324 Answers, continued

Problem Set B Answer

4.

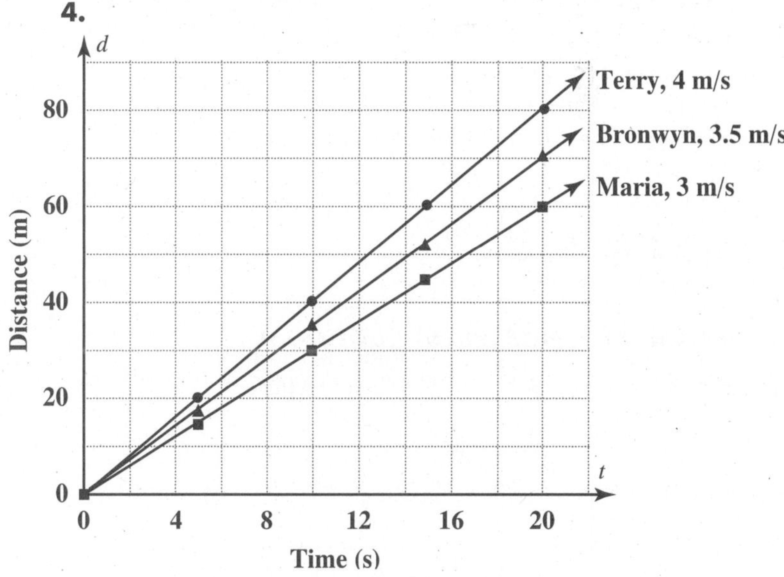

Page 326 Answers, continued

Problem Set C Answer

3.

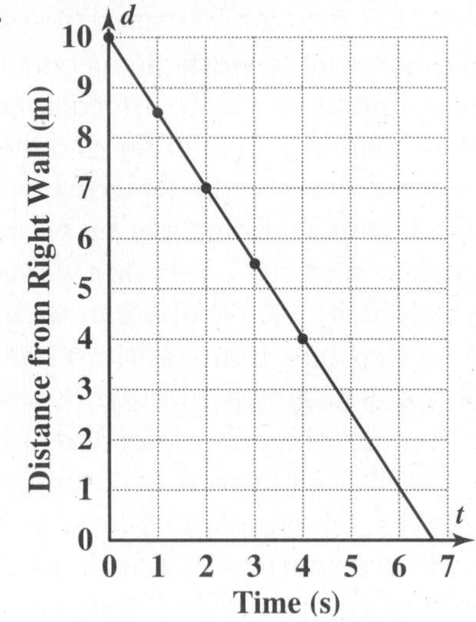

Page 335 Answers, continued

3b. Possible graph:

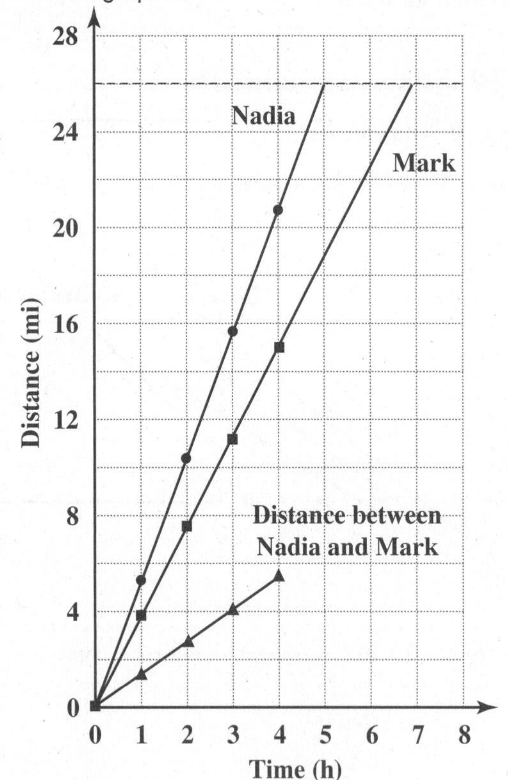

Page 340 Answers, continued

26a. about 10 ft/min

26b.

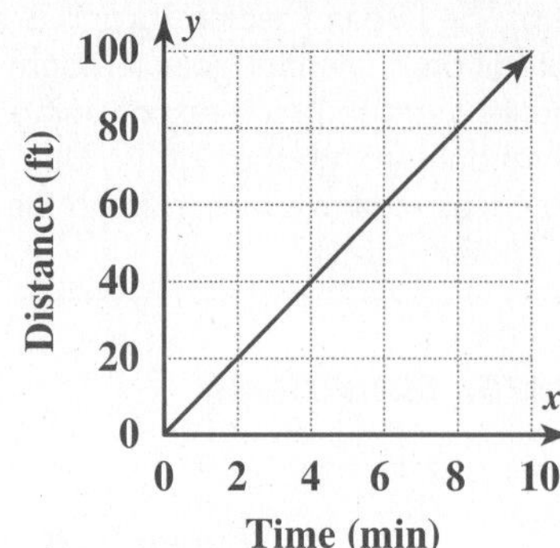

26c. about 10

27a. about 3,000 ft/min

27b.

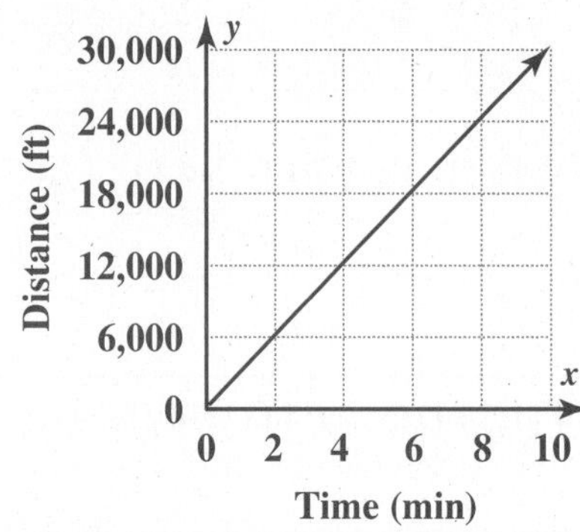

27c. about 3,000

28a. about 3,300 ft/min

28b.

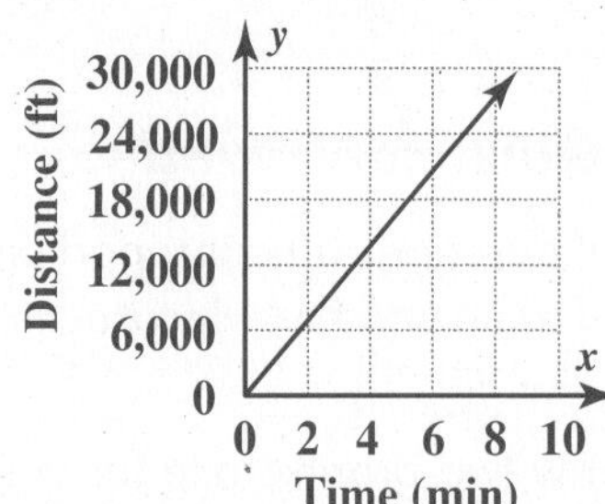

28c. about 3,300

29a. 2,700 ft/min

29b.

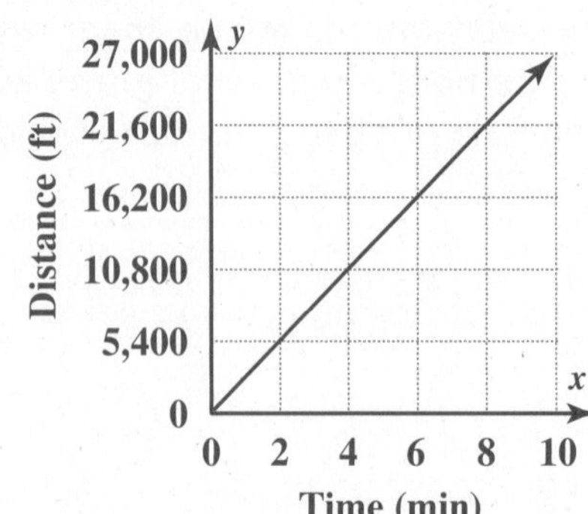

29c. 2,700

30a. 6,600 ft/min

30b.

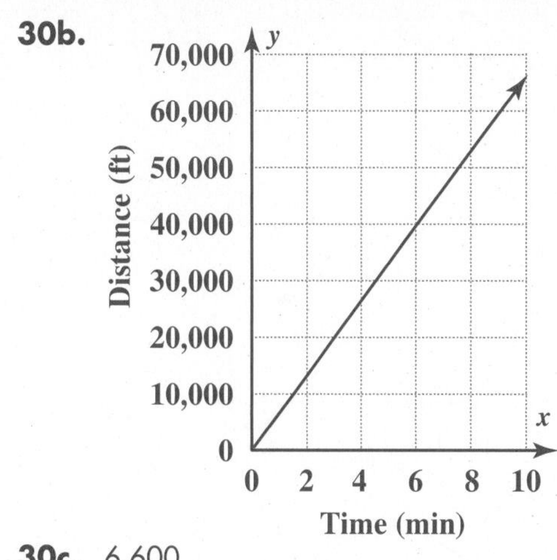

30c. 6,600

Page 341 Answers, continued

33b.

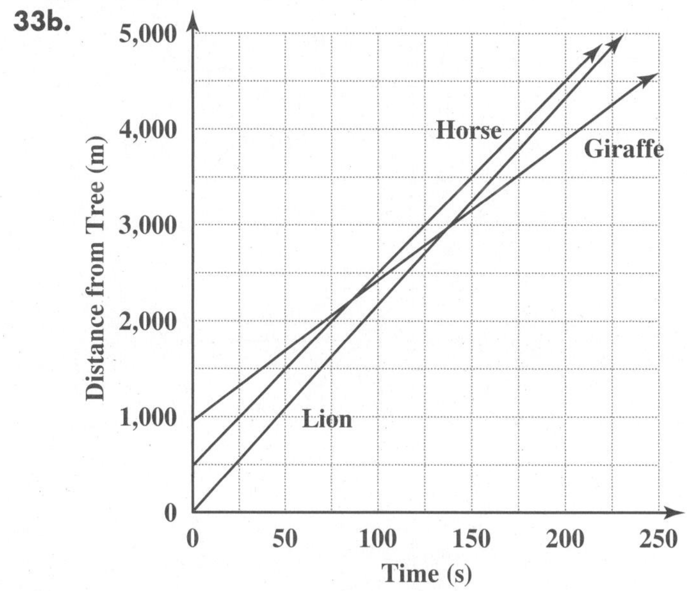

33c.

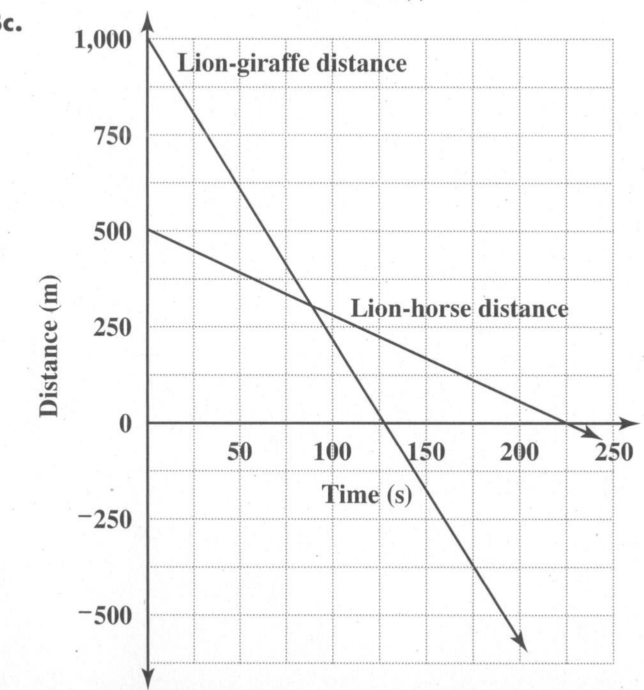

33d. All the graphs are straight lines. The graphs in Part b increase from left to right; the graphs in Part c decrease from left to right. The graph of the lion's distance from the tree is different from the others because it starts at (0, 0).

Page 343 Quick Quiz, continued

Quick Quiz

1. Below are five graphs and their rules. Match the graphs to the rules. $p = q + 2$, graph b; $p = 5 - q$, graph a; $p = 2q$, graph e; $p = 2$, graph c; $p = 2q + 1$, graph d

$p = q + 2$ $\qquad$ $p = 5 - q$

$p = 2q$ $\qquad$ $p = 2$

$p = 2q + 1$

a

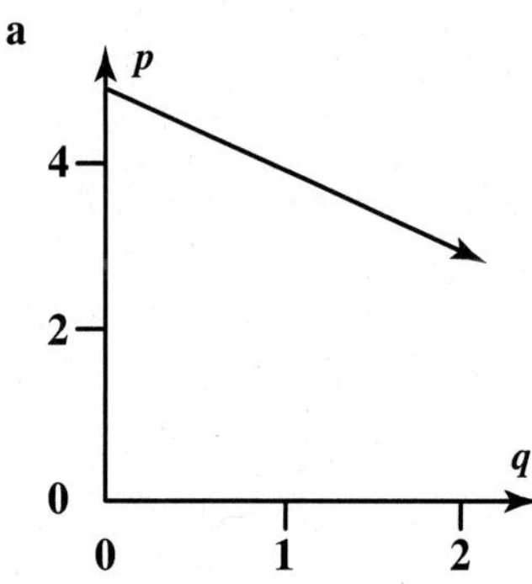

b

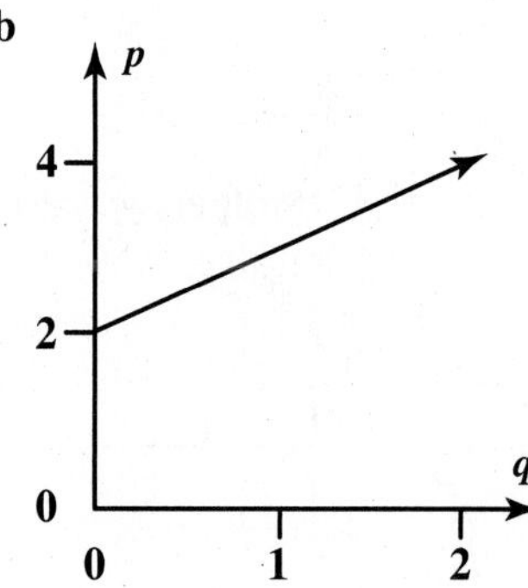

c

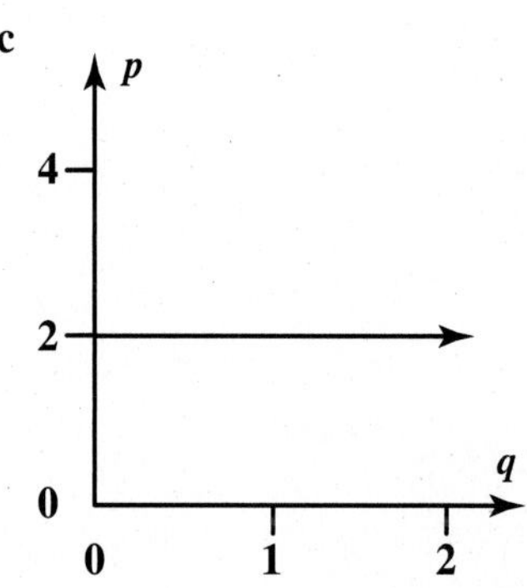

d

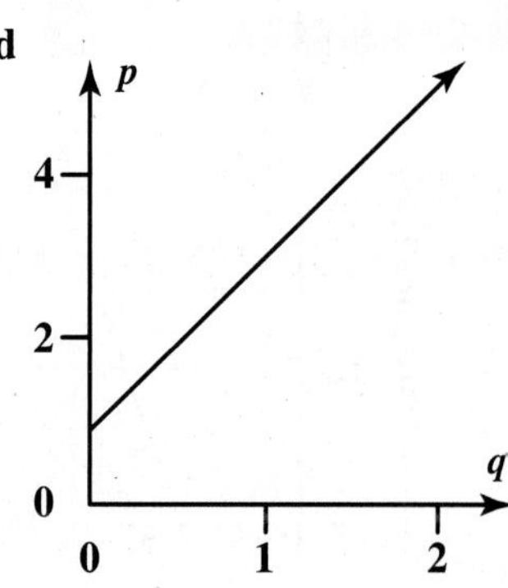

e

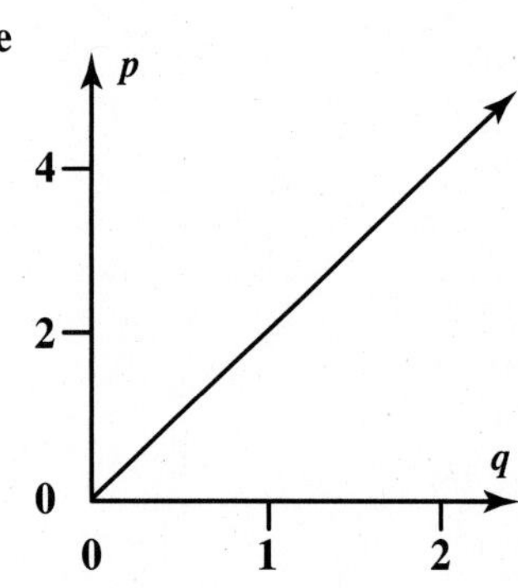

2. A strip of cloth 12 yards long is cut into two smaller pieces. If A stands for the number of yards in one piece and B stands for the number of yards in the other piece, they are related by the rule $A + B = 12$.

a. Draw a graph for this rule. Completing a table of values first may help you.

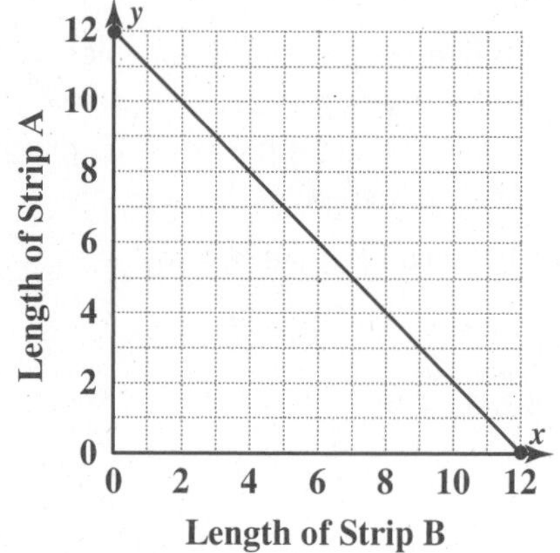

b. Find another way to write the rule that relates the two lengths. *Possible answers:* $A = 12 - B$, $B = 12 - A$

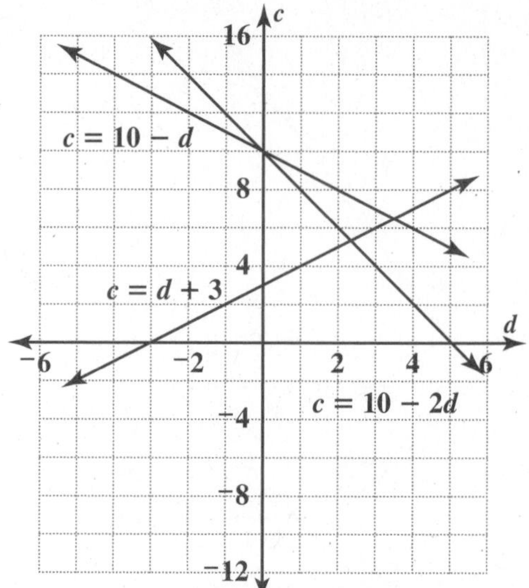

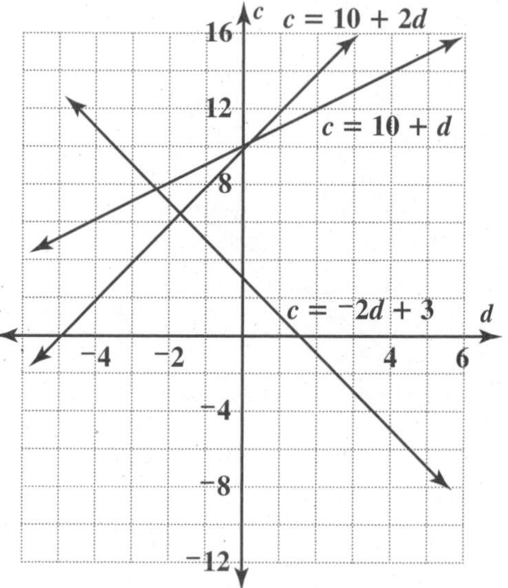

Lesson 5.3

Page 352 Answers, continued

Problem Set F Answers

1.

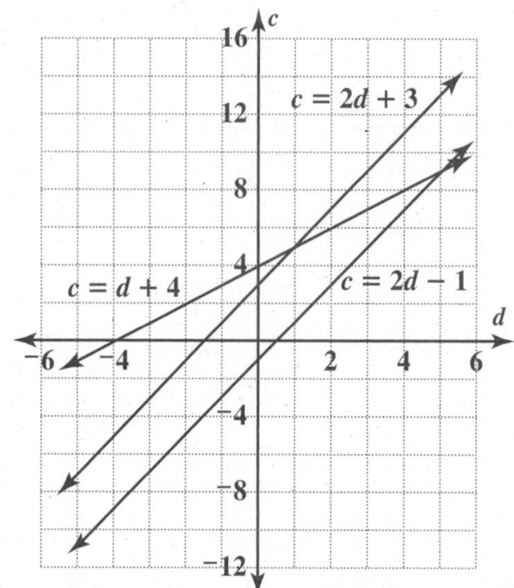

3.

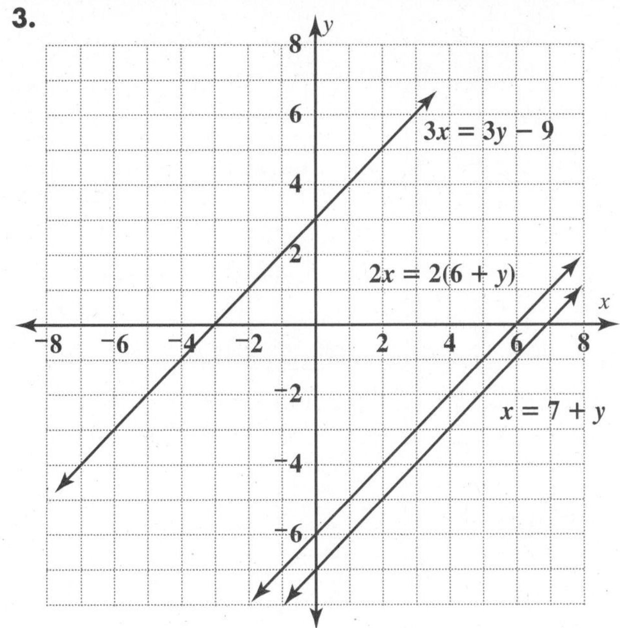

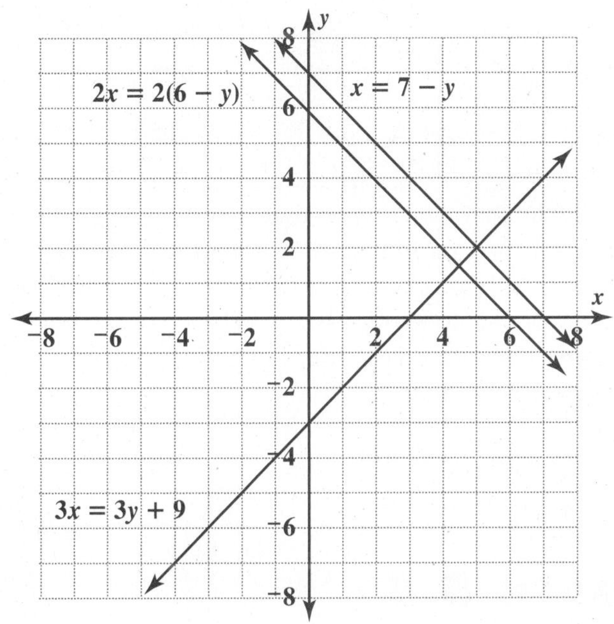

Page 355 Answers, continued

3c.

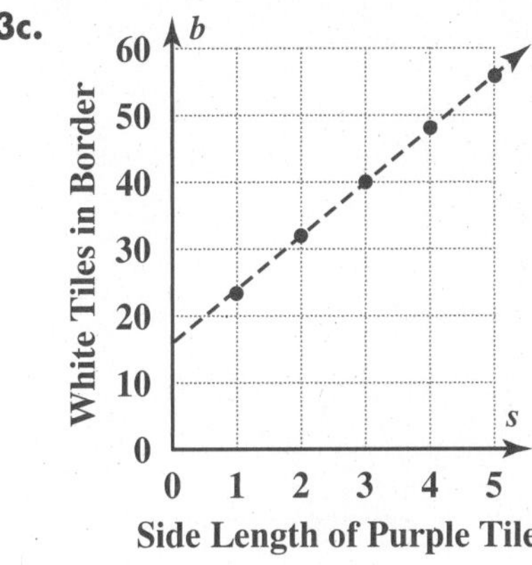

Page 356 Answers, continued

5–8.

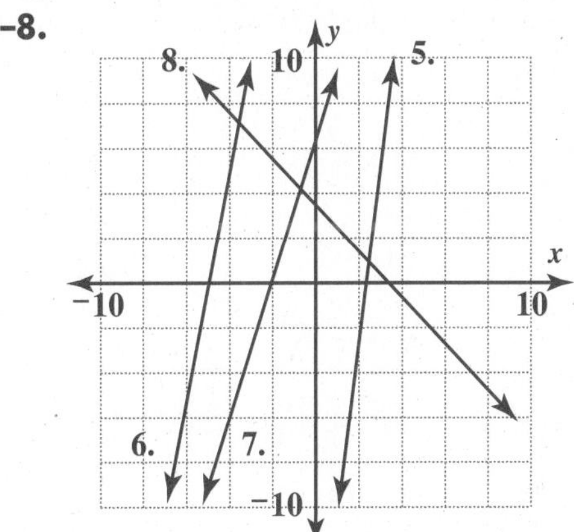

Page 357 Answers, continued

10b.

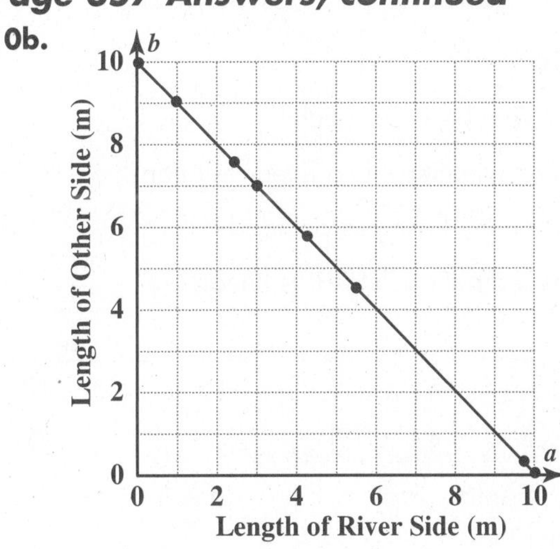

10e. Possible answer: 1×6, 2×4, 2×3, 4×5, 7.5×1

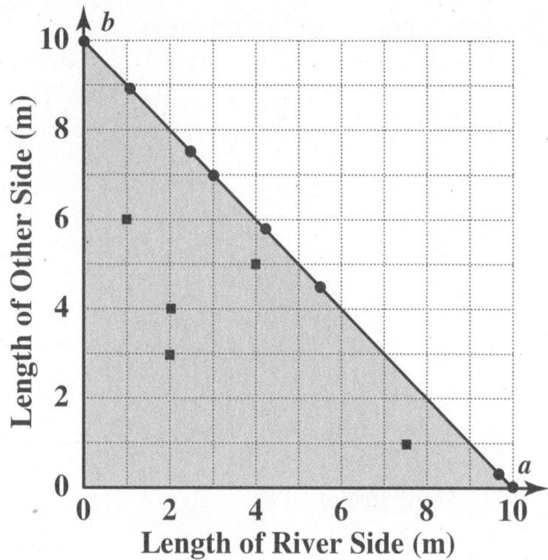

Page 359 Answers, continued

15d.

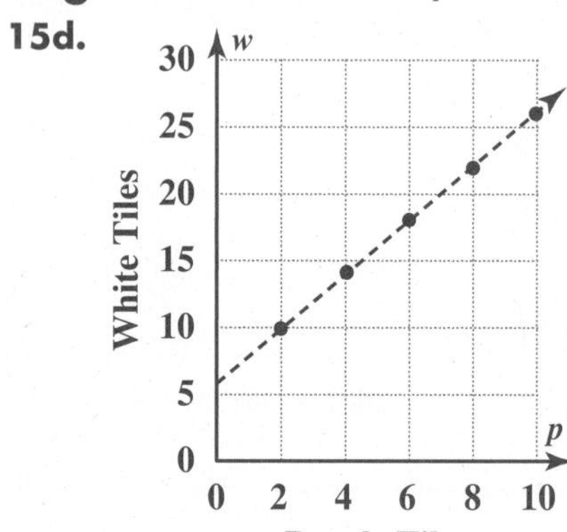

Page 361 Quick Quiz, continued

Quick Quiz

1. Here are five tables. For each,
   - determine whether it is a linear relationship.
   - explain briefly how you decided.
   - write its symbolic rule (if it is linear).

a.

Input	6	8	10	12	14
Output	4	3	2	1	0

linear; Possible explanation and rule: rate of change is constant, $y = {}^{-}\frac{1}{2}x + 7$

b.

Input	6	5	4	3	2
Output	0	1	4	9	16

nonlinear; Possible explanation: rate of change is not constant

c.

Input	$^{-}1$	0	1	2	3
Output	8	16	24	32	40

linear; Possible explanation and rule: rate of change is constant, $y = 8x + 16$

d.

Input	1	2	3	4	5
Output	4	8	16	32	64

nonlinear; Possible explanation: rate of change is not constant

e.

Input	0.2	0.3	0.4	0.5	0.6
Output	3.5	3.4	3.3	3.2	3.1

linear; Possible explanation and rule: rate of change is constant, $y = {}^{-}x + 3.7$

2. Explain in your own words how a and b affect the graph of $y = {}^{-}ax + b$. Possible answer: Increasing a makes the graph steeper and negative a makes the graph go downward from left to right. The variable b is the point where the graph crosses the vertical or y-axis.

Lesson 5.4

Page 363 Answers, continued

5. Possible answer: She could find the slope using the rise and run from one point to another. Then she could multiply the slope by one input and subtract the result from the output. The rule is the slope times an input plus the result from the subtraction.

Page 364 Answers, continued

Problem Set B Answer

3. Estimates will vary, but those for Games 1–3 should be close; actual outputs: Game 1: ⁻8; Game 2: ⁻14; Game 3: 35; Game 4: 0. Possible explanation: The estimates for Games 1–3 are probably accurate, because you can draw a line through the points and read the output for an input of ⁻3. Game 4 isn't linear, so you can't be sure how the graph curves beyond the data points.

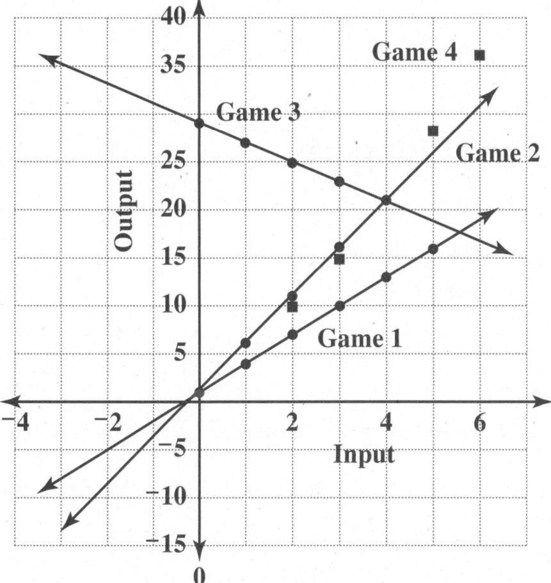

Page 367 Answers, continued

8. 1.

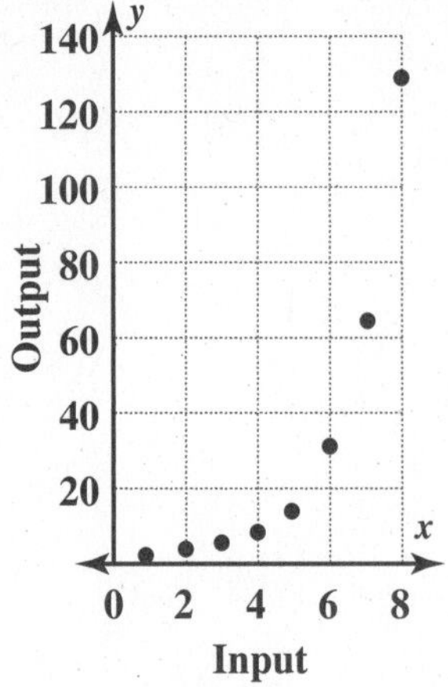

2.

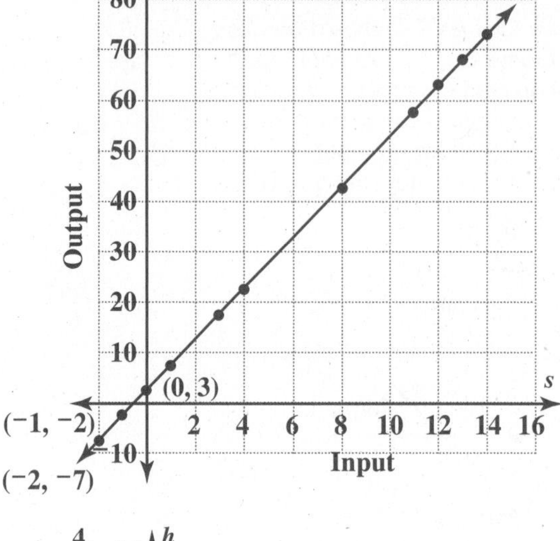

3.

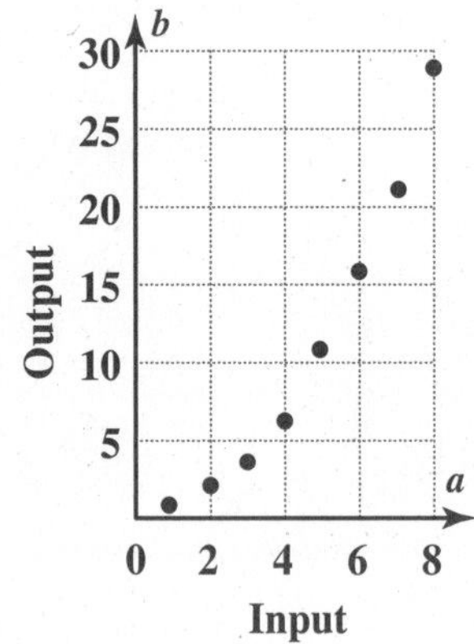

4.

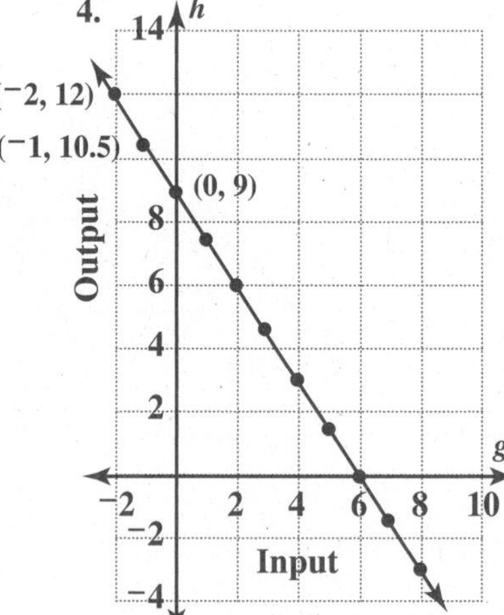

5.

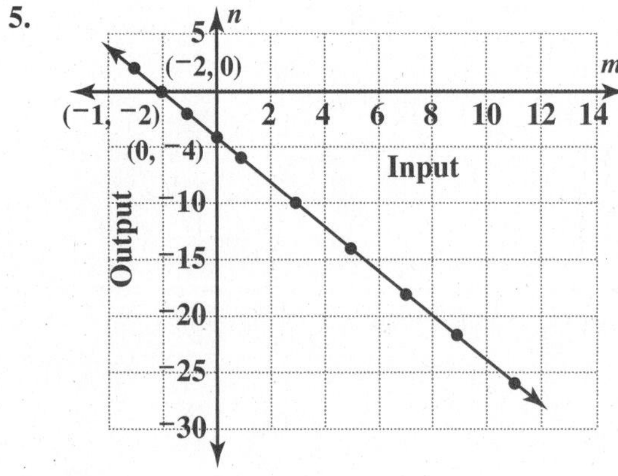

6.

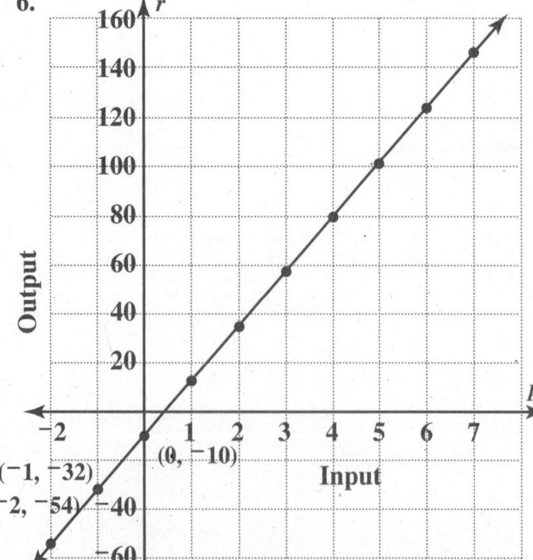

Page 368 Answers, continued

Problem Set F Answer

3b.

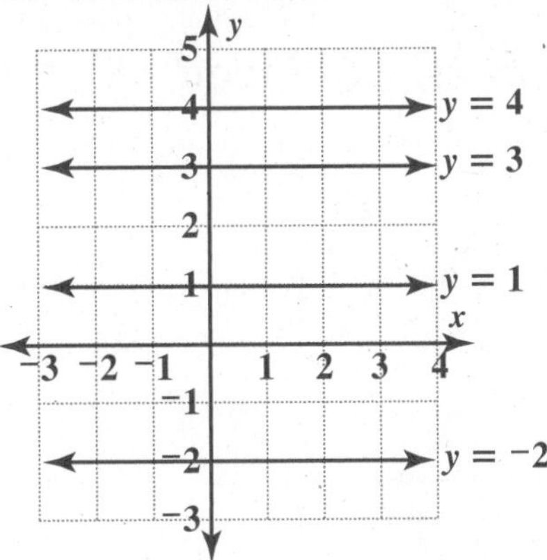

Page 369 Answers, continued

5b.

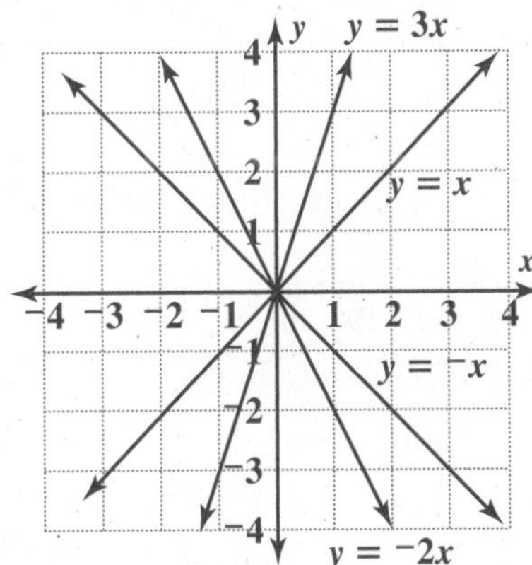

7. Students will likely guess two quadrants, but the graph does not pass through any.

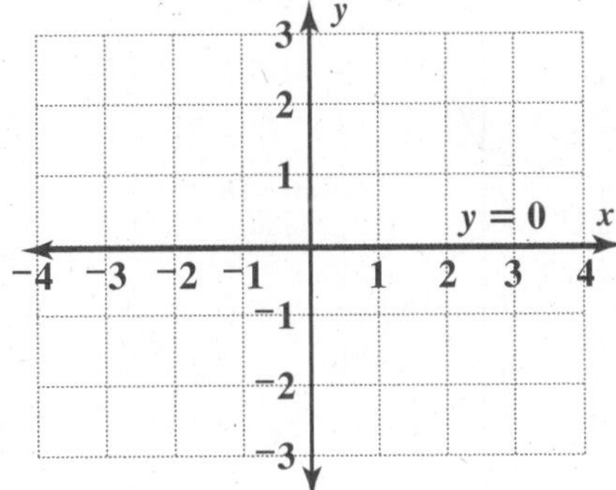

Page 371 Answers, continued

1a. could be linear

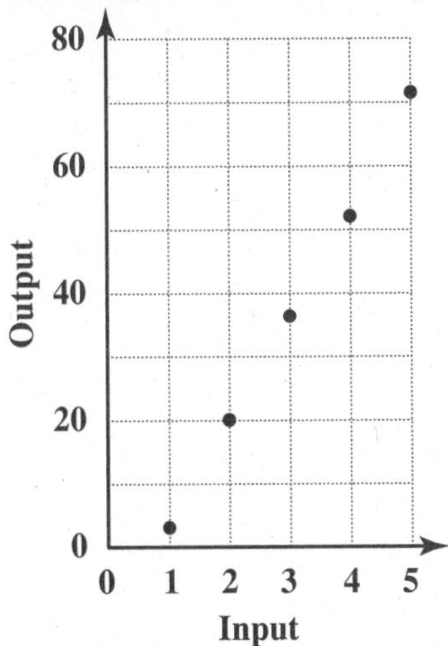

1b. $o = 17i - 14$

2a. could be linear

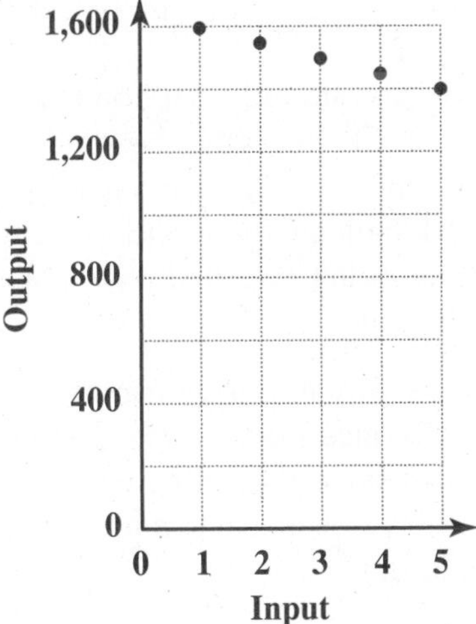

2b. $o = 1{,}637 - 38i$

3a. not linear

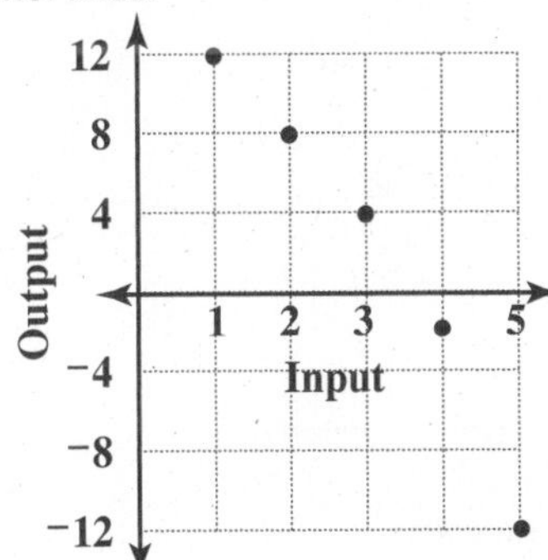

Page 377 Quick Quiz, continued

b. Graph this relationship. Possible answer: graph showing $d = 1.2 - 2.05t$

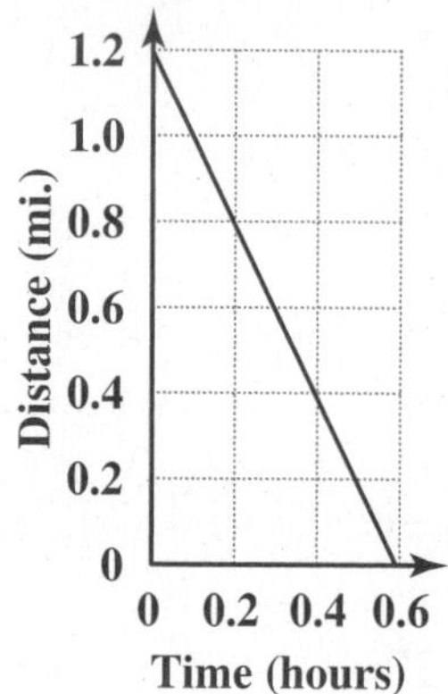

c. What is the slope of the line on the graph? Possible answer: For $d = 1.2 - 2.05t$, the slope is $^{-}2.05$.

d. Is this relationship proportional? No

2. Hillary went for a trip. She started from home at a speed of 55 miles/hour. On her way, she passed the Ice Cream Shoppe 15 miles away from her home. (Ever since she passed the Ice Cream Shoppe, she has been sorry that she didn't stop and now thinks that maybe she needs some ice cream.)

a. Write a rule which shows the relationships between Hillary's distance from the Ice Cream Shoppe and the time since she left home. $d = 55t - 15$ where d is distance in meters and t is time in hours

b. Graph this relationship.

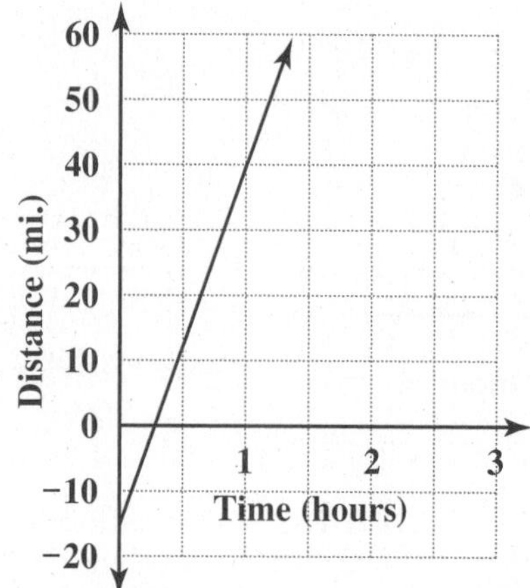

c. What is the slope of the line on the graph? 55

d. How is the constant term shown on the graph? The graph starts at the point (0, −15).

Page 379 Answers, continued

2c.

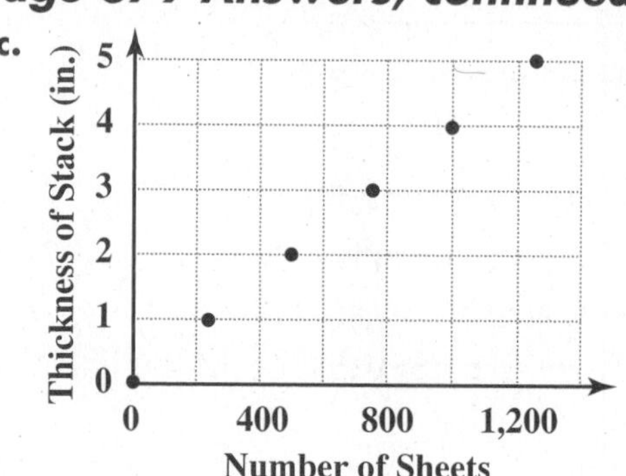

3b.

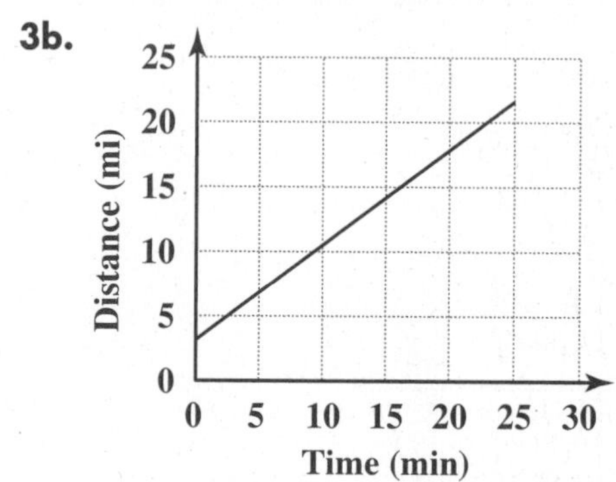

4b.

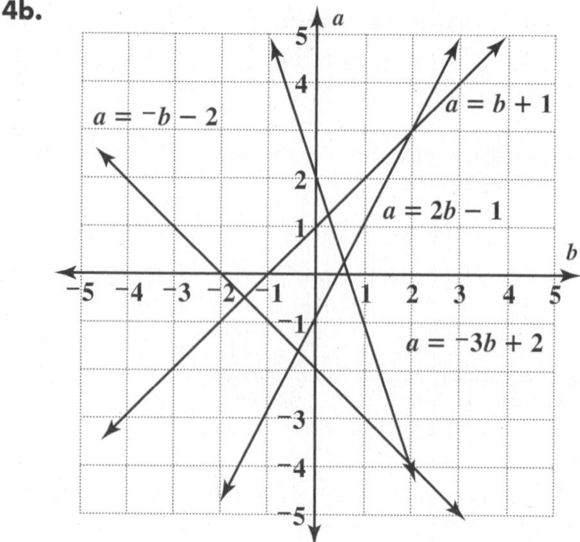

GLOSSARY

algebraic expression

A rule written with numbers and symbols. Examples: $n + n + n + 2$, $3n + 2$. [page 5]

backtracking

A method of solving algebraic equations by working backwards from the known answer to figure out the value of the variable. [page 20]

base

1: The parallel faces of a prism. [page 112]

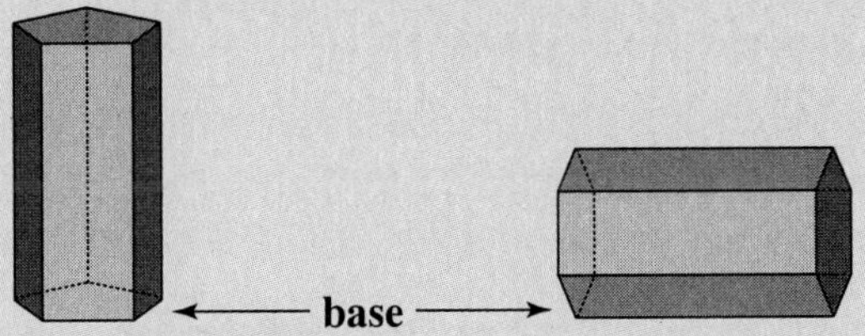

2: The number in an exponential expression that is multiplied by itself. For example, in t^3, t is the *base;* in 10^4, 10 is the *base.* [page 149]

coefficient

A number that is multiplied by a variable. For example, in $y = 3x + 2$, 3 is the *coefficient* of the variable x. [page 367]

congruent

Having the same size and the same shape. [page 450]

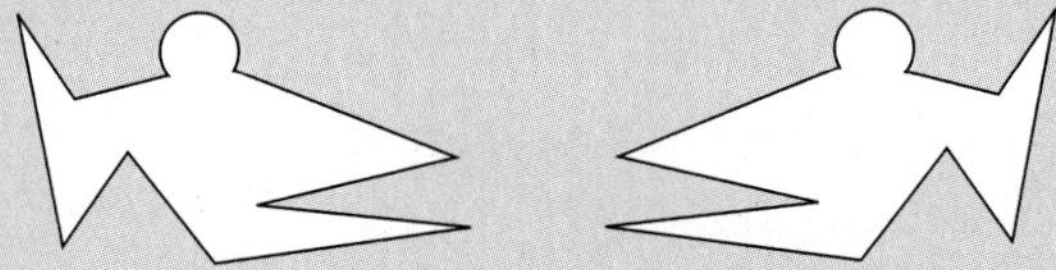

conjecture

A statement that is believed to be true but has not yet been proven. [page 422]

constant term

A number that stands by itself in an expression or equation. For example, in $y = 3x - 2$, -2 is the *constant term.* [page 367]

corresponding angles

Angles of two similar figures that are located in the same place in each figure. For example, in the figure angle B and angle E are *corresponding angles.* [page 457]

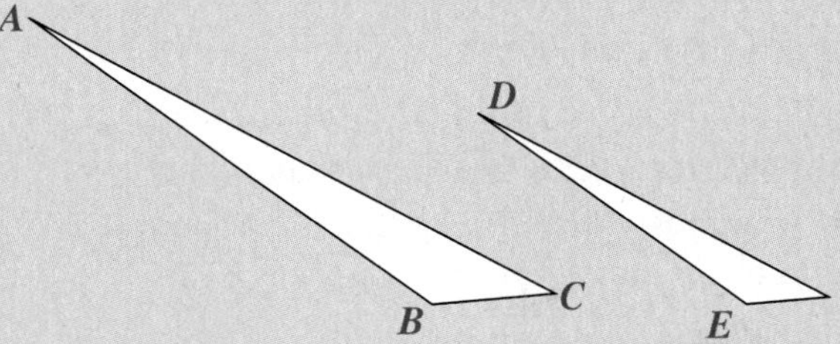

corresponding sides

Sides of two similar figures that are located in the same place in each figure. For example, in the figure above, sides AB and DE are *corresponding sides.* [page 457]

counterexample

In testing a conjecture, an example for which the conjecture is not true. [page 453]

cube

A three-dimensional figure with six square sides, or faces. [page 81]

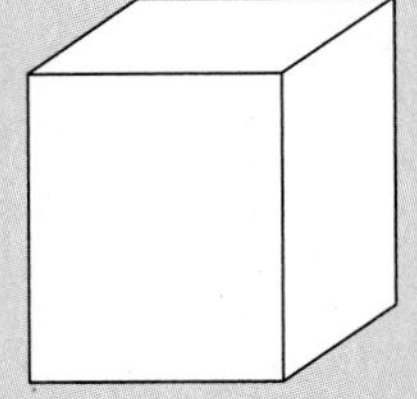

cylinder

A solid with two parallel, congruent bases that are circles. [page 113]

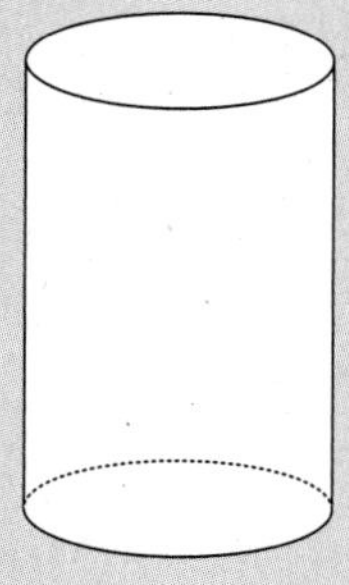

distance formula

The symbolic rule for calculating the distance between any two points, (x_1, y_1) and (x_2, y_2), in the coordinate plane:
distance $= \sqrt{(x_2 - x_1)^2 + (y_2 - y_1)^2}$
[page 274]

distributive property

The *distributive property of multiplication over addition* states that for any numbers n, a, and b, $n(a + b) = na + nb$.
The *distributive property of multiplication over subtraction* states that for any numbers n, a, and b, $n(a - b) = na - nb$. [page 62]

equivalent expressions

Expressions that always give the same result when the same values are substituted for the variables. For example, $2K + 6$ and $2(K + 3)$ are equivalent expressions. [page 57]

equivalent ratios

Two different ratios that represent the same relationship. For example, 1:3 and 4:12 are *equivalent ratios.* [page 457]

expand

To use the distributive property to remove parentheses. [page 64]

exponent

A symbol written above and to the right of a quantity that tells how many times the quantity is multiplied by itself. For example: $t \times t \times t$ is written t^3. [page 13] [page 149]

exponential decay

A decreasing pattern of change in which a quantity is repeatedly multiplied by a number less than 1 and greater than 0. [page 182]

exponential decrease

See *exponential decay.*

exponential growth

An increasing pattern of change in which a quantity is repeatedly multiplied by a number greater than 1. [page 179]

factor

To use the distributive property to insert parentheses. [page 64]

flowchart

A visual diagram that shows each step in evaluating an algebraic expression. [page 19]

formula

An algebraic "recipe" that shows how to calculate a particular quantity. For example, $F = \frac{9}{5}C + 32$ is the *formula* for converting Celsius temperatures to Fahrenheit temperatures. [page 37]

linear relationship

A relationship whose graph is a straight line. *Linear relationships* have a constant rate of change. As one variable changes by 1 unit, the other variable changes by a set amount. For example, $m = 5t$ shows that m changes 5 units per 1-unit change in t. [page 303]

line graph

A graph on which points are connected by line segments. [page 605]

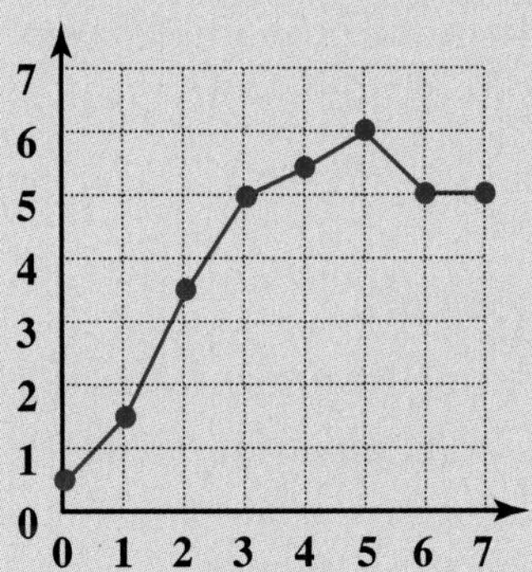

model

Something that has the key characteristics of something else. For example, in mathematics you could use a balance to *model* an equation. [page 395]

multiplicative inverse

The number by which another number is multiplied to get 1. For example, the *multiplicative inverse* of 4 is $\frac{1}{4}$. [page 627]

net

A flat figure that can be folded to form a closed, three-dimensional object called a solid [page 129]

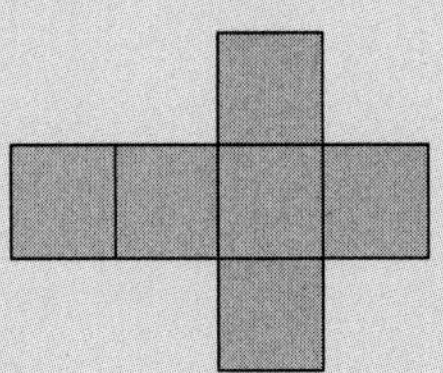

population

A larger group from which a sample is taken. [page 693]

power

An exponent. [page 149]

prism

A figure that has two identical, parallel faces that are polygons, and other faces that are parallelograms. [page 109]

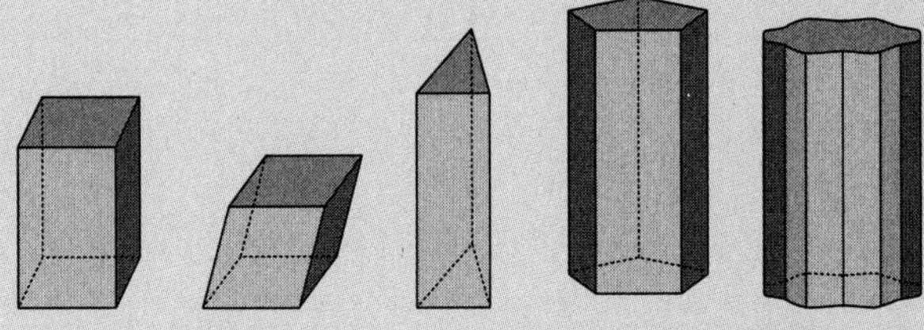

proportion

An equation that states that two ratios are equal. For example, 2:3 = 6:9. [page 545]

proportional

Used to describe the relationship between two variables in which, when the value of one variable is multiplied by a number, the value of the other variable is multipled by the same number. For example, when a someone is paid an hourly rate and works double the hours, that person gets double the pay. When the someone works triple the hours, that person gets triple the pay. The hours worked and rate of pay per hour are *proportional* to each other. [page 309]

quadrant

One of the four sections created by the axes on the coordinate plane. [page 259]

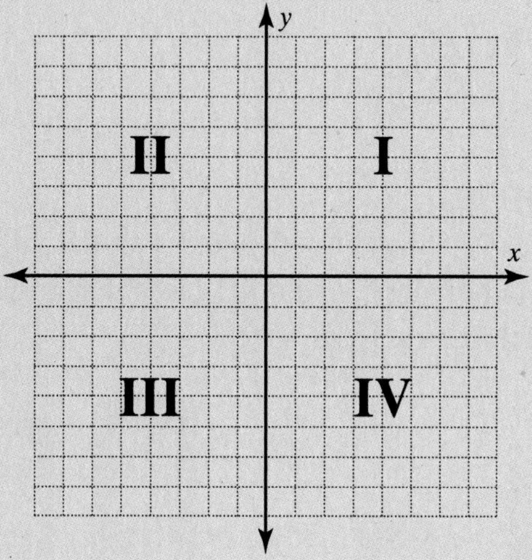

quartile

The values that divide a set of data into four parts; each of which includes about 25% of the data. In a box-and-whisker plot, these values are represented by the ends of the box and a segment inside the box. [page 710]

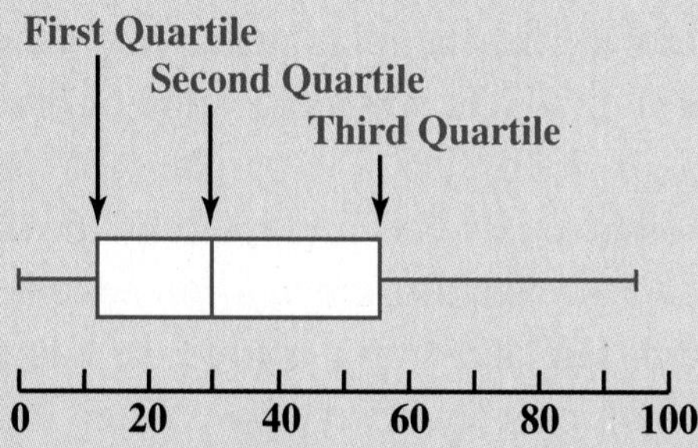

rate

A way to describe how two unlike quantities are related or how they can be compared. For example, in the statement, "David types 30 words per minute," the rate *30 words per minute* describes the relationship between the number of words David types and time in minutes. [page 300]

ratio

A way to compare two numbers. For example, when one segment is twice as long as another, the *ratio* of the length of the longer segment to the length of the shorter segment is 2 to 1, or 2:1. [page 456]

representative sample

A part of a population that has approximately the same proportions as the whole population with respect to the characteristic being studied. [page 698]

sample

A smaller group taken from a population that is used to represent the larger group. [page 693]

scale factor

The number by which you multiply the side lengths of one figure to get the side lengths of a similar figure. [page 482]

scientific notation

A number that is expressed as the product of a number greater than or equal to 1 but less than 10, and a power of 10. For example, 5,000,000 written *scientific notation* is 5×10^6. [page 196]

similar

Having the same shape but possibly different sizes. [page 450]

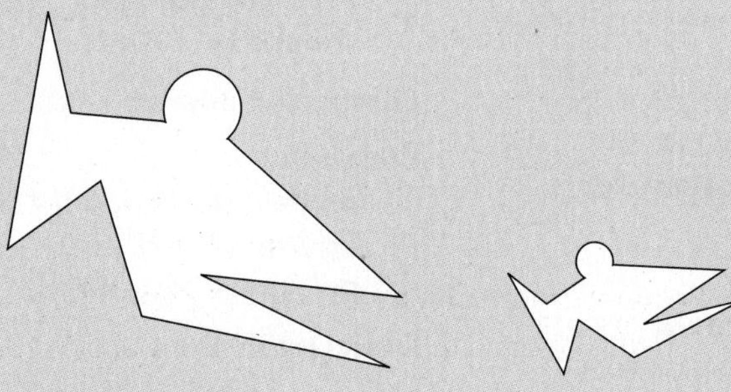

slope

The steepness of a line. [page 324]

speed

How fast an object is going (always positive). [page 329]

surface area

The area of the exterior surface of an object, measured in square units. [page 98]

unit rate

Term used when one of two quantities being compared in a rate is given in terms of one unit. Example: 65 miles per hour or $1.99 per lb. [page 530]

variable

A quantity that can change or vary, or an unknown quantity. [page 5] [page 367]

velocity

The rate at which an object is moving from or toward a designated point (can be positive or negative). [page 329]

volume

The space inside a three-dimensional object, measured in cubic units. [page 98]

y-intercept

A point at which a graph (e.g., line or curve) intersects the *y*-axis. [page 333]

INDEX

PHOTO CREDITS

Chapter 1 **2-3 (background),** Kiell B. Sandved/Visuals Unlimited; **2BL,** Brian Drake/West Stock; **3B,** The Field Museum photo by John Weinstein GEO-859-6.9*c;* **9,** Reuters/Kieran Doherty/Archive Photos; **11B,** Michael Newman/PhotoEdit; **12L,** Archive Photos; **12B,** Connie Geocaris/Tony Stone Images; **16,** Tony Freeman/PhotoEdit; **19,** Bob Fila/*Chicago Tribune;* **23BL,** Jonathan Nourok/PhotoEdit; **25,** Michelle Bridwell/PhotoEdit; **28,** ETHS Yearbook Staff, Evanston, IL; **29,** Gerard Loucel/Tony Stone Images; **31B,** Amy Etra/PhotoEdit; **35,** Jim Steere/Chicago Symphony Orchestra; **39L,** L. Hobbs/West Stock; **41T,** Leonard Lee Rue III/Visuals Unlimited; **41BL,** C.P. Hickman/Visuals Unlimited; **43,** Gary A. Conner/PhotoEdit; **46,** Eric Sanford/West Stock; **48,** James Mayo/*Chicago Tribune;* **50,** Eric Risberg/AP Photo; **53,** Myrleen Ferguson Cate/PhotoEdit; **59,** Rudi Van Briel/PhotoEdit; **61,** Jeff Greenberg/PhotoEdit; **63,** Nick Dolding/Tony Stone Images; **67,** Rick Houchin/AP Photo; **70,** Richard Hutchings/PhotoEdit; **72,** Wayne Eastep/Tony Stone Images

Chapter 2 **76-77 (background),** Clark Borins and Associates; **76L,** The McCall Pattern Company #8934; **77T,** Clark Borins and Associates; **77C, 77B,** Penrod Design, Richard and Jacqueline Penrod; **78B-79B,** Creative Publications; **80,** UPI Photo; **82,** Michael A. Keller/West Stock; **84,** Digital Vision; **86,** Robert Daly/Tony Stone Images; **88,** David Young-Wolff/PhotoEdit; **89,** John D. Cunningham/Visuals Unlimted; **90,** Myrleen Ferguson Cate/PhotoEdit; **92-93B,** Yves Marcoux/Tony Stone Images; **93TL,** William S. Helsel/Tony Stone Images; **96-97,** Nathan Beck/Omni-Photo Communications; **100-101,** C.P. George/Visuals Unlimited; **103,** Creative Publications; **113,** Jack Demuth; **114,** Bill Beatty/Visuals Unlimited; **121,** AP Photo; **123,** David Young-Wolff/PhotoEdit; **124,** Robert Brenner/PhotoEdit; **126CL,** Bob Burch/West Stock; **126CR,** John Cunningham/Visuals Unlimited; **128,** Jeff Schultz/Alaska Stock; **136-137,** Charles Preitner/Visuals Unlimited; **138-139,** Michelle Bridwell/PhotoEdit; **140,** Tom & Pat Leeson/West Stock

Chapter 3 **144-145 (background),** MRPS#81007, Jet Propulsion Laboratory California Institute of Technology; **144-145,** National Aeronautics and Space Administration; **146,** Myrleen Ferguson Cate/PhotoEdit; **148,** Paul Damien/Tony Stone Images; **149,** West Stock; **151,** Justin Lockengs #395/National Geographic; **152,** John D. Cunningham/Visuals Unlimited; **159,** Corbis/Bettmann-UPI; **162,** David Young-Wolff/PhotoEdit; **169,** Robert Crum/West Stock; **171,** Texas Instrument Incorporated, Dallas, Texas; **174TL,** West Stock; **174-175B,** John D. Cunningham/Visuals Unlimted; **176,** Jeff Greenberg/PhotoEdit; **177,** Visuals Unlimited; **179,** Nancy Stone/*Chicago Tribune;* **180TC,** Jack Demuth; **180L,** Elie Bernager/Tony Stone Images; **182,** Sylvan Wittwer/Visuals Unlimited; **183,** Nancy Sheehan/PhotoEdit; **184,** A.H. Benton/Visuals Unlimited; **194,** David Young-Wolff/PhotoEdit; **195,** AP Photo; **196,** Hui Yang, Jeff J. Hester, National Aeronautics and Space Administration; **200-201B,** Hubble Space Telescope Comet Team, National Aeronautics and Space Administration; **208,** National Aeronautics and Space Administration; **214,** Nick Gunderson/Tony Stone Images

Chapter 4 **216-217 (background),** Kevin O. Mooney/Odyssey/Chicago; **216BL,** Sir John Hunt/*Chicago Tribune;* **217T,** Shrinkai 6500/JAMSTEC; **217B,** Warren Lieb/Archive Photos; **219,** Ray Fairall 1991/AP Photo; **223TL,** David Young-Wolff/PhotoEdit; **224,** Davis Barber/PhotoEdit; **225,** David Madison/Tony Stone Images; **228,** Dennis O'Clair/Tony Stone Images; **230,** Ken McVey/Tony Stone Images; **231TL,** Philip and Karen Smith/Tony Stone Images; **241,** Renee Lynn/Tony Stone Images; **242,** Steve McCutcheon/Visuals Unlimited; **244,** Stephen Frink/Tony Stone Images; **249L,** Hulton Getty; **249TR,** Click Chicago/Tony Stone Images; **251,** Jeff Schultz/Alaska Stock; **252,** Jeff Schultz/Alaska Stock; **254,** Peter Cade/Tony Stone Images; **256L,** R.E. Johnson/Alaskan Stock; **260,** Carl Hugare/*Chicago Tribune;* **265,** Science VU/Visuals Unlimited; **267,** Jim Brown; **268,** Chuck Berman/*Chicago Tribune;* **271,** Rod Lankey/*Chicago Tribune;* **272,** Karen Engstrom/*Chicago Tribune;* **273,** Robert Frerck/Odyssey/Chicago; **277,** "The Field Museum" GEO-85906.9c/John Weinstein; **278,** Kevin Miller/Tony Stone Images; **281,** UPI Photo; **292,** Hulton Getty; **295** Richard Hutchings/PhotoEdit

Chapter 5 **298-299 (background),** Orion Press/Tony Stone Images; **298L,** Archive Photos; **298B,** Chris Schrameck/Tony Stone Images; **299T,** Mike Mcqueen/Tony Stone Images; **299C,** Railway Technical Research Institute; **300,** Gary W. Carter/Visuals Unlimited; **301,** Andy Sacks/Tony Stone Images; **302,** Irene Vandermolen/Visuals Unlimited; **303,** W.S. Ormerod Jr./Visuals Unlimited; **306,** Don Smerzer/Tony Stone Images; **308,** Michael Newman/PhotoEdit; **310B,** Chris Walker/*Chicago Tribune;* **312,** Charles Sanders/Visuals Unlimited; **314,** Tony Freeman/PhotoEdit; **316,** *Chicago Tribune;* **318,** Oakland Paramount Theater/Photographer Cathe Centorbe; **319,** Nuccio Dinuzzo/*Chicago Tribune;* **324,** Bonnie Kamin/PhotoEdit; **325,** David Young-Wolff/PhotoEdit; **329,** Chris Cheadle/Tony Stone Images; **330-331B,** Jim Prisching/*Chicago Tribune;* **335,** AP Photo; **336,** Victah Saillor/PhotoRun 1997 Worldwide Copyright; **337,** Brian Rogers/Visuals Unlimited; **340,** National Aeronautics and Space Administration; **344,** Billy E. Barnes/PhotoEdit; **345,** Charles O. Cecil/Visuals Unlimited; **347,** Dan Casper/*Chicago Tribune;* **349,** David Young-Wolff/PhotoEdit; **350,** Glen Allison/Tony Stone Images; **352,** Hulton Getty; **353,** Mary Kate Denny/Tony Stone Images; **354,** Robert Frerck/Tony Stone Images; **357,** Christine Frazer; **358,** Robert Frerck/Tony Stone Images; **359,** Toni Berardi/*Chicago Tribune;* **360,** Tom Pantages/Photographer; **363,** Tony Freeman/

PhotoEdit; **366,** James Frazer; **369,** Bill Hogan/*Chicago Tribune;* **375,** © FOTOPIC/West Stock; **377,** Tony Freeman/PhotoEdit; **378,** John Kringas/*Chicago Tribune;* **379,** Hung T. Vu/ *Chicago Tribune*

Chapter 6 **382-383 (background),** Coug Armand/Tony Stone Images; **382L,** "Bud" Nielsen/Visuals Unlimited; **382B,** Jack Demuth; **383T,** Al Thornton/Tony Stone Images; **387,** Michael Newman/PhotoEdit; **393B,** Charles Mason/Tony Stone Images; **397,** David Young-Wolff/Tony Stone Images; **400,** David Young-Wolff/PhotoEdit; **402,** Jeff Greenberg/ PhotoEdit; **407,** Bonnie Kamin/PhotoEdit; **408,** John Cunningham/Visuals Unlimited; **413,** G and C Merker/Visuals Unlimited; **415,** Frank Siteman/PhotoEdit; **416,** David Young-Wolff/PhotoEdit; **420,** Gary L. Benson/Tony Stone Images; **422,** Bruce Ayres/Tony Stone Images; **428,** Archive Photos; **429CR,** Blank Archives/Archive Photos; **430,** AP Photo; **431,** Gary W. Carter/Visuals Unlimited; **435,** Jack Demuth; **440,** Jack Demuth; **442,** Archive Photos; **445,** Archive Photos

Chapter 7 **448-449 (background),** LEGOLAND California is a 128-acre family theme park for youngsters 2-12. Highlights include rides, shows, miniature LEGO brick cities and a castle. Open daily. (760) 918-LEGO; **449TB,** LEGOLAND California; **452,** Ian O'Leary/Tony Stone Images; **458,** Davis Barber/PhotoEdit; **463,** Frank Associates/ *Chicago Tribune;* **472,** Michael Newman/PhotoEdit; **474,** Science Vu/Visuals Unlimited; **477L,** *Chicago Tribune;* **477CLCCR,** Jack Demuth; **484,** Ryan-Reyer/Tony Stone Images; **486,** Mark E. Gibson/Visuals Unlimited; **488,** C.E. Arnett/Visuals Unlimited; **489,** Bonnie Kamin/PhotoEdit; **493,** Molly Dean/Tony Stone Images; **495BR,** James W. Richardson/Visuals Unlimited; **497,** Tom McCarthy/PhotoEdit; **499,** Russell Kaye/Tony Stone Images; **500,** ETHS Yearbook Staff, Evanston, IL; **503B,** Steve McCutcheon/Visuals Unlimited; **504B,** Jack Demuth; **506,** Bruce Ayres/Tony Stone Images; **509,** Ed Zurbano/*Chicago Tribune;* **513,** Apple Family

Chapter 8 **518-519 (background),** Nuccio Dinuzzo/ *Tribune Olympic Bureau;* **519T,** Walter Kale/*Chicago Tribune;* **519B,** Rusty Kennedy/AP Photo; **521,** Charles Osgood/*Chicago Tribune;* **522,** *Chicago Tribune;* **524,** James Cruimp/*Chicago Tribune;* **528,** Jim Quinn/*Chicago Tribune;* **532,** Rod Kieft/ Visuals Unlimited; **533,** Charles Chemey/*Chicago Tribune;* **546,** van GOGH, Vincent. *The Starry Night.* (1889) Oil on canvas, 29 x 36 1/4" (73.7 x 92.1 cm). The Museum of Modern Art, New York. Acquired through the Lillie P. Bliss Bequest. Photograph © 1999 The Museum of Modern Art, New York; **554,** Jeff Greenberg/Visuals Unlimited; **561,** Fran Brown; **564,** Will Hart/PhotoEdit; **566,** David Young-Wolff/PhotoEdit; **569,** Jim Brown; **571,** Chuck Berman/*Chicago Tribune;* **575,** Bob Handelman/Tony Stone Images; **579,** Keith Wood/ Tony Stone Images; **584,** Kathleen Blanchard/Visuals Unlimited; **585,** Ron Bailey/*Chicago Tribune;* **585,** Dennis MacDonald/ PhotoEdit; **588,** Arthur Morris/Visuals Unlimited

Chapter 9 **601,** David Young-Wolff/Tony Stone Images; **603,** Maria Dominguez; **607,** Jack Demuth; **610,** Nedra Polanski; **616,** Davis Barber/PhotoEdit; **620,** The Newberry Library, Chicago; **624,** Steve Callahan/Visuals Unlimited; **625,** Peter Pearson/Tony Stone Images; **626,** Bayard H. Brattstrom/Visuals Unlimited; **629,** Charles Krebs/Tony Stone Images; **631,** Ovie Carter/*Chicago Tribune;* **633,** McDonald/Visuals Unlimited; **634,** National Aeronautics and Space Administration; **636,** Peter Weber/Tony Stone Images; **645,** David Young-Wolff/PhotoEdit; **647,** Michael Newman/PhotoEdit; **655B,** National Aeronautics and Space Administration; **657,** Ernest Braun/Tony Stone Images; **663,** Fran Brown

Chapter 10 **665CR,** Corbis/Bettmann; **670,** Al Francekevich/The Stock Market; **673,** Luis Leal; **676BL,** Creative Publications; **677,** Myrleen Ferguson Cate/ PhotoEdit; **682,** Columbia Tristar Television; **685,** Bob Langer/ *Chicago Tribune;* **686,** Alan Oddie/PhotoEdit; **688,** Roy Hall/ *Chicago Tribune;* **692,** Creative Publications; **695,** AP Photo; **697,** Michael Newman/PhotoEdit; **700,** Creative Publications; **701,** Kevin Tanaka/*Chicago Tribune* Handout; **702,** *Chicago Tribune;* **705,** Jack Demuth; **706,** ETHS Yearbook Staff, Evanston, IL; **711,** Inga Spence/Visuals Unlimited; **713,** Nicole Martin; **714,** John Elk/Tony Stone Images; **717,** Myrleen Ferguson Cate/PhotoEdit; **718,** ETHS Yearbook Staff, Evanston, IL; **720,** *Chicago Tribune;* **721,** ETHS Yearbook Staff, Evanston, IL; **726,** Andrew Olney/Tony Stone Images

Unlisted photographs are property of Everyday Learning Corporation